THE ENGINEERING DRAWING SERIES

ENGINEERING DRAWING

FRENCH AND VIERCK: *Engineering Drawing*, 8th edition. FRENCH AND VIERCK: *Graphic Science*. VIERCK AND HANG: *Graphic Science Problems*. VIERCK, COOPER, AND MACHOVINA: *Engineering Drawing Problems*, Series 2, 11 × 17, *Engineering Drawing—Basic Problems*, Series A, 8½ × 11. LEVENS AND EDSTROM: *Problems in Engineering Drawing*, Series IV, 8½ × 11. RUSS: *Quiz Questions to Accompany Engineering Drawing*. FRENCH AND TURNBULL: *Lessons in Lettering*, Book I—Vertical Single Stroke Lettering, 3d edition, Book II —Inclined Single Stroke Lettering, 3d edition.

McGRAW-HILL TEXT-FILMS FOR ENGINEERING DRAWING: *A series of directly correlated motion pictures and filmstrips (10 films and 9 follow-up filmstrips).*

GEOMETRY AND GRAPHICS

SHUPE AND MACHOVINA: *Engineering Geometry and Graphics*. SHUPE, MACHOVINA, AND HANG: *Engineering Geometry and Graphics Problems*.

GRAPHIC SCIENCE

ENGINEERING DRAWING
DESCRIPTIVE GEOMETRY
GRAPHICAL SOLUTIONS

NEW YORK   TORONTO   LONDON

GRAPHIC SCIENCE

ENGINEERING DRAWING

DESCRIPTIVE GEOMETRY

GRAPHICAL SOLUTIONS

+31.5	2.67	1.8	29.7	0. 8
+40.0	2.63	1.85	29	0.7660
+50.0	2.58			0.6428
+53.8	2.	2.05	26.2	0.5906

THOMAS E. FRENCH
Late Professor of Engineering Drawing,
the Ohio State University

CHARLES J. VIERCK
Professor of Engineering Drawing,
the Ohio State University

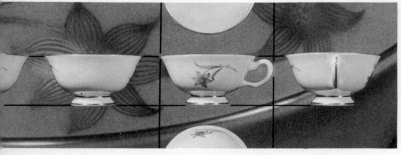

McGRAW-HILL BOOK COMPANY, INC.   **1958**

ENGINEERING DRAWING FILMS

The following 16-mm sound motion pictures are especially recommended for use with various chapters of this book, as indicated below:

According to Plan—An introduction to engineering drawing (9 min). *For Introduction.*

Orthographic Projection—Shape description and the principles of orthographic projection (18 min). *For Chaps. 4 and 5.*

Auxiliary Views: Single Auxiliaries—Reviews orthographic projection and explains auxiliary projection (23 min). *For Chap. 6.*

Auxiliary Views: Double Auxiliaries—The theory and practice of double-auxiliary or oblique view (13 min). *For Chap. 6.*

Sections and Conventions—Theory and practice of sectioning and conventional principles (15 min). *For Chap. 7.*

Pictorial Sketching—Basic principles of axometric, oblique, and perspective pictorial sketching (11 min). *For Chap. 8.*

Drawings and the Shop—Relationships between the drawing and production operations in the shop; basic machines (15 min). *For Chap. 9.*

Selection of Dimensions—Principles governing choice of dimensions and their applications (18 min). *For Chap. 10.*

Simple Developments—What simple developments are and how they are used (11 min). *For Chap. 18.*

Oblique Cones and Transition Developments—Animated drawings illustrate oblique cones and transitions (11 min). *For Chap. 18.*

Prints of these films may be purchased from Text-Film Department, McGraw-Hill Book Company, Inc.

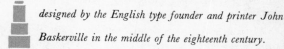

This book is set in monotype Baskerville, a typeface originally designed by the English type founder and printer John Baskerville in the middle of the eighteenth century.

The photographs, taken specially for this text, are by Charles J. Vierck.

PREFACE

FROM THE TIME of hieroglyphic writing down to that of modern graphic description, man has known the need to represent his thoughts, discoveries, and inventions so that others may be informed. As our civilization becomes more complex, graphic representation, paralleling progress in science and engineering, likewise becomes more complex. Moreover, as the history of graphics is studied, one important aspect stands out: the fact that only graphically may some kinds of information be conveyed or certain problems solved—for example, the impossibility of describing complicated mechanisms by other than graphic means is well known.

To the engineer, therefore, graphics is a lifeline, connecting thought, invention, and research with the resulting actualities. To keep pace with advances in science and engineering, graphics in all its varied forms has been and is being refined in many ways.

In the past, graphic training has emphasized engineering drawing as a language of communication. The textbook "Engineering Drawing," by the authors of this volume, promotes the traditional conception and is currently being revised. Future revisions are contemplated as new procedures are developed, as changes come forward in the training of engineers, and as new standards are adopted for industry. Nevertheless, it is well understood today that engineering thinking is directed toward the principle that the "art" of engineering is giving way to the "science" of engineering. Consequently, to progress with this new conception, graphic instruction must now not only stress the communication phase but also emphasize the methods and procedures that will accomplish graphic determination and computation.

Thus engineering drawing, or graphics, by carefully studied refinements and important additions over a period of many years, becomes more than a

language of communication: It is a science embracing both communication and graphic methods of problem solution. Graphic calculation is invaluable in the basic engineering of products, in the scientific investigations of pure and practical research, and in the solution of problems of operation and control. Many departments of instruction have now converted from the representational to the scientific approach to graphics. Others are either engaged in, or are contemplating, modifications of curriculum.

Therefore, upon the premise that graphic methods are extremely important to the scientific training of engineers, this book has been built. It is not a "course book" but a text and reference containing much more than probably will be taught in any formal series of courses. The completeness is deemed necessary because of the varied requirements in different institutions and areas.

The text is divided into three portions: (1) engineering drawing, the fundamentals of projection and the communication phase, (2) descriptive geometry, the solution of space problems of points, lines, planes, and surfaces, and (3) graphical solutions, the solution of mathematical problems of particular interest to engineers.

The graphic procedures used in individual fields, such as architecture, topography, tooling, piping, welding, gearing, cams, and steel structures, are not included here. The particular symbolisms and methods used in these areas are not considered to be fundamental to the training of the engineer but are regarded as specialties that are most advantageously studied in advanced courses or in prejob or on-the-job training.

It is our purpose, then, to present and study the graphic methods as a science, judged by many to be as important to all engineers as any other basic science. In conformity with this conception, the instructional efforts should be aimed toward a complete understanding of graphic methods as they relate to the problems of the engineer, *not* to the problems of the draftsman. In this way, the engineer becomes more competent to specify the graphic procedures to be used in accomplishing engineering work of a wide variety. Also, even though the engineer is competent in the actual work of making drawings, the chances are that he will not often have to do so; and for this reason, the finer points of technique are not now so important. The standard of delineation should be set by correctness and readability rather than by the artistic aspects.

Nevertheless, the engineer must have a knowledge of what is required for readable, well-made drawings so that he may direct the work of others. Because of this, freehand techniques are increasingly important. It is especially significant that the engineer should be so familiar with all methods that he not only will detect errors and omissions but also may be able to specify the procedures making for economy. In employing graphic in place of symbolic solutions, he must be sure that the accuracy of results is within the tolerance set by performance characteristics or by the demands of accuracy in research data.

Consultation may be arranged with teachers who have problems because of changed scope and emphasis. It is hoped that the workbook available for use with this text will solve many of the issues encountered in a choice of problem material for the classroom.

The format of the book in a larger, more "open" style is designed for better readability and to allow space for marginal notes. A notable feature is that illustrations are always on the same page spread as their references. The photographic illustrations attempt not only to augment the appearance of the text but to bring increased interest and response from the student. It is hoped that all this will give the book permanent value in the student's and, later, the engineer's library.

In producing a book of this nature, advice and criticism from friends and associates is quite naturally welcomed, and cooperation received is greatly appreciated. Charles D. Cooper, Ralph S. Paffenbarger, Paul E. Machovina, and Hollie W. Shupe assisted in the eighth edition of "Engineering Drawing," and portions of this material (in revised form) have been used. Richard W. Parkinson, Fairfax E. Watkins, and Paul T. Yarrington assisted with the collection of some of the text and problem essentials. Richard T. Hang and Clyde H. Kearns have been very helpful in collecting text and problem elements and in their collaboration on the workbook. Also noteworthy are the contributions of Irwin Wladaver and B. Leighton Wellman for their careful reading and criticism of the final manuscript.

CHARLES J. VIERCK

CONTENTS

GRAPHICAL SOLUTIONS

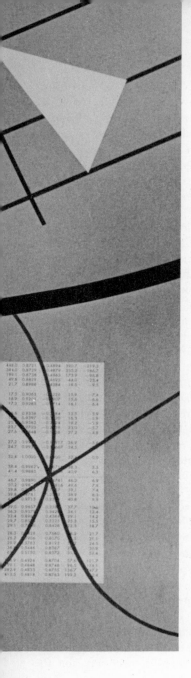

INTRODUCTION

I.1. Through extensive research and analysis carried on in the past and even now in progress, new engineering theories and practices are being developed rapidly. To keep pace with these advances, engineering training has been altered in many ways, particularly in the later stages of study involving the necessary higher mathematics and other subjects indispensable to the engineer in designing and building modern devices and in the research activities of this scientific age. Parallel progress has also been noticed in basic courses such as physics and chemistry. Engineering drawing, formerly thought of and taught as the "language of the engineer" with its importance resting on representation, now through alteration in emphasis and scope takes on a greater value in engineering curricula. The design and construction of modern mechanisms, especially where high speeds, extreme stress and temperature, or a combination of critical conditions is present, bring increasing need for descriptive geometry, also known as "engineering geometry." Complicated space problems are now commonplace. The study of point, line, and plane relationships is very necessary, and a more complete knowledge of surfaces, their generation, and their characteristics is highly desirable.

The engineer finds that his knowledge of descriptive geometry not only aids in understanding complicated relationships but becomes a powerful tool in visualization and subsequent design.

1

Graphics and graphical solutions have likewise taken on an increased importance. A knowledge of vector geometry and of empirical equations is considered essential for engineers engaged in research and design, as well as a knowledge of nomography and graphical calculus for all who deal with problems involving relationship and change of a high order. Many problems that cannot be solved at all by symbolic mathematics, because of the impossibility of writing equations for the relationships, can, however, be solved by graphical calculus.

We have come, therefore, to a realization that engineering drawing must now encompass a wider scope and that graphical instruction cannot have emphasis on representation alone. Engineering geometry and graphical solutions must become a more important part of the training program for engineers. Furthermore, engineers rarely work alone today but are part of a team; they must completely understand, and be familiar with, all basic phases of graphics and graphical representation, with the exception that the actual skills of delineation are not so important as formerly. Therefore, specialized instruction of a "trade" nature can be minimized. For example, an engineer may have no need for a knowledge of architectural, structural, or pipe drawing because of his specialized field of activity, and these items could not then be considered fundamental to the training of all engineers. Instruction in the special field may be given in advanced courses or by on-the-job training. To collect the preceding observations into a few words, it may be said that the "art" of engineering has become subservient to the "science" of engineering.

From the foregoing, the graphical needs of an engineer may be divided into three classifications: (1) *engineering drawing*, the representational or communication phase, including the fundamentals of projection and training in shape and size description; (2) *engineering geometry*, the solution of problems of space and the relationships, characteristics, and uses of points, lines, planes, and surfaces; and (3) *engineering graphics*, the solution of problems involving changes and relationships of variable quantities.

I.2. Engineering Drawing. Engineering drawing is the graphic language used in the industrial world by engineers and designers to express and record the ideas and information necessary for the building of machines and structures.

As distinguished from drawing as a fine art, practiced by artists in pictorial representation, engineering drawing is a descriptive graphical language, whereas art drawing is a means of aesthetic expression. The artist strives to produce, either from the model or landscape before him or through his creative imagination, a picture which will impart to the observer the same mental impression as that produced by the object itself or its visualization in the artist's mind. By employing color, gradation of tone in monochrome light and shade, or line combination in black and white, he is able to suggest his meanings and to depend upon the observer's imagination to visualize the effect of perspective foreshortening and supply the lack of complete detail.

The engineering draftsman has a more exacting task: Limited usually to outline alone (shading is not often used, except for illustrations), he may not depend upon suggested meanings but must give precise and positive information regarding every detail of the machine or structure existing in his imagination. Thus drawing to him is more than pictorial representation; it is a complete graphical language, by whose aid he may describe minutely every operation necessary and may keep a complete record of the work for duplication and repairs. By a logical system of related "views," intricate and complicated shapes are clearly shown, exact and detailed sizes are given without ambiguity, and individual parts are identified for assembly and are located in the machine in their correct functional position. In addition, descriptive notes and specifications give materials, finishes, and directions for manufacture and assembly.

In the artist's case, the result can be understood in greater or less degree by anyone. The draftsman's result does not show the object as it would appear to the eye when finished; consequently his drawing can be read and understood only by one trained in the language.

Thus as the foundation upon which all designing and subsequent manufacture are based, engineering drawing is a very important branch of study in a technical school. Every engineering student must know how to make and how to read drawings. The subject is essential in all types of engineering practice. The drafting room is often the entering gateway into industry, but even one who may never have to make drawings must be able to interpret them and to know whether or not a drawing is correct. An engineer without a working knowledge of the engineer's language would be professionally illiterate.

I.3. Methods of Expression. To serve the many purposes for which drawings may be made, the engineering draftsman has at his disposal several different methods by which he may convey information. For the great bulk of engineering work, the orthographic system will be employed; and this method, with its variations and the necessary symbols and abbreviations, constitutes a most important portion of this book. However, for drawings of proposed construction, illustrations, some working drawings, and others, principally used by the layman, one of the pictorial methods may be better suited to the purpose.

The well-trained engineer, therefore, must be thoroughly familiar with all methods and must be able to specify their use with assurance regarding the final result; the accomplished engineering draftsman must be able, as well, to follow the engineer's directions and produce work of professional grade.

The following outline classifies the various systems of projection according to their theory and includes chapter references:

Systems of Projection
 I. Orthographic projection (projectors perpendicular to planes of projection)
    A. Multiplanar (two or more planes)
       1. Two-view drawings (Chap. 4)
       2. Three-view drawings (Chap. 4)
       3. Orthographic reading (Chap. 4)
       4. Auxiliary views (Chap. 6)
       5. Oblique views (Chap. 6)
       6. Sectional views (Chap. 7)
       7. Intersections (Chap. 18)
       8. Developments (Chap. 18)
    B. Uniplanar (one plane)
       1. Isometric projection (Chap. 8)
       2. Isometric drawing (Chap. 8)
       3. Dimetric drawing (Chap. 8)
       4. Trimetric drawing (Chap. 8)
       5. Axonometric projection from orthographic views (Chap. 8)
 II. Oblique projection (projectors oblique to plane of projection)
    A. Uniplanar
       1. Cavalier projection (Chap. 8)
       2. Cavalier drawing (Chap. 8)
       3. Cabinet drawing (Chap. 8)
       4. Various oblique positions (Chap. 8)
       5. Oblique projection from orthographic views (Chap. 8)
 III. Perspective projection (projectors converging to a station point)
    A. Uniplanar
       1. Parallel perspective (Chap. 8)
       2. Angular perspective (Chap. 8)

Also included as an important part of the method of expression is a study of the description of size, including special notes and specifications. The accomplished draftsman must also understand the special practices peculiar to the separate sections of engineering work. The principal difference between specialized fields is that the dimensioning and notes are prepared in accordance with the accepted standards for each field.

The following outline lists dimensioning practice from the standpoint of drawing type:

Dimensioning Practice
 I. Orthographic drawings
    A. The drawings and the shop (Chap. 9)
    B. Dimensions and notes (Chap. 10)
    C. Precision and limit dimensioning (Chap. 10)
 II. Pictorial drawings
    A. Isometric drawing (Chap. 8)
    B. Dimetric drawing (Chap. 8)

    C. Trimetric drawing (Chap. 8)

    D. Oblique drawing (Chap. 8)

III. Basic machine elements

    A. Screw threads (Chap. 11)

    B. Threaded fasteners (Chap. 11)

    C. Keys, rivets, springs (Chap. 11)

I.4. Technique. To write the graphic language easily and accurately, the aid of drawing instruments is required. When these implements are used, it is called "instrument drawing." When done with the unaided hand, without the assistance of instruments or appliances, it is known as "freehand drawing." Training in both of these methods is necessary for the engineer, the first to develop accuracy and manual dexterity, the second to develop comprehensive observation and to give control and mastery of form and proportion.

In this study, then, we must become familiar with the technique of expression. Important requirements are (1) the ability to use the drawing instruments correctly and (2) the acquisition of freehand skills. Continued practice will develop a capability in delineation that will free the mind from any thought of the elements of expression.

The following subjects are classed as dealing with technique, although some theory may also be included:

Drawing Technique

  I. Fundamentals

    A. Lettering (Chap. 3)

    B. The selection of instruments (Chap. 1)

    C. The use of instruments (Chap. 1)

    D. Applied geometry (Chap. 2)

 II. Freehand drawing

    A. Orthographic freehand drawing (Chap. 5)

    B. Pictorial sketching (Chap. 8)

III. Instrument drawing

    A. Orthographic instrument drawing (Chap. 5)

    B. Pictorial drawing (Chap. 8)

I.5. Objectives. Our object, then, is to study this language so that we may write it, express ourselves clearly to one familiar with it, and read it readily when written by another. To do this we must know its basic theory and its composition and be familiar with its accepted conventions and abbreviations. This language is universal, as its principles are essentially the same throughout the world, and one trained in the practices of one nation can readily adapt himself to the practices of another.

This new language is entirely a graphical or written one. It cannot be read aloud but must be interpreted by acquiring a visual knowledge of the object represented; and the student's success in it will be indicated not alone by his skill in execution but also by his ability to interpret his impressions and to visualize clearly in space.

It is not a language to be learned only by the comparatively few draftsmen who will be professional writers of it but, as already indicated, should be understood by all connected with, or interested in, technical industry. The training its study gives in quick, accurate observation and in the power of reading description from lines is of a value quite unappreciated by those not familiar with it.

I.6. Engineering Geometry. Engineering geometry is the application of the theory of projection to the solution of space problems. Machines and structures are made up, for the most part, of geometrical elements combined in various and sometimes complicated ways. The numerous points, lines, planes, and surfaces are combined to form basic structure, operating components, and housing. These elements of any physical object may involve parallelism, perpendicularity or angularity of lines and planes, and the relationship of these to curved or warped surfaces. Determination of position, clearances, and movement is a basic consideration. In many cases, graphical accuracy is sufficient; in others, graphics is supplemented by mathematical calculations. In either case, in support of graphical knowledge, it may be said that the mathematics can often be simplified by first having a complete understanding of the space problem and a graphical analysis of the relationship of elements.

Engineering geometry is a powerful tool for research, design, and development. Design usually begins with the graphical stage, and there will be a correlated activity involving engineering drawing, engineering geometry, and mathematics, as they relate to the scientific aspects of the design. Engineering geometry will be employed to solve the problems of space and the relationship of the various elements, then will either solve or aid in determining stresses, and will also be invaluable in the visualization of components and the functioning of the completed product.

The following outline classifies problems in engineering geometry according to the geometric elements:

   I. Fundamentals
      A. Engineering drawing (Chaps. 1 to 12)
      B. Point, edge, and normal views (Chap. 13)
  II. Points: points and straight lines (Chap. 14)
 III. Lines
      A. Points and straight lines (Chap. 14)
      B. Straight lines and planes (Chap. 15)
      C. Curved lines (Chap. 16)
 IV. Planes: straight lines and planes (Chap. 15)
  V. Surfaces
      A. Straight lines and planes (Chap. 15)
      B. Curved and warped surfaces (Chap. 17)
      C. Intersections and developments (Chap. 18)

VI. The geometry of forces: vector geometry (Chap. 19)

I.7. Engineering Graphics. Some writers have used the term "graphics" to apply to all drawing of whatever kind that may be necessary in engineering or scientific work. A dictionary definition for the word runs as follows: (1) the art of making drawings, as in architecture or engineering, in accordance with mathematical rules; (2) calculation of stresses, etc., from such drawings. The term "engineering graphics" as used in this text is intended to apply in part to both these definitions but is restricted in meaning to apply to the areas of activity which cannot be classified strictly as engineering drawing or engineering geometry.

There is a graphical counterpart for almost every mathematical procedure or method. One can graphically add, subtract, multiply, divide, determine powers and roots, and solve problems by algebra or the calculus quite as easily as, in many cases as accurately as, and sometimes more quickly than with symbolic mathematics. Any engineer or scientist not familiar with graphical methods of calculation is approaching his job with only part of the desirable equipment.

In the research, design, and development of modern equipment, reactions, stresses, and deflections have to be calculated. The behavior characteristics of electrical currents, solids, fluids, and gases have to be known. The special properties of materials according to their internal structure play an important part in the design of machines and structures. All these problems of basic science may be handled by mathematics and by graphics. The curves obtained from research will be invaluable in predicting the behavior of materials, etc., when employed in the final product. In many cases the equation of a curve may be determined.

For any standard calculation that must be repeated again and again, a nomograph is an invaluable aid. This may be in the form of special slide rules, conversion charts, or alignment charts of a wide variety.

Problems involving rate of change may be solved easily and within the accuracy of the original data by graphical calculus. In cases where the relationship of rate of change is complex and the mathematical equation cannot be written, the graphical method is the only known method of solution.

The following lists various graphical solutions by type:

I. The fundamentals of graphics
    A. Charts, graphs, and diagrams (Chap. 20)
    B. Graphical solutions (Chap. 21)
II. Scales: functional scales (Chap. 22)
III. Curves and equations: empirical equations (Chap. 24)
IV. Computation of forces: vector geometry (Chap. 19)
 V. Aids to computation: nomography (Chap. 23)
VI. Graphical calculus: graphic calculus (Chap. 25)

1

INSTRUMENTS AND THEIR USE

1.1. Historically, the first drawing instruments were probably a stick, bone, or stone used either alone or fastened to a leather thong for use as a compass and employed to scratch lines either in the sand or soil or on stone. From this primitive beginning in prehistory, progress was made by the discovery of pigments and inks, to be applied on parchment with a brush or a quill pen. Later, the same mediums were used on papers. With the development of better papers and inks and with the discovery of metals and the methods of working them into shape came the first true instruments. These were extremely poor at the beginning; but their design has gradually been improved through the ages to the fine modern and efficient instruments of today. Most notable of the early drawings, however, are those of Leonardo da Vinci, surprising in their conciseness and clarity, considering the crude instruments and materials available at the time.

The development of instruments has been brought about quite naturally along with other developments in the fields of art and drawing. The first important change occurred with the discovery of blueprinting, until recently the standard method of reproduction and still much used. Prior to this time drawings were made on paper and were copied if more were needed. With the advent of blueprinting, the drawings were made in pencil and then traced in ink on tracing cloth, from which the reproductions were made.

9

Fig. 1.1. Old instruments.

Figure 1.1 shows a set of instruments made about 1840. These are typical of the period, having no handles on large compasses or dividers and rather long nibs on the pens. The ruling-pen handle comes apart, and the upper end contains a "prick point," used to transfer points from one sheet to another by laying the first on top and pricking through it to the second. The joints of these instruments are made by tongue-and-groove construction with a through screw. A much better joint, called the "pivot joint," was patented by Theodore Alteneder in 1850 and again in 1871. Nevertheless, the design of these instruments did not change materially until, in about 1920, industry began making drawings in pencil on vellum paper and made blueprints directly from the vellum drawings. The prints were not nearly so clear and readable as from inked tracings but were satisfactory for the purpose and could be produced at a great saving of time and expense.

The second major change came about this time. In an effort to get good, opaque, and yet sharp and clear pencil lines on vellum paper, greater rigidity was needed in the instruments. Recent developments have all been directed toward greater strength and rigidity. The large bow (about 6 or $6\frac{1}{2}$ in. over-all), originally called the "automotive bow," was the first really rigid device for drawing circles of small or medium size. Beam compasses have long been used for drawing large circles.

1.2. Selection of Instruments. In the selection of instruments and materials for drawing, the only general advice that can be given is to secure the *best* that can be afforded. For one who expects to do work of professional grade, it is a great mistake to buy inferior instruments. Sometimes a beginner is tempted by the suggestion that he get cheap instruments for learning, with the expectation of getting better ones later. With reasonable care, a set of good instruments will last a lifetime, whereas poor ones will be an annoyance from the start and will be worthless after short usage. As poor instruments look so much like good ones that an amateur is unable to distinguish them, trustworthy advice should be sought before buying.

1.3. Drawing Boards. The drawing surface may be either the table top itself or a separate board. In either case, the working surface should be made of well-seasoned clear white pine or basswood, cleated to prevent warping. The working edge must be straight and should be tested with a steel straightedge. Some boards and table tops are supplied with a hardwood edge or a steel insert on the working edge, thus ensuring a better wearing surface.

1.4. Drawing Paper. Paper for drawing purposes is made in a variety of qualities with varying prices and may be had in either sheets or rolls. White drawing papers that will not turn yellow with age or exposure are used for finished drawings, maps, charts, and drawings for photographic reproduction. For pencil layouts and working drawings, cream or buff detail papers are easier on the eyes, do not show soil so quickly as white papers, and are therefore preferred. In general, paper should have sufficient grain, or "tooth," to take the pencil, be agreeable to the eye, and have a hard surface not easily grooved by the pencil, with good erasing qualities. Formerly imported papers were considered superior to American-made products, but our mills are now making practically all the paper used in this country. The cheap manila papers should be avoided. A few cents more per yard is well spent in the increased satisfaction gained from working on good paper.

1.5. Tracing Paper. Tracing papers are thin papers, either *natural* or *transparentized*, on which drawings are traced, either in pencil or ink, and from which blueprints or similar contact prints can be made. In most drafting rooms, original drawings are being penciled on tracing papers and blueprints made directly from these drawings, a practice increasingly successful because of the improvements both in papers and in printing. Tracing papers vary widely in color, thickness, surface, etc., and the grade of pencil and the technique must be adjusted to suit the paper. With the proper combination, however, good prints may be obtained.

1.6. Tracing Cloth. Finely woven cloth coated with a special starch or plastic is used for making drawings in either pencil or ink. The standard tracing cloth is used for inked tracings and specially made pencil cloth for pencil drawings or tracings. The advantage of cloth is that it will stand more handling than paper and is thus more permanent. Tracing and duplicating processes are described in Chap. 12.

1.7. Drafting Tape. Scotch drafting tape, Fig. 1.3*F*, is usually used as the means of fastening paper to the drawing board. It may be used either by sticking a short piece across each corner or by taping the entire edge of the paper. There is a distinction between drafting tape and masking tape (made by the same company) in that the latter has a heavier coating of adhesive and does not come off the drawing paper so cleanly as the former.

1.8. Thumbtacks (Fig. 1.3*G***).** The best thumbtacks have thin heads with steel points screwed into them. Cheaper ones are made by stamping. Tacks with tapering pins of small diameter should be chosen. Flat-headed (often colored) map pins should not be used, as the heads are too thick and the pins rather large.

1.9. Pencils. The basic instrument is the graphite lead pencil. It is made in a variety of hardnesses, and each manufacturer has certain special methods of processing designed to make the lead strong and yet give a smooth clear line. Figure 1.2 shows five varieties. At the left are two ordinary pencils, with the lead set in wood. (*A*) is of American and (*B*) of foreign manufacture. Both are fine, but the disadvantage is that, in use, the wood must be cut away to expose the lead (a time-consuming annoyance) and the pencil naturally becomes shorter until the last portion must be discarded. More convenient forms are shown at (*C*) to (*E*). These are semiautomatic, employing a chuck to clamp and hold the lead. (*C*) is made with a plastic handle and replaceable tip (for indicating the grade of lead). (*D*) has an aluminum handle and indexing tip for indication of grade. (*E*) is the rather elegant Alteneder pencil with rosewood handle, hardened-steel chuck ring, and eraser tip. All semiautomatic pencils are more convenient to use than the cheaper wooden ones. The manufacturers grade drawing pencils by numbers and letters from 6B, very soft and black, through 5B, 4B, 3B, 2B, B, and HB to F, the medium grade; then H, 2H, 3H, 4H, 5H, 6H, 7H, and 8H to 9H, the hardest. The soft (B) grades are used primarily for sketching and rendered drawings and the hard (H) grades for instrument drawings.

1.10. Pencil Pointer. After the wood of the ordinary pencil is cut away with a pocketknife or mechanical sharpener, the lead must be formed to a long conical point. A lance-tooth file, Fig. 1.3*A*, about 6 in. long is splendid for the purpose. Some draftsmen prefer the standard sandpaper pencil-pointer pad, Fig. 1.3*B*.

1.11. Erasers. The Ruby pencil eraser, Fig. 1.3*C*, large size with beveled ends, is the standard. This eraser not only removes pencil

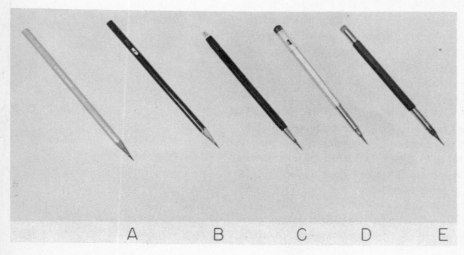

Fig. 1.2. Drafting pencils.

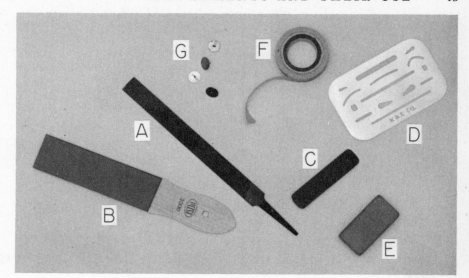

Fig. 1.3. Accessories.

lines effectively but is much better for ink than the so-called ink eraser, as it will remove the ink without seriously damaging the surface of paper or cloth. A good metal erasing shield, Fig. 1.3*D*, aids in getting clean erasures.

Artgum or a *soft*-rubber eraser, Fig. 1.3*E*, is useful for cleaning paper and cloth of finger marks and smears that spoil the appearance of the completed drawing.

1.12. Penholders and Pens. The penholder should have a grip of medium size, small enough to enter the mouth of a drawing-ink bottle easily yet not so small as to cramp the fingers while in use. A size slightly larger than the diameter of a pencil is good.

An assortment of pens for lettering, grading from coarse to fine, may be chosen from those listed in Chap. 3.

A penwiper of lintless cloth or thin chamois skin should always be at hand for both lettering and ruling pens.

1.13. Drawing Ink. Drawing ink is finely ground carbon in suspension, with natural or synthetic gum added to render the mixture waterproof. Nonwaterproof ink flows more freely but smudges very easily. Drawing ink diluted with distilled water or Chinese ink in stick form rubbed up with water in a slate slab is used in making wash drawings and for very fine line work.

Bottleholders prevent the possibility of ruining the drawing table or floor by ink from an upset bottle. They are made in various patterns, one of which is illustrated in Fig. 1.4. As a temporary substitute, the lower half of the paper container in which the ink was sold may be fastened to the table with a thumbtack, or a strip of paper or cloth with a hole for the neck of the bottle may be tacked down over the bottle. Several companies are now supplying ink in small-necked plastic bottles (tubes) which are squeezed to supply

Fig. 1.4. Bottleholder.

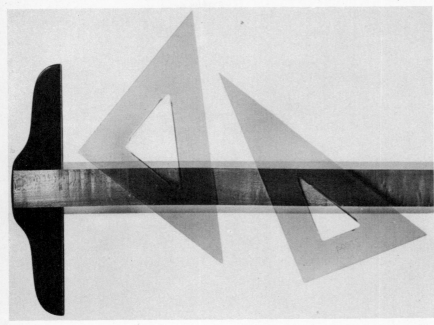

Fig. 1.5. T square and triangles.

the ink, a drop at a time. These containers have the advantage that they prevent spillage, deterioration through evaporation, and contamination.

1.14. The T Square. The fixed-head T square, Fig. 1.5, is used for all ordinary work. It should be of hardwood, and the blade should be perfectly straight. The transparent-edged blade is much the best. A draftsman will have several fixed-head squares of different lengths and will find an adjustable-head square of occasional use.

1.15. Triangles. Triangles, Fig. 1.5, are made of transparent

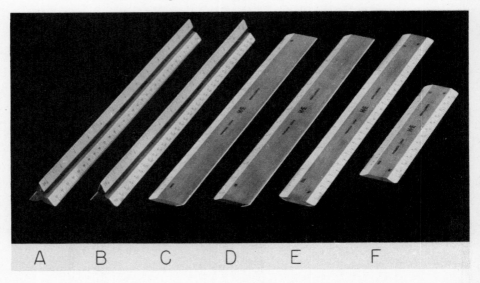

Fig. 1.6. Scale types.

celluloid (fiberloid) or other plastic material. Through internal strains they sometimes lose their accuracy. Triangles should be kept flat to prevent warping. For ordinary work, a 6- or 8-in. 45° and a 10-in. 30°-60° are good sizes.

1.16. Scales. Scales, Fig. 1.6, are made in a variety of types to meet the requirements of many different kinds of work. For convenience, scales are classified according to their most common uses:

Mechanical Engineer's Scales. These are divided and numbered so that fractions of inches represent inches. The most common ranges are ⅛, ¼, ½, and 1 in. to the *inch*. These scales are also known as the *size* scales because the designated reduction also represents the ratio of size, as, for example, *one-eighth* size. A full and half-size scale is illustrated in Fig. 1.7. Mechanical engineer's scales are almost always "full divided," that is, the smallest divisions run throughout the entire length. These scales are also often graduated with the marked divisions numbered from right to left, as well as from left to right, as shown in Fig. 1.7. Mechanical engineer's scales are used mostly for drawings of machine parts and small structures where the drawing size is never less than one-eighth the size of the actual object.

Civil Engineer's Scales. They are divided into decimals with 10, 20, 30, 40, 50, 60, and 80 divisions to the inch (Fig. 1.8). Such a scale is usually full divided and is sometimes numbered both left to right and right to left. These scales are most used for plotting and drawing maps, although they are also very useful for any work where divisions of the inch in tenths is required.

Architect's Scales. Divided into proportional feet and inches, they have divisions indicating ⅛, ¼, ⅜, ½, ¾, 1½, and 3 in. to the *foot* (Fig. 1.9). These are usually "open divided," that is, the units are shown along the entire length, but only the end units are subdivided into inches and fractions. These scales are much used by all engineers, mechanical, industrial, chemical, etc., for both ma-

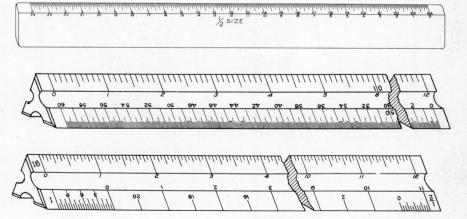

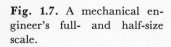
Fig. 1.7. A mechanical engineer's full- and half-size scale.

Fig. 1.8. A civil engineer's scale.

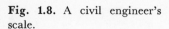
Fig. 1.9. An architect's or mechanical engineer's scale.

Fig. 1.10. Irregular curves.

chine and structural drawings and are sometimes also called *mechanical engineer's* scales.

A variety of special scales, made with divisions specified by the customer, are available from most instrument companies. Compared to standard scales, they are expensive.

Scales are made having various cross-sectional shapes, as shown in Fig. 1.6. The triangular form, either (*A*) or (*B*), has long been favored, because it carries six scales as a unit and is very stiff. However, many draftsmen prefer the flat types as being easier to hold flat to a board and as having any particular working scale more readily available. The "opposite-bevel," scale (*C*) and (*D*), is easier to pick up than the "flat-bevel," scale (*F*); moreover, it shows only one graduation at a time. The "double-bevel," scale (*E*), in the shorter lengths is convenient as a pocket scale, but it can be had in lengths up to 24 in.

Practically all drafting scales of good quality were formerly made of boxwood, either plain or with white edges of celluloid. Although metal scales have been available for more than thirty years, they were seldom used until about 1935, when drafting machines equipped with metal scales made rather important gains in popularity. Extruded medium-hard aluminum alloys are the preferred

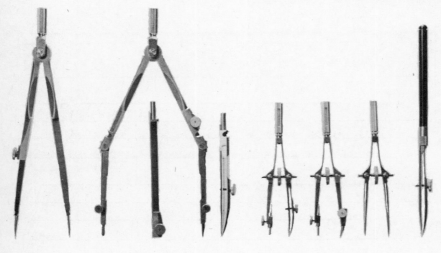

Fig. 1.11. The basic three-bow set.

materials. The Second World War brought a period of considerable experimentation with various types of plastic for all kinds of drafting scales. Up to the present time, the white-edge scale has retained a large measure of its popularity. Another type of scale is now getting considerable attention, a metal scale having a white plastic coating which carries the graduations. Both magnesium and aluminum have been used successfully. These scales have all the reading advantages of a white-edge boxwood scale together with the stability afforded by metal.

1.17. Curves. Curved rulers, called "irregular curves" or "french curves," are used for curved lines other than circle arcs. The patterns for these curves are laid out in parts of ellipses and spirals or other mathematical curves in various combinations. For the student, one ellipse curve of the general shape of Fig. 1.10*A* or *D* and one spiral, either a logarithmic spiral (*B*) or one similar to the one used in Fig. 1.64, will be sufficient. (*C*) is a useful small curve.

1.18. The "Case" Instruments. We have thus far, with the exception of curves, paragraph 1.17, considered the instruments (and materials) needed for drawing straight lines. A major portion of any drawing is likely to be circles and circle arcs, and the so-called case instruments are used for this purpose. The basic instruments are shown in Fig. 1.11. At the left is a divider of the "hairspring" type (having a screw for fine adjustment), used for laying off or transferring measurements. Next is shown the large compass with lengthening bar and pen attachment. The three "bow" instruments next shown are for smaller work. They are almost always made without the conversion feature (pencil to pen). The ruling pen, shown at the extreme right, is used for inking straight lines. A set of instruments of the type shown in Fig. 1.11 is known as a three-bow set.

Until recently, the three-bow set was considered to be the standard, in design and number of pieces, for all ordinary drafting work. However, as described in paragraph 1.1, the trend now is for more rigid construction and fewer pieces. The 6-in. compass of Fig. 1.12 embraces practically a whole set in one instrument. Used as shown, the instrument is a pencil compass; with pencil replaced by pen, it is used to ink circles; with steel point installed in place of pencil point, it becomes a divider; the pen point, placed in handle provided, makes a ruling pen; and a small metal case is supplied for holding steel points and lead. Similar instruments of other manufacture are shown in Figs. 1.13 and 1.14. The instrument at the extreme right of Fig. 1.14 is a "quick-change" design (with vernier adjustment), a great convenience when changing from a very small setting to a large one.

Even though it is possible to make an instrument that serves practically all purposes, naturally it is a convenience to have several instruments, thus saving the time required to convert from pencil leg to ink leg or divider points. Therefore, the newer more rigid

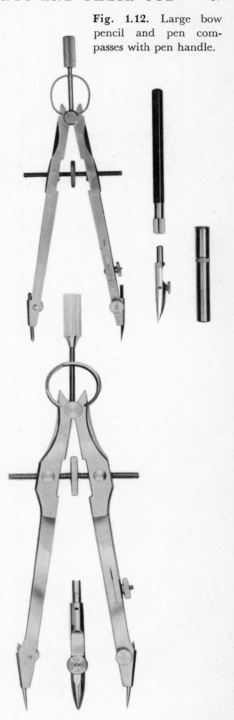

Fig. 1.12. Large bow pencil and pen compasses with pen handle.

Fig. 1.13. Large bow divider, which converts to pen or pencil compasses.

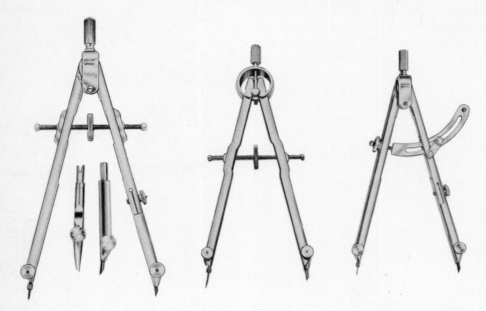

Fig. 1.14. Three different designs of large bow instruments.

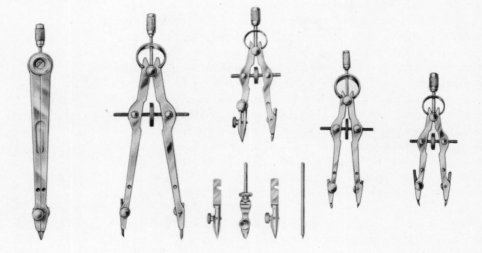

Fig. 1.15. A large- and small-bow set.

Fig. 1.16. Extender for large bow.

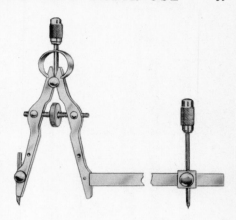

instruments are also made as separate pieces in different sizes. Those shown in Fig. 1.15 are the 6-in. divider and compass, 3-in. pen and pencil compasses, 3-in. divider, and pen points which are used either on the 6-in. compass or in a handle (not shown) to make a ruling pen.

The standard 6-in. compass will open only to approximately 5 in. The lengthening bar of the older-type compass (Fig. 1.11) will extend the radius to about 8 in. Lengthening bars for the newer spring-bow instruments are of the beam type. The instrument of Fig. 1.16 has a center point on the beam, thus employing the pencil and pen of the instrument itself, while the compass of Fig. 1.17 uses the center point of the instrument and separate pen and pencil attachments on the beam. A standard metal beam compass for drawing circles up to about 14-in. radius is shown in Fig. 1.18.

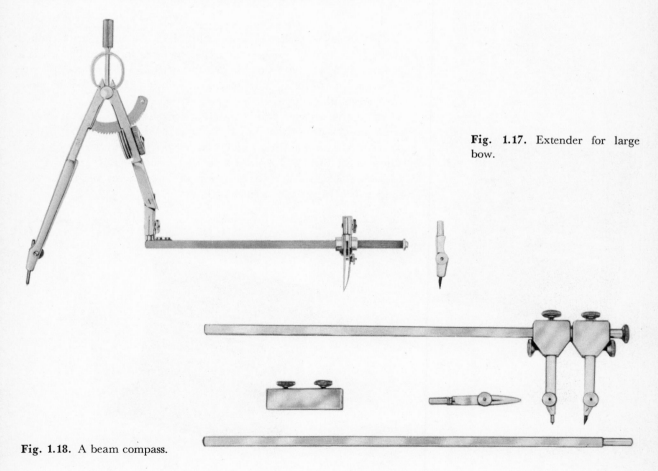

Fig. 1.17. Extender for large bow.

Fig. 1.18. A beam compass.

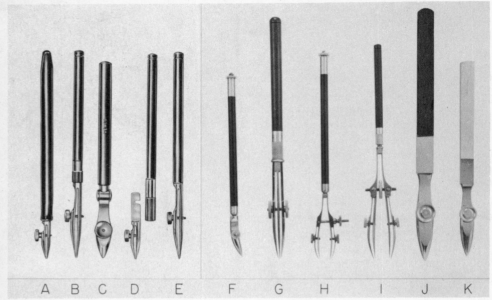

A   B   C   D   E   F   G   H   I   J   K

Fig. 1.19. Various ruling pens.

Various ruling pens are shown in Fig. 1.19. (*A*) to (*E*) are standard types. Note that (*D*) uses the compass-pen leg in a handle. (*F*) is a contour pen, (*G*) is a border pen for wide lines, (*H*) and (*I*) are "railroad" pens for double lines, and (*J*) and (*K*) are border pens with large ink capacity.

All manufacturers supply instruments made up in sets and supplied in a leather or metal case. Figure 1.20 shows a standard three-bow combination and Fig. 1.21 a large-bow set with beam compass. The case of Fig. 1.22 is unique in that inserts may be removed to provide space for any combination of instruments desired at the time of purchase or for additions later.

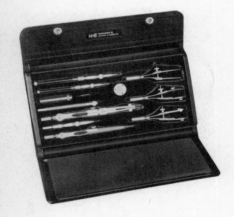

Fig. 1.20. A three-bow set, in case.

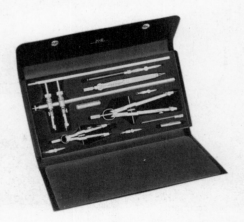

Fig. 1.21. A large-bow (with beam compass) set, in case.

1.19. Lettering Devices. The Ames lettering instrument and the Braddock-Rowe triangle, Figs. 3.2*A* and *B*, are convenient devices used in drawing guide lines for lettering.

Commercial drafting rooms regard mechanical lettering instruments as necessary for producing neat consistent lettering and symbols on inked drawings. The LeRoy set, Figs. 1.23 and 1.24, is one of the most popular. It is available with a wide variety of letter styles and with many electrical, welding, mapping, geological, and mathematical symbols.

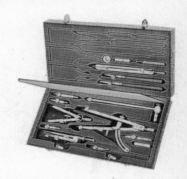

Fig. 1.22. A special case, adaptable to many combinations.

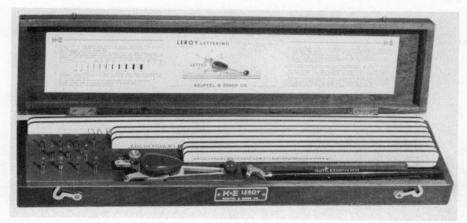

Fig. 1.23. A LeRoy lettering set.

Fig. 1.24. Using the LeRoy lettering instruments.

Fig. 1.25. A drafting machine.

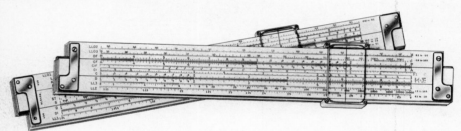

Fig. 1.26. Slide rules.

1.20. Drafting Machines. Since the expiration of the patent on the Universal drafting machine, several makers have come into competition with varied designs of this important instrument, which combines the functions of T square, triangles, scale, and protractor and which is used very extensively in commercial drafting rooms (it is estimated that 35 per cent of time in machine drawing and over 50 per cent in structural drawing is saved by its use). Figure 1.25 shows a band-type drafting machine. Special drafting machines are made for left-handed draftsmen.

1.21. The Slide Rule. Although not a drawing instrument, the slide rule, Fig. 1.26, is essentially an engineer's tool, and proficiency in its use is a requirement of every modern drafting room. A good way for a beginner to learn to use a slide rule is in connection with a drawing course. Its use facilitates the rapid calculation of volumes and weights as an aid in reading drawings or, later, as an essential part of drafting work. Of the several varieties of slide rule, those recommended for prospective engineers are a Polyphase Duplex

Trig,[1] a Polyphase Duplex Decitrig,[1] a Log Log Duplex Trig,[1] a Log Log Duplex Decitrig,[1] or a Versilog [1] in 10-in. size.

1.22. Check List of Instruments and Materials

1. Set of drawing instruments, including the following: 6-in. compasses with fixed needle-point leg, removable pencil and pen legs, and lengthening bar; 6-in. hairspring dividers; 3½-in. bow pencil, bow pen, and bow divider; two ruling pens; box of leads. Or large bow set containing 6½-in. bow compass; 4½-in. bow compass; 6½-in. friction divider and pen attachment for compass; 5½-in. ruling pen; beam compass with extension beam; box for extra leads and points

2. Drawing board

3. T square

4. 45° and 30°-60° triangles

5 Three mechanical engineer's scales, flat pattern, or the equivalent triangular scale

6. Lettering instrument or triangle

7. French curves

8. Drawing pencils, 6H, 4H, 2H, H, and F

9. Pocketknife or pencil sharpener

10. Pencil pointer (file or sandpaper)

11. Pencil eraser (Ruby)

12. Artgum or cleaning rubber

13. Penholder, pens for lettering, and penwiper

14. Bottle of drawing ink and bottleholder

15. Scotch drafting tape or thumbtacks

16. Drawing paper to suit

17. Tracing paper and cloth

18. Dusting cloth or brush

To these may be added:

19. Civil engineer's scale

20. Protractor

21. Erasing shield

22. Slide rule

23. Six-foot steel tape

24. Clipboard or sketchbook

25. Hard Arkansas oiltones

26. Piece of soapstone

27. Cleaning powder or pad

The student should mark all his instruments and materials plainly with his initials or name as soon as they have been purchased and approved.

1.23. Additional Instruments. The instruments and materials described in this chapter are all that are needed for ordinary practice and are, as a rule, with the exception of such supplies as paper,

[1] Registered trade-mark.

pencils, ink, erasers, etc., what a draftsman is expected to take with him into a drafting room.

There are many other special instruments and devices which are not necessary in ordinary work but with which, nevertheless, the draftsman should be familiar, as they may be very convenient in some special cases and are often found as a part of drafting-room equipment. See manufacturer's catalogues.

1.24. The Use of Instruments. In beginning the use of drawing instruments, the student should pay particular attention to the correct method of handling them. Read carefully the instructions given and observe strictly all the details of the technique.

Facility will come with continued practice, but from the outset good *form* must be insisted upon. One might learn to write fairly well holding the pen peculiarly between the fingers or gripped in the closed hand, but it would be poor form. Bad form in drawing is distressingly common and may be traced in every instance to lack of care or knowledge at the beginning and the consequent formation of bad habits. These habits, when once formed, are most difficult to overcome.

All mechanical drawings serve incidentally for practice in the use of instruments, but it is best for the beginner to make a few drawings solely to become familiar with the handling and "feel" of the instruments so that, later, in working a drawing problem, there may be no loss of time on account of faulty manipulation. With practice, the correct skillful use of the instruments will become a subconscious habit.

The requirements of good drawing ability are *accuracy* and *speed*, and in commercial work neither is worth much without the other. Accurate penciling is the first consideration. Inking should not be attempted until real proficiency in penciling has been attained. A good instructor knows that it is mistaken kindness to the beginner to accept faulty or careless work. The standard held at the start will be carried through his professional life, and the beginner should learn that a *good* drawing can be made just as quickly as a *poor* one. Erasing is expensive, and most of it can be avoided. The student allowed to continue in a careless way will grow to regard his erasers as the most important tools in his kit. The draftsman, of course, erases occasionally, and instructions in making corrections should be given, but the beginner should strive for sheets without blemish or inaccuracy.

1.25. Preparation for Drawing. The drawing table should be set so that the light comes from the left and should be adjusted to a convenient height, that is, 36 to 40 in., for use while sitting upon a standard drafting stool or while standing. One may draw with more freedom standing than sitting, especially on large drawings. The board, for use in this manner, should be inclined at a slope of about 1 to 8. Nevertheless, it is more tiring to draw while standing; many modern drafting rooms use tables so made that the board may be used in an almost vertical position and may be raised or lowered so that the draftsman may use a lower stool with swivel seat and a backrest, thus working with comfort and even greater freedom than when an almost horizontal board is used.

The instruments should be placed within easy reach, either on the table or on a special tray or stand beside the table. The table, board, and instruments should be wiped with a dustcloth before starting to draw.

1.26. The Pencil and Its Use. The grade of pencil must be selected carefully, with reference to the surface of the paper used as well as to the line quality desired. For a pencil layout on detail paper of good texture, a pencil as hard as 5H or 6H may be used, while for finished pencil drawings on the same paper, 2H, 3H, or 4H pencils give the blacker line needed. For finished pencil drawings or tracings on vellum, softer pencils, H to 3H, are employed to get printable lines. The F pencil is much used for technical sketching, and the H is popular for lettering. In every case the pencil chosen must be hard enough not to blur or smudge but not so hard as to cut grooves in the paper under reasonable pressure.

To sharpen a pencil, cut away the wood from the unlettered end with a penknife, as shown in Fig. 1.27*A*, and then sharpen the lead to make a long conical point, as at (*B*), by twirling the pencil as the lead is rubbed with long even strokes against the sandpaper pad or file.

A flat or wedge point will not wear away in use so fast as a conical point, and on that account some draftsmen prefer it for straight-line work. The long wedge point illustrated at (*C*) is made by first sharpening, as at (*A*), then making the two long cuts on opposite sides, as shown, then flattening the lead on the sandpaper pad or file, and finishing by touching the corners to make the wedge point narrower than the diameter of the lead.

Have the sandpaper pad within easy reach, and *keep the pencils sharp*. Some hang the pad or file on a cord attached to the drawing table. The professional draftsman sharpens his pencil every few minutes. After sharpening the lead, wipe off excess graphite dust before using the pencil. Form the habit of sharpening the lead as often as you might dip a writing pen into the inkwell. Most com-

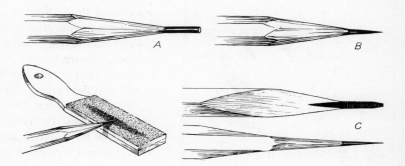

Fig. 1.27. Sharpening the pencil.

mercial and many college drafting rooms are equipped with Dexter or other pencil sharpeners to save the draftsman's time.

Not only must pencil lines be clean and sharp, but for pencil drawings and tracings to be blueprinted, it is absolutely necessary that all the lines of each kind be uniform, firm, and opaque. This means a very careful choice of pencils and the proper use of them. The attempt to make a dark line with too hard a pencil results in cutting deep grooves in the paper. Hold the pencil firmly, yet with as much ease and freedom as possible.

Keep an even constant pressure on the pencil, and when using a conical point, rotate the pencil as the line is drawn so as to keep both the line and pencil sharp. Use a draftsman's brush or soft cloth occasionally to dust off excess graphite from the drawing.

Too much emphasis cannot be given to the importance of clean, careful, accurate penciling. Never entertain the thought that poor penciling can be corrected in tracing.

1.27. Placing the Paper. Since the T-square blade is more rigid near the head than toward the outer end, the paper, if much smaller than the size of the board, should be placed close to the left edge of the board (within an inch or so) with its lower edge several inches from the bottom of the board. With the T square against the left edge of the board, square the top of the paper; hold in this position, slipping the T square down from the edge, and put a thumbtack in each upper corner, pushing it in up to the head so that the head aids in holding the paper. Now move the T square down over the paper to smooth out possible wrinkles, and put thumbtacks in the other two corners. Drafting tape may be used instead of thumbtacks.

1.28. Use of the T Square. The T square is used with its head against the left edge of the drawing board. Manifestly, the T square is used for drawing horizontal lines and is manipulated as follows: Holding the head of the tool, as shown in Fig. 1.28A, the draftsman slides it along the edge of the board to a spot very near the position desired. Then, for closer adjustment, he changes his hold either to that shown at (B), in which the thumb remains on top of the T-square head and the other fingers press against the underside of the board, or more often to that shown at (C), in which the fingers remain on the T square and the thumb is placed on the board.

Figure 1.29 shows the position of the hand and pencil for drawing horizontal lines. Note that the pencil is inclined in the direction the line is drawn, that is, toward the right, and also inclined slightly away from the body so as to bring the pencil point as close as possible to the T-square blade.

In drawing lines, great care must be exercised to keep them accurately parallel to the guiding edge of the T square. The pencil should be held lightly—but close against the edge—and the angle should not vary during the progress of the line. These lines should always be drawn from left to right. A T-square blade may be tested for straightness by drawing a sharp line through two points and then

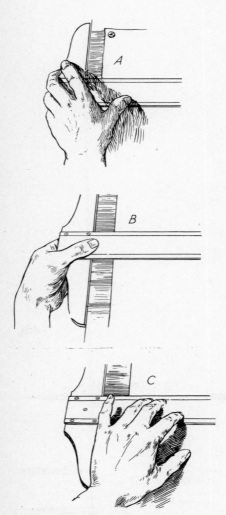

Fig. 1.28. Manipulating the T square.

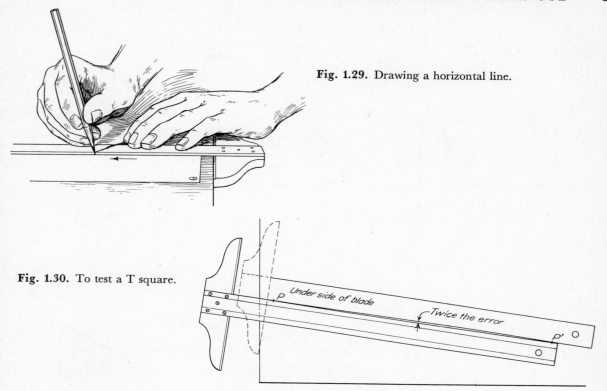

Fig. 1.29. Drawing a horizontal line.

Fig. 1.30. To test a T square.

turning the square over and with the same edge drawing another line through the points, as shown in Fig. 1.30.

1.29. Use of the Triangles. Vertical lines are drawn with the triangle set against the T square, with the perpendicular edge nearest the head of the square and thus toward the light (Fig. 1.31). These lines are always drawn upward, from bottom to top.

In drawing vertical lines, the T square is held in position against the left edge of the board by the thumb and little finger of the left hand while the other fingers of this hand adjust and hold the triangle. One may be sure that the T square is in contact with the board by hearing the little double click as the two come together, and slight pressure of the thumb and little finger toward the right will maintain the position. As the line is drawn, pressure against the board of all the fingers will hold the T square and triangle firmly in position.

As explained before for horizontal lines, care should be exercised to keep the line accurately parallel to the guiding edge. Note the position of the pencil in Fig. 1.31.

In both penciling and inking, the triangles should always be used in contact with a guiding straightedge. To ensure accuracy, never work to the extreme corner of a triangle; to avoid having to do so, keep the T square below the lower end of the line to be drawn.

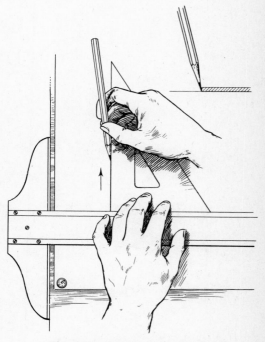

Fig. 1.31. Drawing a vertical line.

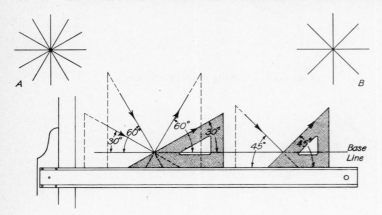

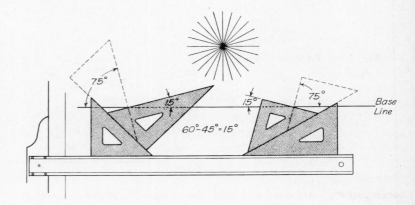

Fig. 1.32. To draw angles of 30°, 45°, and 60°.

Fig. 1.33. To draw angles of 15° and 75°.

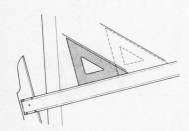

Fig. 1.34. To draw parallel lines.

With the T square against the edge of the board, lines at 45° may be drawn with the standard 45° triangle, and lines at 30° and 60° with the 30-60° triangle, as shown in Fig. 1.32. With vertical and horizontal lines included, lines at increments of 45° may be drawn with the 45° triangle as at (*B*), and lines at 30° increments with the 30-60° triangle as in Fig. 1.32*A*. The two triangles are used in combination for angles of 15, 75, 105°, etc. (Fig. 1.33). Thus any multiple of 15° can be drawn directly; and a circle can be divided with the 45° triangle into 8 parts, with the 30-60° triangle into 12 parts, and with both into 24 parts.

To Draw One Line Parallel to Another (*Fig.* 1.34). Adjust to the given line a triangle held against a straightedge (T square or triangle), hold the guiding edge in position, and slide the triangle on it to the required position.

To Draw a Perpendicular to Any Line (*Fig.* 1.35*A*). Place a triangle with one edge against the T square (or another triangle), and move the two until the hypotenuse of the triangle is coincident with the line; hold the T square in position and turn the triangle, as shown, until its other side is against the T square; the hypotenuse will then

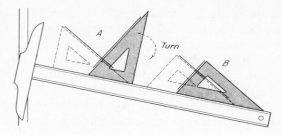

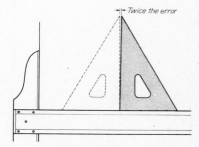

Fig. 1.35. To draw perpendicular lines.

be perpendicular to the original line. Move the triangle to the required position. A quicker method is to set the triangle with its hypotenuse against the guiding edge, fit one side to the line, slide the triangle to the required point, and draw the perpendicular, as shown at (*B*).

Never attempt to draw a perpendicular to a line with only one triangle by placing one leg of the triangle along the line.

Through internal strains, triangles sometimes lose their accuracy. They may be tested by drawing a perpendicular and then reversing the triangle, as shown in Fig. 1.36.

1.30. The Left-handed Draftsman. He reverses the T square and triangles left for right as compared with the regular right-handed position. The head of the T square is used along the right edge of the board. Horizontal lines are drawn from right to left. The triangle is placed with its vertical edge to the right, and the line is drawn from bottom to top. Here the drawing table should be placed with the light coming from the right.

1.31. Use of the Scale. Scale technique is governed largely by the requirements of accuracy and speed. Before a line can be drawn, its relative position must be found by scaling, and the speed with which the scale measurements can be made will greatly affect the total drawing time.

Precise layouts and developments, made for the workmen to scale, must be very accurately drawn, at the expense of speed; conversely, drawings having figured dimensions need not be quite so carefully scaled, and better speed may be attained.

To make a measurement, place the scale on the drawing where the distance is to be laid off, align the scale in the direction of the measurement, and make a *light* short dash with a sharp pencil at the proper graduation mark (Fig. 1.37). In layout work where extreme accuracy is required, a "pricker," or needlepoint set in a wood handle, may be substituted for the pencil, and a *small* hole pricked into the paper in place of the pencil mark. It is best to start with the "zero" of the scale either when setting off lengths or when measuring distances. In using an open-divided scale, *inches* (or fractions) are accounted for in one direction from the zero graduation while *feet* (or units) are recorded in the opposite direction.

Fig. 1.36. To test a triangle.

Fig. 1.37. Making a measurement.

Measurements should not be made on a drawing by taking distances off the scale with dividers, as this method is time-consuming and no more accurate than the regular methods.

To avoid cumulative errors, successive measurements on the same line should, if possible, be made without shifting the scale. In representing objects that are larger than can be drawn to their natural or full size, it is necessary to reduce the size of the drawing in some regular proportion, and for this purpose some one of the standard mechanical engineer's, civil engineer's, or architect's scales is used. Standard scales are given in Fig. 1.38.

The first reduction is to *half size*, or to the scale of 6″ = 1′-0″. In other words, ½ in. on the drawing represents a distance of 1 in. on the object. Stated in terms used for the architect's scales, a distance of 6 in. on the drawing represents 1 ft on the object. This scale is used even if the object is only slightly larger than could be drawn full size. If this reduction is not sufficient, the drawing is made to *quarter size*, or to the scale of 3″ = 1′-0″. If the quarter-size scale is too large, the next reduction is *eighth size*, or 1½″ = 1′-0″, the smallest proportion usually supplied on standard mechanical engineer's scales, but the architect's scales are used down to ³⁄₃₂″ = 1′-0″, as shown by the listings in Fig. 1.38.

In stating the scale used on a drawing, the information should be given in accordance with the scale used to make the drawing. Thus, if a standard mechanical engineer's scale is employed, the statement may read that the scale is (1) *full size*, (2) *half size*, (3) *quarter size*, or (4) *eighth size*. These scales may also be given as (1) 1″ = 1″, (2) ½″ = 1″, (3) ¼″ = 1″, or (4) ⅛″ = 1″. If a standard architect's scale has been used, the statement will be given in terms

$$SIZE = \frac{SCALE}{12}$$

SCALES

Mechanical Engineer's

1″ = 1″ (full size)	½″ = 1″ (½ size)
¼″ = 1″ (¼ size)	⅛″ = 1″ (⅛ size)

Architect's or Mechanical Engineer's

12″ = 1′-0″ (full size)	½″ = 1′-0″ (¹⁄₂₄ size)
6″ = 1′-0″ (½ size)	⅜″ = 1′-0″ (¹⁄₃₂ size)
3″ = 1′-0″ (¼ size)	¼″ = 1′-0″ (¹⁄₄₈ size)
1½″ = 1′-0″ (⅛ size)	³⁄₁₆″ = 1′-0″ (¹⁄₆₄ size)
1″ = 1′-0″ (¹⁄₁₂ size)	⅛″ = 1′-0″ (¹⁄₉₆ size)
¾″ = 1′-0″ (¹⁄₁₆ size)	³⁄₃₂″ = 1′-0″ (¹⁄₁₂₈ size)

Civil Engineer's

10, 20, 30, 40, 50, 60, or 80 divisions to the inch representing feet, 10 ft, 100 ft, rods, miles, or any other necessary unit

Fig. 1.38. Standard scales.

of inches to the foot. Examples are (1) $3'' = 1'-0''$, (2) $1\frac{1}{2}'' = 1'-0''$, or (3) $1'' = 1'-0''$. It should be remembered that, in stating the scale, the first figure always refers to the drawing and the second to the object. Thus $3'' = 1'-0''$ means that 3 in. on the *drawing* represents 1 ft on the *object*.

Drawings to odd proportions, such as $9'' = 1'-0''$, $4'' = 1'-0''$, $5'' = 1'-0''$, etc., are used only in rare cases when it is desired to make it difficult or impossible for a workman to measure them with an ordinary scale.

The two terms scale and size have different meanings: The scale $\frac{1}{4}'' = 1'-0''$ is the usual one for ordinary house plans and is often called by architects the "quarter scale." This term should not be confused with the term "quarter size," as the former means $\frac{1}{4}$ in. to 1 ft and the latter $\frac{1}{4}$ in. to 1 in.

The size of a circle is generally stated by giving its diameter, while to draw it the radius is necessary. Two scales are usually supplied together on the same body, for example, half and quarter size. Therefore, in drawing to half size, it is often convenient to lay off the amount of the diameter with the quarter-size scale and use this distance as the radius.

Small pieces are often made "double size," and very small mechanisms, such as drawings of watch parts, are drawn to greatly enlarged sizes: 10 to 1, 20 to 1, 40 to 1, and 50 to 1, using special enlarging scales.

For plotting and map drawing, the civil engineer's scales of decimal parts, with 10, 20, 30, 40, 50, 60, and 80 divisions to the inch, are used. These scales are not used for machine or structural work but in certain aircraft drawings.

The important thing in drawing to scale is to think and speak of each dimension in its full size and not in the reduced (or enlarged) size it happens to be on the paper. This practice prevents confusion between *actual* and *represented* size.

1.32. Reading the Scale. Reading the standard mechanical engineer's scales is rather simple, because the scale is plainly marked in inches, and the smaller graduations are easily recognized as the regular divisions of the inch into $\frac{1}{2}$, $\frac{1}{4}$, $\frac{1}{8}$, and $\frac{1}{16}$. Thus the scales for half size, quarter size, and eighth size are employed in exactly the same manner as a full-size scale.

The architect's scales, however, being open divided and to stated reductions, such as $3'' = 1'-0''$, may require some study by the beginner in order to prevent confusion and mistakes. As an example, consider the scale of $3'' = 1'-0''$. This is the first reduction scale of the usual triangular scale; on it the distance of 3 in. is divided into 12 equal parts, and each of these is subdivided into eighths. This distance should be thought of not as 3 in. but as a foot divided into inches and eighths of an inch. Notice that the divisions start with the *zero* on the inside, the inches of the divided foot running to the *left* and the open divisions of feet to the *right*, so that dimensions

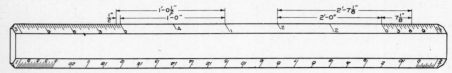

Fig. 1.39. Reading the scale.

Fig. 1.40. Handling the dividers.

Fig. 1.41. Bisecting a line.

given in feet and in inches may be read directly, as 1'-0½" (Fig. 1.39). On the other end will be found the scale of 1½" = 1'-0", or eighth size, with the distance of 1½ in. divided on the right of the zero into 12 parts and subdivided into quarter inches, with the foot divisions to the left of the zero coinciding with the marks of the 3-in. scale. Note again that, in reading a distance in feet and inches, for example, the 2'-7⅛" distance on Fig. 1.39, feet are determined on the left of the zero and inches to the right of it. The other scales, such as ¾" = 1'-0" and ¼" = 1'-0", are divided in a similar way, the only difference being in the value of the smallest graduations. The scale of ³⁄₃₂" = 1'-0", for example, can be read only to the nearest 2 in.

1.33. "Laying out" the Sheet. The paper is usually cut somewhat larger than the desired size of the drawing and is trimmed to size after the work is finished. Suppose the finished size is to be 11 by 17 in. with a ½-in. border inside. Lay the scale down on the paper close to the lower edge, and measure 17 in., marking the distance with the pencil; at the same time, mark ½ in. inside at each end for the border line. Use a short dash forming a continuation of the division line on the scale in laying off a dimension. Do not bore a hole with the pencil. Near the left edge mark 11- and ½-in. borderline points. Through these four marks on the left edge, draw horizontal lines with the T square; and through the points on the lower edge, draw vertical lines, using the triangle against the T square.

1.34. Use of Dividers. Dividers are used for transferring measurements and for dividing lines into any number of equal parts. Facility in their use is most essential, and quick and absolute control of their manipulation must be gained. The instrument should be opened with one hand by pinching the chamfer with the thumb and second finger. This will throw it into correct position with the thumb and forefinger outside the legs and the second and third fingers inside, with the head resting just above the second joint of the forefinger (Fig. 1.40). It is thus under perfect control, with the thumb and forefinger to close it and the other two to open it. This motion should be practiced until an adjustment to the smallest fraction can be made. In coming down to small divisions, the second and third fingers must be gradually slipped out from between the legs while they are closed down upon them. Notice that the little finger is not used in manipulating the dividers.

1.35. To Divide a Line by Trial. In bisecting a line, the dividers are opened at a guess to, roughly, one-half the length. This distance is stepped off on the line, holding the instrument by the handle with the thumb and forefinger. If the division is short, the leg should be thrown out to one-half the remainder (estimated by the eye), without removing the other leg from the paper, and the line spaced again with this new setting (Fig. 1.41). If the result should not come out exactly, the operation may be repeated. With a little experience, a line may be divided very rapidly in this way. Similarly, a line, either straight or curved, may be divided into any number of equal parts, say, five, by estimating the first division, stepping this lightly along the line, with the dividers held vertically by the handle, turning the instrument first in one direction and then in the other. If the last division falls short, one-fifth of the remainder should be added by opening the dividers, keeping the one point on the paper. If the last division is over, one-fifth of the excess should be taken off and the line respaced. If it is found difficult to make this small adjustment accurately with the fingers, the hairspring may be used. It will be found more convenient to use the bow spacers instead of the dividers for small or numerous divisions. Avoid pricking unsightly holes in the paper. The position of a small prick point may be preserved, if necessary, by drawing a small circle around it with the pencil. For most work and until one is very proficient, it is best to divide a line into a number of parts with the scale, as explained on page 53.

1.36. Use of the Compasses. The compasses have the same general shape as the dividers and are manipulated in a similar way. First of all, the needle should be permanently adjusted. Insert the pen in place of the pencil leg, turn the needle with the shoulder point out, and set it a trifle longer than the pen, Fig. 1.42; replace the pencil leg, sharpen the lead to a long bevel, as in Fig. 1.43, and adjust it to the needle point. All this is done so that the needle point will be in perfect position for using the pen; the pencil, which must be sharpened frequently, can then be adjusted, each time, to mate in length with the needle point.

To Draw a Circle. Set the compass on the scale, as shown in Fig. 1.44, and adjust it to the radius needed; then place the needle point

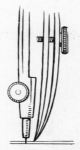

Fig. 1.42. Adjusting the needle point.

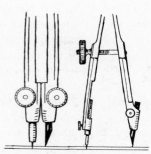

Fig. 1.43. Adjusting the pencil lead.

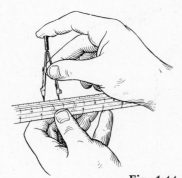

Fig. 1.44. Setting the compasses to radius size.

Fig. 1.45. Guiding the needle point.

Fig. 1.46. Starting circle.

Fig. 1.47. Completing a circle.

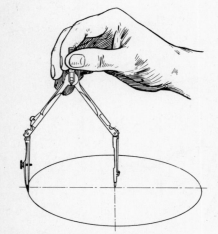

Fig. 1.48. Drawing a large circle.

at the center on the drawing, guiding it with the left hand (Fig. 1.45). Now raise the fingers to the handle and draw the circle in one sweep, rolling the handle with the thumb and forefinger, inclining the compass slightly in the direction of the line (Fig. 1.46).

The position of the fingers after the rotation is illustrated in Fig. 1.47. The pencil line may be brightened, if necessary, by making additional turns. Circles up to perhaps 3 in. in diameter may be drawn with the legs of the compass straight, but for larger sizes, both the needle-point leg and the pencil or pen leg should be bent at the knuckle joints so as to be perpendicular to the paper, Fig. 1.48. The 6-in. compass may be used in this way for circles up to perhaps 10 in. in diameter; larger circles are made by using the lengthening bar, as illustrated in Fig. 1.49, or by using the beam compass, Fig. 1.18. In drawing concentric circles, the *smallest* should always be drawn first before the center hole has become worn.

The bow instruments are used for small circles, particularly when a number are to be made of the same diameter. To avoid wear (on sidewheel instruments), the pressure of the spring against the nut may be relieved in changing the setting by holding the points in the left hand and spinning the nut in or out with the finger. Small adjustments should be made with one hand with the needle point in position on the paper, Fig. 1.50.

When several concentric circles are to be drawn, a saving in time may be had by marking off the several radii on the paper from the scale and then setting the compass to each mark as the circles are made. In some cases it may be advantageous to measure and mark the radius on the paper instead of setting the compass directly on the scale. This method must be used whenever the radius is greater than the length of the scale.

When *extreme accuracy* is required, the compasses are set, a light circle is drawn on the paper, and the diameter is checked with the scale; if the size is not satisfactory, the compasses are adjusted and the operation repeated until the size needed is obtained.

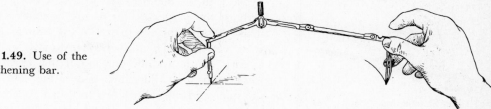

Fig. 1.49. Use of the lengthening bar.

1.37. The Ruling Pen. The ruling pen is for inking straight lines and noncircular curves. Several types are illustrated in Fig. 1.19. The important feature is the shape of the blades; they should have a well-designed ink space between them, and their points should be rounded (actually elliptical in form) equally, as in Fig. 1.51. If pointed, as in Fig. 1.52, the ink will arch up as shown and will be provokingly hard to start. If rounded to a blunt point, as in Fig. 1.53, the ink will flow too freely, the result being bulbs and overruns at the ends of the lines. Pens in constant use become dull and worn, as illustrated in Fig. 1.54. It is easy to tell whether or not a pen is dull by looking for the reflection of light that travels from the side and over the end of the point when the pen is turned in the hand. If the reflection can be seen all the way the pen is too dull. A pen in poor condition is an abomination, but a well-sharpened one is a delight to use. Every draftsman should be able to keep his pens in fine condition.

High-grade pens usually come from the makers well sharpened. Cheaper ones often need sharpening before they can be used.

1.38. To Sharpen a Pen. The best stone for the purpose is a hard Arkansas knife piece. It is well to soak a new stone in oil for several days before using. The ordinary carpenter's oilstone is too coarse for drawing instruments.

The nibs must first be brought to the correct shape, as in Fig. 1.51. Screw the nibs together until they touch and, holding the pen as in drawing a line, draw it back and forth on the stone, starting the

Fig. 1.50. Adjusting the bow pen.

Fig. 1.51. Correct shape of nibs.

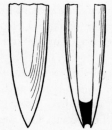

Fig. 1.52. Incorrect shape of ruling-pen nibs.

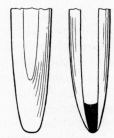

Fig. 1.53. Incorrect shape of ruling-pen nibs.

Fig. 1.54. Incorrect shape of ruling-pen nibs.

Fig. 1.55. Sharpening a pen.

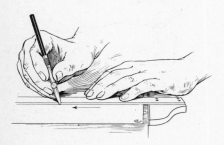

Fig. 1.56. Correct position of ruling pen.

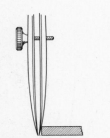

Fig. 1.57. Correct pen position.

stroke with the handle at 30° or less with the stone and swinging it up past the perpendicular as the line across the stone progresses. This will bring the nibs to exactly the same shape and length, leaving them very dull. Then open them slightly, and sharpen each blade in turn, on the outside only, until the bright spot on the end has just disappeared. Hold the pen, as in Fig. 1.55, at a small angle with the stone and rub it back and forth with a slight oscillating or rocking motion to conform to the shape of the blade. A stone 3 or 4 in. long held in the left hand with the thumb and fingers gives better control than one laid on the table. Silicon carbide cloth or paper may be substituted for the stone, and for a fine job, crocus cloth may be used for finishing. A pocket magnifying glass may be of aid in examining the points. The blades should not be sharp enough to cut the paper when tested by drawing a line across it without ink. If oversharpened, the blades should again be brought to touch and a line swung very lightly across the stone as in the first operation. When tested with ink, the pen should be capable of drawing clean sharp lines down to the finest hairline. If these finest lines are ragged or broken, the pen is not perfectly sharpened. It should not be necessary to touch the inside of the blades unless a burr has been formed, which might occur if the metal is very soft, the stone too coarse, or the pressure too heavy. To remove such a burr, or wire edge, draw a strip of detail paper between the nibs, or open the pen wide and lay the entire inner surface of the blade flat on the stone and move it with a very light touch.

1.39. Use of the Ruling Pen. The ruling pen is always used in connection with a guiding edge, T square, triangle, straightedge, or curve. The T square and triangle should be held in the same positions as for penciling.

To fill the pen, take it to the bottle and touch the quill filler between the nibs, being careful not to get any ink on the outside of the blades. If the newer plastic squeeze bottle is employed, place the small spout against the sides of the nibs and carefully squeeze a drop of ink *between* the nibs. Not more than $\frac{3}{16}$ to $\frac{1}{4}$ in. of ink should be put in; otherwise the weight of the ink will cause it to drop out in a blot. The pen should be held in the fingertips, as illustrated in Fig. 1.56, with the thumb and second finger against the sides of the nibs and the handle resting on the forefinger. This hold should be observed carefully, as the tendency will be to bend the second finger to the position used when a pencil or writing pen is held. The position illustrated aids in keeping the pen at the proper angle and the nibs aligned with the ruling edge.

The pen should be held against the straightedge or guide with the blades parallel to it, the screw being on the outside and the handle inclined slightly to the right and always kept in a plane passing through the line and perpendicular to the paper. The pen is thus guided by the upper edge of the guide, as illustrated in actual size in Fig. 1.57. If the pen point is thrown out from the perpendicular, it will run on one blade and a line ragged on one side will result. If the pen is turned in from the perpendicular, the ink is very likely to run under the edge of the guide and cause a blot.

A line is drawn with a steady, even arm movement, the tips of the third and fourth fingers resting on, and sliding along, the straightedge, keeping the angle of inclination constant. Just before the end of the line is reached, the two guiding fingers on the straightedge should be stopped and, without stopping the motion of the pen, the line finished with a finger movement. Short lines are drawn with this finger movement alone. When the end of the line is reached, the pen is lifted quickly and the straightedge moved away from the line. The pressure on the paper should be light but sufficient to give a clean-cut line, and it will vary with the kind of paper and the sharpness of the pen. The pressure against the T square, however, should be only enough to guide the direction.

If the ink refuses to flow, it may be because it has dried in the extreme point of the pen. If pinching the blades slightly or touching the pen on the finger does not start it, the pen should immediately be wiped out and fresh ink supplied. Pens must be wiped clean after using.

In inking on either paper or cloth, the full lines will be much wider than the pencil lines, and thus the beginner must be very careful to have the center of the ink line cover the pencil line, as shown in Fig. 1.58.

Instructions in regard to the ruling pen apply also to the compasses. The instrument should be slightly inclined in the direction of the line and both nibs of the pen kept on the paper, bending the knuckle joints, if necessary, to effect this.

It is a universal rule in inking that *circles and circle arcs must be inked first*. It is much easier to connect a straight line to a curve than a curve to a straight line.

1.40. Tangents. It should be noted particularly that two lines are tangent to each other when the center lines of the lines are tangent and not simply when the lines touch each other; thus at the point of tangency, the width will be equal to the width of a single line, Fig. 1.59. Before inking tangent lines, the point of tangency should be marked in pencil. For an arc tangent to a straight line, this point will be on a line through the center of the arc and perpendicular to the straight line and for two circle arcs will be on the line joining their centers, as described in paragraphs 2.8 to 2.19.

Fig. 1.58. Inking a pencil line.

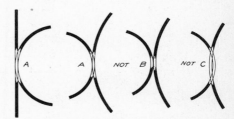

Fig. 1.59. Correct and incorrect tangents.

1.41. The "Alphabet of Lines." As the basis of drawing is the line, a set of conventional symbols covering all the lines needed for different purposes may properly be called an alphabet of lines. Figure 1.60 shows the alphabet of lines adopted by the American Standards Association (ASA) as applied to the following:

1. Layout drawings in pencil on detail paper to be traced on tracing paper or cloth

2. Drawings either made directly or traced in pencil on tracing paper or pencil cloth, from which blueprints or other reproductions are to be made

3. Tracings in ink on tracing cloth or tracing paper and inked drawings on white paper for display or photoreproductions.

The ASA recommends three widths of lines, thick, medium, and thin, for finished drawings, as follows: *thick* for visible outlines and

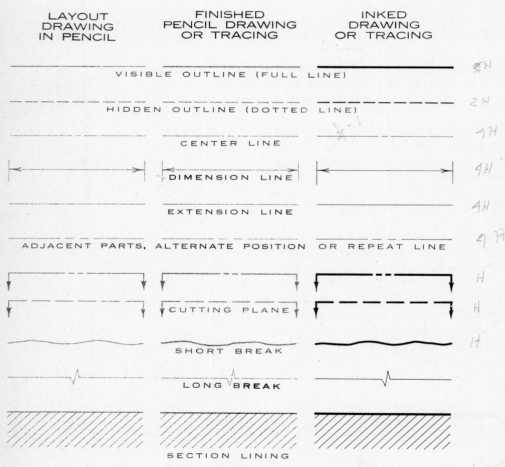

Fig. 1.60. The alphabet of lines.

cutting-plane and short-break lines; *medium* for hidden outlines; and *thin* for section, center, extension, dimension, long-break, adjacent-part, alternate-position, and repeat lines. The actual widths of the three weights of lines, on average drawings, should be about as given in Fig. 1.60. A convenient line gage is illustrated in Fig. 1.61. If applied to Fig. 1.60, this gage would show the heavy lines in ink to be between $\frac{1}{40}$ and $\frac{1}{50}$ in., the medium lines $\frac{1}{80}$ in., and the fine lines $\frac{1}{200}$ in. in width. To use the line gage, draw a line about $1\frac{1}{2}$ in. long in pencil or ink on a piece of the drawing paper, and apply it alongside the gage. By this method a very good comparison can be made. Figure 1.62 shows the application of the alphabet of lines.

1.42. Line Practice. After reading the preceding several paragraphs, the beginner should take a blank sheet of paper and practice making straight lines and circles in all the forms, full, dotted, etc., shown in Fig. 1.60. The practice should include starting and stopping lines, with special attention to tangents and corners.

In pencil, try to get all the lines uniform in width and color for each type. Circle arcs and straight lines should match exactly at tangent points.

In ink, proceed as for pencil practice and pay particular attention to the weight of lines and to the spacing of dashed-in dotted lines and center lines.

If inked lines appear imperfect in any way, the reason should be ascertained immediately. It may be the fault of the pen, the ink,

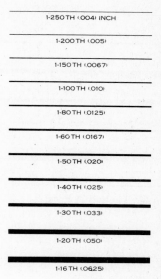

Fig. 1.61. Line gage.

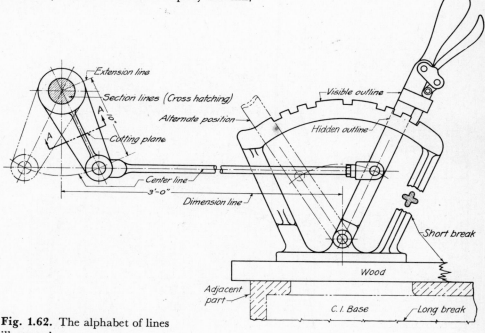

Fig. 1.62. The alphabet of lines illustrated.

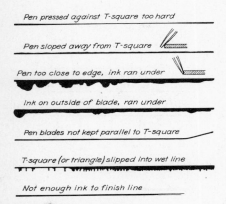

Pen pressed against T-square too hard

Pen sloped away from T-square

Pen too close to edge, ink ran under

Ink on outside of blade, ran under

Pen blades not kept parallel to T-square

T-square (or triangle) slipped into wet line

Not enough ink to finish line

Fig. 1.63. Faulty ink lines.

the paper, or the draftsman; the probabilities are greatly in favor of the last if the faults resemble those of Fig. 1.63, which illustrates the characteristic appearance of several kinds of poor line. The correction in each case will suggest itself.

1.43. Use of the French Curve. The french curve, as has been stated on page 17, is a guiding edge for noncircular curves. When sufficient points have been determined, it is best to sketch in the line lightly in pencil, freehand and without losing the points, until it is clean, smooth, continuous, and satisfactory to the eye. The curve should then be applied to it, selecting a part that will fit a portion of the line most nearly and seeing to it, particularly, that the curve is so placed that the direction in which its curvature increases is the direction in which the curvature of the line increases, Fig. 1.64. In drawing that part of the line matched by the curve, *always* stop a little short of the distance in which the guide and the line seem to coincide. After drawing this portion, shift the curve to find another place that will coincide with the continuation of the line. In shifting the curve, care should be taken to preserve smoothness and continuity and to avoid breaks or cusps. This may be done if, in its successive positions, the curve is always adjusted so that it coincides for a short distance with the part of the line already drawn. Thus at each junction the tangents will coincide.

If the curved line is symmetrical about an axis, marks locating this axis, after it has been matched accurately on one side, may be made in pencil on the curve and the curve then reversed. In such a case exceptional care must be taken to avoid a "hump" at the joint.

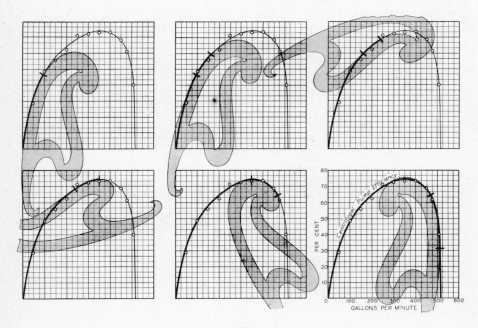

Fig. 1.64. Use of the french curve.

It is often better to stop a line short of the axis on each side and close the gap afterward with another setting of the curve.

When using the curve in inking, the pen should be held perpendicular and the blades kept parallel to the edge. Inking curves will be found to be excellent practice.

Sometimes, particularly at sharp turns, a combination of circle arcs and curves may be used: In inking a long narrow ellipse, for example, the sharp curves may be inked by selecting a center on the major diameter by trial, drawing as much arc as will practically coincide with the ends of the ellipse, and then finishing the ellipse with the curve. The experienced draftsman will sometimes ink a curve that cannot be matched accurately by varying the distance of the pen point from the ruling edge as the line progresses.

1.44. Erasing. The manner of erasing both pencil lines and ink lines is a necessary technique to learn. A designer, working freely but lightly, uses a soft pencil eraser when changing some detail so as not to damage the finish of the paper. Heavier lines are best removed by a Ruby pencil eraser. If the paper has been grooved by the line, it may be rubbed over with a burnisher or even with the back of the thumbnail. In erasing an ink line, hold the paper down firmly and, with a Ruby pencil eraser, rub lightly and patiently, first along the line and then across it, until the ink is removed. A triangle slipped under the paper or cloth gives a good backing surface.

When an erasure is to be made close to other lines, select an opening of the best shape on the erasing shield and rub through it, holding the shield down firmly and first seeing that both of its sides are clean. Wipe off the eraser crumbs from the paper with a dustcloth or brush. Never scratch out a line or a blot with a knife or razor blade, and use so-called ink erasers very sparingly, if at all. A skilled draftsman sometimes uses a sharp blade to trim a thickened spot or overrunning end on a line. For extensive erasing, an electric erasing machine is a great convenience. Several successful models are on the market.

1.45. Special Instruments. Various instruments, such as drafting machines, parallel rules, pantographs, lettering machines, and proportional dividers, not in the usual draftsman's outfit are used in commercial drafting work.

1.46. Exercises in the Use of Instruments. The following may be used as progressive exercises for practice in using the instruments, doing them either as finished pencil drawings or in pencil layout to be inked. Line work should conform to that given in the alphabet of lines, Fig. 1.60.

The problems in Chap. 2 afford excellent additional practice in accurate penciling.

PROBLEMS

Group 1. Straight lines

Prob. 1.1.1

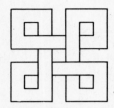

Prob. 1.1.2

Prob. 1.1.3

1.1.1. An exercise for the T square, triangle, and scale. Through the center of the space draw a horizontal and a vertical line. Measuring on these lines as diameters, lay off a 4-in. square. Along the lower side and upper half of the left side measure ½-in. spaces with the scale. Draw all horizontal lines with the T square and all vertical lines with the T square and triangle.

1.1.2. An interlacement. For T square, triangle, and dividers. Draw a 4-in. square. Divide the left side and lower side into seven equal parts with dividers. Draw horizontal and vertical lines across the square through these points. Erase the parts not needed.

1.1.3. A street-paving intersection. For 45° triangle and scale. An exercise in starting and stopping short lines. Draw a 4-in. square. Draw its diagonals with 45° triangle. With the scale, lay off ½-in. spaces along the diagonals from their intersection. With 45° triangle, complete the figure, finishing one quarter at a time.

Prob. 1.1.4

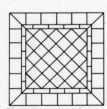

Prob. 1.1.5

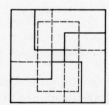

Prob. 1.1.6

1.1.4. A square pattern. For 45° triangle, dividers, and scale. Draw a 4-in. square and divide its sides into three equal parts with dividers. With 45° triangle, draw diagonal lines connecting these points. Measure ⅜ in. on each side of these lines, and finish the pattern as shown.

1.1.5. An acoustic pattern. For 45° triangle, T square, and scale. Draw two intersecting 45° diagonals 4 in. long, to form a field. With the scale lay off ½-in. spaces from their intersection. Add the narrow border 3/16 in. wide. Add a second border ½ in. wide. The length of the border blocks is projected from the corners of the field blocks.

1.1.6. Five cards. Visible and hidden lines. Five cards 1¾ by 3 in. are arranged with the bottom card in the center, the other four overlapping each other and placed so that their outside edges form a 4-in. square. Hidden lines indicate edges covered.

1.1.7. A Maltese cross. For T square, spacers, and both triangles. Draw a 4-in. square and a 1⅜-in. square. From the corners of the inner square, draw lines to the outer square at 15° and 75°, with the two triangles in combination. Mark points with spacers ¼ in. inside each line of this outside cross, and complete the figure with triangles in combination.

Prob. 1.1.7

Group 2. Straight lines and circles

Prob. 1.2.1

Prob. 1.2.2

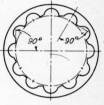

Prob. 1.2.3

1.2.1. Insigne. For T square, triangles, scale, and compasses. Draw the 45° diagonals and the vertical and horizontal center lines of a 4-in. square. With compass, draw a ¾-in.-diameter construction circle and a 2¾- and 3¼-in. circle. Complete the design by adding a square and pointed star as shown.

1.2.2. A six-pointed star. For compass and 30°-60° triangle. Draw a 4-in. construction circle and inscribe the six-pointed star with the T square and 30°-60° triangle. Accomplish this with four successive changes of position of the triangle.

1.2.3. A stamping. For T square, 30°-60° triangle, and compasses. In a 4-in. circle draw six diameters 30° apart. Draw a 3-in. construction circle to locate the centers of ⁵⁄₁₆-in.-radius circle arcs. Complete the stamping with perpendiculars to the six diameters as shown.

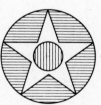

Prob. 1.2.4

Prob. 1.2.5

1.2.4. Aircraft insigne. This device is a white star with a red center on a blue background. Draw a 4-in. circle and a 1¼-in. circle. Divide the large circle into five equal parts with the dividers and construct the star by connecting alternate points as shown. Red is indicated by vertical lines and blue by horizontal lines. Space these by eye approximately ¹⁄₁₆-in. apart.

1.2.5. A 24-point star. For T square and triangles in combination. In a 4-in. circle draw 12 diameters 15° apart, using T square and triangles singly and in combination. With the same combinations, finish the figure as shown.

Group 3. Circles and tangents

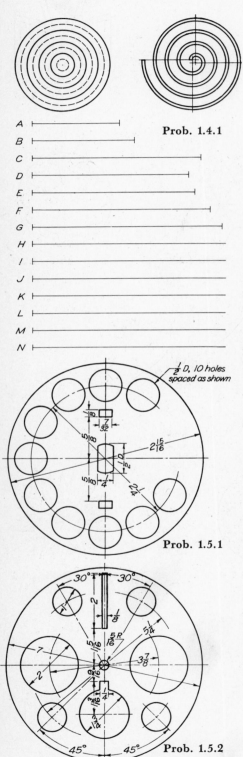

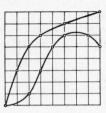

Left to Right:
Prob. 1.3.1
Prob. 1.3.2
Prob. 1.3.3
Prob. 1.3.4

Prob. 1.4.1

1.3.1. Concentric circles. For compasses (legs straight) and scale. Draw a horizontal line through the center of a space. On it mark off radii for eight concentric circles ¼ in. apart. In drawing concentric circles, always draw the smallest first.

1.3.2. A four-centered spiral. For accurate tangents. Draw a ⅛-in. square and extend its sides as shown. With the upper right corner as center, draw quadrants with ⅛- and ¼-in. radii. Continue with quadrants from each corner in order until four turns have been drawn.

1.3.3. A loop ornament. For bow compasses. Draw a 2-in. square, about center of space. Divide AE into four ¼-in. spaces with scale. With bow pencil and centers A, B, C, and D, draw four semicircles with ¼-in. radius, and so on. Complete the figure by drawing the horizontal and vertical tangents as shown.

1.3.4. A rectilinear chart. For french curve. Draw a 4-in. field with ½-in. coordinate divisions. Plot points at the intersections shown, and through them sketch a smooth curve very lightly in pencil. Finish by marking each point with a ⅟₁₆-in. circle and drawing a smooth line with the french curve.

Group 4. Scales

1.4.1. Scale practice. *a.* Measure lines A to G to the following scales: A, full size; B, ½ size; C, 3″ = 1′-0″; D, 1″ = 1′-0″; E, ¾″ = 1′-0″; F, ¼″ = 1′-0″; G, ⁳⁄₁₆″ = 1′-0″.

b. Lay off distances on lines H to N as follows: H, 3³⁄₁₆″, full size; I, 7″, ½ size; J, 2′-6″, 1½″ = 1′-0″; K, 7′-5½″, ½″ = 1′-0″; L, 10′-11″, ⅜″ = 1′-0″; M, 28′-4″, ⅛″ = 1′-0″; N, 40′-10″, ⁳⁄₃₂″ = 1′-0″.

c. For engineer's scale. Lay off distances on lines H to N as follows: H, 3.2″, full size; I, 27′-0″, 1″ = 10′-0″; J, 66′-0″, 1″ = 20′-0″; K, 105′-0″, 1″ = 30′-0″; L, 156′-0″, 1″ = 40′-0″; M, 183′-0″, 1″ = 50′-0″; N, 214′-0″, 1″ = 60′-0″.

Group 5. Combinations

1.5.1. A telephone dial plate. Draw double size.

1.5.2. A film-reel stamping. Draw to scale of 6″ = 1′-0″.

1.5.3. Box cover. Make one-view drawing for rectangular stamping 3 by 4 in., corners rounded with ½-in. radius. Four holes, one in each corner, ³⁄₁₆-in. diameter, 3 and 2 in. center to center, for fasteners. Rectangular hole in center, ⅜ by 1 in., with 1-in. side parallel to 4-in. side. Two slots ¼ in. wide, 2 in. long with semicircular ends, located midway between center and 4-in. edges, with 2-in. side parallel to 4-in. side and centered between 3-in. edges.

Prob. 1.5.1

Prob. 1.5.2

1.5.4. Spacer. Make one-view drawing for circular stamping 4 in. OD, 2 in. ID. Six ¼-in.-diameter holes equally spaced on 3-in.-diameter circle, with two holes on vertical center line. Two semicircular notches 180° apart made with ⅜-in. radius centered at intersections of horizontal center line and 4-in.-OD circle.

1.5.5. Blank for wheel. Make a one-view drawing for stamping 5 in. OD; center hole ½ in. in diameter; eight spokes ⅜ in. wide connecting 1½-in.-diameter center portion with ½-in. rim. Eight ¼-in.-diameter holes with centers at intersection of center lines of spokes and 4½-in. circle; ⅛-in. fillets throughout to break sharp corners.

1.5.6. Cover plate. Make a one-view drawing for rectangular stamping 3 by 4 in., corners beveled ½-in. each way. Four holes, one in each corner, ¼-in. diameter. 3 and 2 in. center to center, for fasteners. Rectangular hole in center, ½ by 1 in. with 1-in. side parallel to 4-in. side. Two holes, ¾-in. diameter, located midway between the slot and short side of rectangle on center line through slot.

A LIST OF CAUTIONS

Never use the scale as a ruler.

Never draw horizontal lines with the lower edge of the T square.

Never use the lower edge of the T square as a horizontal base for the triangles.

Never cut paper with a knife and the edge of the T square as a guide.

Never use the T square as a hammer.

Never put either end of a pencil into the mouth.

Never work with a dull pencil.

Never sharpen a pencil over the drawing board.

Never jab the dividers into the drawing board.

Never oil the joints of compasses.

Never use the dividers as reamers, pincers, or picks.

Never use a blotter on inked lines.

Never screw the pen adjustment past the contact point of the nibs.

Never leave the ink bottle uncorked.

Never hold the pen over the drawing while filling.

Never put into the drawing-ink bottle a writing pen which has been used in ordinary writing ink.

Never try to use the same thumbtack holes in either paper or board when putting paper down a second time.

Never scrub a drawing all over with an eraser after finishing. It takes the life out of the lines.

Never begin work without wiping off the table and instruments.

Never put instruments away without cleaning. This applies with particular force to pens.

Never put bow instruments away without opening to relieve the spring.

Never work with the table cluttered with unneeded instruments or equipment.

Never fold a drawing or tracing.

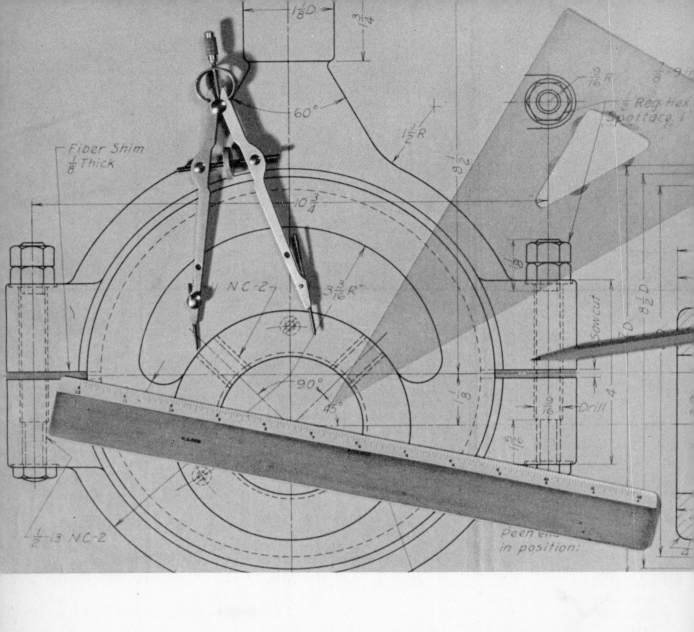

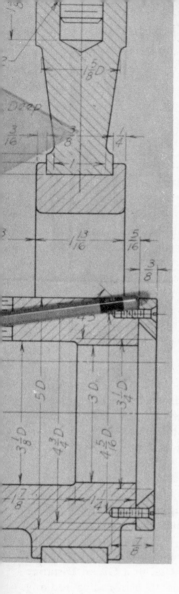

2

APPLIED GEOMETRY

2.1. Strict interpretation of constructional geometry allows only the use of a straightedge and compasses, and with these the geometer, following mathematical theory, accomplishes his solutions. The draftsman constantly employs the principles of geometry, but he is not restricted to the basic instruments. T square, triangles, scale, curves, etc., are used to make constructions with speed and accuracy. Therefore, the methods given in this chapter are the ones which the draftsman will use and with which he should be thoroughly familiar. It is assumed that students using this book are familiar with the elements of plane geometry and will be able to apply their knowledge. In some cases the draftsman's method may appear to differ from the purely geometric method, but the basic geometry will still be present.

Even though the constructions in this chapter are the ones which the draftsman will constantly employ, purely geometric methods appear where the draftsman's and the geometric procedure are identical. Moreover, for large layout and lofting work where the usual drafting instruments could not be used or for cases where extreme accuracy is desired, the geometric methods should be employed. On this account, geometric duplicates of drafting methods are given in the latter portion of the chapter.

The geometry of conic curves (ellipse, parabola, and hyperbola) and the construction of other curves such as the helix are not dis-

47

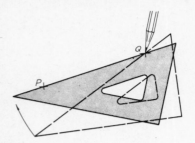

Fig. 2.1. To draw a line through two points.

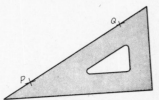

Fig. 2.2. To draw a line through two points.

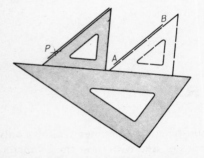

Fig. 2.3. To draw a line parallel to another.

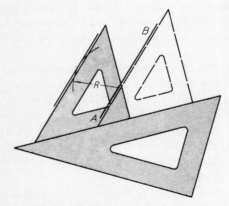

Fig. 2.4. To draw a line parallel to, and at a given distance from, another.

cussed in this chapter because the plane curve is nearly always either derived from or formed on a cylinder, cone, or other geometric surface and are therefore given in Chap. 16, Curved Lines, where the space problems may also be considered.

The constructions given here afford excellent practice in the use of instruments. Remember that the results obtained will be only as accurate as the skill of the draftsman makes them accurate. Therefore, use care in measuring and drawing so that accuracy and a professional appearance will be obtained.

As an aid in recalling the names of various geometrical figures, see Fig. 2.53 at the end of the chapter.

2.2. To Draw a Line through Two Points. *First Method* (*Fig. 2.1*). Place the point of the pencil at Q, bring the triangle or straightedge against the point of the pencil, and using this point as a pivot, swing the triangle until its edge is in alignment with point P. Then draw the line.

Second Method (*Fig. 2.2*). Align the straightedge or triangle with the given points P and Q, and then draw the line.

2.3. To Draw a Straight Line through a Point and Parallel to Another Straight Line (**Fig. 2.3**). Adjust a triangle to the given line AB with a second triangle as a base. Slide the aligned triangle to its position at point P, and draw the required line.

2.4. To Draw a Line Parallel to Another at a Given Distance from It (**Fig. 2.4**). With the given distance R as a radius and any point on the given line as a center, draw an arc. Adjust a triangle to the given line AB, with a second triangle as a base. Slide the

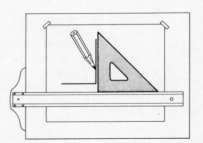

Fig. 2.5. To draw a line perpendicular to another.

Fig. 2.6. To draw a line perpendicular to another.

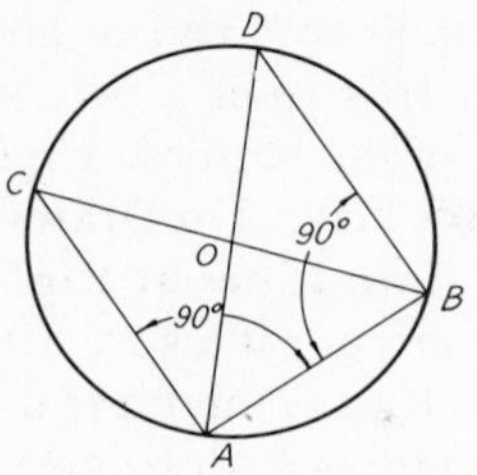

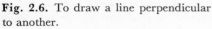

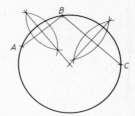

Fig. 2.7. Circle center.

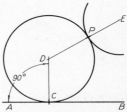

Fig. 2.8. Circle through three points.

aligned triangle to its position tangent to the circle arc, and draw the required line.

2.5. To Erect a Perpendicular to a Given Straight Line. *Given Line Horizontal* (*Fig.* 2.5). With the T square as a base and the triangle in the position shown, draw the required perpendicular.

Given Line Oblique (*Fig.* 2.6). Set a triangle with its hypotenuse against a guiding edge. Fit one side to the line, slide the triangle to the required point, and draw the perpendicular.

2.6. To Locate the Center of a Circle (**Fig. 2.7**). Draw any chord *AB*; then draw *AC* and *BD* perpendicular to *AB*. Then *AD* and *BC* are diameters of the circle and cross at center *O*.

2.7. To Draw a Circle Arc through Three Given Points (**Fig. 2.8**). Given the points *A*, *B*, and *C*, the intersection of the perpendicular bisectors of lines *AB* and *BC* will be the center of the required circle.

2.8. Tangents. One of the most frequent geometrical operations in drafting is the drawing of tangents to circle arcs and the drawing of circle arcs tangent to straight lines or other circles. These should be constructed accurately, and on pencil drawings that are to be inked or traced, the points of tangency should be located by short cross marks to show the stopping points for the ink lines. The method of finding these points is indicated in the following constructions.

2.9. To Locate Tangent Points. *First Case* (*Fig.* 2.9). To find the point of tangency for line *AB* and a circle with the center at *D*, draw *DC* perpendicular to line *AB*. Point *C* is the tangent point.

Second Case (*Fig.* 2.9). To find the point of tangency for two circle arcs, draw the line *DE* joining the centers of the given arcs. Point *P* is the tangent point.

2.10. To Draw a Circle of Given Size Tangent to a Line and Passing through a Point (**Fig. 2.10**). Draw a line *AB*, the given radius distance *R* away from and parallel to the given line; cut line *AB* at *O* with the given radius, using the given point *S* as center; *O* is the center of the circle. Note that there are two possible positions for the circle.

2.11. To Draw a Circle Tangent to a Line at a Point and Passing through a Second Point (**Fig. 2.11**). Connect the two

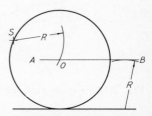

Fig. 2.9. Tangent points.

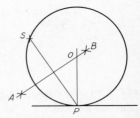

Fig. 2.10. Tangent circle.

Fig. 2.11. Tangent circle.

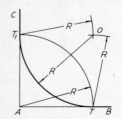

Fig. 2.12. Tangent arc.

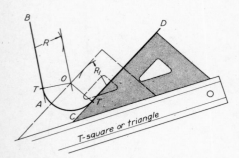

Fig. 2.13. Tangent arc, acute angle.

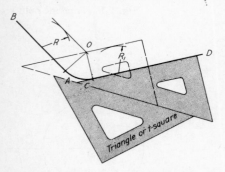

Fig. 2.14. Tangent arc, obtuse angle.

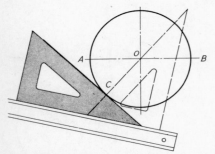

Fig. 2.15. To draw a tangent line at a point on a circle.

points P and S, and draw the perpendicular bisector AB. Where AB crosses a perpendicular to the given line at P is the center O of the required circle.

2.12. To Draw a Circle Arc of Given Radius Tangent to Two Lines at Right Angles to Each Other (Fig. 2.12). Draw an arc of radius R, with center at corner A, cutting the lines AB and AC at T and T_1; then with T and T_1 as centers and with the same radius R, draw arcs intersecting at O, the center of the required arc.

2.13. To Draw an Arc Tangent to Two Straight Lines (Figs. 2.13 and 2.14). Given the lines AB and CD, draw a tangent arc of radius R; set the compass to radius R, and at any convenient point on the given lines, draw the arcs R and R_1. With the method of Fig. 2.3, draw parallels to the given lines through the limits of the arcs. These parallels are the loci of the centers of all circles of radius R tangent to the lines AB and CD, and their intersection at point O will be the center of the required arc. Find the tangent points by erecting perpendiculars, as in Fig. 2.6, to the given lines through the center O. Figure 2.13 is for an acute angle and Fig. 2.14 for an obtuse angle.

2.14. To Draw a Tangent to a Circle at a Point on the Circle (Fig. 2.15). Given the arc ACB, draw a tangent at the point C. Arrange a triangle in combination with the T square (or another triangle) so that its hypotenuse passes through center O and point C. Holding the T square firmly in place, turn the triangle about its square corner and move it until the hypotenuse passes through C; the required tangent then lies along the hypotenuse. (For small constructions or with a large triangle, this may be done more quickly by setting the hypotenuse of the triangle on the T square, as in Fig. 1.35B.)

2.15. To Draw a Tangent to a Circle from a Point Outside (Fig. 2.16). Given the arc ACB and point P, draw a tangent from point P to the given arc; arrange a triangle in combination with another triangle (or T square) so that one side passes through point P and is tangent to the circle arc at C. Now slide the triangle until the right-angle side passes through the center of the circle, and lightly mark the tangent point C. Then bring the triangle back to its original position, and draw the tangent line.

2.16. To Draw a Tangent to Two Circles. *First Case: Open Belt* (*Fig.* 2.17). Arrange a triangle in combination with a T square, or triangle so that one side is in the tangent position. Move to positions 2 and 3, marking lightly the tangent points T_1 and T_2. Return to the original position and draw the tangent line.

2.17. To Draw a Tangent to Two Circles. *Second Case: Crossed Belt (Fig.* 2.18). Arrange a triangle in combination with a T square or triangle so that one side is in the tangent position. Move to positions 2 and 3, marking lightly the tangent points T_1 and T_2. Return to the original position and draw the tangent line. Repeat for the other side.

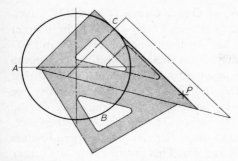

Fig. 2.16. To draw a tangent to a circle from an outside point.

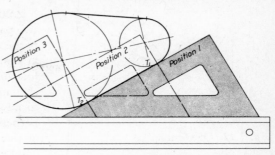

Fig. 2.17. Tangent lines, open belt.

2.18. To Draw a Circle of Radius R Tangent to a Given Circle and a Straight Line (**Fig. 2.19**). Let AB be the given line and R_1 the radius of the given circle. Draw a line CD parallel to AB at a distance R from it. With O as a center and radius $R + R_1$, swing an arc intersecting CD at X, the desired center. The tangent point for AB will be on a perpendicular to AB from X; the tangent point for the two circles will be on a line joining their centers X and O. Note that, when two circles are tangent to each other, the point of tangency must be on a line through their centers.

2.19. To Draw a Circle of Radius R Tangent to Two Given Circles. *First Case* (*Fig. 2.20*). For this case the centers of the given circles are outside the required circle. Let R_1 and R_2 be the radii of the given circles having centers O and P, respectively. With O as a center and a radius $R + R_1$, describe an arc. With P as a center and a radius $R + R_2$, swing another arc intersecting the first arc at Q, which is the center sought. Mark the tangent points in line with OQ and QP.

Second Case (*Fig. 2.21*). For this case the centers of the given circles are inside the required circle. With O and P as centers and radii $R - R_1$ and $R - R_2$, describe arcs that will intersect at the required center Q.

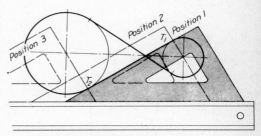

Fig. 2.18. Tangent lines, crossed belt.

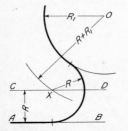

Fig. 2.19. Tangent arcs.

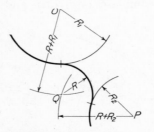

Fig. 2.20. Tangent arcs.

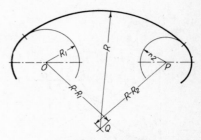

Fig. 2.21. Tangent arcs.

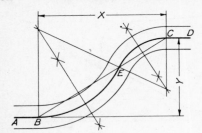

Fig. 2.22. Ogee curve.

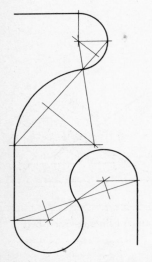

Fig. 2.23. Ogee applications.

2.20. To Draw a Reverse, or Ogee, Curve (Fig. 2.22). Given two parallel lines *AB* and *CD*, join *B* and *C* by a straight line. Erect perpendiculars at *B* and *C*. Any arcs tangent to lines *AB* and *CD* at *B* and *C* must have their centers on these perpendiculars. On the line *BC* assume point *E*, the point through which it is desired that the curve shall pass. Bisect *BE* and *EC* by perpendiculars. Any arc to pass through *B* and *E* must have its center somewhere on the perpendicular from the middle point. The intersection, therefore, of these perpendicular bisectors with the first two perpendiculars will be the centers for arcs *BE* and *EC*. This line might be the center line for a curved road or pipe. The construction may be checked by drawing the line of centers, which *must* pass through *E*. Figure 2.23 illustrates the principle of reverse-curve construction in various combinations.

2.21. To Draw a Reverse Curve Tangent to Two Lines and to a Third Secant Line at a Given Point (Fig. 2.24). Given two lines *AB* and *CD* cut by the line *EF* at points *E* and *F*, draw a perpendicular *JH* to *EF* through a given point *P* on *EF*. With *E* as a center and radius *EP*, intersect *CD* at *G*. Draw a perpendicular from *G* intersecting *JH* at *H*. With *F* as the center and a radius *FP*, intersect *AB* at *K*. Draw a perpendicular to *AB* from *K* intersecting *JH* at *J*. *H* and *J* will be the centers for arcs tangent to the three lines.

2.22. To Lay out a Given Angle. *Tangent Method (Fig. 2.25).* The trigonometrical tangent of an angle is the ratio of the side opposite divided by the side adjacent. Thus $Y/X = \tan A$, or $X \tan A = Y$. To lay out a given angle, obtain the value of the tangent from the table of natural tangents (Appendix), assume any convenient distance *X*, and multiply *X* by the tangent to get distance *Y*. Note that the angle between the sides *X* and *Y* must be a right angle.

2.23. To Lay out a Given Angle. *Chordal Method (Fig. 2.26).* If the length of the chord is known for an arc of given radius and included angle, the angle may be accurately laid out. Given an angle in degrees, lay out the angle as follows: Obtain the chord length for a 1-in. circle arc from the table in the Appendix. Select any convenient arc length *R*, and multiply the chord length for a 1-in. arc by this distance, thus obtaining the chord length *C* for the radius distance selected. Lay out the chord length on the arc with compasses or dividers and complete the sides of the angle.

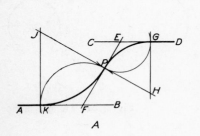

A

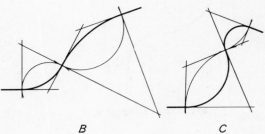

B   *C*

Fig. 2.24. Reverse curve tangent to three lines.

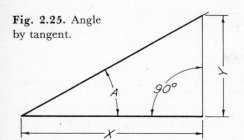

Fig. 2.25. Angle by tangent.

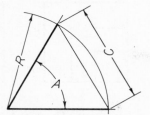

Fig. 2.26. Angle by chord.

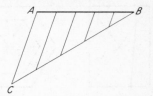

Fig. 2.27. To divide a line.

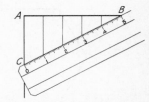

Fig. 2.28. To divide a line.

The chord length for an angle may be had from a sine table by taking the sine of half the given angle and multiplying by two.

2.24. To Divide a Line. *First Method* (*Fig.* 2.27). To divide a line *AB* into, say, five equal parts, draw any line *BC* of indefinite length; on it measure or step off five divisions of convenient length; connect the last point with *A*; and using triangles and a straightedge as shown in Fig. 1.34, draw lines through the points parallel to *CA* intersecting *AB*.

Second Method (*Figs.* 2.28 *and* 2.29). First, draw a perpendicular *AC* from *A*; then place a scale so that five convenient equal divisions are included between *B* and the perpendicular, as in Fig. 2.28. With a triangle and T square draw perpendiculars through the points marked, thus dividing the line *AB* into five parts, as required. Figure 2.29 illustrates an application in laying off stair risers. This method may be used for dividing a line into any series of proportional parts.

2.25. To Construct a Triangle, Given the Three Sides (**Fig. 2.30**). Given the lengths *A*, *B*, and *C*, draw one side *A* in the desired position. With its ends as centers and radii *B* and *C*, draw two intersecting arcs as shown. This construction is used extensively in developments by triangulation.

2.26. To Transfer a Polygon to a New Base. *By Triangulation* (*Fig.* 2.31). Given polygon *ABCDEF* and a new position of base *A'B'*, consider each point as the vertex of a triangle whose base is *AB*. With centers *A'* and *B'* and radii *AC* and *BC*, describe intersecting arcs locating the point *C'*. Similarly, with radii *AD* and *BD*, locate point *D'*. Connect *B'C'* and *C'D'*, and continue the operation always using *A* and *B* as centers.

Box, or Offset, Method (*Fig.* 2.32). Enclose the polygon in a rectangu-

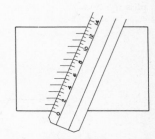

Fig. 2.29. To divide a line.

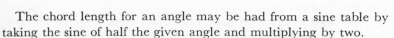
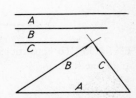

Fig. 2.30. To construct a triangle.

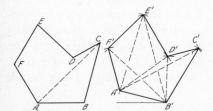

Fig. 2.31. To transfer a polygon by triangulation.

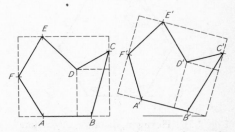

Fig. 2.32. To transfer a polygon by "boxing."

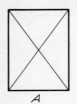
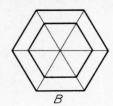

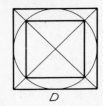

Fig. 2.33. Uses of the diagonal.

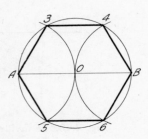

Fig. 2.34. To construct a hexagon, compass method.

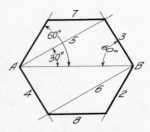

Fig. 2.35. To construct a hexagon, triangle method.

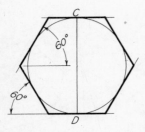

Fig. 2.36. Hexagon, distance across flats given.

lar "box." Draw the box on the new base (method of Fig. 1.35); locate the points *ABCEF* on this box; then set point *D* by rectangular coordinates as shown.

2.27. Uses of the Diagonal. The diagonal may be used in many ways to simplify construction and save drafting time. Figure 2.33 illustrates the diagonal used at (*A*) for locating the center of a rectangle, at (*B*) for enlarging or reducing a geometrical shape, at (*C*) for producing similar figures having the same base, and at (*D*) for drawing inscribed or circumscribed figures.

2.28. To Construct a Regular Hexagon, Given the Distance Across Corners. *First Method* (*Fig.* 2.34). Draw a circle on *AB* as a diameter. With the same radius and *A* and *B* as centers, draw arcs intersecting the circle and connect the points.

Second Method (*without Compasses*). Draw lines with the 30°-60° triangle in the order shown in Fig. 2.35.

2.29. Given the Distance across Flats. The distance across flats is the diameter of the inscribed circle. Draw this circle, and with the 30°-60° triangle, draw tangents to it as in Fig. 2.36.

2.30. To Inscribe a Regular Pentagon in a Circle (**Fig. 2.37**). Draw a diameter *AB* and a radius *OC* perpendicular to it. Bisect *OB*. With this point *D* as center and a radius *DC*, draw arc *CE*. With center *C* and radius *CE*, draw arc *EF*. *CF* is the side of the pentagon. Step off this distance around the circle with the dividers. Instead of using this geometrical method, most draftsmen prefer to guess at *CF* and divide the circle by trial, as described in paragraph 1.36.

2.31. To Draw a Regular Octagon in a Square (**Fig. 2.38**). Draw the diagonals of the square. With the corners of the square as centers and a radius of half the diagonal, draw arcs intersecting the sides of the square, and connect these points.

2.32. To Construct a Regular Polygon, Given One Side (**Fig. 2.39**). Let the polygon have seven sides. With the side *AB* as a radius and *A* as the center, draw a semicircle and divide into seven equal parts with dividers. Through the second division from the left draw radial line *A-2*. Through points 3 to 6, extend radial lines as shown. With *AB* as the radius and *B* as the center, cut line *A-6* at *C*. With *C* as the center and the same radius, cut *A-5* at *D*, and so on at *E* and *F*. Connect the points, *or*, after *A-2* is found, draw the circumscribing circle.

2.33. Geometric Methods. As stated in paragraph 2.1, there are cases when the drafting instruments are impractical, either because

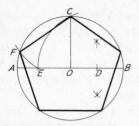

Fig. 2.37. Pentagon.

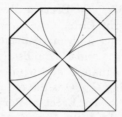

Fig. 2.38. Octagon.

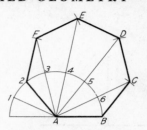

Fig. 2.39. Polygon.

of size limitations or when extreme accuracy is necessary. The geometric methods for common cases of parallelism, perpendicularity, and tangency are given in the paragraphs following.

2.34. To Draw a Line through a Point and Parallel to a Given Line (**Fig. 2.40**). With P as the center and a radius of sufficient length, draw an arc CE intersecting the line AB at C. With C as the center and the same radius, draw the arc PD. With center C and radius DP, draw an arc intersecting CE at E. Then EP is the required line.

2.35. To Draw a Line Parallel to Another at a Given Distance. *For Straight Lines* (*Fig.* 2.41). With the given distance as a radius and two points on the given line as centers (as far apart as convenient), draw two arcs. A line tangent to these arcs will be the required line.

For Curved Lines (*Fig.* 2.42). Draw a series of arcs with centers along the line. Draw tangents to these arcs with a french curve; see Fig. 1.64.

2.36. To Erect a Perpendicular from a Point to a Given Straight Line (**Fig. 2.43**). With point P as the center and any convenient radius R_1, draw a circle arc intersecting the given line at A and B. With any convenient radius R_2 and with centers at A and B, draw intersecting arcs locating Q. The required perpendicular is PQ, with S the intersection of the perpendicular and given line.

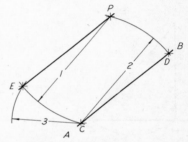

Fig. 2.40. Parallel lines, geometric method.

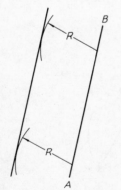

Fig. 2.41. Parallel lines, geometric method.

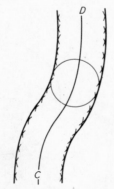

Fig. 2.42. Curved parallel lines, geometric method.

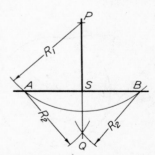

Fig. 2.43. Perpendicular lines, geometric method.

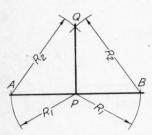

Fig. 2.44. Perpendicular lines, geometric method.

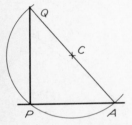

Fig. 2.45. Perpendicular lines, geometric method.

2.37. To Erect a Perpendicular from a Point on a Given Straight Line. *First Method* (*Fig.* 2.44). With point P on the line as center and any convenient radius R_1, draw circle arcs to locate points A and B equidistant from P. With any convenient radius R_2 longer than R_1 and with centers at A and B, draw intersecting arcs locating Q. PQ is the required perpendicular.

2.38. To Erect a Perpendicular from a Point on a Given Straight Line. *Second Method* (*Fig.* 2.45). With any convenient center C and radius CP, draw somewhat more than a semicircle from the intersection of the circle arc with the given line at A. Draw AC extended to meet the circle arc at Q. PQ is the required perpendicular.

2.39. To Draw a Tangent to a Circle at a Point on the Circle (**Fig. 2.46**). Given the arc ACB and to draw a tangent at point C, draw the diameter CD and locate point M; then with any convenient radius R_1, locate point P equidistant from C and M; now with the same radius R_1, draw somewhat more than a semicircle and draw the line MPQ. The line QC is a tangent to the circle at point C. (See also Fig. 2.45.)

2.40. To Draw a Tangent to a Circle from a Point Outside (**Fig. 2.47**). Connect the point P with the center of the circle O. Then draw the perpendicular bisector of OP, and with the intersection at D, draw a semicircle. Its intersection with the given circle is the point of tangency. Draw tangent line from P.

2.41. To Draw a Tangent to Two Circles. *First Case: Open Belt* (*Fig.* 2.48). At center O draw a circle with a radius $R_1 - R_2$. From P draw a tangent to this circle by the method of Fig. 2.47. Extend OT to T_1, and draw PT_2 parallel to OT_1. Join T_1 and T_2.

2.42. To Draw a Tangent to Two Circles. *Second Case: Crossed Belt* (*Fig.* 2.49). Draw OA and O_1B perpendicular to OO_1. From P, where AB crosses OO_1, draw tangents as in Fig. 2.47.

2.43. To Lay off on a Straight Line the Approximate Length of a Circle Arc (**Fig. 2.50**). Given the arc AB, at A draw the tangent AD and the chord produced, BA. Lay off AC equal to half

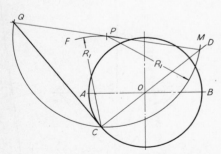

Fig. 2.46. To draw a tangent, geometric method.

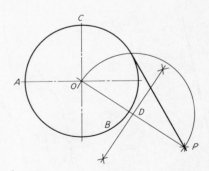

Fig. 2.47. To draw a tangent from an outside point, geometric method.

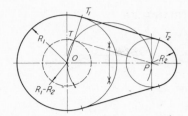

Fig. 2.48. Tangent lines (open belt), geometric method.

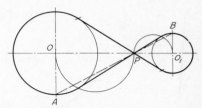

Fig. 2.49. Tangent lines (crossed belt), geometric method.

the chord *AB*. With center *C* and radius *CB*, draw an arc intersecting *AD* at *D*; then *AD* will be equal in length to the arc *AB* (very nearly).[1] If the given arc is between 45° and 90°, a closer approximation will result by making *AC* equal to the chord of half the arc instead of half the chord of the arc.

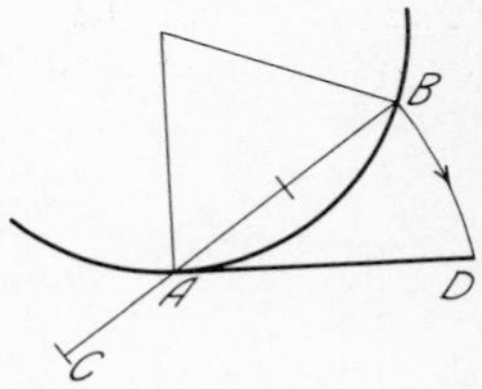

The usual way of rectifying an arc is to set the dividers to a space small enough to be practically equal in length to the corresponding arc. Starting at *B*, step along the arc to the point nearest *A*, and without lifting the dividers, step off the same number of spaces on the tangent, as shown in Fig. 2.51.

2.44. To Lay off on a Given Circle the Approximate Length of a Straight Line (**Fig. 2.52**). Given the line *AB* tangent to the circle at *A*, lay off *AC* equal to one-fourth *AB*. With *C* as a center and a radius *CB*, draw an arc intersecting the circle at *D*. The arc *AD* is equal in length to *AB* (very nearly). If arc *AD* is greater than 60°, solve for one-half *AB*.

Fig. 2.50. Lengths of arcs.

PROBLEMS

To be of value both as drawing exercises and as solutions, geometrical problems should be worked very accurately. The pencil must be kept very sharp, and comparatively light lines must be used. A point should be located by two intersecting lines, and the length of a line should be indicated by short dashes across the line. The following problems are dimensioned to fit in a space of not over 5 by 7 in., except as noted. Thus either one or two may be drawn on a standard 8½- by 11-in. sheet, and either two or four on an 11- by 17-in. sheet.

Fig. 2.51. Lengths of arcs.

Group 1. Lines and plane figures

2.1.1. Near the center of the space, draw a horizontal line 4½ in. long. Divide it into seven equal parts by the method of Fig. 2.28.

2.1.2. Draw a vertical line 1 in. from the left edge of the space and 3⅞ in. long. Divide it into parts proportional to 1, 3, 5, and 7.

[1] For an included angle of 60°, the line will be 1/900 part short; for 30°, it will be only 1/14,400 part short.

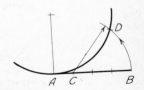

Fig. 2.52. Lengths of arcs.

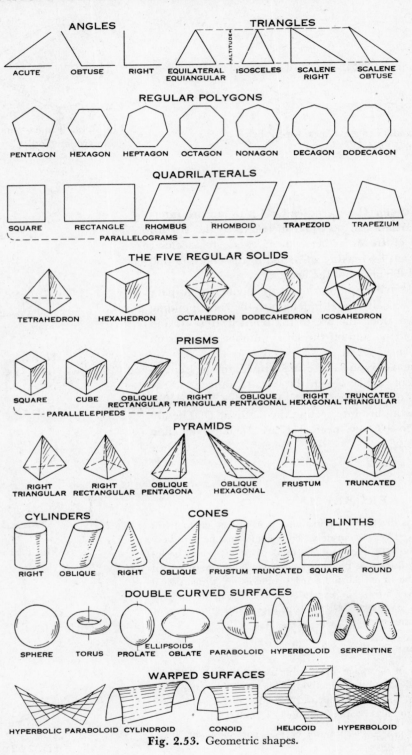

Fig. 2.53. Geometric shapes.

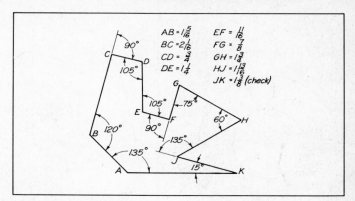

Prob. 2.1.3. Irregular polygon.

2.1.3. Construct a polygon as shown in Prob. 2.1.3, drawing the horizontal line *AK* (of indefinite length) ⅝ in. above the bottom of the space. From *A* draw and measure *AB*. Proceed in the same way for the remaining sides. The angles may be obtained by proper combinations of the two triangles; see Figs. 1.32 and 1.33.

2.1.4. Draw line *AK* making an angle of 15° with the horizontal. With this line as a base, transfer the polygon of Prob. 2.1.3.

2.1.5. Draw a regular hexagon having a distance across corners of 4 in.

2.1.6. Draw a regular hexagon, distance across flats 3⅜ in.

2.1.7. Draw a regular dodecagon, distance across flats 3⅜ in.

Group 2. Tangent problems

These problems are given for practice in the accurate joining of tangent lines. Read carefully paragraphs 2.8 and 2.21 before beginning.

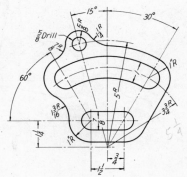

Prob. 2.2.1. Offset swivel plate.

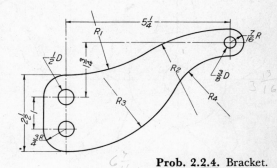

Prob. 2.2.4. Bracket.

2.2.1. Draw the offset swivel plate.

2.2.2. Draw two lines *AB* and *AC* making an included angle of 30°. Locate point *P*, 4 in. from *A* and ½ in. from line *AB*. Draw a circle arc through point *P* and tangent to lines *AB* and *CD* (two solutions).

2.2.3. Construct an ogee curve joining two parallel lines *AB* and *CD* as in Fig. 2.22, making $X = 4$ in., $Y = 2\frac{1}{2}$ in., and $BE = 3$ in. Consider this as the center line for a rod 1¼ in. in diameter, and draw the rod.

2.2.4. Make the contour view of the bracket shown. In the upper ogee curve, the radii R_1 and R_2 are equal. In the lower one, R_3 is twice R_4.

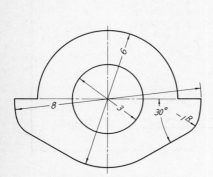

Prob. 2.2.6. Washer.

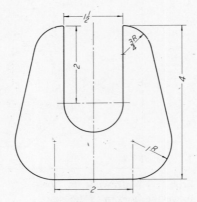

Prob. 2.2.7. Shim.

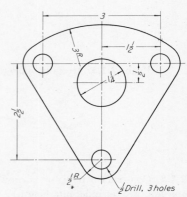

Prob. 2.2.8. Rod guide.

2.2.5. Draw an arc of a circle having a radius of $3^{13}\!/_{16}$ in., with its center ½ in. from the top of the space and 1¼ in. from the left edge. Find the length of an arc of 60° by construction; compute the length arithmetically, and check the result.

2.2.6. Front view of *washer*. Draw half size.

2.2.7. Front view of *shim*. Draw full size.

2.2.8. Front view of *rod guide*. Draw full size.

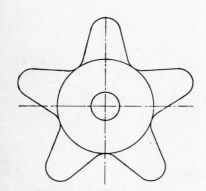

Prob. 2.2.9. Star knob.

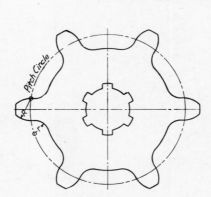

Prob. 2.2.10. Sprocket.

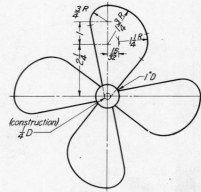

Prob. 2.2.11. Fan.

2.2.9. Front view of a *star knob*. Radius of circumscribing circle 2⅜ in. Diameter of hub 2½ in. Diameter of hole ¾ in. Radius at points ⅜ in. Radius of fillets ⅜ in. Mark tangent points in pencil.

2.2.10. Front view of *sprocket*. Outside diameter 4¼ in., pitch diameter 4 in., root diameter 3¼ in., bore 1¼ in. Thickness of tooth at the pitch line is ⁹⁄₁₆ in. Splines ¼ in. wide by ⅛ in. deep. Mark tangent points in pencil.

2.2.11. Front view of a *fan*. Draw full size to dimensions given (9- by 9-in. space).

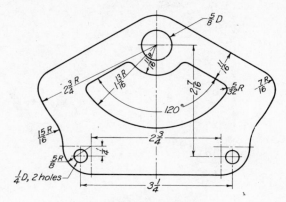

Prob. 2.2.12. Level plate.

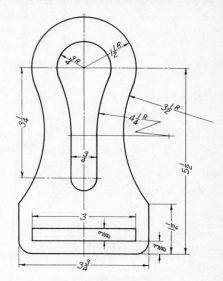

Prob. 2.2.13. Eyelet.

2.2.12. Front view of a *level plate*. Draw to full size.

2.2.13. Front view of an *eyelet*. Draw to dimensions given (5- by 8-in. space).

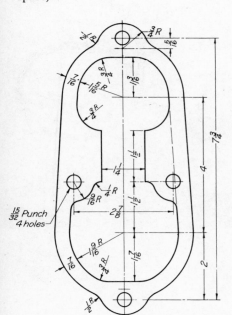

Prob. 2.2.14. Stamping.

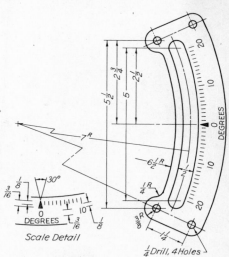

Prob. 2.2.15. Spline lock.

2.2.14. Front view of a *stamping*. Draw to dimensions given (5- by 9-in. space).

2.2.15. Front view of *spline lock*.

2.2.16. Front view of *gage cover plate*.

Prob. 2.2.16. Gage cover plate.

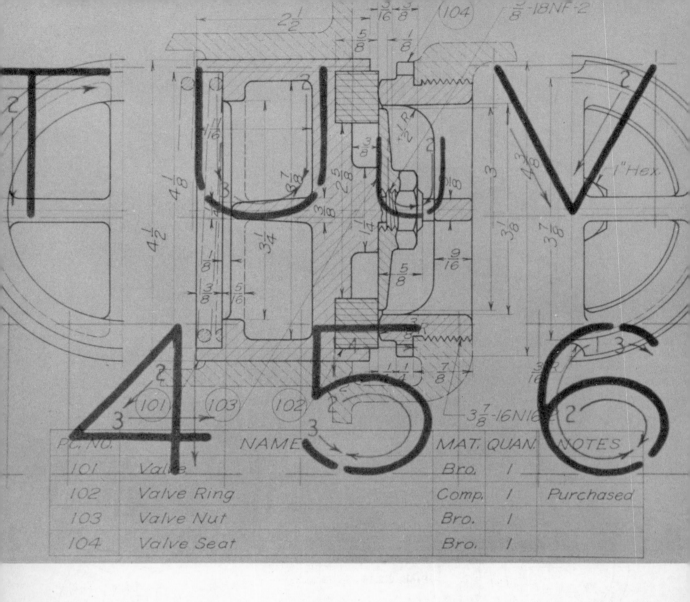

PC. NO.	NAME	MAT.	QUAN.	NOTES
101	Valve	Bro.	1	
102	Valve Ring	Comp.	1	Purchased
103	Valve Nut	Bro.	1	
104	Valve Seat	Bro.	1	

3

LETTERING

3.1. To give all the information necessary for the complete construction of a machine or structure, there must be added to the "graphical language" of lines describing its shape figured dimensions, notes on material and finish, and a descriptive title—all of which must be lettered, freehand, in a style that is perfectly legible, uniform, and capable of rapid execution. As far as the appearance of a drawing is concerned, no part is so important as the lettering. A good drawing may be ruined, not only in appearance but in usefulness, by lettering done ignorantly or carelessly because illegible figures are very apt to cause mistakes in the work.

In a broad sense, the subject of lettering is a distinct branch of design. There are two general classes of persons who are interested in its study: (1) those who have to use letters and words to convey information on drawings and (2) those who use lettering in applied design, such as art students, artists, and craftsmen. The first group is concerned mainly with legibility and speed, the second with beauty of form and composition. In our study of engineering drawing, we are concerned only with the problems of the first group. The engineering student takes up lettering as his first work in drawing and continues its practice throughout his course, becoming more and more skillful and proficient.

3.2. Single-stroke Lettering. By far the greatest amount of lettering on drawings is done in a rapid single-stroke letter, either vertical

63

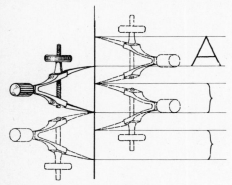

Fig. 3.1. To space guide lines.

or inclined, and every engineer must have absolute command of these styles. The ability to letter well can be acquired only by continued and careful practice, but it can be acquired by anyone with normal muscular control of his fingers who will practice faithfully and intelligently and take the trouble to observe carefully the shapes of the letters, the sequence of strokes in making them, and the rules for their composition. It is not a matter of artistic talent or even of dexterity in handwriting. Many draftsmen who write very poorly letter well.

The term "single-stroke," or "one-stroke," does not mean that the entire letter is made without lifting the pencil or pen but that the width of the stroke of the pencil or pen is the width of the stem of the letter.

3.3. General Proportions. There is no one standard for the proportions of letters, but there are certain fundamental points in design and certain characteristics of individual letters that must be thoroughly learned by study and observation before composition into words and sentences may be attempted. Not only do the widths of letters in any alphabet vary, from *I*, the narrowest, to *W*, the widest, but different alphabets vary as a whole. Styles narrow in their proportion of width to height are called **"COMPRESSED"** and are used when space is limited. Styles wider than the normal are called **"EXTENDED."**

The proportion of the thickness of stem to the height varies widely, ranging all the way from one-third to one-twentieth. Letters with heavy stems are called **"BOLDFACE,"** or **"BLACKFACE,"** those with thin stems **"LIGHTFACE."**

3.4. The Rule of Stability. In the construction of letters, the well-known optical illusion in which a horizontal line drawn across the middle of a rectangle appears to be below the middle must be provided for. In order to give the appearance of stability, such letters as B, E, K, S, X, and Z and the figures *3* and *8* must be drawn smaller at the top than at the bottom. To see the effect of this illusion, turn a printed page upside down and notice the letters mentioned.

3.5. Guide Lines. Light guide lines for both tops and bottoms of letters should always be drawn, using a sharp pencil. Figure 3.1

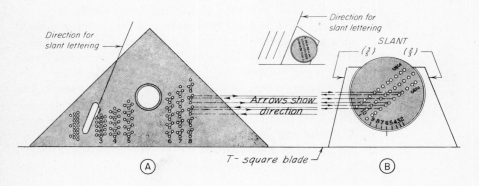

Fig. 3.2. (*A*) Braddock-Rowe and (*B*) Ames lettering instruments.

shows a method of laying off a number of equally spaced lines of letters. Draw the first base line, and above it mark the desired height of the letters; then set the bow spacers to the distance wanted between base lines, and step off the required number of base lines. With the same setting, step down again from the upper point, thus obtaining points for the top of each line of letters.

The Braddock-Rowe triangle, Fig. 3.2*A*, and the Ames lettering instrument, Fig. 3.2*B*, are convenient devices for spacing lines of letters. A sharp pencil is inserted in the proper row of countersunk holes, and the instrument, guided by a T-square blade, is drawn back and forth by the pencil, as indicated by Fig. 3.3. The holes are grouped for capitals and lower case, the numbers indicating the height of capitals in thirty-seconds of an inch; thus No. 6 spacing means that the capitals will be $6/32$, or $3/16$, in. high.

3.6. Lettering in Pencil. In the previous chapters, the necessity for good technique in drawing was mentioned. This is equally true for lettering, either as finished work to be reproduced by one of the printing processes or as part of a pencil drawing to be inked. In the first case, the penciling will be clean, firm, and opaque; in the second case, it may be lighter. The lettering pencil should be selected carefully by trial on the paper. In one case, the same grade as that used for the drawing may be chosen; in another case, a grade or two softer may be preferred. Sharpen the pencil to a long conical point, and then round the lead slightly on the end so that it is not so sharp as a point used for drawing.

The first requirement in lettering is the correct holding of the pencil or pen. Figure 3.4 shows the pencil held comfortably with the thumb, forefinger, and second finger on alternate flat sides and the third and fourth fingers on the paper. Vertical, slanting, and curved strokes are drawn with a steady, even, *finger* movement; horizontal strokes are made similarly but with some pivoting of the hand at the wrist (Fig. 3.5). Exert a firm, uniform pressure, but not so heavy as to cut grooves in the paper. To keep the point symmetri-

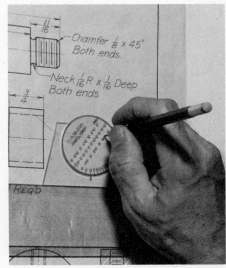

Fig. 3.3. Using the Ames lettering instrument.

Fig. 3.4. Vertical strokes.

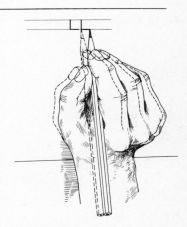

Fig. 3.5. Horizontal strokes.

LEONARDT 516 F: 506 F
HUNT 512: ESTERBROOK 968
Esterbrook 1000 Spencerian No.1
Gillott 404: Gillott 303

For very fine lines Gillott 170 and 290
or Esterbrook 356 and 355

Fig. 3.6. Pen strokes, full size.

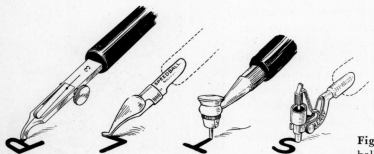

Fig. 3.7. Barch-Payzant, Speedball, Edco, and LeRoy pens.

Fig. 3.8. Henry tank pen.

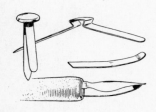

Fig. 3.9. Ink holder.

cal, the habit of rotating the pencil after every few strokes should be formed.

3.7. Lettering Pens. There are many steel writing pens either adaptable to, or made especially for, lettering. The sizes of the strokes of a few popular ones are shown in full size in Fig. 3.6. Several special pens made in sets of graded sizes have been designed for single-stroke lettering, among which are those illustrated in Fig. 3.7. These are particularly useful for large work. The ink-holding reservoir of the Henry tank pen, Fig. 3.8, assists materially in maintaining uniform weight of line. A similar device may be made by bending a brass strip from a paper fastener, a piece of annealed watch spring, or—perhaps best—a strip cut from a piece of shim brass into the shape shown in Fig. 3.9 and inserting it in the penholder so that the curved end just touches the nibs of the pen.

To remove the oil film, always wet a new pen and wipe it thoroughly before using. A lettering pen well broken in by use is worth much more than a new one. It should be kept with care and never lent. A pen that has been dipped into writing ink should never be put into drawing ink. When in use, a pen should be wiped clean frequently with a cloth penwiper.

3.8. Using the Pen. A penholder with cork grip (the small size) should be chosen and the pen set in it firmly. Many prefer to ink the pen with the quill filler, touching the quill to the underside of the pen point, rather than to dip it into the ink bottle. If the pen is dipped, the surplus ink should be shaken back into the bottle or the pen touched against the neck of the bottle as it is withdrawn. Lettering with too much ink on the pen is responsible for results of the kind shown in Fig. 3.10.

The penholder should be held in the fingers firmly but without pinching in the position shown in Fig. 3.11. The strokes of the letters should be made with a steady, even motion and a slight, uniform pressure on the paper that will not spread the nibs of the pen.

3.9. Single-stroke Vertical Capitals. The vertical single-stroke commercial gothic letter is a standard for titles, reference letters, etc. As for the proportion of width to height, the general rule is that the smaller the letters are, the more extended they should be in width. A low extended letter is more legible than a high compressed one and, at the same time, makes a better appearance.

The basic requirement is to learn the form and peculiarity of each of the letters. Too many persons think that lettering is simply "printing" of the childish kind learned in the primary grades. There is an individuality in lettering often nearly as marked as in handwriting, but it must be based on a careful regard for the fundamental letter forms.

3.10. Order of Strokes. In the following figures, an alphabet of slightly extended vertical capitals has been arranged in family groups. The shape of each letter, with the order and direction of the strokes forming it, must be studied carefully and the letter repeatedly practiced until its form and construction are perfectly familiar. The first studies should be made in pencil to large size, perhaps ⅜ in. high, afterward to smaller size, and finally directly in ink.

To aid in seeing the proportions of widths to heights and in learning the subtleties in the shapes of the letters, they are shown against a square background with its sides divided into sixths. It will be noted that several of the letters in this alphabet, such as A and T, fill the square; that is, they are as wide as they are high. Some others, such as H and D, are approximately five spaces wide, or five-sixths of their height. *These proportions must be learned visually* so well that letters of various heights can be drawn in correct proportion without hesitation.

The I-H-T Group (*Fig.* 3.12). The letter I is the foundation stroke. It may be found difficult to keep the stems vertical. If so, direction lines may be drawn lightly an inch or so apart to aid the eye. The H is nearly square (five-sixths), and in accordance with the rule of stability, the crossbar is just above the center. The top of the T is drawn first to the full width of the square, and the stem is started accurately as its middle point.

The L-E-F Group (*Fig.* 3.13). The L is made in two strokes. Note that the first two strokes of the E are the same as the L, that the third, or upper, stroke is slightly shorter than the lower, and that the last

EHMNWTZ

Fig. 3.10. Too much ink.

Fig. 3.11. Holding the pen.

Fig. 3.12

Fig. 3.13

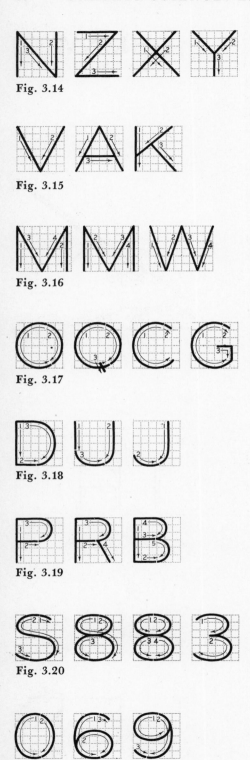

Fig. 3.14

Fig. 3.15

Fig. 3.16

Fig. 3.17

Fig. 3.18

Fig. 3.19

Fig. 3.20

Fig. 3.21

stroke is two-thirds as long and just above the middle. *F* has the same proportions as *E*.

The N-Z-X-Y Group (Fig. 3.14). The parallel sides of *N* are generally drawn first, but some prefer to make the strokes in consecutive order. *Z* and *X* are both started inside the width of the square on top and run to full width on the bottom. This throws the crossing point of the *X* slightly above the center. The junction of the *Y* strokes is at the center.

The V-A-K Group (Fig. 3.15). *V* is the same width as *A*, the full breadth of the square. The *A* bridge is one-third up from the bottom. The second stroke of *K* strikes the stem one-third up from the bottom; the third stroke branches from it in a direction starting from the top of the stem.

The M-W Group (Fig. 3.16). These are the widest letters. *M* may be made either in consecutive strokes or by drawing the two vertical strokes first, as with the *N*. *W* is formed of two narrow *V*'s, each two-thirds of the square in width. Note that with all the pointed letters the width at the point is the width of the stroke.

The O-Q-C-G Group (Fig. 3.17). In this extended alphabet, the letters of the *O* family are made as full circles. The *O* is made in two strokes, the left side a longer arc than the right, as the right side is harder to make. Make the kern of the *Q* straight. A large-size *C* and *G* can be made more accurately with an extra stroke at the top, whereas in smaller letters the curve is made in one stroke, Fig. 3.25. Note that the bar on the *G* is halfway up and does not extend past the vertical stroke.

The D-U-J Group (Fig. 3.18). The top and bottom strokes of *D* must be horizontal. Failure to observe this is a common fault with beginners. *U* in larger letters is formed of two parallel strokes, to which the bottom stroke is added. For smaller letters, it may be made in two strokes curved to meet at the bottom. *J* has the same construction as *U*, with stroke 1 omitted.

The P-R-B Group (Fig. 3.19). With *P*, *R*, and *B*, the number of strokes used depends upon the size of the letter. For large letters, the horizontal lines are started and the curves added; but for smaller letters, only one stroke for each lobe is needed. The middle lines of *P* and *R* are on the center line; that of *B* observes the rule of stability.

The S-8-3 Group (Fig. 3.20). The *S*, *8*, and *3* are closely related in form, and the rule of stability must be observed carefully. For a large *S*, three strokes may be used; for a smaller one, two strokes; and for a very small size, one stroke only is best. The *8* may be made on the *S* construction in three strokes, or in "head and body" in four strokes. A perfect *3* should be capable of being finished into an *8*.

The 0-6-9 Group (Fig. 3.21). The cipher is an ellipse five-sixths the width of the letter *O*. The backbones of the *6* and *9* have the same curve as the cipher, and the lobes are slightly less than two-thirds the height of the figure.

The 2-5-7-& Group (Fig. 3.22). The secret in making the *2* lies in getting the reverse curve to cross the center of the space. The

Fig. 3.22

bottom of *2* and the tops of *5* and *7* should be horizontal straight lines. The second stroke of *7* terminates directly below the middle of the top stroke. Its stiffness is relieved by curving it slightly at the lower end. The ampersand (*&*) is made in three strokes for large letters and two for smaller ones and must be carefully balanced.

The Fraction Group (Fig. 3.23). Fractions are always made with horizontal bar. Integers are the same height as capitals. The total fraction height is best made twice the height of the integer. The numerator and denominator will be about three-fourths the height of the integer. Be careful to leave a clear space above and below the horizontal bar. Guide lines for fractions are easily obtained with lettering instruments by using the set of uniformly spaced holes or by drawing the integer height above and below the center, the position of the horizontal bar.

3.11. Vertical Lower-case Letters. The single-stroke vertical lower-case letter is not commonly used on machine drawings but is used extensively in map drawing. It is the standard letter for hypsography in government topographical drawing. The bodies are made two-thirds the height of the capitals with the ascenders extending to the capital line and the descenders dropping the same distance below. The basic form of the letter is the combination of a circle and a straight line, Fig. 3.24. The alphabet with some alternate shapes is shown in Fig. 3.25, which also gives the capitals in alphabetical order.

3.12. Single-stroke Inclined Capitals. The inclined, or slant, letter is used in preference to the upright by many draftsmen. The order and direction of strokes are the same as in the vertical form.

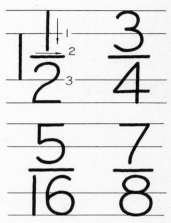

Fig. 3.23. Fractions.

Fig. 3.24. Basic forms for lower-case letters.

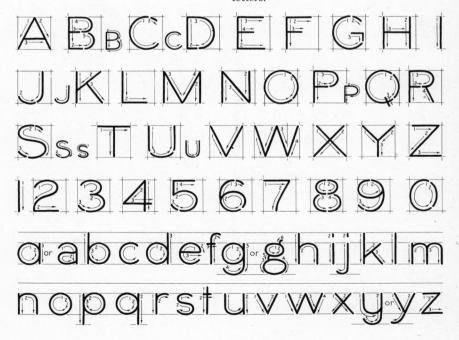

Fig. 3.25. Single-stroke vertical capitals and lower case.

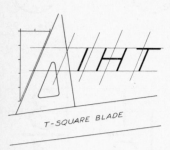

Fig. 3.26. Slope guide lines.

After ruling the guide lines, slanting "direction lines" should be drawn across the sheet to aid the eye in keeping the slope uniform. These slope lines may be drawn with a special lettering triangle of about $67\frac{1}{2}°$, or the slope of 2 to 5 may be fixed on the paper by marking two units on a horizontal line and five on a vertical line and using T square and triangle as shown in Fig. 3.26. The Braddock-Rowe triangle and the Ames instrument both provide for the drawing of slope lines, Fig. 3.2*A* and *B*. The form taken by the rounded letters when inclined is illustrated in Fig. 3.27, which shows that curves are sharp in all upper right-hand and lower left-hand corners and flattened in the other two corners. Particular care must be observed with the letters having sloping sides, such as *A*, *V*, and *W*. The sloping sides of these letters must be drawn so that they appear to balance about a slope guide line passing through the intersection, as in Fig. 3.28. The alphabet is given in Fig. 3.29. Study the shape of each letter carefully.

The snap and swing of professional work are due to three things: (1) keeping to a uniform slope, (2) having the letters full and well shaped, and (3) keeping them close together. The beginner's invariable mistake is to cramp the individual letters and space them too far apart.

Fig. 3.27. Form of curved-stroke letters.

Fig. 3.28. Form of straight-stroke letters.

Fig. 3.29. Single-stroke inclined capitals and lower case.

3.13. Single-stroke Inclined Lower-case Letters. The inclined lower-case letters, Fig. 3.29, have the bodies two-thirds the height of the capitals with the ascenders extending to the capital line and the descenders dropping the same distance below the base line. Among older engineers, particularly civil engineers, this letter is generally known as the "Reinhardt letter," in honor of Charles W. Reinhardt, who first systematized its construction. It is very legible and effective and, after its swing has been mastered, can be made very rapidly. The lower-case letter is suitable for notes and statements on drawings for the two reasons indicated: (1) It is much more easily read than all capitals since we read words by the word shapes; (2) it can be done much faster.

All the letters of the Reinhardt alphabet are based on two elements, the straight line and the ellipse, and have no unnecessary hooks or appendages. They may be divided into four groups, as shown in Figs. 3.30 to 3.33. The dots of *i* and *j* and the top of the *t* are on the "*t* line," halfway between the waistline and the capital line. The loop letters are made with an ellipse whose long axis is inclined about 45° in combination with a straight line. In lettering rapidly, this ellipse tends to assume a pumpkin-seed form that should be guarded against.

The *c*, *e*, and *o* are based on an ellipse of the shape of the capitals but not inclined quite so much as the loop-letter ellipse. In rapid small work, the *o* is often made in one stroke, as are also *e*, *v*, and *w*. The *s* is similar to the capital but, except in letters more than ⅛ in. high, is made in one stroke. In the hook-letter group, note particularly the shape of the hook.

The single-stroke letter may, if necessary, be very much compressed and still be clear and legible (Fig. 3.34). It is also used sometimes in extended form.

3.14. For Left-handers Only. The order and direction of strokes in the preceding alphabets have been designed for right-handed persons. The principal reason that left-handers sometimes find lettering difficult is that, whereas the right-hander progresses away from the body, the left-hander progresses toward the body; consequently his pencil and hand partially hide the work he has done, making it

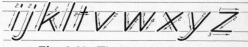

Fig. 3.30. The straight-line letters.

Fig. 3.31. The loop letters.

Fig. 3.32. The ellipse letters.

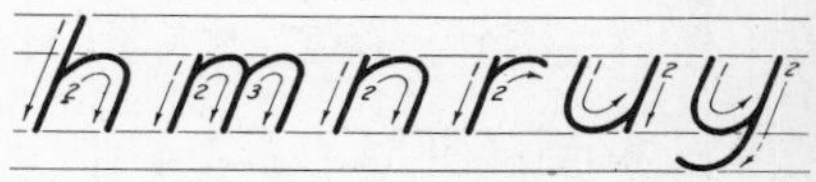

Fig. 3.33. The hook letters.

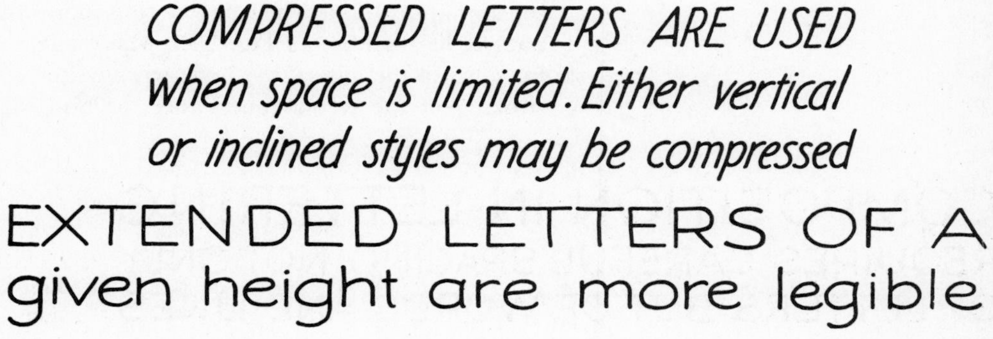

Fig. 3.34. Compressed and extended letters.

COMPRESSED LETTERS ARE USED when space is limited. Either vertical or inclined styles may be compressed EXTENDED LETTERS OF A given height are more legible

A A B B C C D D E E F F G G H H
I J J K L L M N O O P Q Q
R S T T T U U U V V W X Y Z Z
1 2 3 4 5 5 6 7 7 8 9 0
a b b c c d e f f g h i j k l m n o o p
q r s t t u v w x y z

Fig. 3.35. Strokes for left-handers.

LETTERING
LETTERING

Fig. 3.36. Background areas.

harder to join strokes and to preserve uniformity. Also, in the case of inclined lettering, the slope direction, instead of running toward his eye, runs off into space to the left of his body, making this style so much harder for him that the left-hander is strongly advised to *use vertical letters exclusively*.

For the natural left-hander, whose writing position is the same as a right-hander except reversed left for right, a change in the sequence of strokes of some of the letters will obviate part of the difficulty caused by interference with the line of sight. Figure 3.35 gives an analyzed alphabet with an alternate for some letters. In *E* the top bar is made before the bottom bar, and *M* is drawn from left to right to avoid having strokes hidden by the pencil or pen. Horizontal portions of curves are easier to make from right to left; hence the starting points for *O*, *Q*, *C*, *G*, and *U* differ from the standard right-hand stroking. *S* is the perfect letter for the left-hander and is best made in a single smooth stroke. *6* and *9* are difficult and require extra practice. In the lower-case letters *a*, *d*, *g*, and *q*, it is better to draw the straight line before the curve even though it makes spacing a little harder.

The hook-wrist left-handed writer, who pushes his strokes from top to bottom, finds vertical lettering more difficult than does the natural left-hander. In Fig. 2.35, where alternate strokes are given for some of the letters, the hook-wrist writer will probably find the stroking of the second one easier for him than that of the first.

COMPOSITION IN LETTERING
REQUIRES CAREFUL SPACING, NOT ONLY
OF LETTERS BUT OF WORDS AND LINES

Fig. 3.37. Word composition.

WORDS I SPACED I BY I SKETCHING I AN III BETWEEN

Fig. 3.38. Word spacing.   WORDS SPACED BY SKETCHING AN I BETWEEN

Some prefer to reverse *all* the strokes, drawing vertical strokes from bottom to top and horizontal strokes from right to left.

By way of encouragement it may be said that many left-handed draftsmen letter beautifully.

3.15. Composition. Composition in lettering has to do with the selection, arrangement, and spacing of appropriate styles and sizes of letters. On engineering drawings, the selection of the style is practically limited to vertical or inclined single-stroke lettering, so that composition here means arrangement into pleasing and legible form. After the shapes and strokes of the individual letters have been learned, the entire practice should be on composition into words and sentences since proper spacing of letters and words does more for the appearance of a block of lettering than the forms of the letters themselves. Letters in words are not spaced at a uniform distance from each other but are arranged so that the areas of white spaces (the irregular backgrounds between the letters) are approximately equal, thus making the spacing *appear* approximately uniform. Figure 3.36 illustrates these background shapes. Each letter is spaced with reference to its shape and the shape of the letter preceding it. Thus adjacent letters with straight sides would be spaced farther apart than those with curved sides. Sometimes combinations such as *LT* or *AV* may even overlap. Definite rules for spacing are not successful; it is a matter of the draftsman's judgment and sense of design. Figure 3.37 illustrates word composition. The sizes of letters to use in any particular case may be determined better by sketching them lightly than by judging from the guide lines alone. A finished line of letters always looks larger than the guide lines indicate. Avoid the use of a coarse pen for small sizes and one that makes thin wiry lines for large sizes. When capitals and small capitals are used, the height of the small capitals should be about four-fifths that of the capitals.

In spacing words, a good method is to leave the space that would be taken by an assumed letter *I* connecting the two words into one, as in Fig. 3.38. The space would never be more than the height of the letters.

The clear distance between lines may vary from ½ to 1½ times the height of the letter but, for the sake of appearance, should not be exactly the same as the letter height. The instruments of Figs. 3.2 and 3.3 provide spacing two-thirds the letter height. Paragraphs should always be indented.

3.16. Titles. The most important problem in lettering composition that the engineering draftsman will meet is the design of titles. Every drawing has a descriptive title giving the necessary informa-

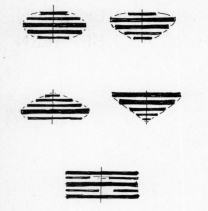

Fig. 3.39. Shapes in symmetrical composition.

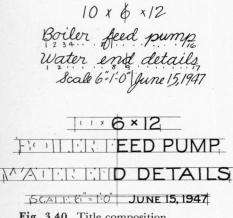

Fig. 3.40. Title composition.

tion concerning it, which is either all hand-lettered or filled in on a printed form. This information is not the same for all kinds of drawing (see the section on working-drawing titles in Chap. 12).

The usual form of lettered title is the *symmetrical title*, which is balanced or "justified" on a vertical center line and designed with an elliptical or oval outline. Sometimes the wording necessitates a pyramid or inverted-pyramid ("bag") form. Figure 3.39 illustrates several shapes into which titles can be composed. The lower right-hand corner of the sheet is, from long custom and on account of convenience in filing, the usual location for the title, and in laying out a drawing, this corner is reserved for it. The space allowed is a matter of judgment and depends on the size and purpose of the drawing. On an 11- by 17-in. working drawing, the title may be about 3 in. long.

3.17. To Draw a Title. When the wording has been determined, write out the arrangement on a separate piece of paper as in Fig. 3.40 (or, better, typewrite it). Count the letters, including the word spaces, and make a mark across the middle letter or space of each line. The lines must be displayed for prominence according to their relative importance as judged from the point of view of the persons who will use the drawing. Titles are usually made in all capitals. Draw the base line for the most important line of the title, and mark on it the approximate length desired. To get the letter height, divide this length by the number of letters in the line, and draw the capital line. Start at the center line, and sketch very lightly the last half of the line, drawing only enough of the letters to show the space each will occupy. Lay off the length of this right half on the other side, and sketch that half, working either forward or backward. When this line is satisfactory in size and spacing, draw the remainder in the same way. Study the effect, shift letters or lines if necessary, and complete in pencil. Use punctuation marks only for abbreviations.

3.18. Scratch-paper Methods. Sketch each line of the title separately on a piece of scratch paper, using guide lines of determined height. Find the middle point of each of these lines, fold the paper along the base line of the letters, fit the middle point to the center line on the drawing, and draw the final letters directly below the sketches. *Or* draw the letters along the edge of the scratch paper, using either the upper or the lower edge as one of the guide lines. *Or* letter the title on scratch paper, cut apart and adjust until satisfactory, and then trace it.

PROBLEMS

Group 1. Single-stroke vertical capitals

3.1.1. Large letters in pencil for careful study of the shapes of the individual letters. Starting $\frac{9}{16}$ in. from the top border, draw guide lines for five lines of $\frac{3}{8}$-in. letters. Draw each of the straight-line letters *I, H, T, L, E, F, N, Z, Y, V, A, M, W,* and *X* four times in pencil only, studying carefully Figs. 3.12 to 3.16. The illustration is a full-sized reproduction of a corner of this exercise.

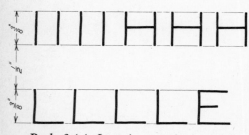

Prob. 3.1.1. Lettering practice in pencil.

3.1.2. Same as Prob. 3.1.1 for the curved-line letters *O, Q, C, G, D, U, J, B, P, R,* and *S.* Study Figs. 3.17 to 3.20.

3.1.3. Same as Prob. 3.1.1 for the figures *3, 8, 6, 9, 2, 5,* $\frac{1}{2}$, $\frac{3}{4}$, $\frac{5}{8}$, $\frac{7}{16}$, and $\frac{9}{32}$. Study Figs. 3.21 to 3.23.

3.1.4. Composition. Same layout as for Prob. 3.1.1. Read paragraph on composition; then letter the following five lines in pencil: (*a*) WORD COMPOSITION, (*b*) TOPOGRAPHIC SURVEY, (*c*) TOOLS AND EQUIPMENT, (*d*) BRONZE BUSHING, (*e*) JACK–RAFTER DE–TAIL.

3.1.5. Quarter-inch vertical letters in pencil and ink. Starting $\frac{1}{4}$ in. from top, draw guide lines for nine lines of $\frac{1}{4}$-in. letters. In the group order given, first draw each letter four times in pencil and then four times directly in ink, as shown in the illustration.

3.1.6. Composition. Make a three-line design of the quotation from Benjamin Lamme on the Lamme medals: "THE ENGINEER VIEWS HOPEFULLY THE HITHERTO UNATTAINABLE."

3.1.7. Eighth-inch vertical letters. Starting $\frac{1}{4}$ in. from top, draw guide lines for 18 lines of $\frac{1}{8}$-in. letters. Make each letter and numeral eight times directly in ink. Fill the remaining lines with a portion of paragraph 3.15 on composition.

3.1.8. Composition. Letter the following definition: "Engineering is the art and science of directing and controlling the forces and utilizing the materials of nature for the benefit of man. All engineering involves the organization of human effort to attain these ends. It also involves an appraisal of the social and economic benefits of these activities."

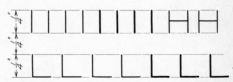

Prob. 3.1.5. Lettering practice in pencil and ink.

Group 2. Single-stroke inclined capitals

3.2.1. to 3.2.8. Same spacing and specifications as for Group 1, Probs. 3.1.1 to 3.1.8, but for inclined letters. Study paragraph 3.12 and Figs. 3.26 to 3.29.

Group 3. Single-stroke inclined lower case

3.3.1. Large letters in pencil for use with $\frac{3}{8}$-in. capitals. The bodies are $\frac{1}{4}$ in., the ascenders $\frac{1}{8}$ in. above, and the descenders $\frac{1}{8}$ in. below. Starting $\frac{3}{8}$ in. from top, draw guide lines for seven lines of letters. This can be done quickly by spacing $\frac{1}{8}$ in. uniformly down the sheet and bracketing capital and base lines. Make each letter of the alphabet four times in pencil only. Study Figs. 3.29 to 3.33.

3.3.2. Lower case for $\frac{3}{16}$-in. capitals. Starting $\frac{1}{2}$ in. from top, draw capital, waist-, and base lines for 13 lines of letters (Braddock or Ames No. 6 spacing). Make each letter six times in pencil and then six times in ink.

3.3.3. Composition. Same spacing as Prob. 3.3.2. Letter opening paragraph of this chapter.

3.3.4. Letter paragraph 3.4.

Group 4. Titles

3.4.1. Design a title for the assembly drawing of a rear axle, drawn to the scale of 6 in. = 1 ft, as made by the Chevrolet Motor Co., Detroit. The number of the drawing is C82746. Space allowed is 3 by 5 in.

3.4.2. Design a title for the front elevation of a powerhouse, drawn to $\frac{1}{4}$-in. scale by Burton Grant, Architect, for the Citizens Power and Light Company of Punxsutawney, Pennsylvania.

4

THEORY OF PROJECTION
DRAWING

4.1. The previous chapters have been preparatory to the real
subject of engineering drawing as a language. In the Introduction,
attention was directed to the difference between the representation
of an object by the artist, in which he seeks to convey certain impressions or emotions, and the representation by the engineer, where
the main intent is to convey information. The facts required from
the engineer include the description of the *shape* of the object and the
specification of the *size* of every detail. In this chapter, we are concerned with the method of describing *shape*.

Orthographic projection provides a means of describing the exact
shape of any material object. Practically, the drawing is made up of
a set of separate views of the object taken by the observer from different positions and arranged relative to each other in a definite way.
Each of these views will show the shape of the object for a particular
view direction, and a combination of two or more views will completely describe the object.

4.2. Fundamental Theory. On the supposition that a transparent plane may be set up between an object and the station point
of an observer's eye, Fig. 4.1, the intersection of this plane with the
rays formed by lines of sight from the eye to all points of the object
will give a picture that will be practically the same as the image
formed in the eye of the observer.

If the observer will then imagine himself as walking backward

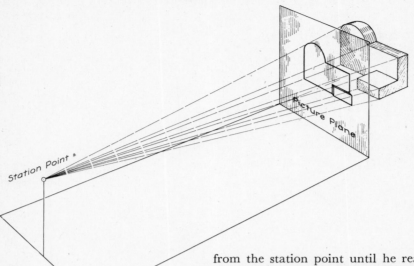

Fig. 4.1. Perspective projection.

from the station point until he reaches a theoretically *infinite* distance, the rays formed by lines of sight from his eye to the object will grow longer and finally become infinite in length, *parallel to each other* and perpendicular to the picture plane. The picture so formed on the picture plane is what is known as "orthographic projection." See Fig. 4.2.

4.3. Definition. Basically, orthographic [1] projection could be defined as any single projection made by dropping perpendiculars to a plane. However, it has been accepted through long usage and common consent to mean the combination of two or more such views; hence the following definition: *Orthographic projection is the method of representing the exact shape of an object in two or more views on planes generally at right angles to each other, by extending perpendiculars*

[1] "Right writing."

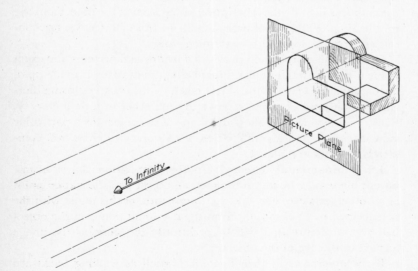

Fig. 4.2. Orthographic projection (projection on a plane with station point at infinity).

from the object to the planes. (The term "orthogonal"[2] is sometimes used for this system of drawing.)

4.4. Orthographic Views. As stated in the definition just given, the rays from the picture plane to infinity, as described in paragraph 4.3, may be discarded and the picture, or "view," thought of as being found by extending perpendiculars to the plane from all points of the object, as shown in Fig. 4.3. This picture, or projection on a frontal plane, will show the shape of the object when viewed from the front, but it will not tell the shape or distance from front to back; hence more than one projection will be required to describe the object.

In addition to the frontal plane, another transparent plane is then imagined as placed horizontally above the object, as in Fig. 4.4. The projection on this plane, found by extending perpendiculars to it from the object, will give the appearance of the object as if viewed from directly above and will show the distance front to rear. If this horizontal plane is now revolved into coincidence with the frontal plane, as in Fig. 4.5, the two views of the object will then be in the same plane, as if on a sheet of paper. A third plane, called a "profile plane," may be imagined, perpendicular to the first two, Fig. 4.6, and on it a third view may be projected. The third view will show the shape of the object when viewed from the side and the distance bottom to top and front to rear. The horizontal and profile planes are shown revolved into the same plane as the frontal plane (again thought of as the plane of the drawing paper) in Fig. 4.7; moreover, thus related in the same plane, they will correctly give the three-dimensional shape of the object.

[2] "Right-angled."

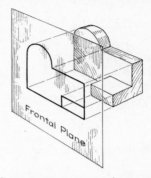

Fig. 4.3. Frontal plane of projection.

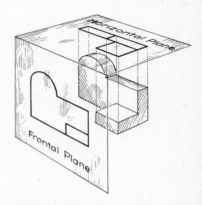

Fig. 4.4. Frontal and horizontal planes of projection.

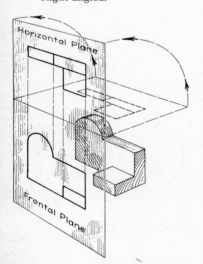

Fig. 4.5. The horizontal plane revolved to coincide with the frontal plane.

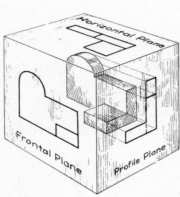

Fig. 4.6. The three planes of projection.

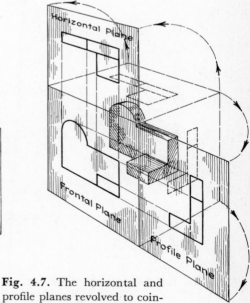

Fig. 4.7. The horizontal and profile planes revolved to coincide with the frontal plane.

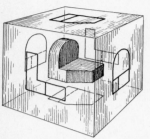

Fig. 4.8. The transparent box.

In orthographic projection, the picture planes are called "planes of projection"; and the perpendiculars, "projecting lines," or "projectors."

In looking at these theoretical projections, or views, the observer should not think of the views as being flat surfaces on the transparent planes but should imagine himself as looking **through** the transparent planes at the object itself.

4.5. The Six Principal Views. If now we consider the fact that the object can be entirely surrounded by a set of six mutually perpendicular planes, as shown by Fig. 4.8, views may be obtained by looking at the object from the top, front, right side, left side, bottom, and rear.

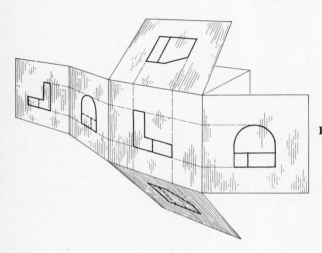

Fig. 4.9. The box as it opens.

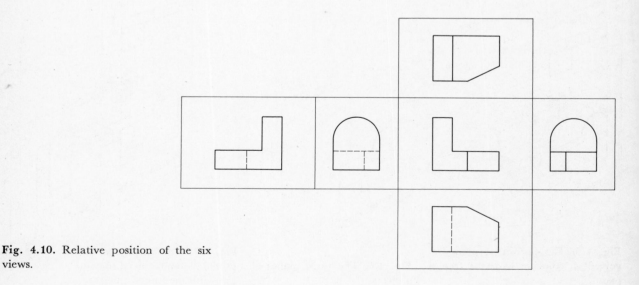

Fig. 4.10. Relative position of the six views.

The six sides, or planes, of the box are then thought of as being opened up, as illustrated in Fig. 4.9, into one plane, the plane of the paper. The front is considered to be originally in the plane of the paper, and the other sides are considered to be hinged and rotated into position as shown. The projection on the frontal plane is known as the *front view, vertical projection,* or *front elevation;* that on the horizontal plane, the *top view, horizontal projection,* or *plan;* that on the side, or "profile," plane, the *side view, profile projection, side elevation,* or sometimes *end view* or *end elevation.* By reversing the direction of sight, a *bottom view* will be obtained instead of a *top view* or a *rear view* instead of a *front view.* In comparatively rare cases, either a bottom view or a rear view or both may be required to show some detail of shape or construction. Figure 4.10 shows the relative positions of the six views as set by the ASA. In actual work, there is rarely ever an occasion where all six principal views would be needed on one drawing; but no matter how many are required, their positions relative to each other would be as given in Fig. 4.10. All these views are principal views. Each one of the six views shows two of the three dimensions of height, width, and depth.

4.6. Combination of Views. The most usual combination selected from the six possible views consists of the *top, front,* and *right-side* views, as shown in Fig. 4.11, which, in this case, best describes the shape of the given block. Sometimes the left-side view will help describe an object more clearly than the right side would. Figure 4.12 shows the arrangement of *top, front,* and *left-side* views (in this case, the right-side view would be preferred, as it has no hidden lines). Note that the *side view of the front face of the object is adjacent to the front view* and that the side view of any point will be the same distance from the front surface as is its distance from the front surface on the top view. The combination of *front, right-side,* and *bottom views* is shown in Fig. 4.13 and that of *front, top, left-side,* and *rear* views in Fig. 4.14.

4.7. "Alternate-position" Views. The top of the enclosing transparent box may be thought of as in a fixed position with the

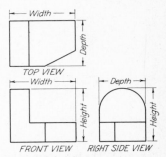

Fig. 4.11. Three projections.

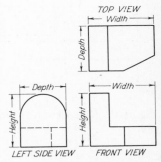

Fig. 4.12. Three projections.

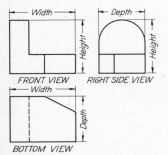

Fig. 4.13. Three projections.

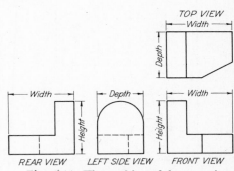

Fig. 4.14. The position of the rear view.

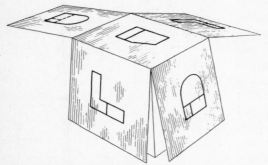

Fig. 4.15. The box opening for alternate-position views.

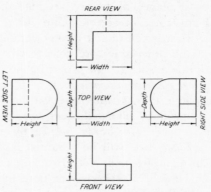

Fig. 4.16. Alternate-position views.

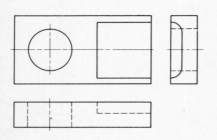

Fig. 4.17. Side view in alternate position.

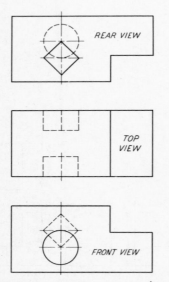

Fig. 4.18. Rear view in alternate position.

front, rear, and sides hinged as illustrated in Fig. 4.15, thus bringing the sides in line with the top view and the rear view above the top view, Fig. 4.16. This alternate-position arrangement is of occasional use in drawing a broad flat object, Fig. 4.17, as it saves space on the paper. The alternate position for the rear view may be used if this arrangement makes the drawing easier to read, Fig. 4.18.

4.8. The Three Space Dimensions. As all material objects from single pieces to complicated structures are definitive and measurable by three space dimensions,[1] it is desirable for drawing purposes to define these dimensions and to fix their direction.

Height is the difference in elevation between any two points, measured as the perpendicular distance between a pair of horizontal planes that contain the points (Fig. 4.19). Edges of the object may or may not correspond with the height dimensions. Edge *AB* corresponds with the height dimension, while edge *CD* does not, but the space heights of *A* and *C* are the same, as are *B* and *D*. Height is always measured in a vertical direction and has no relationship whatever to the shape of the object.

Width is the positional distance of left to right, between any two points measured as the perpendicular distance between a pair of profile planes containing the points. The relative width between points *E* and *G* on the left and *H* and *F* on the right of an object is shown by the dimension marked "width," Fig. 4.20. The object edge *EF* is parallel to the width direction and corresponds with the width dimension, but edge *GH* slopes downward from *G* to *H*, thus making the actual object edge longer than the width separating points *G* and *H*.

Depth[2] is the positional distance, front to rear, between any two points measured as the perpendicular distance between two frontal planes containing the points. Figure 4.21 shows two frontal planes,

[1] *Space dimensions* and *dimensions of the object* should not be confused. The primary function of orthographic projection is to show the shape. Size is not established until the figured dimensions and/or the scale are placed on the drawing. Space dimensions are *only* the measure of three-dimensional space.

[2] The term "depth" is used in the civil-engineering sense, as the depth of a lot.

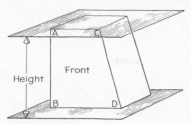

Fig. 4.19. Measurement of height.

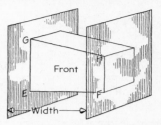

Fig. 4.20. Measurement of width.

one at the front of the object containing points J and L, the other at the rear containing points K and M. The relative depth separating the front and rear of the object is the perpendicular distance between the planes as shown.

Any point may be located in space by giving its height, width, and depth relative to some other known point. Figure 4.22 shows a cube with four identified corners A, B, C, and D. Assuming that the plane containing points A and B is the front of the object, height, width, and depth would be as marked. Assuming also that point A is fixed in space, point B may be located from point A by giving the width dimension, including the statement that height and depth measurements are zero. C may be located from A by giving width, height, and zero depth. D may be located from A by giving width, height, and depth measurements.

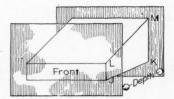

Fig. 4.21. Measurement of depth.

4.9. The Relationship of Planes, View Directions, and Space Dimensions. Under the theory explained in paragraphs 4.4 and 4.5, the object to be drawn may be thought of as surrounded by transparent planes upon which the actual views are projected. The three space dimensions, height, width, and depth, and the planes of projection are unchangeably oriented and connected with each other and with the view directions, Fig. 4.23. Each of the planes of projection is perpendicular, respectively, to its own view direction. Thus the frontal plane is perpendicular to the front-view direction, the horizontal plane is perpendicular to the top-view direction, and the profile plane is perpendicular to the side-view direction. The two space measurements for a view are parallel to the plane of that view and perpendicular to the view direction. Therefore height and width are parallel to the frontal plane and perpendicular to the front-view direction; width and depth are parallel to the horizontal plane and perpendicular to the top-view direction; height and depth are parallel to the profile plane and perpendicular to the side-view direction. Note that the three planes of projection are *mutually* perpendicular, as are the three space measurements and the three view directions. Carefully study the views of Figs. 4.11 to 4.17 and note the space dimensions marked on each figure.

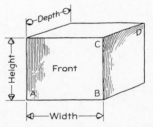

Fig. 4.22. Location of points in space.

4.10. Classification of Surfaces and Lines. Any object, depending upon its shape and space position, may or may not have some surfaces parallel or perpendicular to the planes of projection.

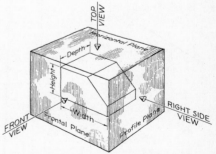

Fig. 4.23. The relationship of space directions and the planes of projection.

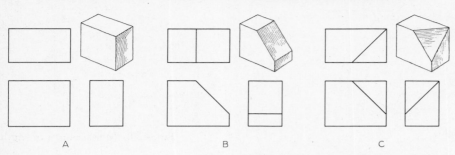

Fig. 4.24. Surface positions.

Surfaces are classified according to their space relationship with the planes of projection. *Horizontal*, *frontal*, and *profile* surfaces are illustrated in Fig. 4.24*A*. When a surface is inclined to two of the planes of projection (but perpendicular to the third), as at *B*, the surface is said to be *auxiliary*. If the surface is at an angle to all three planes, as at *C*, the term *oblique* is used.

The edges (represented by lines) bounding a surface may, because of object shape or position, also be either in a simple position or inclined to the planes of projection. A line in, or parallel to, a plane of projection receives its name from the plane. Thus a *horizontal line* is a line in a horizontal plane, a *frontal line* is a line in a frontal plane, and a *profile line* is a line in a profile plane. When a line is parallel to two planes, the line takes the name of both planes, as *horizontal-frontal*, *horizontal-profile*, or *frontal-profile*. A line not parallel to any plane of projection is called an *oblique line*. Figure 4.25 illustrates various positions of lines.

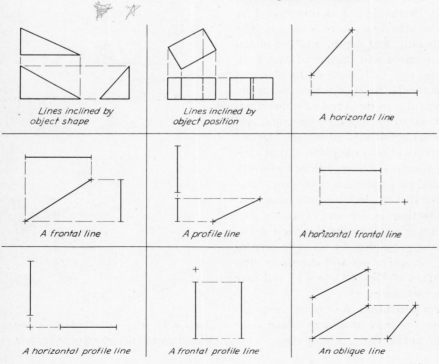

Fig. 4.25. Different line positions.

An edge relative to a plane of projection appears in true length when parallel, as a point when perpendicular, and shorter than true length when inclined. Similarly, a surface relative to a plane of projection appears in its true shape when parallel, as a line when perpendicular, and foreshortened when inclined. As an example, Fig. 4.24*A* shows an object with its faces parallel to the planes of projection; top, front, and right-side surfaces are shown in true shape; and the object edges appear either in true length or as points. The inclined surface of the object at (*B*) does not show in true shape in any of the views but appears as an edge in the front view. The front and rear edges of the inclined surface are in true length in the front view and foreshortened in the top and side views. The top and bottom edges of the inclined surface appear in true length in top and side views and as points in the front view. The oblique surface of the object at (*C*) does not show in true shape in any of the views, but each of the bounding edges shows in true length in one view and is foreshortened in the other two views.

4.11. Representation of Lines. Although uniform in appearance, the lines on a drawing may indicate three different types of directional change on the object. An *edge view* is a line showing the edge of a receding surface (a surface perpendicular to the plane of projection). An *intersection* is the line formed by the meeting of two surfaces. A *surface limit* is the reversal element line of a curved surface (or the series of points of reversal on a warped surface). Figure 4.26 illustrates the different line meanings.

4.12. Hidden Features. To describe an object completely, a drawing should contain lines representing all the edges, intersections, and surface limits of the object. *In any view there will be some parts of the object that cannot be seen from the position of the observer, as they will be covered by portions of the object closer to the observer's eye.* The edges, intersections, and surface limits of these hidden parts are indicated by a line made up of short dashes, sometimes called a "dotted line" by draftsmen. In Fig. 4.27, the drilled hole[1] that is visible in the right-side view is hidden in the top and front views, and therefore it is

[1] See Glossary and Index.

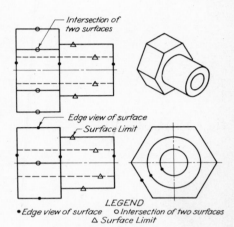

Fig. 4.26. What a line indicates.

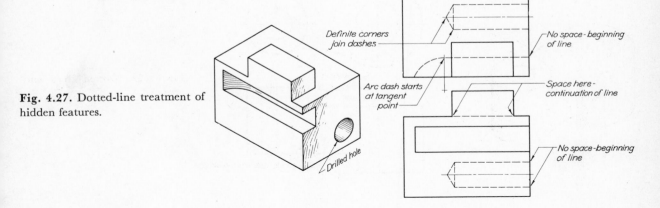

Fig. 4.27. Dotted-line treatment of hidden features.

indicated by a dotted line showing the hole and the shape as left by the drill point. The milled slot (see Glossary) is visible in the front and side views but is hidden in the top view.

The beginner must pay particular attention to the execution of these dotted lines. If carelessly drawn, they not only will ruin the appearance of a drawing but will make it much harder to read. The line is drawn lighter than the full lines, of short dashes uniform in length with the space between them very short, about one-fourth the length of the dash. It is important that they start and stop correctly. A dotted line always starts with a dash except when it would form a continuation of a full line, in which case a space is left, as shown in Fig. 4.27. Dashes always meet at corners. An arc must start with a dash at the tangent point except when it would form a continuation of a straight or curved full line. The number of dashes used in a tangent arc should be carefully judged to maintain a uniform appearance (Fig. 4.28). Study carefully all dotted lines in Figs. 4.27 and 4.29.

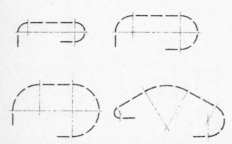

Fig. 4.28. Dotted arcs (actual size).

4.13. Center Lines. In general, the first lines to be drawn in the layout of an engineering drawing are the center lines, thereby forming the axes of symmetry for all symmetrical views or portions of views: (1) Every part with an axis, as a cylinder or a cone, will have the axis drawn as a center line before the part is drawn. (2) Every circle will have its center at the intersection of two center lines.

The standard symbol for center lines on finished drawings is a fine line made up of alternate long and short dashes, as shown in the alphabet of lines, Fig. 1.60. They are always extended slightly beyond the outline of the view or portion of the view to which the center line applies. Center lines form the skeleton construction of the drawing, from and to which the important measurements are made and dimensions given. Study the center lines in Probs. 5.4.1 to 5.5.6.

4.14. Precedence of Lines. In any view, there is likely to be a coincidence of lines. Hidden portions of the object may project

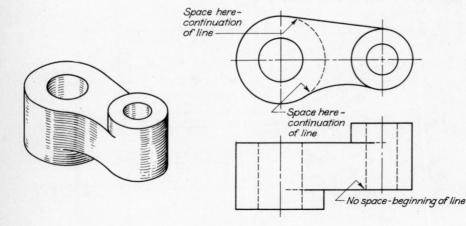

Fig. 4.29. Dotted lines and arcs.

identically with visible portions. Center lines may likewise occur where there is the visible or hidden outline of some part of the object.

Since the physical features of the object *must* be represented, full and dotted lines take precedence over all other lines. Since the visible outline is more prominent by space position, full lines take precedence over dotted lines. A full line could cover a dotted line, but a dotted line could not cover a full line. It is evident also that a dotted line could not occur as one of the boundary lines of a view.

When a center line and cutting-plane line coincide, the one that is more important for the readability of the drawing should take precedence over the other.

Break lines should be placed so that they do not spoil the readability of the over-all view.

Dimension and extension lines must always be placed so as not to coincide with other lines of the drawing.

The following list gives the order of precedence of lines:

1. Full line
2. Dotted line
3. Center line or cutting plane
4. Break lines
5. Dimension and extension lines
6. Crosshatch lines

Note the coincident lines in Fig. 4.30.

4.15. First-angle Projection. The system of orthographic projection explained in this chapter is known as "third-angle projection." It is the official American Standard universally adopted in the United States and Canada.

If the horizontal and vertical planes of projection were to be extended beyond their intersection, four dihedral angles would be formed, which are called, in order, " first," "second," "third," and "fourth" angles, numbered as illustrated in Fig. 4.31. Theoretically, the object might be placed in any one of the four angles or quadrants, projected to the planes, and the planes folded about their inter-

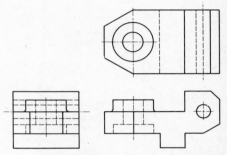

Fig. 4.30. Coincident-line study.

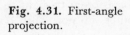
Fig. 4.31. First-angle projection.

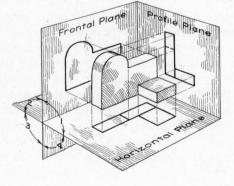

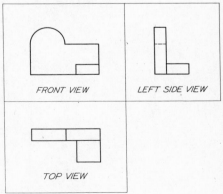

FRONT VIEW   LEFT SIDE VIEW   TOP VIEW

section. Practically, the second and fourth angles would be eliminated, leaving the first and third as possibilities. If the object is placed in the *first angle* and is projected to the planes and the planes are opened up into one plane, the top view would evidently fall below the front view; and if a profile plane were added, the view of the left side of the figure would be to the right of the front view. The system of first-angle projection was formerly in universal use but was generally abandoned in this country some 70 years ago. The student should understand and recognize it, however, as it may be encountered occasionally in old drawings and illustrations as well as in drawings from some foreign countries. Argument and confusion have arisen and sometimes expensive mistakes have occurred through the misreading of first-angle drawings as made by foreign-trained engineers.

4.16. Orthographic Reading. As already stated, the engineer must be able to *read* and *write* the orthographic language. The necessity of learning to read is absolute because everyone connected with technical industry must be able to read a drawing without hesitation. Not to have that ability would be an admission of technical illiteracy.

Since reading is a mental process, a drawing is not read aloud. To describe even a simple object with words will be found to be an uncertain and almost impossible task. Reading proficiency develops with experience, for similar conditions and shapes repeat so often that one gradually acquires a background of knowledge that enables him to visualize the shapes shown. Experienced readers will read quickly because they can draw upon their knowledge and easily recognize familiar shapes and combinations without hesitation; but, even so, reading a drawing should be done carefully and deliberately. One cannot expect to read a whole drawing at once any more than he would expect to read a whole page of print at a glance.

4.17. Prerequisites and Definition. Before attempting to read a drawing, one should be thoroughly familiar with the principles of orthographic projection as explained in paragraphs 4.1 to 4.15. The arrangement of views and their projection, the space measurements of height, width, and depth, what each line represents, etc., must constantly be kept in mind and used where they apply.

Visualization is the medium through which the shape information on a drawing is translated to give the reader an understanding of the object represented. The *ability to visualize* is often thought to be a "gift," which some people possess and others do not. This, however, is not true. Proof that anyone of reasonable intelligence has a visual memory lies in the fact that he is able to recall and describe scenes at home, actions at sporting events, and even the details of acting and facial expression in a play or motion picture.

The ability to visualize a shape shown on a drawing is almost completely governed by the knowledge of the principles of orthographic projection possessed by the individual. The common adage that "the best way to learn to read a drawing is to learn how to make one" is quite correct, because in learning to make a drawing one is forced to study and apply the principles of orthographic projection.

From the foregoing statements, then, the following definition is derived: *"Reading a drawing" is an ability to recognize and apply the principles of orthographic projection to interpret the shape of an object from the orthographic views.*

4.18. Method of Reading. A drawing is read by visualizing units or details one at a time from the orthographic projection and mentally orienting and combining these details to interpret the whole object finally. The form taken in this visualization, however, may not be the same for all readers or for all drawings. Reading is primarily a reversal of the process of making drawings; and inasmuch as drawings are usually first made from a picture of the object, the beginner often attempts to carry the reversal too completely back to the pictorial. The result is that the orthographic views of an object like that shown in Fig. 4.32 are translated to the accompanying picture, with the thought of the object as positioned in space or placed on a table or similar surface. Another will need only to recognize in the drawing the geometry of the solid, which in the case of Fig. 4.32 would be a rectangular prism so high, so wide, and so deep with a hole passing vertically through the center of it. This second reader will have read the views just as completely as the first but with much less mental effort.

To most it is a mental impossibility (and surely an unnecessary requirement) to translate more than just the simplest set of orthographic views into a complete pictorial form that can be pictured in its entirety. Actually, the reader will go through a routine pattern of procedure (listed in paragraph 4.19). Much of this will be done subconsciously. For example, consider the object of Fig. 4.33. One observes a visible circle in the top view. From memory of previous projection experience, this must be either a hole or the end of a cylinder. The eyes rapidly shift back and forth from the top view to the front view, aligning features of the same size ("in projection"), with the mind assuming the several possibilities and finally accepting the fact that, because of the dotted lines and their extent in the front view, the circle represents a hole that extends through the prism. Following a similar pattern of analysis, the reader will find that Fig. 4.34 represents a rectangular prism surmounted by a cylinder. All is done so rapidly that the reader is scarcely aware of the steps and processes involved.

Presumably the foregoing is the usual method, but how does the beginner develop this ability?

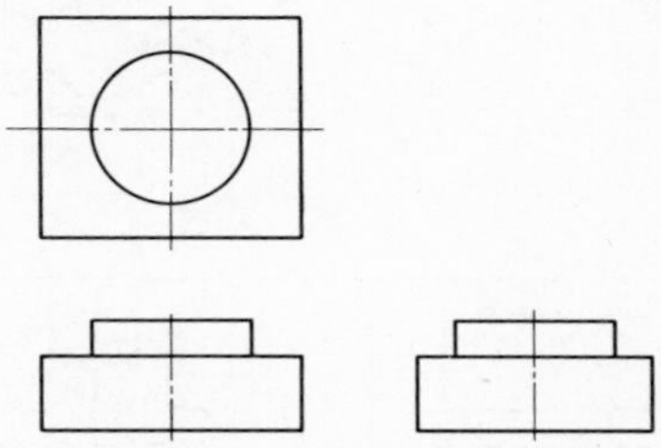

First, as stated in paragraph 4.17, a reasonable knowledge of the principles of orthographic projection is necessary.

Second, as described in paragraphs 4.20 and 4.21, a complete

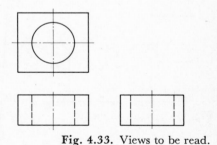

Fig. 4.32. Orthographic views and picture.

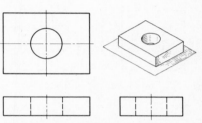

Fig. 4.33. Views to be read.

Fig. 4.34. Views to be read.

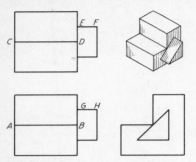

Fig. 4.35. The meaning of lines.

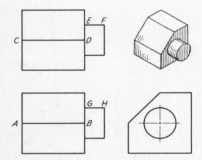

Fig. 4.36. The meaning of lines.

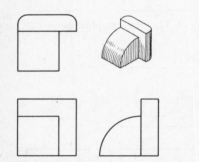

Fig. 4.37. Read all views.

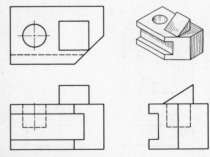

Fig. 4.38. Read all lines.

understanding of the meaning of lines, areas, etc., and the mental processes involved must be acquired. To read, one applies these principles. There is very little additional learning required. Careful study of all these items plus practice will develop the ability and confidence needed.

4.19. Procedure for Reading. The actual steps in reading will not always be identical because of the wide variety of subject matter (drawings). Nevertheless, the following outline gives the basic procedure and will serve as a guide:

First, orient yourself with the views given.

Second, obtain a general idea of the over-all shape of the object. Think of each view as the object itself, visualizing yourself in front, above, and at the side as the draftsman did in making the views. Study the dominant features and their relation to each other.

Third, start reading the simpler individual features, beginning with the most dominant and progressing to the subordinate. Look for familiar shapes or conditions that your memory retains from previous experience. Read all views of these familiar features to note the extent of holes, thickness of ribs and lugs, etc.

Fourth, read the unfamiliar or complicated features. Remember that every point, line, surface, and solid appears in every view and that you must find the projection of every detail in the given views to learn the shape.

Fifth, as the reading proceeds, note the relationship between the various portions or elements of the object. Such items as the number and spacing of holes, placement of ribs, tangency of surfaces, and the proportions of hubs, etc., should be noted and remembered.

Sixth, reread any detail or relationship not clear at the first reading.

4.20. The Meaning of Lines. As explained in paragraph 4.14, a line on a drawing indicates (1) the *edge of a surface*, (2) an *intersection of two surfaces*, or (3) a *surface limit*. Because a line on a view may mean any one of these three conditions, the corresponding part of another view must be consulted to determine the meaning. For example, the meaning of line *AB* on the front view of Fig. 4.35 cannot be determined until the side view is consulted. The line is then found to be the edge view of the horizontal surface of the cutout corner. Similarly, line *CD* on the top view cannot be fully understood without consulting the side view, where it is identified as the edge view of the vertical surface of the cutout corner. Line *EF* on the top view and *GH* on the front view are identical in appearance. However, the side view shows that line *EF* represents the edge view of the rear surface of the triangular block and that line *GH* is the intersection of the front and rear surfaces of the triangular block.

The top and front views of the objects shown in Figs. 4.35 and 4.36 are identical. Nevertheless, lines *AB* and *CD* in Fig. 4.36 do not represent what they did in Fig. 4.35 but are in Fig. 4.36 the intersection of two surfaces. Also, lines *EF* and *GH* in Fig. 4.36 are

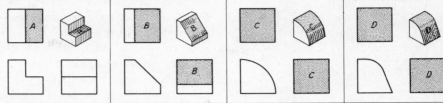

Fig. 4.39. The meaning of areas.

identical in appearance with those in Fig. 4.35, but in Fig. 4.36 they represent the surface limits of the circular boss.

From Figs. 4.35 and 4.36, it is readily seen that one cannot read a drawing by looking at a single view. Two views will not always describe an object, and when three or more views are given, all must be consulted to be sure that the shape has been read correctly. To illustrate with Fig. 4.37, the front and top views show what appears to be a rectangular projection on the front of the object, but the side view shows this projection to be quarter round. Similarly, the front and side views apparently indicate the rear portion of the object to be a rectangular prism, but the top view shows that the two vertical rear edges are rounded.

One cannot assume a shape from one or two views—*all the views must be read carefully.*

From the foregoing, it should be evident that the several *lines,* representing some feature, must be read in all the views. As an exercise in reading the lines on an orthographic drawing, find *all* the lines representing the hole, triangular prism, slot, and cutoff corner of Fig. 4.38.

4.21. The Meaning of Areas. The term "area" as used here means the contour limits of a surface or combination of tangent surfaces as seen in the different orthographic views. To illustrate, an area of a view as shown in Fig. 4.39 may represent (1) a surface in true shape as at *A*, (2) a foreshortened surface as at *B*, (3) a curved surface as at *C*, or (4) a combination of tangent surfaces as at *D*.

When a surface is in an oblique position, as surface *E* of Fig. 4.40, all principal views of the surface will appear as an area. A study of the surfaces in Figs. 4.39, 4.40, and others will establish with the force of a rule that *a plane surface, whether it be positioned in a horizontal, frontal, profile, or an auxiliary or oblique position, will always appear in a principal orthographic view either as a line or an area.* Principal views of an oblique surface that appear as an area in more than one view will always have like shapes. As an example, surface *A* of Fig. 4.41 will appear as a triangular area in all the principal views. The length of the edges and the angles between the edges may change, but all views will have the same number of sides. It should be noted that a plane surface bounded by a certain number of sides could never appear to have more or fewer sides except when the surface appears as an edge. Moreover, the sides in any view will always connect in

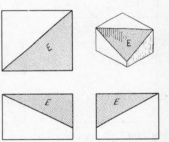

Fig. 4.40. The meaning of areas.

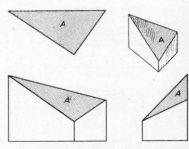

Fig. 4.41. The meaning of areas.

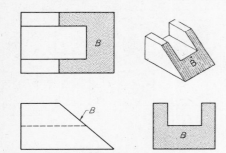

Fig. 4.42. Similar shapes of areas.

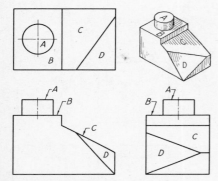

Fig. 4.43. Adjacent areas.

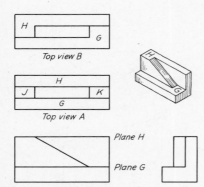

Fig. 4.44. Adjacent areas.

the same sequence. Illustrating these principles with the block of Fig. 4.42, the front view shows surface *B* as an edge. The top and side views show the surface as an area having a similar shape, the same number of sides, and with the corners in the same sequence.

4.22. Adjacent Areas. No two adjacent areas can lie in the same plane. It is simple logic that, if two adjacent areas *did* lie in the same plane, there would be no boundary between the areas, and therefore, orthographically, the two adjacent areas could not exist. In illustration of these statements, note that in Fig. 4.43 areas *A*, *B*, *C*, and *D* are shown in the front and side views to lie in different planes.

Further proof of these principles is given by Fig. 4.44, in which two top views are shown. By analysis of the projection between top and front views, it is seen that areas *G* and *H* shown on the top views must lie in planes *G* and *H*, respectively, shown on the front view. Also, by projection, it is seen that area *J* of top view *A* must lie in plane *H* and that area *K* must lie in plane *G*. Because areas *H* and *J* lie in plane *H* and areas *G* and *K* lie in plane *G*, the correct top view, therefore, is top view *B*.

Hidden areas may sometimes be confusing to read because the areas may overlap or even correspond with each other. For example, areas *A*, *B*, and *C* of Fig. 4.45 are not separate areas because they are all formed by the slot on the rear of the object. The apparent separation into separate areas is caused by the dotted lines from the rectangular hole, which, of course, is not connected with the slot in any way.

4.23. Reading Lines and Areas. The foregoing principles regarding the meaning of lines and areas must be used to analyze any given set of views by correlating a surface appearing as a line or an area with the other views, in which the surface may appear as a line or an area. Illustrating with Fig. 4.46, first orient yourself with the given views. From their arrangement, the views are evidently top, front, and right side. An over-all inspection of the views does not reveal familiar geometric shapes, such as a hole or boss, so that an analysis of the surfaces is necessary. Beginning with the trapezoidal area *A* in the top view and then moving to the front

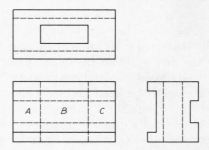

Fig. 4.45. Reading hidden areas.

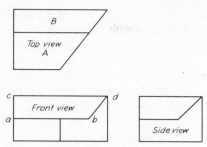

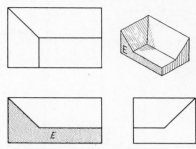

Fig. 4.46. Reading lines and areas.

Fig. 4.47. Identical areas may have different meanings.

view, a similar-shaped area of the same width is not shown; therefore, the front view of area *A* must appear as an edge, the line *ab*. Next, consider area *B* in the top view. It is seen to be a trapezoidal area (four sides) the full width of the view. Again, going to the front view for a mating area or line, the area *abcd* is of similar shape and has the same number of sides with the corners in projection. Area *abcd*, therefore, satisfies the requirements of orthographic projection and is the front view of area *B*. The side view should be checked along with the other views to see if it agrees. Proceed in like manner to additional areas, correlating them one with another to visualize the shape of the complete object.

Memory and experience will aid materially in reading any given drawing. However, every new set of views must be approached with an open mind because sometimes a shape that looks like a previously known condition will crowd the correct interpretation from the mind of the reader. For example, area *E* in Fig. 4.47 is in a vertical position. The front view of Fig. 4.48 is identical with the front view of Fig. 4.47, but in 4.48 the surface *F* is inclined to the rear and is not vertical.

4.24. Reading of Corners and Edges. The corners and edges of areas may be numbered or lettered to identify them for making additional views or as an aid in reading some complicated shape. If there are no coincident conditions, they are easily named by projection; that is, the top view is directly over the front view, and the side view lies on a horizontal projector to the front view. When coincident conditions are present, it may be necessary to coordinate a point with an adjacent point as shown by Fig. 4.49. Corner *c* in the front view (c_F) may be in projection with c_T at any one of the three positions marked 1, 2, 3. However, the point *c* is one end of an edge *dc*, and the front view of *c* must therefore be at position 2. An experienced reader could probably make the above observations without marking the points, but a beginner in many cases can gain much valuable experience by marking corners and edges, especially if the problem is some unusual combination of surfaces.

4.25. Learning to Read by Sketching. A drawing is interpreted by mentally understanding the shape of the object represented. Proof that the drawing has been read and understood may be shown

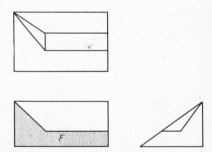

Fig. 4.48. Identical areas may have different meanings.

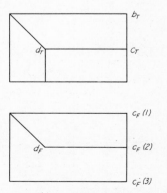

Fig. 4.49. Identification of corners.

by making the piece in wood or metal, by modeling it in clay, or by making a pictorial sketch of it, the latter being the usual method. Since facility in freehand sketching is so important to every engineer, its practice should be started early. Before attempting to make a pictorial sketch, a preliminary study of the method of procedure will be required. Pictorial sketching may be based on a skeleton of three axes, one vertical and the other two at 30°,[1] representing three mutually perpendicular lines (Fig. 4.50). On these axes are marked the proportionate width, depth, and height of any rectangular figure. Circles are drawn in their circumscribing squares.

In Fig. 4.51, look at the views given, as described in paragraph 4.19. Then with a soft pencil (F) and notebook paper make a *very light* pictorial construction sketch, estimating the height, width, and depth of the object and laying the distances off on the axes as at *A*; then sketch the rectangular box that would enclose the piece, or the block from which it could be cut, Fig. 4.51*B*. On the top face of this box, sketch very lightly the lines that occur on the top view of the orthographic drawing, Fig. 4.51*C*. Note that, as will be found later, some of the lines on top views may not be in the top plane. Next sketch lightly the lines of the front view on the front face of the box or block, and if a side view is given, outline it similarly, Fig. 4.51*D*. Now begin to cut the figure from the block, strengthening the visible edges and adding the lines of intersection where faces of the object meet, as in Fig. 4.51*E*. Edges that do not appear as visible lines are omitted unless necessary to describe the piece. Finish the sketch, checking back to the three-view drawing. The construction lines need not be erased unless they confuse the sketch.

4.26. Learning to Read by Modeling. An interesting and effective learning method is to model the object in clay or modeling wax, working in much the same way as when reading by pictorial sketching. Some shapes may be modeled by cutting out from the enclosing block; others may be modeled more easily by first analyzing

[1] Isometric position. Oblique or other pictorial methods may also be used.

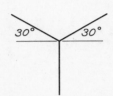

Fig. 4.50. Pictorial axes.

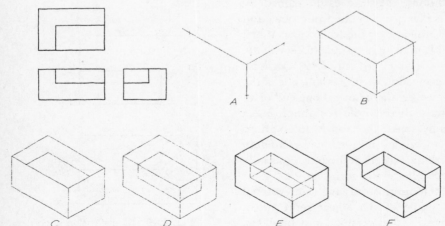

Fig. 4.51. Stages in making a pictorial sketch.

and dividing the object into its basic geometric shapes and then combining these shapes.

Starting with a rectangular block of clay, perhaps 1 in. square and 2 in. long, read Fig. 4.52 by cutting the figure from the solid. Scribe very lightly, with the point of the knife or a scriber, the lines of the three views on the three corresponding faces of the block (Fig. 4.53*A*). Evidently the first cut could be as shown at (*B*) and the second as at (*C*). Successive cuts are indicated at (*D*) and (*E*), and the finished model is indicated at (*F*).

Figure 4.54 illustrates the type of model that can be made by building up the shapes of which the object is composed.

4.27. Calculation of Volume As an Aid in Reading. In calculating the volume of an object, one is forced to break the part down into its simple geometrical elements and then to analyze carefully the shape of each element before computation is possible. Thus the calculation of volume is primarily an exercise in reading a drawing. Before the computations are completed, the object has usually been visualized, but the mathematical record of the volume of each portion and the correct total volume and weight are proof that the drawing has been read and understood.

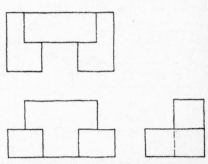

Fig. 4.52. A drawing to be read.

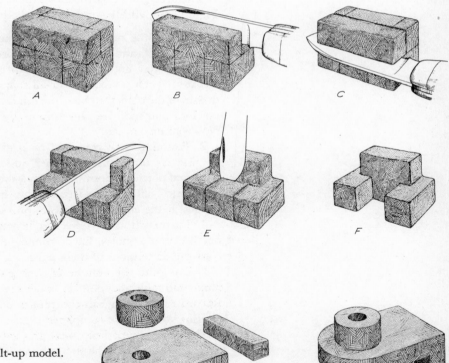

Fig. 4.53. Stages in modeling.

Fig. 4.54. A built-up model.

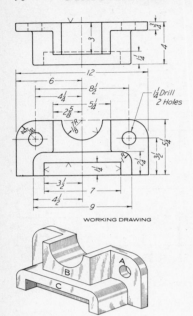

WORKING DRAWING

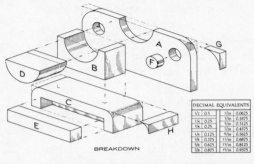

BREAKDOWN

DECIMAL EQUIVALENTS			
1/2	0.5	1/16	0.0625
1/4	0.25	3/16	0.1875
3/4	0.75	5/16	0.3125
		7/16	0.4375
1/8	0.125	9/16	0.5625
3/8	0.375	11/16	0.6875
5/8	0.625	13/16	0.8125
7/8	0.875	15/16	0.9375

Fig. 4.55. Shape breakdown for volume and weight calculations.

BEARING REST	MATERIAL	WT. — LB. PER CU. IN.		
PART	DIMENSIONS		PLUS VOLUME	MINUS VOLUME
A				
B				
C				
D				
E				
F				
G				
H				
		TOTALS		

WEIGHT PER CUBIC INCH		
GRAY CAST IRON 0.260 LB	TOTAL NET VOLUME IN CUBIC INCHES	
TOBIN BRONZE 0.304 LB		
CAST STEEL 0.282 LB	WEIGHT IN POUNDS	

The procedure closely follows the usual steps in reading a drawing. Figure 4.55 will illustrate the method.

1. Study the orthographic drawing and pick out the principal masses (A, B, and C shown on the breakdown and in the pictorial drawing). Pay no attention in the beginning to holes, rounds, etc., but study each principal over-all shape and its relation to the other masses of the object. Record the dimensions of each of these principal portions and indicate plus volume by placing a check mark in the plus-volume column.

2. Examine each principal mass and find the secondary masses (D and E) that must be either added to or subtracted from the principal portions. Bosses, lugs, etc., must be added; cutout portions, holes, etc., subtracted. Record the dimensions of these secondary masses, being careful to indicate plus or minus volume.

3. Further limit the object to its actual shape by locating smaller details, such as holes, fillets, rounds, etc. (parts F, G, and H). Record the dimensions of these parts.

4. Compute the volume of each portion. This may be done by longhand multiplication or, more conveniently, with a slide rule. Record each volume in the proper column, plus or minus. When all unit volumes are completed, find the net volume by subtracting total minus volume from total plus volume.

5. Multiply net volume by the weight per cubic inch of metal to compute the total weight.

The calculations are simplified if all fractional dimensions are converted to the decimal form. When a slide rule is employed, fractions *must* be converted to decimals. A partial conversion table is given in Fig. 4.55 and a more complete table in the Appendix.

The complete volume and weight calculation not only gives training in recognition of the fundamental geometrical portions of an object but also serves to teach neat and concise working methods in the recording of engineering data.

4.28. Exercises in Projection. As can be seen from the foregoing paragraphs of this chapter, the principal problem in learning orthographic projection is first to become thoroughly familiar with the theory and then to practice this theory by translating from a picture of the object to the orthographic views. Figures 4.56 and 4.57 contain a variety of objects shown by a pictorial sketch and the translation into orthographic views. Study the objects in these figures and

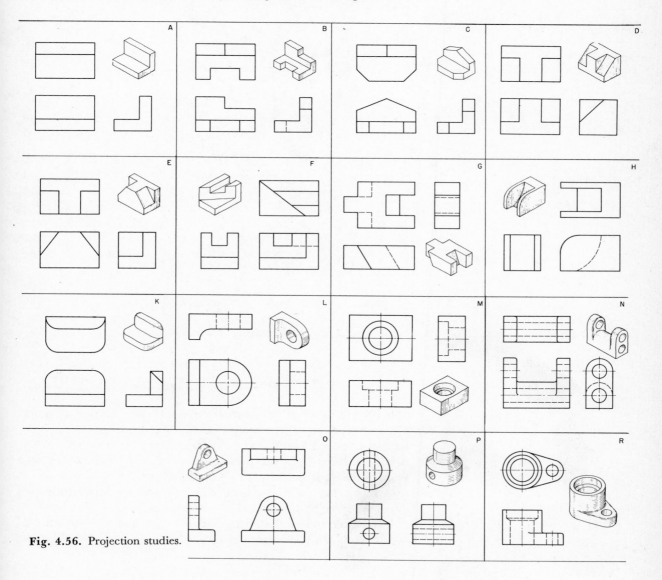

Fig. 4.56. Projection studies.

Fig. 4.57. Projection studies.

note (1) how the object is oriented in space, (2) why the orthographic views are chosen, (3) the projection of visible features, (4) the projection of hidden features, and (5) center lines.

4.29. Orthographic Representation. The end point of orthographic theory is not simply to understand the theory but to apply it in the making of drawings. Chapter 5 gives the application for drawings made both freehand and with instruments.

4.30. Exercises in Reading. Figures 4.58 and 4.59 contain a number of three-view drawings of block shapes made for exercises

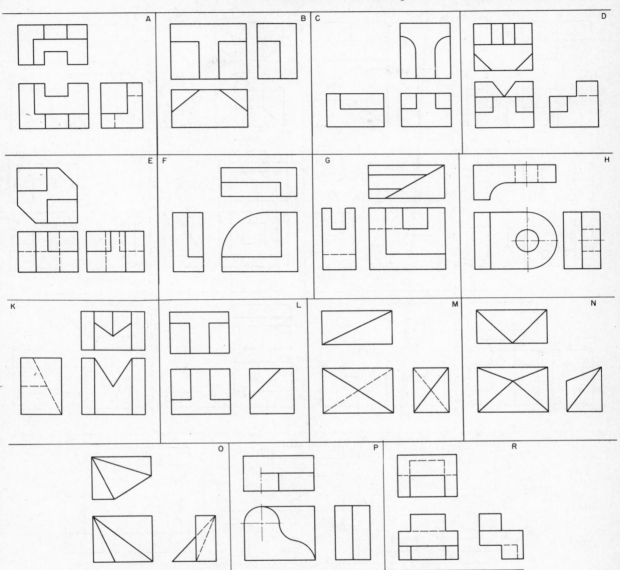

Fig. 4.58. Reading exercises.

in reading orthographic projection and translating into pictorial sketches or models. Proceed as described in the previous paragraphs, making sketches not less than 4 in. over-all. Check each sketch to be sure that all intersections are shown and that the original three-view drawing could be made from the sketch.

In each three-view drawing of Fig. 4.60, some lines have been intentionally omitted. Read the drawings and supply the missing lines.

4.31. Volume and Weight Calculations with Slide Rule. In

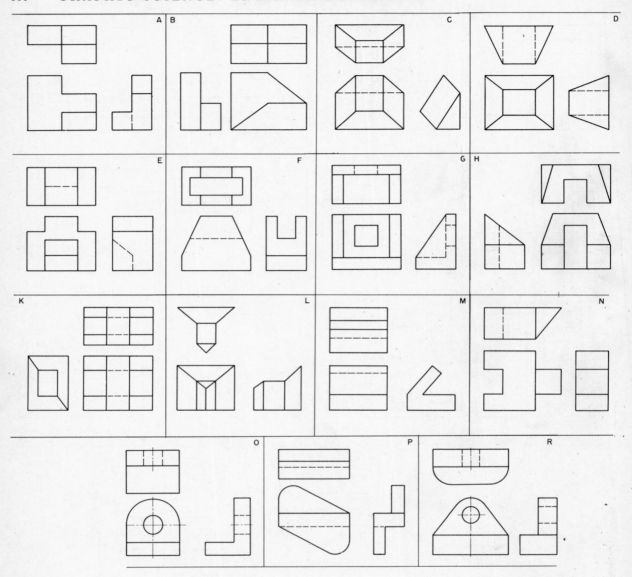

Fig. 4.59. Reading exercises.

calculating the weight of a piece from the drawings, the object should be divided or broken up into the geometric solids (prisms, cylinders, pyramids, or cones) of which it is composed. The volume of each of these shapes should be calculated, and these should be added—or sometimes subtracted—to find the total volume which, multiplied by the weight of the material per unit of volume, will give the weight of the object.

A table of weights of materials will be found in the Appendix.

Fig. 4.60. Missing-line exercises.

The following problems are suggested:
1. Find the weight of the cast-iron jig block, Prob. 8.1.1.
2. Find the weight of the bearing brass, Prob. 8.1.10.
3. Find the weight of the wrought-iron guide block, Prob. 8.1.6.
4. Find the weight of the cast-steel dovetail stop, Prob. 8.1.7.
5. Find the weight of the malleable-iron bracket, Prob. 8.1.15.

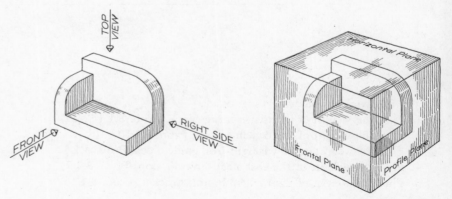

Fig. 5.1. Object orientation.

5

PRACTICE OF PROJECTION DRAWING

5.1. Orthographic drawing is the major objective in any drawing course. Before attempting an orthographic drawing, one must have a knowledge of orthographic projection as explained in Chap. 4. In addition, instrument drawing demands, for technique, some skill and facility in the use of instruments, Chap. 1, and a knowledge of applied geometry, Chap. 2. Lettering, Chap. 3, should also be studied and practiced. Careful attention should always be paid to accuracy and neatness.

Speed and accuracy are of prime importance, but neither one should be slighted for the benefit of the other. Unnecessary extreme accuracy will waste time, while excessive speed will result in inaccurate, poorly made drawings. Good drawing habits and practices must be acquired. Instruments must be kept clean and in good working order. The drawing board and table should not be cluttered with unneeded equipment. Have a definite place for everything so that time is not lost looking for instruments and tools.

5.2. Object Orientation. An object may, of course, be drawn in any of several possible positions. *The simplest position should be used,* with the object oriented so that the principal faces are perpendicular to the sight directions for the views and parallel to the planes of projection as shown in Fig. 5.1. Any other position with the faces of the object at some angle to the planes of projection would complicate the drawing, foreshorten the object faces, and make the drawing difficult to make and to read.

103

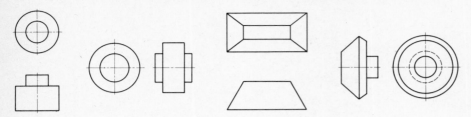

Fig. 5.2. Two-view drawings.

5.3. Selection of Views.

In practical work, it is very important to choose the combination of views that will describe the shape of an object in the best and most economical way. Often only two views are necessary, as, for example, a cylindrical shape, which, if on a vertical axis, would require only a front and top view and, if on a horizontal axis, only a front and side view. Conical and pyramidal shapes also may be described in two views. Figure 5.2 illustrates two-view drawings. On the other hand, some shapes will need more than the three regular views for adequate description.

Objects may be thought of as being made up of combinations of simple geometrical solids, principally cylinders and rectangular prisms, and the views necessary to describe any object would be determined by the directions from which it would have to be viewed to see the characteristic contour shapes of these parts. Figure 5.3, for example, is made up of several prisms and cylinders. If each of these simple shapes is described and their relation to each other is shown, the object will be fully represented. In the majority of cases, the three regular views, top, front, and side, are sufficient to do this.

Sometimes two views are proposed as sufficient for some object on the assumption that the contour in the third direction would be of the shape that would naturally be expected. For instance, Fig. 5.4*A* would be assumed to have a uniform cross section and be a square prism. But the two views *might* be the top and front views of a wedge, as shown in three views at (*B*). Two views of an object, as drawn at (*C*), do not describe the piece at all. It might be assumed to be square in section, but it could as easily be round, triangular, quarter round, or other shape, which should have been indicated by a required side view. Sketch several different front views for each top view, Fig. 5.5*A* to *C*.

With the object preferably in its functioning position and *with its principal surfaces parallel to the planes of projection*, visualize the object, mentally picturing the orthographic views one at a time to decide on the best combination. In Fig. 5.6, the arrows show the direction of observation for the six principal views of an object, and indicate the mental process of the draftsman. He notes that the front view should show the two horizontal holes as well as the width and height of the piece, that a top view is needed to show the contour of the vertical cylinder, and that the cutout corner will require a side view to show its shape. He notes further that the right-side view would show this cut in full lines, while on the left side it would be hidden. He notes, incidentally, that neither a bottom view nor a

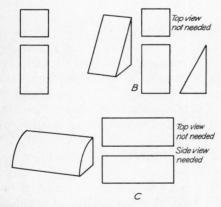

Fig. 5.3. Geometric shapes combined.

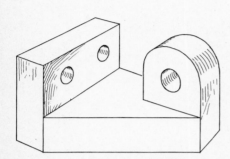

Top view not needed

Top view not needed

Side view needed

Fig. 5.4. A study of views.

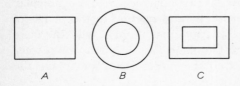

Fig. 5.5. Top views given.

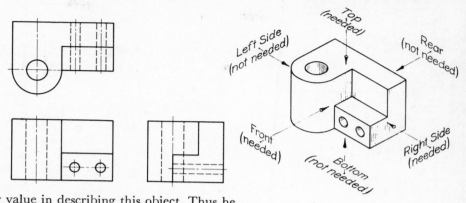

Fig. 5.6. Selection of views.

rear view would be of any value in describing this object. Thus he has arrived at the correct choice of front, top, and right-side views for the best description of the piece. As a rule, the side view containing the fewer dotted lines should be preferred. If there is no choice, the right-side view is preferred in standard practice.

In inventive and design work, any simple object should be visualized mentally and the view selected without a picture sketch. In complicated work, a pictorial or orthographic sketch may be used to advantage, but it should not be necessary, in any case, to sketch all possible views in order to make a selection.

Study the drawings in Fig. 5.7 and determine why the views are so chosen.

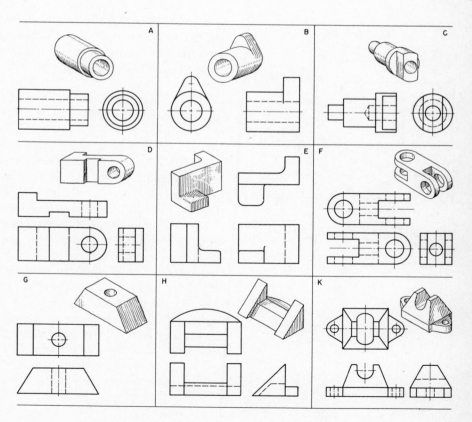

Fig. 5.7. Selection-of-view study.

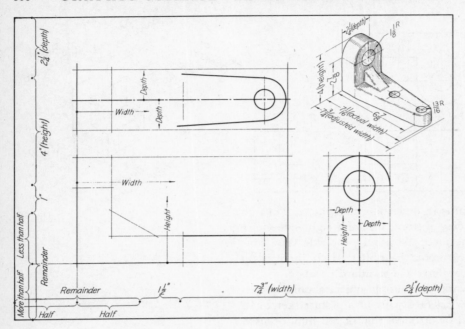

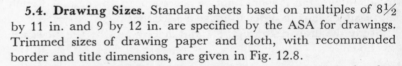

Fig. 5.8. Spacing the views.

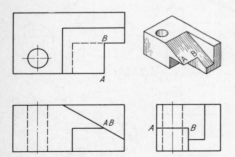

Fig. 5.9. Projection of lines.

5.4. Drawing Sizes. Standard sheets based on multiples of $8\frac{1}{2}$ by 11 in. and 9 by 12 in. are specified by the ASA for drawings. Trimmed sizes of drawing paper and cloth, with recommended border and title dimensions, are given in Fig. 12.8.

5.5. Spacing the Views. View spacing is necessary in order that the drawing may be balanced within the space provided. The draftsman, therefore, must do a little preliminary measuring to locate the views. The following example will describe the procedure: Suppose the piece illustrated in Fig. 5.8 is to be drawn full size on an 11- by 17-in. sheet. With an end-title strip, the working space inside the border will be $10\frac{1}{2}$ by 15 in. The front view will require $7\frac{11}{16}$ in., and the side view $2\frac{1}{4}$ in. This leaves $5\frac{1}{16}$ in. to be distributed between the views and at the ends.

This preliminary planning need not be to exact dimensions, that is, small fractional values, such as $\frac{15}{64}$ in. or $\frac{31}{32}$ in., may be adjusted to $\frac{1}{4}$ and 1 in., respectively, to speed up the planning. In this case the $7\frac{11}{16}$-in. dimension may be adjusted to $7\frac{3}{4}$ in.

The draftsman locates the views graphically and very quickly by measuring with his scale along the bottom border line. Starting at the lower right corner, lay off first $2\frac{1}{4}$ in. and then $7\frac{3}{4}$ in. The distance between views may now be decided upon. It is chosen arbitrarily to separate the views without crowding, yet sufficiently close to have the drawing read easily (in this case $1\frac{1}{2}$ in.) and the distance measured; half the remaining distance to the left corner is the starting point of the front view. For the vertical location, the front view is 4 in. high, and the top view $2\frac{1}{4}$ in. deep. Starting at the upper left corner, lay off first $2\frac{1}{4}$ in. and then 4 in.; judge the distance between views (in this case 1 in.), and lay it off; then a point marked

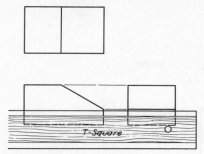

Fig. 5.10. Making a horizontal projection.

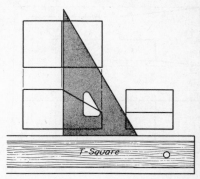

Fig. 5.11. Making a vertical projection.

at less than half the remaining space will locate the front view, allowing more space at the bottom than at the top for appearance.

Spaces for the views are blocked out lightly, and the over-all arrangement is studied, because changes can be easily made at this stage. If satisfactory, next select reference lines in each view from which the space measurements of height, width, and depth that appear in the view may be measured. This may be an edge or a center line through some dominant feature, as indicated on Fig. 5.8 by the center lines in the top and side views and the medium weight lines in all the views. The directions for height, width, and depth measurements for the views are also shown.

5.6. Projecting the Views. After the views have been laid out, the various features of the object may be located and drawn. In accomplishing this, the views should be *carried along together*, that is, *not* attempting to complete one view before proceeding to another. The most characteristic view of a feature should be drawn first and then projected and drawn in the other views before going on to a second feature. As an example, the vertical hole of Fig. 5.9 should be drawn first in the top view, and then the dotted lines representing the limiting elements should be projected and drawn in the front and side views.

In some cases, a view cannot be completed before a feature has been located and drawn in another view. For illustration of this point, study the pictorial drawing of Fig. 5.9, and note from the orthographic views that the horizontal slot must be drawn on the front view before the edge AB on the slanting surface can be found in the top view.

Projections (horizontal) between the front and side views are made by employing the T square to draw the required horizontal line (or to locate a required point), as illustrated in Fig. 5.10.

Projections (vertical) between the front and top views are made by using the T square and a triangle as illustrated in Fig. 5.11.

Projections between the top and side views cannot be projected directly but must be measured and transferred or found by special construction. In carrying the top and side views along together, the draftsman usually transfers the depth measurement from one to the other either with his dividers, as in Fig. 5.12*A*, or with his scale, as

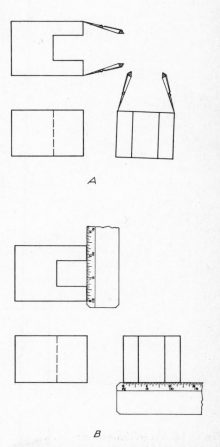

Fig. 5.12. Transferring depth measurements.

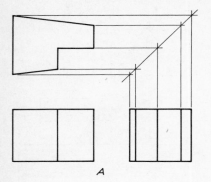

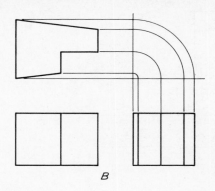

Fig. 5.13. Projecting depth measurements.

at (*B*). Sometimes, however, as in the case of an irregular figure, he prefers to "miter" the points around, using a 45° line drawn through the point of intersection of the top and side views of the front face, extended as shown in Fig. 5.13*A*, or, going back to the method of the glass box, to swing them around with the compasses, as at (*B*). The methods of Fig. 5.13, however, require more time and care to maintain accuracy than do the methods of Fig. 5.12 and are *not*, therefore, recommended.

5.7. Projections of Surfaces Bounded by Linear Edges. In the drawing of projections of inclined surfaces, in some cases the corners of the bounding edges may be used, and in other cases the bounding edges themselves may be projected. In illustration of these methods Fig. 5.14*A* shows a vertical hexagonal hole that may be laid out from specifications in the top view. Then the front view may be drawn by projecting from the six corners of the hexagon and drawing the four dotted lines to complete the front view. To get the side view, a horizontal projection may be made from each corner on the front view to the side view, thus locating the height of the points needed on the side view. Measurements D_1, D_2, and D_3 then taken from the top view and transferred to the side view will locate all six corners in the side view. Connecting these corners and drawing the three vertical dotted lines complete the view. The object in Fig. 5.14*B* shows a horizontal slot running out on an inclined surface. In the front view, the true width and height of this slot may be laid out from specifications. The projection to the side view is a simple

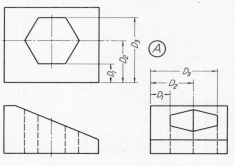

Fig. 5.14. Projections of surfaces bounded by linear edges.

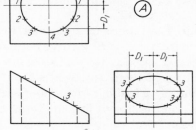

Fig. 5.15. Projection of elliptical boundaries.

horizontal projection for the dotted line, indicating the top surface of the slot. To get the top view, the width may be projected from the front view and then the position of the runout line measured (distance D_1) and transferred to the top view.

In summary, it may be stated that, if a line will appear at some angle on a view, its two ends must be projected; if a line will appear parallel to its path of projection, the complete line may be projected.

5.8. Projections of an Elliptical Boundary. The intersection of a cylindrical hole (or cylinder) with a slanting (auxiliary or oblique) surface, as shown in Fig. 5.15, will be an ellipse, and some projections of this elliptical edge will appear as another ellipse. The projection may be made as shown in Fig. 5.15A by assuming a number of points on the circular view and projecting them to the edge view and then to an adjacent view. Thus, as an example, points 1 to 4 are located in the top view and projected to the front view, and the projectors are then drawn to the side view. Measurements of depth taken from the top view (as D_1) will locate the points in the side view. A smooth curve is then drawn through the points, employing a french curve for the job.

For an ellipse on an auxiliary surface, the projection may also be made by establishing the major and minor diameters of the ellipse, as shown in Fig. 5.15B. A pair of diameters positioned so as to give the largest and smallest extent of the curve will give the required major and minor diameters. Thus, in Fig. 5.15B, AB will project to the side view as the smaller, or minor, diameter A_SB_S, and CD will project as the larger, or major, diameter C_SD_S. The ellipse may then be drawn by one of the methods of paragraphs 16.6, 16.9, and 16.11.

If the surface intersected by the cylinder is oblique, as shown in Fig. 5.16, a pair of perpendicular diameters located in the circular view will give a pair of conjugate diameters in an adjacent view. Therefore, A_TB_T and C_TD_T projected to the front view will give conjugate diameters, which may be employed as explained in paragraphs 16.10, 16.12, and 16.13 to draw the required ellipse.

In projecting the axes, they may be extended to the straight-line

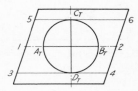

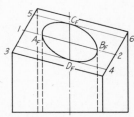

Fig. 5.16. Projection of an elliptical boundary by employing conjugate diameters.

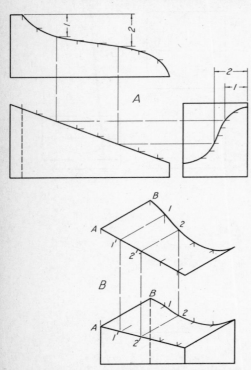

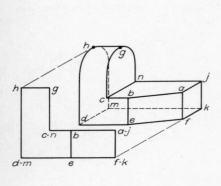

Fig. 5.17. Projection of curved boundaries.

boundary of the oblique surface. Thus the line 1–2 located in the front view and intersected by projection of $A_T B_T$ from the top view locates $A_F B_F$. Similarly, lines 3–4 and 5–6 at the ends of the axis CD locate $C_F D_F$.

5.9. Projections of a Curved Boundary. Any nongeometrical curve (or a geometrical curve not having established axes) must be projected by locating points on the curve. If the surface is in an auxiliary position, as shown in Fig. 5.17A, points may be assumed on the curve laid out from data (assumed in this case to be the top view) and projected first to the edge view (front) and then to an adjacent (side) view. Measurements, such as 1, 2, etc., from the top view transferred to the side view complete the projection. A smooth curve is then drawn through the points.

If the surface is oblique, as illustrated in Fig. 5.17B, elements of the oblique surface, such as 1'-1, 2'-2, etc., located in an adjacent view (by drawing the elements parallel to some known line of the oblique surface, such as AB) make it possible to project points on the curve 1, 2, etc., to the adjacent view, as shown.

5.10. Projections by Identifying Corners. In projecting orthographic views or in comparing the views with a picture, it will be of much help in some cases to letter or number the corners of the object and, with these identifying marks, to letter, similarly, the corresponding points on each of the views, as in Fig. 5.18. Hidden points directly behind visible points are lettered to the right of the letter of the visible point, and in this figure, they have been further differentiated by the use of "phantom," or dotted, letters. Study Fig. 5.19, and number or letter the corners of the three views to correspond with the pictorial view.

5.11. Order of Drawing. The order of working is important, as speed and accuracy depend largely upon the methods employed in laying down lines. Duplications of the same measurement should be avoided, and changing from one instrument to another should be kept at a minimum. Naturally, *all* measurements cannot be made with the scale at one time or *all* circles and arcs drawn before laying

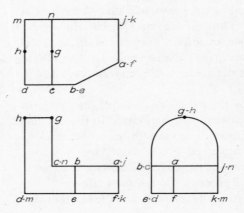

Fig. 5.18. Identified corners.

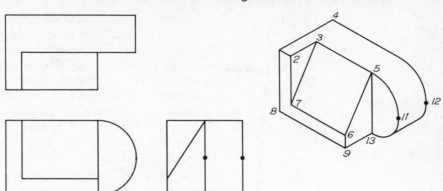

Fig. 5.19. Projection study.

down the compasses, but as much work as possible should be done before shifting to another instrument. An orderly placement of the working tools on the drafting table will save much time when changing from the use of one instrument to another. The usual order of working is illustrated in Fig. 5.20.

1. Decide what combination of views will best describe the object. A freehand sketch will aid in choosing the views and in planning the general arrangement of the sheet.

2. Decide what scale is to be used, and by calculation or measurement, find a suitable standard sheet size; or pick one of the standard drawing sizes, and find a suitable scale.

3. Space the views on the sheet, as described in paragraph 5.5.

4. Lay off the principal dimensions, and then "block in" the views with light, sharp, accurate outlines and center lines. Center lines are drawn for the axes of all symmetrical views or parts of views. Thus every cylindrical part should have a center line—the projection of the axis of the piece. Every circle should have two center lines intersecting at its center.

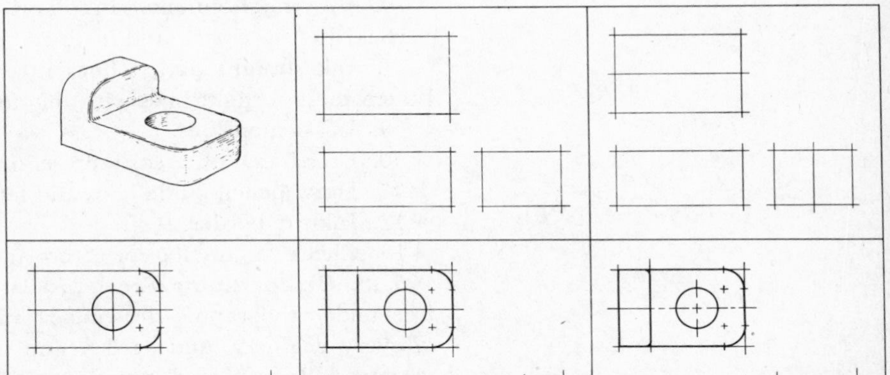

Fig. 5.20. Stages in penciling.

5. Draw in the details of the part, beginning with the dominant characteristic shape and progressing to the minor details, such as fillets and rounds. The different views should be carried along together, projecting a characteristic shape, as shown on one view to the other views, not finishing one view before starting another. Use a minimum of construction and draw the lines to finished weight, if possible, as the views are carried along. *Do not make the drawing lightly and then "heavy" the lines later.*

6. Lay out and letter the title.

7. Check the drawing carefully.

5.12. Order of Tracing. If the drawing is to be traced in ink as an exercise in the use of instruments or for a finished orthographic drawing without dimensions, the order of working is as follows:

1. Place the pencil drawing to be traced on the drawing board, carefully align it with the T square, and put thumbtacks in the two upper corners. Then place the tracing paper or cloth (dull side up) over the drawing. Holding the cloth in position, lift the tacks one at a time and replace them to hold both sheets. Then put tacks in the two lower corners.

2. To remove any oily film, prepare the surface of the cloth or paper by dusting it lightly with prepared pounce or soft white chalk. *Then wipe the surface perfectly clean with a soft cloth.*

3. Carefully set the compasses to the correct line width, and ink all full-line circles and circle arcs, beginning with the smallest. Correct line weights are given in Fig. 1.60.

4. Ink dotted circles and arcs in the same order as full-line circles.

5. Carefully set the ruling pen to draw exactly the same width line as the full-line circles. The best way to match the straight lines to the circles is to draw with the compasses and ruling pen outside the trim line of the sheet or on another sheet of the same kind and adjust the ruling pen until the lines match.

6. Ink irregular curved lines.

7. Ink straight full lines in this order: horizontal (top to bottom), vertical (left to right), and inclined (uppermost first).

8. Ink straight dotted lines in the same order. Be careful to match these straight lines with the dotted circles.

9. Ink center lines.

10. Crosshatch all areas representing cut surfaces.

11. Draw pencil guide lines and letter the title.

12. Ink the border.

13. Check the tracing for errors and omissions.

5.13. Orthographic Freehand Drawing. Facility in making a freehand orthographic drawing is an essential part of the ability of every engineer, and as sketching requires some mastery of the various skills employed, practice should be started early. Full proficiency in freehand drawing means the mastery of the graphic language and is gained only after much knowledge and skill of drawing with instruments have been acquired. Nevertheless, sketching

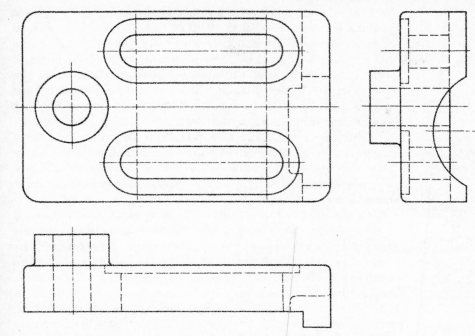

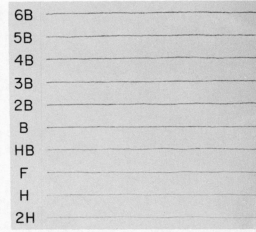

Fig. 5.21. A freehand drawing.

is an excellent method of learning the fundamentals of orthographic projection and may be employed by the beginner even before much practice with instruments. Time can be saved by working freehand instead of with instruments, thus making it possible to solve more problems in the same amount of time.

Although some experienced teachers advocate the making of freehand sketches before practice in the use of instruments, some knowledge of the use of instruments and especially of applied geometry is a great help before starting to sketch because the essentials of line tangents, connections, and intersections as well as the basic geometry of the part should be well defined on the freehand drawing. In favor of starting to sketch early, it may be said that freehand drawing is excellent exercise in accuracy of observation. Figure 5.21 is an example of a well-made freehand drawing.

5.14. Line Quality for Freehand Work. A freehand drawing may be made on a wide variety of papers, ranging from inexpensive notebook or writing grades to the finer drawing and tracing papers or even pencil cloth. The surface texture, smooth, medium, or rough, combined with the grade of pencil and pressure used, will govern the final result. If a bold rough effect is wanted for a scheming or idea sketch, a soft pencil and possibly rough paper would be employed. On the other hand, for a working sketch or for representation of an object having much small or intricate detail, a harder pencil and smoother paper will help in producing the necessary line quality.

Figure 5.22 is a photograph (reproduced about half size) of various pencil grades with medium pressure on paper of medium texture.

Fig. 5.22. Different pencil grades, using medium pressure on paper of medium texture.

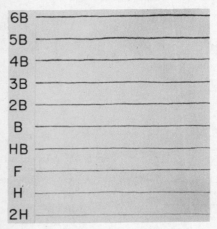

Fig. 5.23. Different pencil grades, using firm pressure on paper of medium texture.

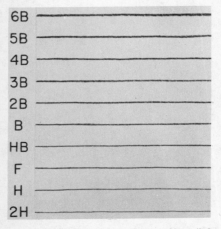

Fig. 5.24. Different pencil grades, using firm pressure on smooth paper.

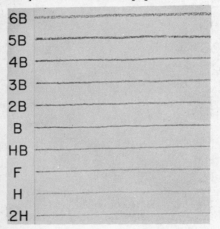

Fig. 5.25. Different pencil grades, using firm pressure on rough paper.

Note that the 6B pencil gives a rather wide and rough line. As the hardness increases from 5B to 4B, etc., up to 2H, the line becomes progressively narrower and lighter in color. This does not mean that a wide line cannot be made with a fairly hard pencil, but with ordinary sharpening and with uniform pressure, the softer grades wear down much faster than the harder grades. Unless a soft pencil such as 6B, 5B, or 4B is sharpened after each short stroke, fine lines are impossible. Also, the harder grades such as F, H, and 2H, once sharpened, will "hold their point" for some time, and fairly fine lines may be obtained without much attention to the point. Thus with ordinary pressure and normal use, the soft grades give bold rough results and, comparably, the harder grades give light smooth lines.

5.15. Range of Pencil Grades. The 6B grade is the softest pencil made and gives black rough lines. With normal pressure, the line erases easily but is likely to leave a slight smear. As mentioned before, the 6B, 5B, and 4B pencils should be employed when a rather rough line is wanted. Examples of use are scheming or idea sketches, architectural renderings, and illustrations. The range from 3B to HB, inclusive, is usually employed for engineering sketches on medium-textured paper. For example, a sketch of a machine part having a normal amount of small detail may be effectively made with a 2B or B pencil. The smoothness and easy response to variations in pressure make these grades stand out as the preferred grades for a wide variety of work. However, for more critical work where there is much detail and also where the "smearing" of the soft grades is objectionable, the grades from F to 2H may be adopted. For a sketch on fairly smooth paper, F or H are quite satisfactory. Grades harder than 2H are rarely used for freehand work. Incidentally, a very fine pencil for ordinary writing is the 2B grade.

5.16. Sharpening the Pencil. The pencil should be sharpened to a fairly long conical point, as explained in paragraph 1.26. However, for freehand work, a point not quite so sharp as for instrument drawing gives the desired line width without too much pressure. If, after sharpening in the regular way, the point is too fine, it may be rounded off slightly on an extra piece of scratch paper before use on the drawing.

5.17. Pencil Pressure and Paper Texture. As indicated before, the pencil grade, the pressure, and the paper texture all have an effect on the final result. Figure 5.22 shows the various pencil grades with medium pressure on paper of medium texture. To mark the difference in line quality obtainable by increasing the pressure, Fig. 5.23 shows the same paper but with firm pressure on the pencil. Note that the lines of Fig. 5.23 are much blacker than those of Fig. 5.22. The line quality of Fig. 5.23 is about right for most en-

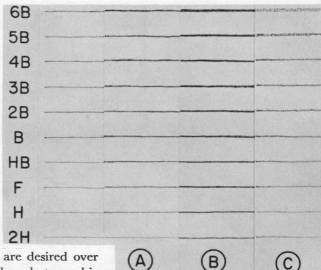

Fig. 5.26. Comparison of different pencil pressures and paper surfaces.

gineering sketches. The rather firm opaque lines are desired over the type of Fig. 5.22, especially if reproductions, either photographic or transparency process, are to be made from the sketch.

To show the difference in line quality produced by paper texture, Fig. 5.24 shows the same firm pressure used in Fig. 5.23, but this time on smooth paper. In Fig. 5.25, again the same pressure has been used on rough paper. Figure 5.26 is given so that a comparison between pressure and texture may be easily made. On the left is the medium pressure on medium-textured paper and, at (*A*), firm pressure on the same paper. Then at (*A*), (*B*), and (*C*), the same firm pressure has been used but at (*A*) on medium, at (*B*) on smooth, and at (*C*) on rough-textured paper.

5.18. Kinds of Paper. *Plain and Coordinate.* Sketches are made for many purposes and under a variety of circumstances, and as a result may be made on a number of different paper types and surfaces. A field engineer in reporting information to the central office may include a sketch made on notebook paper or a standard letterhead. On the other hand, a sketch made in the home office or drafting room may be as important as any instrument drawing and for this reason will probably be made on good-quality drawing or tracing paper and, afterward, filed and preserved with other drawings in a set. Figure 5.27 is an example of a sketch made on plain paper.

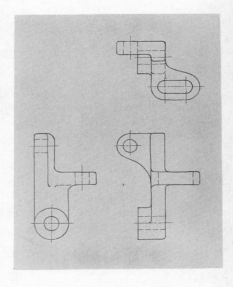

Fig. 5.27. A freehand drawing on plain paper.

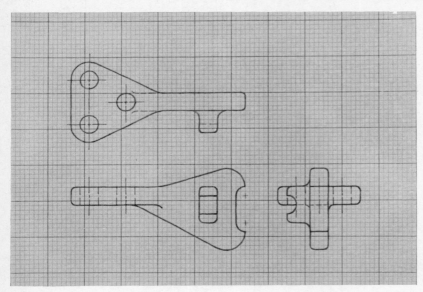

Fig. 5.28. A freehand drawing on coordinate tracing paper.

This might be the letterhead paper of the field engineer or a piece of fine drawing or tracing paper. The principal difficulty in using plain paper is that proportions and projections must be estimated by eye. A good sketch on plain paper requires better-than-average ability and experience. A great aid in producing good results is to employ some variety of coordinate paper. There are many kinds of paper and coordinate divisions available, from smooth to medium texture and coordinate divisions of ⅛ or ⅒ to ½ in., printed on either tracing paper or various weights of drawing paper. Usually one coordinate size on tracing paper and another (or the same)

Fig. 5.29. A freehand drawing on standard coordinate notebook paper.

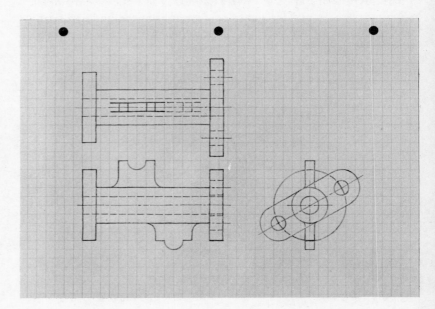

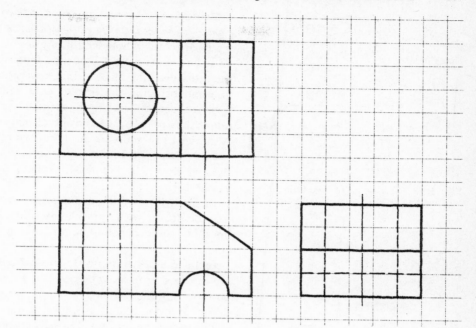

Fig. 5.30. A freehand drawing on coordinate paper (actual size).

on drawing paper will supply the needs of an engineering office. Figure 5.28 is an example of a sketch on paper having coordinate divisions of ⅛ in. Figure 5.29 has divisions of ¼ in. Figure 5.30 is a sketch on ¼-in. coordinate paper, actual size.

The paper type, tracing or regular, may also be an important factor. Reproduction by any of the transparency methods demands the use of tracing paper. However, if coordinate paper is employed, it may be desirable to obtain prints on which the coordinate divisions do not show. Figure 5.28 is an example of a sketch on tracing paper having the coordinate divisions printed on the back of the paper in faint purplish-blue ink. Since the divisions are on the back, erasures and corrections may be made without erasing the coordinate divisions. The divisions will not normally reproduce, giving prints appearing as though the sketch was made on plain paper. Figure 5.29 is a sketch on standard three-hole notebook paper having ¼-in. divisions in pale blue ink.

The use of coordinate paper is a distinct advantage. The projections are much easier to make than when plain paper is used. Also, to transfer distances from top to side view, the divisions may be counted. The use of coordinate paper speeds up the work considerably.

5.19. Technique. The pencil should be held with freedom and not close to the point. Vertical lines are drawn downward with a finger movement in a series of overlapping strokes, with the hand somewhat in the position of Fig. 5.31. Horizontal lines are drawn with the hand shifted to the position of Fig. 5.32, using a wrist motion for short lines and a forearm motion for longer ones. In

Fig. 5.31. Sketching a vertical line.

Fig. 5.32. Sketching a horizontal line.

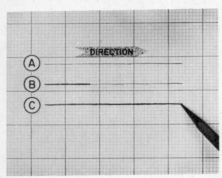

Fig. 5.33. Technique of sketching lines.

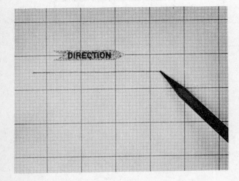

Fig. 5.34. Sketching a horizontal line.

drawing any straight line between two points, *keep the eyes on the point to which the line is to go rather than on the point of the pencil.* Do not try to draw the whole length of a line in a single stroke. It may be an aid to draw a very light line first, as shown in Fig. 5.33*A*, and then to sketch the finished line, correcting the direction of the light line and bringing the line to final width and blackness by using strokes of convenient length, as indicated in Fig. 5.33*B*. The finished line is shown at (*C*). Do not be disturbed by any nervous waviness. Accuracy of direction is more important than smoothness of line.

5.20. Straight Lines. Horizontal lines are drawn from left to right as shown in Fig. 5.34, vertical lines from top to bottom as in Fig. 5.35.

Inclined lines running downward from right to left (Fig. 5.36) may be drawn with approximately the same movement as vertical lines, but the paper may be turned and the line drawn as a vertical (Fig. 5.37).

Inclined lines running downward from left to right (Fig. 5.38) are the hardest to draw because the hand is in a somewhat awkward position; for this reason, the paper should be turned and the line drawn as a horizontal, as shown in Fig. 5.39.

The sketch paper may be easily turned in any direction in order to facilitate drawing the lines because there is no necessity of fastening the paper to a drawing-table top. The paper may, of course, be taped to a drawing board or attached to a clip board.

It is legitimate in freehand drawing to make long vertical or horizontal lines by using the little finger as a guide along the edge of the pad or clip board. The three important things about a straight line are that it (1) be essentially straight, (2) be the right length, and (3) go in the right direction.

5.21. Circles. Circles may be drawn by marking the radius on

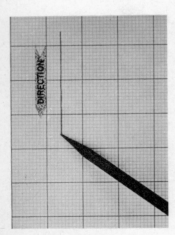

Fig. 5.35. Sketching a vertical line.

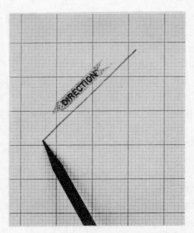

Fig. 5.36. Sketching an inclined line sloping downward, right to left.

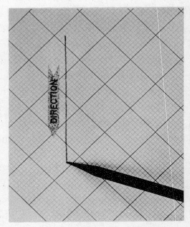

Fig. 5.37. Paper turned to sketch as a vertical line.

each side of the center lines or, more accurately, by drawing two diagonals in addition to the center lines and marking points equidistant from the center of the eight radii. At these points, draw short arcs perpendicular to the radii, and then complete the circle as shown in Fig. 5.40. A modification is to use a slip of paper as a trammel. Large circles can be done very smoothly, after a little practice, by using the third or fourth finger as a pivot, holding the pencil stationary and rotating the paper under it, or by holding two pencils and using one as a pivot about which to rotate the paper. Another way of drawing a circle is to sketch it in its circumscribing square.

5.22. Projection. In making an orthographic sketch, the principles of projection and applied geometry are to be remembered and applied. Sketches are *not* made to scale but are made to show fair proportions of objects sketched. It is legitimate, however, when coordinate paper is employed, to count the spaces or rulings as a means of proportioning the views and as an aid in making projections. Particular care should be exercised in having the various details of the views in good projection from view to view. An inexcusable mistake is to have a detail sketched to a different size on one view than on another.

When working on plain paper, projections between the top and front views or between the front and side views are easily made by simply "sighting" between the views or employing *very* light construction lines as indicated in Fig. 5.41. Projections between the top and side views are laid off by judging the distance by eye, by measuring the distance by holding the finger at the correct distance from the end of the pencil and transferring to the view, or by marking the distance on a small piece of paper and transferring to the view. Note in Fig. 5.41 that distances A, B, and others could be transferred from the top to the side view by the methods just mentioned.

Even though freehand lines are somewhat "wavy" and not so accurate in position as ruled lines, a good freehand drawing should

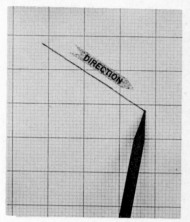

Fig. 5.38. Sketching an inclined line sloping downward, left to right.

Fig. 5.39. Paper turned to sketch as a horizontal line.

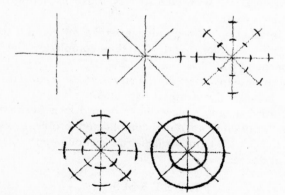

Fig. 5.40. Method of drawing freehand circles.

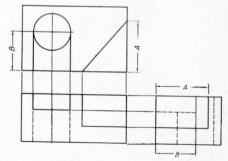

Fig. 5.41. Freehand projections.

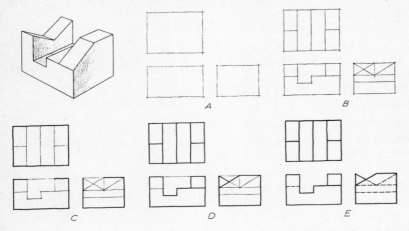

Fig. 5.42. Stages in making an orthographic freehand drawing.

present the same clean appearance as a good instrument drawing.

Cross-section paper, ruled with light lines as in Fig. 5.30, aids greatly in keeping the views "in projection." By counting divisions, distances are easily transferred either from top to side or from side to top view.

5.23. Method. Practice in orthographic freehand drawing should be started by drawing the three views of a number of simple pieces, developing the technique and the ability to "write" the orthographic language, while exercising the constructive imagination in visualizing the object by looking at the three projections. Observe the following order of working:

1. Study the pictorial sketch and decide what combination of views will best describe the shape of the piece.

2. Block in the views, as in Fig. 5.42*A*, using a very light stroke of a soft pencil (2B, B, HB, or F), spacing the views so as to give a well-balanced appearance to the drawing.

3. Build up the detail in each view, carrying the three views along together as at (*B*).

4. Brighten the outline of each view with bold strokes as at (*C*).

5. Brighten the detail with bold strokes, thus completing the full lines of the sketch as at (*D*).

6. Sketch in all dotted lines, using a stroke of medium weight, lighter than the full lines, as at (*E*), thus completing the shape description of the block.

7. Check the drawing carefully; then cover the pictorial sketch and visualize the object from the three views.

After a number of simple pieces have been drawn freehand, the student may "graduate" to more complicated problems such as Probs. 5.3.9 and 5.3.28. Faintly ruled cross-section paper (Fig. 5.30) may be used if desired.

PROBLEMS

Selections from the following groups of problems are to be made for practice in orthographic freehand drawing. Group 1 gives practice in drawing the three views of an object, and Group 2 provides exercises in reading a drawing as well as practice in freehand drawing.

Group 1. Freehand projections from pictorial views

5.1.1 to 5.1.16. These figures contain a number of pictorial sketches of pieces of various shapes. These are to be translated into three-view orthographic freehand drawings. Make them of fairly large size, the front view, say, 2 to 2½ in. in length, and estimate the proportions of the different parts by eye or from the proportionate marks shown but without measuring. The problems are graduated in difficulty so that a selection may be made, depending on ability and experience.

Problem 5.1.16 gives a series that may be used for advanced work in freehand drawing or, later on, by adding dimensions, that may be used as dimensioning studies or freehand working-drawing problems.

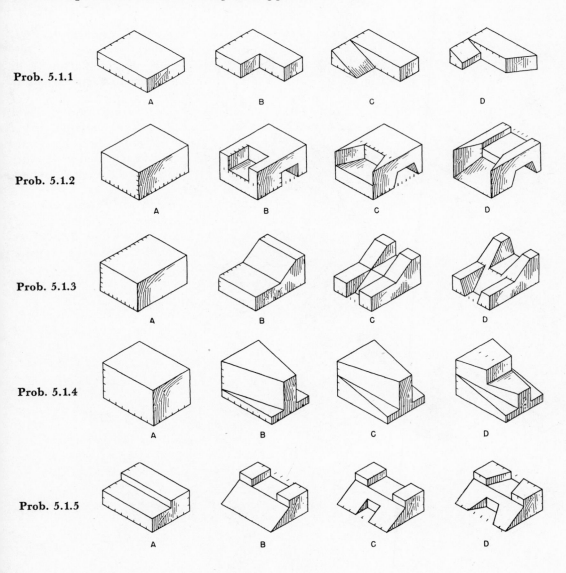

Prob. 5.1.1   A   B   C   D

Prob. 5.1.2   A   B   C   D

Prob. 5.1.3   A   B   C   D

Prob. 5.1.4   A   B   C   D

Prob. 5.1.5   A   B   C   D

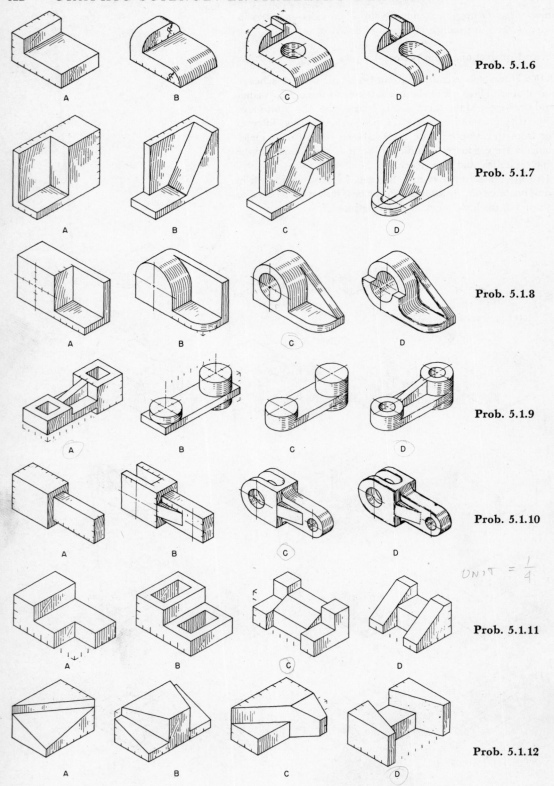

Prob. 5.1.6

A   B   C   D

Prob. 5.1.7

A   B   C   D

Prob. 5.1.8

A   B   C   D

Prob. 5.1.9

A   B   C   D

Prob. 5.1.10

A   B   C   D

UNIT = $\frac{1}{4}$

Prob. 5.1.11

A   B   C   D

Prob. 5.1.12

A   B   C   D

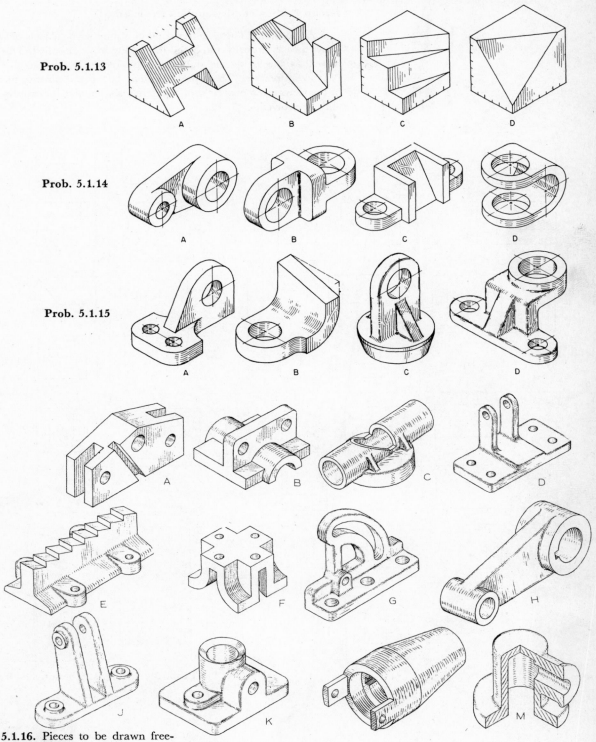

Prob. 5.1.13

A   B   C   D

Prob. 5.1.14

A   B   C   D

Prob. 5.1.15

A   B   C   D

A   B   C   D

E   F   G   H

J   K   L   M

Prob. 5.1.16. Pieces to be drawn free-hand in orthographic projection.

Group 2. Views to be supplied freehand

5.2.1 to 5.2.3. These figures contain a number of objects of which two views have been drawn and the third view to be supplied. This exercise, as well as developing the ability to draw freehand, will also give valuable practice in reading. These problems may be worked directly in the book, or the views given may be copied to larger size on plain or coordinate paper and then solved.

Prob. 5.2.1. Views to be supplied freehand.

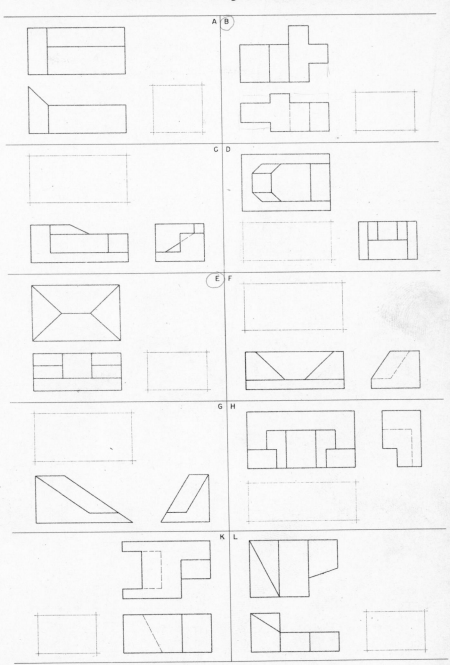

Prob. 5.2.2. Views to be supplied freehand.

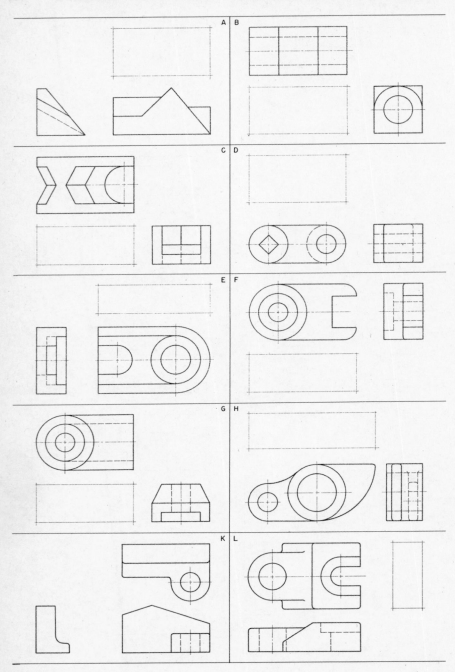

Prob. 5.2.3. Views to be supplied freehand.

Selections from several groups of the problems following are to be made for practice in projection drawing. Most of them are intended to be drawn with instruments but will give valuable training done freehand on either plain or coordinate paper.

The groups are as follows:

3. Projections from pictorial views
4. Views to be supplied
5. Views to be changed
6. Drawing from memory
7. Volume and weight calculations with slide rule

Group 3. Projections from pictorial views

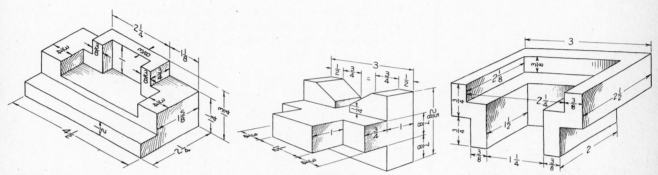

Prob. 5.3.1. Beam support.   **Prob. 5.3.2.** Vee rest.   **Prob. 5.3.3.** Saddle bracket.

5.3.1. Draw the top, front, and right-side views of the beam support.
5.3.2. Draw the top, front, and right-side views of the vee rest.
5.3.3. Draw three views of the saddle bracket.

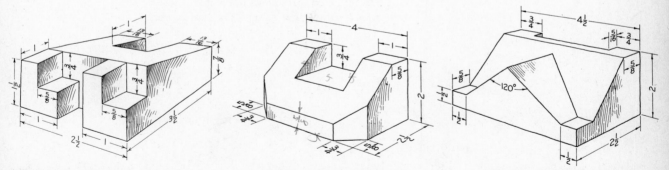

Prob. 5.3.4. Wedge block.   **Prob. 5.3.5.** Slotted wedge.   **Prob. 5.3.6.** Pivot block.

5.3.4. Draw three views of the wedge block.
5.3.5. Draw three views of the slotted wedge.
5.3.6. Draw three views of the pivot block.

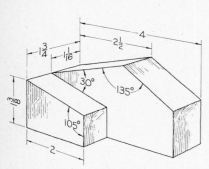

Prob. 5.3.7. Inclined support.

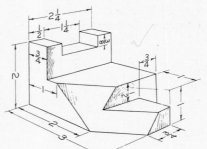

Prob. 5.3.8. Corner stop.

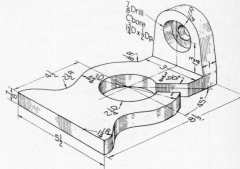

Prob. 5.3.9. Switch base.

5.3.7. Draw three views of the inclined support.
5.3.8. Draw three views of the corner stop.
5.3.9. Draw three views of the switch base.

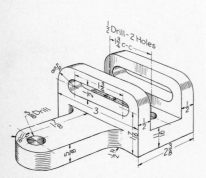

Prob. 5.3.10. Adjusting bracket.

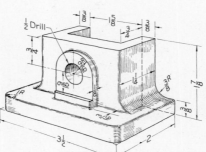

Prob. 5.3.11. Guide base.

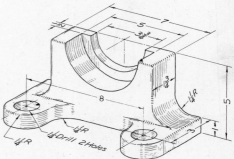

Prob. 5.3.12. Bearing rest.

5.3.10. Draw three views of the adjusting bracket.
5.3.11. Draw three views of the guide base.
5.3.12. Draw three views of the bearing rest.

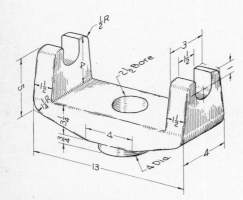

Prob. 5.3.13. Swivel yoke.

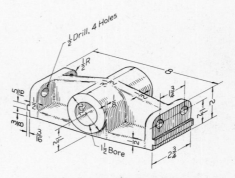

Prob. 5.3.14. Truss bearing.

5.3.13. Draw three views of the swivel yoke.
5.3.14. Draw three views of the truss bearing.

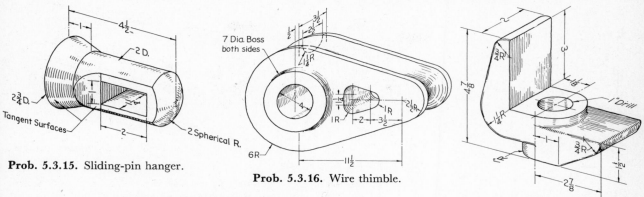

Prob. 5.3.15. Sliding-pin hanger.

Prob. 5.3.16. Wire thimble.

Prob. 5.3.17. Hanger jaw.

5.3.15. Draw three views of the sliding-pin hanger.
5.3.16. Draw two views of the wire thimble.
5.3.17. Draw three views of the hanger jaw.

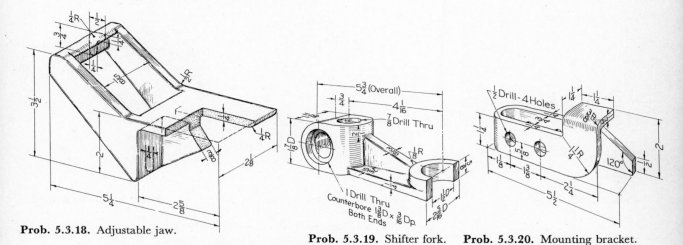

Prob. 5.3.18. Adjustable jaw.

Prob. 5.3.19. Shifter fork.

Prob. 5.3.20. Mounting bracket.

5.3.18. Draw three views of the adjustable jaw.
5.3.19. Draw two views of the shifter fork.
5.3.20. Draw three views of the mounting bracket.

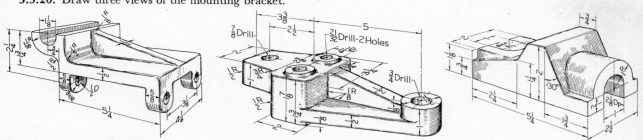

Prob. 5.3.21. Hinged bearing.

Prob. 5.3.22. Clamp lever.

Prob. 5.3.23. Bedplate stop.

5.3.21. Draw three views of the hinged bearing.
5.3.22. Draw two views of the clamp lever.
5.3.23. Draw three views of the bedplate stop.

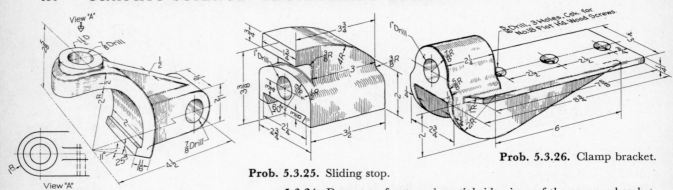

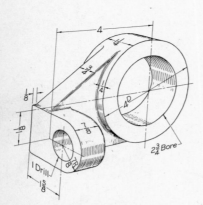

Prob. 5.3.24. Spanner bracket.

Prob. 5.3.25. Sliding stop.

Prob. 5.3.26. Clamp bracket.

5.3.24. Draw top, front, and partial-side views of the spanner bracket.
5.3.25. Draw two views of the sliding stop.
5.3.26. Draw three views of the clamp bracket.

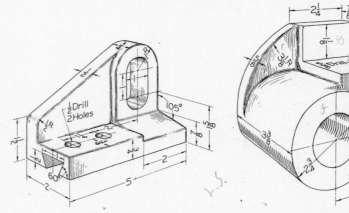

Prob. 5.3.27. Tube hanger.

Prob. 5.3.28. Gage holder.

Prob. 5.3.29. Shaft guide.

5.3.27. Draw three views of the tube hanger.
5.3.28. Draw three views of the gage holder.
5.3.29. Draw three views of the shaft guide.

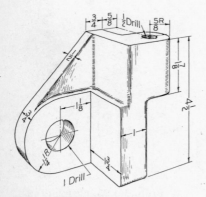

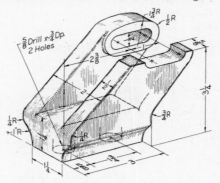

Prob. 5.3.30. Clamp block.

Prob. 5.3.31. Offset yoke.

5.3.30. Draw three views of the clamp block.
5.3.31. Draw three views of the offset yoke.

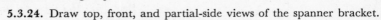

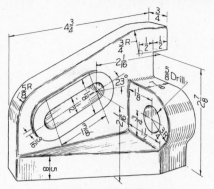

Prob. 5.3.32. Angle connector.

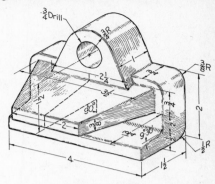

Prob. 5.3.33. Buckstay clamp.

5.3.32. Draw three views of the angle connector.
5.3.33. Draw three views of the buckstay clamp.

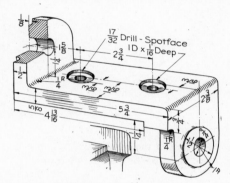

Prob. 5.3.34. Stop base.

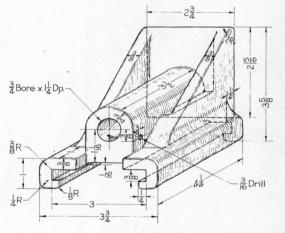

Prob. 5.3.35. Sliding buttress.

5.3.34. Draw three views of the stop base.
5.3.35. Draw three views of the sliding buttress.

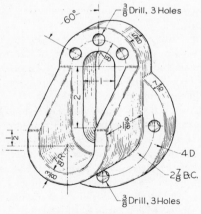

Prob. 5.3.36. End plate.

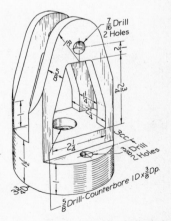

Prob. 5.3.37. Switch base.

5.3.36. Draw two views of the end plate.
5.3.37. Draw three views of the plastic switch base.

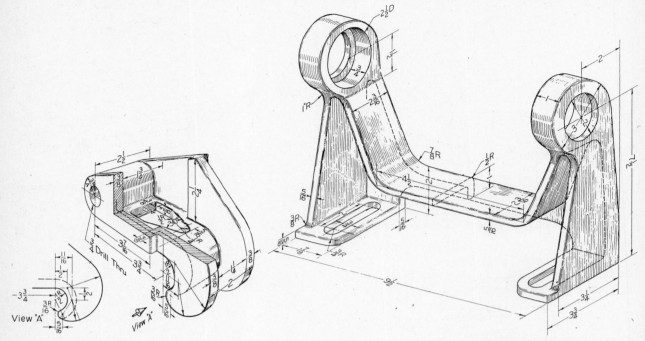

Prob. 5.3.38. Pawl hook.

Prob. 5.3.39. Step-pulley frame.

5.3.38. Draw two views of the pawl hook.

5.3.39. Draw three views of the step-pulley frame.

Group 4. Views to be supplied

These problems supply valuable training in reading orthographic views, as well as supplying further practice in the principles of orthographic projection.

In reading the views given, refer to Chap. 4 and apply the principles given there. Pay particular attention to the meaning of lines, the meaning of areas, and the meaning of adjacent areas. Corners or edges of the object may be numbered or lettered, if preferred, to aid in the reading or, later, to aid in the projection.

A pictorial sketch may be used, if desired, as an aid in reading the views. This sketch may be made either before the views are drawn and completed or at any time during the making of the drawing. For some of the simpler objects, a clay model may be of assistance.

After the views given have been read and drawn, project the third view or complete the views as specified in each individual case.

Remember that every line representing an edge view of a surface, an intersection of two surfaces, or a surface limit will have a mating projection in the other views. Be careful to represent all hidden features and pay attention to the precedence of lines.

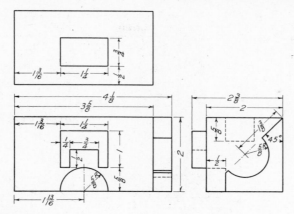

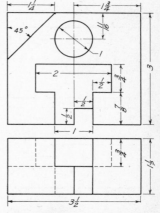

Prob. 5.4.1. Projection study.

Prob. 5.4.2. Projection study.

5.4.1. Draw the views given, completing the top view from information given on the front and side views. Carry the views along together.

5.4.2. Given top and front views of the block, top, front, and side views are required. See that dotted lines start and stop correctly.

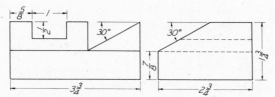

Prob. 5.4.3. Projection study.

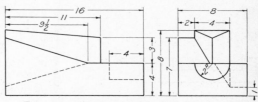

Prob. 5.4.4. Bit-point forming die.

5.4.3. Given front and right-side views, add top view.
5.4.4. Given front and right-side views, add top view.

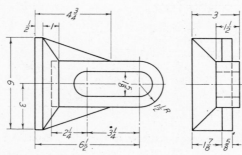

Prob. 5.4.5. Rabbeting-plane guide.

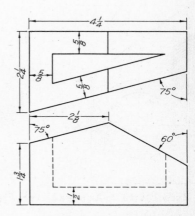

Prob. 5.4.6. Wedge block.

5.4.5. Given front and top views, add right-side view.
5.4.6. Given top and front views, add right-side view.

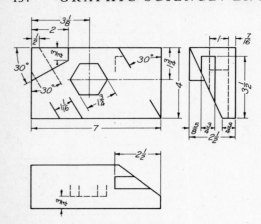

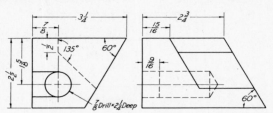

Prob. 5.4.8. Burner-support key.

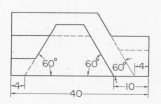

Prob. 5.4.7. Projection study.

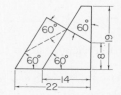

Prob. 5.4.9. Abutment block.

5.4.7. Complete the three views given.
5.4.8. Given front and left-side views, add top view.
5.4.9. Given front and right-side views, add top view.

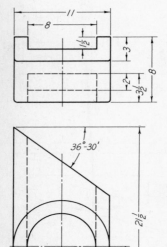

Prob. 5.4.10. Sliding port.

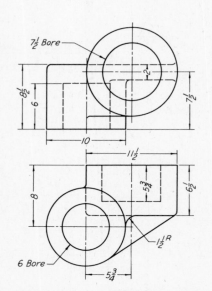

Prob. 5.4.11. Bumper support and post cap.

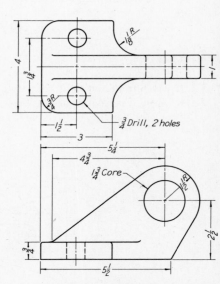

Prob. 5.4.12. Anchor bracket.

5.4.10. Given front and top views, add right-side view.
5.4.11. Assume this part to be right-hand. Draw three views of left-hand part.
5.4.12. Given front and top views, add side view.

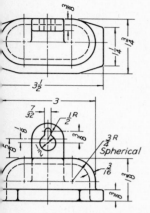

Prob. 5.4.13. Entrance head.

Prob. 5.4.14. Yoked link.

Prob. 5.4.15. Rubber-mounting bracket.

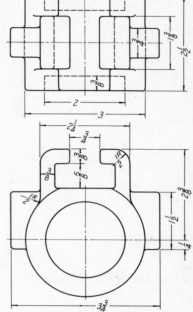

5.4.13. Given front and top views, add side view.
5.4.14. Given top and front views, add left-side view.
5.4.15. Given front and top views, add side view.

Prob. 5.4.16. Crosshead.

Prob. 5.4.17. Tool holder.

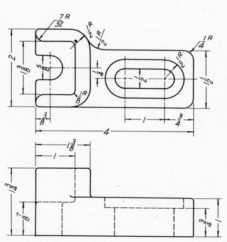

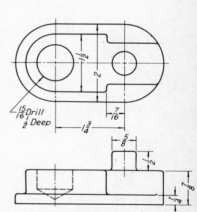

Prob. 5.4.18. Lock plate.

5.4.16. Given front and top views, add side view.
5.4.17. Given front and top views, add side view.
5.4.18. Given top and front views, add side view.

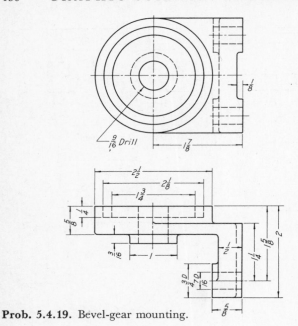

Prob. 5.4.19. Bevel-gear mounting.

Prob. 5,4.20. Cylinder support.

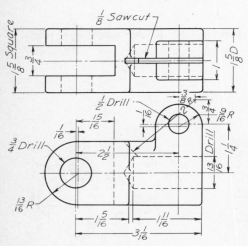

Prob. 5.4.21. Rod yoke.

5.4.19. Given top and front views, add left-side view.
5.4.20. Given top and front views, add side view.
5.4.21. Given front and top views, add side view.

Group 5. Views to be changed

These problems are given to develop the ability to visualize the actual piece in space and, from this mental picture, to draw the required views as they would appear if the object were looked at in the directions specified.

In addition to the training that these problems afford in the reading of orthographic views and in orthographic projection, they are valuable exercises in developing drawing technique. Note that all the problems given are castings containing the usual features found on such parts, that is, fillets, rounds, runouts, etc., on the unfinished surfaces. Also, sharp corners are formed either by the intersection of an unfinished and finished surface or by two finished surfaces. After finishing one of these problems, check the drawing carefully to make sure that all details of construction have been represented correctly.

5.5.1. Given front and top views, new front, top, and side views are required, turning the block so that the back becomes the front and the top the bottom. The rib contour is straight.

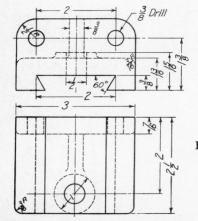

Prob. 5.5.1. Sliding block.

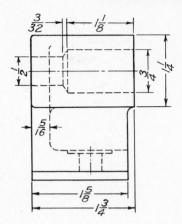

Prob. 5.5.2. Plunger bracket.

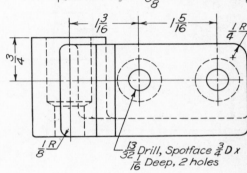

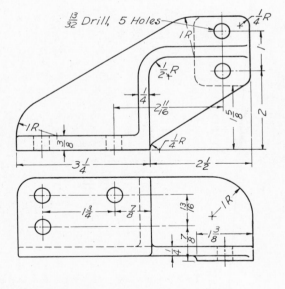

Prob. 5.5.3. Offset bracket.

5.5.2. Given front, left-side, and bottom views, draw front, top, and right-side views.

5.5.3. Given front, right-side, and bottom views, draw front, top, and left-side views.

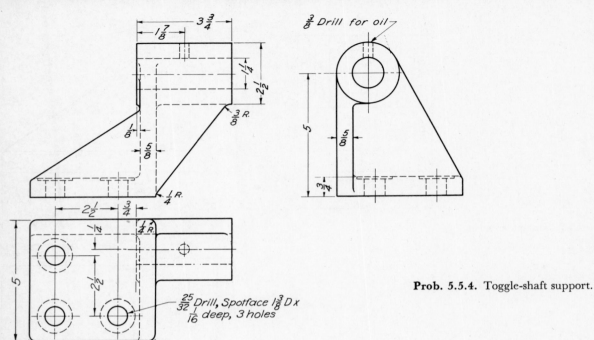

Prob. 5.5.4. Toggle-shaft support.

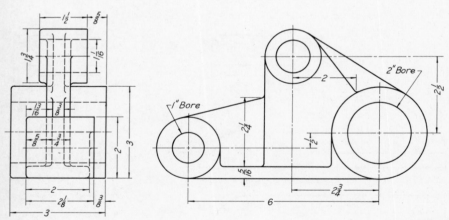

Prob. 5.5.5. Compound link.

5.5.4. Given front, right-side, and bottom views, draw new front, top, and right-side views, turning the support so that the back becomes the front.

5.5.5. Given front and left-side views of the left-hand part, draw the right-hand part.

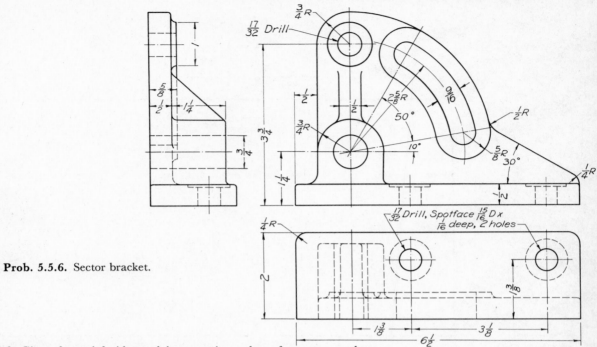

Prob. 5.5.6. Sector bracket.

5.5.6. Given front, left-side, and bottom views, draw front, top, and right-side views.

Group 6. Drawing from memory

One of the valuable assets of an engineer is a trained memory for form and proportion. The graphic memory may be developed to a surprising degree in accuracy and power by systematic exercises in drawing from memory. This training may be commenced as soon as a knowledge of orthographic projection has been acquired.

Select an object not previously used; look at it with concentration for a certain time (from 5 sec to $\frac{1}{2}$ min or more), close the book, and make an accurate orthographic sketch. Check with the original, and correct any mistakes or omissions. Follow with several different figures. The next day, allow a 2-sec view of one of the objects, and repeat the orthographic views of the previous day.

Group 7. Volume and weight calculations with slide rule

In calculating the weight of a piece from the drawings, the object should be divided or broken up into the geometric solids (prisms, cylinders, pyramids, or cones) of which it is composed. The volume of each of these shapes should be calculated and these added, or sometimes subtracted, to find the total volume, which, multiplied by the weight of the material per unit of volume, will give the weight of the object.

A table of weights of materials will be found in the Appendix.

5.7.1. Find the weight of the cast-iron anchor bracket, Prob. 5.4.12.

5.7.2. Find the weight of the cast-iron bracket, Prob. 5.4.15.

5.7.3. Find the weight of the wrought-iron tool holder, Prob. 5.4.17.

5.7.4. Find the weight of the cast-steel cylinder support, Prob. 5.4.20.

5.7.5. Find the weight of the malleable-iron sliding block, Prob. 5.5.1.

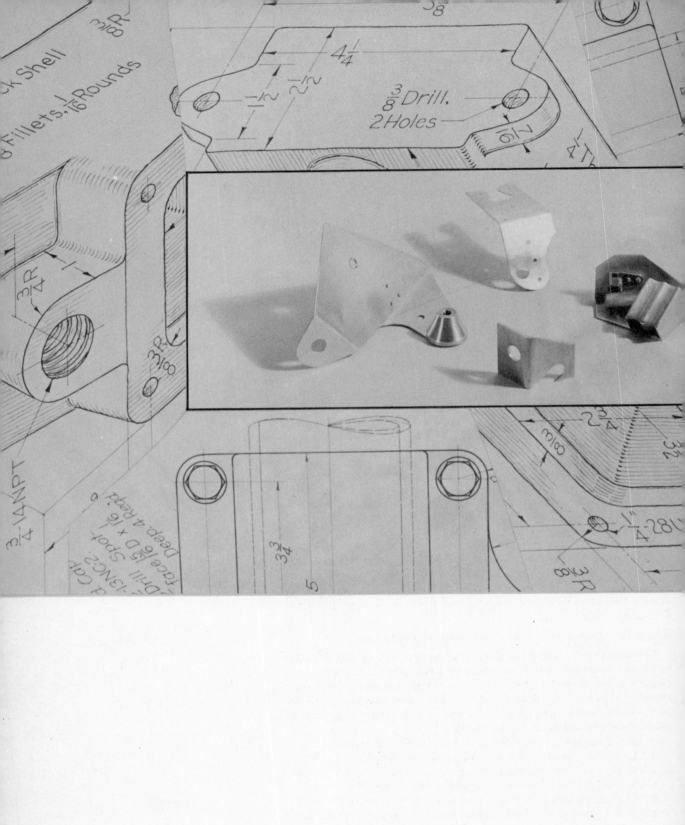

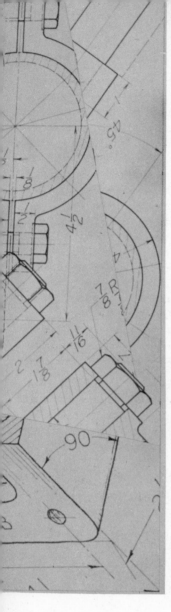

6

AUXILIARY AND OBLIQUE VIEWS

6.1. Basic Concepts. A surface is shown in true shape when projected on a plane parallel to that surface. A line is shown in true length when projected on a plane parallel to the line. Also, a line will appear as a point when projected on a plane perpendicular to the line, and a surface will appear as an edge when projected on a plane perpendicular to the surface. Any view showing the true shape of a surface or the true length of a line is known as a *normal view*. A view in which a line appears as a point is known as an *end view*. A view showing the edge of a plane surface is known as an *edge view*.

As most objects are rectangular, they may be placed with their faces parallel to the three principal planes of projection and be fully described by the principal views. In Fig. 6.1, the top, front, and right-side views are normal views, respectively, of the top, front, and right-side surfaces of the object. Also, the front view shows the *true length* of all the lines in the front face of the object. The top view shows the end view of lines *AC* and *BD*, and the right-side view shows the end view of lines *AB* and *CD*. The top and side views show the front surface (bounded by lines *AB*, *BD*, *DC*, and *CA*) as an edge. Thus it may be seen that the three principal views will give normal and edge views of the major, or important, surfaces of any rectangular object.

Sometimes, however, the object may have one or more inclined

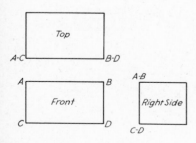

Fig. 6.1. All faces parallel to the principal planes of projection.

141

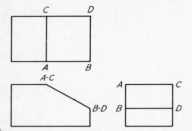

Fig. 6.2. One face inclined to two principal planes of projection.

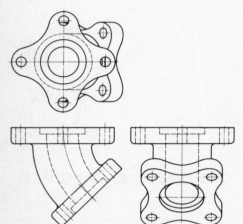

Fig. 6.3. Front, top, and right-side views.

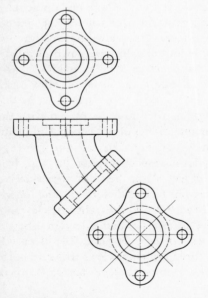

Fig. 6.4. Front, partial top, and auxiliary views.

faces whose true shape it is desirable or necessary to show, especially if irregular in outline. Figure 6.2 shows an object with one inclined face *ABDC*. Note that the front view shows the edge view of the inclined surface and also the point view of *AC* and *BD* and the true length of *AB* and *CD*. The side and top views show the true length of *AC* and *BD*. Nevertheless, none of the views shows the normal view (true shape) of the inclined surface. In order to show the true shape of the inclined surface, a view known as an *auxiliary* will have to be made, *looking in a direction perpendicular to the slanting surface*.

A practical example is the flanged 45° elbow of Fig. 6.3, a casting having an irregular inclined face, which not only cannot be shown in true shape in any of the principal views but also is difficult to draw in its foreshortened position. An easier and more practical selection of views for this piece is shown in Fig. 6.4, where an auxiliary view looking in a direction perpendicular to the inclined face shows the true shape of the surface and also allows for simplification of the views.

6.2. Definition. *An auxiliary view is an orthographic projection on a plane perpendicular to one of the principal planes of projection but inclined to the other two, specifically:*

1. An *elevation auxiliary view*, a projection on a plane perpendicular to the horizontal plane and inclined to the frontal and profile planes

2. A *right or left auxiliary view*, a projection on a plane perpendicular to the frontal plane and inclined to the horizontal and profile planes

3. A *front or rear auxiliary view*, a projection on a plane perpendicular to the profile plane and inclined to the horizontal and frontal planes

6.3. Purposes of Auxiliary Views. In practical drafting, the

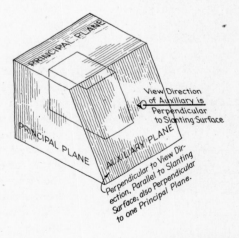

Fig. 6.5. View-direction and auxiliary-plane relationship.

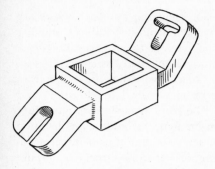

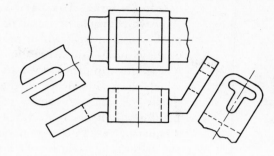

Fig. 6.6. Use of partial views.

chief reason for using an auxiliary view is to show the true shape of a slanting surface. In such cases, the view direction must be perpendicular to the slanting surface, and the auxiliary plane will be parallel to the slanting surface. The edge view of the auxiliary plane, therefore, will be parallel to the edge view of the slanting surface, and both the surface and auxiliary plane will appear as edges on the principal plane to which they are perpendicular. The auxiliary plane is revolved into the plane of the paper by considering it to be hinged to the plane to which it is perpendicular. Figure 6.5 illustrates the principles just mentioned.

In projecting an object on an auxiliary plane, the inclined surface will be shown in its true shape, but the other faces of the object will evidently be foreshortened. In practical work, these foreshortened parts are usually omitted, as in Fig. 6.6. Views thus drawn are called *partial views*. The exercise of drawing a complete view, however, may aid the student in understanding the subject.

Another important use of an auxiliary view is in the case where a principal view has some part in a foreshortened position, which cannot be drawn without first constructing an auxiliary view in its true shape from which the part can be projected back to the principal view. Figure 6.7 is an illustration of this principle. Note in this figure that the view direction is set up looking along the semi-hexagonal slot and perpendicular to the face which is at a right angle to the slot. From the auxiliary showing the true semihexagonal shape, the side view and then the front view may be completed.

In most cases the auxiliary view cannot be projected from the principal views but *must be drawn from dimensional specifications of the surface shape.* The explanations and figures following will illustrate this point.

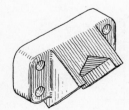

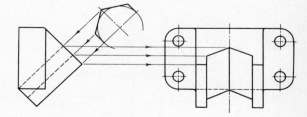

Fig. 6.7. Use of constructional auxiliary.

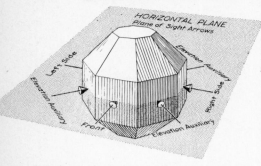

Fig. 6.8. Directions from which elevation auxiliaries are taken.

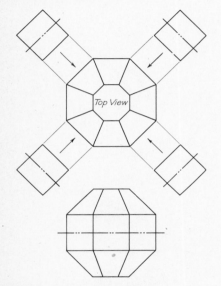

Fig. 6.9. Elevation auxiliaries.

6.4. Elevation Auxiliary Views. Elevation auxiliary views are those which would be seen if one walked around the object, starting at the position from which the front view is taken and following a circle with all sight arrows in a horizontal plane, as shown in Fig. 6.8. In this trip the observer would successively pass the points from which the right-side view, the rear view, the left-side view, and finally the front view again would be seen. A view from any other point in this plane, as indicated on the figure, would be an elevation auxiliary view. An elevation auxiliary view may thus be taken from the right-front, right-rear, left-rear, or left-front directions. Figure 6.9, an orthographic representation of Fig. 6.8, shows the complete top and front views of the object and indicates the view directions with the partial elevation auxiliary views that show the true shape of the slanting faces. On any drawing, the front, side, and rear views are *elevation* views since they show the *height* of the object. Front, side, rear, and elevation auxiliary views are all made by looking in some particular *horizontal* direction; hence the height of any point on an elevation auxiliary will be the same as the height of the same point in the front and side views. Therefore, all height measurements will be made from some fixed horizontal plane called a "reference plane."

In Fig. 6.10, the right end of the piece is at an angle to the frontal and profile planes but is perpendicular to the horizontal plane; thus its edge will show in the top view, but its true shape will not appear in either the front or side views. *An elevation auxiliary taken as if looking directly at the surface will show the true shape.* The pictorial drawing of Fig. 6.10A shows the direction for top, front, and elevation auxiliary views. The auxiliary view direction is perpendicular to the slanting surface to be shown in true shape. Note that the auxiliary projection plane is perpendicular to the view direction and parallel to the slanting surface. The projection planes are shown opened up

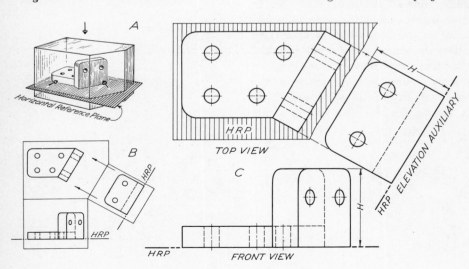

Fig. 6.10. Elevation auxiliary.

into one plane (the plane of the drawing paper) at (*B*), directly below the pictorial drawing. In this illustration, note that the rays of projection for the auxiliary will be parallel to the view direction and that the reference plane will be perpendicular to both the view direction and rays of projection. In this case, the reference plane has been taken at the base of the object. The larger orthographic illustration (*C*) shows the outline of projection planes removed. Note from both the orthographic views and the pictorial sketch that measurements of height on the auxiliary will be identical with those on the front view. The auxiliary view of the base is not completed, as it is fully described by the front and top views.

6.5. To Draw an Elevation Auxiliary View. The first operation in drawing *any* auxiliary is to locate and draw the direction of observation for the view. This is done by studying the object and locating the principal view, in which the slanting (auxiliary) surface will appear as an edge. Figure 6.11*A* and *B* shows the direction of observation will be horizontal and perpendicular to the slanting surface.

1. Draw the partial top and front views, as at (*B*), and locate the view direction by drawing projectors perpendicular to the edge view of the slanting surface, as shown.

2. Locate the reference plane *HRP* in the front view. The reference plane may be taken above, below, or through the view and is chosen for convenience in measuring. In this case (Fig. 6.11), it is taken through the natural center line of the front view. The reference plane (*HRP*) in the auxiliary will be perpendicular to the rays of projection already drawn, and is located at a convenient distance from the top view, as shown at (*C*).

3. As shown at (*D*), measure the distance (height) from the reference plane of various points needed, as, for example, H and H_1, and transfer these measurements with dividers or scale to the auxiliary view, measuring from the reference plane in the auxiliary view.

4. Complete the auxiliary from specifications of the rounds, etc.,

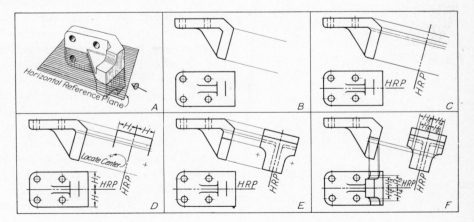

Fig. 6.11. Stages in drawing an elevation auxiliary.

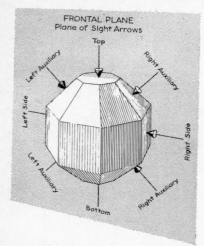

Fig. 6.12. Directions from which right and left auxiliaries are taken.

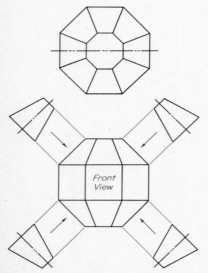

Fig. 6.13. Right and left auxiliaries.

as shown at (E). Note that any measurement in the front view, made *toward* the top view, is transferred to the *auxiliary view, toward* the top view. Note also in Fig. 6.11 that the front view could not be completed without using the auxiliary view.

5. To get the front view of the circular portions, the true shape of which shows only on the auxiliary as circle arcs, points are selected on the auxiliary view, projected back to the top view, and then to the front view. On these projectors the heights H_2 and H_3 are transferred from the auxiliary to find the corresponding points in the front view. H_4, H_5, and others will complete the curve in the front view.

6.6. Right and Left Auxiliary Views. The right and left auxiliary views are those which would be seen if one traveled around the object with all sight arrows in a frontal plane, as shown in Fig. 6.12. Right auxiliary views are those obtained from the right side of the circle, and left auxiliary views are those obtained from the left side of the circle. Thus a right auxiliary view is had by looking in a frontal direction somewhere between the right-side view and either the top or bottom view. Similarly, a left auxiliary view is made by looking in a frontal direction somewhere between the left-side view and either the top or bottom view.

The top, right-side, bottom, left-side, and right and left auxiliary views all have two common features: (1) They are all made by looking in some particular frontal direction; (2) they all show the depth of the object as a true (not foreshortened) distance. Thus all depth measurements for right and left auxiliary views will be made from a frontal reference plane (*FRP*), and the distance front to back of any particular point will be identical on top, right-side, bottom, left-side, and right and left auxiliary views. Figure 6.13, an orthographic representation of Fig. 6.12, shows the complete top and front views of the object and indicates the view directions with partial right and left auxiliary views that show the true shape of the slanting faces.

In Fig. 6.14, the right and left surfaces of the object are at an angle to the horizontal and profile planes but are perpendicular to the frontal plane; thus the edges of these slanting surfaces will show in the front view, but the true shape will not appear in any principal view. *Right and left auxiliary views taken as if looking directly at the surfaces will show the true shapes.* The pictorial drawing Fig. 6.14A shows the view directions for top, front, and right and left auxiliary views. The auxiliary-view directions are perpendicular to the surfaces to be shown in true shape. In each case, the auxiliary projection plane is perpendicular to the view direction and parallel to the slanting surface. The projection planes are shown opened up into one plane (the plane of the drawing paper) in Fig. 6.14B, directly below the pictorial drawing. Note that the rays of projection for the auxiliary will be parallel to the view direction and that the reference plane

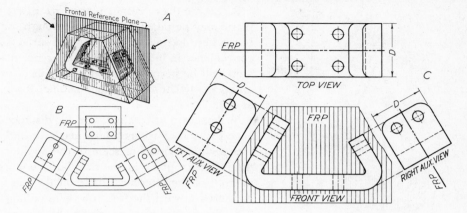

Fig. 6.14. Right and left auxiliaries.

will be perpendicular to both the view direction and the rays of projection. In this case the reference plane *FRP* has been taken through the center of the object because of symmetry, front to rear. The larger orthographic illustration (*C*) shows the outline of projection planes removed. Note from the orthographic views and the pictorial sketch that measurements of depth on the auxiliaries will be identical with those on the top view.

6.7. To Draw a Right or Left Auxiliary View. The first step is to visualize the object to be drawn and determine the direction of observation for the auxiliary. This is done by studying the object and locating the principal view in which the slanting (auxiliary) surface will appear as an edge and then imagining a view direction perpendicular to the slanting surface. Figure 6.15*A* and *B* shows that the slanting surface appears as an edge in the front view; therefore, the direction of observation for the auxiliary will be frontal and perpendicular to the slanting surface.

1. Draw the partial top and front views, as at (*B*), and locate the view direction by drawing projectors perpendicular to the slanting surface, as shown.

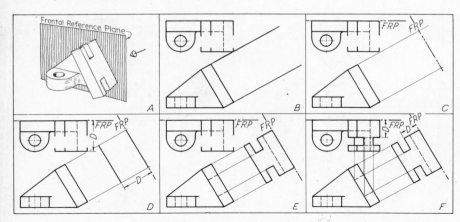

Fig. 6.15. Stages in drawing a right auxiliary.

R - L   AUX ELEV

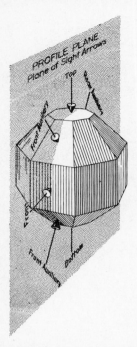

2. Locate the reference plane *FRP* in the top view. The reference plane may be taken in front of, through, or to the rear of the view but is here located at the rear flat surface of the object because of convenience in measuring. The reference plane *FRP* in the auxiliary view will be perpendicular to the rays of projection already drawn and is located at a convenient distance from the front view, as shown at (*C*).

3. As shown at (*D*), measure the distance (depths) from the reference plane (of various points needed), and transfer these measurements with dividers or scale to the auxiliary view, measuring from the reference plane in the auxiliary view. Note that the points are in front of the reference plane on the top view and, therefore, are measured toward the front on the auxiliary view.

4. From specifications, complete the auxiliary view, as shown at (*E*).

5. Complete the drawing, as shown at (*F*). In this case, the top view could have been completed before the auxiliary was drawn. However, it is considered better practice to lay out the true-shape view (auxiliary) before completing the view that will show the surface foreshortened.

The auxiliary view just discussed is a *right auxiliary view*, as explained in paragraph 6.6. Obviously, a left auxiliary view would be used if the object had a slanting face on the left rather than on the right side. The order of drawing would, of course, be the same.

6.8. Front or Rear Auxiliary Views. The front and rear auxiliary views are those which would be seen if one traveled around the object with all sight arrows in a profile plane, as shown in Fig. 6.16. Front auxiliary views are those obtained from the front half of the circle, and rear auxiliary views are those obtained from the rear half of the circle. Thus a front auxiliary view is had by looking in a profile direction somewhere between the front view and either the top or bottom view. Similarly, a rear auxiliary view is made by

Fig. 6.16. Directions from which front and rear auxiliaries are taken.

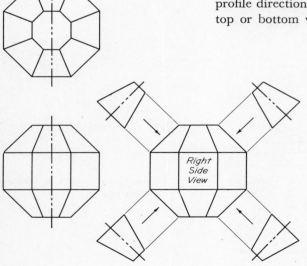

Fig. 6.17. Front and rear auxiliaries.

looking in a profile direction somewhere between the rear view
and either the top or bottom view.

The front, top, rear, and bottom views and the front and rear
auxiliary views all have two common features: (1) They are all
made by looking in some particular profile direction; (2) they all
show the width of the object as a true (not foreshortened) distance.
Thus all width measurements for front and rear auxiliary views
will be made from a profile reference plane *PRP*, and the distance
left to right of any particular point will be identical on front, top,
rear, bottom, and front and rear auxiliary views. Figure 6.17, an
orthographic representation of Fig. 6.16, shows the complete top,
front, and side views of the object and indicates the view directions
with partial front and rear auxiliary views that show the true shape
of the slanting faces.

In Fig. 6.18, the upper portion of the object is at an angle to the
horizontal and frontal planes but is perpendicular to the profile
plane; thus the edge of this slanting surface will show in either side
view, but the true shape will not appear in any principal view. *A
front auxiliary view, taken as if looking directly at the surface, will show the
true shape*. The pictorial drawing in Fig. 6.18*A* shows the view directions for front, right-side, and front auxiliary views. The auxiliary-
view direction is perpendicular to the surface to be shown in true
shape. Note that the auxiliary projection plane is perpendicular to
the view direction and parallel to the slanting surface. The projection planes are shown opened up into one plane (the plane of the

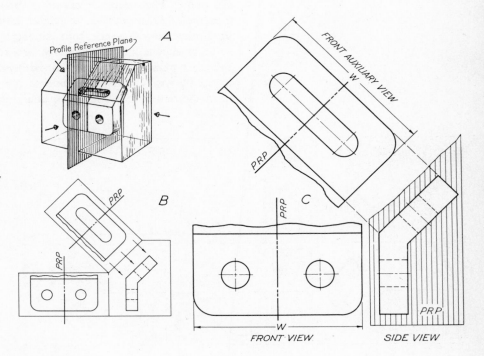

Fig. 6.18. Front auxiliary
view.

drawing paper) at (*B*), directly below the pictorial drawing. In this illustration, note that the rays of projection for the auxiliary will be parallel to the view direction and that the reference plane will be perpendicular to both the view direction and the rays of projection. In this case the profile reference plane *PRP* has been taken through the center of the object, because of symmetry, right to left. The larger orthographic illustration (*C*) shows the outline of projection planes removed. Note from the orthographic views and the pictorial sketch that measurements of width on the auxiliary will be identical with those on the front view.

6.9. To Draw a Front or Rear Auxiliary View. The first step is to visualize the object to be drawn and determine the direction of observation for the auxiliary. This is done by locating the principal view in which the slanting (auxiliary) surface will appear as an edge and then imagining a viewing direction perpendicular to the slanting surface. Figure 6.19*A* and *B* shows that the slanting surface appears as an edge in the right-side view; therefore, the direction of observation for the auxiliary will be profile and perpendicular to the slanting surface.

1. Draw the partial front, top, and right-side views, as at (*B*), and locate the view direction by drawing projectors perpendicular to the slanting surface, as shown.

2. Locate the profile reference plane *PRP* in the front view. This reference plane is taken at the left side of the object, because both the vertical and slanting portions have a left surface in the same profile plane. The reference plane in the auxiliary view will be perpendicular to the rays of projection already drawn, and is located at a convenient distance from the right-side view, as shown at (*C*).

3. As shown at (*D*), measure the distances (widths) from the reference plane (of various points needed), and transfer these measurements with dividers or scale to the auxiliary view, measuring from the reference plane in the auxiliary view. Note that points to

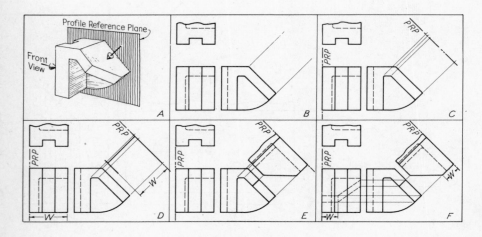

Fig. 6.19. Stages in drawing a rear auxiliary.

the right of the reference plane on the front view will be measured in a direction *toward* the right-side view on the auxiliary.

4. From specifications of the surface contour, complete the auxiliary, as shown at (E).

5. Complete the right-side and front views by projecting and measuring from the auxiliary view. As an example, one intersection of the cut corner is projected to the right-side view and from there to the front view; the other intersection is measured (distance W) from the auxiliary view and then laid off on the front view.

The auxiliary view just discussed is a rear auxiliary view, as explained in paragraph 6.8. Obviously, a front auxiliary view would require that the object have a slanting face on the front rather than on the rear. The general order of drawing would, of course, be the same.

6.10. Summary. The following outline is given as an aid in review and for reference while learning the basic principles and steps in drawing auxiliary views:

I. General procedure for drawing an auxiliary view.
  A. Determine the view direction.
  B. Determine the type of auxiliary which will result (elevation auxiliary view, right or left auxiliary view, or front or rear auxiliary view).
  C. Lay out partial principal views (top, front, etc.), planning the sheet to leave room for the auxiliary.
  D. Draw projection rays (parallel to the view direction) for the auxiliary.
  E. Locate the reference plane in the proper principal view and also on the auxiliary view (perpendicular to the rays of projection).
  F. Draw the auxiliary view.
    1. By laying out the shape from dimensional specifications.
    2. Or, if distances can be obtained from the principal view, measure them from the reference plane and transfer to the auxiliary (measuring from the reference plane).
    3. Note that, in measuring from the reference plane, a distance *toward* the view projected from will be laid off on the auxiliary *toward* the view projected from.

II. Digest of facts.
  A. Elevation auxiliary view.
    1. Always projected from the top view.
    2. Viewing direction will be horizontal.
    3. Shows true *height*.
    4. Reference plane is horizontal (HRP).
    5. Top of object will always be nearest the top view.
  B. Right or left auxiliary views.
    1. Always projected from the front view.
    2. Viewing direction will be frontal.

[handwritten margin notes:]
RIGHT OR LEFT ELEV. AUX
RIGHT OR LEFT FRONTAL AUX
FRONT OR REAR PROFILE AUX

3. Shows true *depth*.
4. Reference plane is frontal (*FRP*).
5. Front of object will always be nearest the front view.
C. Front or rear auxiliary views.
1. Always projected from a side view.
2. Viewing direction will be profile.
3. Shows true *width*.
4. Reference plane is profile (*PRP*).
5. Orientation of auxiliary.
    a. From a right-side view, right side of object will be nearest the right-side view.
    b. From a left-side view, left side of object will be nearest the left-side view.

6.11. Oblique Views. As explained in paragraph 6.1, the majority of objects will have their surfaces parallel to the three principal planes of projection and can, therefore, be described by some combination of principal views. Other objects, as described in paragraphs 6.1 to 6.10, may have some faces perpendicular to one of the principal planes but inclined to the other two, thus requiring an auxiliary view to describe their true shape. A third possibility is that some face of an object may be inclined to *all* the principal planes of projection, in which case the surface is said to be oblique and the view required to show its true shape is known as an *oblique view*.

6.12. Definition. *An oblique view is a projection on a plane inclined to all three principal planes of projection.*

6.13. Basic Concepts. To find the true shape (normal view) of an oblique surface, that is, a surface not perpendicular to any one of the principal planes, as illustrated by the pictorial drawing of Fig. 6.20, two operations are required: (1) an auxiliary view of the object made in a direction so that the oblique surface appears as an edge and (2) an auxiliary view made in a direction perpendicular to the edge view. *This second auxiliary is the oblique view.*

The principle is illustrated by Fig. 6.21, an orthographic representation of Fig. 6.20. Surfaces *A* and *B* shown on the figure are oblique surfaces because they are not parallel or perpendicular to any of the principal planes of projection. If an elevation auxiliary is made looking in direction 1, an edge view of the oblique surface *A* will be obtained because, as shown on the figure, the *end views* of the horizontal lines *ab* and *cd* of the surface will be had, *and if one looks along one line of a surface, the surface will appear as an edge.* Next, if a second auxiliary is made looking in direction 2, perpendicular to the edge view, the surface will appear in true shape because the direction of observation is now perpendicular to the surface.

Thus we see that two operations (mentioned before) are necessary: (1) the edge view and (2) the oblique view or normal view of the surface. Also, the *edge*-view step is necessary so that the second auxiliary may be set up having a direction of observation perpendicular to the oblique surface.

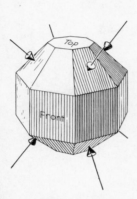

Fig. 6.20. Directions from which oblique views are taken.

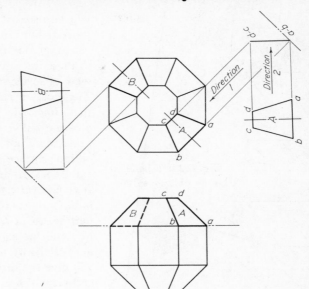

Fig. 6.21. Oblique views.

6.14. The True Length of a Line in an Auxiliary Position. The true length of a line in an auxiliary position will appear in the principal view of the plane to which the line is parallel. Thus a horizontal line appears in true length in the top view, a frontal line appears in true length in the front view, and a profile line appears in true length in either side view. Study Fig. 6.22.

6.15. The End View of a Line in an Auxiliary Position. The end view of a line in an auxiliary position will appear in an auxiliary view taken in a direction looking along the line. Therefore, if the line is horizontal, an elevation auxiliary will be employed; if frontal, a right or left auxiliary view; and if profile, a front or rear auxiliary view. All three basic positions and the end views are illustrated in Fig. 6.22.

6.16. Edge Views. As indicated in paragraph 6.13, the key to determining the direction of observation necessary in order to obtain an edge view is to find a direction that will give an end view of *one line* of the surface. This can be easily done if the surface contains a horizontal, frontal, or profile line as a part of the surface outline. Referring again to Fig. 6.22, if a line is horizontal, an elevation auxiliary will give the end view; if frontal, a right or left auxiliary view

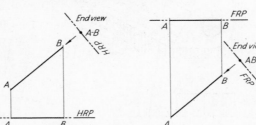

Fig. 6.22. True length and end views of horizontal, frontal, and profile lines.

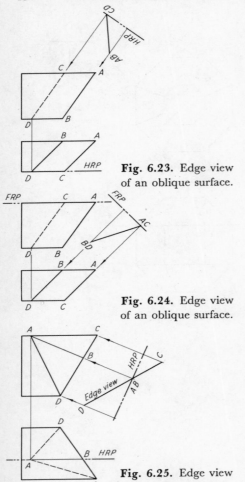

Fig. 6.23. Edge view of an oblique surface.

Fig. 6.24. Edge view of an oblique surface.

Fig. 6.25. Edge view of an oblique surface.

will be used; if profile, a front or rear auxiliary view will be employed. Thus in Fig. 6.23, lines *AB* and *CD* are horizontal, and the elevation auxiliary shown having a direction of observation parallel to these lines gives the required end view of the lines and the edge view of surface *ABDC*. In Fig. 6.24, lines *AC* and *BD* are frontal. Therefore, a right auxiliary view taken in a direction parallel to these lines will give the required edge view. Study Figs. 6.23 and 6.24 carefully, and note that in each case the auxiliary must be projected from the view showing the true length of a line of the oblique surface. The objects shown in Figs. 6.23 and 6.24 are identical. Edges *AB* and *CD* are horizontal. Edges *AC* and *BD* are frontal. If no *horizontal, frontal,* or *profile* line is present as a part of the surface outline, one is then laid out on the surface. In Fig. 6.25, the surface outlines *AC, CD,* and *DA* are all oblique lines and cannot be used to obtain an edge view in the first auxiliary. However, the horizontal line *AB* drawn on the front view and then projected to the top view will give the direction for an elevation auxiliary that will show the end view of line *AB* and the edge view of surface *ADC*.

6.17. Oblique Views. After an edge view of an oblique surface has been obtained, the direction for an oblique view showing the normal view of the surface may be made. The direction of observation for the oblique view (in order to give a normal view) will be perpendicular to the surface and will, therefore, be perpendicular to the edge view. Figure 6.26*A* shows the pictorial representation of an object with a horizontal base and an oblique notched surface extending upward. The intersection of the oblique surface and the base is a horizontal line, thus giving the direction (1) for an auxiliary showing the edge view of the oblique surface, as described in paragraph 6.16. Perpendicular to the edge view (and perpendicular to the oblique surface) is the direction of observation (2) for the oblique view.

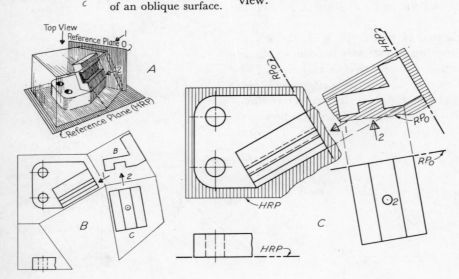

Fig. 6.26. Oblique view.

At (B) is shown the planes of projection opened out into one plane, the paper. Note that (1) the direction of observation is parallel to the lower horizontal edge of the oblique surface and that (2) the direction for the oblique is perpendicular to the edge view.

Illustration (C) shows the views enlarged and includes the necessary reference planes. The reference plane for the first auxiliary (edge) view will be horizontal (HRP) and is, for convenience in measuring, taken at the bottom surface of the horizontal base. The reference plane (HRP) in the auxiliary view will be perpendicular to the view direction and to the rays of projection. The reference plane (RP_O) for the oblique view must be (as with any other auxiliary view) *in the oblique view*, perpendicular to the view direction and to the rays of projection. The other view of the reference plane will in this case be placed in the top view perpendicular to the rays between the top view and edge view *because the distance along the oblique face in the direction of view direction* (1) *is the measurement that must be made*. A study of pictorial drawing (A) in connection with orthographic illustration (C) will show that the oblique reference plane is shown in normal view in the first auxiliary (edge) view. Therefore, the two views that are in projection with the edge view of the oblique surface will show the edge view of the reference plane (RP_O), and both views of the reference plane (RP_O) will be perpendicular to the rays between the edge view and the two views in direct projection with the edge view.

6.18. To Draw an Oblique View. Figure 6.27 illustrates the progressive steps in drawing an oblique view. The pictorial illustration (A) shows a typical object having an oblique surface. The line of intersection between the oblique portion and the horizontal base is line AB. In order to get an edge view of the oblique surface, a

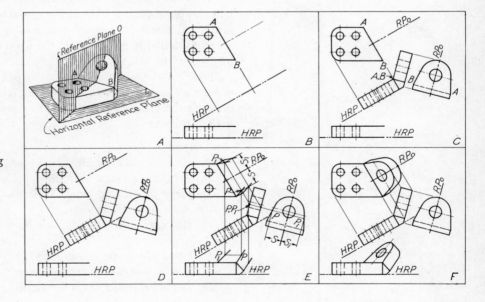

Fig. 6.27. Stages in drawing an oblique view.

view may be taken looking in the direction of line AB, thus giving an end view of AB. Because AB is a line of the oblique surface, the edge view will result. The reference plane for this view will be horizontal (HRP) because an elevation auxiliary will be used. The direction of observation for the oblique view will be perpendicular to the oblique surface. The reference plane (RP_O) for the oblique view will be perpendicular to the edge-view direction and thus be perpendicular to edge AB, as shown in illustration (A).

(B) shows partial top and front views. The projectors and reference plane for the required edge view are also shown.

At (C), the edge view has been drawn. Note that line AB appears as a point in the edge view. The angle that the oblique surface makes with the base is laid out in this view from specifications.

(D) illustrates the addition of the oblique view. The projectors for the view are perpendicular to the edge view. The reference plane is drawn perpendicular to the projectors for the oblique view and at a convenient distance from the edge view. The reference plane in the top view is drawn perpendicular to the rays between the top and edge views and is taken midway between points A and B on the top view because the oblique surface is symmetrical about this reference plane. The oblique view is then drawn from specifications of the shape. The projection back to the edge view may then be made.

The views thus completed at (D) describe the object, but if it is desired for illustrative purposes or as an exercise in projection, the top and front views may be completed. (E) and (F) illustrate the method. Any point, say P, may be selected and projected back to the edge view. From this view a projector is drawn back to the top view. Then the distance S from the oblique view is transferred to the reference plane in the top view. A number of points so located will complete the top view of the circular portion, and the straight-line portion may be projected in similar manner. The front view is found by drawing projectors to the front view for the points needed, measuring the heights from the reference plane in the edge view and transferring these distances to the front view. Note that this procedure for completion of the top and front views is the same as for drawing the views originally but in reverse order.

6.19. Summary

I. General.
   A. .An oblique view must be projected from an auxiliary view.
   B. An oblique view can show the normal view of an oblique plane or the end view of an oblique line.
II. To draw an oblique view.
   A. Determine direction for auxiliary view (to show edge of plane or true length of line).
   B. Determine type of auxiliary.
   C. Lay out partial principal views.
   D. Draw projection rays for auxiliary.

E. Locate reference plane in auxiliary and principal views.
F. Draw auxiliary view.
G. Determine direction for oblique view.
  1. Perpendicular to edge view for normal view of plane.
  2. Aligned with true length of line for end view.
H. Locate reference plane in oblique and principal views.
  1. Perpendicular to rays between auxiliary view and oblique view.
  2. Perpendicular to rays between auxiliary view and principal view.
  I. Draw oblique view.
  J. Complete auxiliary and principal views if required.

PROBLEMS

Group 1. Auxiliary studies

6.1.1 to 6.1.7. Draw views given, and add auxiliary views, using reference planes indicated.

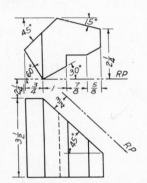

Prob. 6.1.1. Auxiliary study.

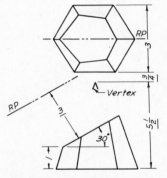

Prob. 6.1.2. Auxiliary study.

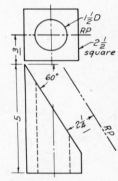

Prob. 6.1.3. Auxiliary study.

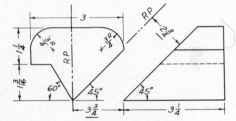

Prob. 6.1.4. Auxiliary study.

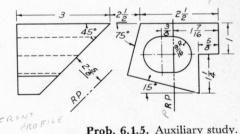

Prob. 6.1.5. Auxiliary study.

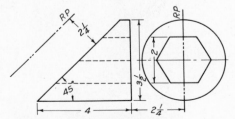

Prob. 6.1.6. Auxiliary study.

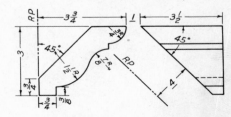

Prob. 6.1.7. Auxiliary study.

Group 2. Auxiliary views

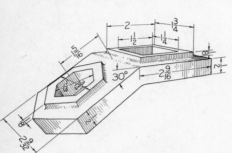

Prob. 6.2.1. Holder.

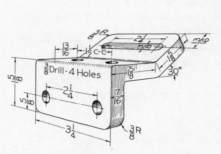

Prob. 6.2.2. Slotted anchor.

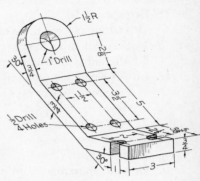

Prob. 6.2.3. Connector strip.

6.2.1. Draw front view, partial top view, and partial left auxiliary.

6.2.2. Draw partial front view, right-side view, partial top view, and partial front auxiliary.

6.2.3. Draw front view, partial top view, and partial right and left auxiliaries.

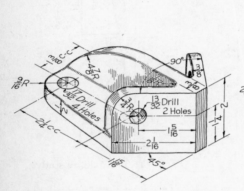

Prob. 6.2.4. Push plate.

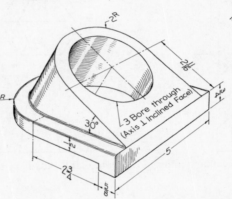

Prob. 6.2.5. Bevel washer.

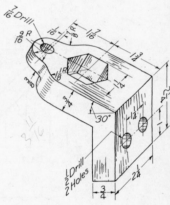

Prob. 6.2.6. Jig angle.

6.2.4. Draw top view, partial front view, and partial elevation auxiliaries.

6.2.5. Draw front view, partial top view, and partial right auxiliary.

6.2.6. Draw front view, partial right-side view, and partial right auxiliary. Draw auxiliary before completing the front view.

6.2.7. Draw front view, partial top view, and partial right auxiliary.

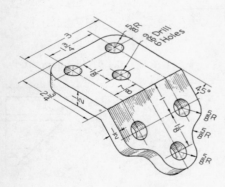

Prob. 6.2.7. Angle clip.

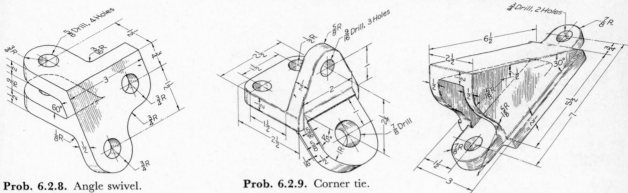

Prob. 6.2.8. Angle swivel.

Prob. 6.2.9. Corner tie.

Prob. 6.2.10. Channel support.

6.2.8. Draw front view, partial top view, and partial right auxiliary.

6.2.9. Draw front view, partial top and right-side views, and partial right auxiliary.

6.2.10. Draw front, partial top, and left-side views, and partial right auxiliary.

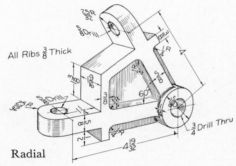

Prob. 6.2.11. Radial swing block.

6.2.11 and 6.2.12. Determine what views and part views will best describe the piece. Submit sketch before starting the drawing.

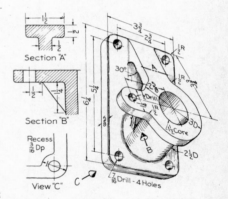

Prob. 6.2.12. Angle-shaft base.

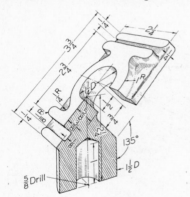

Prob. 6.2.13. Catenary clip.

6.2.13. Draw front view, partial bottom view, and partial left auxiliary.

6.2.14. Draw front view, partial left-side and bottom views, and partial right auxiliary.

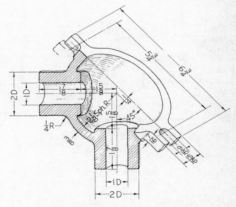

Prob. 6.2.14. Bevel-gear housing.

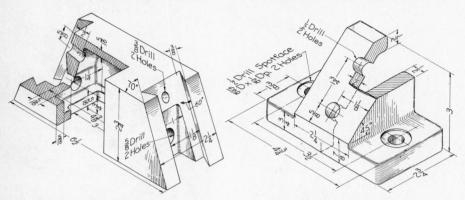

Prob. 6.2.15. Slide base.

Prob. 6.2.16. Idler bracket.

6.2.15 and 6.2.16. Determine what views and part views will best describe the piece.

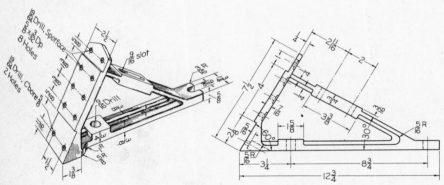

Prob. 6.2.17. Corner brace.

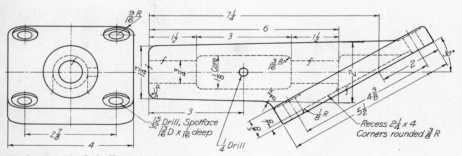

Prob. 6.2.18. Spindle support.

6.2.17. Draw given front view; add necessary views to describe the piece.

6.2.18. Draw front view, partial left-side view, and partial right auxiliary.

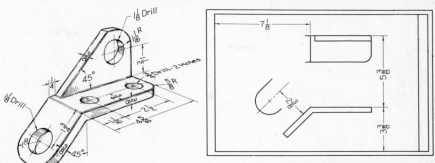

Prob. 6.2.19. Spar clip, 90°.

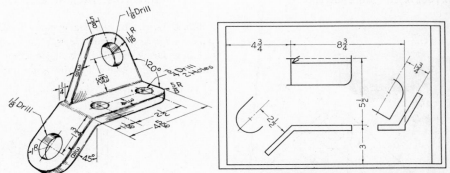

Prob. 6.2.20. Spar clip, 120°.

6.2.19 and 6.2.20. This pair of similar objects has the upper lug in two different positions. Layouts are for 11- by 17-in. paper. Draw views and part views as indicated on layouts.

Group 3. Oblique views

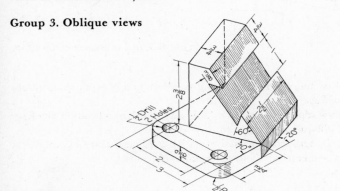

Prob. 6.3.1. Dovetail clip.

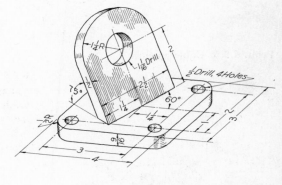

Prob. 6.3.2. Anchor base.

6.3.1. Draw partial front, partial top, partial elevation auxiliary (edge), and oblique views. Edge view is to show the true size of dovetail slot; oblique view is to show the true size of slanting face.

6.3.2. Draw partial front, partial top, elevation auxiliary showing edge view of slanting lug, and oblique view showing true size and shape of slanting lug. Lay out oblique view before completing elevation auxiliary.

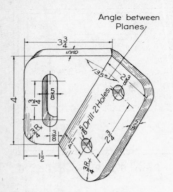

Prob. 6.3.3. Adjusting clip.

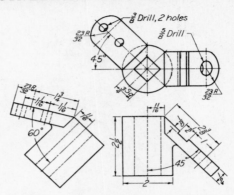

Prob. 6.3.4. Bar-strut anchor.

6.3.3. Draw the necessary views to describe the adjusting clip, using partial edge and oblique views.

6.3.4. Draw the views given, omitting lugs on top view. Add right auxiliary and oblique view to show true shape of lugs.

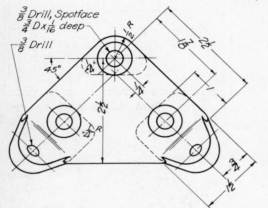

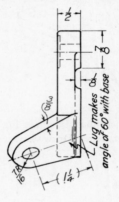

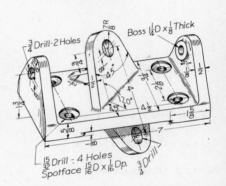

Prob. 6.3.6. Transverse connection.

Prob. 6.3.5. Cable anchor.

6.3.5. Draw the views given, using auxiliary and oblique views to obtain shape of lugs.

6.3.6. Draw top, front, left-side (alternate position), elevation auxiliary (edge), and oblique views.

6.3.7. Draw top, front, partial elevation auxiliary, and oblique views. The piece is symmetrical about the main axis.

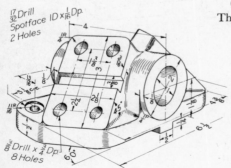

Prob. 6.3.7. Chamfer-tool base.

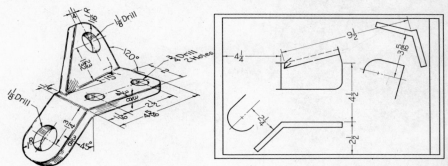

Prob. 6.3.8. Spar clip.

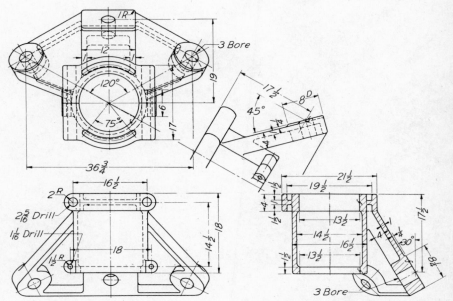

Prob. 6.3.9. Crane-masthead collar and cap.

6.3.8. Draw the spar clip, using layout for 11- by 17-in. paper as shown. Note that left auxiliary, elevation auxiliary (edge), and oblique views are required.

6.3.9. Draw the layout of the views given and such additional auxiliary and oblique views as are necessary for the description of the piece.

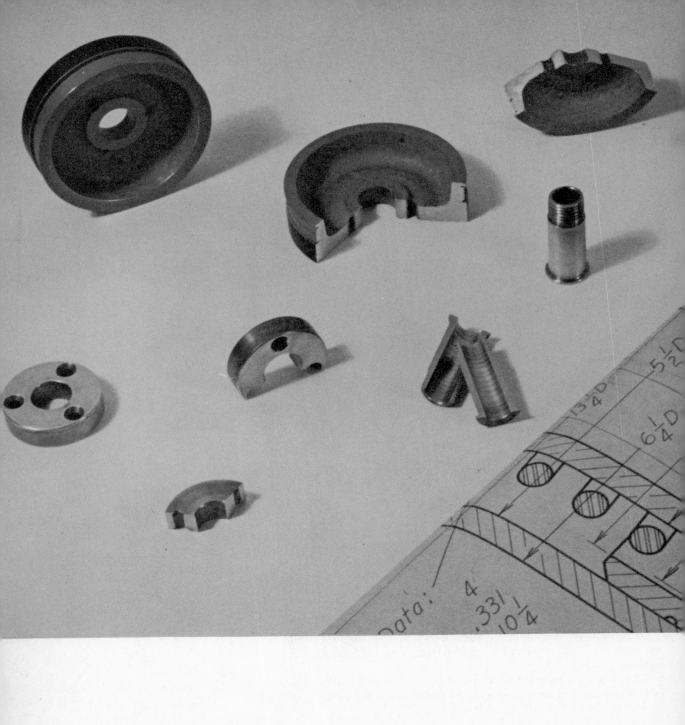

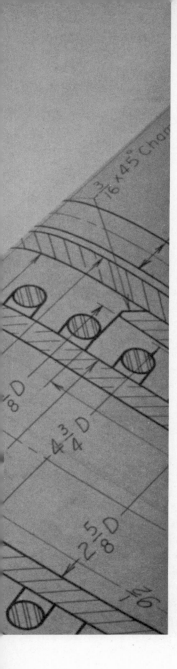

7

SECTIONS AND CONVENTIONS

7.1. Sections. Previous chapters have dealt with the method of describing the shape of an object by orthographic views, using dotted lines to indicate hidden parts. If the object is very simple in its interior construction, these hidden lines are not hard to read and understand. Often, however, when the interior is complicated or when several different pieces are assembled in place, an attempt to show the construction on an exterior view would result in a confusing mass of dotted lines, annoying to draw and difficult, if not impossible, to read clearly. In such cases one (or more) of the views is made "in section." Even for simple objects where the orthographic views may be read easily, sectional views are often preferred because they give emphasis to the material of which the objects are made and to the void spaces, such as holes, resulting in views which may be read with much less mental effort than exterior views.

The following is a definition: *A section is an imaginary cut taken through an object so as to reveal the shape or interior construction.*

A *sectional view* is either (1) a conventional representation in which a part of an object or machine is imagined to be cut or broken away and removed so as to expose the interior or (2) a conventional representation in which a slice of negligible thickness is taken through an object and then revolved, removed, or aligned to show the shape or interior construction.

7.2. Cutting Planes. A cutting plane is the imaginary medium
165

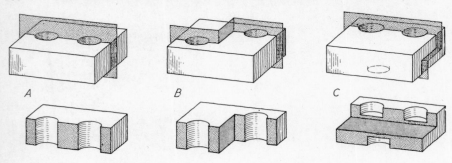

Fig. 7.1. Cutting planes.

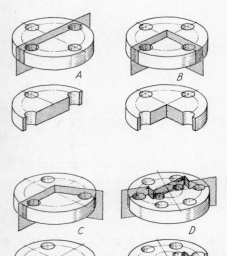

Fig. 7.2. Cutting planes.

used to show the path of cutting an object to make a section. Figure 7.1 pictures several objects intersected by cutting planes, giving the *appearance* that the castings have actually been cut through by the plane and the front parts removed to expose the interior. The cutting plane may pass directly across the object as in Fig. 7.1*A*, or it may offset, changing direction forward or backward, so as to pass through features it would otherwise miss, as at (*B*) and (*C*).

Figure 7.2 shows several examples of how the cutting plane may pass through a symmetrical object, permitting the removal of a portion of the object so as better to describe the shape. Note how the cutting planes may change direction so as to pass through the holes.

Figure 7.3*A* shows the use of more than one plane on the same object. When more than one view is drawn in section, each sectional view should be considered separately without any reference to what has been removed for other views. Thus Fig. 7.3*B* shows the front half removed for one sectional view; and Fig. 7.3*C*, a different part removed for another sectional view.

Figure 7.4*A* shows an object cut part way through and the front portion broken out and removed. The cutting plane in this case cannot be extended through the length of the object, for to do so would remove features that would not then be described. For some objects a portion is broken out and removed to expose the interior, as in Fig. 7.4*B*, and even though no cutting plane is used, the principles of sectional drawing will apply in making the orthographic views.

The cutting plane may also be imagined to pass through an object cutting a slice of negligible thickness, which may then be removed,

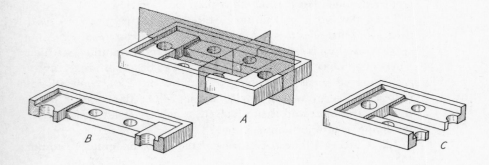

Fig 7.3. Cutting planes.

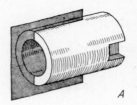
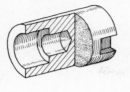
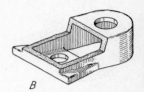

Fig. 7.4. Cutting planes.

revolved, or aligned to show a shape that otherwise would be difficult to see or describe, Fig. 7.5.

7.3. The Cutting-plane Symbol. It may be shown on the orthographic view where the cutting plane appears as an edge and may be more completely identified with reference letters along with arrows to show the direction in which the view is taken. The cutting-plane line symbol is shown in the alphabet of lines, Fig. 1.60. For an example of its use, see Fig. 7.16. Often when the position of the section is evident, the cutting-plane symbol is omitted, Fig. 7.12. It is not always possible to show the symbol through its entire length; so, in such cases, the beginning and ending of the plane is shown as in section *A-A*, Prob. 12.3.14.   Removed sections usually need the cutting-plane symbol with arrows to show the direction of sight and with letters to name the resulting sectional view (Fig. 7.20).

7.4. Section Lining. Wherever material has been cut by the section plane, the cut surface is indicated by section lining, sometimes called "crosshatching," done with fine lines generally at 45° with the principal lines in the view and spaced uniformly to give an even tint. They are spaced entirely by eye except when some form of mechanical section liner is used. The pitch, or distance between lines, is governed by the size of the surface. For ordinary working drawings, it will not be much less than $\frac{1}{16}$ in. and rarely more than $\frac{1}{8}$ in. *Very* small pieces may require a spacing closer than $\frac{1}{16}$ in. Care should be exercised in setting the pitch by the first two or three lines, and one should glance back at the first lines often in order that the pitch may not gradually increase or decrease. Nothing mars the appearance of a drawing more than poor section lining. The alphabet of lines, Fig. 1.60, gives the weight of crosshatch lines.

Two adjacent pieces in an assembly drawing are crosshatched in opposite directions. If three pieces adjoin, one of them may be sectioned at other than 45° (usually 30° or 60°, Fig. 7.6), or all pieces

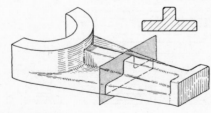

Fig. 7.5. Cutting plane.

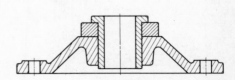

Fig. 7.6. Adjacent parts.

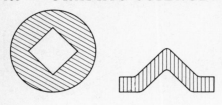
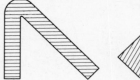

Fig. 7.7. Section-line directions for unusual shapes.

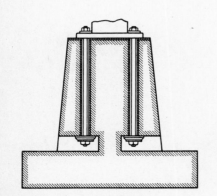

Fig. 7.8. Outline sectioning.

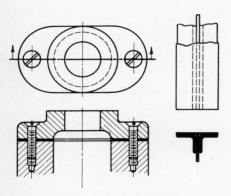

Fig. 7.9. Thin material in section.

may be crosshatched at 45° by using a different pitch for each piece. If a part is so shaped that 45° sectioning runs parallel, or nearly so, to its principal outlines, another direction should be chosen (Fig. 7.7).

Large surfaces are sometimes sectioned around the edge only, as illustrated by Fig. 7.8.

Very thin sections, as of gaskets, sheet metal, or structural-steel shapes to small scale, may be shown in solid black, with white spaces between the parts where thin pieces are adjacent (Fig. 7.9).

7.5. Code for Materials in Section. Symbolical section lining is not commonly used on ordinary working drawings, but sometimes in an assembly section it is desired to show a distinction between materials, and a recognized standard code is of obvious advantage. The ASA symbols for indicating different materials will be found in the Appendix. Code section lining is used only as an aid in reading the drawing and is not to be taken as the official specification of the materials. Exact specifications of the material for each piece are always given on the detail drawing.

7.6. Projecting the Section. In general, the rules of projection are followed in making sectional views. Figure 7.10 shows the picture of a casting intersected by a cutting plane, giving the appearance that the casting has been cut through by the plane A-A and the front part removed, exposing the interior. Figure 7.11 shows the drawing of the casting with the front view in section. The edge of the cutting plane is shown on the top view by the cutting-plane symbol, with reference letters and arrows to show the direction in which the view is taken. It must be understood clearly that, in thus removing the nearer portion of the object to make the sectional view, the portion assumed to be removed is not omitted in making other views. Therefore, the top and right-side views of the object in Fig. 7.10 are full and complete, and only in the front view has part of the object been represented as removed.

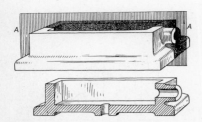

Fig. 7.10. The cutting plane.

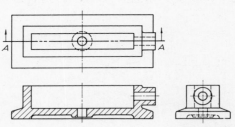

Fig. 7.11. Section A-A.

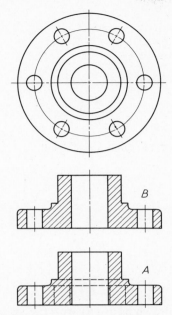

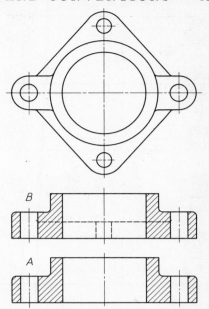

Fig. 7.12. Hidden edges and surfaces not shown.

Fig. 7.13. Hidden edges and surfaces shown.

7.7. Unnecessary Hidden Detail. Hidden edges and surfaces are not shown unless needed to describe the object. Much confusion may occur if all detail behind the cutting plane is drawn. Figure 7.12A shows a sectional view with all the hidden edges and surfaces shown by dotted lines. These lines complicate the view and do not add any information. View 7.12B is preferred because it is much simpler, is less time-consuming to draw, and is read with less mental effort than the view at (A). The holes lie on a circular center line; and where similar details repeat, all may be assumed to be alike.

7.8. Necessary Hidden Detail. Hidden edges and surfaces are shown if necessary for the description of the object. Figure 7.13A is inadequate since it does not show the thickness of the lugs. The correct treatment is in view (B), where the lugs are shown by dotted lines.

7.9. Visible Detail Shown on Sectional Views. Figure 7.14 shows an object pictorially with the front half removed, thus exposing edges and surfaces behind the cutting plane.

Figure 7.14A shows a sectional view of the cut surface only, with the visible elements omitted. This treatment should never be used.

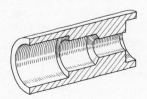 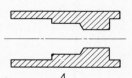 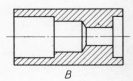

Fig. 7.14. Visible edges shown.

A

B

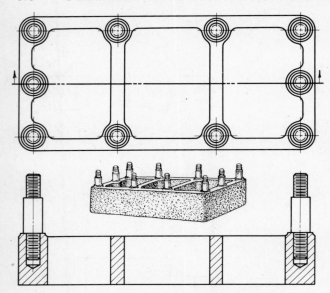

Fig. 7.15. Omission of detail.

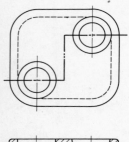

Fig. 7.16. Full section.

The view should be drawn as at (*B*) with the visible edges and surfaces behind the cutting plane included in the sectional view.

7.10. Visible Detail Not Shown on Sectional Views. Sometimes confusion may occur if all visible detail behind the cutting plane is drawn. Omission of such detail should be carefully considered and may be justified as time saved in drawing. It will apply more often on assembly drawings, where the function of the drawing is to show how the pieces fit together rather than to give complete information for making the parts. For an example of omitted detail, see Fig. 7.15.

7.11. Names of Sectional Views. The many different types of sectional views have been given names for purposes of identification during discussion and instruction and for specifying the kind of sectional view desired from a draftsman. Sectional views are not named on the drawings, and workmen do not need the names to use or read the drawings. Different kinds of sectional views may have more than one appropriate name. For example, a revolved, removed, or aligned section may also be a full section. The portion of the object that is assumed to be removed has nothing to do with the name of the section. Names have been assigned in all cases by the amount of the view in section or the manner in which the view is arranged in relation to the other views of the object.

7.12. Full Section. This is one in which the cutting plane cuts entirely across the object, showing all the view in section. The path of the cutting plane may go straight along the principal axis or center line, as in Fig. 7.10, or it may be offset and change direction, as in Fig. 7.16. Observe that the change in plane direction on the sectional view is not shown, for the cut is purely imaginary and no edge is present on the object at this position.

7.13. Half Section. This is a view sometimes used for symmetrical objects, in which one half is drawn in section and the other half as a regular exterior view. The cutting plane is imagined to extend half-way across, stopping at the axis or center line (Fig. 7.17). A half section has the advantage of showing both the exterior and the interior on one view without using dotted lines but has the disadvantage that inside diameters cannot be dimensioned well. However, the hidden edges may be shown in the exterior portion for clarity and assistance in dimensioning (Fig. 7.17*B*). *Note that a center line separates the exterior and interior portions of the sectional view.*[1]

7.14. Broken-out Section. It is a partial section used on an exterior view to show some interior detail without drawing a complete full or half section. Note the irregular break line, which limits the extent of the section, Fig. 7.18.

7.15. Revolved Section. This is made directly on an exterior view and provides a very convenient and useful method of showing the shape of the cross section of some detail of construction, such as a rib or the arm of a wheel. The cutting plane is passed perpendicular to the center line or axis of the part to be sectioned and the resulting section revolved or turned up in place (Fig. 7.19). The revolved section is used primarily for shape description rather than size description. When lines of the outline interfere with the section, as is sometimes the case, the view may be broken away to make a clear space for the sectional view. Figures 7.34 and 7.35 contain some examples of revolved sections.

7.16. Removed Sections. They are used for the same purpose as revolved sections, but instead of being drawn on the view, they are set off, or shifted, to some adjacent place on the paper (Fig. 7.20).

[1] The reason why a center line is used is that, theoretically, the cutting of the object is imaginary and, in addition, no edge, edge view of a surface, or surface limit producing a solid line exists at the center of the object. An unfortunate mistake exists in some drafting manuals in which a solid line is also allowed for the line of demarcation between sectioned and exterior portions of a half section. It is certainly hoped that, sometime in the near future, this mistake will be corrected.

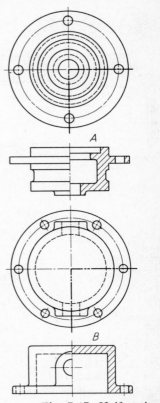

Fig. 7.17. Half sections.

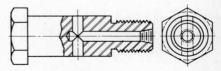

Fig. 7.18. A broken-out section.

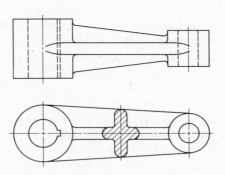

Fig. 7.19. A revolved section.

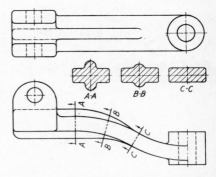

Fig. 7.20. Removed sections.

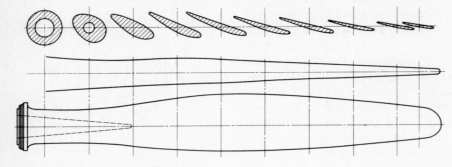

Fig. 7.21. Removed sections.

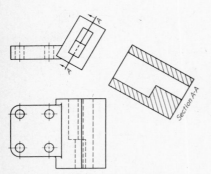

Fig. 7.22. Auxiliary section.

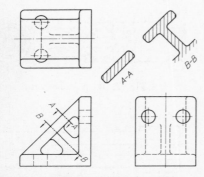

Fig. 7.23. Auxiliary sections (partial).

The cutting plane with reference letters should always be indicated unless the place from which the section has been taken is obvious. Removed sections are used whenever restricted space for the section or the dimensioning of it prevents the use of an ordinary revolved section. When the shape of a piece changes gradually or is not uniform, several sections may be required (Fig. 7.21). It is often an advantage to draw them to larger scale than that of the main drawing in order to show dimensions more clearly. Sometimes sections are removed to a separate drawing sheet. When this practice is employed, the section must be carefully shown on the main drawing with cutting plane and identifying letters. Often these identifying letters are made as a fraction in a circle, with the numerator a letter identifying the section and the denominator a number identifying the sheet. The sectional view is then marked with the same letters and numbers. The American Standard recommends that, whenever possible, a removed section should be drawn in its natural projected position. Note in Fig. 7.21 that this practice is followed.

7.17. Auxiliary Section. This is a sectional view made on an auxiliary plane and conforms to all the principles of auxiliary views as explained in Chap. 6; thus there may be an elevation auxiliary section, a right or left auxiliary section, a front or rear auxiliary section, or an oblique section. Similarly, half sections, broken-out sections, revolved sections, and removed sections may be used on auxiliary views. Figure 7.22 is an example of an auxiliary in section. Figure 7.23 shows the use of right auxiliary partial sections.

7.18. Assembly Sections. As the name implies, an assembly section is one taken through a combination of parts making up a machine or structure. All the previously mentioned types of sections (full, revolved, broken-out, etc.) may be used for increasing the clarity and readability of assembly drawings. Problems 12.3.3, 12.3.5, and 12.3.7 are examples of assembly sections.

The purpose of an assembly section is to reveal the interior of the machine or structure so that the separate parts may be clearly shown and identified, but the separate parts do not need to be completely described. Thus only such hidden details as are necessary for part identification are shown. Also, the small amount of clearance

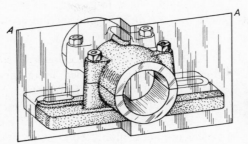

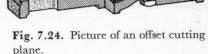

Fig. 7.24. Picture of an offset cutting plane.

between mating or moving parts is not shown because, if shown, the clearance would have to be greatly exaggerated, thus confusing the drawing. Even the clearance between a bolt and its hole, which may be as much as $\frac{1}{16}$ in., is rarely shown.

Crosshatching practice for assembly sections is explained in paragraph 7.4 and is also shown in Fig. 7.25.

7.19. Five Principles in Sectioning

1. The cutting plane need not be a continuous single plane but may be offset or changed in direction so as to show the construction to the best advantage (Fig. 7.24).

2. Section lining, either (a) for the same piece in different views or (b) for the same piece in different parts of the same view, should be identical in spacing and direction.[1]

3. Invisible lines beyond the plane of the section should not be drawn unless necessary for the description or identification of the piece.

4. Adjacent pieces are section-lined in opposite directions and are often brought out more clearly by varying the pitch of the section lines for each piece, using closer spacing for the smaller pieces (Figs. 7.6 and 7.25).

[1] An exception to this rule is made for the crosshatching of an auxiliary view in order to avoid crosshatch lines either parallel or perpendicular, or nearly so, to the outlines of the view.

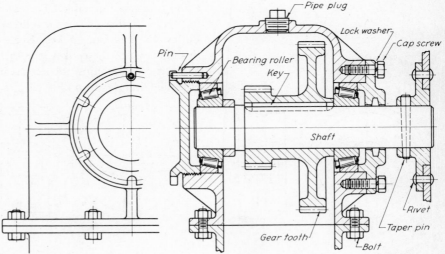

Fig. 7.25. Section study.

5. Shafts, bolts, nuts, rods, rivets, keys, and the like whose axes occur in the plane of the section are left in full and not sectioned (Fig. 7.25).

7.20. Conventional Sections. All sections are conventions in that they represent an assumed imaginary cut from which, following rather closely the rules of projection, the sectional views are made. However, added clearness will sometimes be obtained by violating the strict rules of projection, resulting in a type of view called a "conventional section." Some conventions must be used with caution because they are not always readily understood by the workman. It is impossible to illustrate all the conditions that might occur, but the following discussions and illustrations show the principles that are recognized and accepted as good practice since they result in added clearness and readability.

7.21. Parts Not Sectioned. Many machine elements, such as fasteners, pins, and shafts, have no internal construction and, in addition, are more easily recognized by their exterior views. These parts often lie in the path of the section plane, but if they are sectioned (crosshatched), they are more difficult to read because their typical identifying features (boltheads, rivet heads, chamfers on shafts, etc.) are removed. Thus features of this kind should be left in full view and *not sectioned*. To justify this treatment, the assembly is thought of as being sectioned on a particular plane, and then the nonsectioned parts are placed in the half holes remaining after the section is made. Figure 7.24 shows a full section made on an offset cutting plane that passes through a bolt. The treatment shown with the bolt in full view illustrates the above statements. Figure 7.25 shows several nonsectioned parts. It should be evident in this figure that, if the shaft, bolts, nuts, rivets, etc., were sectioned, the drawing would be confusing and difficult to read.

7.22. Section Lines Omitted. A basic principle for sectioning circular parts is that any element not continuous (solid) around the axis of the part should be drawn without crosshatching in order to avoid a misleading effect. For example, consider the two pulleys of Fig. 7.26. Pulley (*A*) has a solid web connecting the hub and rim. Pulley (*B*) has four spokes. Even though the cutting plane passes through two of the spokes, the sectional view of (*B*) must be made without crosshatching the spokes in order to avoid the appearance of a solid web, as in pulley (*A*).

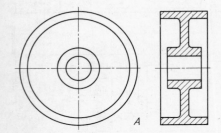

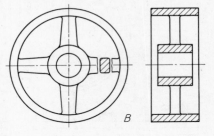

Fig. 7.26. Section lines omitted.

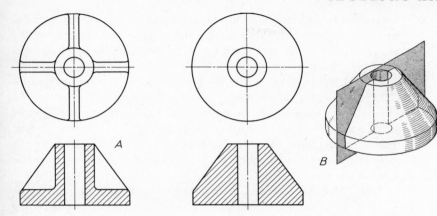

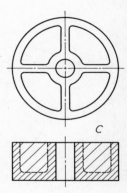

Fig. 7.27. Ribs in section.

Other machine elements treated in this manner are teeth of gears and sprockets, vanes and supporting ribs of cylindrical parts, equally spaced lugs, and other similar portions.

7.23. Ribs in Section. For reasons very similar to those given in paragraph 7.22, when the cutting plane passes longitudinally through the center of a rib or web as in Fig. 7.27*A*, the crosshatching should be eliminated from the ribs as if the cutting plane were just in front of them or as if they were temporarily removed and replaced after the section is made. A true sectional view with the ribs crosshatched gives a heavy misleading effect suggesting a cone shape, as shown at (*B*). When the cutting plane cuts a rib transversely, that is, at right angles to its length or axis direction (the direction that shows its thickness), it should always be crosshatched. For an example, see Fig. 7.15.

7.24. Alternate Crosshatching. In some cases omitting the crosshatching of ribs or similar parts will give an inadequate and sometimes ambiguous treatment. To illustrate, Fig. 7.28*A* shows a full section of an idler pulley. At (*B*), four ribs have been added, and (note) the top surfaces of the ribs are flush with the top of the pulley. Without crosshatching, the section at (*B*) is identical with (*A*) and the ribs of (*B*) are not identified at all on the sectional view. A better

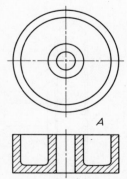

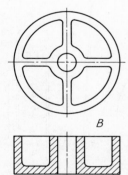

Fig. 7.28. Alternate crosshatching.

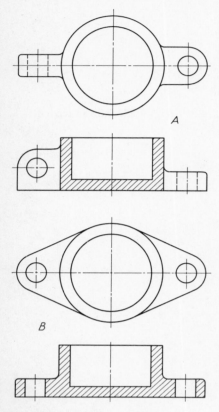

Fig. 7.29. Lugs in section.

treatment in this case is to use alternate crosshatching for the ribs, as at (*C*), where half (alternating) the crosshatch lines are carried through the ribs. Note that the line of demarcation between rib and solid portions is a *dotted* line.

7.25. Lugs in Section. For the same reasons given in paragraphs 7.22 to 7.24, a lug or projecting ear, Fig. 7.29*A*, usually of *rectangular* cross section, should not be crosshatched. Note that, in this case, crosshatching either of the lugs would suggest a circular flange. However, the somewhat similar condition at (*B*) should have the projecting ears crosshatched as shown because these ears *are* the base of the part.

7.26. Aligned Sections. Any part having an odd number (3, 5, 7, etc.) of spokes or ribs will give an unsymmetrical and misleading section if the principles of true projection are strictly adhered to, as illustrated by the drawing of a handwheel in Fig. 7.30. The preferred projection is shown in the second sectional view, where one arm is drawn as if aligned, or in other words, the arm is revolved to the path of the vertical cutting plane and then projected to the side view. Note that neither arm should be sectioned for reasons given in paragraph 7.22.

This practice of alignment is well justified logically because a part having an odd number of equally spaced elements is just as symmetrical as a part with some even number and, therefore, should be shown by a symmetrical view. Moreover, the symmetrical view shows the true *relationship* of the elements, while a true projection does not.

7.27. Aligned Ribs, Lugs, and Holes. Following the principles given in paragraph 7.26, ribs, lugs, and holes often occur in odd numbers and, therefore, should be aligned to show the true relationship of the elements. In Fig. 7.31*A*, true projection of the ribs would show the pair on the right foreshortened, suggesting in the sectional view that they would not extend to the outer edge of the base. Here, again, the alignment as shown in Fig. 7.31*A* gives a symmetrical section of a symmetrical part and shows the ribs in their true relationship to the basic part. To illustrate further, in Fig. 7.31*B* and *C*, the lugs and holes are aligned, thus showing the holes at their true

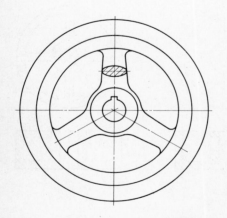

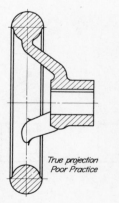

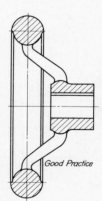

Fig. 7.30. Aligned section.

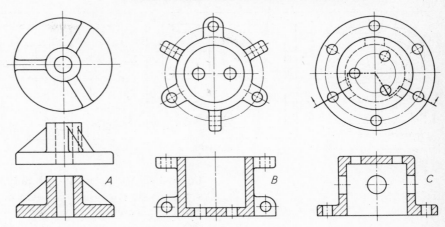

Fig. 7.31. Aligned ribs, lugs, and holes.

radial distance from the axis, and, incidentally, eliminating some difficult projections.

In all cases of alignment, one may think of the element as being swung around to a common cutting plane and then projected to the sectional view. Note in Fig. 7.31*C* that, because an offset cutting plane is used, each hole is brought separately into position on a common cutting plane before projection to the sectional view.

7.28. Conventional Practices. There are violations of the rules of projection in full views, as well as in sectional views, that are desirable because they add to the clearness of the drawing. One statement can be made with the force of a rule: *If anything in clearness can be gained by violating a principle of projection, violate it.* Permissible violations usually are not readily apparent to the reader. This is true since they describe, in a better and usually simpler form, the actual conditions. Some care and judgment must be used in applying conventional treatments. Draftsmen usually understand their meaning, but workmen often do not. Some unusual convention may be more harmful than helpful and result in greater ambiguity than true projection.

Some typical examples in which true lines of intersection are of no value as aids in reading and are therefore ignored are shown in Fig. 7.32. In contrast with the above practices, very similar condi-

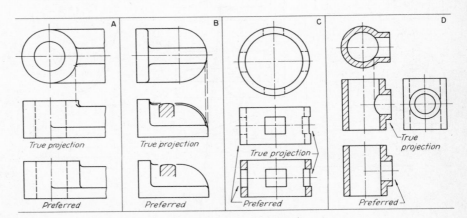

Fig. 7.32. Conventional practices.

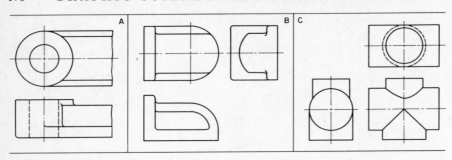

Fig. 7.33. Intersections not conventionalized.

tions where the proportions differ should show the true line of intersection. Compare the treatment of the similar objects in Figs. 7.32 and 7.33. It would not be good practice to conventionalize the intersections on the objects of Fig. 7.33 because the difference between true projection and the convention is too great.

7.29. Fillets and Rounds. In designing a casting, sharp internal angles must never be left because of the liability to fracture at those points. The radius of the fillet depends on the thickness of the metal and other design conditions. When not dimensioned, it is left to the patternmaker. External angles may be rounded for appearance or comfort, with radii ranging from enough merely to remove the

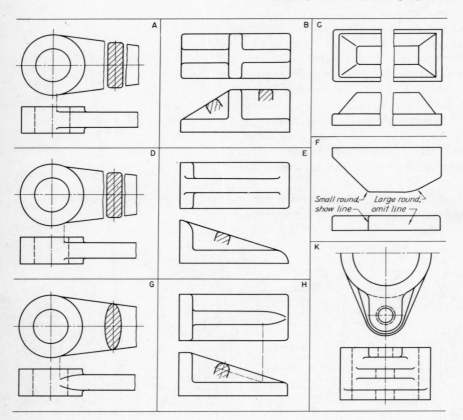

Small round, show line   Large round, omit line

Fig. 7.34. Conventional fillets, rounds, and runouts.

sharp edges to an amount nearly equal to the thickness of the piece. An edge made by the intersection of two unfinished surfaces of a casting should always be "broken" by a very small round. A sharp corner on a drawing thus indicates that one or both of the intersecting surfaces are machined. Small fillets, rounds, and "runouts" are best put in freehand, both in pencil and ink. Runouts, or "dieouts," as they are sometimes called, are conventional indications of filleted intersections where, theoretically, there would be no line because there is no abrupt change in direction. Figure 7.34 shows some conventional representations of fillets and rounds with runouts of arms and ribs intersecting other surfaces.

7.30. Conventional Breaks. In making the detail of a long bar or piece having a uniform shape of cross section, there is rarely any necessity for drawing its whole length. It may be shown to a larger and thus better scale by breaking out a piece, moving the ends together, and giving the true length by a dimension, as in Fig. 7.35. The shape of the cross section is indicated either by a revolved section or, more often, by a semipictorial break line as in Fig. 7.36. This figure also shows some other conventional symbols.

7.31. Conventional Symbols. Draftsmen use conventional representation for indicating many details, such as screw threads, springs, pipe fittings, and electrical apparatus. These have been standardized by the ASA, whose code for materials in section has already been referred to in paragraph 7.5.

The symbol of two crossed diagonals is used for two distinct purposes: (1) to indicate on a shaft the position of finish for a bearing and (2) to indicate that a certain surface (usually parallel to the

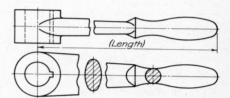

Fig. 7.35. Broken view with revolved sections.

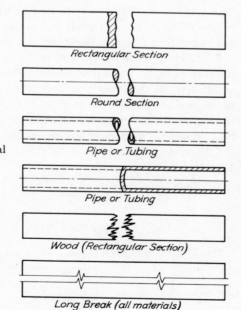

Fig. 7.36. Conventional breaks and other symbols.

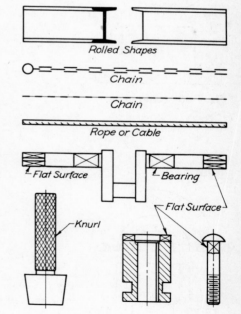

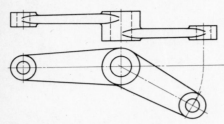

Fig. 7.37. Aligned view.

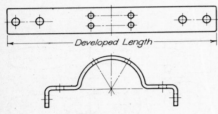

Developed Length

Fig. 7.38. Developed view.

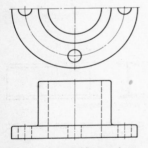

Fig. 7.39. Half top view.

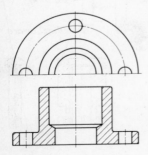

picture plane) is flat. These two uses are not apt to be confused (Fig. 7.36).

Because of constant recurrence, the representation of screw threads is one of the most important items under conventional symbols. Up to the time of their official standardization by the ASA, there were a dozen different thread symbols in use. Now one regular symbol and one simplified one are adopted for American drawings, and both are understood internationally. The symbols for indicating threads on bolts, screws, and tapped holes are given in Chap. 11.

The conventional symbols mentioned in the previous paragraph are used principally on machine drawings. Architectural drawing, because of the small scales employed, uses many conventional symbols, and topographic drawing is made up entirely of symbols.

7.32. Aligned and Developed Views. There are violations of the rules of true projection in full views, as well as in sectional views, that are recognized as good practice because they add to the clearness of the drawing. For example, if a front view shows a hexagonal bolthead "across corners," the theoretical projection of the side view would be "across flats"; but in a working drawing, when boltheads occur, they should be drawn across corners in both views to show better the shape and the space needed.

Pieces that have elements at an angle to each other, as the lever of Fig. 7.37, may be shown straightened out or aligned in one view. Similarly, bent pieces of the type of Fig. 7.38 should have one view made as a developed view of the *blank* to be punched and formed. Extra metal must be allowed for bends.

Lugs or parts cast on for holding purposes and to be machined off are shown by phantom lines. If such parts are in section, the section lines are dotted. Phantom lines are also used for indicating the limiting positions of moving parts and for showing adjacent parts that aid in locating the position or use of a piece.

7.33. Half Views. When space is very limited, it is allowable practice to make the top or the side view of a symmetrical piece as a half view. If the front is an exterior view, the *front* half of the top or the side view would be used, as in Fig. 7.39; but if the front view is a sectional view, the *rear* half would be used, as in Fig. 7.40. Figure 7.41 shows another space-saving combination of a half view with a half section. Examples of half views occur in Probs. 12.3.6 to 12.3.8.

Fig. 7.40. Half top view and full section.

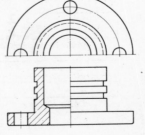

Fig. 7.41. Half top view and half section.

PROBLEMS

Selections from the following problems may be used for shape description only or as working drawings by adding dimensions:

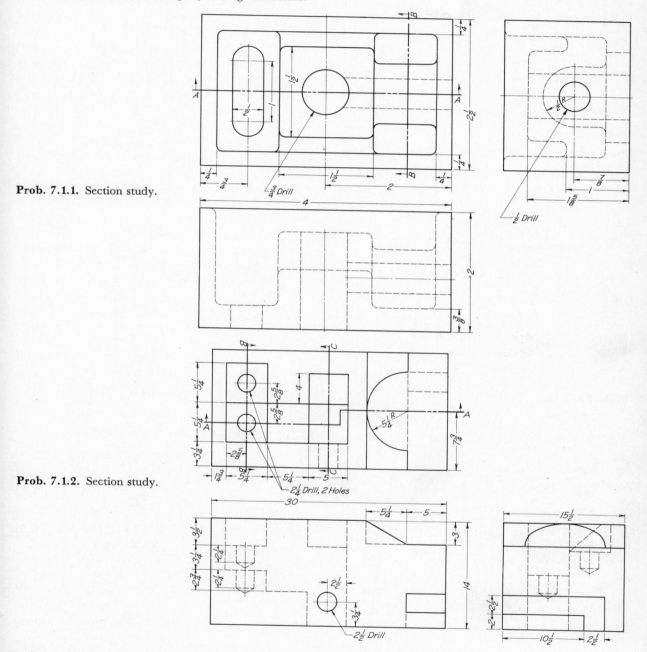

Prob. 7.1.1. Section study.

Prob. 7.1.2. Section study.

7.1.1. Draw top view, and change front and side views to sectional views as indicated.

7.1.2. Draw top view, and make front and two side views in section on cutting planes as indicated. Scale to suit.

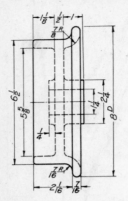

Prob. 7.1.3. Flanged wheel.

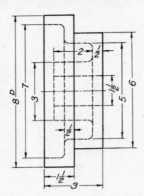

Prob. 7.1.4. Step pulley.

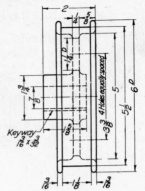

Prob. 7.1.5. Flanged pulley.

7.1.3 to 7.1.5. Given side view, draw full front and side view in section. Scale to suit.

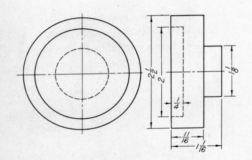

Prob. 7.1.6. Cap.

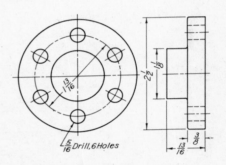

Prob. 7.1.7. Flanged cap.

7.1.6 and 7.1.7. Change right-side view to a full section.

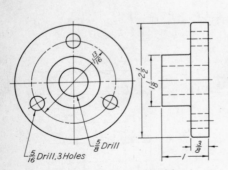

Prob. 7.1.8. Pump-rod guide.

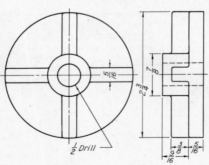

Prob. 7.1.9. Face plate.

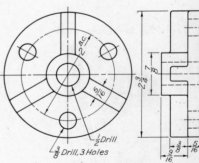

Prob. 7.1.10. Ribbed support.

7.1.8 and 7.1.9. Change right-side view to a full section.
7.1.10. Change right-side view to a full section.

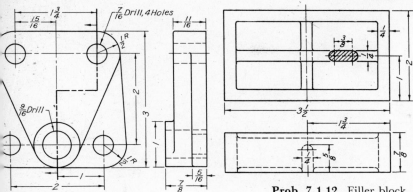

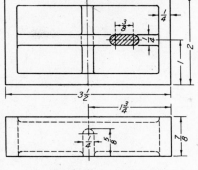

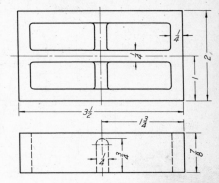

Prob. 7.1.11. Housing cover.

Prob. 7.1.12. Filler block.

Prob. 7.1.13. Filler block.

7.1.11. Change right-side view to sectional view as indicated.
7.1.12 and 7.1.13. Change front view to a full section.

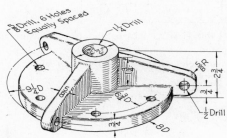

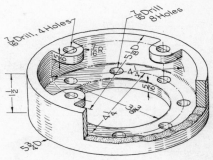

Prob. 7.1.14. End plate.

Prob. 7.1.15. Piston cap.

7.1.14 and 7.1.15. Select views that will best describe the piece.

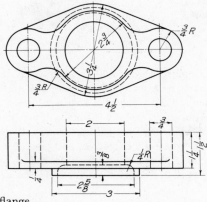

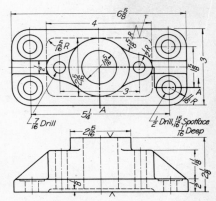

Prob. 7.1.16. Pump flange.

Prob. 7.1.17. Brake-rod bracket.

7.1.16. Draw top view as shown and front view as a full section.
7.1.17. Draw top view as shown and front view in half section on *A-A*.

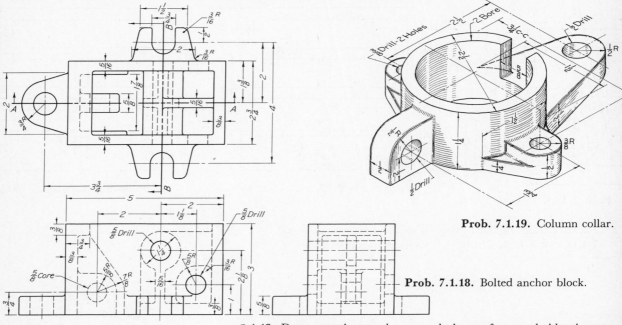

Prob. 7.1.19. Column collar.

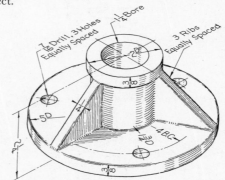

Prob. 7.1.18. Bolted anchor block.

7.1.18. Draw top view as shown, and change front and side views to sections as indicated.

7.1.19. Draw top view and sectional view or views to best describe the object.

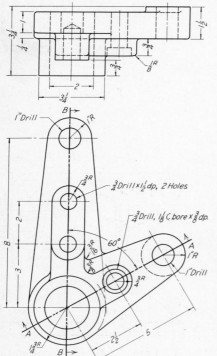

Prob. 7.1.20. Compound bell crank.

Prob. 7.1.21. Stem support.

7.1.20. Turn object through 90°, and draw given front view as new top view; then make new front view as section *B-B* and auxiliary section *A-A*. Refer to paragraph 7.17, where instructions for auxiliary sections have been given. Also, paragraphs 6.5 and 6.6 may be referred to for the method of projection for the auxiliary section. Note in this case that the new top view, front-view section *B-B*, and auxiliary section *A-A* will completely describe the object. However, if desired, the side view may also be drawn, either as shown or as an aligned view as described in paragraph 7.32.

7.1.20*A.* As an alternate for Prob. 7.1.20, views may be drawn as follows: with object in position shown, draw front view as shown, draw left-side view as section *B-B*, and draw new top view as an aligned view.

7.1.21. Draw top view and front view in section.

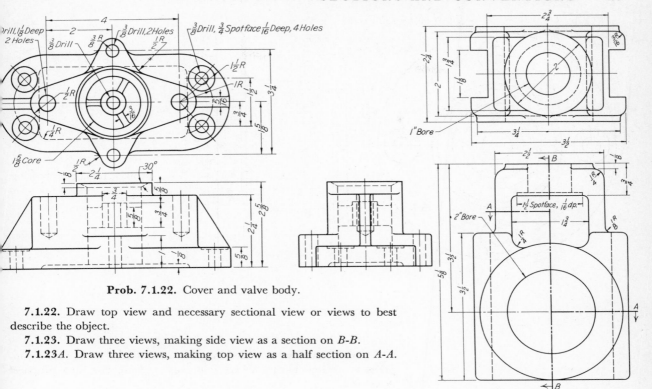

Prob. 7.1.22. Cover and valve body.

7.1.22. Draw top view and necessary sectional view or views to best describe the object.

7.1.23. Draw three views, making side view as a section on *B-B*.

7.1.23A. Draw three views, making top view as a half section on *A-A*.

Prob. 7.1.23. Crosshead.

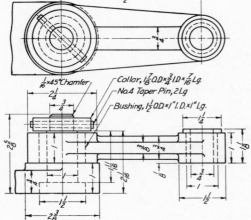

Prob. 7.1.24. Link assembly.

7.1.24. Draw top view as shown and new front view in section. Show shape (right section) of link with revolved or removed section. The assembly comprises a cast-steel link, two bronze bushings, steel toggle pin, steel collar, steel taper pin, and part of the cast-steel supporting lug.

7.1.25. Select views that will best describe the piece.

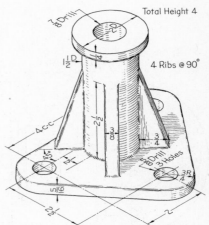

Prob. 7.1.25. Spindle support.

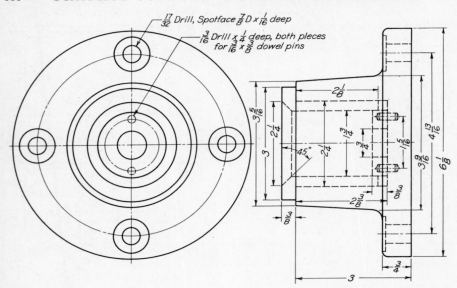

Prob. 7.1.26. Step bearing.

7.1.26. Draw front view and longitudinal section. The assembly comprises a cast-iron base, a bronze bushing, a bronze disk, and two steel dowel pins.

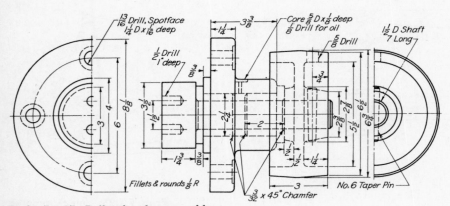

Prob. 7.1.27. Pulley bracket assembly.

7.1.27. Draw two half end views and longitudinal section. The assembly consists of cast-iron body, two bronze bushings, steel shaft, cast-iron pulley, and steel taper pin.

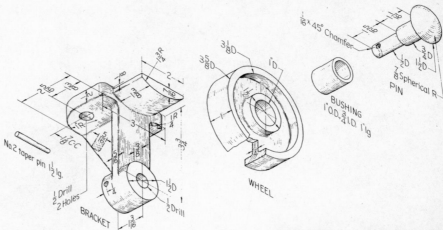

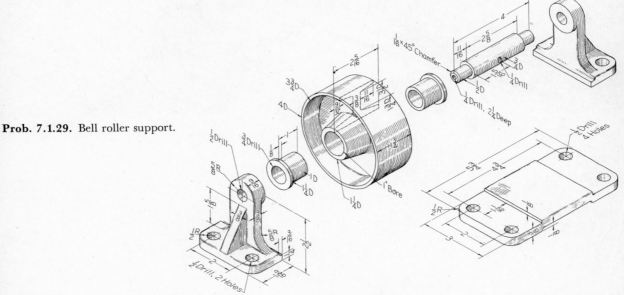

Prob. 7.1.28. Sliding-door guide.

7.1.28. Make an assembly drawing in section. The bracket is cast iron, the wheel is cast steel, the bushing is bronze, and the pin and taper pin are steel. Scale: full size.

7.1.28*A.* Make a drawing of the bracket with one view in section. Material is cast iron. Scale: full size.

7.1.28*B.* Make a drawing of the wheel with one view in section. Material is cast steel. Scale: full size.

Prob. 7.1.29. Bell roller support.

7.1.29. Make an assembly drawing in section. The assembly comprises two cast-iron brackets, two bronze bushings, steel shaft, cast-steel roller, and cast-iron base. The bushings are pressed into the roller, and the shaft is drilled for lubrication. Scale: full size.

7.1.29*A.* Make a drawing of the roller and bushing assembly with one view in section. See Prob. 7.1.29 for materials. Scale: full size.

8

PICTORIAL DRAWING

8.1. In the study of the theory of projection in Chap. 4, it was found that perspective projection shows the object as it appears to the eye but that its lines cannot be measured directly, while orthographic projection, with two or more views, shows it as it really is in form and dimensions, but requiring a trained imagination to visualize the object from the views. To combine the pictorial effect of perspective drawing with the possibility of measuring the principal lines directly, several forms of one-plane projection or conventional picture methods have been devised in which the third dimension is taken care of by turning the object in such a way that three of its faces are visible. Along with the advantages of these methods go some disadvantages which limit their usefulness. The distorted effect is often unreal and unpleasant; only certain lines can be measured; the execution occasionally requires more time, particularly if curved lines occur, and it is often difficult to show certain dimensions; but, even with their limitations, a knowledge of these methods is extremely desirable as they can be used to great advantage.

Mechanical or structural details not clear in orthographic projection may be drawn pictorially or illustrated by supplementary pictorial views. Technical illustrations, patent-office drawings, and the like are advantageously made in one-plane projection; layouts, piping plans, and many other applications will occur to draftsmen

189

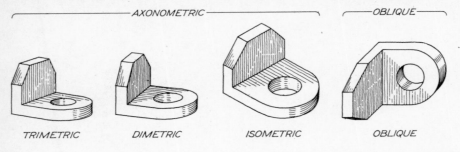

AXONOMETRIC

OBLIQUE

TRIMETRIC   DIMETRIC   ISOMETRIC   OBLIQUE

Fig. 8.1. Pictorial methods.

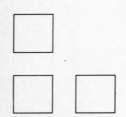

Fig. 8.2. Object faces parallel to picture plane.

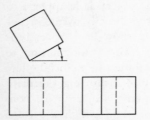

Fig. 8.3. Object rotated about a vertical axis.

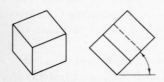

Fig. 8.4. Object rotated about a profile axis.

who can use these methods with facility. One of the most important reasons for learning them is that they are so useful in making free-hand sketches.

8.2. Pictorial Methods. Aside from perspective drawing, there are two main divisions of pictorial projection: (1) *axonometric*, with its divisions into trimetric, dimetric, and isometric, and (2) *oblique* projection, with several variations. Both methods are illustrated and compared by the drawings of Fig. 8.1. The trimetric form gives the most pleasing effect and allows almost unlimited freedom in orienting the object but is the most difficult to draw. The dimetric method is less pleasing and allows less freedom in orientation but is easier to draw than trimetric. The isometric form is less pleasing than either dimetric or trimetric but is the easiest to draw and, in addition, has the distinct advantage that it is easier to dimension. The oblique method is used principally for objects having circular or curved features only on one face or on parallel faces, and for objects of this type the oblique is very easy to draw and dimension.

The isometric and oblique forms of pictorial projection are the ones most commonly used.

8.3. Axonometric Projection. As shown in the tabular classification on page 4, this is theoretically orthographic projection in which only one plane is used, the object being turned so that three faces show. Imagine a transparent vertical plane with a cube behind it, one face of the cube being parallel to the plane. The projection on the plane, that is, the front view of the cube, will be a square, Fig. 8.2. Rotate the cube about a vertical axis through any angle less than 90°, and the front view will now show two faces, both fore-shortened, Fig. 8.3. From this position, tilt the cube forward (rotation axis perpendicular to profile) any amount less than 90°. Three faces will now be visible on the front view, Fig. 8.4. Thus there can be an infinite number of axonometric positions, only a few of which are ever used for drawing. The simplest of these is the *isometric* (equal-measure) position, in which the three faces are foreshortened equally.

8.4. Isometric Projection. If a cube in Fig. 8.5*A* is rotated about a vertical axis through 45°, as shown in (*B*), and then tilted forward, as in (*C*), until the edge *RU* is foreshortened equally with *RS* and *RT*, the front view of the cube in this position is said to be an "iso-

Fig. 8.5. The isometric cube.

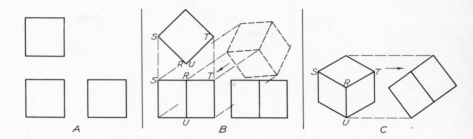

metric projection." (The cube has been tilted forward until the body diagonal through R is perpendicular to the front plane. This makes the top face slope approximately 35°16'.[1]) The projections of the three mutually perpendicular edges RS, RT, and RU meeting at the front corner R make equal angles, 120°, with each other and are called "isometric axes." Since the projections of parallel lines are parallel, the projections of the other edges of the cube will be, respectively, parallel to these axes. Any line parallel to an edge of the cube, whose projection is thus parallel to an isometric axis, is called an "isometric line." The planes of the faces of the cube and all planes parallel to them are called "isometric planes."

The isometric axes RS, RT, and RU are all foreshortened equally because they are at the same angle to the picture plane.

8.5. Isometric Drawing. In nearly all practical use of the isometric system, this foreshortening of the lines is disregarded, and *their full lengths are laid off on the axes*, as explained in paragraph 8.6. This gives a figure of exactly the same shape but larger in the proportion of 1.23 to 1, linear, or in optical effect 1.23^3 to 1.00^3 (Fig. 8.6). Except when drawn beside the same piece in orthographic projection, the effect of increased size is usually of no consequence, and as the advantage of measuring the lines directly is of such great convenience, isometric drawing is used almost exclusively instead of isometric projection.

In isometric projection the isometric lines have been foreshortened to approximately $81/100$ of their length, and an isometric scale to this proportion can be made graphically as shown in Fig. 8.7 if it becomes necessary to make an isometric projection by the method of isometric drawing.

8.6. To Make an Isometric Drawing. If the object is rectangular, start with a point representing a front corner and draw from it the three isometric axes 120° apart, one vertical, the other two with the

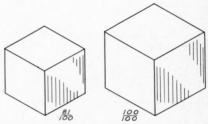

Fig. 8.6. Isometric projection and isometric drawing compared.

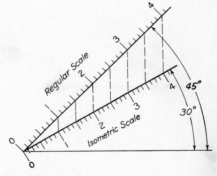

Fig. 8.7. To make an isometric scale.

---

[1] The only difference between rotation and auxiliary projection is that in the former the object is moved and in the latter the plane is moved. Thus an auxiliary view on a plane perpendicular to a body diagonal of the cube in position (*B*) would be an isometric projection, as illustrated by the dotted view.

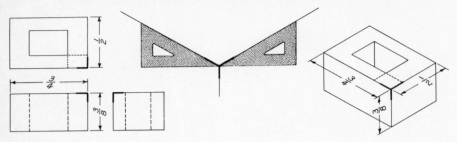

Fig. 8.8. Isometric axes, first position.

30° triangle (Fig. 8.8). On these three lines measure the height, width, and depth of the object, as indicated; through the points so determined draw lines parallel to the axes, completing the figure. To draw in isometric, it is necessary to remember the direction of the three principal isometric planes. Hidden lines are omitted except when needed for the description of the piece.

It is often more convenient to build up an isometric drawing from the lower front corner, as illustrated in Fig. 8.9, starting from axes in what may be called the "second position."

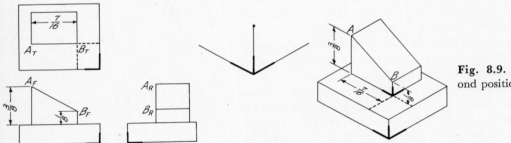

Fig. 8.9. Isometric axes, second position.

8.7. Nonisometric Lines. Edges whose projections or drawings are not parallel to one of the isometric axes are called "nonisometric lines." The one important rule is that *measurements can be made only on the drawings of isometric lines;* conversely, measurements *cannot* be made on the drawings of *nonisometric* lines. For example, the diagonals of the face of a cube are nonisometric lines; although equal in length, their isometric drawings will not be at all of equal length on the isometric drawing of the cube. Since a nonisometric line does not appear in the isometric drawing in its true length, the isometric view of each end of the line must be located and the isometric view of the line found by joining these two points. In Fig. 8.9, *AB* is a nonisometric line whose true length could not be measured on the isometric drawing.

In locating edge *AB* the vertical distances above the base to points *A* and *B* are parallel to the vertical isometric axis and can, therefore, be laid off as shown in Fig. 8.9.

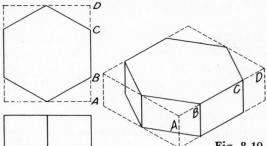

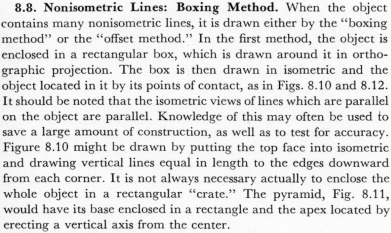

Fig. 8.10. Box construction.

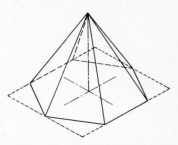

Fig. 8.11. Semibox construction.

8.8. Nonisometric Lines: Boxing Method. When the object contains many nonisometric lines, it is drawn either by the "boxing method" or the "offset method." In the first method, the object is enclosed in a rectangular box, which is drawn around it in orthographic projection. The box is then drawn in isometric and the object located in it by its points of contact, as in Figs. 8.10 and 8.12. It should be noted that the isometric views of lines which are parallel on the object are parallel. Knowledge of this may often be used to save a large amount of construction, as well as to test for accuracy. Figure 8.10 might be drawn by putting the top face into isometric and drawing vertical lines equal in length to the edges downward from each corner. It is not always necessary actually to enclose the whole object in a rectangular "crate." The pyramid, Fig. 8.11, would have its base enclosed in a rectangle and the apex located by erecting a vertical axis from the center.

The object shown in Fig. 8.12 is composed almost entirely of nonisometric lines. In such cases, the isometric cannot be drawn without first making the orthographic views necessary for boxing. In general, the boxing method is adapted to objects which have the nonisometric lines in isometric planes.

8.9. Nonisometric Lines: Offset Method. When the object is made up of planes at a number of different angles, it is better to locate the ends of the edges by the offset method. In this method, perpendiculars are extended from each point to an isometric reference plane. These perpendiculars, which are isometric lines, are located on the drawing by isometric coordinates, the dimensions being taken from the orthographic views. In Fig. 8.13, line *AB* is used as a base line and measurements are made from it as shown.

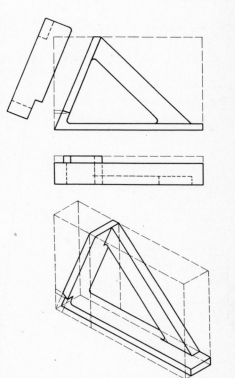

Fig. 8.12. Box construction.

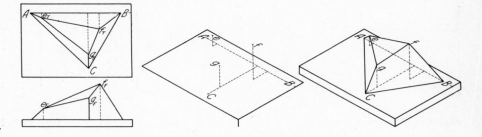

Fig. 8.13. Offset construction.

Figure 8.14 is another example of offset construction, using a vertical plane as a reference plane.

8.10. Angles in Isometric. The three isometric axes, referred back to the isometric cube, are mutually perpendicular but in the isometric drawing appear at 120° to each other. For this reason, angles specified in degrees do not appear in their true size on the isometric drawing and must, therefore, be laid off by coordinates which will be parallel to the isometric axes. Thus if an orthographic drawing has edges specified by angular dimensions as in Fig. 8.15*A*, *a view to the same scale as the isometric drawing* is made as at (*B*), from which the coordinate dimensions *a*, *b*, and *c* can be transferred with dividers or scale to the isometric drawing.

8.11. Curves in Isometric. For the same reasons given in paragraphs 8.7 and 8.10, a circle or any other curve will not show in its true shape when drawn in isometric. A circle on any isometric plane will be an ellipse, and a curve will be shown as the isometric projection of the true curve.

Any curve may be drawn by plotting points on it from isometric reference lines (coordinates) which are parallel to the isometric axes, as shown in Fig. 8.16. A circle plotted in this way is shown in Fig. 8.17. Note in both these figures that coordinates *a* and *b* are parallel to the isometric axes and that the coordinate distances must be obtained from an orthographic view drawn to the same scale as the isometric.

8.12. Isometric Circles. These occur so frequently that they are usually drawn by a four-centered approximation, which is sufficiently accurate for all ordinary work. Geometrically, the center for any arc tangent to a straight line lies on a *perpendicular from the point of tangency*, Fig. 8.18*A*. In isometric, if perpendiculars are drawn from the middle point of each side of the circumscribing square, the intersections of these perpendiculars will be centers for arcs tangent to two sides, Fig. 8.18*B*. Two of these intersections will evidently fall at the corners *A* and *C* of the isometric square, as the perpendiculars are altitudes of equilateral triangles. The construction of Fig. 8.18*B*

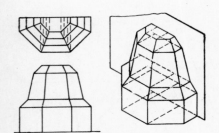

Fig. 8.14. Offset construction.

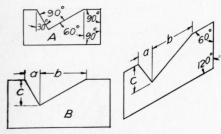

Fig. 8.15. Angles in isometric.

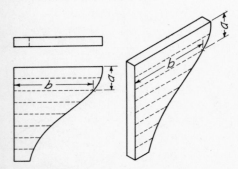

Fig. 8.16. Curves in isometric.

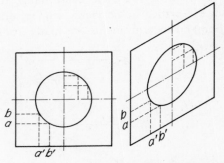

Fig. 8.17. Isometric circle, points plotted.

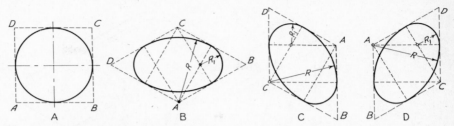

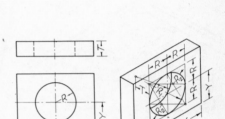

Fig. 8.18. Isometric circles, four-center approximation.

to D may thus be made by simply drawing 60° lines from the corners A and C and then drawing arcs with radii R and R_1, as shown.

Figure 8.19 shows the method of locating and laying out a hole in isometric from the given orthographic views. First locate and then draw the center lines for the hole by laying out the distances X and Y, as shown. Construct an isometric square on these lines with sides equal to the diameter of the hole by laying out the radius R in each direction from the intersection of these center lines. The four-center method is then used as shown in Fig. 8.18. Should the piece be thin enough, a portion of the back side of the hole will be visible. To determine this, drop the thickness T back on an isometric line and swing the large radius R_1 of the isometric circle with this point as a center. If the arc thus drawn comes within the boundary of the isometric circle, that portion of the back would be visible. In extra-thin pieces, portions of the small arcs R_2 might be visible. These would be determined in a similar manner.

If a true ellipse is plotted by the method of paragraph 8.11, in the same square as this four-center approximation, it will be a little longer and narrower and of much more pleasing shape, but in the great majority of drawings, the difference is not sufficient to warrant the extra expenditure of time required in execution.

The isometric drawing of a *sphere* is a circle with its diameter equal to the long axis of the ellipse inscribed in the isometric square of a great circle of the sphere. It would thus be 1.23/1.00 of the actual diameter (the isometric *projection* of a sphere would be a circle of the actual diameter of the sphere).

8.13. Isometric Circle Arcs. To draw any circle arc, the isometric square of its diameter should be drawn in the plane of its face, with as much of the four-center construction as is necessary to find centers for the part of the circle needed, as has been illustrated in Fig. 8.20.

Fig. 8.19. Locating and laying out a hole in isometric.

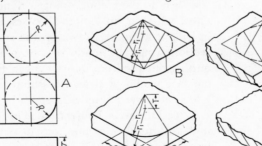

Fig. 8.20. Isometric quarter circles (approximate method).

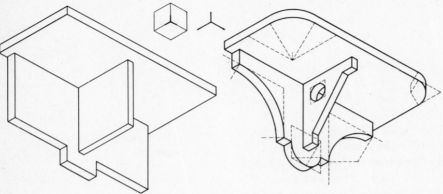

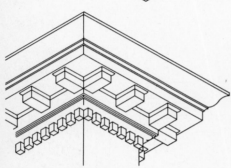

Fig. 8.21. Construction with reversed axes.

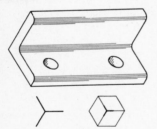

Fig. 8.22. An architectural detail on reversed axes.

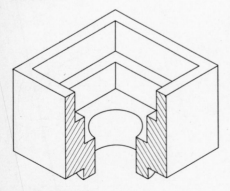

Fig. 8.23. Isometric with main axis horizontal.

Fig. 8.24. Isometric half section.

The arc occurring most frequently is the quarter circle. Note that in illustrations (*D*) and (*E*) only two construction lines are needed to find the center of a quarter circle in an isometric plane. Measure the true radius *R* of the circle from the corner on the two isometric lines as shown, and draw *actual* perpendiculars from these points. Their intersection will be the required center for radius R_1 or R_2 of the isometric quadrant. (*F*) illustrates the construction for the two vertical isometric planes.

8.14. Reversed Isometric. It is often desirable to show the lower face of an object by tilting it *back* instead of *forward*, thus reversing the usual position so as to show the underside. The construction is just the same, but the directions of the principal isometric planes must be kept clearly in mind. Figure 8.21 shows the reference cube and the position of the axes, as well as the application of reversed-isometric construction to circle arcs. A practical use of this construction is in the representation of such architectural features as are naturally viewed from below. Figure 8.22 is an example.

Sometimes a piece may be shown to better advantage with the main axis horizontal, as in Fig. 8.23.

8.15. Isometric Sections. Isometric drawings are, from their pictorial nature, usually outside views, but sometimes a sectional view may be employed to good advantage to show a detail of shape or interior construction. The cutting planes are taken as isometric planes, and the section lining is done in a direction to give the best effect which is, in almost all cases, in the direction of the long diagonal of a square drawn on the surface. As a general rule, a half section would be made by outlining the figure in full and then cutting out the front quarter, as in Fig. 8.24. For a full section, the cut face would be drawn first and the part of the object behind it added afterward (Fig. 8.25).

8.16. Dimetric Projection. The reference cube can be rotated into any number of positions in which two edges will be equally foreshortened, and the direction of axes and ratio of foreshortening for any one of these positions might be taken as a basis for a system of dimetric drawing. A simple dimetric position is one with the ratios 1 to 1 to ½. In this position, the tangents of the angles are ⅛ and ⅞, making the angles approximately 7° and 41°. Figure 8.26 shows a drawing in this system. Dimetric is seldom used because of the difficulty of drawing circles.

8.17. Trimetric Projection. Any position with three unequal axes would be called "trimetric." Although with some of these positions the effect of distortion might be lessened, the added time required makes trimetric drawing impractical, except when drawn by projection as explained in paragraph 8.26.

8.18. Oblique Projection. When the projectors make an angle other than 90° with the picture plane, the resulting projection is called "oblique projection." The name *cavalier projection* is given to that special and most used case of *oblique projection* in which the projectors make an angle of 45° with the plane of projection. It is often called by the general name *oblique projection*, or *oblique drawing*. The principle is as follows: Imagine a vertical plane with a rectangular block behind it, having its long edges parallel to the plane. Assume a system of parallel projecting lines in any direction making an angle of 45° with the picture plane (they could be parallel to any one of the elements of a 45° cone with its base in the picture plane). Then that face of the block which is parallel to the plane is projected in its true size, and the edges perpendicular to the plane are projected in their true length. Figure 8.27 illustrates this principle. The first panel shows the regular orthographic projection of a rectangular block with its front face in the frontal plane. An oblique projector from the back corner B is the hypotenuse of a 45° right triangle of which AB is one side and the projection of AB on the plane is the other side. When this triangle is horizontal, the projection on the plane will be AC. If the triangle is rotated about AB through any angle β, C will revolve to C' and $A_F C_F'$ will be the oblique projection of AB.

8.19. To Make an Oblique Drawing. Oblique drawing is similar to isometric drawing in having three axes, representing three mutually perpendicular edges, upon which measurements can be made. Two of the axes are always at right angles to each other, being in a

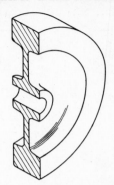

Fig. 8.25. Isometric full section.

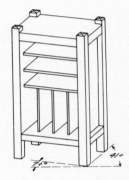

Fig. 8.26. Dimetric drawing.

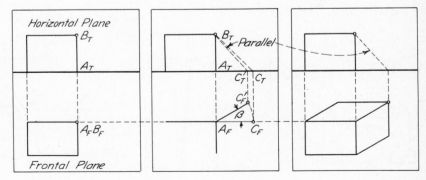

Fig. 8.27. Oblique projection.

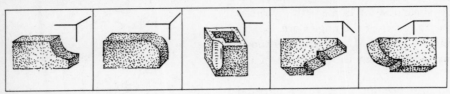

Fig. 8.28. Various positions of oblique axes.

plane parallel to the picture plane. The third, or depth, axis may be at any angle to the horizontal, 30° or 45° being generally used (Fig. 8.28). It is thus more flexible than isometric drawing. For a rectangular object, Fig. 8.29, start with a point representing a front corner (A) and draw from it the three oblique axes, one vertical, one horizontal, and one at an angle. On these three axes measure the height, width, and depth of the object. In this case, the width is made up of the 2½-in. distance and the 1⁵⁄₁₆-in. radius. Locate the center of the arc, and draw it as shown. When the hole in the figure is drawn, the center for the arc will be at the same point as the center

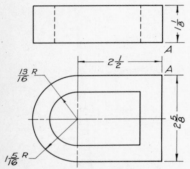

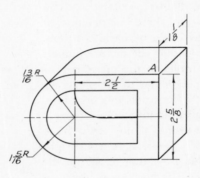

Fig. 8.29. Oblique drawing.

for the outside arc on the front face. The center for the rear arc of the hole will be 1⅛-in. rearward on a depth axis line through the front center.

8.20. Object Orientation for Oblique. Any face parallel to the picture plane will evidently be projected without distortion, an advantage over isometric of particular value in the representation of objects with circular or irregular outline.

The *first rule* for oblique projection is to *place the object with the irregular outline or contour parallel to the picture plane.* Note in Fig. 8.30 the distortion of (B) and (C) over that of (A).

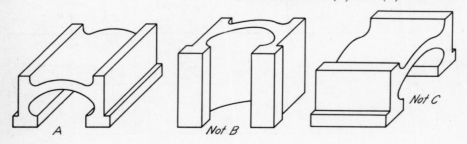

Fig. 8.30. Illustration of first rule.

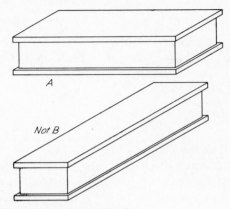

Fig. 8.31. Illustration of second rule.

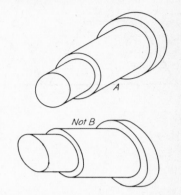

Fig. 8.32. Precedence of first rule.

One of the greatest disadvantages in the use of either isometric or oblique drawing is the effect of distortion produced by the lack of convergence in the receding lines—the violation of perspective. In some cases, particularly with large objects, this becomes so painful as practically to preclude the use of these methods. It is perhaps even more noticeable in oblique than in isometric and, of course, increases with the length of the depth dimension.

Hence the *second rule: preferably, the longest dimension should be parallel to the picture plane.* Figure 8.31*A* is preferable to (*B*).

In case of conflict between these two rules, *the first should always have precedence*, as the advantage of having the irregular face without distortion is greater than that gained by the second rule, as illustrated in Fig. 8.32. The first rule should be given precedence even with shapes that are not irregular if, in the draftsman's judgment, the distortion can be lessened, as in the example of Fig. 8.33, where (*B*) is perhaps preferable to (*A*).

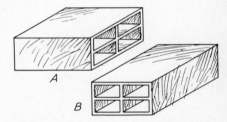

Fig. 8.33. Choice of position.

8.21. Starting Plane. It will be noted that, as long as the front of the object is in one plane parallel to the plane of projection, the front face of the oblique projection is exactly the same as the orthographic. When the front is made up of more than one plane, particular care must be exercised in preserving the relationship by selecting one of these planes as the starting plane and working from it. In such a piece as the link, Fig. 8.34, the front bosses may be

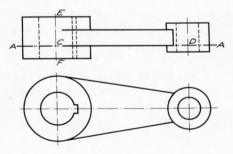

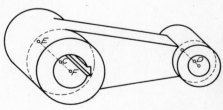

Fig. 8.34. Offsets from reference plane.

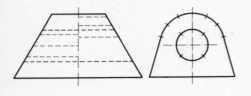

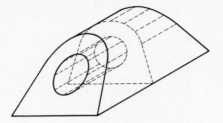

Fig. 8.35. Offsets from right section.

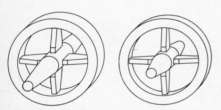

Fig. 8.36. Oblique circle construction.

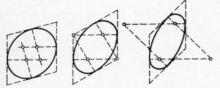

Fig. 8.37. Oblique and cabinet drawing compared.

imagined as cut off on the plane *A-A* and the front view, that is, the section on *A-A*, drawn as the front of the oblique projection. On depth axes through the centers *C* and *D*, the distances, for example, *CE* behind and *CF* in front of the plane *A-A*, may be laid off.

When an object has no face perpendicular to its base, it may be drawn in a similar way by cutting a right section and measuring offsets from it, as in Fig. 8.35. This offset method, previously illustrated in the isometric drawings of Figs. 8.13, 8.14, and 8.16, be found to be a most rapid and convenient way for drawing almost any figure, and it should be studied carefully.

8.22. Circles in Oblique. When it is necessary to draw circles that lie on oblique faces, they may be drawn as circle arcs, with the compasses, on the same principle as the four-center isometric approximation shown in Fig. 8.18. In isometric it happens that *two of the four intersections of the perpendiculars from the middle points* of the containing square fall at the corner of the square, and advantage is taken of the fact. In oblique, the position of the corresponding points depends on the angle of the depth axis. Figure 8.36 shows three squares in oblique positions at different angles and the construction of their inscribed circles.

8.23. Arcs in Oblique. Circle arcs representing rounded corners, etc., are drawn in oblique by the same method given for isometric arcs in paragraph 8.13. The only difference will be that the angle of the sides tangent to the arc will vary according to the angle of depth axis chosen.

8.24. Cabinet Drawing. This is that case of oblique projection in which the parallel projectors make with the picture plane an angle of such a value that distances measured parallel to the depth axis are reduced one-half that of cavalier projection. The appearance of excessive thickness that is so disagreeable in cavalier projection is entirely overcome in cabinet projection. The depth axis may be at any angle with the horizontal but is usually taken at either 30° or 45°. The comparative appearances of cavalier and cabinet drawing are illustrated in Fig. 8.37.

8.25. Other Forms. Cabinet drawing, explained above, is popular because of the easy ratio, but the effect is often too thin. Other oblique drawing ratios, such as 2 to 3 or 3 to 4, may be used with pleasing effect.

8.26. Axonometric Projection from Orthographic Views. In making pictorial drawings of complicated parts, especially whenever curves must be plotted, projection from orthographic views may give an advantage in speed and ease of drawing. Any position, isometric, dimetric, or trimetric, may be used.

The three axes of an axonometric drawing are *three mutually perpendicular edges* in space. If the angle of rotation and the angle of tilt of the object are known or decided upon, the three axes for the pictorial drawing and the location of the orthographic views for projection to the pictorial may easily be found. Figure 8.38 will illustrate the procedure. At (G) is shown the three orthographic views of a cube. The three mutually perpendicular edges OA, OB, and OC will be foreshortened differently when the cube is rotated in space for some axonometric position, but the ends of the axes A, B, and C will always lie on the surface of a sphere whose radius is $OA = OB = OC$, as illustrated by (G'). At any particular angle of tilt of

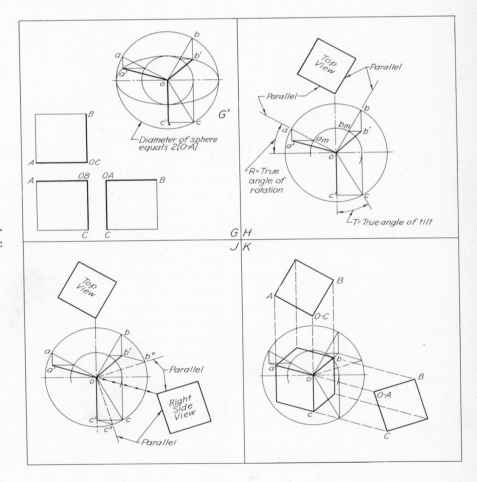

Fig. 8.38. Axonometric projection from orthographic views.

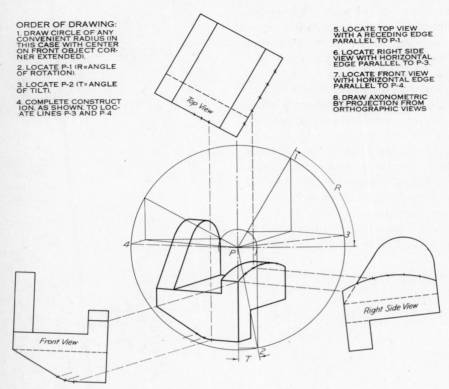

ORDER OF DRAWING:
1. DRAW CIRCLE OF ANY CONVENIENT RADIUS (IN THIS CASE WITH CENTER ON FRONT OBJECT CORNER EXTENDED).

2. LOCATE P-1 (R=ANGLE OF ROTATION).

3. LOCATE P-2 (T=ANGLE OF TILT).

4. COMPLETE CONSTRUCTION, AS SHOWN, TO LOCATE LINES P-3 AND P-4

5. LOCATE TOP VIEW WITH A RECEDING EDGE PARALLEL TO P-1.

6. LOCATE RIGHT SIDE VIEW WITH HORIZONTAL EDGE PARALLEL TO P-3.

7. LOCATE FRONT VIEW WITH HORIZONTAL EDGE PARALLEL TO P-4.

8. DRAW AXONOMETRIC BY PROJECTION FROM ORTHOGRAPHIC VIEWS

Fig. 8.39. An axonometric drawing by projection.

the cube, the axis ends A and B will describe an ellipse, as shown, if the cube is rotated about the axis OC. The axis OC will appear foreshortened at oc'. Thus for any particular position of the cube in space, representing some desired axonometric position, the axes may be located and their relative amounts of foreshortening found.

Moreover, if a face of the cube is rotated about a *frontal axis perpendicular to the axis which is at right angles to the face,* an orthographic view of the face, in projection with the axonometric view, will result. Thus, the top and right-side views may be located as at (J) and projected as at (K) to give the axonometric drawing.

The drawings at (H), (J), and (K) will illustrate the practical use of the theory of rotation just described. The actual size of the sphere is unimportant, as it is used only to establish the direction of the axes. First, the desired angle of rotation R and the angle of tilt T are decided upon and laid out as at (H). The minor diameter for the ellipse upon which A and B will lie is found by projecting vertically from c and drawing the circle as shown. A and B on the major-diameter circle of the ellipse will be at a and b; on the minor-diameter circle, they will be at a_m and b_m; and they are found in the axonometric position by projecting, as in the concentric-circle ellipse method, to a' and b'. The foreshortened position of C is found by projecting horizontally across from c to c'.

The top orthographic view of the cube (or object) will be parallel to *oa* and *ob*, and projection from the orthographic view to the axonometric will be vertical (parallel to *aa'* and *bb'*).

Projection from an orthographic right-side view would be as shown at (*J*). The right side of the cube, containing axes *OC* and *OB*, is found by projecting from *b'* and *c'*, parallel to *oa'*, to locate *b''* and *c''* on the circle representing the sphere. The sides of the cube (or object) are parallel to *ob''* and *oc''*, as shown at (*J*). Projection from the right-side view to the axonometric view is in the direction of *oa'*, as indicated.

The axonometric drawing is shown projected at (*K*). The dashed lines indicate the actual projectors, and the light solid lines and circles show the necessary construction just described.

One advantage of this method is that the angle of rotation and tilt can be decided upon so that the object may be shown in the best position. Figure 8.39 is an example of an axonometric drawing made by projection. The curved faces are plotted by projecting points as shown.

8.27. Isometric Projection from Orthographic Views. Isometric is, of course, a special case of axonometric projection in which all three axes are foreshortened equally. The work of finding the axes for isometric projection from orthographic views is reduced if the views are located by angle, as illustrated in Fig. 8.40.

8.28. Oblique Projection from Orthographic Views. In oblique projection, the projectors make some oblique angle with the picture plane. The actual angle of the projectors (with horizontal and frontal planes) is not critical, and a variety of angles may be used. The making of an oblique drawing by projection from the views is very simple, as illustrated by Fig. 8.41. The picture plane is located, and one face of the object is made coincident with the

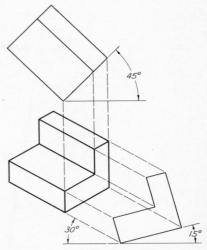

Fig. 8.40. Isometric by projection.

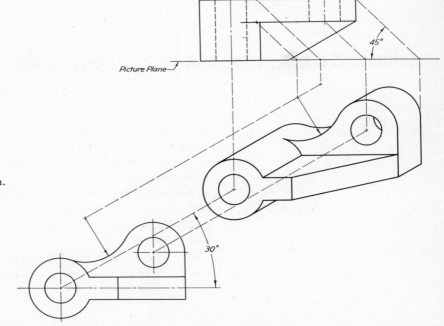

Fig. 8.41. Oblique by projection.

picture plane. The front view is located at a convenient place on the paper, as shown. The angle of the projectors in the top view may be assumed (in this case 45°) and projections made to the picture plane as shown. The angle of the projectors in the front view may be then assumed (in this case 30°). Projection from the front view at the assumed angle and vertically from the picture plane, as shown, will locate the necessary lines and points for the oblique view.

Reversed axes may be obtained by projecting downward from the front view. An axis to the left may be had by changing the direction of the projectors in the top view. Any desired oblique axes may be had by altering the angles (top and front) for the projectors.

8.29. Perspective Drawing. Perspective drawing is the representation of an object as it appears to an observer stationed at a particular position relative to it. Geometrically, it is the figure resulting when visual rays from the eye to the object are cut by a picture plane. There is a difference between "artists' perspective" and "geometrical perspective" in that the artist draws the object as he sees it before him or as he visualizes it through his creative imagination, while geometrical perspective is projected mechanically on a plane from views or measurements of the object represented. Projected geometrical perspective is, theoretically, very similar to the optical system in photography.

In a technical way, perspective is used more in architecture and in illustration than in other branches, but every engineer will find it of advantage to know the principles of the subject.

8.30. Fundamental Concepts. Let one imagine himself standing on the sidewalk of a city street, as in Fig. 8.42, with the picture plane erected between him and the street scene ahead. Visual rays from the observer's eye to the ends of the lamppost A intercept a distance

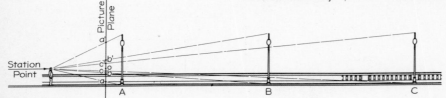

Fig. 8.42. The observer and the picture plane.

aa' on the picture plane. Similarly, rays from post B intercept bb', a smaller distance than aa'. This apparent diminution in the size of like objects as the distance from the objects to the eye increases agrees with our everyday experience and is the keynote of perspective drawing. It is evident from the figure that succeeding lampposts will intercept shorter distances on the picture plane than the preceding ones, and that a post at infinity would show only as a point o at the level of the observer's eye.

In Fig. 8.43, the plane of the paper is the picture plane, and the intercepts aa', bb', etc., show as the heights of their respective lamp-

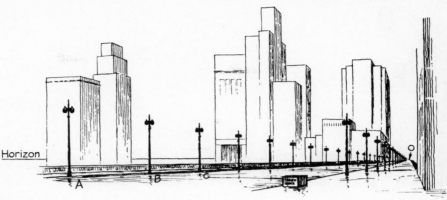

Fig. 8.43. The perspective drawing.

posts as they diminish in their projected size and finally disappear on the horizon. In a similar way the curbings and balustrade appear to converge at the same point O. Thus a system of parallel horizontal lines will vanish at a single point on the horizon, and all horizontal planes will vanish on the horizon. Verticals such as the lampposts and the edges of the buildings, being parallel to the picture plane, pierce the picture plane at an infinite distance and therefore show as vertical lines in the picture.

8.31. Definitions and Nomenclature. Figure 8.44 illustrates perspective theory and names the points, lines, and planes used. An observer in viewing an object selects his *station point* and thereby determines the *horizon plane* as the horizontal plane at eye level. This horizon plane is normally above the horizontal *ground plane* upon which the object is assumed to rest. The *picture plane* is usually located between the station point and the object being viewed and is ordinarily a vertical plane perpendicular to the horizontal projection of the line of sight to the object's center of interest. The *horizon line* is the intersection of the horizon plane and picture plane, and the *ground line* is the intersection of the ground plane and picture plane. The *axis of vision* is the line through the station point that is per-

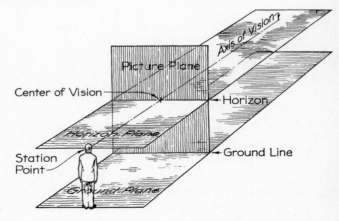

Fig. 8.44. Perspective nomenclature.

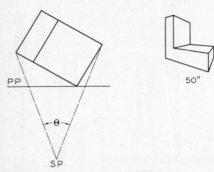

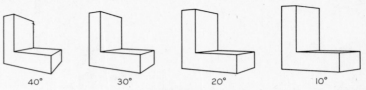

Fig. 8.46. Comparative lateral angles of view.

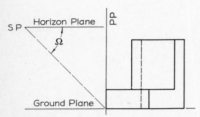

Fig. 8.45. Lateral angle of view.

Fig. 8.47. Elevation angle of view.

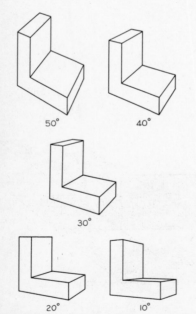

pendicular to the picture plane. The piercing point of the axis of vision with the picture plane is the *center of vision.*

8.32. Selection of the Station Point. Care must be exercised in selecting the station point, for an indiscriminate choice may result in a distorted drawing. If the station point is placed to one side of the drawing, the same effect is had as when a theater screen is viewed from a position close to the front and well off to one side; heights are seen properly but not horizontal distances. Therefore, the *center of vision should be somewhere near the picture's center of interest.*

Wide angles of view will result in a violent convergence of horizontal lines and so should be avoided. The angle of view is the included angle θ between the widest visual rays, Fig. 8.45. Figure 8.46 shows the difference in perspective foreshortening for different lateral angles of view. In general, an angle of about 20° will give the most natural picture.

The station point should be located where the object will be seen to best advantage, and for this reason, on large objects such as buildings, etc., the station point is usually taken at a normal standing height of about 5 ft above the ground plane. For small objects, however, the best representation demands that the top, as well as the lateral surfaces, be seen, and the station point must be elevated accordingly. Figure 8.47 shows the angle of elevation Ω between the horizon plane and the extreme visual ray. By contrasting several different angles of elevation (Ω), Fig. 8.48 shows the effect of elevation of the station point. In general, the best picturization is had at an angle of about 20° to 30°.

Fig. 8.48. Comparative elevation angles of view.

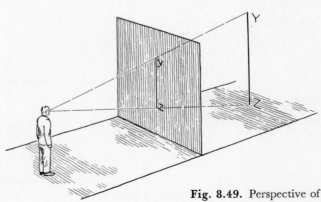

Fig. 8.49. Perspective of a line.

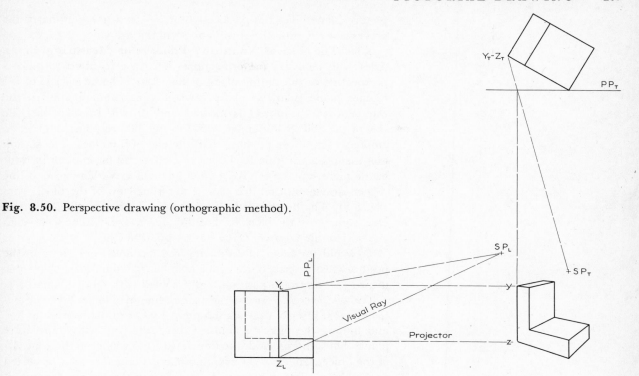

Fig. 8.50. Perspective drawing (orthographic method).

It may be established, therefore, that *the visual rays to the object should be kept within a right-circular cone whose elements make an angle of not more than 15° with the cone axis.*

In choosing the station point, its position should always be offset to one side and also offset vertically from the exact middle of the object, or a rather stiff and awkward perspective will result. Similarly, in locating the object with reference to the picture plane, the faces should not make identical angles with the picture plane, or the same stiffness will appear.

8.33. To Draw a Perspective. Perspective projection is based on the theory that visual rays from the object to the eye pierce the picture plane, and form an image of the object on the plane. Thus in Fig. 8.49, the image of line YZ is formed by the piercing points y and z of the rays. Several projective methods may be used. The simplest method, basically, but the most laborious to draw is illustrated by the purely orthographic method of Fig. 8.50, in which the top and side views are drawn in orthographic. The picture plane (edge view) and the station point are located in each view. Assuming that the line YZ of Fig. 8.49 is one edge of the L-shaped block of Fig. 8.50, visual rays from Y and Z will intersect the picture plane in the top view, thus locating the perspective of the points laterally. Similarly, the intersections of the rays in the side view give the perspective heights of Y and Z. Projection from the top and side views of the

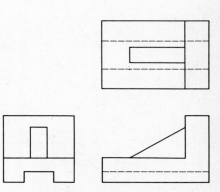

Fig. 8.51. Sliding block.

picture plane gives the perspective of *YZ*, and a repetition of the process for the other lines will complete the drawing.

8.34. The Use of Vanishing Points and Measuring Lines. These will facilitate the projections. Let it be required to make a perspective of the sliding block of Fig. 8.51. The edge view of the picture plane (plan view) is drawn, Fig. 8.52, and behind it the top view of the object is located and drawn. In this case, one side of the object is oriented at 30° to the picture plane in order to emphasize the L shape more than the end of the block. The station point is located a little to the left of center and far enough in front of the picture plane to give a good angle of view. The ground line is then drawn, and on it is placed the front view of the block from Fig. 8.51. The height of the station point is then decided—in this case, well above the block so that the top surfaces will be seen—and the horizon line drawn at the station-point height.

To avoid the labor of redrawing the top and front views in the positions just described, the views may be cut from the orthographic drawing, oriented in position, and fastened with tacks or tape.

The *vanishing point* for any horizontal line may be found by drawing a visual ray from the station point *parallel* to the horizontal line and finding the piercing point of this visual ray with the picture plane. Thus, in Fig. 8.52, the line *SP* to *R* is parallel to the edge *AB* of the object, and *R* is the piercing point. Point *R* is then projected to the horizon line, locating *VR*, the vanishing point for *AB* and all edges parallel to *AB*. The vanishing point *VL* for *AC* and edges parallel to *AC* is found similarly, as shown.

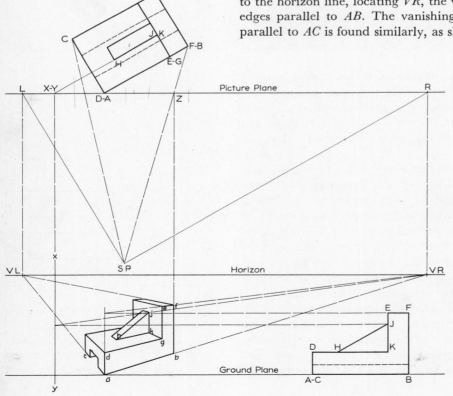

Fig. 8.52. Use of vanishing points and measuring lines.

In visualizing the location of a vanishing point, imagine that the edge, for example, *AB*, is moved to the right along the ground, still making the same angle with the picture plane; the intercept of *AB* will become less and less until, when *A* is in coincidence with *R*, the intercept will be zero. *R* then must be the top view of the vanishing point for all lines parallel to *AB*.

Point *A* lies in both the picture plane and the ground plane and will therefore be shown in the perspective at *a*, on the ground line, and in direct projection with the top view. The perspective of *AB* is determined by drawing a line from *a* to *VR* (the perspective *direction* of *AB*) and then projecting the intercept *Z* (of the visual rays *SP* to *B*) to the line, thus locating *b*.

All lines behind the picture plane are foreshortened in the picture, and only those lying in the picture plane will appear in their true length. For this reason, *all measurements must be made in the picture plane*. Since *AD* is in the picture plane, it will show in its actual height as *ad*.

A *measuring line* will be needed for any verticals such as *BF* that do not lie in the picture plane. If a vertical is brought forward to the picture plane along some established line, the true height can be measured in the picture plane. If, in Fig. 8.52, *BF* is imagined as moved forward along *ab* until *b* is in coincidence with *a*, the true height can be measured vertically from *a*. This vertical line at *a* is then the measuring line for all heights in the vertical plane containing *a* and *b*. The height of *f* is measured from *a*, and from this height point, a vanishing line is drawn to *VR*; then from *Z* (the piercing point in the picture plane of the visual ray to *F*), *f* may be projected to the perspective.

The measuring line may also be thought of as the intersection of the picture plane with a vertical plane that contains the distance to be found. Thus *ad*, extended, is the measuring line for all heights in surface *ABFEGD*. The triangular rib of Fig. 8.52 is located by continuing surface *HJK* until it intersects the picture plane at *XY*, thereby establishing *xy* as the measuring line for all heights in *HJK*. In the figure, the height of *J* is measured on the measuring line *xy*, and *j* is found as described for *f*.

Note that heights can either be measured with a scale on the measuring line or they can be projected from the front view, as indicated in Fig. 8.52.

Summary

1. Draw the top view (edge of the picture plane).
2. Orient the object relative to the picture plane so that the object will appear to advantage, and draw the top view of the object.
3. Select a station point that will best show the shape of the object.
4. Draw the horizon and ground line.
5. Find the top view of the vanishing points for the principal hori-

zontal edges by drawing lines parallel to the edges, through the station point, and to the picture plane.

6. Project from the top views of the vanishing points to the horizon line, thus locating the vanishing points for the perspective.

7. Draw the visual rays from the station point to the corners of the object in the top view, locating the piercing point of each ray with the picture plane.

8. Start the picture, building from the ground up and from the nearest corner to the more distant ones.

8.35. Planes Parallel to the Picture Plane. Objects having circles or other curves in a vertical plane may be oriented with their curved faces parallel to the picture plane. The curves will then appear in true shape. This method, often called "parallel perspective," is also suitable for interiors and for street vistas and similar scenes where considerable depth is to be represented.

The object of Fig. 8.53 has been placed so that the planes containing the circular contours are parallel to the picture plane. The

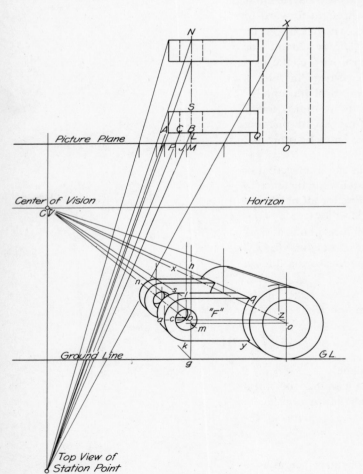

Fig. 8.53. Planes parallel to the picture plane (parallel perspective).

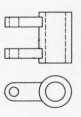

horizontal edges parallel to the picture plane will appear horizontal in the picture and will have no vanishing point. Horizontals perpendicular to the picture plane are parallel to the axis of vision and will vanish at the center of vision *CV*. Except for architectural interiors, the station point is usually located above the object and either to the right or left, yet not so far in any direction as to cause unpleasant distortion. For convenience, one face of the object is usually placed in the picture plane and is therefore not reduced in size in the perspective.

In Fig. 8.53, the end of the hub is in the picture plane; thus the center *o* is projected from *O* in the top view, and the circular edges are drawn in their true size. The center line *ox* is vanished from *o* to *CV*. To find the perspective of center line *MN*, a vertical plane is passed through *MN* intersecting the picture plane in measuring line *gh*. A horizontal line from *o* intersecting *gh* locates *m*, and *m* vanished to *CV* is the required line.

By using the two center lines from *o* and *m* as a framework, the remaining construction is simplified. A ray from the station point to *B* pierces the picture plane at *J*, which, projected to *mn*, locates *b*. The horizontal line *bz* is the center line of the front face of the nearer arm, and the intercept *IJ* gives the perspective radius *ab*. The circular hole having a radius *CB* has an intercept *PJ*, giving *cb* as the perspective radius. The arc *qy* has its center on *ox* at *z*. On drawing the tangents *lq* and *ky*, the face "*F*" is completed.

The remaining construction for the arms is exactly the same as that for "*F*." The centers are moved back on the center lines, and the radii are found from their corresponding intercepts on the picture plane.

8.36. Circles in Perspective. The perspective of a circle is a circle only when its plane is parallel to the picture plane; the circle appears as a straight line when its plane is receding from the station point. In all other positions the circle projects as an ellipse whose major and minor diameters are not readily determinable. The major diameter of the ellipse will be at some odd angle except when a vertical circle has its center on the horizon plane; then the major diameter will be vertical. Also, when a horizontal circle has its center directly above, below, or on the center of vision, the major diameter will be horizontal. It should be noted that in all cases the center of the circle is not coincident with the center of the ellipse representing the circle and that concentric circles are not represented by concentric ellipses. The major and minor diameters of the ellipses for concentric circles are not even parallel except in special cases.

The perspective of a circle may be plotted point by point, but the most rapid solution is had by enclosing the circle in a square, as shown in Fig. 8.54, and plotting points at the tangent points and at the intersections of the diagonals. The eight points thus determined are usually sufficient to give an accurate curve. The square, with its diagonals, is first drawn in the perspective. From the intersection

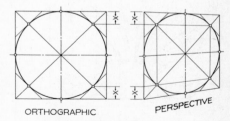

ORTHOGRAPHIC   PERSPECTIVE

Fig. 8.54. Perspective of a circle.

of the diagonals, the vertical and horizontal center lines of the circle are established; where these center lines cross the sides of the square are four points on the curve. In the orthographic view, the measurement X is made, then laid out *in the picture plane* and vanished, crossing the diagonals at four additional points.

It must be realized that the curve is tangent to the lines enclosing it and that the *direction* of the curve is established by these tangent lines; if the lines completing the circumscribing octagon are projected and drawn, the direction of the curve is established at eight points.

8.37. Graticulation. The perspectives of irregular curves may be had by projecting a sufficient number of points to establish the curve, but if the curve is complicated, the method of graticulation may be used to advantage. A square grid is overlaid on the orthographic view as shown in Fig. 8.55; then the grid is drawn in perspective and the outlines of the curve transferred by inspection from the orthographic view.

8.38. Measuring Points. It has been shown that all lines lying in the picture plane will be their own perspectives and may be scaled directly on the perspective drawing. The adaptation of this principle has an advantage in laying off a series of measurements, such as a row of pilasters, because it avoids a confusion of intercepts on the picture plane and the inaccuracies due to long projection lines.

In the measuring-points method, a surface, such as the wall between A and B of Fig. 8.56, is rotated into the picture plane for the purpose of making measurements, as shown at AB'. While in the picture plane, the entire surface can be laid out directly to the same scale as the top view; therefore, ab' and other horizontal dimensions of the surface are established along the ground line as shown. The counterrotation of the wall to its actual position on the building and the necessary projections in the perspective are based on the principle that the rotation has been made about a vertical axis and that any point has traveled in a horizontal plane. By drawing, as

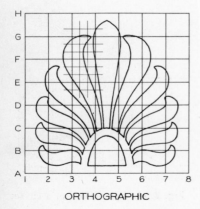

ORTHOGRAPHIC

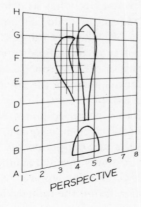

PERSPECTIVE

Fig. 8.55. Graticulation.

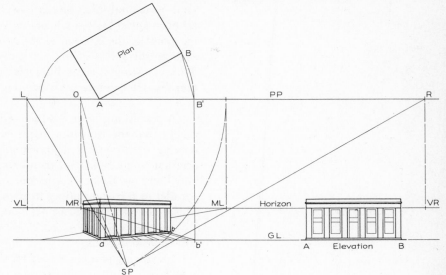

Fig. 8.56. Use of measuring points.

usual, a line parallel to BB', from the station point to the picture plane, and then projecting to the horizon, the vanishing point MR is found. This vanishing point is termed a *measuring point* and may be defined as the vanishing point for lines joining corresponding points of the actual and rotated positions of the face considered. The divisions on ab' are therefore vanished to MR; where this construction intersects ab (the perspective of AB), the lateral position of the pilasters, in the perspective, is determined. Heights are scaled on the vertical edge through a, as this edge lies in the picture plane. The perspective of the wall between A and B is completed by the regular methods previously described. For work on the end of the building, the end wall is rotated as indicated, measuring point ML is found, and the projections are continued as described for the front wall.

Measuring points may be more readily located if the draftsman will recognize that the triangles ABB' and $R\,O\,SP$ are similar. Therefore, a measuring point is as far from its corresponding vanishing point as the station point is from the picture plane, measuring the latter parallel to the face concerned. MR can then be found by measuring the distance from the station point to R and laying off RO equal to the measurement or by swinging an arc, with R as center, from the station point to O, as shown. The measuring point MR is then projected from O.

8.39. Inclined Lines. Any line neither parallel nor perpendicular to either the picture plane or the horizon plane is termed an inclined line. Any line may have a vertical plane passed through it, and if the vanishing line of the plane is found, a line in the plane will vanish at some point on the vanishing line of the plane. Vertical planes will vanish on vertical lines, just as horizontal planes vanish on a horizontal line, the horizon. In Fig. 8.57, the points *a* to *e* have all been found by regular methods previously described. The vanishing point of the horizontal *ab* is *VR*. The vertical line through *VR* is the vanishing line of the plane of *abc* and all planes *parallel to abc*. This vanishing line is intersected by the extension of *de* at *UR*, thereby determining the vanishing point for *de* and all edges *parallel to de*.

The vanishing point for inclined lines may also be located on the theory that the vanishing point for any line may be determined by moving the line until it appears as a point, while still retaining its original angle with the picture plane. The vanishing point of *de* may therefore be located by drawing a line through the station point parallel to *DE* and finding its piercing point with the picture plane. This is done by laying out *SP T* at the angle β to *SP R* and erecting *RT* perpendicular to *SP R*. Then *RT* is the height of the vanishing point *UR* above *VR*.

If measuring points are used for the initial work on the perspective, it will be an advantage to recognize which one of the measuring points was used for determining horizontal measurements in the parallel vertical planes containing the inclined lines; at that measuring point, the angle β is laid out, either above or below the horizon depending upon whether the lines slope up or down as they go into the distance. Where this construction intersects the vanishing line for the vertical planes containing the inclined lines, the vanishing point is located.

8.40. Inclined Planes. An inclined plane is any plane neither parallel nor perpendicular to either the picture plane or the horizon plane. The vanishing line for an inclined plane may be found by

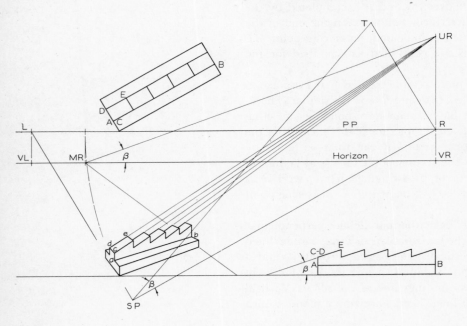

Fig. 8.57. Vanishing point of inclined lines.

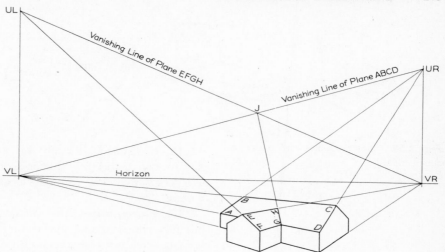

Fig. 8.58. Vanishing lines of inclined planes and vanishing point for the intersection of two inclined planes.

locating the vanishing points for any two systems of parallel lines in the inclined plane. For determining the vanishing line of plane *ABCD* of Fig. 8.58, the vanishing point *VL* of the horizontal edges *AD* and *BC* is one point, and the vanishing point *UR* for the inclined edges *AB* and *DC* gives a second point on the vanishing line *VL UR* for plane *ABCD*.

It is often necessary to draw the line of intersection of two inclined planes. The intersection will vanish at the point of intersection of the vanishing lines of both planes. The intersection *J* of the two vanishing lines of the roof planes of Fig. 8.58 is the vanishing point of the line of intersection of the two planes.

8.41. Pictorial Sketching. The necessity that the engineer be trained in freehand sketching was emphasized in Chap. 5. What was said there, however, referred particularly to sketching in orthographic projection; now let it be remarked that, before the engineer can be said to be adequately equipped to use the graphic language, he must possess the ability to sketch *pictorially* with skill and facility.

In designing and inventing, the first ideas come into the mind in pictorial form, and preliminary sketches made in this form preserve the ideas as visualized. From this record, the preliminary orthographic design sketches are made. A pictorial sketch of an object or of some detail of construction can often be used to explain it when the orthographic projection cannot be read intelligently by a client or a workman. If a working drawing is difficult to understand, one of the best ways of reading it is to start a pictorial sketch of it. Usually before the sketch is finished, the orthographic drawing is perfectly clear. Often again, a pictorial sketch may be made more quickly and may serve as a better record than would orthographic views of the same piece. The young engineer should not be deterred by any fancied lack of "artistic ability." An engineer's sketch is a record of information, not a work of art. The one requirement for both is *good proportion.*

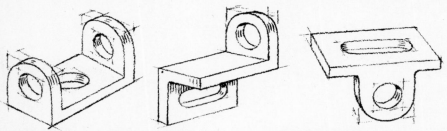

Fig. 8.59. Choice of axes and basic construction.

8.42. Methods. Although not a complete classification, there may be said to be three pictorial methods: axonometric, oblique, and perspective. The mechanical construction has been explained in detail.

8.43. Prerequisites. At the outset, it should be clearly understood that pictorial sketching means the making of a pictorial drawing *freehand*. The same construction for locating points and lines and for drawing circles and arcs with instruments will be used in pictorial sketching. From this standpoint, a knowledge of the constructions given previously is necessary before pictorial sketching is attempted. Note in Fig. 8.59 that the ellipses representing holes and rounded

Fig. 8.60. Ellipse method of establishing axes.

contours have been "boxed in" first with construction lines representing the enclosing square in exactly the same manner as for an instrument drawing.

8.44. Materials and Technique. The same materials, pencil grades, etc., used for orthographic freehand drawing, described in Chap. 5, are employed for pictorial sketching. Also, the directions given there for drawing straight lines, circles, and arcs will apply.

8.45. Axonometric Sketching: Choice and Direction of Axes. After a clear visualization, the first step in the procedure is to select

Fig. 8.61. Relationship of major and minor diameters of ellipse to the central axis.

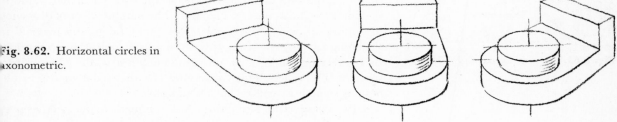

Fig. 8.62. Horizontal circles in axonometric.

the best position from which to view the object and thus determine the direction of the axes. It will be remembered that there are an infinite number of positions for the three axes that represent three mutually perpendicular lines and that the simplest is the isometric position. Sketches may be made on isometric axes, but unless it is important to show some feature on the top, a much better effect is gained and the distortion greatly lessened by drawing the depth axes at a much smaller angle with the horizontal (Fig. 8.59). Since measurements are not made on sketches, the axes may be foreshortened until the proportion is satisfactory to the eye; moreover, the effect of distortion may be overcome still further by slightly converging the receding lines. Objects of rectangular outline are best adapted to sketching in axonometric projection. Figures 8.59, 8.62, and 8.64 show examples of pictorial sketches.

8.46. Ellipse Method of Establishing Axes. A successful method of establishing the direction of the two horizontal axes for cylindrical objects (but adaptable for other shapes) is to sketch first a horizontal ellipse (with a little practice this can be done with a free sweep of the arm), Fig. 8.60. At some point, as *A*, draw a tangent. Through *A* and the center of the ellipse, draw one of a pair of conjugate diameters of the ellipse; at the other end of this diameter, draw a second tangent parallel to the first. Complete the axonometric square by drawing the other two sides parallel to the diameter. Then add the vertical axis and necessary edges parallel to it, as in Fig. 8.60.

8.47. Axonometric Circles. A circle in pictorial drawing is always an ellipse whose major diameter is at right angles to the shaft, or rotation axis, of the circle. Thus its minor diameter coincides on the drawing with the picture of the shaft axis, Fig. 8.61.

Note particularly that by the above rule *all* circles on horizontal planes are drawn as ellipses *with the major diameter horizontal* (Fig. 8.62).

In almost every case, it is best to draw the enclosing square for the ellipse as indicated in Fig. 8.63. By this method, the size of the ellipse and the thickness of the cylindrical portion represented are easily judged. Note in Fig. 8.63 that the center lines, or "rotation axes," of the cylindrical features and the directions for the major diameters of the ellipses are drawn as an aid in sketching the curves. Figure 8.64 shows the ellipses and the sketch completed.

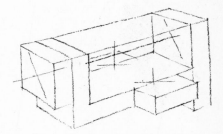

Fig. 8.63. Blocking in a sketch.

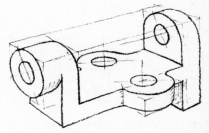

Fig. 8.64. Completing a sketch.

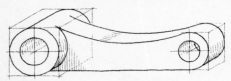

Fig. 8.65. An oblique sketch.

Fig. 8.66. Method of estimating proportion.

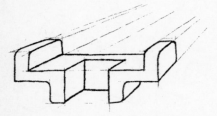

Fig. 8.67. A perspective sketch (one plane parallel to the picture plane).

8.48. Oblique Sketching. The advantage of oblique projection in preserving one face without distortion is of particular value in sketching, as illustrated by Fig. 8.65. The painful effect of distortion in oblique drawing done mechanically may be greatly lessened in sketching by foreshortening the depth axis to a pleasing proportion. By converging the lines parallel to the depth axis, the effect of perspective is obtained. This converging in either axonometric or oblique is sometimes called "fake perspective."

8.49. Perspective Sketching. A sketch made in perspective gives a better effect than either axonometric or oblique. For constructing a perspective drawing of a proposed structure from its plans and elevations, a knowledge of the principles of perspective drawing is required, but for making a perspective sketch from the object, one may get along by observing the ordinary phenomena of perspective which affect everything we see: the fact that objects appear proportionately smaller as their distance from the eye increases, that parallel lines appear to converge as they recede, and that horizontal lines and planes appear to "vanish" on the horizon.

In perspective sketching from the model, the drawing is made simply by observation, the directions and proportionate lengths of lines being estimated by sighting and measuring on the pencil held at arm's length, one's knowledge of perspective phenomena being used as a check. With the drawing board or sketch pad held in a comfortable drawing position perpendicular to the line of sight from the eye to the object, the direction of a line is tested by holding the pencil at arm's length parallel to the board, rotating the arm until the pencil appears to coincide with the line on the model, and then moving it parallel to this position back to the board. The apparent lengths of lines are estimated in the same way; holding the pencil in a plane perpendicular to the line of sight, one marks with the thumb the length of pencil which covers the line of the model, rotates the arm with the thumb held in position until the pencil coincides with another line, and then estimates the proportion of this measurement to the second line (Fig. 8.66).

The sketch should be made lightly, with free sketchy lines, and no lines should be erased until the whole sketch has been blocked in. *Do not make the mistake of getting the sketch too small.*

In starting a sketch from the object, set it in a position to give the most advantageous view, and sketch the directions of the principal lines, running them past the limits of the figure toward their vanishing points. Block in the enclosing squares for all circles and circle arcs and proceed with the figure, drawing the main outlines first and adding details later; then brighten the sketch with heavier lines. A good draftsman often adds a few touches of surface shading, but the beginner should be cautious in attempting it. Figure 8.67 shows the general appearance of a "one-point" perspective sketch before the construction lines have been erased. Figure 8.68 is an example showing the object turned at an angle to the picture plane.

8.50. Order of Sketching. Because of the variety of objects that will require representation, the order of procedure will not always be the same. The following, however, will serve as a guide:

1. Visualize the object's shape and proportions from the orthographic views, a model, or other source.

2. Mentally picture the object in space, and decide the pictorial position that will best describe its shape.

3. Decide on what type of pictorial to use (axonometric, oblique, or perspective).

4. Pick a suitable paper size.

5. Sketch suitable axes for the type of pictorial to be used, and lightly block in the enclosing "box" or "boxes" for the part.

6. Sketch in the construction for details, as illustrated by Figs. 8.59, 8.63, 8.65, and 8.68, starting with the most dominant and progressing to the subordinate, being careful the while to preserve the proportions and relationships of the various features. Draw the enclosing parallelogram for ellipses, representing cylindrical features, and use other construction as needed.

7. Complete the details, as in Fig. 8.64, by sketching them directly to the final weight desired. Complicated features, however, may be sketched lightly and, when satisfactory to the eye, then heavied. Do not use any hidden lines unless necessary for the description of the piece.

8. Check the sketch for errors of shape or proportion, and correct if necessary.

9. Remove any construction that may be objectionable or that may confuse the representation.

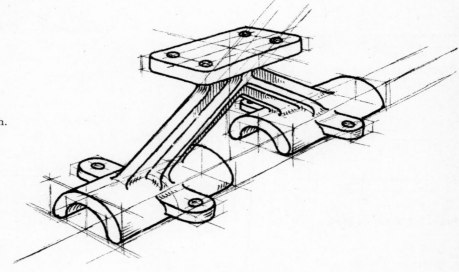

Fig. 8.68. A perspective sketch.

PROBLEMS

The following problems are intended to serve two purposes: (1) furnish practice in the various methods of pictorial representation and (2) furnish practice in reading and translating orthographic projections.

In reading a drawing remember that a line on any view always means an edge or a change in direction of the surface of the object and that one must always look at another view to interpret the meaning of the line.

Group 1. Isometric drawings

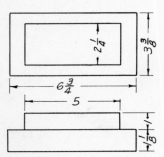

Prob. 8.1.1. Jig block.

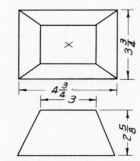

Prob. 8.1.2. Frustum of pyramid.

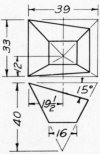

Prob. 8.1.3. Hopper.

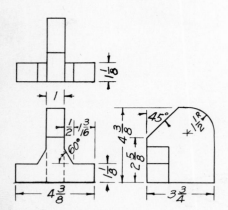

Prob. 8.1.4. Stop block.

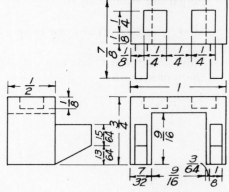

Prob. 8.1.5. Skid mount.

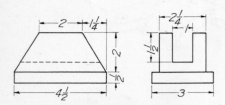

Prob. 8.1.6. Guide block.

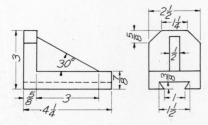

Prob. 8.1.7. Dovetail stop.

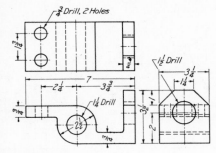

Prob. 8.1.8. Bracket.

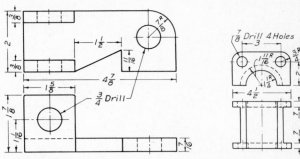

Prob. 8.1.9. Hinged catch.   **Prob. 8.1.10.** Bearing.

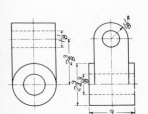

Prob. 8.1.11. Cross link.

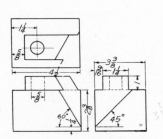

Prob. 8.1.12. Wedge block.

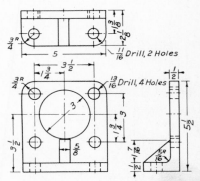

Prob. 8.1.13. Head attachment.

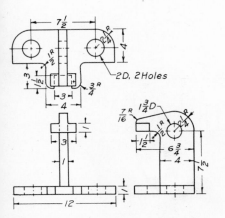

Prob. 8.1.14. Slide stop.

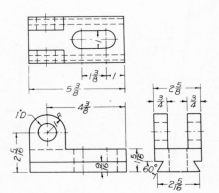

Prob. 8.1.15. Dovetail bracket.

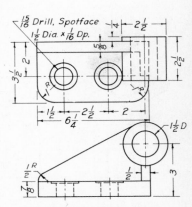

Prob. 8.1.16. Offset bracket.

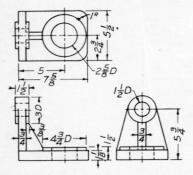

Prob. 8.1.17. Cradle bracket.

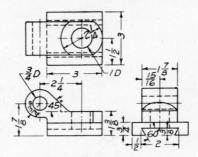

Prob. 8.1.18. Dovetail hinge.

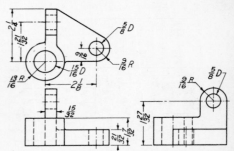

Prob. 8.1.19. Cable clip.

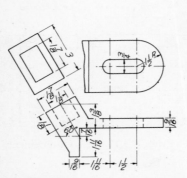

Prob. 8.1.20. Strut anchor.

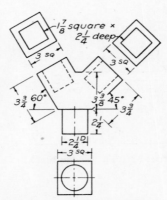

Prob. 8.1.21. Strut swivel.

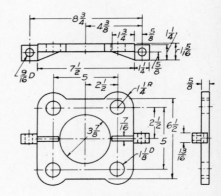

Prob. 8.1.22. Tie plate.

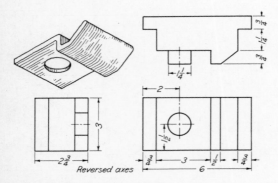

Prob. 8.1.23. Forming punch.

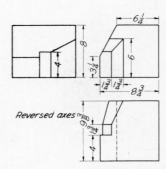

Prob. 8.1.24. Springing stone.

Group 2. Isometric sections

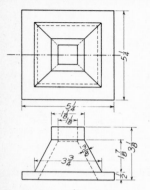

Prob. 8.2.1. Column base.

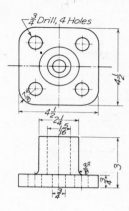

Prob. 8.2.2. Base plate.

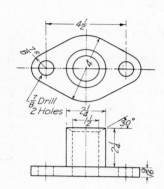

Prob. 8.2.3. Gland.

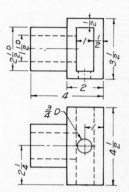

Prob. 8.2.4. Squared collar.

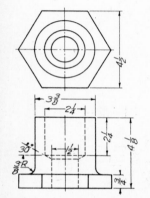

Prob. 8.2.5. Blank for gland.

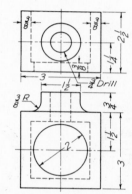

Prob. 8.2.6. Sliding cover.

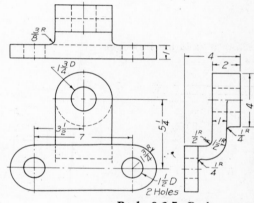

Prob. 8.2.7. Rod support.

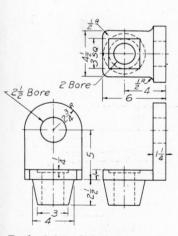

Prob. 8.2.8. Side-beam bracket.

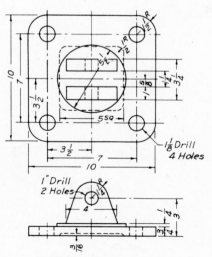

Prob. 8.2.9. Head yoke.

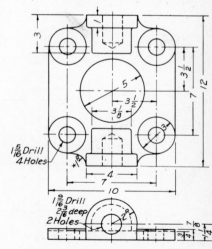

Prob. 8.2.10. Trunnion plate.

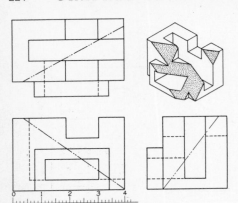

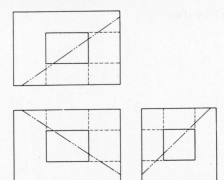

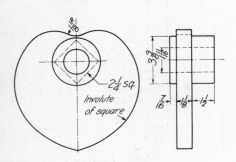

Prob. 8.2.11. Section study.

Prob. 8.2.12. Section study.

Group 3. Oblique drawings

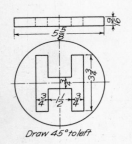

Prob. 8.3.1. Letter die.

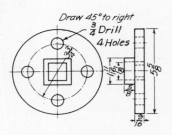

Prob. 8.3.2. Guide plate.

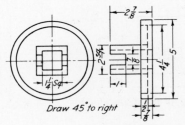

Prob. 8.3.3. Brace base.

Prob. 8.3.4. Heart cam.

Prob. 8.3.5. Ratchet wheel.

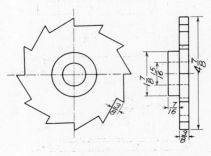

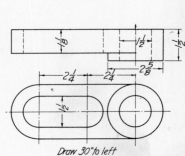

Prob. 8.3.6. Slotted link.

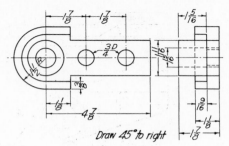

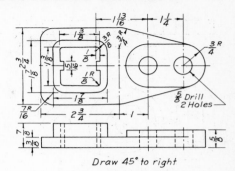

Prob. 8.3.7. Swivel plate.

Draw 45° to right

Prob. 8.3.8. Slide bracket.

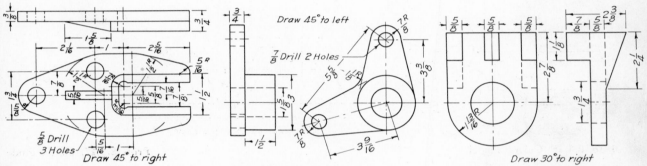

Prob. 8.3.9. Jaw bracket.

Prob. 8.3.10. Bell crank.

Prob. 8.3.11. Stop plate.

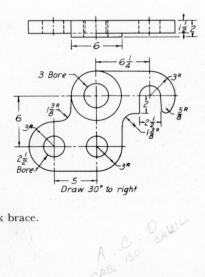

Prob. 8.3.12. Hook brace.

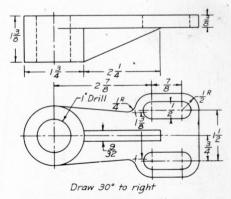

Draw 30° to right

Prob. 8.3.13. Adjusting-rod support.

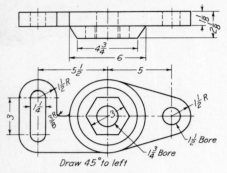

Prob. 8.3.14. Link.

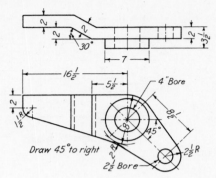

Prob. 8.3.15. Pawl.

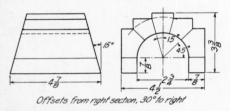

Offsets from right section, 30° to right

Prob. 8.3.16. Culvert model.

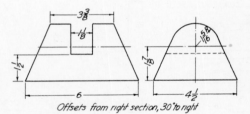

Offsets from right section, 30° to right

Prob. 8.3.17. Slotted guide.

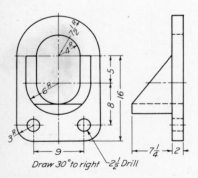

Draw 30° to right   *2½ Drill*

Prob. 8.3.18. Support bracket.

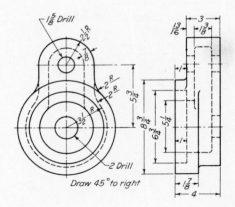

Draw 45° to right

Prob. 8.3.19. Port cover.

Group 4. Oblique sections

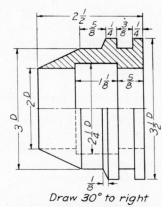

Draw 30° to right

Prob. 8.4.1. Sliding cone.

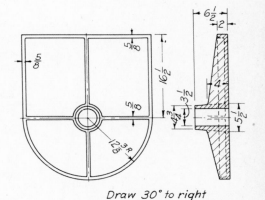

Draw 30° to right

Prob. 8.4.2. Conveyer-trough end.

8.4.1. Oblique full section of sliding cone.
8.4.1*A*. Oblique half section of sliding cone.
8.4.2. Oblique full section of conveyer-trough end.
8.4.2*A*. Oblique half section of conveyer-trough end.

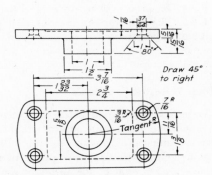

Draw 45°
to right

Prob. 8.4.3. Ceiling flange.

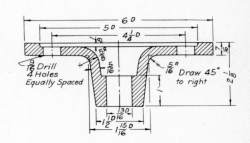

Draw 45°
to right

Prob. 8.4.4. Hanger flange.

8.4.3. Oblique full section of ceiling flange.
8.4.3*A*. Oblique half section of ceiling flange.
8.4.4. Oblique full section of hanger flange.
8.4.4*A*. Oblique half section of hanger flange.
8.4.5. Oblique half section of the base plate of Prob. 8.2.2.
8.4.6. Oblique half section of the gland of Prob. 8.2.3.

Group 5. Dimetric and cabinet drawing

8.5.1. Make a dimetric drawing of the jig block, Prob. 8.1.1.
8.5.2. Make a dimetric drawing of the guide block, Prob. 8.1.6.
8.5.3. Make a cabinet drawing of the gland, Prob. 8.2.3.
8.5.4. Make a cabinet drawing of the ceiling flange, Prob. 8.4.3.

Group 6. Axonometric and oblique projection from orthographic views

Any of the problems given in this chapter may be used for making axonometric or oblique projections from the orthographic views by first drawing the orthographic views to suitable scale and then employing these views as described in paragraphs 8.26 to 8.28 to obtain the pictorial projection.

Group 7. Pictorial drawings from machine parts

Machine parts, either rough castings and forgings or finished parts, offer valuable practice in making pictorial drawings. Choose pieces to give practice in isometric and oblique drawing. Use the most appropriate form of representation, and employ sections and half-section treatments where necessary to give clearer description.

Group 8. Pictorial working drawings

Any of the problems in this chapter offer practice in making complete pictorial working drawings. Follow the principles of dimensioning in Chap. 10. The form and placement of the dimension figures are given in paragraph 10.37.

8.8.1. Pictorial working drawing of dovetail stop, Prob. 8.1.7.
8.8.2. Pictorial working drawing of hinged catch, Prob. 8.1.9.
8.8.3. Pictorial working drawing of tie plate, Prob. 8.1.22.
8.8.4. Pictorial working drawing of head yoke, Prob. 8.2.9.
8.8.5. Pictorial working drawing of jaw bracket, Prob. 8.3.9.
8.8.6. Pictorial working drawing of adjusting-rod support, Prob. 8.3.13.
8.8.7. Pictorial working drawing of port cover, Prob. 8.3.19.
8.8.8. Pictorial working drawing of ceiling flange, Prob. 8.4.3.

Group 9. Reading exercises

These figures are to be sketched freehand in one of the pictorial systems as a test of the ability to read orthographic projections. They may also be used as reading problems by requiring other orthographic views, particularly the figures with two views given. All surfaces are plane or cylindrical surfaces, and several of the two-view problems may have two or more possible solutions.

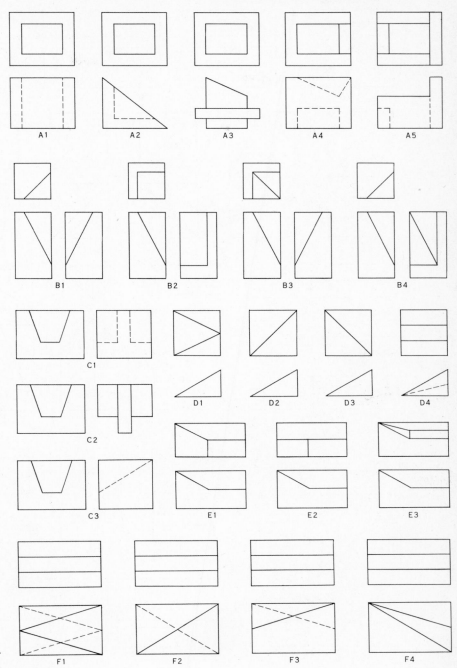

Prob. 8.9.1. Reading exercises.

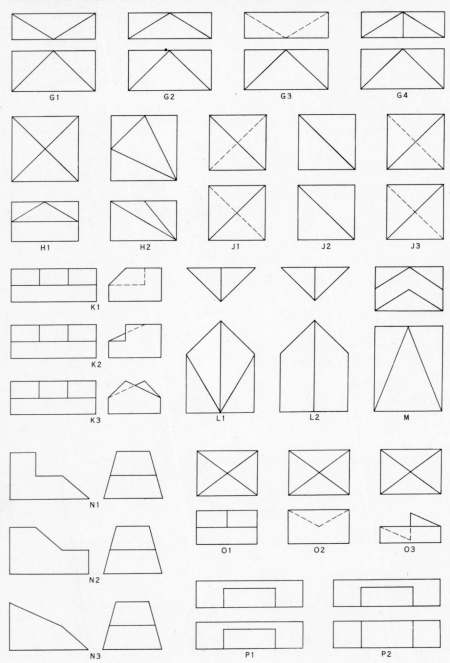

Prob. 8.9.2. Reading exercises.

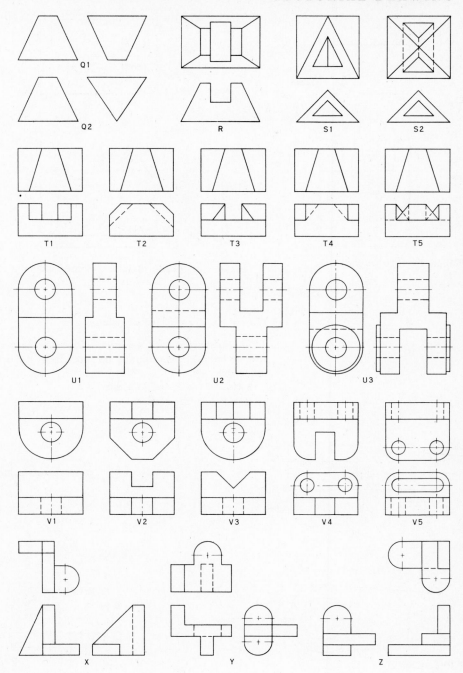

Prob. 8.9.3. Reading exercises.

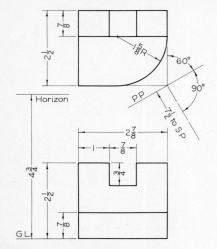

Prob. 8.10.1. Double wedge block.

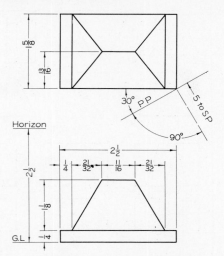

Prob. 8.10.2. Notched holder.

Group 10. Perspective drawings

The following give a variety of different objects to be drawn in perspective. A further selection may be made from the orthographic drawings in other chapters.

8.10.1. Double wedge block.
8.10.2. Notched holder.

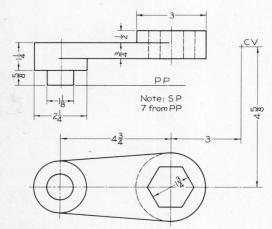

Prob. 8.10.3. Crank.

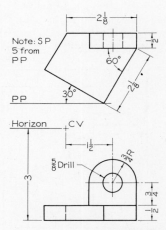

Prob. 8.10.4. Corner lug.

8.10.3. Crank.
8.10.4. Corner lug.

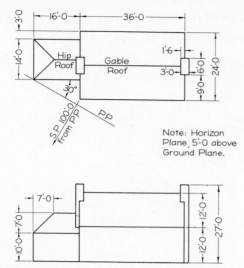

Prob. 8.10.5. House.

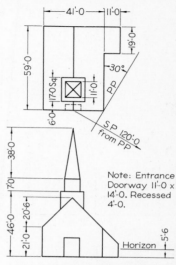

Prob. 8.10.6. Church.

8.10.5. House.
8.10.6. Church.

The problems following are to be used to develop not only an ability in pictorial sketching but also the ability to read orthographic drawings. Make the sketches to suitable size on 8½- by 11-in. paper, choosing the most appropriate form of representation, axonometric, oblique, or perspective, with partial, full, or half sections as needed. Small fillets and rounds may be ignored and shown as sharp corners.

Group 11. Pictorial sketching

Make pictorial sketches of the objects shown.

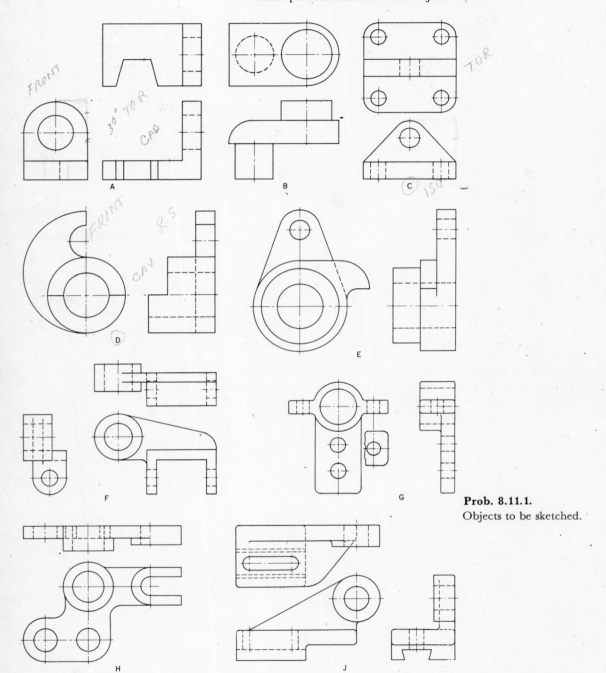

Prob. 8.11.1.
Objects to be sketched.

Group 12. Axonometric sketching

Select an object not previously drawn with instruments, and make an axonometric sketch.

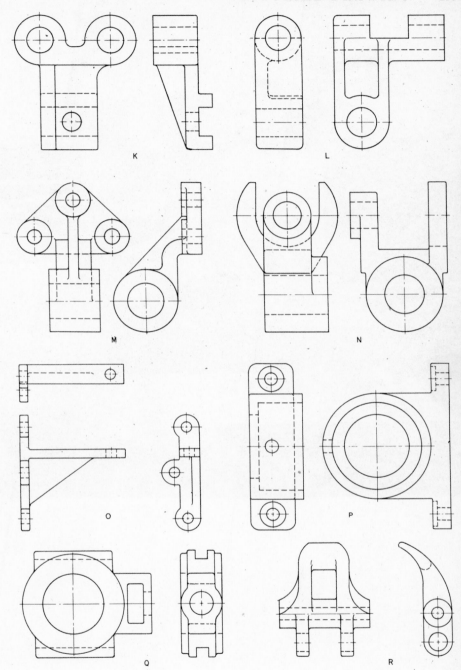

Prob. 8.11.2.
Objects to be sketched.

Group 13. Oblique sketching

Select an object not previously drawn with instruments, and make an oblique sketch.

Group 14. Perspective sketching

Select an object not previously drawn with instruments, and make a perspective sketch.

9

THE DRAWINGS AND THE SHOP

9.1. The test of any working drawing for legibility, completeness, and accuracy is the production of the object or assembly by the shop without further information than that given on the drawing. A knowledge of shop methods will, to a great extent, govern the effectiveness and completeness of the drawing. The glossary of shop terms should be studied to gain an acquaintance with the terms and the form of designation in notes. This chapter is thus given as an introduction to those following on dimensioning and working drawings.

The relation of drawings and the prints made from them to the operations of production is illustrated in the graphical chart, Fig. 9.1. This chart shows in diagrammatic form the different steps in the development of the drawings and their distribution and use in connection with the shop operations from the time the order is received until the finished machine is delivered to the shipping room.

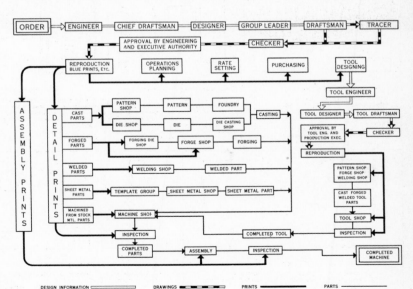

Fig. 9.1. Development and distribution of drawings.

9.2. Effect of the Basic Manufacturing Method on the Drawing. In the drawing of any machine part, a first consideration is the manufacturing process to be used, as on this depends the representation of the detailed features of the part and, to some extent, the choice of dimensions. Special or unusual methods may occasionally be used, but most machine parts are produced by (1) casting, (2) forging, (3) machining from standard stock, (4) welding, or (5) forming from sheet stock.

Each of the different methods will produce a characteristic detailed shape and appearance of the parts, and these features must be shown on the drawing. Figure 9.2 shows and lists typical features of each method and indicates the differences in drawing practice.

9.3. The Drawings. For the production of any part, a detail working drawing is necessary, complete with shape and size description and giving, where needed, the operations that are to be performed by the shop. Machined surfaces must be clearly indicated, with dimensions chosen and placed so as to be useful to the various shops without the necessity of adding or subtracting dimensions or scaling the drawing.

Two general practices may be followed: (1) the "single-drawing" system, in which only one drawing, showing the finished part, is made to be used by all the shops involved in producing the part and (2) the "multiple-drawing" system, in which different drawings are prepared, one for each shop, giving only the information required by the shop for which the drawing is made.

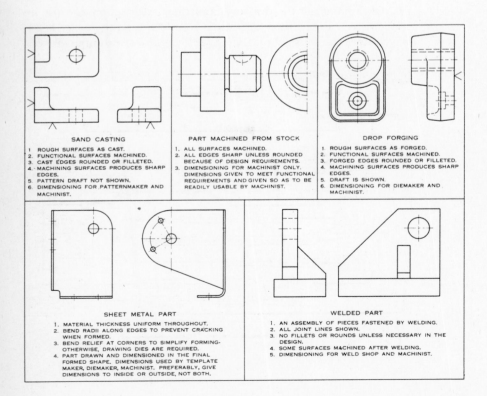

SAND CASTING

1. ROUGH SURFACES AS CAST.
2. FUNCTIONAL SURFACES MACHINED.
3. CAST EDGES ROUNDED OR FILLETED.
4. MACHINING SURFACES PRODUCES SHARP EDGES.
5. PATTERN DRAFT NOT SHOWN.
6. DIMENSIONING FOR PATTERNMAKER AND MACHINIST.

PART MACHINED FROM STOCK

1. ALL SURFACES MACHINED.
2. ALL EDGES SHARP UNLESS ROUNDED BECAUSE OF DESIGN REQUIREMENTS.
3. DIMENSIONING FOR MACHINIST ONLY. DIMENSIONS GIVEN TO MEET FUNCTIONAL REQUIREMENTS AND GIVEN SO AS TO BE READILY USABLE BY MACHINIST.

DROP FORGING

1. ROUGH SURFACES AS FORGED.
2. FUNCTIONAL SURFACES MACHINED.
3. FORGED EDGES ROUNDED OR FILLETED.
4. MACHINING SURFACES PRODUCES SHARP EDGES.
5. DRAFT IS SHOWN.
6. DIMENSIONING FOR DIEMAKER AND MACHINIST.

SHEET METAL PART

1. MATERIAL THICKNESS UNIFORM THROUGHOUT.
2. BEND RADII ALONG EDGES TO PREVENT CRACKING WHEN FORMED.
3. BEND RELIEF AT CORNERS TO SIMPLIFY FORMING—OTHERWISE, DRAWING DIES ARE REQUIRED.
4. PART DRAWN AND DIMENSIONED IN THE FINAL FORMED SHAPE, DIMENSIONS USED BY TEMPLATE MAKER, DIEMAKER, MACHINIST. PREFERABLY, GIVE DIMENSIONS TO INSIDE OR OUTSIDE, NOT BOTH.

WELDED PART

1. AN ASSEMBLY OF PIECES FASTENED BY WELDING.
2. ALL JOINT LINES SHOWN.
3. NO FILLETS OR ROUNDS UNLESS NECESSARY IN THE DESIGN.
4. SOME SURFACES MACHINED AFTER WELDING.
5. DIMENSIONING FOR WELD SHOP AND MACHINIST.

Fig. 9.2. Drawing requirements for different manufacturing methods.

The second practice is recommended, as the drawings are much easier to dimension without ambiguity and are somewhat simpler and more direct, therefore being easier for the shop to use. Figure 9.3 is a single drawing, to be used by both the pattern shop and the machine shop. Figures 10.90 and 10.91 are multiple drawings, Fig. 10.90 for the patternmaker and Fig. 10.91 for the machine shop.

9.4. Sand Castings. Figure 9.3 shows (in the title strip) that the material to be used is cast iron (*C.I.*), indicating that the part will be formed by pouring molten iron into a mold (in this case a "sand mold"), resulting in a sand casting. Before the part can be cast, however, the shape of the part must be produced in the sand mold.

9.5. The Pattern Shop. The drawing is first used by the pattern-maker who will make a pattern, or "model," of the part in wood. From this, if a large quantity of castings is required, a metal pattern, often of aluminum, is made. The patternmaker provides for the shrinkage of the casting by making the pattern oversize, using a "shrink rule" for his measurements. He also provides additional metal (machining allowance) for the machined surfaces, indicated on the drawing by (1) finish marks, (2) dimensions indicating a degree of precision attainable only by machining, or (3) notes giving machining operations. The patternmaker also provides the "draft," or slight taper, not shown on the drawing, so that the pattern can be withdrawn easily from the sand. A "core box," for the making of sand cores for the hollow parts of the casting, is also made in the pattern shop. A knowledge of patternmaking is of great aid in dimensioning, as almost all the dimensions are used by the pattern-

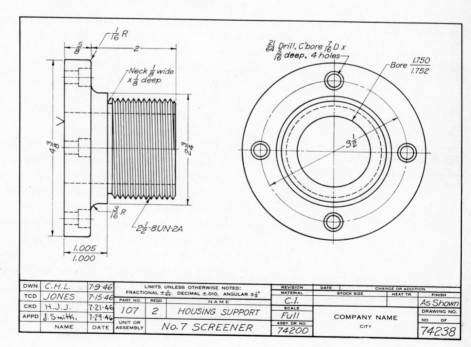

Fig. 9.3. A working drawing.

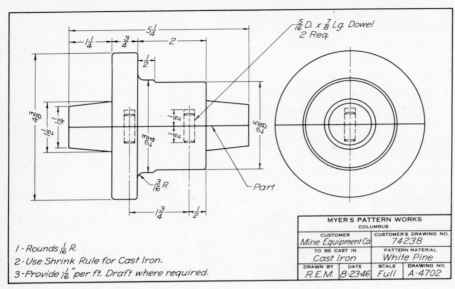

1 - Rounds $\frac{1}{16}$ R.

2 - Use Shrink Rule for Cast Iron.

3 - Provide $\frac{1}{16}$″ per ft. Draft where required.

MYERS PATTERN WORKS			
COLUMBUS			
CUSTOMER		CUSTOMER'S DRAWING NO.	
Mine Equipment Co.		74238	
TO BE CAST IN		PATTERN MATERIAL	
Cast Iron		White Pine	
DRAWN BY	DATE	SCALE	DRAWING NO.
R.E.M.	8-23-46	Full	A-4702

Fig. 9.4. A pattern drawing.

maker, while only the dimensions for finished features will be used by the machine shop.

9.6. Drawings of Castings. Casting drawings are usually made as a single drawing of the machined casting, having dimensions for both the patternmaker and machinist, Fig. 9.3. If the multiple-drawing system is followed, a drawing of the unmachined casting, with allowances for machining accounted for and having no finish marks or finish dimensions, will be made for the patternmaker; then a second drawing for the machinist shows the finished shape and gives machining dimensions.

For complicated or difficult castings, a special "pattern drawing" may be made, Fig. 9.4, showing every detail of the pattern, including the amount of draft, the parting line, "core prints" for supporting the cores in the mold, and the pattern material. Similar detail drawings may also be made for the core boxes.

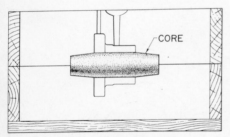

Fig. 9.5. Cross section of a two-part mold.

9.7. The Foundry. The pattern and core box or boxes are sent to the foundry and sand molds made so that molten metal may be poured into the molds and allowed to cool, forming the completed rough casting. Figure 9.5 is a cross section of a two-part mold, showing the space left by the pattern and the core in place. Only in occasional instances does the foundryman call for assistance from the drawing, as his job is simply to reproduce the pattern in metal.

Permanent molds, made of cast iron coated on the molding surfaces with a refractory material, are sometimes an advantage in that the mold may be used over and over again, thus saving the time to make an individual sand mold for each casting. This method is usually limited to small castings.

Die castings are made by forcing molten metal under pressure into a steel die mounted in a special die-casting machine. Alloys with a low melting point are used in order to avoid damaging the die. Because of the accuracy possible in making the die, a fine finish and accurate dimensions of the part may be obtained; thus machining may be unnecessary.

9.8. Forgings. Forgings are made by heating metal to make it plastic and then forming the metal to shape on a power hammer with or without the aid of special steel dies. Large parts are often hammered with dies of generalized all-purpose shape. Smaller parts in quantity may warrant the expense of making special dies. Some small forgings are made with the metal cold.

Drop forgings are the most common and are made in dies of the kind shown in Fig. 9.6. The lower die is held on the bed of the drop hammer, and the upper die is raised by the hammer mechanism. The hot metal is placed between the dies and the upper die dropped several times, causing the metal to flow into the cavity of the dies. The slight excess of material will form a thin fin, or "flash," surrounding the forging at the parting plane of the dies (Fig. 9.6). This flash is then removed in a "trimming" die made for the purpose. Considerable draft must be provided for release of the forging from the dies.

9.9. Drawings of Forgings. Forging drawings either are prepared according to the multiple system, one drawing for the diemaker and one for the machinist, Fig. 10.93, or are made as a single drawing for both, Fig. 9.7. In either case, the parting line and draft should be shown and the amount of draft specified. On the single

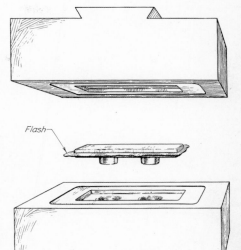

Fig. 9.6. Drop-forging dies and the forged part.

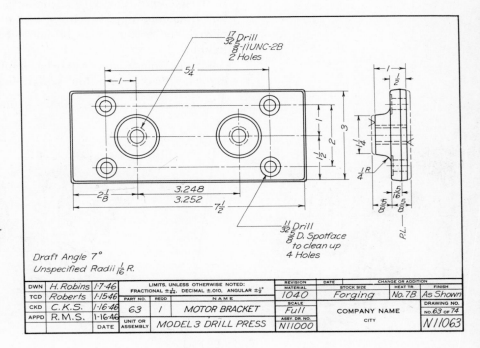

Fig. 9.7. A working drawing.

drawing, the shape of the finished forging is shown in full outline, and the machining allowance is indicated by "alternate-position" lines, thus completing the shape of the rough forging. This single drawing, therefore, combines two drawings into one, with complete dimensions for both diemaker and machinist.

9.10. The Machine Shop. The machine shop produces parts machined from stock material and finishes castings, forgings, etc., requiring machined surfaces. Cylindrical and conical surfaces are machined on a lathe. Flat or plane surfaces are machined on a planer, shaper, milling machine, broaching machine, or in some cases (facing) a lathe. Holes are drilled, reamed, counterbored, and countersunk on a drill press or lathe; holes are bored on a boring mill or lathe. For exact work, grinding machines with wheels of abrasive material are used. Grinders are also coming into greatly increased use for operations formerly made with cutting tools. In quantity production, many special machine tools and automatic machines are in use. The special tools, jigs, and fixtures made for the machine parts are held in the toolroom ready for the machine shop.

9.11. Fundamentals of Machining. All machining operations remove metal, either to make a smoother and more accurate surface, as by planing, facing, milling, etc., or to produce a surface not previously existing, as by drilling, punching, etc. The metal is removed by a hardened steel, carbide, or diamond cutting tool (machining) or an abrasive wheel (grinding); the product, or "work piece," as well as the tool or wheel, being held and guided by the machine. When steel cutting tools are used, the product must remain relatively soft until after all machining has been performed upon it, but if diamond-tipped tools are used or if grinding wheels are employed, the product may be hardened by heat-treatment before finishing.

All machining methods may be classified according to the operating principle of the machine performing the work:

1. The surface may be *generated* by moving the work with respect

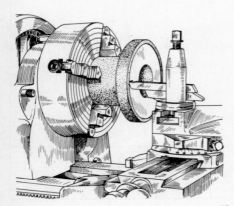

Fig. 9.8. Facing.

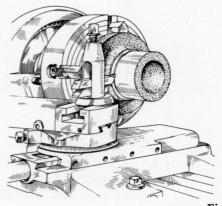

Fig. 9.9. Turning.

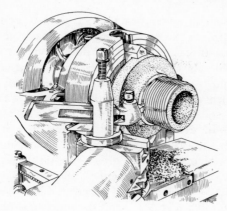

Fig. 9.10. Threading.

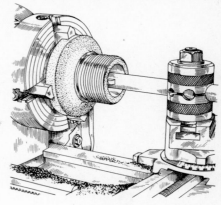

Fig. 9.11. Boring.

to a cutting tool or the tool with respect to the work, following the geometric laws for producing the surface.

2. The surface may be *formed* with a specially shaped cutting tool, moving either work or tool while the other is stationary.

The forming method is, in general, less accurate than the generating method, as any irregularities in the cutter are reproduced on the work. In some cases, a combination of the two methods is used.

9.12. The Lathe. Called the "king of machine tools," the lathe is said to be capable of producing all other machine tools. Its primary function is for machining cylindrical, conical, and other surfaces of revolution, but with special attachments a great variety of operations can be performed. Figure 9.8 shows the casting made from the drawing of Fig. 9.3 held in the lathe chuck. As the work revolves, the cutting tool is moved across perpendicular to the axis of revolution, removing metal from the base and producing a plane surface by generation. This operation is called *facing*. After being faced, the casting is turned around and the finished base is aligned against the face of the chuck, bringing the cylindrical surface into position for *turning* to the diameter indicated in the thread note on the drawing. The neck shown at the intersection of the base with the body is turned first, running the tool into the casting to a depth slightly greater than the depth of the thread. The cylindrical surface is then turned (generated) by moving the tool parallel to the axis of revolution, Fig. 9.9. Figure 9.10 shows the thread being cut on the finished cylinder. The tool is ground to the profile of the thread space, carefully lined up to the work, and moved parallel to the axis of revolution by the lead screw of the lathe. This operation is a combination of the fundamental processes, the thread profile being formed while the helix is generated.

The hole through the center of the casting, originally cored, is now finished by *boring*, as the cutting of an interior surface is called, Fig. 9.11. The tool is held in a boring bar and moved parallel to the axis of revolution, thus generating an internal cylinder.

Note that in these operations the dimensions used by the machinist have been (1) the finish mark on the base and thickness of the base, (2) the thread note and outside diameter of the thread, (3) the dimensions of the neck, (4) the distance from the base to the shoulder, and (5) the diameter of the bored hole.

Long cylindrical pieces to be turned in the lathe are supported by conical centers, one at each end. Figure 9.19 illustrates the principle.

9.13. The Drill Press. The partially finished piece of Fig. 9.3 is now taken to the drill press for drilling and counterboring the holes in the base according to the dimensions on the drawing. These dimensions give the diameter of the drill, the diameter and depth of the counterbore, and the location of the holes. The casting is clamped to the drill-press table, Fig. 9.12, and the rotating drill brought into the work by a lever operating a rack and pinion in the head of the machine. The cutting is done by two ground lips on the end of the drill, Fig. 9.21A. Drilling can also be done in a lathe, the work revolving while the drill is held in and moved by the tailstock. In Fig. 9.13, the drill has been replaced by a counterboring tool, Fig. 9.21C, of which the diameter is the size specified on the drawing and which has a cylindrical pilot on the end to fit into the drilled hole, thus ensuring concentricity. This tool is fed in to the depth shown on the drawing.

Study the drawing of Fig. 9.3 with the illustrations of the operations, and check, first, the dimensions that would be used by the patternmaker and, second, those required by the machinist.

9.14. The Shaper and the Planer. The drop forging of Fig. 9.7 requires machining on the base and boss surfaces.

Flat surfaces of this type may be machined on a shaper or a planer. In this case, the shaper, Fig. 9.14, is used because of the relatively small size of the part. The tool is held in a ram which moves back and forth across the work, taking a cut at each pass forward. Be-

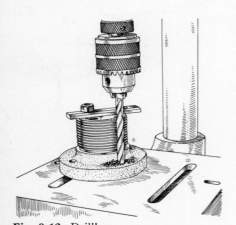

Fig. 9.12. Drilling.

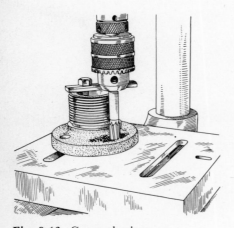

Fig. 9.13. Counterboring.

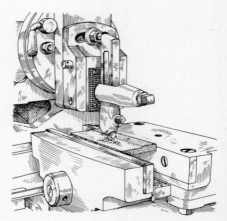

Fig. 9.14. Shaping.

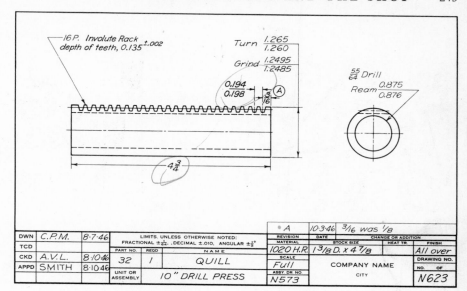

Fig. 9.15. A working drawing.

tween the cuts, the table moves laterally so that closely spaced parallel cuts are made until the surface is completely machined.

The planer differs from the shaper in that its bed, carrying the work, moves back and forth under a stationary tool. It is generally used for a larger and heavier type of work than that done on a shaper.

9.15. Parts Machined from Standard Stock. The shape of a part will often lend itself to machining directly from standard stock, such as bars, rods, tubing, plates, and blocks, or from extrusions and rolled shapes, such as angles and channels. Hot-rolled (HR) and cold-rolled (CR) steel are common materials.

Parts produced from stock are usually finished on all surfaces, and the general note "Finish all over" on the drawing eliminates the use of finish marks. Figure 9.15 is the drawing of a part to be made from bar stock. Note the specification of material, stock size, etc., in the title.

9.16. The Turret Lathe. The *quill* of Fig. 9.15, produced in quantity, may be made on a turret lathe, except for the rack teeth and the outside-diameter grinding. The stock is held in the collet chuck of the lathe. First the end surface is faced, and then the cylindrical surface (OD) is turned. The work piece is then ready for drilling and reaming. The turret holds the various tools and swings them around into position as needed. A center drill starts a small hole to align the larger drill, and then the drill and reamer are brought successively into position. The drill provides a hole slightly undersize, and then the reamer, cutting with its fluted sides, cleans out the hole and gives a smooth surface finished to a size within the

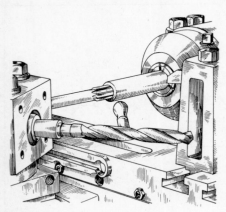

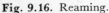

Fig. 9.16. Reaming.

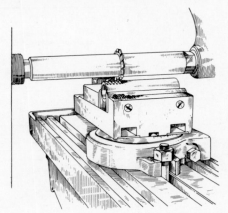

Fig. 9.17. Milling.

dimensional limits on the drawing. Figure 9.16 shows the turret indexed so that the drill is out of the way and the reamer is in position. At the right is seen the cutoff tool ready to cut the piece to the length shown on the drawing.

9.17. The Milling Machine. The dimensions of the rack teeth, Fig. 9.15, give the depth and spacing of the cuts and the specifications for the cutter to be used. This type of work may be done on a milling machine. The work piece is held in a vise and moved horizontally into the rotating milling cutter, which, in profile, is the shape of the space between the teeth (Fig. 9.17). The cuts are spaced by moving the table of the machine to correspond with the distance shown on the drawing. Note that this operation is a forming process, as the shape depends upon the contour of the cutter. With several cutters mounted together (gang milling), a number of teeth can be cut at the same time.

There are many types of milling cutters made to cut on their peripheries, their sides, or their ends, for forming flat, curved, or special surfaces. Three milling cutters are shown in Fig. 9.18.

9.18. The Grinder. The general purpose of grinding is to make a smoother and more accurate surface than can be obtained by turning, planing, milling, etc. In many cases, pieces hardened by heat-treatment will warp slightly; and as ordinary machining methods are impractical with hardened materials, such parts are finish-ground after hardening.

The limit dimensions for the outside diameter of the quill, Fig. 9.15, indicate a grinding operation on a cylindrical grinder, Fig. 9.19. The abrasive wheel rotates at high speed, while the work piece, mounted on a mandrel between conical centers, rotates slowly in the opposite direction. The wheel usually moves laterally to cover the surface of the work piece. The work piece is gaged carefully during the operation to bring the size within the dimensional limits shown on the drawing and to check for a cylindrical surface without

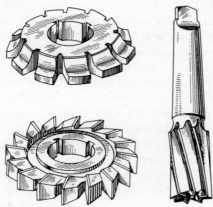

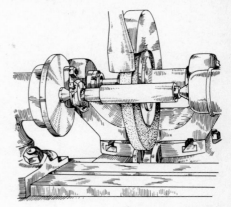

Fig. 9.18. Milling cutters.

Fig. 9.19. Grinding.

taper. The machine for flat surfaces, called a "surface grinder," holds the work piece on a flat table moving back and forth under the abrasive wheel. The table "indexes" laterally after each pass under the work.

9.19. Lapping, Honing, and Superfinishing. These are methods of producing smooth, accurate, mirrorlike surfaces after grinding. All three methods use very fine abrasives, (1) powdered and carried in oil on a piece of formed soft metal (lapping) or (2) in the form of fine-grained compact stones (honing and superfinishing) to rub against the surface to be finished and reduce scratches and waviness.

9.20. The Broaching Machine. A broach is a long tapered bar having a series of cutting edges (teeth), each successively removing a small amount of material until the last edge forms the shape desired. For flat or irregular external surfaces, the broach and work piece are held by the broaching machine, and the broach is passed across the surface of the work piece. For internal surfaces, the broach is either pulled or pushed through a hole to give the finished size and shape.

Some machined shapes can be more economically produced by broaching than by any other method. Figure 9.20 shows several forms of broaches and the shapes they produce.

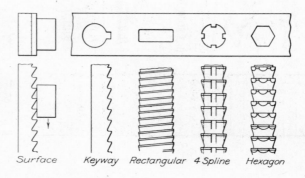

Fig. 9.20. Broaches.

Surface   Keyway   Rectangular   4 Spline   Hexagon

9.21. Small Tools. The shop uses a variety of small tools, both in powered machines and as hand tools. Figure 9.21A shows a *twist drill*, available in a variety of sizes (numbered, lettered, fractional, and metric) for producing holes in almost any material; at (B), a *reamer*, used to enlarge and smooth a previously existing hole and to give greater accuracy than is possible by drilling alone; at (C), a *counterbore* and at (D), a *countersink*, both used to enlarge and alter the end of a hole (usually for screwheads). A *spot-facing tool* is similar to a counterbore. *Taper*, *plug*, and *bottoming taps* for cutting the thread of a tapped hole are shown at (E), (F), and (G). A die for threading a rod or shaft is shown at (H).

9.22. Welded Parts. Simple shapes cut from standard rod, bar, or plate stock may be combined by welding to form a finished part. Some machining after welding is frequently necessary.

9.23. Parts from Standard Sheet. A relatively thin sheet or strip of standard thickness may first be cut to size "in the flat" and then bent, formed, punched, etc., to form the final required part. The drawing should be made so as to give information for the "template maker" and the information required for bending and forming the sheet. Sometimes separate developments (Chap. 18) are made. The thickness of sheet stock is specified by giving (1) the gage (see table, Appendix) and the equivalent thickness in decimals of an inch or (2) only the decimal thickness (the practice followed in specifying aluminum sheet). Figure 10.94 is a working drawing of a sheet-metal part.

9.24. Plastics. Plastics are available either in standard bar, rod, tubing, sheet, etc., from which parts can be made by machining or in granular form to be used in "molding," a process similar to die-casting, in which the material is heated to a plastic state and compressed by a die (compression molding) or injected under pressure into a die (injection molding). Metal inserts for threads, wear bush-

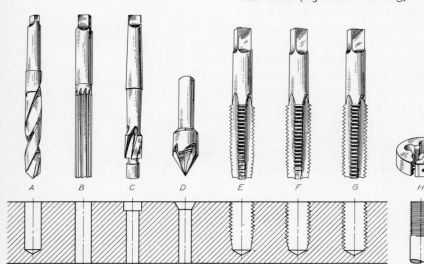

Fig. 9.21. Small tools.

ings, etc., are sometimes cast into the part. Consideration should be given the diemaker when dimensioning the drawing.

9.25. Heat-treatment. This is a general term applied to the processing of metals by heat and chemicals to change the physical properties of the material.

The glossary of shop terms gives definitions of such heat-treatment processes as annealing, carburizing, casehardening, hardening, normalizing, and tempering.

The specification of heat-treatment may be given on the drawing in several ways: (1) by a general note listing the steps, temperatures, and baths to be used, (2) by a standard heat-treatment number (SAE or company standard) in the space provided in the title block, (3) by giving the Brinell or Rockwell hardness number to be attained, or (4) by giving the tensile strength, in pounds per square inch, to be attained through heat-treatment.

Figures 9.7, 10.59, 10.89, and 10.93 illustrate these methods.

9.26. Tools for Mass Production. Many special machine tools, either semiautomatic or fully automatic, are used in modern factories. These machines are basically the same as ordinary lathes, grinders, etc., but contain mechanisms to control the movements of cutting tools and produce identical parts with little attention from the operator once the machine is "tooled up." Automatic screw machines and centerless grinders are examples.

9.27. Jigs and Fixtures. Jigs for holding the work and guiding the tool or fixtures for holding the work greatly extend the production rate for general-purpose machine tools.

9.28. Inspection. Careful inspection is an important feature of modern production. Good practice requires inspection after each operation. For production in quantity, special gages are usually employed, but in small-quantity production, the usual measuring instruments, calipers and scale, micrometers, dial gages, etc., are used. For greater precision in gaging, electrical, air, or optical gages are often employed.

9.29. Assembly. The finished separate pieces come to the assembly department to be put together according to the assembly drawings. Sometimes it is desirable or necessary to perform some small machining operation during assembly, often drilling, reaming, or hand finishing. In such cases the assembly drawing should carry a note explaining the required operation and give dimensions for the alignment or location of the pieces. If some parts are to be combined before final assembly, either a subassembly drawing or the detail drawings of each piece will give the required information. "$\frac{1}{8}$ drill in assembly with piece No. 107" is a typical note form for an assembly machining operation.

10

DIMENSIONS, NOTES, LIMITS, AND PRECISION

10.1. After the shape of an object has been described by orthographic (or pictorial) views, the value of the drawing for the construction of the object depends upon dimensions and notes to give the description of *size*. In general, the description of shape and size together gives complete information for producing the object represented.

The dimensions put on the drawing are *not necessarily* those used in making the drawing but are those required for the proper functioning of the part after assembly, selected so as to be readily usable by the workers who are to make the piece. The draftsman must thus first study the machine and understand its functional requirements and then put himself in the place of the patternmaker, diemaker, machinist, etc., and mentally construct the object to discover which dimensions would best give the information.

10.2. Method. Three basic steps are involved in the study of dimensioning practice:

Fundamentals and Technique. One must first have a thorough knowledge of the lines and symbols used for dimensions and notes and of the weight and spacing of the lines on the drawing. These lines, symbols, and techniques are the "tools" for clear, concise representation of size. (See paragraphs 10.3 to 10.13, inclusive.)

Selection of Distances to Be Given. The most important consideration from the standpoint of ultimate operation of a machine and the

251

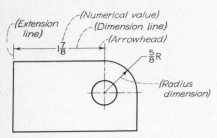

Fig. 10.1. Dimensions.

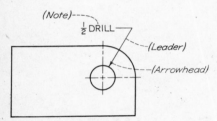

Fig. 10.2. A note.

proper working of the individual parts is the selection of distances to be given. From the functional requirements, the "breakdown" of the part into its geometrical elements, and the requirements of the shop for production, this selection is made. (See paragraphs 10.14 to 10.19, inclusive.)

Placement. After the distances to be given have been decided upon, the next step is the actual placement of the dimensions showing these distances on the drawing. The dimensions should be placed in an orderly arrangement clear and easy to read and in positions where they may be readily found without undue search by persons reading the drawing. (See paragraphs 10.20 to 10.40, inclusive.)

10.3. Dimension Forms. Two basic methods are used to give a distance on the drawing, a *dimension* (Fig. 10.1) or a *note* (Fig. 10.2). A dimension is used to give the distance between two points, lines, or planes or some combination of points, lines, and planes. The numerical value gives the actual distance, the dimension line indicates the direction in which the value applies, and the arrowheads indicate the points between which the value applies. Extension lines refer the dimension to the view when the dimension is placed outside the view. A note provides a means of giving explanatory information along with a size. The leader and arrowhead refer the word statement of the note to the proper place on the drawing. Notes applying to the object as a whole are given without a leader in some convenient place on the drawing.

The lines and symbols used in dimensioning are dimension lines, arrowheads, extension lines, leaders, numerical values, notes, finish marks, etc.

10.4. Line Weights. Dimension lines, extension lines, and leaders are made with fine full lines the same width as the center lines so as to contrast with the heavier outlines of the views. Note the line widths given in the alphabet of lines, Fig. 1.60.

10.5. Arrowheads. These are carefully drawn freehand, making the sides either in one stroke or in two strokes toward the point, as shown in enlarged form in Fig. 10.3. The general preference is for the solid head, Fig. 10.4. The solid head is usually made thinner and slightly longer than the open head and has practically no curvature to the sides. It is made in one stroke and then filled, if necessary, without lifting the pen or pencil; a rather blunt pencil or pen is required with this style of head. The bases of arrowheads should not be made wider than one-third the length. All arrowheads on the same drawing should be the same type, either open or solid, and the same size, except in restricted spaces. Arrowhead lengths will vary somewhat depending upon the drawing size. One-eighth inch is a good general length for small drawings and $3/16$ in. for larger drawings.

Poor arrowheads ruin the appearance of an otherwise carefully made drawing. Avoid the incorrect shapes and placements shown in Fig. 10.5.

Fig. 10.3. Open-style arrowhead strokes.

Fig. 10.4. Solid-style arrowhead strokes.

Fig. 10.5. Incorrect arrowheads.

10.6. Extension Lines. They extend from the view to a dimension placed outside the view. They should not touch the outline of the view but should start about $\frac{1}{16}$ in. from it and extend about $\frac{1}{8}$ in. beyond the last dimension line, Fig. 10.6A. This example is printed approximately one-half size.

Dimensions are preferably kept outside the views but occasionally may be placed to better advantage inside. Thus dimensions may terminate at *center lines* or visible *outlines of the view*, Fig. 10.6B and C.

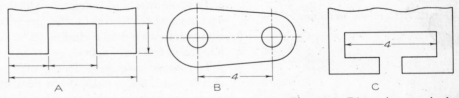

Fig. 10.6. Dimension terminals.

Where a measurement between centers is to be shown, as at (B), the center lines are continued to serve as extension lines, extending about $\frac{1}{8}$ in. beyond the last dimension line. Usually the outline of the view becomes the terminal for arrowheads, as at (C), when a dimension must be placed inside the view. This might occur because of limited space, when extension lines in crossing parts of the view would cause confusion, or when very long extension lines would make the dimension difficult to read.

10.7. Leaders. These are *straight* (not curved) lines leading from a dimension value or an explanatory note to the feature on the drawing to which the note applies (Fig. 10.7). An arrowhead is used on the pointing end of the leader but never on the note end. The note end of the leader should terminate with a short horizontal

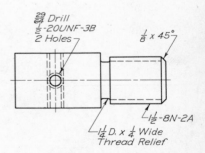

Fig. 10.7. Leaders for notes.

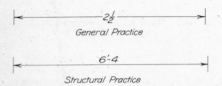

General Practice

Structural Practice

Fig. 10.8. Placing dimension values.

bar at the mid-height of the lettering and should run either to the beginning or the end of the note, never to the middle.

Leaders should be drawn at an angle to contrast with the principal lines of the drawing, which are mainly horizontal and vertical. Thus leaders are usually drawn at 30°, 45°, or 60° to the horizontal; 60° looks best. When several leaders are used, the appearance of the drawing is improved if the leaders can be kept parallel.

10.8. Figures. For dimension values they must be carefully lettered in either vertical or inclined style. In an effort for neatness the beginner often gets them too small. One-eighth inch for small drawings and $\frac{5}{32}$ in. for larger drawings are good general heights.

The general practice is to leave a space in the dimension line for the dimension value (Fig. 10.8). It is universal in structural practice and common in architectural practice to place the values above a continuous dimension line (Fig. 10.8).

10.9. Common Fractions. These should be made with the fraction bar parallel to the guide lines of the figure and with the numerator and denominator each somewhat smaller than the height of the whole number so that the total fraction height is twice that of the integer (Fig. 10.9). Avoid the incorrect forms shown. The figures should not touch the fraction bar.

10.10. Feet and Inches. Indicate these thus: 9'-6". When there are no inches, it should be so indicated, as 9'-0", 9'-0½". When dimensions are all in inches, the inch mark is preferably omitted from all the dimensions and notes unless there is some possibility of misunderstanding; thus "1 bore" is clearer as, and should be, "1" bore."

In some machine industries, all dimensions are given in inches. In others where feet and inches are used, the ASA recommends that dimensions up to and including 72 in. be given in inches and greater lengths in feet and inches.

In structural drawing, length dimensions should be given in feet and inches. Plate widths, beam sizes, etc., are given in inches. Inch marks are omitted, even though the dimension is in feet and inches, Fig. 10.8.

In the United States, if no foot or inch marks appear on the drawing, the dimension values indicate inches unless a different unit of measurement is indicated by general note. Drawings made in foreign countries employing the metric system are commonly dimensioned in millimeters.

Correct   **Avoid**

Fig. 10.9. Common fractions.

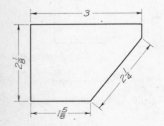

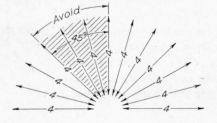

Fig. 10.10. Reading direction (aligned system).

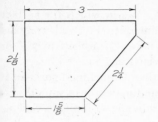

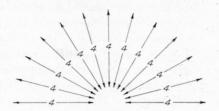

Fig. 10.11. Reading direction (uni-directional system).

10.11. Reading Direction of Figures. This is arranged according to either the aligned system or the unidirectional system.

The *aligned system* is the older of the two methods. The figures are oriented to be readable from a position *perpendicular* to the dimension line; thus the guide lines for the figures will be parallel to the dimension line, and the fraction bar in line with the dimension line, Fig. 10.10. The figures should be arranged so as to be readable from the *bottom* or *right side* of the drawing. Avoid running dimensions in the directions included in the shaded area; if this is unavoidable, they should read downward with the line.

The *unidirectional system* originated in the automotive and aircraft industries. Sometimes called the "horizontal system," all figures are oriented to read from the bottom of the drawing. Thus the guide lines and fraction bars are horizontal regardless of the direction of the dimension, Fig. 10.11. The "avoid" zone of Fig. 10.10 has no significance with this system.

Notes must be lettered horizontally and read from the bottom of the drawing in either system.

10.12. Finish Marks. These are used to indicate that certain surfaces of metal parts are to be machined and that allowance must therefore be provided for finish. Finish marks need not be used for parts made by machining from rolled stock, as the surfaces are necessarily machined. Neither are they necessary on drilled, reamed, or counterbored holes nor on similar machined features when the machining operation is specified by note.

The standard mark recommended by the ASA is a 60° **V** with its point touching the line representing the edge view of the surface to be machined. The **V** is placed on the "air side" of the surface. Figure 10.12 shows the normal size of the **V** and its position for lines in various directions as applied on a drawing.

The symbol which has been in use for many years is an italic *f* with its cross mark intersecting the line representing the surface to be finished, Fig. 10.13.

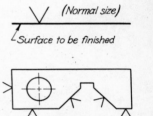

Fig. 10.12. ASA finish mark.

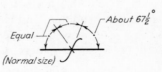

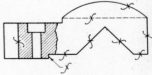

Fig. 10.13. Italic-*f* finish mark.

Finish marks should be placed on all views in which the surface to be machined appears as a line, including dotted lines. If the part is to be machined on all surfaces, the note "Finish all over," or "FAO," is used, and the marks on the views are omitted.

In addition to the finish mark indicating a machined surface, it may be necessary in some cases to indicate the degree of smoothness of the surface. The ASA gives a set of symbols to indicate various conditions of *surface quality*. These symbols are explained and illustrated in paragraph 10.61.

10.13. Systems of Writing Dimension Values. Dimension values may be given either as common fractions, ¼, ⅜, etc., or as decimal fractions, 0.26, 0.375, etc.; and from these, three systems are evolved.

The *common-fraction system*, used in general drawing practice, including architectural and structural work, has all dimension values written as units and common fractions, as 3½, 1¼, ⅜, ¹⁄₁₆, ³⁄₃₂, ¹⁄₆₄. Values thus written can be laid out with a steel tape or scale graduated in sixty-fourths of an inch.

The *common-fraction, decimal-fraction system* is used principally in machine drawing whenever the degree of precision calls for fractions of an inch smaller than those on the ordinary steel scale. To continue the use of common fractions below ¹⁄₆₄, such as ¹⁄₁₂₈ or ¹⁄₂₅₆, is considered impractical. The method followed is to give values (1) in units and common fractions for distances not requiring an accuracy closer than ¹⁄₆₄ in. and (2) in units and decimal fractions, as 2.375, 1.250, 0.1875, etc., for distances requiring greater precision. The decimal fractions are given to as many decimal places as the degree of precision requires.

The *complete decimal system* uses decimal fractions exclusively for all dimension values. This system has the advantages of the metric system but uses the inch as its basis, thus making it possible to use present measuring equipment.

The ASA complete decimal system [1] uses a two-place decimal for all values where common fractions would ordinarily be used. The digits after the decimal point are preferably written to even fiftieths, .02, .10, .36, etc., so that when halved, as for radii, etc., two-place decimals will result. Writing the values in even fiftieths allows the use of scales divided in fiftieths, Fig. 10.14, which are much easier to read than scales divided in hundredths.

Dimension values for distances requiring greater precision than that expressed by the two-place decimal are written to three, four, or more decimal places as the degree of precision may require.

Figure 10.15 is a detail drawing dimensioned according to the ASA decimal system. The advantage of this system in calculating, adding, and checking and in doing away with all conversion tables, as well as in lessening chances for error, is apparent.

Designers and draftsmen working in the complete decimal system

Fig. 10.14. Decimal scale.

[1] Z14.1—1946.

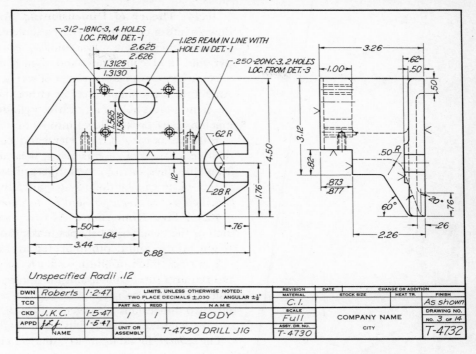

Fig. 10.15. A drawing dimensioned in the ASA complete decimal system.

will find it necessary to think in terms of tenths and hundredths of inches instead of thinking in common fractions. New designs must be made in decimal sizes without reference to common fractional sizes. However, until standard-stock materials, tools, and commercial parts are available in decimal sizes, some dimensions will have to be given as the decimal equivalent of a common fraction. Thus, for example, a standard ⅜-16UNC-2A thread would be given as 0.375-16UNC-2A.

Decimal equivalents of some common fractions come out to a greater number of decimal places (significant digits) than is necessary or desirable for use as a dimension value, and in such cases, the decimal should be adjusted, or "rounded off," to a smaller number of decimal places. The following procedure from the American Standards [1] is recommended:

When the figure beyond the last figure to be retained is less than 5, the last figure retained should not be changed. *Example.* 3.46325, if cut off to three places, should be 3.463.

When the figures beyond the last place to be retained amount to more than 5, the last figure retained should be increased by 1. *Example.* 8.37652, if cut off to three places, should be 8.377.

When the figure beyond the last place to be retained is exactly 5 with only zeros following, the preceding number, if even, should be unchanged; if odd, it should be increased by 1. *Example.* 4.365 becomes 4.36 when cut off to two places. Also 4.355 becomes 4.36 when cut off to two places.

[1] Z25.1—1940.

10.14. Theory of Dimensioning. Any object can be "broken down" into a combination of basic geometrical shapes, principally prisms and cylinders. Occasionally, however, there will be parts of pyramids and cones, now and then a double-curved surface, and very rarely, except for surfaces of screw threads, a warped surface. Any of the basic shapes may be either positive or negative, taken in the sense that a hole is a negative cylinder. Figure 4.55 illustrates a machine part broken down into its fundamental shapes.

If the *size* of each of these elemental shapes is dimensioned and the relative location of each is given, measuring from center to center, from base lines, or from the surfaces of each other, the dimensioning of any piece can be done systematically. Dimensions may thus be classified as *size dimensions* and *location dimensions*.

10.15. Size Dimensions. As every solid has three dimensions, each of the geometrical shapes making up the object must have its height, width, and depth indicated in the dimensioning.

The *prism*, often in plinth or flat form, is the most common shape and requires three dimensions for square, rectangular, or triangular (Fig. 10.16A). For regular hexagonal or octagonal types, usually only two dimensions are given, either the distance "across corners" and the length or "across flats" and the length.

The *cylinder*, found on nearly all mechanical pieces as a shaft, boss, or hole, is the second most common shape. A cylinder obviously requires only two dimensions, diameter and length (Fig. 10.16B). Partial cylinders, such as fillets and rounds, are dimensioned by radius instead of diameter. A good general rule is to dimension complete circles with a diameter and circle arcs (partial circles) with a radius.

Right cones may be dimensioned with the altitude and the diameter of the base. They usually occur as frustums, however, and require the diameters of the ends and the length (Fig. 10.16C). Sometimes it is desirable to dimension cone frustums as *tapers* or with an angular dimension, as described in paragraph 10.29.

Right pyramids are dimensioned by giving the dimensions of the

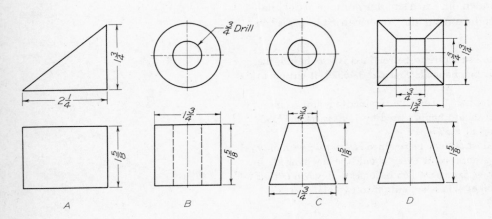

Fig. 10.16. Size dimensions: prism, cylinder, cone, and pyramid.

base and the altitude. These also are often frustums, requiring dimensions of both bases (Fig. 10.16*D*).

Oblique cones and *pyramids* are dimensioned in the same way as right cones and pyramids but with an additional dimension parallel to the base to give the offset of the vertex.

Spheres are dimensioned by giving the diameter and other surfaces of revolution by dimensioning the generating curve.

Warped surfaces are dimensioned according to their method of generation; and as their representation requires numerous sections, each of these must be fully dimensioned by ordinate and abscissa dimensions.

10.16. Location Dimensions. After the basic geometric shapes have been dimensioned for size, the location of each relative to the others must be given. *Location must be established in height, width, and depth directions.* Rectangular shapes are located with reference to their faces, cylindrical and conical shapes to their center lines and their ends.

A basic shape will often coincide or align with another on one or more of its faces. In such cases, the alignment serves partially to locate the parts and eliminates the need of a location dimension in a direction perpendicular to the line of coincidence. Thus in Fig. 10.17, prism *A* requires only one dimension for complete location with respect to prism *B*, as two surfaces are in alignment and two in contact.

Coincident center lines often eliminate the need of location dimensions. In the cylinder, Fig. 10.16*B*, the center lines of the hole and cylinder coincide, and no location dimensions are needed. The two holes of Fig. 10.17 are on the same center line, and the dimension perpendicular to the coincident center line locates both holes in that direction.

10.17. Selection of Dimensions. The dimensions arrived at by reducing the part to its basic geometry will, in general, fulfill the requirements of practical dimensioning. These dimensions, however, sometimes require alteration to ensure satisfactory functioning of

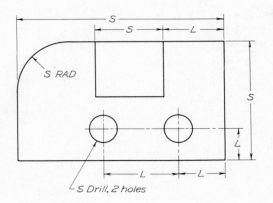

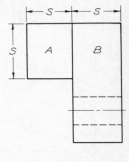

Fig. 10.17. Size and location dimensions.

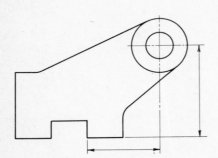

Fig. 10.18. Location by offsets.

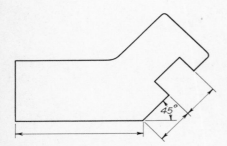

Fig. 10.19. Location by angle.

the part and to give the information in the best way from the standpoint of production. *The draftsman must therefore correlate the dimensions on drawings of mating parts to ensure satisfactory functioning and, at the same time, select dimensions convenient for the workmen to use.*

Here our study of drawing as a language must be supplemented by a knowledge of shop methods. To be successful, the machine draftsman must have an intimate knowledge of patternmaking, foundry practice, forging, and machine-shop practice, as well as, in some cases, sheet-metal working, metal and plastic die casting, welding, and structural-steel fabrication.

The beginning student without this knowledge should not depend upon his instructor alone but, as recommended in the previous chapter, should set about to inform himself by observing work going through the shops and reading books and periodicals on methods used in modern production work.

The *selection of size dimensions* arrived at by "shape breakdown" will usually meet the requirements of the shop since the basic shapes result from the fundamental shop operations. However, size dimensions are often preferred in note form instead of a regular dimension whenever a shop process is involved, such as drilling, reaming, counterboring, and punching.

The *selection of location dimensions* ordinarily requires more consideration than for size dimensions because there are, usually, several ways in which a location might be given. In general, location dimensions will be given between finished surfaces, center lines, or a combination thereof (Fig. 10.20). Remember that rough castings or forgings will vary in size, and do not locate machined surfaces from unfinished surfaces. The only exception is when an *initial*, or *starting, dimension* is given to locate the first surface to be machined from which, in turn, the other machined surfaces are located. *Coinciding center lines of unfinished and finished surfaces often take the place of a starting dimension.*

The location of a point or center by offset dimensions from two

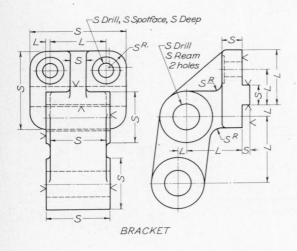

BRACKET

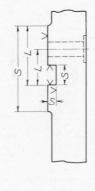

BODY

Fig. 10.20. Correlation of dimensions.

center lines or surfaces, Fig. 10.18, is preferred over angular dimensions, Fig. 10.19, unless the angular dimension is more practical from the standpoint of construction.

10.18. Correlation of Dimensions. Mating parts must have their dimensions correlated so that the two parts will fit and function as intended. Figure 10.20 illustrates this principle. Note that the tongue of the bracket is to fit the groove in the body, and note that the drilled holes in both pieces must align. Study the dimensioning of both pieces and observe that the location dimensions are correlated so that the intended alignment and fitting of the parts will be accomplished.

Not only must dimensions be correlated with the dimensions of the mating part, but the accuracy to which these distances are produced must meet certain requirements, or the parts still may not fit and function properly. Distances between the surfaces or center lines of finished features of an object must usually be more accurately made than unfinished features. In Fig. 10.21, note that the location dimensions between center lines or surfaces of finished features are given as three-place decimals, as dimension *A*. Location dimensions for unfinished features are given as common fractions, as dimension *B*. The decimal dimensions call for greater precision in manufacture than do the common fractions. Dimension *B* is in this case used by the patternmaker to locate cylinder *C* from the right end of the piece. The machinist will first locate the finished hole in this cylinder, making it concentric with the cylinder; then all other machined surfaces are located from this hole, as, for example, the spline loca-

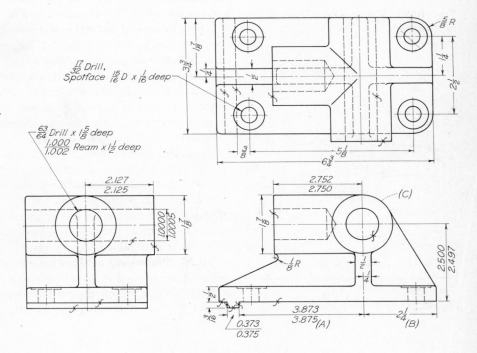

Fig. 10.21. An example of dimensioning.

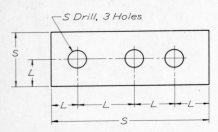

Fig. 10.22. One unnecessary dimension.

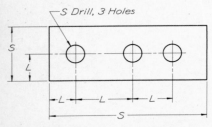

Fig. 10.23. Unnecessary dimension omitted.

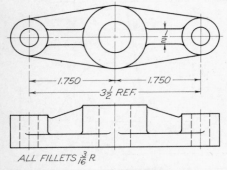

Fig. 10.24. One reference dimension.

tion by dimension *A*. The four spot-faced holes are located with reference to each other with fractional dimensions since the holes are oversize for the fastenings used, allowing enough shifting of the fastenings in the holes so that great accuracy in location is not necessary. The mating part, with its holes to receive the screws, would be similarly dimensioned.

Study Fig. 10.21 and note the classification, size, or location of each dimension.

10.19. Superfluous Dimensions. *Duplicate* or *unnecessary* dimensions are to be avoided because of the confusion and delay they may cause. When a drawing is changed or revised, a duplicate dimension may not be noticed and changed along with its counterpart; hence the distance will have two different values, one incorrect. An unnecessary dimension is any dimension, other than a duplicate, that is not essential in making the piece. Because of the allowable variation permitted the manufacturer on each dimension, difficulties will be encountered if unnecessary dimensions occur when parts are to be interchangeable. Actually, under these circumstances, it should only be possible to establish a point on the object in any given direction with but one dimension. Unnecessary dimensions will always occur when all the individual dimensions are given, in addition to the over-all dimension (Fig. 10.22). One dimension of the series must be omitted if the over-all is used, thus allowing only one possible location from each dimension (Fig. 10.23). Occasionally it is desirable, for reference or checking purposes, to give all dimensions in a series and give the over-all dimension. In such cases, one dimension not to be used in manufacturing is marked with the abbreviation "Ref.," as indicated in Fig. 10.24.

In architectural and structural work, where the interchangeability of parts usually has no consideration, unnecessary dimensions cause no difficulty and all dimensions are given as in Fig. 10.22.

Although, as pointed out, it is important not to "overdimension" a part, it is equally important that sufficient dimensions be given to locate every point, line, or surface of the object. The workman should never be required to scale a dimension from the drawing. All necessary distances must be given.

However, dimensions for similar features, such as the thickness of several ribs obviously of the same size, need not be repeated (Fig. 10.24). Also, such details as the size of fillets and rounds can be provided for with a general note. If the draftsman will mentally go through the manufacture or even the drawing of the part, checking each dimension as he needs it, he will easily discover any superfluous or omitted dimensions.

10.20. Placement of Dimensions. After the distances have been selected as outlined in paragraph 10.2, it is then possible to decide (1) the *view* on which the distance will be indicated, (2) the particular *place* on that view, and (3) the *form* of the dimension itself.

Numerous principles, some with the force of a rule, can be given, but in any case the important consideration is *clarity*.

10.21. Views: The Contour Principle. One of the views of an object will usually describe the shape of some detailed feature better than will the other view or views, and the feature is then said to be "characteristic" in that particular view. In reading a drawing, it is natural to look for the dimensions of a given feature wherever that feature appears most characteristic, and an advantage in clarity and in ease of reading will certainly result by following this principle in dimensioning the drawing. In Fig. 10.25, the rounded corner, the drilled hole, and the lower notched corner are all characteristic in, and dimensioned on, the front view. The projecting shape on the front of the object is more characteristic in the top view and is dimensioned there.

Dimensions for prisms should be placed so that two of the three dimensions are on the view showing the contour shape and the third on one of the other views (Figs. 10.16 and 10.25).

Dimensions for cylinders, the diameter and length, are usually best placed on the noncircular view (Fig. 10.26*A*). This practice keeps the dimensions on one view, a convenience for the workman. Oc-

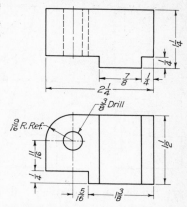

Fig. 10.25. The contour principle applied.

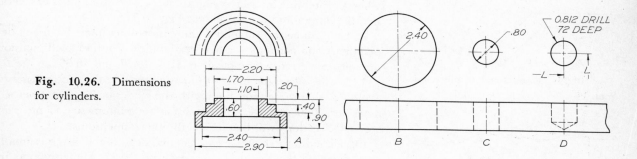

Fig. 10.26. Dimensions for cylinders.

casionally a cylindrical hole may be dimensioned with the diameter at an angle on the circular view, as indicated at (*B*). This practice should never be used unless there is a clear space for the dimension value. In some cases, however, the value can be carried outside the view, as in (*C*). When a round hole is specified by a note, as at (*D*), the leader should point to the circular view if possible. The note has an advantage in that the diameter, operation, and depth may all be given together. Giving the diameter on the circular view as at (*B*), (*C*), or (*D*) may make for ease of reading, as the location dimensions will likely be given there also, as indicated at (*D*). When it is not obvious from the drawing, a dimension may be indicated as a diameter by following the value with the letter *D*, as shown in Fig. 10.27.

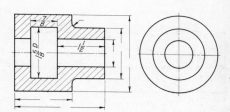

Fig. 10.27. Dimensions inside the view.

PRINCIPLES FOR THE PLACEMENT OF DIMENSIONS

1. Dimensions outside the view are preferred, unless added clearness, simplicity, and ease of reading will result from placing some of them inside. For good appearance, they should be kept off the cut surfaces of sections. When it is necessary that they be placed there, the section lining is omitted around the numbers (Fig. 10.27).

2. Dimensions between the views are preferred unless there is some reason for placing them elsewhere, as there was in Fig. 10.25, where the dimension for the lower notched corner and the location of the hole must come at the bottom of the front view.

3. Dimensions should be applied to one view only; that is, with dimensions between views, the extension lines should be drawn from one view, not from both views (Fig. 10.28).

4. Dimensions should be placed on the view that shows the distance in its true length (Fig. 10.29).

5. Dimension lines should be spaced, in general, ½ in. away from the outlines of the view. This applies to a single dimension or the first dimension of several in a series.

6. Parallel dimension lines should be spaced uniformly with at least ⅜ in. between lines.

7. Values should be midway between the arrowheads, except when a center line interferes, Fig. 10.30, or when the values of several parallel dimensions are staggered, Fig. 10.31.

8. Continuous or staggered dimension lines may be used, depending upon convenience and readability. Continuous dimension lines are preferred where possible (Figs. 10.32 and 10.33).

9. Always place the longer dimension outside the shorter ones to avoid crossing dimension lines with the extension lines of other dimensions. Thus an over-all dimension (maximum size of piece in a given direction) will be outside all other dimensions.

10. Dimensions should never be crowded. If the space is small, follow one of the methods of paragraph 10.22, Dimensioning in Limited Space.

11. Center lines are used to indicate the symmetry of shapes and as such frequently eliminate the need of a location dimension. They should be considered as part of the dimensioning and drawn in finished form at the time of dimensioning. They should extend about ⅛ in. beyond the shape for which they indicate symmetry unless

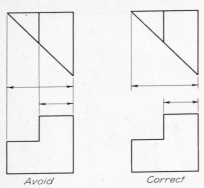

Fig. 10.28. Dimensions applied to one view only.

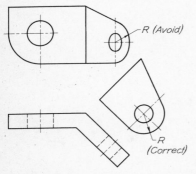

Fig. 10.29. Dimensioned distance normal.

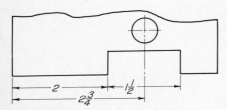

Fig. 10.30. Values midway between arrowheads.

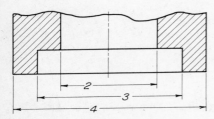

Fig. 10.31. "Staggered" values.

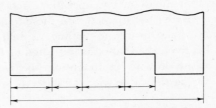

Fig. 10.32. Continuous dimensions.

hey are carried farther to serve as extension lines. Center lines
hould not be continued between views.

12. All notes must read horizontally (from the bottom of the
lrawing).

STUDY

PRACTICES TO AVOID

1. Never use a center line, a line of a view, or an extension line
ıs a dimension line.

2. Never place a dimension line on a center line or place a dimension line where a center line should properly be.

3. Never allow a line of any kind to pass through a dimension
figure.

4. Avoid the crossing of two dimension lines or the crossing of an
extension line and a dimension line.

5. Avoid dimensioning to dotted lines if possible.

10.22. Dimensioning in Limited Space. Dimensions should
never be crowded into a space too small to contain them. One of the
methods of Fig. 10.34 may be used to avoid the difficulty. Sometimes
a note may be appropriate. If the space is very small and crowded,
an enlarged removed section or part view may be used (Fig. 10.35).

10.23. Arcs and Curves. Arcs should be dimensioned by giving
the radius on the view that shows the true shape of the curve. The
dimension line for a radius should always be drawn as a radial line
at an angle (Fig. 10.36), never horizontal or vertical; and only one
arrowhead is used. There is no arrowhead at the arc center. The
numerical value should be followed by the letter R. Depending
upon the size of the radius and the available space for the value, the
dimension line and value are either both inside or the line inside
and the value outside or, for small arcs, both outside, as shown in
the illustration.

When the center of an arc lies outside the limits of the drawing,
the center is moved closer along a center line of the arc and the dimension line is jogged to meet the new center (Fig. 10.37). The

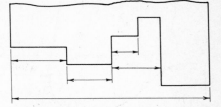

Fig. 10.33. "Staggered" dimensions.

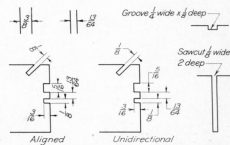

Fig. 10.34. Limited space.

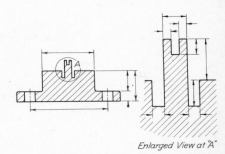

Fig. 10.35. Use of enlarged view.

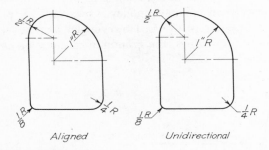

Fig. 10.36. Radius dimensions.

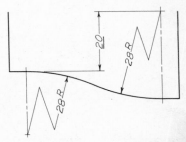

Fig. 10.37. Inaccessible centers.

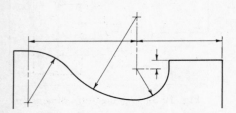

Fig. 10.38. Curve dimensioned by radii.

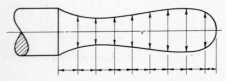

Fig. 10.39. Curve dimensioned by offsets.

portion of the dimension line adjacent to the arc is a radial line of the true center.

A curved line made up of circle arcs is dimensioned by radii with the centers located, as in Fig. 10.38. Irregular curves are usually dimensioned by offsets, as in Fig. 10.39, or by ordinate and abscissa dimensions.

10.24. Angles. The dimension line for an angle is a circle arc with its center at the intersection of the sides of the angle (Fig. 10.40). The value is placed to read horizontally with the exception that, in the aligned system, large arcs only have the value aligned with the dimension arc. Angular values should be written in the form 35°7′ with no dash between the degrees and minutes.

10.25. Notes. Notes are word statements giving information that cannot be given by the views and dimensions. They may be classified as either *general* or *specific*. A general note applies to the entire part, and a specific note applies to an individual feature. Occasionally a note will save making an additional view or even, for example, with a note used to indicate right- and left-hand parts, save making an entire drawing.

Do not be afraid to put notes on drawings. Supplement the graphic language by the English language whenever added information can be conveyed, but be careful to word it so clearly that the meaning cannot possibly be misunderstood.

General notes do not require the use of a leader and should be grouped together above the title block. Examples are "Finish all over," "Fillets ¼R, rounds ⅛R, unless otherwise specified," "All draft angles 7°," "Remove burs," etc.

Much of the information provided in the title strip of a machine drawing is a grouping of general notes. Stock size, material, heat-treatment, etc., are general notes in the title of the drawing of Fig. 10.59.

Specific notes almost always require a leader and should therefore be placed fairly close to the feature to which they apply. Most common are notes giving an operation with a size, as "½ Drill, 4 holes."

Recommended forms for the wording of notes occurring more or less frequently are given in Fig. 10.41.

When lower-case lettering is used, capitalization of words in notes depends largely on company policy. One common practice is to capitalize all important words. However, for long notes, as on civil or architectural drawings, the grammatical rules for capitalization usually prevail.

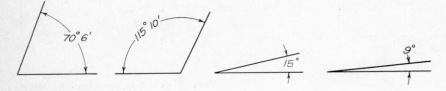

Fig. 10.40. Dimensions for angles.

Up to Here For Final

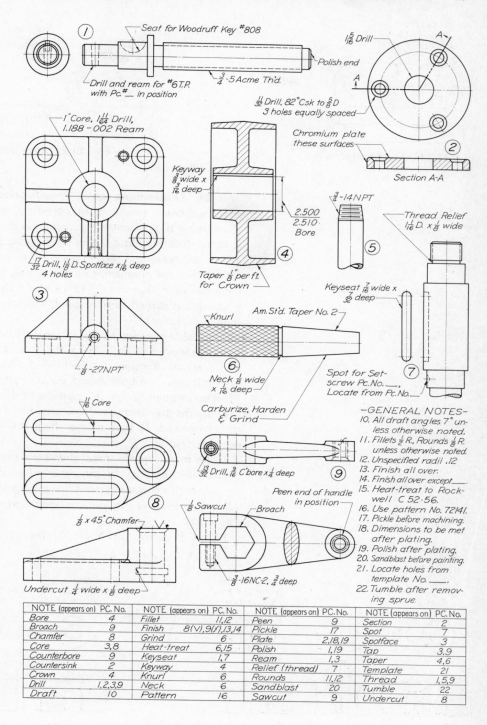

GENERAL NOTES

10. All draft angles 7° unless otherwise noted.
11. Fillets ½ R, Rounds ⅛ R. unless otherwise noted.
12. Unspecified radii .12
13. Finish all over.
14. Finish all over except____.
15. Heat-treat to Rockwell C 52-56.
16. Use pattern No. 72141.
17. Pickle before machining.
18. Dimensions to be met after plating.
19. Polish after plating.
20. Sandblast before painting.
21. Locate holes from template No. ____.
22. Tumble after removing sprue.

NOTE (appears on)	PC. No.	NOTE (appears on)	PC. No.	NOTE (appears on)	PC. No.	NOTE (appears on)	PC. No.
Bore	4	Fillet	11,12	Peen	9	Section	2
Broach	9	Finish	8(V),9(f),13,14	Pickle	17	Spot	7
Chamfer	8	Grind	6	Plate	2,18,19	Spotface	3
Core	3,8	Heat-treat	6,15	Polish	1,19	Tap	3,9
Counterbore	9	Keyseat	1,7	Ream	1,3	Taper	4,6
Countersink	2	Keyway	4	Relief (thread)	7	Template	21
Crown	4	Knurl	6	Rounds	11,12	Thread	1,5,9
Drill	1,2,3,9	Neck	6	Sandblast	20	Tumble	22
Draft	10	Pattern	16	Sawcut	9	Undercut	8

Fig. 10.41. Approved wording for notes on drawings.

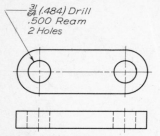

Fig. 10.42. Dimensioning of holes.

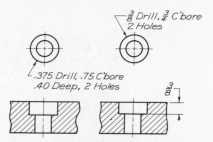

Fig. 10.43. Dimensioning of counterbored holes

10.26. Dimensions and Specifications for Holes. Drilled reamed, bored, punched, or cored holes are usually specified by note giving the diameter, operation, and depth if required. If there is more than one hole of the same kind, the leader needs to point to but one hole, and the number of holes is stated in the note (Fig. 10.42). Several operations involving one hole may be grouped in a common note. Figures 10.42 to 10.45 show typical dimensioning practice for drilled and reamed, counterbored, countersunk, and spot-faced holes.

The ASA specifies that standard drill sizes be given as decimal fractions, such as 0.250, 0.375, 0.750, and 1.500. If the size is given as a common fraction, the decimal equivalent should be added.

The leader to a hole should point to the circular view if possible. With concentric circles, the arrowhead should touch the inner circle (usually the first operation) unless an outer circle would pass through the arrowhead. In such a case, the arrow should be drawn to touch the outer circle.

Holes made up of several diameters and involving several stages of manufacture may be dimensioned as shown in Fig. 10.46. This method of dimensioning combines notes with the regular dimensions.

Threaded holes are dimensioned and specified as described in Chap. 11.

10.27. Location of Holes. Mating parts held together by bolts,

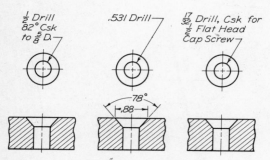

Fig. 10.44. Dimensioning of counter-sunk holes.

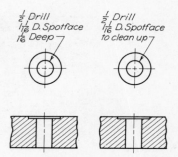

Fig. 10.45. Dimensioning of spot-faced holes.

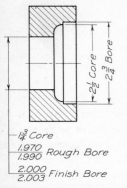

Fig. 10.46. Specifying several operations on large holes.

Fig. 10.47. Location of holes.

Fig. 10.48. Location of holes.

screws, rivets, etc., must have their holes for fastenings located from common datum surfaces or lines in order to assure matching of the holes. When two or more holes are on an established center line, the holes will require location in one direction only (Fig. 10.47). If the holes are not on a common center line, they will require location in two directions, as in Fig. 10.48. The method at (*B*), where the locations are referred to a common base line, is preferred for precision work.

Hole circles are circular center lines, often called "bolt circles," on which the centers of a number of holes are located.

One practice is to give the diameter of the hole circle and a note specifying the size of the holes, the number required, and the spacing, as in Fig. 10.49*A*. If one or more holes are not in the regular equally spaced position, their location may be given by an offset dimension, as shown at (*B*). An angular dimension is sometimes used for this purpose but, in general, should be avoided in more precise work.

The coordinate method for locating holes, Fig. 10.49*C*, is preferred in precision work. The hole circle is often drawn and its diameter given for reference purposes, as indicated on the figure. The diameter of a hole circle is invariably given on the circular view.

10.28. Chamfers. Chamfers may be dimensioned by note, as in

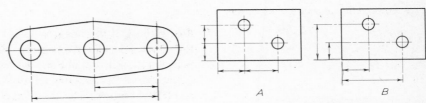

Fig. 10.49. Hole circles.

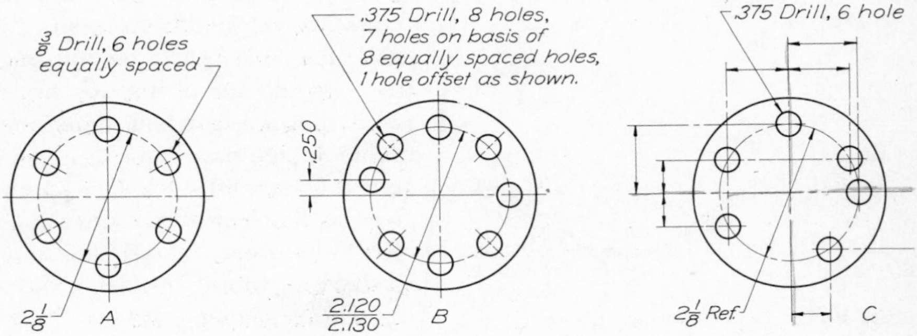

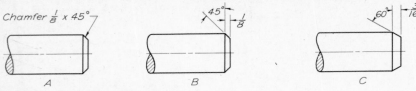

Fig. 10.50. Dimensioning of chamfers.

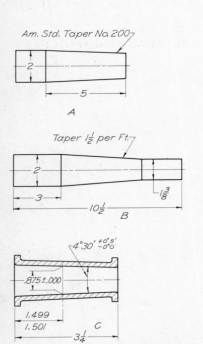

Fig. 10.51. Dimensioning of tapers.

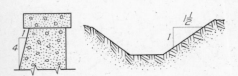

Fig. 10.52. Dimensioning of batters and slopes.

Fig. 10.50*A*, if the angle is 45°. The linear size is understood to be the short side of the chamfer triangle in conformity with the dimensioning without a note, as shown at (*B*). If the chamfer angle is other than 45°, it should be dimensioned as at (*C*).

10.29. Tapers. The term "taper" as used in machine work usually means the surface of a cone frustum. The dimensioning will depend on the method of manufacture and the accuracy required. If a standardized taper (see Appendix) is used, the specification should be accompanied by one diameter and the length (Fig. 10.51*A*). At (*B*) is illustrated the general method of giving the diameters of both ends and the taper per foot. An alternate method is to give one diameter, the length, and the taper per foot. Taper per foot is defined as the difference in diameter in inches for 1 ft of length. (*C*) illustrates the method of dimensioning for precision work, where a close fit between the parts as well as a control of entry distance is required. Because of the inaccuracy resulting from measuring at one of the ends, a gage line is established where the diameter is to be measured. The entry distance is controlled through the allowable variation in the location of the gage line, and the fit of the taper is controlled by the accuracy called for in the specification of the angle.

10.30. Batters, Slopes, and Grades. *Batter* is a deviation from the vertical, such as is found on the sides of retaining walls, piers, etc., and *slope* is a deviation from the horizontal. Both are expressed as a ratio with one factor equal to unity, as illustrated in Fig. 10.52. *Grade* is identical to slope but is expressed in percentage, the inclination in feet per hundred feet. In structural work, angular measurements are shown by giving the ratio of run to rise with the larger side 12 in.

10.31. Shapes with Rounded Ends. These should be dimensioned according to their method of manufacture. Figure 10.53 shows several similar contours and the typical dimensioning for each. The link (*A*), to be cut from thin material, has the radius of the ends and the center distance given as it would be laid out. At (*B*) is shown a cast pad dimensioned as (*A*), with dimensions most usable for the patternmaker. The drawing at (*C*) shows a slot machined from solid stock with an end-milling cutter. The dimensions give the diameter of the cutter and the travel of the milling-machine table. The slot at (*D*) is similar to (*C*) but is dimensioned for quantity production, where, instead of the table travel, the over-all length is wanted for gaging purposes. Pratt and Whitney keys and key seats are dimensioned by this method.

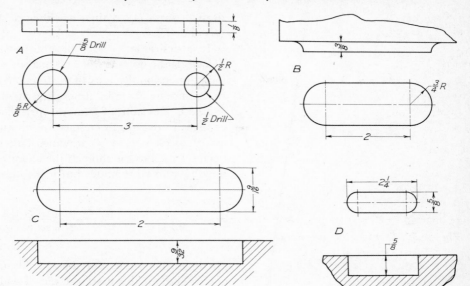

Fig. 10.53. Dimensioning of round-end shapes.

10.32. Order of Dimensioning. A systematic order of working is a great help in placing dimensions. Figure 10.54 will illustrate the procedure. At (A) the shape description is complete. (B) shows the extension lines placed and center lines extended where necessary, thus planning for the positions of both size and location dimensions. Here the placement of each dimension can be studied and alterations made if desirable or necessary. At (C) the dimension lines have been added. Next, arrowheads and leaders for notes are

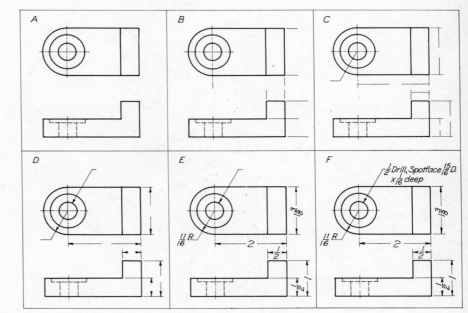

Fig. 10.54. Order of dimensioning.

drawn as at (*D*). Values are then added and notes lettered as at (*E*) and (*F*).

It is desirable to add the notes *after* the dimensions have been placed. If the notes are placed first, they may occupy a space desired for a dimension. Because of the freedom allowed in the use of leaders, notes may be given in almost any available space.

10.33. Revision of Dimensions. As a project is being developed, changes in design, in engineering methods, etc., may make it necessary to change some drawings either before or after they have been released to the shop. If the change is a major one, the drawing may have to be remade; but if the change is minor, in many cases

Fig. 10.55. Out-of-scale dimensions.

the dimension values may be altered and the shape description left unchanged. In this case, the out-of-scale dimensions should be indicated by one of the methods of Fig. 10.55. Drawing changes should be listed in tabular form, either in connection with the title block or in the upper right corner, with reference letters and the date, as explained in paragraph 12.19.

10.34. Dimensioning of Auxiliary Views. In placing dimensions on an auxiliary view, all the principles of dimensioning will apply as for any other drawing, but with special attention paid to the contour principle described in paragraph 10.21. An auxiliary view is made for the purpose of showing the true contour and *size* of some slanting face, and for this reason the dimensioning of the face should be placed where it is easiest to read, *which will be on the auxiliary view*. Note in Fig. 10.56 that the spacing and size of holes

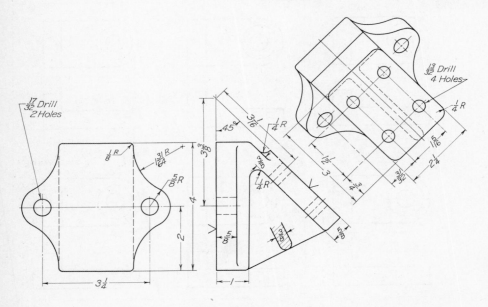

Fig. 10.56. Dimensioning on an auxiliary view.

as well as the size of the inclined face are dimensioned on the auxiliary view. Note further that the angle and location dimension tying the inclined face to the rest of the object could not be placed on the auxiliary view.

10.35. Dimensioning of Sectional Views. Dimensions that must be placed on sectional views may, in most cases, be placed outside the view so as not to be crowded within crosshatched areas. However, sometimes a dimension *must* be placed across a crosshatched area; and when this is necessary, the crosshatching is left out around the dimension figures, as illustrated in Fig. 10.27. Examples showing dimensioning practice on sectional views are given in Probs. 12.2.3, 12.2.4, and 12.3.3.

10.36. Dimensioning a Half Section. In general, the half section is difficult to dimension clearly without some possibility of giving misleading, ambiguous, or crowded information. Generous use of notes and careful placement of the dimension lines, leaders, and figures will in most cases make the dimensioning clear; but if a half section cannot be clearly dimensioned, an extra view or part view should be added on which to describe the size.

Inside diameters should be followed by the letter *D* and the dimension line carried over the center line, as in Fig. 10.57, to prevent the possibility of reading the dimension as a radius. Sometimes the view and the dimensioning may both be clarified by showing the dotted lines on the unsectioned side. Dimensions of internal parts, if placed inside the view, will prevent the confusion between extension lines and the outline of external portions.

10.37. Dimensioning of Pictorial Drawings. Pictorial drawings are often more difficult to dimension than orthographic drawings because there is only one view instead of several, and the dimensioning may become crowded unless the placement is carefully planned. In general, the principles of dimensioning for orthographic drawings

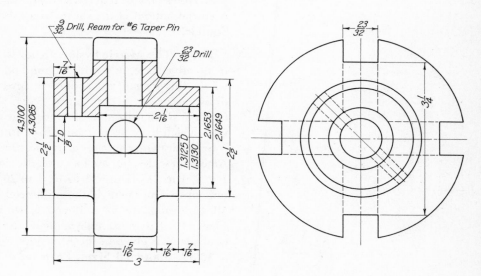

Fig. 10.57. Dimensioning a half section.

should be followed whenever possible. The following rules should be observed:

1. Dimension and extension lines should be placed so as to lie either *in* or *perpendicular to* the face on which the dimension applies. See Probs. 5.3.19 and 5.3.20.

2. Dimension numerals should be placed so as to lie in the plane in which the dimension and extension lines lie. See Probs. 5.3.22 and 5.3.38.

3. Leaders for notes and the lettered note should be placed so as to lie in a plane either parallel or perpendicular to the face on which the note applies. See Probs. 6.2.2 and 6.2.20.

4. Finish may be indicated by the standard finish (**V**) symbol. The symbol is applied *perpendicular to* the face with its point touching a short line lying in the surface. The symbol and line should be parallel to one of the principal axes. If the symbol cannot be applied in the above manner, the finish symbol may be attached to a leader pointing to the face. See Probs. 12.1.5 and 12.1.18.

5. Lettering of dimension values and of notes should be made so that the lettering appears to lie in or parallel to one of the principal faces of the pictorial drawing. To do this the lettering must be the *pictorial representation of vertical figures*. Note the placement and lettering of the dimension values and the notes of Probs. 12.4.4 and 12.4.7.

The American Standard also allows the use of the unidirectional system with either vertical or slant lettering for pictorial drawings. This is done principally to make possible the use of mechanical lettering devices. If this system is employed, the following should be observed:

1. Dimension values may be lettered to read from the bottom of the sheet.

2. Notes may be lettered so that they lie *in the picture plane*, to read from the bottom of the sheet. Notes should be kept off the view, if possible.

10.38. The Metric System. Knowledge of the metric system will be an advantage, as it will be found on all drawings from countries where this system is standard and with increasing frequency on drawings made in the United States. The first instance of international standardization of a mechanical device is that of ball bearings, which have been standardized in the metric system.

Scale drawings in the metric system are not made to English or American scales, but are based on divisions of 10 as full size and then 1 to 2, 1 to 2½, 1 to 5, 1 to 10, 1 to 20, 1 to 50, and 1 to 100. The unit of measurement is the millimeter (mm), and the figures are all understood to be millimeters, without any indicating marks. Figure 10.58 is an example of metric dimensioning. A table of metric equivalents is given in the Appendix.

10.39. Standard Sizes, Parts, and Tools. In the dimensioning

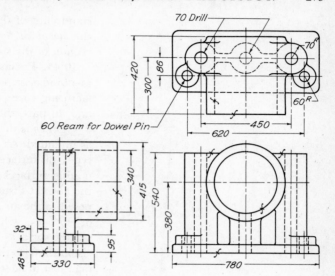

Fig. 10.58. A metric drawing.

of any machine part, there is often the necessity of specifying some standard thickness or diameter or the size produced by some standard tool. The American Standard, prevailing company standard, or manufacturer's standard should be consulted in order to assure giving correct information.

Wire and sheet-metal gages are given by number and are followed by the equivalent thickness or diameter in decimal form.

Bolts and screws are supplied in fractional and numbered sizes.

Keys are available in manufacturer's numbered sizes or, for square and flat keys, in fractional sizes.

Rivets, depending upon the variety, are to be had in fractional or numbered sizes.

Drills are available in numbered, lettered, fractional, and metric sizes.

Reamers, *milling cutters*, and other standard tools are available in a variety of standard sizes.

The Appendix gives tables of standard wire and metal gages, bolt and screw sizes, key sizes, etc. ASA or manufacturer's standards will give further information required.

10.40. Obligation of Engineering Groups. Modern production methods are based on the principle that the engineering department is responsible for the correctness and completeness of the drawings and that manufacturing then proceeds in the various shops to produce exactly what is called for by the drawings. This procedure clearly defines the responsibility of the designing and manufacturing groups, minimizes confusion in the drafting room and in the shop, ensures the interchangeability of parts, and guarantees, in so far as is possible, proper functioning of a completed machine. Thus working drawings must be clearly and completely dimensioned from the standpoint of the *functioning of the part*, the *method of production*, and the *manufacturing process to be used* so that nothing is left to the discretion of the shop.

10.41. Precision and Tolerance. In the manufacture of any machine or structure, quality is a primary consideration. The manufacturing care put into the product determines the relative quality and, in part, the accompanying relative cost and selling price.

Precision is the degree of accuracy necessary to ensure functioning as intended. As an example, a cast part will usually have on it two types of surfaces: mating surfaces and nonmating surfaces. The mating surfaces will be machined to the proper smoothness and at the correct distance from each other. The nonmating surfaces, exposed to the air and having no important relationship to other parts or surfaces, will be left in the original rough-cast form. Thus the mating surfaces ordinarily require much greater manufacturing precision than do the nonmating surfaces. The dimensions on the drawing must indicate which surfaces are to be finished and the precision required in finishing. However, because of the impossibility of producing any distance to an absolute size, some variation must be allowed in manufacture.

Tolerance is the allowable variation for any given size and provides a practical means of achieving the precision required. The tolerance on any given dimension varies according to the degree of precision necessary for that particular dimension. For nonmating surfaces, the tolerance may vary from 0.01 in. for small parts to as much as 1 in. on very large parts. For mating surfaces, tolerances as small as a few millionths of an inch are sometimes necessary (for extremely close-fitting surfaces), but usually surfaces are finished to an accuracy of 0.001 to 0.010, depending upon the function of the part. Figure

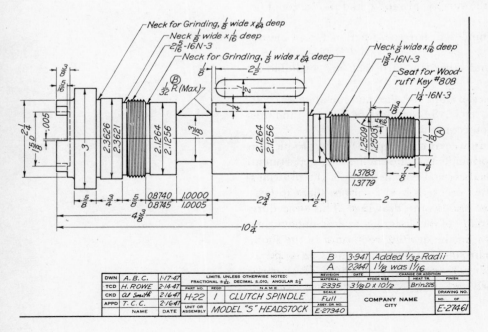

Fig. 10.59. Toleranced dimensions.

10.59 shows variously toleranced dimensions on a machine drawing.

In some cases, particularly in structural and architectural work, tolerances are not stated on the drawing but are given in a set of specifications or are understood to be of an order standard for the industry.

10.42. Fits of Mating Parts. The working parts of any machine will have some definite relationship to their mating parts in order to achieve a particular function, as free rotation, free longitudinal movement, clamping action, permanent fixed position, etc. In accomplishing these, the old practice was to mark the drawings of both parts with the same fractional dimension and add a note such as "running fit" or "drive fit," leaving the difference in size required (allowance) to the experience and judgment of the machinist.

The tongue of Fig. 10.60 is to slide longitudinally in the slot. Thus, if the slot is machined first and measures 1.499 in. and the machinist, from his experience, assumes an allowance of 0.004 in., he then carefully machines the tongue to 1.495 in.; the parts will fit and function as desired. In making up a second machine, if the slot measures, say, 1.504 in. after machining, the tongue is made 1.500 in. and an identical fit obtained; but the tongue of the first machine would be much too loose in the slot of the second machine, and the tongue of the second would not enter the slot of the first. The parts are, therefore, not interchangeable.

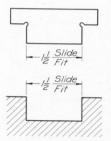

Fig. 10.60. Dimensioning a fit (old practice).

Since it is not possible to work to absolute sizes, it is necessary where interchangeable assembly is required to give the dimensions of mating parts with "limits," that is, the maximum and minimum sizes within which the actual measurements must fall in order for the part to be accepted. The dimensions for each piece are given by three- or four-place decimals, the engineering department taking all the responsibility for the correctness of fit required.

Figure 10.61 shows the same tongue and slot of Fig. 10.60 but dimensioned for interchangeability of parts. In this case, for satisfactory functioning, it is decided that the tongue must be at least 0.002 in. smaller than the slot but not more than 0.006 in. smaller. This would provide an average fit similar to that used in the previous example. The maximum and minimum sizes acceptable for each part can then be figured.

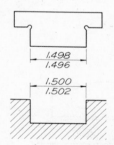

Fig. 10.61. Dimensioning a fit with limits.

The value 1.500 in. has been assigned as the size of the minimum acceptable slot. This value minus the minimum clearance, 0.002 in., gives a size for the maximum tongue of 1.498. The maximum allowable clearance, 0.006, minus the minimum allowable clearance, 0.002, gives the amount, 0.004, available as the total manufacturing tolerance for both parts. This has been evenly divided and applied as 0.002 to the slot and 0.002 to the tongue. Thus the size of the maximum slot will be the size of the minimum slot *plus* the slot tolerance, or 1.500 + 0.002 = 1.502. The size of the minimum tongue will be the size of the maximum tongue *minus* the tongue tolerance, or 1.498 − 0.002 = 1.496.

A study of Fig. 10.61 will show that, made in any quantity, the

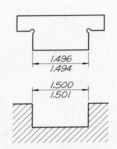

Fig. 10.62. An example of limit dimensioning.

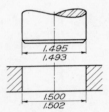

Fig. 10.63. A clearance fit.

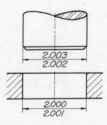

Fig. 10.64. An interference fit.

two parts will allow interchangeable assembly and that any pair will fit approximately as any other pair, as planned. This system is essential in modern quantity-production manufacture.

10.43. Nomenclature. The terms used in limit dimensioning are so interconnected that their meaning should be clearly understood before a detailed study of the method is attempted.

The ASA gives the following definitions:

Nominal Size. A designation given to the subdivision of the unit of length having no specified limits of accuracy but indicating a close approximation to a standard size.

Basic Size. The exact theoretical size from which all limiting variations are made.

Allowance (*Neutral Zone*). An intentional difference in the dimensions of mating parts, that is, the minimum clearance space (or maximum interference) which is intended between mating parts. It represents the condition of the tightest permissible fit, or the largest internal member mated with the smallest external member. It is to provide for different classes of fit.

Tolerance. The amount of variation permitted in a size of a part.

Limits. The extreme permissible dimensions of a part.

In illustration of these terms, a pair of mating parts is dimensioned in Fig. 10.62. In this example the *nominal size* is 1½ in. The *basic size* is 1.500. The *allowance* is 0.004. The *tolerance* on the tongue is 0.002, and on the slot it is 0.001. The *limits* are, for the tongue, 1.496 (maximum) and 1.494 (minimum) and, for the slot, 1.501 (maximum) and 1.500 (minimum).

Sometimes a somewhat broader definition is used for *basic size*, in which both parts are considered to be basic in their most desirable size. Following this conception, the basic tongue of Fig. 10.62 would be 1.496, and the basic slot would be 1.500.

10.44. General Fit Classes. The fits established on machine parts may be classified as follows:

A *clearance fit* is the condition in which the internal part is smaller than the external part, as illustrated by the dimensioning of Fig. 10.63. In this case, the largest shaft is 1.495 in. and the smallest hole 1.500 in., leaving a clearance of 0.005 for the tightest possible fit.

An *interference fit* is the opposite of a clearance fit, having a definite interference of metal for all possible conditions. The parts must be assembled by pressure or by heat expansion of the external member. Figure 10.64 is an illustration, where the shaft is 0.001 in. larger than the hole for the loosest possible fit. The allowance in this case is 0.003 in. interference.

A *transition fit* is the condition in which either a clearance fit or an interference fit may be had; a minimum shaft in a maximum hole will give clearance, and a maximum shaft in a minimum hole will give interference. Figure 10.65 illustrates a transition fit where the smallest shaft in the largest hole results in 0.0003 in. clearance and the largest shaft in the smallest hole results in 0.0007 in. interference.

10.45. Selective Assembly. Sometimes the fit desired may be so close and the tolerances so small that the cost of producing interchangeable parts is prohibitive. In this case, tolerances as small as practical are established; then the parts are gaged and graded as, say, *small*, *medium*, and *large*. A small shaft in a small hole, medium in medium, or large in large will produce approximately the same fit allowance. Transition and interference fits often require a selection of parts in order to get the amount of clearance or interference desired. Antifriction bearings are usually assembled selectively.

10.46. Basic-hole and Basic-shaft Systems. Production economy depends to some extent upon which mating part is taken as a standard size. In the *basic-hole system*, the hole can often be made with a standard tool, and the minimum size of the hole is taken as a base from which all variations are made.

Where a number of different fits of the same nominal size are required on one shaft, as, for example, when bearings are fitted to line shafting, the *basic-shaft system* is employed, in which the maximum shaft size is taken as the basic size.

10.47. Unilateral and Bilateral Tolerances. A unilateral tolerance is one in which the total allowable variation is in *one* direction, either plus or minus (not both) from the basic value. A bilateral tolerance is one in which the tolerance is divided, with part plus and the remainder minus from the basic value.

In general, mating surfaces should be toleranced unilaterally and nonmating surfaces toleranced bilaterally. One important exception is in the location of holes that *mate* with other holes or pins, as shown in Fig. 10.80. In this case, the basic size is the same for both parts, and the tolerances are bilateral as the variation is equally dangerous in either direction. The sizes of the pins and holes, however, are dimensioned with unilateral tolerances.

10.48. Methods of Expressing Tolerances. Tolerances may be either *specific*, given with the dimension value, or they may be *general*, as a note in the title block. The general tolerances apply to all dimensions not carrying a specific tolerance. The general tolerance should be allowed to apply whenever possible, using specific tolerances only when necessary. If no tolerances are specified, the value usually assumed for fractional dimensions is $\pm\frac{1}{64}$ in., for angular dimensions $\pm\frac{1}{2}°$, and for decimal dimensions plus or minus the nearest significant figure, as, for example, ±0.01 in. for a two-place decimal and ±0.001 in. for a three-place decimal.

There are several methods for expressing tolerances. The method preferred in quantity-production work, where gages are extensively employed, is to write the two limits representing the maximum and minimum acceptable sizes as in Fig. 10.66. An internal dimension has the *minimum* size above the line, and an external dimension has the *maximum* size above the line. This is for convenience in machining.

Another method is to give the basic size followed by the tolerance, plus and minus (with the plus above the minus), Fig. 10.67*A*. If

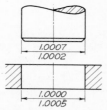

Fig. 10.65. A transition fit.

Fig. 10.66. A tolerance expressed as limits.

Fig. 10.67. Tolerances, plus and minus.

only one tolerance value is given, as at (B), the other value is assumed to be zero.

Unilateral tolerances may be expressed by giving the two limits, as in Fig. 10.66, or by giving one limiting size and the tolerance, as 2.750 +0.005 or 2.750 $\begin{smallmatrix}+0.005\\-0.000\end{smallmatrix}$; for fractional dimensions, $\frac{1}{2} - \frac{1}{32}$ or $\frac{1}{2} \begin{smallmatrix}+0\\-\frac{1}{32}\end{smallmatrix}$; for angular dimensions, $64°15'30'' +0°45'0''$ or $64°15'30'' \begin{smallmatrix}+0°45'0''\\-0°\ 0'0''\end{smallmatrix}$.

Bilateral tolerances are expressed by giving the basic value followed by the divided tolerance, both plus and minus (commonly equal in amount), as 1.500 $\begin{smallmatrix}+0.002\\-0.002\end{smallmatrix}$ or 1.500 ±0.002; for fractional dimensions, $1\frac{1}{2} \begin{smallmatrix}+\frac{1}{64}\\-\frac{1}{64}\end{smallmatrix}$ or $1\frac{1}{2} \pm\frac{1}{64}$; for angular dimensions, $30°0' \begin{smallmatrix}+0°10'\\-0°10'\end{smallmatrix}$ or $30°0' \pm0°10'$.

10.49. Decimal Places. A dimension value should be carried to the same number of decimal places as the tolerance. For example, with a tolerance of 0.0005 on a nominal dimension of $1\frac{1}{2}$ in., the basic value should be written 1.5000. Tolerances for common fractional values should be given as common fractions, as $\frac{7}{8} \pm\frac{1}{64}$. Tolerances for decimal values should be given as decimal fractions, as 0.750 ±0.010.

10.50. Fundamentals for Tolerance Selection. Experience in manufacturing is needed as well as a study of the particular mechanism involved before the engineer can decide on the precision necessary and specify the proper fits and tolerances. The following quotation from the ASA Standard is pertinent:

In choosing the class of fit for manufacture, the engineer should keep in mind that cost usually increases proportionately to the accuracy required, and no finer class of fit should be chosen than the functional requirements actually demand. It is axiomatic that the closer the fit the smaller the manufacturing tolerance, and usually the greater the cost. The length of engagement of the fit also plays an important part in the selection of the class of fit for a piece of work. It is obvious that a long engagement will tolerate more looseness than a short one, and due regard should be paid to this feature.

A table of fits, such as the ASA table of cylindrical fits explained in paragraph 10.53, may be taken as a guide for ordinary work.

In many cases, practical experience is necessary in determining the fit conditions guaranteeing proper performance. Often it is difficult to determine the definite size at which performance fails, and critical tolerances are sometimes determined through exhaustive testing of experimental models.

It is essential to know the precision attainable with various machine tools and machining methods. As an example, holes to be produced by drilling must not be specified to a smaller tolerance than can be attained by drilling. Attainable manufacturing precision is discussed in paragraph 10.51. A knowledge of kinds and types of equipment is needed to assure that the tolerances specified can be attained.

10.51. Manufacturing Precision. The different manufacturing processes all have inherent minimum possible accuracies, depending upon the size of the work, the condition of the equipment, and, to some extent, the skill of the workmen. The following *minimum* tolerances are given as a guide and are based on the assumption that the work is to be done on a quantity-production basis with equipment in good condition. Greater precision may be attained by highly skilled workmen on a unit-production basis.

In general, the following are recommended as tolerances for dimensions having *no effect on the function of the part:* for sizes of 0 to 6 in., $\pm \frac{1}{64}$; 6 to 18 in., $\pm \frac{1}{32}$; 18 in. and larger, $\pm \frac{1}{16}$ (or more).

Sand Castings. For the unmachined surfaces, a tolerance of $\pm \frac{1}{32}$ is recommended for small castings and a tolerance of $\pm \frac{1}{16}$ for medium-size castings. On larger castings, the tolerance should be increased to suit the size. Small and medium-size castings will rarely be below the nominal size since the pattern is "rapped" for easy removal from the sand, thus tending to increase the size.

Die Castings and Plastic Molding. A tolerance of $\pm \frac{1}{64}$ or less can easily be held with small and medium-size parts; for large parts, the tolerance should be increased slightly. Hole-center distances can be maintained within 0.005 to 0.010, depending on the distance of separation. Certain alloys may be die-cast to tolerances of 0.001 or less.

Forgings. The rough surfaces of drop forgings weighing 1 lb or less can be held to $\pm \frac{1}{32}$; for weights up to 10 lb, $\pm \frac{1}{16}$; for weights up to 60 lb, $\pm \frac{1}{8}$. Because of die wear, drop forgings tend to increase in size as production from the die increases.

Drilling. For drills from No. 60 to No. 30, +0.002 − 0.000; No. 29 to No. 1, +0.004 − 0.000; from $\frac{1}{4}$ to $\frac{1}{2}$ in., +0.005 − 0.000; from $\frac{1}{2}$ to $\frac{3}{4}$ in., +0.008 − 0.000; from $\frac{3}{4}$ to 1 in., +0.010 − 0.000; from 1 to 2 in., +0.015 − 0.000.

Reaming. In general, a tolerance of +0.0005 − 0.0000 can be held with diameters up to $\frac{1}{2}$ in. For diameters from $\frac{1}{2}$ to 1 in., +0.001 − 0.000; from 1 in. and larger, +0.0015 − 0.0000.

Lathe Turning: Rough Work. For diameters of $\frac{1}{4}$ to $\frac{1}{2}$ in., allow a total tolerance of 0.005; for diameters of $\frac{1}{2}$ to 1 in., 0.007; for diameters of 1 to 2 in., 0.010; for diameters of 2 in. and larger, 0.015.

Finish Turning. For diameters of $\frac{1}{4}$ to $\frac{1}{2}$ in., a total tolerance of 0.002; for diameters of $\frac{1}{2}$ to 1 in., 0.003; for diameters of 1 to 2 in., 0.005; for diameters of 2 in. and larger, 0.007.

Milling. When single surfaces are to be milled, tolerances of 0.002 to 0.003 can be maintained. With two or more surfaces to be milled, the most important may be toleranced to 0.002 and the remainder as 0.005. In general, 0.005 is a good value to use with most milling work.

Planing and Shaping. These operations are not commonly used with small parts in quantity-production work. For larger parts, tolerances of 0.005 to 0.010 may be maintained.

Broaching. Diameters up to 1 in. may be held within 0.001; diameters of 1 to 2 in., 0.002; diameters of 2 to 4 in., 0.003. Surfaces up to 1 in. apart may be held within 0.002; 1 to 4 in. apart, 0.003; 4 in. apart and over, 0.004.

Threads. Tolerances for ASA threads are provided on the pitch diameter through the thread class given with the specification. For a given class, the tolerances increase as the size of the thread increases. These tolerances may be found in ASA B1.1—1949.

Grinding. For both cylindrical and surface grinding, a tolerance of 0.0005 can be maintained.

10.52. Selection of Tolerances. A common method of determining and applying tolerances is to determine at the outset how much clearance or interference there can be between the mating parts and *still allow the parts to function properly.* The difference between the tightest and loosest conditions will be the *sum* of the tolerances of both parts. This value may be then halved to obtain tolerances for the individual parts; or if it is believed desirable because of easier machining on one part, slightly less tolerance may be used on that part, with a proportionately larger tolerance on the part more difficult to machine. The following example will illustrate the procedure:

Assume that a running fit is to be arranged between a 2-in. shaft and bearing and that, in order to provide clearance for a film of oil, it is determined that the parts cannot fit closer than 0.002 in. Also, in order to prevent excessive looseness and radial movement of the shaft, it is determined that the parts cannot be looser than 0.007 in. Then we have the following calculations:

Loosest fit, 0.007 (maximum clearance)
Tightest fit, 0.002 (minimum clearance—allowance)
Difference, 0.005 (sum of tolerances)
½ of difference, 0.0025 (possible value for each tolerance)

Assuming that the shaft will be ground and the bearing reamed, 0.002 may be used for the shaft tolerance and 0.003 for the bearing tolerance since these values conform better to the precision attainable by these methods of production.

Figure 10.68 illustrates the completed dimensions. Note that the minimum hole is taken as the basic size of 2.000 and the tolerance of 0.003 applied. Then the largest shaft size will be the basic size minus the value for the tightest fit (allowance); the shaft tolerance then subtracted from the maximum shaft size gives the minimum shaft size. From the figure, the 2.003 bearing minus the 1.996 shaft gives 0.007, the loosest fit; the 2.000 bearing minus the 1.998 shaft gives 0.002, the tightest fit.

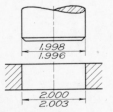

Fig. 10.68. Limits calculated from maximum and minimum clearances.

10.53. ASA Cylindrical Fits. The ASA has made a classification of eight kinds of fit and has compiled tables of limits for external and internal members, for different sizes in each class. These limits are tabulated in the Appendix.

ASA CLASSIFICATION OF FITS

Loose Fit (Class 1): Large Allowance. This fit provides for considerable freedom and embraces certain fits where accuracy is not essential.

Examples. Machined fits of agricultural and mining machinery; controlling apparatus for marine work; textile, rubber, candy, and bread machinery; general machinery of a similar grade; some ordnance material.

Free Fit (Class 2): Liberal Allowance. For running fits with speeds of 600 rpm or over and journal pressures of 600 lb per sq in. or over.

Examples. Dynamos, engines, many machine-tool parts, and some automotive parts.

Medium Fit (Class 3): Medium Allowance. For running fits under 600 rpm and with journal pressures less than 600 lb per sq in.; also for sliding fits and the more accurate machine-tool and automotive parts.

Snug Fit (Class 4): Zero Allowance. This is the closest fit that can be assembled by hand and necessitates work of considerable precision. It should be used where no perceptible shake is permissible and where moving parts are not intended to move freely under a load.

Wringing Fit (Class 5): Zero to Negative Allowance. This is also known as a "tunking fit," and it is practically metal-to-metal. Assembly is usually selective and not interchangeable.

Tight Fit (Class 6): Slight Negative Allowance. Light pressure is required to assemble these fits, and the parts are more or less permanently assembled, such as the fixed ends of studs for gears, pulleys, rocker arms, etc. These fits are used for drive fits in thin sections or extremely long fits in other sections and also for shrink fits on very light sections. Used in automotive, ordnance, and general machine manufacturing.

Medium Force Fit (Class 7): Negative Allowance. Considerable pressure is required to assemble these fits, and the parts are considered permanently assembled. These fits are used in fastening locomotive wheels, car wheels, armatures of dynamos and motors, and crank disks to their axles or shafts. They are also used for shrink fits on medium sections or for long fits. These fits are the tightest which are recommended for cast-iron holes or external members as they stress cast iron to its elastic limit.

Heavy Force and Shrink Fit (Class 8): Considerable Negative Allowance. These fits are used for steel holes where the metal can be highly stressed without exceeding its elastic limit. These fits cause excessive stress for cast-iron holes. Shrink fits are used where heavy force fits are impractical, as on locomotive wheel tires, heavy crank disks of large engines, etc.

Example of Limit Dimensioning and Use of the ASA Tables. Suppose a 1-in. shaft is designed to run with a class 1 fit, basic-hole system. The *nominal size* is then 1 in., and the *basic size* is 1.000 in. The ASA table (Appendix) shows that the hole may vary from 0.000 to +0.003, which is the *tolerance on the hole*. The tolerance applied to

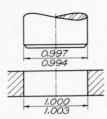

Fig. 10.69. An ASA clearance fit.

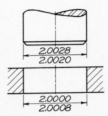

Fig. 10.70. An ASA interference fit.

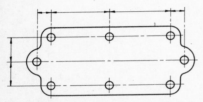

Fig. 10.71. Successive dimensioning.

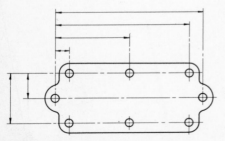

Fig. 10.72. Base-line dimensioning.

the basic size of 1.000 would give 1.000 as the minimum size of the hole and 1.003 as the maximum (Fig. 10.69).

The table shows that the shaft may vary from −0.003 to −0.006. The *actual tolerance on the shaft* is the difference between these two minus values, or 0.003 in. The two minus values applied to the basic size of 1.000 would give 0.997 as the maximum size of the shaft and 0.994 as the minimum. From the definition of allowance, the difference between maximum shaft (0.997) and minimum hole (1.000) would be 0.003 clearance.

The foregoing example is a clearance fit. The first four classes of the ASA fits will all result in clearance fits. Number 5 is a transition fit. The last three classes will give interference fits except in the smaller sizes, where transition fits will result unless selective assembly is used.

In the following example, the shaft is to be permanently assembled in a hole (hub) with an interference fit (Fig. 10.70):

Nominal size, 2 in.; class 8 fit; basic size, 2.000; from the ASA table (Appendix): hole, or external member, +0.0008 and 0.0000; shaft, or internal member, +0.0028 and +0.0020.

These values applied to the basic size give the limit dimensioning (Fig. 10.70):

Tolerance on hole, 2.0008 − 2.0000 = 0.0008
Tolerance on shaft, 2.0028 − 2.0020 = 0.0008
Allowance, 2.0000 − 2.0028 = −0.0028 (interference)

10.54. Base-line Dimensioning. Dimensions may be given either (1) in *successive* form, having each dimension from the one immediately preceding (Fig. 10.71), or (2) in *coordinate*, or "base-line," form, having all dimensions referred to a common datum or reference (Fig. 10.72). To save space, base-line dimensions are sometimes arranged along a single line in *progressive* fashion, as indicated by the horizontal dimensions of Fig. 10.73. This method should be used only in limited space and when many dimensions are needed. The position of a point dimensioned by the base-line system is not dependent upon the cumulative tolerances of preceding dimensions.

10.55. Cumulative Tolerances. Tolerances are said to be cumulative when a position in a given direction is controlled by more than one tolerance. Thus in Fig. 10.74, the position of surface Y with respect to surface W is controlled by the additive tolerances on dimensions A and B. If it is important, functionally, to hold surface Y with respect to surface X, the dimensioning used is good. If, however, it is more important to hold surface Y with respect to surface W, the harmful effect of cumulative tolerances can be avoided by dimensioning as in Fig. 10.75. Cumulative tolerance, however, is always present; thus in Fig. 10.75, the position of surface Y with respect to surface X is now subject to the cumulative tolerances of dimensions A and C.

In machine drawing, confusion in the shop may result from cumu-

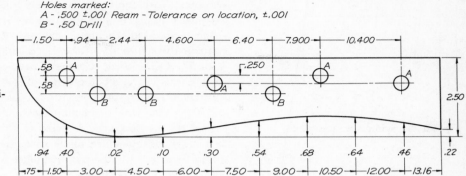

Holes marked:
A - .500 ±.001 Ream - Tolerance on location, ±.001
B - .50 Drill

Fig. 10.73. Progressive dimensioning.

lative tolerances when the drawing is overdimensioned. This is illustrated in Fig. 10.76, where one of the surfaces will be positioned by two dimensions, both of which are subject to a tolerance. Thus surface Z may be positioned with respect to surface W by means of dimensions A, B, and D and be within ±0.003 in. of the basic position; this variation is inconsistent with the tolerance on dimension E. The situation may be clarified by assigning smaller tolerances to dimensions A, B, and D so that, cumulatively, they will be equal to ±0.001 or less. This is poor practice, however, since it will probably increase the production cost. Another solution is to increase the tolerance on dimension E to ±0.003 if the function of the part will permit. The best solution, however, is to eliminate one of the four dimensions since one dimension is superfluous. If all four dimensions are given, one should be marked "Ref.," and its tolerance thus eliminated.

10.56. Tolerance for Symmetry. Older practice in dimensioning symmetrical pieces frequently took advantage of the symmetry to avoid giving certain location dimensions. Following this practice, the part illustrated in Fig. 10.77, which is symmetrical about the vertical center line, has no horizontal dimension to locate the hole. The assumption is that the shop will center the hole in the part.

The above practice is to be avoided on drawings intended for quantity production, however, since with no locating dimension there is no tolerance to indicate how much the hole can be out of

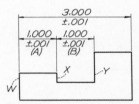

Fig. 10.74. Control of surface position through different toleranced dimensions.

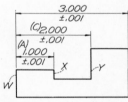

Fig. 10.75. Control of surface position through different toleranced dimensions.

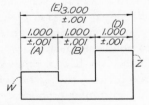

Fig. 10.76. Control of surface position through different toleranced dimensions.

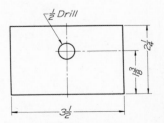

Fig. 10.77. Symmetry assumed.

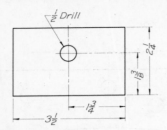

Fig. 10.78. Symmetry controlled.

symmetry with the rest of the part and still function satisfactorily. Modern practice is to give a center-line locating dimension with a value of one-half the total size; the tolerance on this dimension controls the symmetry of the piece (Fig. 10.78).

10.57. Coinciding Center Lines and Dimensions. In many cases, there will be a coincidence of the center lines for two different features of a part. Often one center line is for an unfinished feature and the other (and coincident) center line for a finished feature. Figure 10.79*A* shows the drawing of a link dimensioned for the patternmaker. If holes are to be machined in this link, the drawing would be as at (*B*); the patternmaker would not use the dimension between centers, as shown, but would assume the nominal dimension of 1½ in. with the usual pattern tolerance of ±⅟₃₂ in. The clearest dimensioning in this case would be as at (*C*).

In any case where there is a coincidence of centers, it may be difficult to indicate the limits within which the coincidence must be maintained. In Fig. 10.79*C*, there are actually two horizontal center

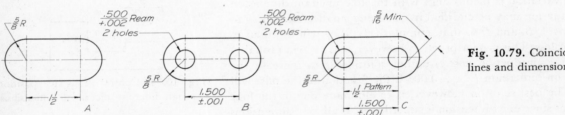

Fig. 10.79. Coinciding center lines and dimensions.

lines, one for the cast link and another for hole centers. One method of controlling the deviation from coincidence is to give the wall thickness as a minimum, which is understood to apply in all radial directions.

In cases where the coincident center lines are both for finished features with differing tolerances, there may be a serious ambiguity on the drawing unless the dimensioning is specially arranged. Figure 10.80*A* shows a milled slot with nominal dimensions and, on the coincident center lines, two accurate holes with a closely toleranced center distance. Unless the dimensioning is cleared by two separate dimensions as shown, the machinist would not know the difference in tolerance. A somewhat more difficult case is shown at (*B*) where pairing holes are diagonally opposite. Unless all the holes are to be toleranced the same on their center distance, the dimensioning must be made clear with notes as shown.

The Army Ordnance method of dimensioning and tolerancing, described in paragraph 10.62, provides a simple and direct means of handling the above and similar problems.

10.58. Tolerance of Concentricity. Tolerance of concentricity is a special case of tolerance for symmetry in which there is a coin-

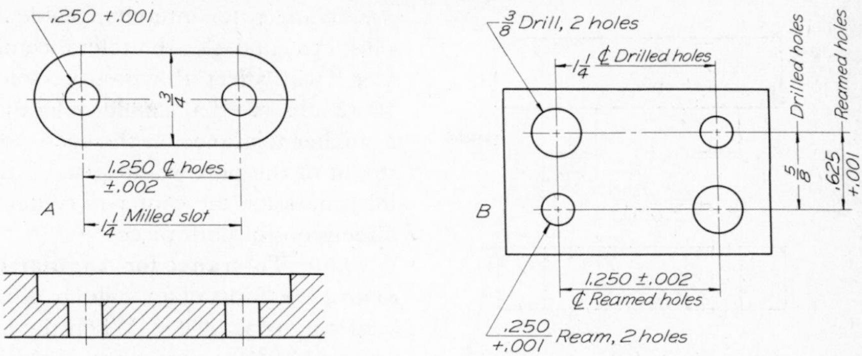

Fig. 10.80. Coinciding center lines and dimensions.

idence of centers. In most cases, concentric cylinders, cones, etc., generated about common axes in manufacture, will be concentric to a degree of precision more than adequate for functional requirements, and no statement is required on the drawing concerning the allowable variation. However, mating pairs of two (or more) precise, close-fitting, machined cylindrical surfaces must have the axes of adjoined cylinders closely coinciding in order to permit assembly of the parts; thus a method of giving the permissible deviation from concentricity is sometimes necessary. Since the center lines of adjoining cylinders coincide on the drawing, the tolerance cannot be given as a dimension. One method is to mark the diameters with reference letters and give the tolerance in note form as in Fig. 10.81*A*. The reference letters may be dispensed with if the note is applied directly to the surfaces, as at (*B*).

10.59. Tolerance between Centers. In any case where centers

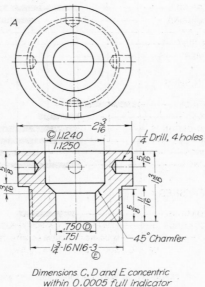

Fig. 10.81. Tolerance of concentricity.

Dimensions C, D and E concentric within 0.0005 full indicator reading.

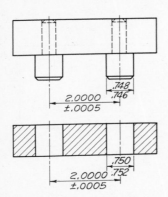

Fig. 10.82. Tolerance on centers.

are arranged for interchangeable assembly, the tolerance on shafts, pins, etc., and also the tolerance on bearings or holes in the mating piece will affect the possible tolerance between centers. In Fig. 10.82, observe that smaller tolerances on the holes would necessitate a smaller tolerance on the center distances. A smaller allowance for the fit of the pins would make a tighter fit and reduce the possible tolerances for the center-to-center dimensions. Study carefully the dimensions of both pieces.

10.60. Tolerance for Angular Dimensions. When it is necessary to give the limits of an angular dimension, the tolerance is generally bilateral, as $32 \pm \frac{1}{2}°$. When the tolerance is given in minutes, it is written $\pm 0°10'$; and when given in seconds, it is written $\pm 0'30''$. Where the location of a hole or other feature is dependent upon an angular dimension, the length along the leg of the angle governs the angular tolerance permitted. A tolerance of $\pm 1°$ gives a variation of 0.035 in. for a length of 1 in. and may be used as a basis for computing the tolerance in any given problem.

As an example, assume an allowable variation of 0.007 in.; then $(0.007/0.035) \times 1° = \frac{1}{5}°$ is the angular tolerance at 1 in. If the

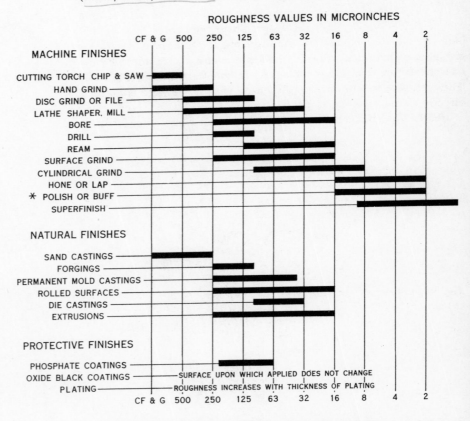

Fig. 10.83. Surface-roughness values.

length is assumed as 2 in., then the tolerance would be one-half the tolerance computed for 1 in., or $\frac{1}{5}° \times \frac{1}{2} = \frac{1}{10}°$, or 0°6'.

10.61. Surface Quality. The proper functioning and wear life of a part frequently depends upon the smoothness quality of its surfaces. American Standard B46 defines the factors of surface quality and describes the meaning and use of symbols for use on drawings. Any surface, despite its apparent smoothness, will be found to have minute peaks and valleys, the height of which is termed "surface roughness" and which may or may not be superimposed on a more general *waviness*. The most prominent direction of tool marks and minute scratches is called "lay."

The degree of surface roughness may be measured as the maximum peak-to-valley height, average peak-to-valley height, or average deviation from the mean (root-mean-square value). The latter is usually preferred and may be measured with instruments such as the Profilometer.[1] The ability to make accurate measurements of roughness permits precise specification of the surface required. Figure 10.83 is a chart adapted from the U.S. Army Ordnance Standard (URAX6), which gives the range of roughness in microinches for surfaces produced by various means.

The following explanations pertaining to symbols for the control of surface quality are adapted from the ASA Standard:

A surface whose quality is to be specified should be marked with a symbol having the general form of a check mark ($\checkmark$) so that the point of the symbol is (1) on the line indicating the surface, or (2) on a leader pointing to the surface.

Where it is desired to specify only the surface-roughness height, and the width of roughness or direction of tool marks is not important, the simplest form of the symbol should be used, Fig. 10.84*A*. The numerical value may be any one of the three roughness values mentioned above in connection with surface roughness, placed in the $\checkmark$ as shown.

Where it is desired to specify waviness height in addition to roughness height, a straight horizontal line should be added to the top of the simple symbol, Fig. 10.84*B*, and the numerical value of waviness height shown above this line.

[1] Physicists Research Co., Ann Arbor, Mich.

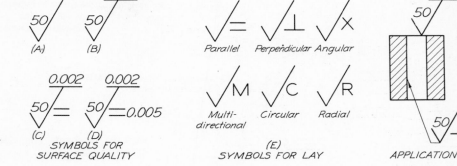

Fig. 10.84. ASA surface-quality symbols.

(A)   (B)

(C)   (D)
SYMBOLS FOR
SURFACE QUALITY

Parallel   Perpendicular   Angular

Multi-directional   Circular   Radial

(E)
SYMBOLS FOR LAY

APPLICATION

If the nature of the preferred lay is to be shown, it is indicated by the addition of a combination of lines as shown in Fig. 10.84C, D, and E.

The parallel and perpendicular part of the symbol indicates that the dominant tool marks on the surface are parallel or perpendicular to the boundary line of the surface in contact with the symbol. The complete symbol, including the roughness width placed to the right of the lay symbol, is shown in Fig. 10.84D.

The use of only one number to specify the height or width of roughness or waviness indicates the maximum value. Any lesser degree of roughness will be satisfactory. When two numbers separated by a dash are used, they indicate the maximum and minimum permissible values.

The surface-quality symbol should not be thought of as a finish mark in the same sense as the old symbol f and the newer V. These marks indicate the removal of material, whereas the surface-roughness symbol may be used to indicate the quality of a surface from which no material is to be removed, as, for example, a die-cast or even a sand-cast surface. On the other hand, should a metal-removal process be required in order to obtain the surface quality specified, the surface-roughness symbol is used in place of the finish mark.

10.62. Positional and Locational Tolerances.[1] The language of engineering drawing has developed along with the improvement of manufacturing methods. As quantity-production systems have been developed and accuracies improved, demands have been made for the drawings to depict the parts with greater exactness, particularly in the dimensioning. Examples of the trend in dimensioning are found in the methods of specifying tolerances, surface quality, and similar modern practices. Finished holes are now often specified by limit dimensions with, in addition, the surface-roughness specification instead of the older practice of giving the size and operation, such as drilling, reaming, etc.

With improved manufacturing methods and higher precisions, a demand has developed for a workable method of controlling the parallelism, perpendicularity, concentricity, and symmetry of surfaces. Along this line, the Ordnance Department of the U.S. Army has developed a set of symbols for indicating positional tolerances. Figure 10.85 illustrates the procedure.

[1] Adapted from the Ordnance Department's "Manual on Dimensioning and Tolerancing," prepared by the inspection-gage suboffice, Office of the Chief of Ordnance, A.S.F., U.S. Army.

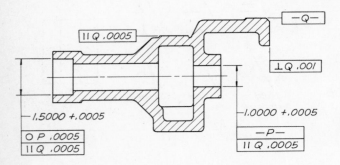

Fig. 10.85. Army Ordnance positional tolerance symbols.

The letter *P*, preceded and followed by dashes (—*P*—), connected to the diameter dimension of the small hole at the right, indicates that this hole is serving as a datum or reference surface with which one or more other surfaces will be checked for parallelism, perpendicularity, concentricity, or symmetry. Thus the concentricity symbol ⊙, the datum letter *P*, and the tolerance value 0.0005 connected to the diameter dimension of the hole at the left indicate that this surface is to be concentric, with the datum surface —*P*— or within 0.0005 in. full indicator reading, or that the total permissible eccentricity (runout) is 0.0005 in.

The datum symbol —*Q*— will be found assigned to the horizontal surface at the upper right, while the adjoining vertical surface carries the perpendicularity symbol (⊥), the datum letter *Q*, and the tolerance 0.001; therefore, this surface must be perpendicular to the datum surface —*Q*— within 0.001 in. over its entire surface.

The method for specifying permissible errors in parallelism is similar to that used for concentricity and perpendicularity. Accordingly, the three surfaces in Fig. 10.85 carrying the parallelism symbol (‖) must each be parallel to the indicated datum surface —*Q*— within 0.0005 in. over their entire surface.

The U.S. Army Ordnance Department has also developed a system for expressing *locational tolerances*.[1] The new system simplifies design calculations for the size and locational tolerances on mating parts, simplifies the appearance and readability of the drawing, and allows a maximum manufacturing variation without affecting the function of the parts.

Figure 10.86 illustrates the usual method for dimensioning a part, and Fig. 10.87 shows the Ordnance method. In the Ordnance system, dimensions for locating the centers of cylindrical shapes are given as basic values followed by the letter *B*. Beneath the size dimension for the cylinder, an additional positional tolerance value enclosed in a rectangle is given, which represents the permissible variation for the location of the cylinder and indicates that its center must lie within an imaginary circle of a diameter equal to the positional tolerance. The center of this positional tolerance circle must, of course, be at the center located by the basic dimensions. In Fig. 10.88, the symbol *P*.010 indicates that the centers of the small holes must be located by the dimensions given within a positional-tolerance circle of 0.010 in. (diameter) with reference to the datum —*P*— (the large hole, whose position is basic).

An important advantage of the Ordnance system, compared with the conventional method, is that an increase in manufacturing variation is permitted without affecting the functioning of the parts. In the conventional method, having direct tolerances given on location dimensions, the positional-variation area is an inscribed square of the Ordnance positional-tolerance circle. Also, the effective area for

<hr>

[1] This system is based on ideas first proposed by G. A. Gladman of the National Physical Laboratory, Great Britain, and is now included, in essence, in proposed British standards.

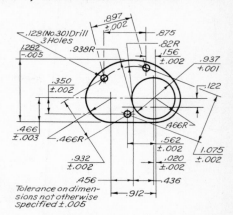

Fig. 10.86. Locational tolerances.

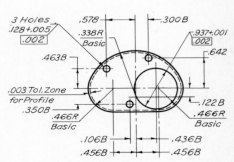

Fig. 10.87. Locational tolerances (Army Ordnance).

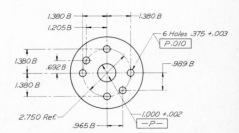

Fig. 10.88. Locational tolerances (Army Ordnance).

gaging acceptable parts is usually restricted to the inscribed circle of the square. Thus parts rejected by inspection according to the conventional system may prove to be acceptable by the Ordnance method.

The Ordnance tolerancing system may also be applied to the location of rectangular shapes. The only difference is that the tolerance circle used with cylindrical shapes will be replaced by a tolerance rectangle within which the center of the form may vary.

10.63. Production Methods and Dimensioning Practice. Production methods may be classified as (1) *unit production*, the term applied when one or only a few devices or structures are to be built, and (2) *quantity* or *mass production*, indicating that a large number of practically identical machines or devices are to be made with the parts interchangeable from one machine to another.

Unit-production methods almost always apply to large machines and structures, especially if custom made. The large size to some extent eliminates the need for great accuracy. Each individual part is produced to fit or is fitted to the adjacent parts, frequently on the job, by experienced workmen in accordance with common fractional dimensions and directions given on the drawings. Since interchangeability of parts is no object, tolerances are not ordinarily used.

Similar methods are employed for unit production of smaller machines and mechanical devices. The drawings may have common fractional dimensions exclusively on the assumption that the parts will be individually fitted in the shop. Thus, in this case, the manufacturing group accepts the responsibility for the proper functioning of the machine and, in some cases, even the design of some of the parts. Skilled workmen are employed for this work. Usually each machine is completed before another is started, and the parts will not be interchangeable.

Quantity-production methods will be employed whenever a great number of identical products are to be made. After a part has been detailed, the operations-planning group of the engineering department will plan the shop operations step by step. Then special tools are designed by the tool-design group so that, in production, semiskilled workmen may perform operations that would otherwise require skilled workmen. These tools, built by the highly skilled tool-maker, simplify and greatly increase the rate of production.

One workman performs a single operation on the part, after which it is passed to a second workman, who performs another operation, and so on until the completed part results. The specially designed tools and equipment make it possible to produce parts of high quality at low cost; moreover, it is relatively simple to produce parts with dimensional exactness consistent with the requirements for interchangeability. The assembly may also be made by semiskilled workers using special assembly fixtures and tools.

With this system, nothing can be left to the judgment of the workman. In preparing drawings intended for quantity production, it is necessary for the engineering department to assume full responsibility for the success of the resulting machine by making the drawings so exact and complete that, if followed to the letter, the resulting parts cannot fail to be satisfactory. The engineering department alone is in a position to correlate corresponding dimensions of mating parts, establish dimensional tolerances, and give complete directions for the entire manufacturing job.

It is sometimes expedient for concerns doing unit or small-production work to follow the methods of the quantity-production system. The advantage is interchangeable parts, which may be produced without reference or fitting to each other.

10.64. Principles for the Selection of Dimensions. Systematic selection of dimensions demands attention to the *use* or *function* of the part and the *manufacturing process* to be used in producing the part.

The *functional principle* recognizes that it is essential to dimension between points or surfaces associated through their functional relationship with points or surfaces of mating parts. This is accomplished by correlating the dimensions on a drawing of one part with the mating dimensions on the drawing of a mating part and arranging the tolerances of these dimensions to ensure interchangeability and proper functioning.

The *process principle*, or "workman's rule," as it is sometimes called, recognizes that the work of manufacture may be made easier by giving directly the dimensions the shop will find most convenient to "work to" in producing the part. Here a knowledge of manufacturing processes and procedure is necessary, as explained in Chap. 9.

In some cases, there may be a conflict between these two principles; and whenever this occurs, the functional principle must take precedence; any attempt to satisfy both principles in this case would result in overdimensioning, as described in paragraph 10.19, causing confusion for the workmen and possible malfunctioning of the part. With few exceptions, however, dimensions can be chosen to satisfy both principles.

10.65. Procedure for the Selection of Dimensions. A systematic procedure is, of course, desirable. The following steps will illustrate and serve as a guide:

1. The part should be carefully studied along with the mating part or parts. Pay particular attention to the mating and controlling surfaces. Dimensions meeting functional requirements are planned before any dimensions are placed on the drawing so that the correlation with dimensions of mating parts may be made.

2. Study the part to determine whether or not the manufacturing processes may be simplified by some alteration of any of the functional dimensions. Changes should not be made if the functioning of the part would be impaired in any way.

3. Select the nonfunctional dimensions, being guided by the proc-

ess principle, so that the dimensions are readily usable by the workmen. Avoid overdimensioning and duplication.

In general, dimensions for mating surfaces are governed by the functional and process principles, and the dimensions for nonmating surfaces are governed by the process principle only.

Occasionally the manufacturing process will not be known at the time of dimensioning. This may happen either when there are optional methods of manufacture, all equally good, or when the details of the manufacturing equipment of a contracting firm are unknown. In such cases, the dimensions should be selected and toleranced in a logical manner so that the part, regardless of how produced, cannot fail to be satisfactory. The size and location dimensions arrived at by the shape-breakdown system described in paragraph 10.17 will apply here to a great extent since these dimensions will fulfill most production requirements. Contracting firms will often redraw incoming part drawings, dimensioning them to result in the most economical production with their own shop equipment.

10.66. Methods of Part Production. In following the process principle, the basic method of part production, casting, forging, etc., as described in Chap. 9, must be known. The manufacturing procedures followed with the particular type of part involved are then considered in selecting the dimensions. The only workman to be considered in dimensioning a part cut from solid stock is the machinist. For parts produced by casting, the workmen to be considered are the patternmaker (for sand castings) or the diemaker (for die castings) and, for finishing, the machinist. Forged parts subject to quantity production will be dimensioned for the diemaker and machinist. For parts produced from sheet stock, the template maker, the diemaker, and the machinist must be considered; information for making the template and for forming the blank is obtained from a detail drawing showing the part as it should be when completed. In any case, one drawing, appropriately dimensioned, must show the finished part.

The several paragraphs following give examples of the dimensioning of machine parts for quantity production.

10.67. Dimensioning a Part Machined from Stock. Figure 10.89 is a detail drawing of the stud from the rail-transport hanger, Prob. 12.3.11. This assembly drawing should be studied to determine the function of the stud. The stud is produced by machining on a lathe. Cold-rolled steel stock, $1\frac{1}{4}$ in. in diameter, is used. The stock diameter is the same as the large end of the stud, thus eliminating one machining operation.

Shape breakdown of the part results in a series of cylinders each requiring two dimensions, diameter and length. The important functional dimensions have been marked (on Fig. 10.89) with the letters A, B, C, and D. Diameter A is given to correlate with the bore of the bearings; a four-place decimal limit provides for the desired

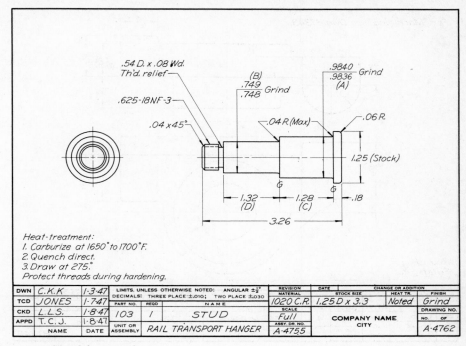

Fig. 10.89. Dimensioning of a part machined from stock.

fit. Dimension B is a three-place decimal limit to correlate with a similar dimension for the hole in the hanger. Dimension C is made 0.03 in. larger than the combined width of the two bearings in order to allow the inner races of the bearings to "creep." Dimension C, a two-place decimal, can vary by ± 0.010 in., but clearance for the bearings is assured under all conditions. Dimension D is made approximately 0.05 in. less than the length of the hanger hub to ensure that the nut will bear against the hanger rather than on the shoulder of the stud.

Functional dimensions need not always be extremely accurate. Note that dimensions C and D, with the relatively broad tolerance of two-place decimals, will allow the part to function as intended.

The thread specification may be considered as a functional dimension wherein the tolerance is provided through the thread class.

The remainder of the dimensions have been selected to best suit shop requirements. Note that the thread length and over-all dimension cannot both be given, or the part would be overdimensioned.

10.68. Dimensioning a Casting. The dimensions required for sand castings may be classified as those used by the patternmaker, those used by the machinist, and those used by the patternmaker and machinist. Since a cast part has two distinct phases in its manufacture, the drawings, in this case, have been made according to the

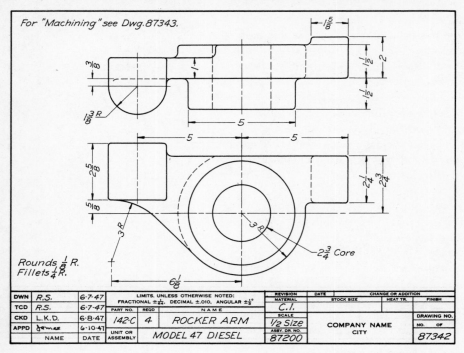

Fig. 10.90. Dimensioning of an unmachined casting.

multiple system explained in Chap. 9, one for the patternmaker, Fig. 10.90, and one for the machinist, Fig. 10.91.

The *casting drawing* gives the shape of the unmachined casting and

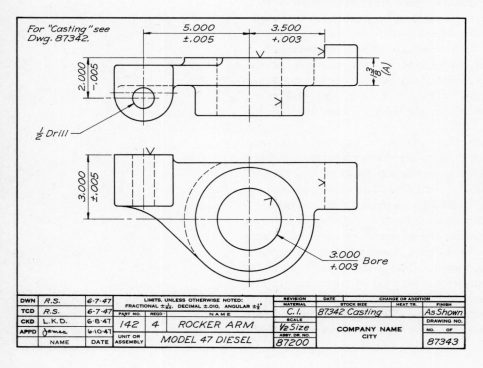

Fig. 10.91. Dimensions for machining a casting.

carries dimensions for the patternmaker only. Shape breakdown will show that each geometric shape has been dimensioned for size and then located, resulting in dimensions easily usable by the workman. Some of the dimensions might be altered, depending upon how the pattern is made; the most logical and easily usable combination should be used. Note that the main central shape is dimensioned as it would be laid out on a board. Note also that several of the dimensions have been selected to agree with required functional dimensions of the machined part although the dimensions employed have been selected so as to be directly usable by the patternmaker; they also achieve the *main objective*, which is to state *the sizes that the un-machined casting must fulfill when produced*.

The *machining drawing* shows only the dimensions required by the machinist. These are almost all functional dimensions and have been selected to correlate with mating parts. It is important to note that a starting point must be established in each of the three principal directions for machining the casting. In this case, a starting point is provided by (1) the coincidence of the center lines of the large hole and cylinder (location in two directions) and (2) dimension A to locate the machined surface on the back, from which is located the drilled hole. Dimension A is a common fraction carrying the broad tolerance of $\pm\frac{1}{64}$ in., as there is no functional reason for working to greater precision.

Figure 10.92 is a drawing for the same part used in Figs. 10.90 and 10.91 but with the casting drawing dispensed with and the

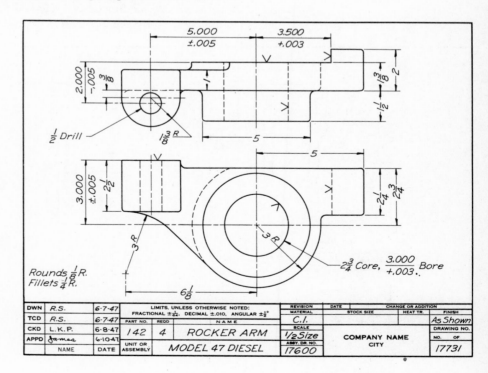

Fig. 10.92. All dimensions for a casting.

patternmaker's dimensions incorporated in the drawing of the finished part. In combining the two drawings, some dimensions are eliminated, as the inclusion of all the dimensions of both drawings would result in overdimensioning; thus the patternmaker must make use of certain machining dimensions in his work. In working from the drawing of Fig. 10.92, the patternmaker provides for machining allowance, being guided by the finish marks. If the drawing of Fig. 10.90 is used, the engineering department provides for the machining allowance by showing and dimensioning the rough casting oversize where necessary for machining, and no finish marks are used.

10.69. Dimensioning a Drop Forging. Figure 10.93 is a drawing of a drop forging showing, at the left, the unmachined forging and, at the right, the machined forging. The drawing of the unmachined forging carries the dimensions it must fulfill when produced; these dimensions have been selected so as to be most useful to the diemaker for producing the forging dies. As the draft on drop forgings is considerable, it is shown on the drawing and dimensioned (usually) by a note. If the draft varies for different portions of the part, the angles may be given on the views. The dimensions parallel to the horizontal surfaces of the die are usually given so as to specify the size at the *bottom of the die cavity*. Thus, in dimensioning, one may visualize the draft as stripped off; then its apparent complication will no longer be a difficulty.

The machining drawing shows the dimensions for finishing. These dimensions are all functional, selected from the required function of the part. Study the illustration carefully.

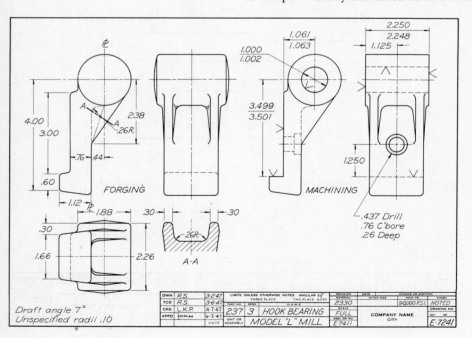

Fig. 10.93. Dimensioning of a drop forging.

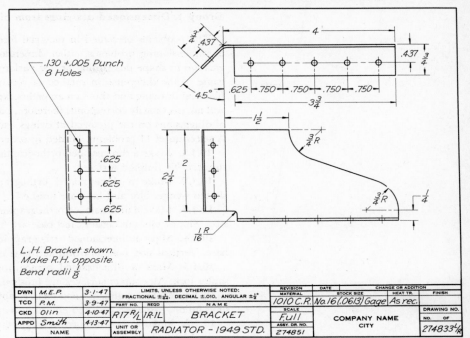

Fig. 10.94. Dimensioning of
a sheet-metal part.

10.70. Dimensioning a Sheet-metal Part. Parts to be made of
thin materials are usually drawn showing the part in its finished
form, as in Fig. 10.94. The template maker first uses this drawing
to lay out a flat pattern of the part. If only a few parts are to be
made, this template will serve as a pattern for cutting the blanks.
Then the part is formed and completed by hand. If a large number
of parts are to be made, the diemaker will use the template and
drawing in making up the necessary dies for blanking, punching,
and forming. The work of both template maker and diemaker is
simplified by giving the dimensions to the same side of the material
(either inside or outside, whichever is more important from the
functional standpoint), as shown in Fig. 10.94. Dimensions to
rounded edges (bends) are given to the theoretical sharp edges,
which are called *mold lines*. The thickness of the material is given in
the "stock" block of the title strip. Note that, in the figure, the holes
are located in groups (because of functional requirements) and that
important functional dimensions are three-place decimals.

PROBLEMS

The problems following are given as studies in dimensioning in which to
apply the principles of this chapter. Attention should be given to the methods
of manufacture as described in Chap. 9. A function for the part should be
assumed in order to fix the location of finished surfaces and to limit the
possibilities in the selection of dimensions.

Group 1. Dimensioned drawings from pictorial views

The problems presented in pictorial form in Chaps. 5 to 8 may be used as dimensioning problems, either dimensioning one already drawn as an exercise in shape description or, for variety, one not previously made. Because of the difference in method of representation, the dimensions on a pictorial drawing and those on an orthographic drawing of the same object will not necessarily correspond; therefore, pay no attention to the placement of dimensions on the pictorial drawings except for obtaining sizes needed. A selection of 11 problems, graded in order of difficulty, is given below.

10.1.1. Make a dimensioned orthographic drawing of Prob. 5.3.1, beam support. No finished surfaces.

10.1.2. Make a dimensioned orthographic drawing of Prob. 5.3.5, slotted wedge. Slot and base are finished.

10.1.3. Make a dimensioned orthographic drawing of Prob. 5.3.8, corner stop. Slot at top, cut corner, and base are finished.

10.1.4. Make a dimensioned orthographic drawing of Prob. 5.3.11, guide base. Vertical slot, boss on front, and base are finished.

10.1.5. Make a dimensioned orthographic drawing of Prob. 5.3.19, shifter fork. All contact surfaces are finished.

10.1.6. Make a dimensioned orthographic drawing of Prob. 5.3.29, shaft guide. L-shaped pad and end of hub are finished.

10.1.7. Make a dimensioned orthographic drawing of Prob. 6.2.6, jig angle. Finished all over.

10.1.8. Make a dimensioned orthographic drawing of Prob. 6.2.12, angle-shaft base. Base and slanting surface are finished.

10.1.9. Make a dimensioned orthographic drawing of Prob. 6.2.11, radial-swing block. All contact surfaces are finished.

10.1.10. Make a dimensioned orthographic drawing of Prob. 6.3.6, transverse connection. Base pads are finished.

10.1.11. Make a dimensioned orthographic drawing of Prob. 6.3.7, chamfer-tool base. Contact surfaces are finished.

Group 2. Dimensioned drawings from models

An excellent exercise in dimensioning is to make a detail drawing from a pattern, casting, or forging or from a model made for the purpose. Old or obsolete patterns can often be obtained from companies manufacturing a variety of small parts, and "throw-out" castings or forgings are occasionally available. In taking measurements from a pattern, a shrink rule should always be used, and allowance must be made for finished surfaces.

Group 3. Pieces to be drawn and dimensioned

The illustrations are printed to scale, as indicated in each problem. Transfer distances with dividers or by scaling, and draw the objects to a convenient scale on a paper size to suit. For proper placement of dimensions, more space should be provided between views than is shown in the illustrations.

Use the aligned or horizontal dimensioning systems as desired. It is suggested that some problems be dimensioned in the complete decimal system.

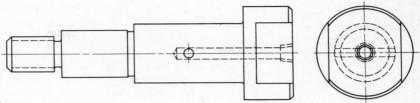

Prob. 10.3.1. Stud shaft.

10.3.1. Stud shaft, shown half size. Machined from steel-bar stock.

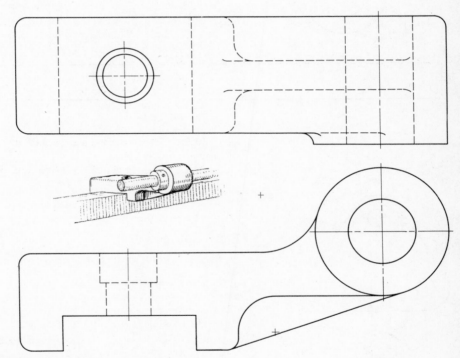

Prob. 10.3.2. Shaft bracket.

10.3.2. Shaft bracket, shown half size. Malleable iron. Hole in base is drilled and counterbored for a socket-head cap screw. Base slot and front surface of hub are finished. Hole in hub is bored and reamed. The function of this part is to support a shaft at a fixed distance from a machine bed, as indicated by the small pictorial view.

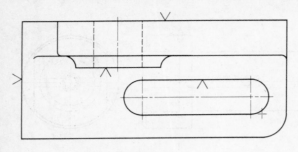

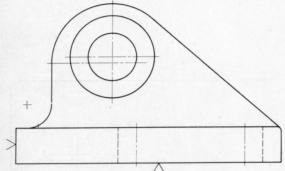

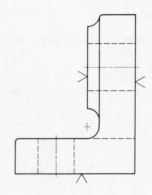

Prob. 10.3.3. Idler bracket, left-hand.

10.3.3. Idler bracket, shown half size. Cast iron. Hole is bored and reamed. Slot is milled.

10.3.3A. See Prob. 10.3.3. Draw and dimension the right-hand part.

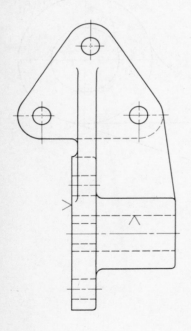

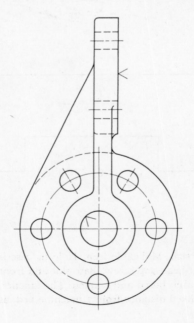

Prob. 10.3.4. Filter flange.

10.3.4. Filter flange, shown half size. Cast aluminum. The small holes are drilled. Add spot faces.

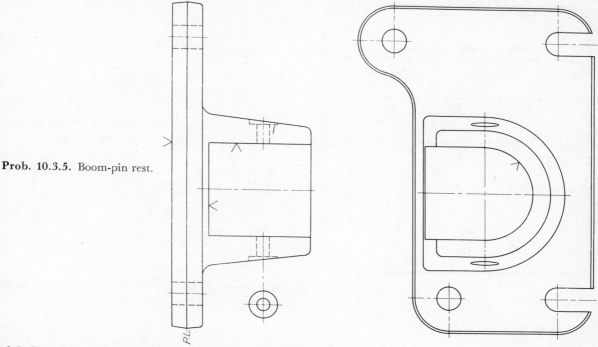

Prob. 10.3.5. Boom-pin rest.

10.3.5. Boom-pin rest. Steel drop forging. Shown half size, draw half size or full size. Add top view if desired. Show machining allowance with alternate position lines, and dimension as in Fig. 9.7. All draft angles 7°. Holes are drilled; corner notches milled.

10.3.5A. Same as Prob. 10.3.5, but make two drawings: (a) the unmachined forging dimensioned for the diemaker and (b) the machined forging dimensioned for the machinist. Reference: Fig. 10.93.

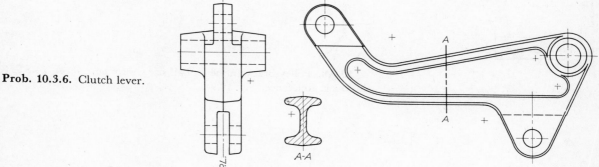

Prob. 10.3.6. Clutch lever.

10.3.6. Clutch lever. Aluminum drop forging. Shown half size, draw full size or twice size. Add top view if desired. Holes are drilled and reamed; ends of hub are finished; left-end lug is straddle milled; slot in lower lug is milled. Show machining allowance with alternate position lines, and dimension as in Fig. 9.7. All draft angles 7°.

10.3.6A. Same as Prob. 10.3.6, but make two drawings: (a) the unmachined forging dimensioned for the diemaker and (b) the machined forging dimensioned for the machinist. Reference: Fig. 10.93.

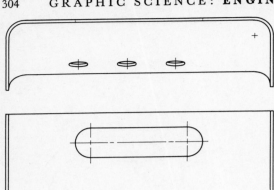

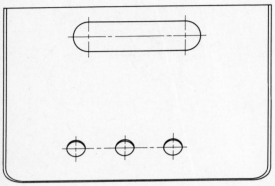

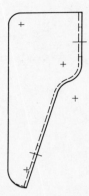

Prob. 10.3.7. Radiator mounting clip, left-hand.

10.3.7. Radiator mounting clip, LH, No. 16 (0.0625) steel sheet. Shown half size. Holes and slot are punched. Reference: Fig. 10.94.

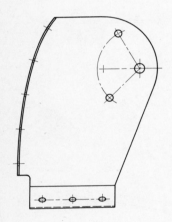

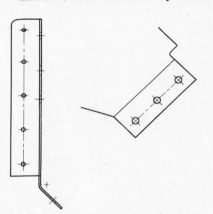

Prob. 10.3.8. Pulley bracket.

10.3.8. Pulley bracket. Shown half size. Aluminum sheet, 24-ST, 0.032 in. thick. Reference: Fig. 10.94.

roup 4. Dimensioned drawings from an assembly or design drawing

The assembly drawings of Chap. 12 are well suited for exercises in dimensioning detail working drawings. The assembly shows the position of ach part, and the function may be understood by a study of the motion, elationship, etc., of the different parts. Note particularly the mating and ontrolling surfaces and the logical reference surfaces for dimensions of ocation. Inasmuch as the dimensioning of an assembly drawing is crowded nd probably does not even have the same views as will the detail drawing f one of the parts, disregard the position and selection of the assembly imensions, and use them only to obtain sizes. The following are suggested:

10.4.1. Detail drawing of shaft, Prob. 12.3.3.
10.4.2. Detail drawing of bushing, Prob. 12.3.3.
10.4.3. Detail drawing of bracket, Prob. 12.3.3.
10.4.4. Detail drawing of body, Prob. 12.3.7.
10.4.5. Detail drawing of hanger, Prob. 12.3.11.
10.4.6. Detail drawing of rack, Prob. 12.3.9.
10.4.7. Detail drawing of rack housing, Prob. 12.3.9.
10.4.8. Detail drawing of cover, Prob. 12.3.9.
10.4.9. Detail drawing of base, Prob. 12.3.1.
10.4.10. Detail drawing of base, Prob. 12.6.6.
10.4.11. Detail drawing of jaw, Prob. 12.6.6.
10.4.12. Detail drawing of screw, Prob. 12.6.6.
10.4.13. Detail drawing of screw bushing, Prob. 12.6.6.
10.4.14. Detail drawing of frame (drop forging), Prob. 12.6.2.
10.4.15. Detail drawing of base, Prob. 12.6.4.
10.4.16. Detail drawing of frame, Prob. 12.6.4.
10.4.17. Detail drawing of frame, Prob. 12.6.5.
10.4.18. Detail drawing of ram, Prob. 12.6.5.
10.4.19. Detail drawing of pinion shaft, Prob. 12.6.5.
10.4.20. Detail drawing of base, Prob. 12.3.5.
10.4.21. Detail drawing of cover, Prob. 12.3.5.
10.4.22. Detail drawing of sleeve ball, Prob. 12.3.5.
10.4.23. Detail drawing of stud ball, Prob. 12.3.5.
10.4.24. Detail drawing of body, Prob. 12.5.6.
10.4.25. Detail drawing, with development, of spring, Prob. 12.5.6.

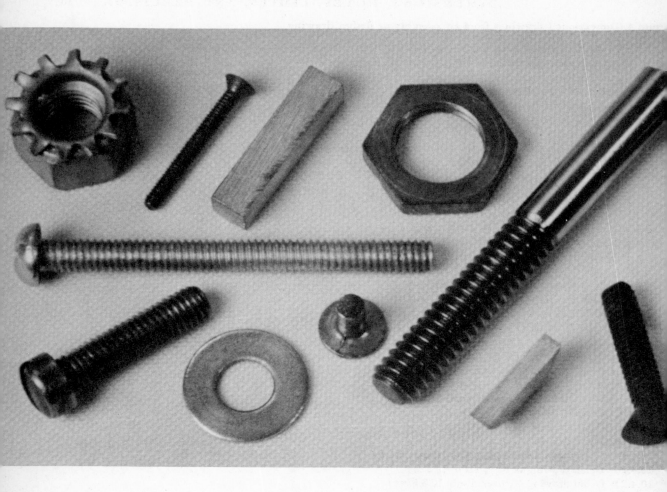

11

SCREW THREADS, FASTENERS, KEYS, RIVETS, AND SPRINGS

Screw Threads, Fasteners, Keys, Rivets, and Springs

11.1. A screw thread is the operating element used on bolts, nuts, cap screws, wood screws, and the like and on shafts or similar parts employed either for transmitting power or for adjustment. Screw threads occur in one form or another on practically all engineering products. Consequently, in the making of working drawings, there is the repeated necessity to *represent* and *specify* screw threads.

11.2. Historical. The earliest records of the screw are found in the writings of Archimedes (278 to 212 B.C.). Although specimens of ancient Greek and Roman screws are so rare as to indicate that they were seldom used, in the later Middle Ages many are found; and it is known that both lathes and dies were used to cut threads. Most early screws, however, were made by hand, forging the head, cutting the slot with a saw, and fashioning the screw with a file. In Colonial times, wood screws were blunt on the ends, the gimlet point not appearing until 1846. Iron screws were made for each threaded hole. There was no interchanging of parts, and nuts had to be tied to their own bolts. Sir Joseph Whitworth made the first attempt at a uniform standard in 1841. This was generally adopted in England but not in the United States.

11.3. Standardization. The initial attempt to standardize screw threads in the United States came in 1864 with the adoption of a report prepared by a committee appointed by the Franklin Institute. This system, designed by William Sellers, came into general use

307

and was known as the "Franklin Institute thread," the "Sellers thread," or the "United States thread." It fulfilled the need of a general-purpose thread for that period; but with the coming of the automobile, the airplane, and other modern equipment, it became inadequate. Through the efforts of the various engineering societies, the Bureau of Standards, and others, the National Screw Thread Commission was authorized by act of Congress in 1918 and inaugurated the present standards. This work has been carried on by the ASA and by the Interdepartmental Screw Thread Committee of the U.S. Departments of War, Navy, and Commerce. Later, these organizations, working in cooperation with representatives of the British and Canadian governments and standards associations, developed an agreement covering a general-purpose thread that fulfills the basic requirements for interchangeability of threaded products produced in the three countries. The "Declaration of Accord" establishing the Unified Screw Thread was signed in Washington, D.C., on November 18, 1948.

Essential features of the Unified and other threads are given in this chapter, while standards covering them are listed in the Appendix.

11.4. Screw-thread Terminology

Screw Thread (*Thread*). A ridge of uniform section in the form of a helix on the external or internal surface of a cylinder or cone.

Straight Thread. A thread formed on a cylinder, Fig. 11.1.

Taper Thread. A thread formed on a cone.

External Thread (*Screw*). A thread on the external surface of a cylinder or cone, Fig. 11.1.

Internal Thread (*Nut*). A thread on the internal surface of a cylinder or cone, Fig. 11.1.

Right-hand Thread. A thread which, when viewed axially, winds in a clockwise and receding direction. Threads are always right-hand unless otherwise specified.

Left-hand Thread. A thread which, when viewed axially, winds in a counterclockwise and receding direction. All left-hand threads are designated "LH."

Form. The profile (cross section) of the thread. Figure 11.3 shows various forms.

Crest. The edge or surface which joins the sides of a thread and is farthest from the cylinder or cone from which the thread projects, Fig. 11.1.

Root. The edge or surface which joins the sides of adjacent thread forms and coincides with the cylinder or cone from which the thread projects, Fig. 11.1.

Pitch. The distance between corresponding points on adjacent thread forms measured parallel to the axis, Fig. 11.1. This distance is a measure of the size of the thread form used.

Lead. The distance a threaded part moves axially, with respect to

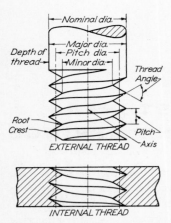

Fig. 11.1. Screw-thread terminology.

a fixed mating part, in one complete revolution. See Multiple Thread and Fig. 11.2.

Threads per Inch. The reciprocal of the pitch and the value specified to govern the size of the thread form.

Major Diameter. The largest diameter of a screw thread, Fig. 11.1.

Minor Diameter. The smallest diameter of a screw thread, Fig. 11.1.

Pitch Diameter. On a straight thread, the diameter of an imaginary cylinder, the surface of which cuts the thread forms where the width of the thread and groove are equal, Fig. 11.1. The clearance between two mating threads is controlled largely by closely toleranced pitch diameters.

Depth of Thread. The distance between crest and root measured normal to the axis, Fig. 11.1.

Single Thread. A thread having the thread form produced on but one helix of the cylinder, Fig. 11.2 (see Multiple Thread). On a single thread, the lead and pitch are equivalent. Threads are always single unless otherwise specified.

Multiple Thread. A thread combination having the same form produced on two or more helices of the cylinder, Fig. 11.2. For a multiple thread, the lead is an integral multiple of the pitch, that is, on a *double thread* the lead is twice the pitch, on a *triple thread*, three times the pitch, etc. A multiple thread permits a more rapid advance without a coarser (larger) thread form. Note that the helices of a double thread start 180° apart; those of a triple thread, 120° apart; and those of a quadruple thread, 90° apart.

11.5. Thread Forms. Screw threads are used on fasteners, on devices for making adjustments, and for the transmission of power and motion. For these different purposes, a number of thread forms are in use (Fig. 11.3). The dimensions given are those of the basic thread forms. In practical usage, clearance must be provided between the external and internal threads.

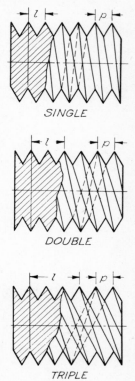

Fig. 11.2. Multiple threads.

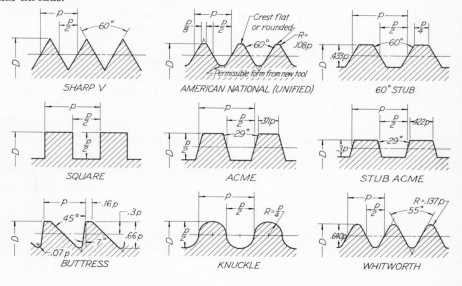

Fig. 11.3. Thread profiles.

The *sharp V*, formerly used to a limited extent, is rarely employed now; it is difficult to maintain sharp roots in quantity production. The form is of interest, however, as the basis of more practical V-type threads; also, because of its simplicity, it is used on drawings as a conventional representation for other (V-type) threads.

V-type threads are employed primarily on fasteners and for making adjustments. For these purposes, the standard thread form in the United States is the *American National*. This form is also the basis for the Unified Screw Thread standard of the United States, Canada, and Britain and as such is known as the *Unified* thread. As illustrated in Fig. 11.3, the form is that of the maximum external thread. Observe that, while the crest may be either flat or rounded, the root is rounded by design or as the result of tool wear. The American National thread is by far the most commonly used thread in this country.

The 60° *stub* form is sometimes preferred when, instead of multiple threads, a single National-form thread would be too deep.

The former British standard was the *Whitworth*, at 55°, with crests and roots rounded. The *British Association Standard*, at 47½°, measured in the metric system, is used for small threads. The *French* and the *International Metric Standards* have a form similar to the American National but are dimensioned in the metric system.

For transmitting power, the V shapes are not desirable since part of the thrust tends to burst the nut. The *square thread* avoids this as it transmits all the forces nearly parallel to the axis of the screw. It can have, evidently, only half the number of threads in the same axial space as a V thread of the same pitch, and thus in shear it is only half as strong. Because of manufacturing difficulties, the square-thread form is sometimes modified by providing a slight (5°) taper to the sides.

The *Acme* has generally replaced the square thread in use. It is stronger, more easily produced, and permits the use of a disengaging or split nut that cannot be used on a square thread.

The *Stub Acme* form results in a very strong thread suited to power applications where space limitation makes it desirable.

The *buttress*, for transmitting power in only one direction, has the efficiency of the square and the strength of the V thread. It was formerly produced with a perpendicular pressure flank (face), but the newer 7° slope results in simplified manufacture. Sometimes called the "breech-block" thread, it is used to withhold the pressure on breech blocks of large guns.

The *knuckle* thread is especially suitable when threads are to be molded or rolled in sheet metal. It can be observed on glass jars and in a shallow form on the bases of ordinary incandescent lamps.

Internal screw threads are produced by cutting, while external threads may be made by cutting or rolling. Tests show that rolled threads are considerably stronger than cut threads. Through cold

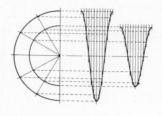

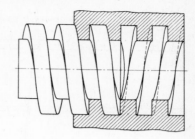

Fig. 11.4. True representation of a square thread, external and internal.

forging, rolling adds toughness and strength to the threaded portion of the metal.

11.6. Thread Representation. The true representation of a screw thread is almost never used in making working drawings. In true representation, the crest and root lines, Fig. 11.4, appear as the projections of helices (see Helix, paragraph 16.34), the drawing of which is extremely laborious. For instances where true representation is desirable, that is, on advertising, elaborate display drawings, etc., templates can be made of cardboard or celluloid to assist in drawing the helices.

On practical working drawings, threads are represented with either a semiconventional or symbolic treatment, which provides thread pictures adequate for manufacturing purposes. These methods of thread representation are discussed in the following paragraphs.

11.7. Semiconventional Representation. This simplifies the drawing of the thread principally by conventionalizing the projection of the helix into a straight line. Where applicable with certain thread forms, further simplifications are made. For example, the 29° angle of the Acme and 29° stub forms may be drawn at 30°, and the American National form is represented by the sharp V. In general, true pitch should be shown, although a small increase or decrease in pitch is permissible so as to have even units of measure in making the drawing. Thus seven threads per inch may be increased to eight, or four and one-half may be decreased to four. The student must keep in mind that this is only to simplify the drawing and that the actual threads per inch must be specified in the dimensioning.

To draw a thread semiconventionally, we must know whether it is external or internal, the form, the major diameter, the pitch, its multiplicity, and whether it is right- or left-hand. Figure 11.5 illustrates the stages in drawing an American National, or sharp V;

Fig. 11.5. Stages in drawing a single V thread.

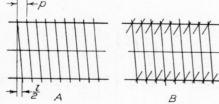

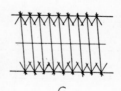

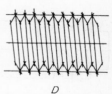

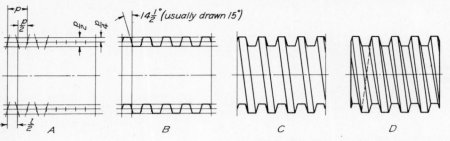

Fig. 11.6. Stages in drawing a single Acme thread.

Fig. 11.6, an Acme; and Fig. 11.7, a square thread. The V thread of Fig. 11.5 will illustrate the principle. At (*A*) the diameter is laid out, and on it the pitch is measured on the upper line. This thread is a single thread; therefore, the pitch is equal to the lead, and the helix will advance $p/2 = l/2$ in 180°. This distance is laid off on the bottom diameter line, and the crest lines are drawn in. At (*B*), one side of the V form is drawn and is completed at (*C*). At (*D*), the root lines have been added. As can be seen from the three figures, 11.5 to 11.7, the stages in drawing any thread semiconventionally are similar, the principal difference being in the thread form. The

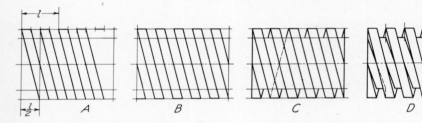

Fig. 11.7. Stages in drawing a double square thread.

square thread of Fig. 11.7 is double, while that of Fig. 11.8 is single and left-hand. Observe in Fig. 11.8 that it is unnecessary to draw the threads on the whole length of a long screw. If the thread is left-hand, the crest and root lines are slanted in the opposite direction to those shown in Figs. 11.5 to 11.7, as illustrated by the left-hand square thread of Fig. 11.8. Figure 11.9 illustrates semiconventional treatment for both external and internal V threads. Note that the crest and root lines are omitted on internal threads.

In general, threads should be represented semiconventionally except for the smaller sizes, which are ordinarily pictured by means of the ASA thread symbols. It is suggested that threads of 1 in. and

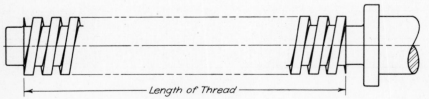

Fig. 11.8. Thread representation on a long screw.

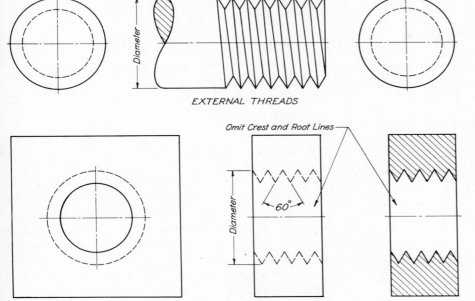

EXTERNAL THREADS

Omit Crest and Root Lines

60°

INTERNAL THREADS

Fig. 11.9. Semiconventional thread representation (suggested for V threads drawn 1 in. or over on both assembly and detail drawings).

larger in actual measurement on the drawing be represented semiconventionally.

11.8. Thread Symbols. The ASA provides two systems of thread symbols, "regular" and "simplified." It is recommended that these symbols be used for indicating the smaller threads (under 1 in.) and that the regular symbols be used on assembly drawings and the simplified symbols on detail drawings.

11.9. ASA Regular Thread Symbols (Fig. 11.10). They omit the profile on longitudinal views and indicate the crests and roots by lines perpendicular to the axis. However, exceptions are made for internal threads not drawn in section and external threads drawn in section as shown by the figure.

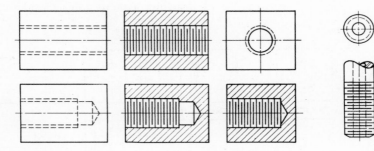

Fig. 11.10. ASA regular thread symbols.

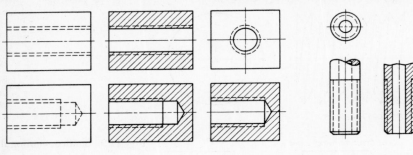

Fig. 11.11. ASA simplified thread symbols.

11.10. ASA Simplified Symbols (Fig. 11.11). They omit both form and crest lines and indicate the threaded portion by dotted lines parallel to the axis at the approximate depth of thread. The simplified method does not have the descriptive effect of the regular symbol, but as it saves much time, it is preferred on detail drawings.

11.11. To Draw the ASA Symbols. The two sets of symbols should be carefully studied and compared. Note that the regular and simplified symbols are identical for hidden threads. Also note that the end view of an external thread differs from the end view of

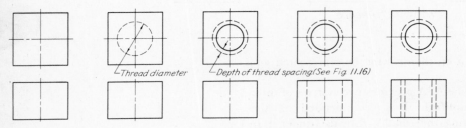

Fig. 11.12. Stages in drawing regular and simplified internal-thread symbols in external views.

an internal thread but that regular and simplified end-view symbols are identical.

No attempt need be made to show either the actual pitch of the threads or their depth by the spacing of lines in the symbol. Identical symbols may be used for several threads of the same diameter but of different pitch. It is possible only in the larger sizes to show the actual pitch and the true depth of thread without a confusion of lines that would defeat the purpose of the symbol. The symbols should therefore be made so as to read clearly and look well on the drawing, without other considerations.

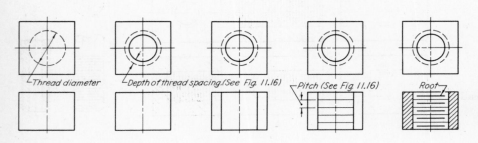

Fig. 11.13. Stages in drawing regular internal-thread symbols in section.

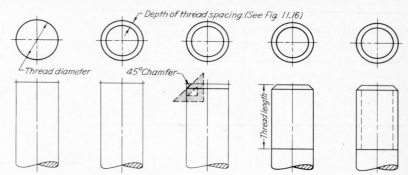

Fig. 11.14. Stages in drawing simplified external-thread symbols.

To draw a symbol for any given thread, only the major diameter and length of thread must be known, and for a blind tapped hole, the depth of the tap drill is also needed.

A *regular or simplified symbol for a tapped hole* is drawn in the stages shown by Fig. 11.12. As already stated, the lines representing depth of thread are not drawn to actual scale but are spaced so as to look well on the drawing and to avoid crowding of the lines.

A *regular symbol for a tapped hole in section* is drawn in the stages shown by Fig. 11.13. The lines representing the crests are spaced by eye or scale to look well and need not conform to the actual thread pitch. The lines representing the roots of the thread are equally spaced by eye between the crest lines and are usually drawn heavier. Their length need not indicate the actual depth of thread but should be kept uniform by using light guide lines.

A *simplified symbol for an external thread* is drawn in the stages shown by Fig. 11.14. The 45° chamfer extends to the root line of the thread. Note that in the end view the chamfer line is shown.

A *regular symbol for external threads* is drawn in the stages shown by Fig. 11.15. The chamfer is 45° and to the depth of thread. Crest lines are spaced by eye or scale. Root lines are spaced by eye, are usually drawn heavier, and need not conform to actual thread depth.

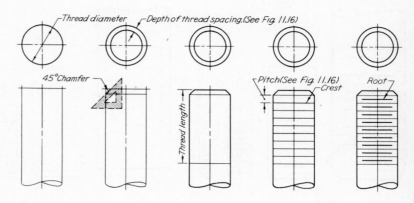

Fig. 11.15. Stages in drawing regular external-thread symbols.

Major diam. of thread D	Pitch p for dwg. purposes	Depth of thread $p/2$ for dwg. purposes
⅛ and 3⁄16	1⁄16 scant	1⁄32 scant
¼ and ⅜	1⁄16	1⁄32
½ and ⅝	⅛	1⁄16
¾ and ⅞	3⁄16	3⁄32

Fig. 11.16. Suggested values for drawing thread symbols.

Line Spacings. The table, Fig. 11.16, gives suggested values of "pitch" and "depth of thread" for purposes of drawing the ASA symbols. Figure 11.17 shows both regular and simplified symbols, full size, drawn according to the values given in Fig. 11.16. No distinction is made in the symbol between coarse and fine threads.

11.12. Threads in Section. Figure 11.4 shows the true form of an internal square thread in section. Observe that the far side of the thread is visible, causing the root and crest lines to slope in the opposite direction from those on the external thread. Figure 11.9 shows the semiconventional treatment for V threads over 1 in. in diameter. Note that the crest and root lines are omitted. The regular and simplified symbols for threads in section are shown in Figs. 11.10 and 11.11. When two pieces screwed together are shown in section, the thread form should be drawn to aid in reading (Fig. 11.18). In small diameters, it is desirable to decrease the number of threads per inch, thus eliminating monotonous detail and greatly improving the readability of the drawing.

11.13. Unified and American (National) Screw Threads. The Unified thread standards adopted by the United States, Canada, and the United Kingdom for the bulk of threaded products basically constitutes the American Standard "Unified and American Screw Threads" (ASA B1.1—1949). The form of thread employed has been described in paragraph 11.5 and is essentially that of the former (1935) American Standard. Threads produced according to the

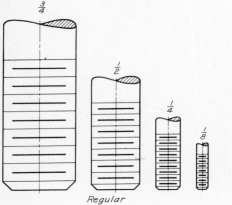

Regular

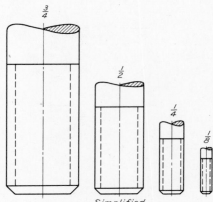

Simplified

Fig. 11.17. Thread symbols, actual drawing size.

former and present American Standards will interchange. Important differences between the two standards are in the liberalization of manufacturing tolerances, the provision of allowances for most classes of threads, and the changes in thread designations. The new American Standard contains, in addition to the Unified diameter-pitch combinations and thread classes (adopted in common by the three countries), additional diameter-pitch combinations and two thread classes retained from the 1935 standard.

11.14. Thread Series. Threads are classified in "series" according to the number of threads per inch used with a specific diameter. For example, an American (Unified) thread having 20 threads per inch applied to a ¼-in. diameter results in a thread belonging to the coarse-thread series, while 28 threads per inch on the same diameter gives a thread belonging to the fine-thread series.

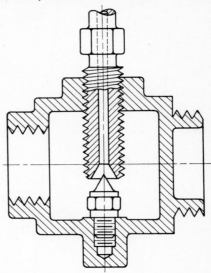

Fig. 11.18. Threads in section, drawing size.

In the United States, the thread forms which have been subjected to series standardization by the ASA include the Unified or American National, the Acme, stub Acme, pipe threads, buttress, and the knuckle thread as used on electric sockets and lamp bases. Except for the Unified, or American National, only one series is provided for each of the thread forms so standardized (see Appendix for Acme and stub Acme threads and for pipe threads).

The American Standard "Unified and American (National) Screw Threads" covers six series of screw threads and, in addition, certain other preferred special diameter-pitch combinations. In the descriptions of the series which follow, the letters "U" and "N" used in the series designations stand for the words "Unified" and "National (form)," respectively.

The *coarse-thread series*, designated "UNC" or "NC," is recommended for general use where conditions do not require a fine thread.

The *fine-thread series*, designated "UNF" or "NF," is recommended for general use in automotive and aircraft work and where special conditions require a fine thread.

The *extrafine-thread series*, designated "UNEF" or "NEF," is used particularly in aircraft work, where an extremely shallow thread or a maximum number of threads within a given length is required.

The *8-thread series*, designated "8N," is a uniform-pitch series using eight threads per inch for all diameters concerned. Bolts for high-pressure pipe flanges, cylinder-head studs, and similar fasteners against pressure require that an initial tension be set up by elastic deformation of the fastener and that the components be held together so that the joint will not open when steam or other pressure is applied. To secure a proper initial tension, it is not practicable that the pitch should increase with the diameter of the thread, as the torque required to assemble would be excessive. Accordingly, for such purposes, the 8-thread series has come into general use in many classes of engineering work and as a substitute for the coarse-thread series.

The 12-*thread series*, designated "12UN" or "12N," is a uniform-pitch series using 12 threads per inch for all diameters concerned. Sizes of 12-pitch threads from $\frac{1}{2}$ to $1\frac{3}{4}$ in. in diameter are used in boiler practice, which requires that worn stud holes be retapped with the next larger size. The 12-thread series is also widely used in machine construction for thin nuts on shafts and sleeves and provides continuation of the fine-thread series for diameters larger than $1\frac{1}{2}$ in.

The 16-*thread series*, designated "16UN" or "16N," is a uniform-pitch series using 16 threads per inch for all diameters concerned. This series is intended for applications requiring a very fine thread, such as threaded adjusting collars and bearing retaining nuts. It also provides continuation of the extrafine-thread series for diameters larger than 2 in.

Special threads, designated "UN," "UNS," or "NS," as covered in the standards include nonstandard or special combinations of diameter, pitch, and length of engagement.

The diameter-pitch combinations of the above series will be found in the Appendix, where the Unified combinations (combinations common to the standards of the United States, Canada, and Great Britain) are printed in bold type.

11.15. Unified and American Screw-thread Classes. A class of thread is distinguished by the tolerance and allowance specified for the member threads and is therefore a control of the looseness or tightness of the fit between mating screws and nuts. The Unified and American (National) and Acme are at present the only threads in this country standardized to the extent of providing several thread classes to control the fit.

The classes provided by the American Standard "Unified and American Screw Threads" are classes 1A, 2A, and 3A, applied to *external threads only;* classes 1B, 2B, and 3B, applied to *internal threads only;* and classes 2 and 3, applied to *both external and internal threads.* These classes are achieved through toleranced thread dimensions given in the standards.

Classes 1A and 1B are intended for ordnance and other special uses where free assembly and easy production are important. Tolerances and allowance are largest with this class.

Classes 2A and 2B are the recognized standards for the bulk of screws, bolts, and nuts produced and are suitable for a wide variety of applications. A moderate allowance provides a minimum clearance between mating threads to minimize galling and seizure.

Classes 3A and 3B provide a class where accuracy and closeness of fit are important. No allowance is provided.

Classes 2 and 3, each applying to both external and internal threads, have been retained from the former (1935) American Standard. No allowance is provided with either class, and tolerances are in general closer than with the corresponding new classes.

11.16. Unified Threads. Not all the diameter-pitch combinations listed in the American Standard "Unified and American Standard Screw Threads" appear in the British and Canadian standards. Combinations used in common by the three countries are called Unified threads and are identified by the letter U in the series designation; they are printed in bold type in the Appendix table. Unified threads may employ classes 1A and 1B, 2A and 2B, and 3A and 3B only. When one of these classes is used and the U does not appear in the designation, the thread conforms to the principles on which Unified threads are based.

The Unified and American National screw-thread table (Appendix) indicates the classes for which each series has data tabulated in the standards. Threads of standard diameter-pitch combinations but of a class for which data are not tabulated in the standard are designated UNS if a Unified combination and NS if not.

11.17. Acme and Stub Acme Threads. Acme and stub Acme threads have been standardized by the ASA in one series of diameter-pitch combinations (see Appendix). In addition, the standard provides for two general applications of Acme threads: general purpose and centralizing. The three thread classes 2G, 3G, and 4G, standardized for general-purpose applications, have clearances on all diameters for free movement. Centralizing Acme threads have a close fit on the major diameter to maintain alignment of the screw and nut and are standardized in five thread classes, 2C, 3C, 4C, 5C, and 6C. The stub Acme has only one thread class for general usage.

11.18. Buttress Threads. Buttress threads have been standardized in a different fashion from the other types. Thread form and class of fit is completely defined. Thread series is not defined, but a table of recommended thread diameters and associated thread pitches is provided. Since the number of associated thread pitches varies from three to eleven (depending upon the thread diameter), the designation of a thread series would merely add complication. Three classes of fit are standard: class 1 (free), class 2 (medium), and class 3 (close).

11.19. Thread Specification. The orthographic views of a thread are necessary in order to locate the position of the thread dimensionally on the part. In addition, the views describe whether the thread is external or internal. All other information, called the "specification," is normally conveyed by means of either a note or dimensions and a note. In addition to appearing on drawings, the specification may be needed in correspondence, on stock and parts lists, etc.

Features of a thread on which information is essential for manufacture are form, nominal (major) diameter, threads per inch, and thread class or toleranced dimensions. In addition, if the thread is left-hand, the letters LH must be included in the specification; also, if the thread is other than single, its multiplicity must be indicated.

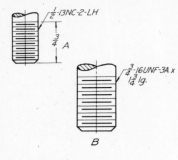

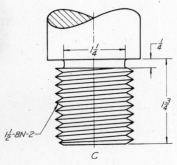

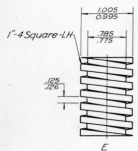

Fig. 11.19. Specifications of external threads.

In general, threads other than the Unified and American National, Acme, stub Acme, and buttress will require toleranced dimensions to control the fit (Fig. 11.19E).

Unified and American National threads are specified completely by note. The form of the specification always follows the same order: The nominal size is given first, then the number of threads per inch and the series designation (UNC, NC, etc.), and then the thread class (Fig. 11.19A to C). If the thread is left-hand, the letters LH follow the class (Fig. 11.19A).

Examples

¼-20UNC-3A	1-12UNF-2B-LH	2-8N-2	2-16UN-2B
¼-20NC-2	1-20NEF-3	2-12UN-2A	2-6NS-2A

Note that, when the Unified-thread classes are employed, the letters A and B indicate whether the thread is external or internal.

Acme and stub Acme threads are also specified by note. The form of the specification follows that of the Unified, Fig. 11.19D.

Examples

1¾-4Acme-2G (general-purpose class 2 Acme; 1¾ in. major diameter, 0.25 in. pitch; single, right-hand)

1-5Acme-4C-LH (centralizing class 4 Acme; 1 in. major diameter, 0.2 in. pitch; single, left-hand)

2½-0.333p-0.666L-Acme-3G (general-purpose class 3 Acme; 2½ in. major diameter, 0.333 in. pitch, 0.666 in. lead; double, right-hand)

¾-6Stub Acme (stub Acme; ¾ in. major diameter, 0.1667 in. pitch; right-hand)

Buttress threads can be completely specified by note but require one additional item of information in addition to diameter, threads per inch, type of thread, and class of fit: the direction of pressure as exerted by the internal member (screw). The following symbols are recommended for this purpose:

(← screw *pushing* to left (screw pressure flank facing left)

←(screw *pulling* to right (screw pressure flank facing right)

Note that the arrow points left but that the parenthesis mark indicates the direction of pressure flank.

Where the buttress thread is multiple, the pitch and lead distances should be given instead of threads per inch.

Examples

⅝-20(←N. Butt.-1

4-8←(N. Butt.-2LH

10-0.1p-0.2L(←N. Butt.-1

11.20. Tapped-hole Specifications. Always specify by note, giving the tap-drill diameter and depth of hole followed by the thread specification and length of thread (Fig. 11.20). For tap-drill sizes, see Appendix. It is general commercial practice to use 75 per cent of the theoretical depth of thread for tapped holes. This gives

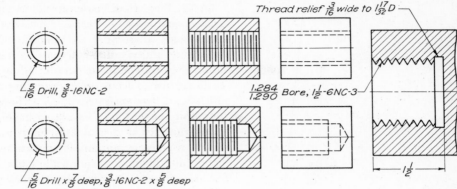

Fig. 11.20. Specifications of internal threads.

about 95 per cent of the strength of a full thread and is much easier to cut.

11.21. Depth of Tapped Holes and Entrance Length. For threaded rods, studs, cap screws, machine screws, and similar fasteners, these may be found by using an empirical formula based on the diameter of the fastener and the material tapped (see Fig. 11.21 and the accompanying table).

Material	Entrance length for cap screws, etc., A	Thread clearance at bottom of hole B	Thread depth C	Unthreaded portion at bottom of hole E	Depth of drilled hole F
Aluminum	$2D$	$4/n$	$2D + 4/n$	$4/n$	$C + E$
Cast iron	$1\frac{1}{2}D$	$4/n$	$1\frac{1}{2}D + 4/n$	$4/n$	$C + E$
Brass	$1\frac{1}{2}D$	$4/n$	$1\frac{1}{2}D + 4/n$	$4/n$	$C + E$
Bronze	$1\frac{1}{2}D$	$4/n$	$1\frac{1}{2}D + 4/n$	$4/n$	$C + E$
Steel	D	$4/n$	$D + 4/n$	$4/n$	$C + E$

A = entrance length for fastener.
B = thread clearance at bottom of hole.
C = total thread depth.
D = diameter of fastener.
E = unthreaded portion at bottom of hole.
F = depth of tap-drill hole.
n = threads per inch.

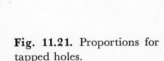

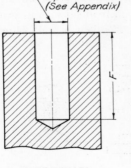

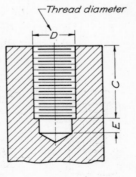

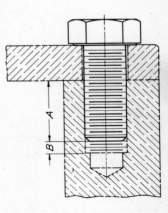

Fig. 11.21. Proportions for tapped holes.

HOLE DRILLED   HOLE TAPPED   CAP SCREW IN TAPPED HOLE

11.22. Threaded Fasteners. All engineering products, structures, etc., are composed of separate parts which must be held together by some means of fastening. Compared with permanent methods, such as welding and riveting, threaded fasteners provide an advantage in that they may be removed, thus allowing disassembly of the parts. As distinguished from other fastening devices such as pins, rivets, and keys, a *threaded* fastener is a cylinder of metal having a screw thread on one end and, usually, a head on the other.

The quantity of threaded fasteners used each year is tremendous. Many varieties are obtainable, some standardized and others special. The standardization of such widely used products results in uniform and interchangeable parts obtainable without complicated and detailed specification and at low cost. Standardized fasteners should be employed wherever possible.

Most fasteners have descriptive names, as the "setscrew," which holds a part in a set, or fixed, position. The bolt derives its name from an early-English use, where it was employed as a fastener or pin for bolting a door. Five types—the bolt, stud, cap screw, machine screw, and setscrew—represent the bulk of threaded fasteners.

11.23. American Standard Bolts and Nuts. A *bolt*, Fig. 11.22*A*, having an integral head on one end and a thread on the other end, is passed through clearance holes in two parts and draws them together by means of a nut screwed on the threaded end.

Two major groups of bolts have been standardized: round-head bolts and wrench-head bolts (sometimes called "machine bolts").

Round-head bolts are used as through fasteners with a nut, usually square. Eleven head types have standard proportions and include carriage bolts, step bolts, elevator bolts, and spline bolts. Several head types are intended for wood construction and have square sections, ribs, or fins under the head to prevent the bolts from turning. These bolts are hot or cold formed, with no machining except threading; hence they present a somewhat coarse and irregular appearance. A table in the Appendix shows the various head forms and gives nominal dimensions suitable for drawing purposes.

Wrench-head (machine) bolts have two standard head forms, square and hexagonal. Although intended for use as a through fastener with a nut, machine bolts are sometimes used as cap screws. Nuts to match the bolthead form and grade are available, but any nut of correct thread will fit a bolt. Machine bolts vary in grade from

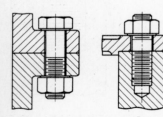
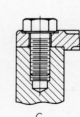

A   B   C   D   E

Fig. 11.22. Common types of fastener.

coarsely finished products resembling round-head bolts to a well-finished product matching a hexagon cap screw in appearance. Dimensions for drawing purposes are given in the Appendix.

11.24. Studs. A *stud*, Fig. 11.22*B*, is a rod threaded on each end. As used normally, the fastener passes through a clearance hole in one piece and screws permanently into a tapped hole in the other. A nut then draws the parts together. The stud, Fig. 11.23, is used when through bolts are not suitable for parts that must be removed frequently, such as cylinder heads and chest covers. One end is screwed tightly into a tapped hole, and the projecting stud guides the removable piece to position. The end to be screwed permanently into position is called the "stud end"; and the opposite end, the "nut end." The nut end is sometimes identified by rounding instead of chamfering. Studs have not been standardized by the ASA. The length of thread on the stud end is governed by the material tapped, as indicated in paragraph 11.21. The threads should jam at the top of the hole to prevent the stud from turning out when the nut is removed. The fit of the thread between the stud and tapped hole should be tight.

The length of thread on the nut end should be such that there is no danger of the nut binding before the parts are drawn together. The name "stud bolt" is often applied to a stud used as a through fastener with a nut on each end. The stud, a nonstandard part, is usually described on a detail drawing (Fig. 11.23*B*). The nut, being a standard part, is described by note on the assembly drawing (Fig. 11.23*A*) or on the parts list.

11.25. Cap Screws. A *cap screw*, Fig. 11.22*C*, passes through a clearance hole in one piece and screws into a tapped hole in the other. The head, an integral part of the screw, draws the parts together as the screw enters the tapped hole. Cap screws are used on machine tools and other products requiring close dimensions and finished appearances. They are well-finished products; for example, the heads of the slotted and socket head screws are machined, and all have chamfered points. The five types of heads shown in Fig. 11.24 are standard. Detail dimensions and length increments are given in the Appendix.

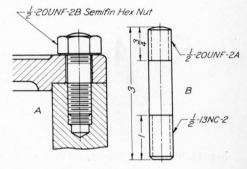

Fig. 11.23. Stud and nut.

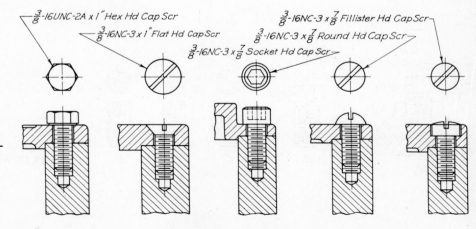

Fig. 11.24. American Standard cap screws.

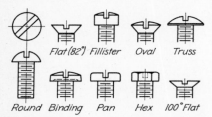

Flat (82°) *Fillister* *Oval* *Truss*

Round *Binding* *Pan* *Hex* *100° Flat*

Fig. 11.25. American Standard machine-screw heads.

Fig. 11.26. Recessed head and driver.

11.26. Machine Screws. A *machine screw*, Fig. 11.22*D*, is a small fastener used with a nut to function in the same manner as a bolt; or without a nut, to function as a cap screw. Machine screws are small fasteners used principally in numbered diameter sizes. The finish is regularly bright, and the material used is commonly steel or brass. The nine standardized head shapes, Fig. 11.25, except for the hexagon, are available in slotted form as shown or with cross recesses (Fig. 11.26). The size of the recess varies with the size of the screw. Two recess types occur: intersecting slots with parallel sides converging to a sharp apex at the bottom of the recess (the same driver is used for all size recesses) and large center opening, tapered wings, and a blunt bottom (five sizes of drivers needed).

The hexagon machine screw is not made with a cross recess but may be optionally slotted. Dimensions for drawing machine screw heads will be found in the Appendix.

11.27. Setscrews. A *setscrew*, Fig. 11.22*E*, screws into a tapped hole in an outer part, often a hub, and bears with its point against an inner part, usually a shaft. Setscrews are made of hardened steel and hold two parts in relative position by having the point set against the inner part. The American Standard square-head and headless screws are shown in Fig. 11.27. Types of points are shown in Fig. 11.28. Headless setscrews are made to comply with the safety code of factory-inspection laws, which are very strict regarding the use of projecting screws on moving parts. Square-head setscrews have head proportions following the formulas of Fig. 11.27 and can be drawn by using the radii suggested there. A neck or a radius may be used under the head, and the points have the same dimensions as headless screws. Dimensions for headless setscrews are given in the Appendix.

11.28. American Standard Nuts. These are available in two wrench-type styles, square and hexagonal. In addition to the plain form usually associated with bolts, several special-purpose styles are available. Jam, hexagonal slotted, and hexagonal castle nuts are shown in Fig. 11.29. Machine screw and stove-bolt nuts are available in small sizes only.

11.29. Standard Fasteners. The ASA Standards provide uniform dimensions and proportions for all fasteners (except studs) listed in

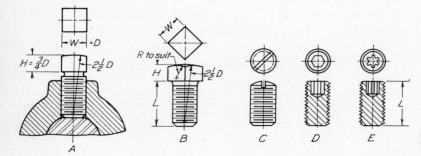

Fig. 11.27. American Standard setscrews.

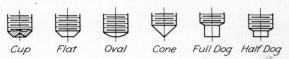

Fig. 11.28. American Standard setscrew points.

Cup   Flat   Oval   Cone   Full Dog   Half Dog

the preceding paragraphs. With the exception of machine bolts, the only options for any of the preceding fasteners are the head style and thread series. Wrench head bolts are available in two head styles, two head weights, three finishes, and three thread series. The following table lists the available standard options, and paragraph 11.30 describes the differences:

Fastener group	Head styles	Thread series	Thread class
Round-head bolts	All	UNC	2A
Cap screws	Hexagonal Slotted Socket	UNC, UNF, 8UN	2A 2A 3A
Machine screws	All	NC, NF	2
Setscrews	Socket Square Slotted	UNC, UNF, 8UN, UNC, UNF	3A 2A 2A

Wrench-head (machine) bolts

Finish class	Square		Hexagonal		Thread	
	Regular	Heavy	Regular	Heavy	Series	Class
Unfaced	X	...	X	X	UNC	2A
Semifinished	...	...	X	X	UNC	2A
Finished	...	...	X	X	UNC, UNF, 8UN	2A

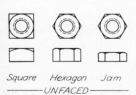

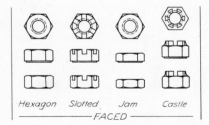

Square   Hexagon
Hexagon   Jam
———UNFACED———

Hexagon   Slotted   Jam   Castle
————————FACED————————

Square   Hexagon

MACHINE SCREW AND
STOVE BOLT NUTS

Fig. 11.29. American Standard nuts.

American Standard nuts

Finish class	Square		Hexagonal			Hexagonal slotted		
	Regular	Heavy	Regular	Heavy	Thick	Regular	Heavy	Thick
Unfaced	X	X	X*	X				
Semifinished	...	...	X*	X	...	X*	X	
Finished	...	...	X	...	X	X	...	X

* ASA Standard B18.2—1955 lists $\frac{1}{4}$ to $\frac{5}{8}$ sizes as not recommended for new designs.

11.30. Fastener Terms. *Nominal Diameter.* The basic major diameter of the thread.

Width across Flats W. The distance separating parallel sides of the square or hexagonal head or nut, corresponding with the nominal size of the wrench. See table in Appendix for dimension W.

Tops of Boltheads and Nuts. The tops of heads and nuts are flat with a chamfer to remove the sharp corners. The angle of chamfer with the top surface is 25° for the square form and 30° for the hexagonal form; both are drawn at 30°. The diameter of the top circle is equal to the width across flats.

Washer Face. The washer face is a circular boss turned or otherwise formed on the bearing surface of a bolthead or nut to make a smooth surface. The diameter is equal to the width across flats. The thickness is $\frac{1}{64}$ in. for all fasteners. A circular bearing surface may be obtained on a nut by chamfering the corners. The angle of chamfer with the bearing face is 30°, and the diameter of the circle is equal to the width across flats.

Fastener Length. The nominal length is the distance from the bearing surface to the point. For flat-head fasteners and for headless setscrews it is the over-all length.

Regular Series. Regular boltheads and nuts are for general use. The dimensions and the resulting strengths are based on the theoretical analysis of the stresses and on results of numerous tests.

Heavy Series. They are for use where greater bearing surface is necessary. Therefore, for the same nominal size, they are larger in over-all dimensions than regular heads and nuts. They are used where a large clearance between the bolt and hole or a greater wrench-bearing surface is considered essential.

Thick Nuts. They have the same dimensions as regular nuts, except that they are higher.

Class of Finish. Unfaced bolts and nuts are not machined on any surface except the threads. The bearing surface is plain. Dimensional tolerances are as large as practicable.

Semifinished Boltheads and Nuts. These have a smooth bearing surface machined or formed at right angles to the axis (see Fig. 11.30). For boltheads, this is a washer face; and for nuts, either a washer

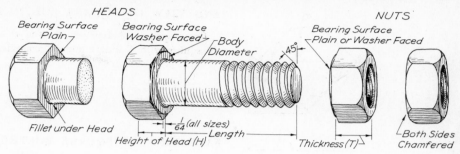

Fig. 11.30. Hexagonal bolt and nuts.

face or a circular bearing surface produced by chamfering the corners. Dimensional tolerances of the fastener are otherwise the same as the unfaced group.

Finished Bolts and Nuts. These differ from the semifinished in two ways: The bearing surface may be either washer-faced or produced by double chamfering (see Fig. 11.30). Dimensional tolerances are smaller than the semifinished form. Finished hexagonal bolts have dimensional tolerances and workmanship similar to hexagonal cap screws.

11.31. Standard Fastener Specifications. All standard fasteners may be specified on drawings or parts lists by notes.

The following items may be included in a fastener specification in the order listed. Obviously, many of the items will not apply to some fastener types.

1. Thread specification (without length)
2. Fastener length
3. Fastener series (bolts only)
4. Class of finish (bolts only)
5. Material (if other than steel)
6. Head style or form
7. Point type (setscrews only)
8. Fastener group name

Sample specifications follow. Note carefully the wording of the machine-bolt notes.

½-13UNC-2A × 3 Reg Sq Bolt
¼-20UNC-2A × 4 Reg Semifin Hex Bolt
⅜-16UNC-2A × 3½ Hvy Semifin Hex Bolt
¾-16UNF-2A × 2½ Finished Hex Bolt (omit Reg)
⅝-11UNC-2A × 4¼ Hvy Finished Hex Bolt
#10-24NC-2 × 2 Brass Slotted Flat Hd Mach Scr
#6-32NC-2 × ½ Recess Fil Hd Mach Scr
¼-20UNC-2A × ¾ Sq Hd Cone Pt Setscrew
½-13UNC-3A × 2 Soc, Flt Pt Setscrew

See Fig. 11.24 for cap-screw notes.

END VIEW OF SQUARE BOLTHEAD

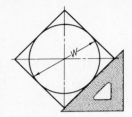

Draw a circle of diameter W, and then draw the square with T square and 45° triangle.

FACE VIEW OF SQUARE BOLTHEAD

1. Establish the diameter and the height of head.

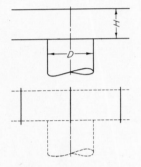

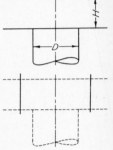

2. Draw, lightly, the vertical edges of the faces, projecting from the end view.

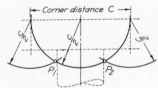

3. Set compass to radius of $C/2$, and draw the circle arcs locating centers P_1 and P_2.

3. Set compass to radius of W, and draw the circle arc locating the center P.

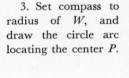

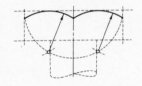

4. Draw chamfer arcs, using radii and centers shown.

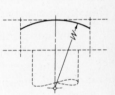

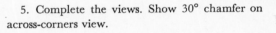

5. Complete the views. Show 30° chamfer on across-corners view.

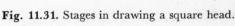

Fig. 11.31. Stages in drawing a square head.

11.32. The Drawing of Fasteners. Before drawing a fastener, its *type*, *nominal diameter*, and *length*, if a bolt or screw, must be known. Knowing the type and diameter, other dimensions can be sought in the tables (see Appendix).

11.33. To Draw Square and Hexagon-form Fasteners. Square and hexagonal heads and nuts are drawn "across corners" on all views showing the faces unless a special reason exists for drawing them "across flats." Figure 11.31 shows stages for drawing square heads both across corners and across flats, and Fig. 11.32 shows the

END VIEW OF HEXAGONAL BOLTHEAD

Draw a circle of diameter W, and then draw the hexagon with T square and 30°-60° triangle.

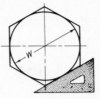

FACE VIEW OF HEXAGONAL BOLTHEAD

1. Establish the diameter, height of head, and washer-face thickness. The actual thickness of the washer face for all fasteners is $\frac{1}{64}$ in. but may be increased up to $\frac{1}{32}$ in. for the drawing.

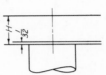

2. Draw, lightly, the vertical edges of the faces, projecting from the end view.

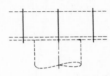

3. With radius of $W/2$ draw the circle arcs locating centers P_1 and P_2.

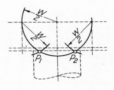

4. Draw chamfer arcs, using radii and centers shown.

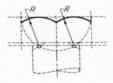

5. Complete the views. Washer-face diameter is equal to W. For across-corners view, show 30° chamfer.

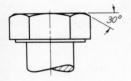

Fig. 11.32. Stages in drawing a hexagonal head.

same for hexagonal heads. The principles apply equally to the drawing of nuts. The following information must be known: (1) type of head or nut, (2) whether regular or heavy, (3) whether unfinished or semifinished, and (4) the nominal diameter. Using this information, additional data W (width across flats), H (height of head), and T (thickness of nut) are obtained from the tables (see Appendix).

Figure 11.33 shows a regular semifinished hexagonal bolt and nut, drawn by the method of Fig. 11.32, showing the head across flats and the nut across corners. The length is selected from the bolt-

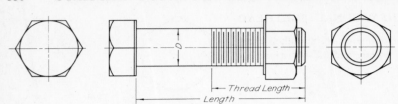

Fig. 11.33. American Standard regular hexagonal semifinished bolt and nut.

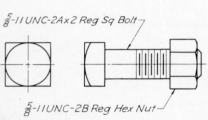

$\frac{5}{8}$-11 UNC-2Ax2 Reg Sq Bolt

$\frac{5}{8}$-11UNC-2B Reg Hex Nut

Fig. 11.34. ASA regular square bolt and regular unfaced hexagonal nut.

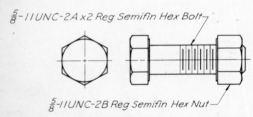

$\frac{5}{8}$-11UNC-2A x2 Reg Semifin Hex Bolt

$\frac{5}{8}$-11UNC-2B Reg Semifin Hex Nut

Fig. 11.35. ASA regular semifinished hexagonal bolt and regular semifinished hexagonal nut.

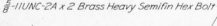
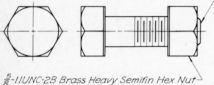

$\frac{5}{8}$-11UNC-2A x 2 Brass Heavy Semifin Hex Bolt

$\frac{5}{8}$-11UNC-2B Brass Heavy Semifin Hex Nut

Fig. 11.36. ASA heavy semifinished hexagonal bolt and heavy semifinished hexagonal nut.

length tables and the length of thread determined from the footnote to the bolt table (see Appendix). Observe that the washer face shown in Fig. 11.32 will occur only with semifinished hexagonal fasteners and is sometimes omitted from the drawings of these. Other views of bolts and nuts are shown in Figs. 11.34 to 11.37.

The drawing may require considerable time when, for example, clearance conditions necessitate an accurately drawn fastener, using exact dimensions from tables. Often, however, their representation may be approximate or even symbolic because the note specifications invariably accompany and exactly specify them. If an accurate drawing of the fastener is not essential, the W, H, and T dimensions of hexagonal and square heads and nuts may be obtained from the nominal diameter and the following formulas; the resulting values will be quite close to the actual dimensions. For the regular series, $W = 1\frac{1}{2}D$, $H = \frac{2}{3}D$, and $T = \frac{7}{8}D$; for the heavy series, $W = 1\frac{1}{2}D + \frac{1}{8}$ in., $H = \frac{3}{4}D$, and $T = D$.

A wide variety of *templates* to facilitate the drawing of fasteners is available. See paragraph 12.36 and Fig. 12.31.

11.34. Specialized Fasteners. There are a great many special fasteners, a number of which are the developments of the companies that supply a variety of forms. The following are common types:

11.35. Shoulder Screws (Fig. 11.38). These are widely used for holding machine parts together and providing pivots, such as with cams, linkages, etc. They are also used with punch and die sets for attaching stripper plates and are then commonly called "stripper bolts." Threads are coarse series, class 3. Detail dimensions are given in the Appendix.

11.36. Plow Bolts (Fig. 11.39). These are used principally in agricultural equipment. The No. 3 and No. 7 heads are recommended for most new work. Threads are coarse series, class 2A. For particulars and proportions, see ASA B18.9—1950.

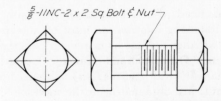

$\frac{5}{8}$-11NC-2 x 2 Sq Bolt & Nut

Fig. 11.37. ASA regular unfaced square bolt and nut.

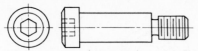

11.38. American Standard shoulder
screw.

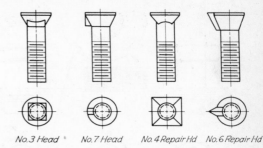

No.3 Head No.7 Head No.4 Repair Hd No.6 Repair Hd

Fig. 11.39. American Standard plow
bolts.

11.37. American Standard Tapping Screws. Tapping screws
are hardened fasteners which form their own mating internal threads
when driven into a hole of the proper size. For certain conditions
and materials, these screws give a combination of speed and low
production cost, which makes them preferred. Many special types
are available. The ASA has standardized head types conforming
with all machine-screw heads except the binding and 100° flat
heads. For drawing purposes, dimensions of machine-screw heads
may be used. Sizes conform, in general, with machine-screw sizes.
The ASA provides three types of threads and point combinations
(Fig. 11.40). The threads are 60° with flattened crest and root; types
(A) and (B) are interrupted threads, and all fasteners are threaded
to the head. Full details will be found in ASA B18.6—1947.

11.38. Fasteners for Wood. Many forms of threaded fasteners
for use in wood are available. Some are illustrated in Fig. 11.41.
Threads are interrupted, 60° form, with a gimlet point. The ASA
has standardized lag bolts having square heads and also wood screws
having flat, round, and oval heads. Lag boltheads follow the same
dimensions and, in general, the same nominal sizes as regular square
bolts. Specific information will be found in ASA B18—1951. Wood
screws follow the same head dimensions and, in general, the same
nominal sizes as the corresponding flat-, round-, and oval-head
machine screws. The nominal sizes, however, are carried to higher
numbers. See table in the Appendix. Like machine screws, wood-
screw heads may be plain slotted or have either style of cross recess.
Several kinds of finish are available, for example, bright steel, blued,
or nickel-plated. Material is usually steel or brass.

11.39. Other Forms of Threaded Fasteners. Many other forms
of threaded fasteners, most of which have not been standardized,
are in common use. Figure 11.42 illustrates some of these.

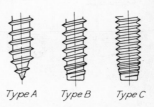

Type A Type B Type C

Fig. 11.40. American Standard tapping-
screw points.

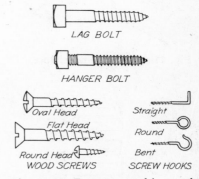

LAG BOLT

HANGER BOLT

Oval Head Straight

Flat Head Round

Round Head Bent

WOOD SCREWS SCREW HOOKS

Fig. 11.41. Fasteners used in wood.

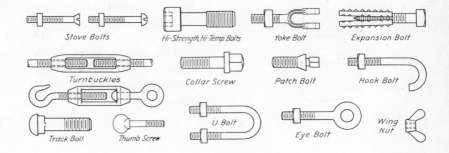

Stove Bolts Hi-Strength, Hi-Temp. Bolts Yoke Bolt Expansion Bolt

Turnbuckles Collar Screw Patch Bolt Hook Bolt

Track Bolt Thumb Screw U Bolt Eye Bolt Wing Nut

Fig. 11.42. Miscellaneous threaded
fasteners.

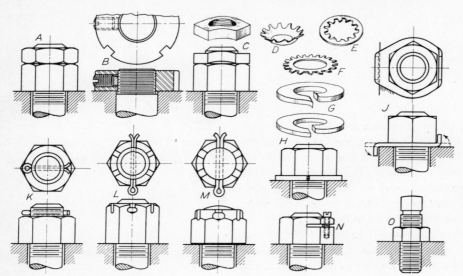

Fig. 11.43. Locking devices.

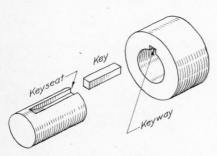

Fig. 11.44. Key nomenclature.

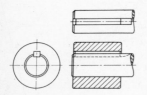

Fig. 11.45. Square (or flat) key.

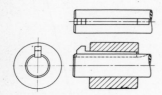

Fig. 11.46. Gib-head key.

11.40. Lock Nuts and Locking Devices (Fig. 11.43). Man different locking devices are used to prevent nuts from workin loose. A screw thread holds securely unless the parts are subject t impact and vibration, as in a railroad-track joint or an automobil engine. A common device is the *jam nut* (*A*) *Slotted nuts* (*L*) an *castle nuts* (*M*), to be held with a cotter or wire, are commonly use in automotive and allied work. For additional information on jam slotted, and castle nuts, see paragraph 11.28.

At (*B*) is shown a *round nut* locked by means of a setscrew. A bras plug is placed under the setscrew to prevent damage to the thread This is a common type of adjusting nut used in machine-tool prac tice. (*C*) is a *lock nut*, in which the threads are deformed after cutting. Patented *spring washers*, such as are shown at (*D*), (*E*), and (*F*), are common devices. Special patented nuts with plastic or fiber inserts or with distorted threads are in common use as locking devices. The locking action of (*J*), (*K*), (*N*), and (*O*) should be evident from the figure.

11.41. ASA Standard Plain and Lock Washers. There are four standard ASA spring lock washers: light, medium, heavy, and extra heavy; these are shown in Fig. 11.43*G* and *H* and are specified by giving nominal diameter and series.

Example

½ Heavy Lock Washer

ASA plain washers are also standardized in four series, light, me dium, heavy, and extra heavy, and are specified by giving nominal diameter and series.

Example

$\frac{7}{16}$ Light Plain Washer

Dimensions of ASA plain and lock washers will be found in the ppendix.

11.42. Keys. In the making of machine drawings there is fre-uent occasion for representing key fasteners, used to prevent rota-on of wheels, gears, etc., on their shafts. A key is a piece of metal, ig. 11.44, placed so that part of it lies in a groove, called the "key-eat," cut in a shaft. The key then extends somewhat above the shaft nd fits into a "keyway" cut in a hub. Thus, after assembly, the key partly in the shaft and partly in the hub, locking the two together o that one cannot rotate without the other.

11.43. Key Types. The simplest key, geometrically, is the square ey, placed *half* in the shaft and *half* in the hub, Fig. 11.45. A flat ey is rectangular in cross section and is used in the same manner s the square key. The gib-head key, Fig. 11.46, is tapered on its pper surface and is driven in to form a very secure fastening. Both quare and flat (parallel and tapered stock) keys have been stand-rdized by the ASA. Tables of standard sizes are given in the Ap-endix.

The Pratt and Whitney key, Fig. 11.47, is a variation on the quare key. It is rectangular in cross section and has rounded ends. t is placed two-thirds in the shaft and one-third in the hub. The ey is proportioned so that the keyseat is square and the keyway is alf as deep as it is wide. See Appendix for sizes.

Perhaps the most common key is the Woodruff, Fig. 11.48. This ey is a flat segmental disk with either a flat (*A*) or round (*B*) ottom. The keyseat is semicylindrical and cut to a depth so that *half* the *width* of the key extends above the shaft and into the hub. Tables of dimensions are given in the Appendix. A good basic rule for proportioning a Woodruff key to a given shaft is to have the width of the key one-fourth the diameter of the shaft and its radius equal to the radius of the shaft, selecting the standard key that comes nearest to these proportions. In drawing Woodruff keys, care should be taken to place the center for the arc above the top of the key to a distance equal to one-half the thickness of the saw used in splitting the blank. This amount is given in column *E* of the table in the Appendix.

Figure 11.49 shows three keys for light duty: the saddle key (*A*), the flat key (*B*), and the pin, or Nordberg, key (*C*), which is used at the end of a shaft, as, for example, in fastening a handwheel.

Figure 11.50 shows some forms of heavy-duty keys. (*A*) is the Barth key, (*B*) the Kennedy key, and (*C*) the Lewis key for driving in one direction. In the latter two, the line of shear is on the diagonal.

For very heavy duty, keys are not sufficiently strong and splines (grooves) are cut in both shaft and hub, arranged so that they fit one within the other, Fig. 11.51. (*A*) and (*B*) are two forms of splines widely used instead of keys. (*B*) is the newer ASA involute spline (B5.15—1946).

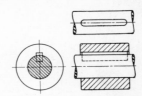

Fig. 11.47. Pratt and Whitney key.

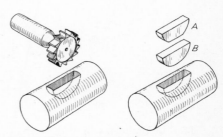

Fig. 11.48. Woodruff keys, cutter, and keyseat.

Fig. 11.49. Keys for light duty.

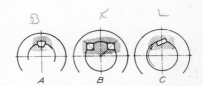

Fig. 11.50. Keys for heavy duty.

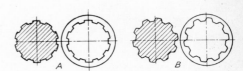

Fig. 11.51. Splined shafts and hubs.

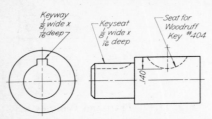

Fig. 11.52. Nominal dimensions (square and Woodruff keys).

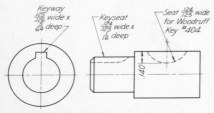

Fig. 11.53. Limit dimensions (square and Woodruff keys).

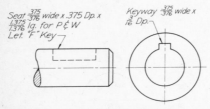

Fig. 11.54. Dimensioning for a Pratt and Whitney keyseat and keyway.

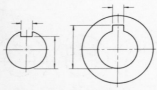

Fig. 11.55. Dimensions for interchangeable assembly.

11.44. Specification of Keys. Keys are specified by note or number, depending upon the type.

Square and flat keys are specified by a note giving the width, height, and length.

Examples

½ Square Key 2½ Lg
½ × ⅜ Flat Key 2½ Lg

Plain taper stock keys are specified by giving the width, the height at the large end, and the length. The height at the large end is measured at the distance W (width) from the large end. The taper is 1 to 96. See Appendix.

Examples

⅜ × ⅜ × 1½ Square Plain Taper Key
½ × ⅜ × 1¼ Flat Plain Taper Key

Gib-head taper stock keys are specified by giving, except for name, the same information as for square or flat taper keys. See Appendix.

Examples

¾ × ¾ × 2¼ Square Gib-head Taper Key
⅞ × ⅝ × 2½ Flat Gib-head Taper Key

Pratt and Whitney keys are specified by number or letter. See Appendix.

Example

Pratt and Whitney Key No. 6

Woodruff keys are specified by number. See Appendix.

Dimensions and specifications of other key types may be found in handbooks or manufacturers' catalogues.

11.45. Dimensioning Keyseats and Keyways. The dimensioning of the *seat* and *way* for keys depends upon the purpose for which the drawing is intended. For unit production, when the keys are expected to be fitted by the machinist, nominal dimensions may be given, as in Fig. 11.52. For quantity production, the limits of width (and depth, if necessary) should be given as in Fig. 11.53. Pratt and Whitney keyseats and keyways are dimensioned as in Fig. 11.54. Note that the *length* of the keyseat is given to correspond with the specification of the key. If interchangeability is important and when careful gaging is necessary, the dimensions should be given as in Fig. 11.55 and the values expressed with limits.

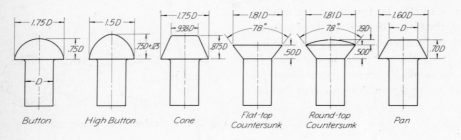

Button   High Button   Cone   Flat-top Countersunk   Round-top Countersunk   Pan

Fig. 11.56. Large rivet heads.

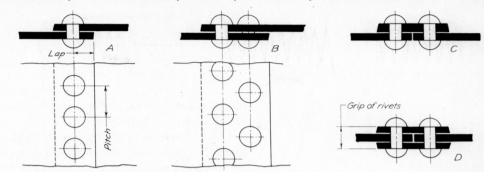

Fig. 11.57. Lap and butt joints.

11.46. Rivets. Rivets are used for making permanent fastenings, generally between pieces of sheet or rolled metal. They are round bars of steel or wrought iron with a head formed on one end and are often put in place red hot so that a head may be formed on the other end by pressing or hammering. Rivet holes are punched, punched and reamed, or drilled larger than the diameter of the rivet, and the shank of the rivet is made just long enough to give sufficient metal to fill the hole completely and make the head.

Large rivets are used in structural-steel construction and in boiler and tank work. In structural work, only a few kinds of heads are normally needed: the button, high button, and flat-top countersunk heads, Fig. 11.56.

For boiler and tank work, the button, cone, round-top countersunk, and pan heads are used. Plates are connected by either lap or butt joints. Figure 11.57A is a single-riveted lap joint; (B) is a double-riveted lap joint; (C) is a single-strap and (D) a double-strap butt joint.

Large rivets are available in diameters of $\frac{1}{2}$ to $1\frac{3}{4}$ in., by increments of even $\frac{1}{8}$ in. The length needed is governed by the "grip," as shown at Fig. 11.57D, plus the length needed to form the head. Length of rivets for various grip distances may be found in the handbook "Steel Construction" published by the American Institute of Steel Construction.

Small rivets are used for fabricating light structural shapes and sheet metal. ASA small-rivet heads are shown in Fig. 11.58. Small rivets are available in diameters of $\frac{3}{32}$ to $\frac{7}{16}$ in., by increments of even $\frac{1}{32}$ in. to $\frac{3}{8}$ in. diameter.

Tinners', coopers', and belt rivets are used for fastening thin sheet

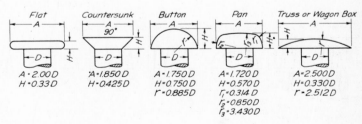

Fig. 11.58. American Standard small-rivet heads.

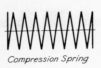

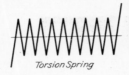

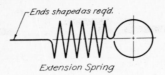

Compression Spring   Torsion Spring   Extension Spring

Fig. 11.59. Single-line representation of springs.

metal, wood, leather, rubber, etc. Standard heads and proportions are given in the Appendix.

11.47. Springs. A spring may be defined as an elastic body designed to store energy when deflected. Springs are classified according to their geometrical form: helical or flat.

11.48. Helical Springs. These are further classified as (1) compression, (2) extension, or (3) torsion, according to the intended action. On working drawings, helical springs are drawn either as a single-line convention, as in Fig. 11.59, or semiconventionally, as shown in Figs. 11.60 to 11.62, by laying out the diameter (D) and pitch (P) of coils and then drawing a construction circle for the wire size at the limiting positions and conventionalizing the helix with straight lines. Helical springs may be wound of round-, square-, or special-section wire.

Compression springs are wound with the coils separated so that the unit may be compressed, and the ends may be either open or closed and may be left plain or ground, as shown in Fig. 11.60. The information that must be given for a compression spring is as follows:

1. Controlling diameter: (*a*) outside, (*b*) inside, (*c*) operates inside a tube, or (*d*) operates over a rod
2. Wire or bar size
3. Material (kind and grade)
4. Coils: (*a*) total number and (*b*) right- or left-hand
5. Style of ends
6. Load at deflected length of ___
7. Load rate between ___ inches and ___ inches
8. Maximum solid height
9. Minimum compressed height in use

Extension springs are wound with the loops in contact so that the unit may be extended, and the ends are usually made as a loop, as shown in Fig. 11.61. Special ends are sometimes required and are described by the ASA. The information that must be given for an extension spring is as follows:

1. Free length: (*a*) over-all, (*b*) over coil, or (*c*) inside of hooks

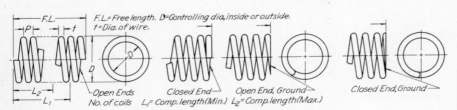

F.L.= Free length. D=Controlling dia, inside or outside.
t=Dia. of wire.

Open Ends   Closed End   Open End, Ground   Closed End, Ground
No. of coils L_1= Comp. length (Min.) L_2= Comp. length (Max.)

Fig. 11.60. Representation and dimensioning of compression springs.

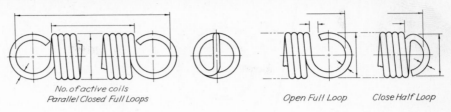

No. of active coils
Parallel Closed Full Loops

Open Full Loop   *Close Half Loop*

2. Controlling diameter: (*a*) outside diameter, (*b*) inside diameter,
r (*c*) operates inside a tube

3. Wire size

4. Material (kind and grade)

5. Coils: (*a*) total number and (*b*) right- or left-hand

6. Style of ends

7. Load at inside hooks

8. Load rate, pounds per 1-in. deflection

9. Maximum extended length

Torsion springs are wound with either closed or open coils, and the
oad is applied torsionally (at right angles to the spring axis). The
ends may be shaped as hooks or as straight torsion arms, as indicated
n Fig. 11.62. The information that must be given for a torsion
pring is as follows:

1. Free length (dimension *A*, Fig. 11.62)

2. Controlling diameter: (*a*) outside diameter, (*b*) inside diameter,
c) operates inside a hole, or (*d*) operates over a rod

3. Wire size

4. Material (kind and grade)

5. Coils: (*a*) total number and (*b*) right- or left-hand

6. Torque, pounds at ___ degrees of deflection

7. Maximum deflection (degrees from free position)

8. Style of ends

11.49. Flat Springs. A flat spring may be classified as any spring
made of flat or strip material. Flat springs, Fig. 11.63, may be
classified as (1) simple flat springs, formed so that the desired force
will be applied when the spring is deflected in a direction opposite
to the force; (2) power springs, made as a straight piece and then

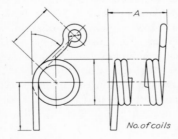

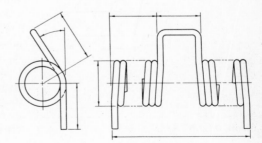

No. of coils

Fig. 11.62. Representation and
dimensioning of torsion springs.

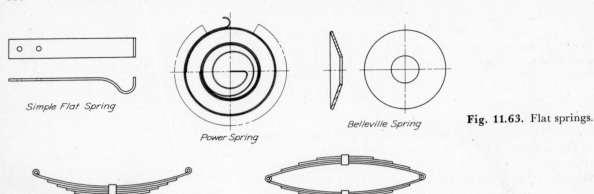

Fig. 11.63. Flat springs.

coiled inside an enclosing case; (3) Belleville springs, stamped of thin material and shaped so as to store energy when deflected; and (4) leaf springs, in either elliptic or semielliptic form, made of several pieces of varying length, shaped so as to straighten when a load is applied. The information that must be given for a flat spring is as follows:

1. A drawing showing the detailed shape and dimensions of the spring
2. Material and heat-treatment
3. Finish

PROBLEMS

Group 1. Helices

11.1.1. Draw three complete turns of a helix; diameter, 3 in.; pitch, 1¼ in. See Chap. 16.

11.1.2. Draw three complete turns of a conical helix, end and front views, with 1½-in. pitch, whose large diameter is 4 in. and small diameter is 1½ in. See Chap. 16.

Group 2. Screw threads

11.2.1. Draw in section the following screw-thread forms, 1-in. pitch: American National, Acme, stub Acme, square.

11.2.2. Draw two views of a square-thread screw and a section of the nut separated; diameter, 2½ in.; pitch, ¾ in.; length of screw, 3 in.

11.2.3. Same as Prob. 11.2.2 but for V thread with ½-in. pitch.

11.2.4. Draw screws 2 in. diameter and 3½ in. long: single square thread, pitch ½ in.; single V thread, pitch ¼ in.; double V thread, pitch ½ in.; left-hand double square thread, pitch ½ in.

11.2.5. Working space, 7 by 10½ in. Divide space as shown and in left space draw and label thread profiles, as follows: at *A*, sharp V, ½-in. pitch; at *B*, American National (Unified), ½-in. pitch; at *C*, square, 1-in. pitch; at *D*, Acme, 1-in. pitch. Show five threads each at *A* and *B* and three at *C* and *D*.

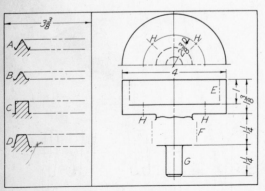

Prob. 11.2.5. Screw threads.

In right space, complete the views of the object by showing at E a 3½-4UNC-2B threaded hole in section. The thread runs out at a $3^{17}/_{32}$-in.-diameter by ¼-in.-wide thread relief. The lower line for the thread relief is shown. At F, show a 1¾-5UNC-3A thread. The thread is 1 in. long and runs out at a neck which is 1⅜ in. diameter by ¼ in. wide. The free end of the thread should be chamfered at 45°. At G, show the shank threaded ⅝-18UNF-3A by 1 in. long; at H, show ⅜-16UNC-2B through tapped holes in section, four required. Completely specify all threads.

11.2.6. Working space, 7 by 10½ in. Complete the views and show threaded features as follows: at A, a ½-20UNF-3B through tapped hole; at B, a ⅝-11UNC-2B by ¾-in.-deep tapped hole with tap drill 1⅛ in. deep; at C, a ⅜-16UNC-2B by ¼-in.-deep tapped hole with the tap drill through to the 1-in. hole; at D, a 1½-8N-2 threaded hole running out at the large cored hole. Completely specify all threads.

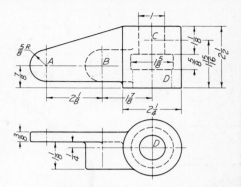

Prob. 11.2.6. Intermediate lever.

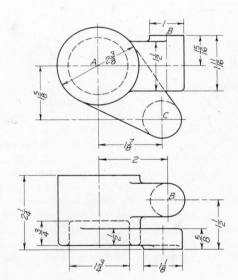

Prob. 11.2.7. Offset support.

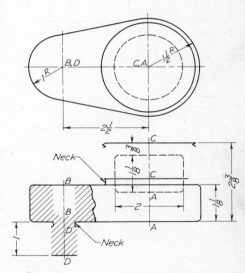

Prob. 11.2.8. Rocker.

11.2.7. Complete the offset support, showing threaded holes as follows: at A, 1⅜-6UNC-2B; at B, ½-13NC-2; at C, ⅝-18UNF-3B. A and C are through holes. B is a blind hole to receive a stud. Material is cast iron. Specify the threaded holes.

11.2.8. Complete the views of the cast-steel rocker, showing threads as follows: on center line A-A, 2-8N-2; on center line B-B, a ½-20UNF-2B tapped hole, ⅝ in. deep, with tap drill ⅞ in. deep; on center line C-C, a 2¾-12UN-2A external thread; on center line D-D, a ⅞-14UNF-3A external thread.

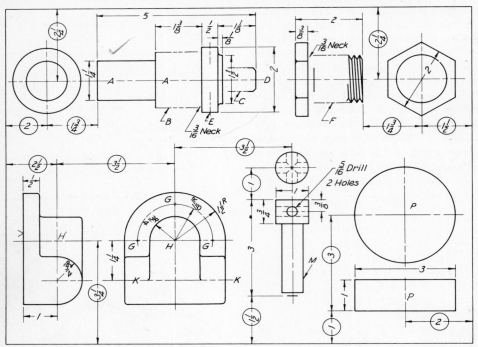

Prob. 11.2.9. Screw threads.

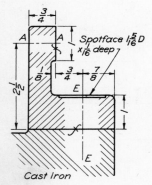

Prob. 11.3.5

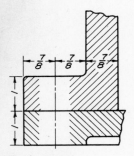

Prob. 11.3.6

11.2.9. Minimum working space, 10½ by 15 in. Complete the views of the objects, and show threads and other details as follows: *upper left,* on center line *A-A,* show in section a ¾-10UNC-2B tapped hole, 1½ in. deep, with tap-drill hole 2½ in. deep. At *B,* show a 1¾-8N-2 external thread in section. At *C,* show a ¾-10UNC-2A thread in section. From *D* on center line *A-A,* show a ¼-in. drilled hole extending to the tap-drill hole. At *E,* show six ¼-in. drilled holes, ¼ in. deep, equally spaced for spanner wrench. *Upper right,* at *F,* show a 1½-6UNC-2A thread. *Lower left,* at *G,* show (three) ⅜-16UNC-2B through holes. At *H,* show a ⅞-9UNC-2B tapped hole, 1⅛ in. deep, with the tap-drill hole going through the piece. On center line *K-K,* show a ⅞-14UNF-3B through tapped hole. *Lower center,* at *M,* show a ⅝-18UNF-3A thread 1¾ in. long. *Lower right,* on center line *P,* show a 2-4½UNC-2B hole in section. Completely specify all threads.

Group 3. Threaded fasteners

11.3.1. Draw one view of regular semifinished hexagonal bolt and nut, across corners; diameter, 1 in.; length, 5 in.

11.3.2. Same as Prob. 11.3.1 for a heavy unfinished bolt and nut.

11.3.3. Same as Prob. 11.3.1 for a square bolt and nut.

11.3.4. Draw four ½- by 1½-in. cap screws, each with a different kind of head. Specify each.

11.3.5. Show the pieces fastened together on center line *E-E* with a ¾-in. hexagonal-head cap screw and light lock washer. On center line *A-A* show a ⅝- by 1½-in. shoulder screw.

11.3.6. Show pieces fastened together with a ¾-in. square bolt and heavy square nut. Place nut at bottom.

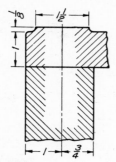

Prob. 11.3.7

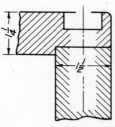

Prob. 11.3.8

11.3.7. Fasten pieces together with a ¾-in. stud and regular semifinished hexagonal nut.

11.3.8. Fasten pieces together with a ¾-in. fillister-head cap screw.

11.3.9. Draw one view of a round-head square-neck (carriage) bolt; diameter, 1 in.; length, 5 in.; with regular square nut.

11.3.10. Draw one view of a round-head rib-neck (carriage) bolt; diameter, ¾ in.; length, 4 in.; with regular square nut.

11.3.11. Draw two views of a shoulder screw; diameter, ¾ in.; shoulder length, 5 in.

11.3.12. Draw two views of a socket-head cap screw; diameter, 1¼ in.; length, 6 in.

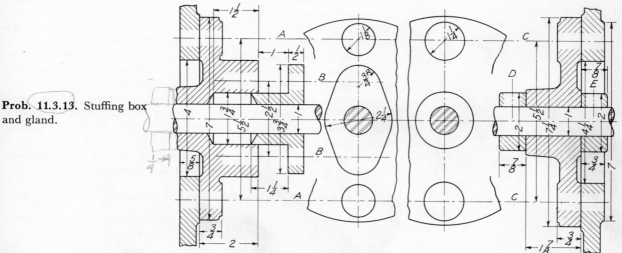

Prob. 11.3.13. Stuffing box and gland.

Prob. 11.3.14. Bearing plate.

11.3.13. Draw the stuffing box and gland, showing the required fasteners. At A, show ½-in. hexagon-head cap screws (six required). At B, show ½-in. studs and regular semifinished hexagon nuts. Specify fasteners.

11.3.14. Draw the bearing plate, showing the required fasteners. At C, show ½-in. regular semifinished hexagon bolts and nuts (four required). At D, show ½-in. socket setscrew. At E, show ½-in. square-head setscrew. Setscrews to have cone points. Specify fasteners.

Problems 11.3.13 and 11.3.14 may be drawn together on an 11- by 17-in. sheet or on separate sheets, showing full diameter of flanges.

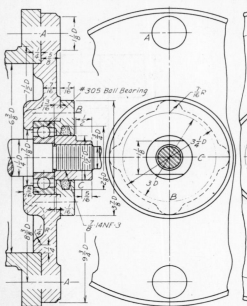

Prob. 11.3.15. Ball-bearing head.

Prob. 11.3.16.
Plain bearing head.

11.3.15. Draw the ball-bearing head, showing the required fasteners. At *A*, show ½- by 1¾-in. regular semifinished hexagon bolts and nuts (six required), with heads to left and across flats. Note that this design prevents the heads from turning. At *B*, show 5⁄16- by ¾-in. fillister-head cap screws (four required). At *C*, show a ⅜- by ½-in. slotted flat-point setscrew with fiber disk to protect threads of spindle. Specify fasteners.

11.3.16. Draw the plain bearing head, showing the required fasteners. At *D*, show ½- by 2-in. studs and regular semifinished hexagon nuts (six required); spot-face 1 in. diameter by 1⁄16 in. deep. At *E*, show ⅜- by 1-in. hexagon-head cap screws (four required). At *F*, show a 7⁄16- by ⅞-in. square-head cup-point setscrew. At *G*, show a ⅛-27NPT hole with a pipe plug. Show the 11⁄32-in. tap drill through for gun packing the gland. Specify fasteners.

Problems 11.3.15 and 11.3.16 may be drawn together on an 11- by 17-in. sheet or on separate sheets, showing full diameter of flanges.

Group 4. Keys (key sizes will be found in Appendix)

11.4.1. Draw hub and shaft as shown, with a Woodruff key in position.
11.4.2. Draw hub and shaft as shown, with a square key 2 in. long in position.

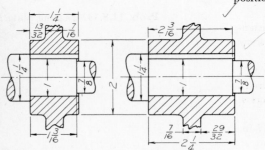

Prob. 11.4.1   **Prob. 11.4.2**

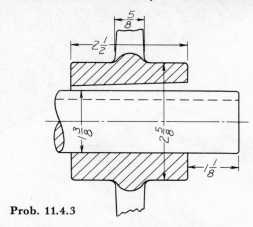

Prob. 11.4.3

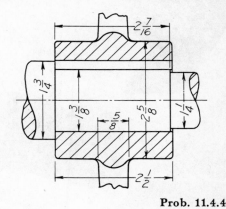

Prob. 11.4.4

11.4.3. Draw hub and shaft as shown, with a gib-head key in position.

11.4.4. Draw hub and shaft as shown, with a Pratt and Whitney key in position.

Group 5. Rivets

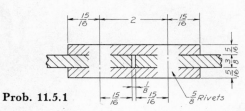

Prob. 11.5.1

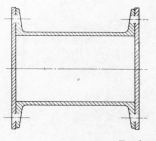

Prob. 11.5.2

11.5.1. Draw top view and section of a single-riveted butt joint $10\frac{5}{8}$ in. long. Pitch of rivets is $1\frac{3}{4}$ in. Use cone-head rivets.

11.5.2. Draw a column section made of 15-in. by 33.9-lb channels with cover plates as shown, using $\frac{7}{8}$-in. rivets (dimensions from the handbook of the American Institute of Steel Construction). Use button-head rivets on left side and flat-top countersunk-head rivets on right side so that the outside surface is flush.

Group 6. Springs

11.6.1. Draw a compression spring as follows: inside diameter, $\frac{3}{4}$ in.; wire size, $\frac{1}{8}$ in. diameter; coils 14, right-hand; squared and ground ends; free length, $3\frac{1}{2}$ in.

11.6.2. Draw a compression spring as follows: outside diameter, 1 in.; wire size, $\frac{3}{32}$ in. diameter; coils 12, left-hand; open ends, not ground; free length, 4 in.

11.6.3. Draw an extension spring as follows: free length over coils, 2 in.; outside diameter, $1\frac{1}{8}$ in.; wire size, $\frac{1}{8}$ in. diameter; coils 11, right-hand; ends parallel, closed loops.

11.6.4. Draw an extension spring as follows: free length inside hooks, $2\frac{3}{4}$ in.; inside diameter, $\frac{3}{4}$ in.; wire size, $\frac{1}{8}$ in. diameter; coils 11, left-hand; ends parallel, closed half loops.

11.6.5. Draw a torsion spring as follows: free length over coils $\frac{3}{4}$ in.; inside diameter, $1\frac{1}{8}$ in.; wire size, $\frac{1}{8}$ in. diameter; coils 5, right-hand; ends straight and turned to follow radial lines to center of spring and extend $\frac{1}{2}$ in. from outside diameter of spring.

12

WORKING DRAWINGS

12.1. Definition. A working drawing is any drawing used to give information for purposes of manufacture, construction, or erection of a machine or structure. Complete knowledge for the production of a machine or structure is given by a *set* of working drawings conveying all the facts fully and explicitly so that further instruction is not required.

The description given by the set of drawings will thus include:

1. The full graphical representation of the shape of each part (shape description).

2. The figured dimensions of all parts (size description).

3. Explanatory notes, general and specific, on the individual drawings, giving the specifications of material, heat-treatment, finish, etc. Often, particularly in architectural and structural work, the notes of explanation and information concerning details of materials and workmanship are too extensive to be included on the drawings and so are made up separately in typed or printed form and called the "specifications"—thus the term "drawings and specifications."

4. A descriptive title on each drawing.

5. A description of the relationship of each part to the others (assembly).

6. A parts list or bill of material.

A set of drawings will include, in general, two classes: (1) *detail drawings* giving the information included in items 1 to 4 and (2) an *assembly drawing*, item 5, giving the location and relationship of the parts.

12.2. Engineering Procedure. In designing a new machine or structure, the first drawings are usually in the form of freehand sketches on which the original ideas, scheming, and inventing are worked out. These are either accompanied or followed by calculations to prove the suitability of the design. Working from the sketches and calculations, the design department produces a *design assembly* (also called a "design layout" or "design drawing"), Fig. 12.1. This is a preliminary pencil drawing on which more details of the design are worked out. It is accurately made with instruments, full size if possible, and shows the shape and position of the various parts, but little attempt is made to show all the intricate detail. Only the essential dimensions, such as basic calculated sizes, are given. On the drawing or separately as a set of written notes will be the designer's general specifications for materials, heat-treatments, finishes, clearances or interferences, etc., and any other information needed by the draftsman in making up the individual drawings of the separate parts.

Working from the design drawing and notes, a draftsman (detailer) then makes up the individual detail drawings illustrated by the detail drawing of Fig. 12.2, taken from the design drawing of Fig. 12.1. On the detail drawing, all the views necessary for complete shape description are provided, and all the necessary dimensions and manufacturing directions are given. Dimension values for non-mating surfaces are obtained by scaling the design drawing, and the more critical values are had from the design notes and from drafting-

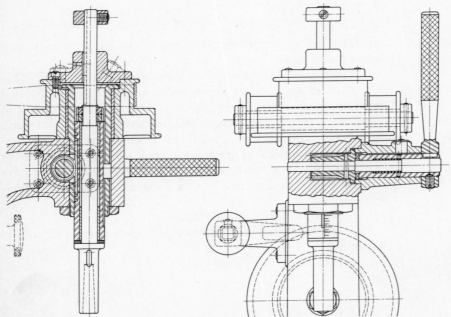

Fig. 12.1. A portion of a design drawing.

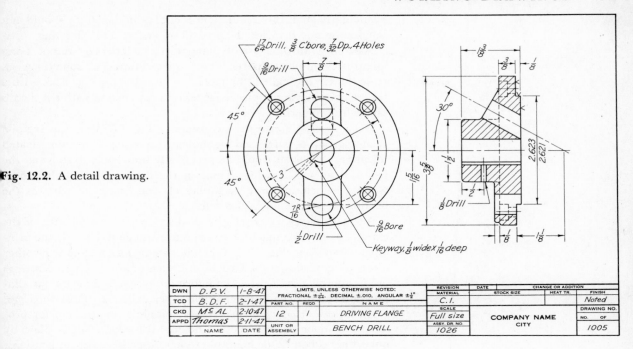

Fig. 12.2. A detail drawing.

DWN	D.P.V.	1-8-47	LIMITS, UNLESS OTHERWISE NOTED: FRACTIONAL ±1/64. DECIMAL ±.010. ANGULAR ±1/2°				REVISION	DATE	CHANGE OR ADDITION		
							MATERIAL		STOCK SIZE	HEAT TR.	FINISH
TCD	B.D.F.	2-1-47	PART NO.	REQD		N A M E	C.I.				Noted
CKD	McAL	2-10-47	12	1		DRIVING FLANGE	SCALE		COMPANY NAME		DRAWING NO.
APPD	Thomas	2-11-47					Full size		CITY		NO. OF
	NAME	DATE	UNIT OR ASSEMBLY			BENCH DRILL	ASSY. DR. NO.				
							1026				1005

room standards. The detailer will correlate the dimensions of mating parts and give all necessary manufacturing information.

The set of drawings is completed by making an assembly drawing and a parts list or bill of material.

If the machine is to be quantity produced, "operation" or "job" sheets will be prepared describing the separate manufacturing steps required and indicating the use and kind of special tools, jigs, fixtures, etc. The tool-design group, working from the detail drawings and the operation sheets, designs and makes the drawings for the special tools needed.

12.3. Assembly Drawings. An assembly drawing is, as its name implies, a drawing of the machine or structure put together, showing the relative positions of the different parts.

Under the term "assembly drawings" are included preliminary design drawings and layouts, piping plans, unit assembly drawings, installation diagrams, and final complete drawings used for assembling or erecting the machine or structure.

The design drawing, as already indicated, is the preliminary layout on which the scheming, inventing, and designing are accurately worked out. The *assembly drawing* is in some cases made by tracing from the design drawing. More often it is drawn from the dimensions of the detail drawings. This provides a valuable check on the correctness of the detail drawings.

The assembly drawing may give the over-all dimensions and the distances between centers or from part to part of the different pieces, thus fixing the relation of the parts to each other and aiding in the erection of the machine. It should not be overloaded with detail, particularly invisible detail. Unnecessary hidden lines should not be used on any drawing, least of all on an assembly drawing.

Assembly drawings usually have reference letters or numbers designating the different parts. These "piece numbers," sometimes enclosed in circles (called "balloons" by draftsmen), Fig. 12.3, with a leader pointing to the piece, are used in connection with the details and bill of material.

A *unit assembly drawing* or subassembly, Fig. 12.3, is a drawing of a related group of parts used for showing the assembly of complicated machinery where it would be practically impossible to show all the features on one drawing. Thus, in the drawing of a lathe, there would be included unit assemblies of such groups of parts as the headstock, tailstock, gearbox, etc.

An *outline assembly drawing* is used to give a general idea of the exterior shape of a machine or structure and contains only the principal dimensions, Fig. 12.4. When it is made for catalogues or other illustrative purposes, dimensions are often omitted. These drawings are frequently used to give the information required for the installation or erection of equipment and are then called *installation drawings*.

An *assembly working drawing* gives complete information for producing a machine or structure on one drawing. This is done by providing adequate orthographic views together with dimensions, notes, and a descriptive title. The figure for Prob. 12.3.7 may be considered an example.

A *diagram drawing* is an assembly showing, symbolically, the erection or installation of equipment. Erection and piping and wiring

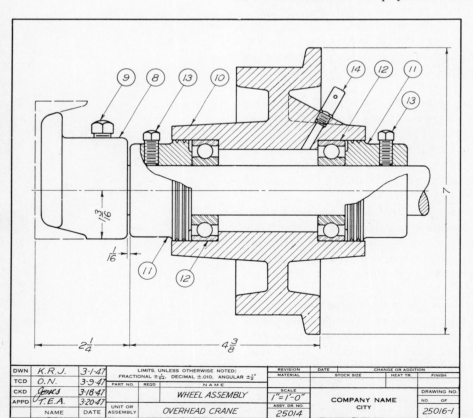

Fig. 12.3. A unit assembly.

DWN	K.R.J.	3-1-47	LIMITS. UNLESS OTHERWISE NOTED: FRACTIONAL ±1/64. DECIMAL ±.010. ANGULAR ±1/2°		REVISION	DATE	CHANGE OR ADDITION		
TCD	O.N.	3-9-47			MATERIAL		STOCK SIZE	HEAT TR.	FINISH
CKD	Jones	3-18-47	PART NO.	REQD	N A M E				
APPD	T.E.A.	3-20-47			WHEEL ASSEMBLY	SCALE 1"=1'-0"	COMPANY NAME CITY		DRAWING NO.
	NAME	DATE	UNIT OR ASSEMBLY		OVERHEAD CRANE	ASSY. DR. NO. 25014		NO. OF 25016-1	

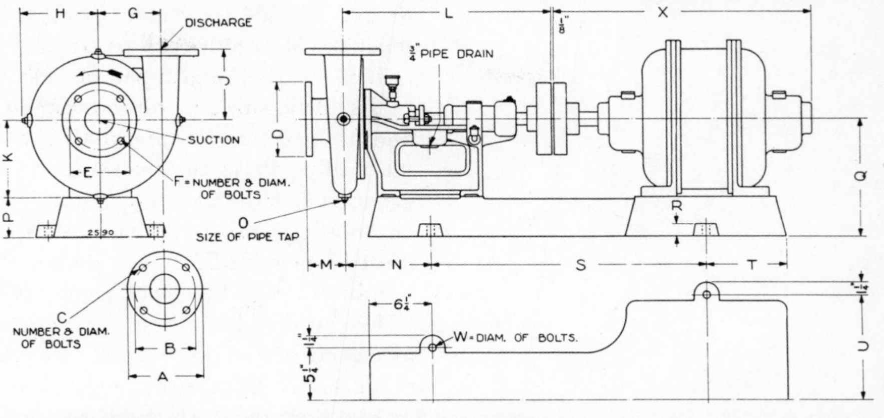

CODE WORD	PIPE SIZES DISCH.	SUCT'N.	A	B	C	D	E	F	G	H	J	K	L	M	N	O	P	Q	R	S	T	U	W	X
			DIMENSIONS IN INCHES																					
JAY	$1\frac{1}{2}$"	2"	TAPPED OPENINGS						$5\frac{13}{16}$	$6\frac{7}{8}$	$6\frac{1}{2}$	$7\frac{3}{4}$	$20\frac{3}{8}$	$3\frac{1}{4}$	$8\frac{3}{16}$	$\frac{3}{8}$								
JABBER	2"	$2\frac{1}{2}$"	6	$4\frac{3}{4}$	$4-\frac{5}{8}$	7	$5\frac{1}{2}$	$4-\frac{5}{8}$	$5\frac{29}{32}$	$7\frac{1}{4}$	$6\frac{1}{2}$	$7\frac{3}{4}$	$20\frac{7}{16}$	3	$8\frac{1}{4}$	$\frac{3}{8}$								
JACKET	3"	3"	$7\frac{1}{2}$	6	$4-\frac{5}{8}$	$7\frac{1}{2}$	6	$4-\frac{5}{8}$	$6\frac{1}{4}$	$7\frac{11}{16}$	7	$7\frac{3}{4}$	$20\frac{11}{16}$	$3\frac{3}{4}$	$8\frac{1}{2}$	$\frac{3}{8}$	ABOVE DIMENSIONS DETERMINED BY SIZE OF MOTOR AND BASE USED							
JACK	4"	4"	9	$7\frac{1}{2}$	$8-\frac{5}{8}$	9	$7\frac{1}{2}$	$8-\frac{5}{8}$	$7\frac{11}{16}$	$8\frac{3}{4}$	$7\frac{3}{4}$	$8\frac{13}{16}$	$22\frac{11}{16}$	$4\frac{1}{2}$	10	$\frac{1}{2}$								
JACOBUS	5"	5"	10	$8\frac{1}{2}$	$8-\frac{3}{4}$	10	$8\frac{1}{2}$	$8-\frac{3}{4}$	$8\frac{1}{8}$	$9\frac{1}{8}$	$8\frac{1}{4}$	$8\frac{13}{16}$	$22\frac{15}{16}$	5	$10\frac{1}{4}$	$\frac{1}{2}$								

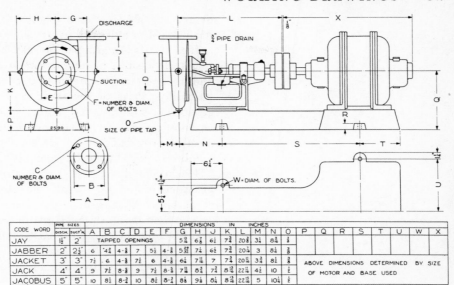

Fig. 12.4. An outline assembly drawing (tabular).

diagrams are examples. Diagram drawings are often made in pictorial form.

12.4. Detail Drawings. A detail drawing is the drawing of a single piece, giving a complete and exact description of its form, dimensions, and construction. A successful detail drawing will tell the workman *simply* and *directly* the shape, size, material, and finish of each part; what shop operations are necessary; what limits of accuracy must be observed; the number of parts wanted; etc. It should be so exact in description that, if followed, a satisfactory part will result. Figure 12.5 illustrates a commercial detail drawing.

Detailing practice will vary somewhat according to the industry and the requirements of the shop system. For example, structural

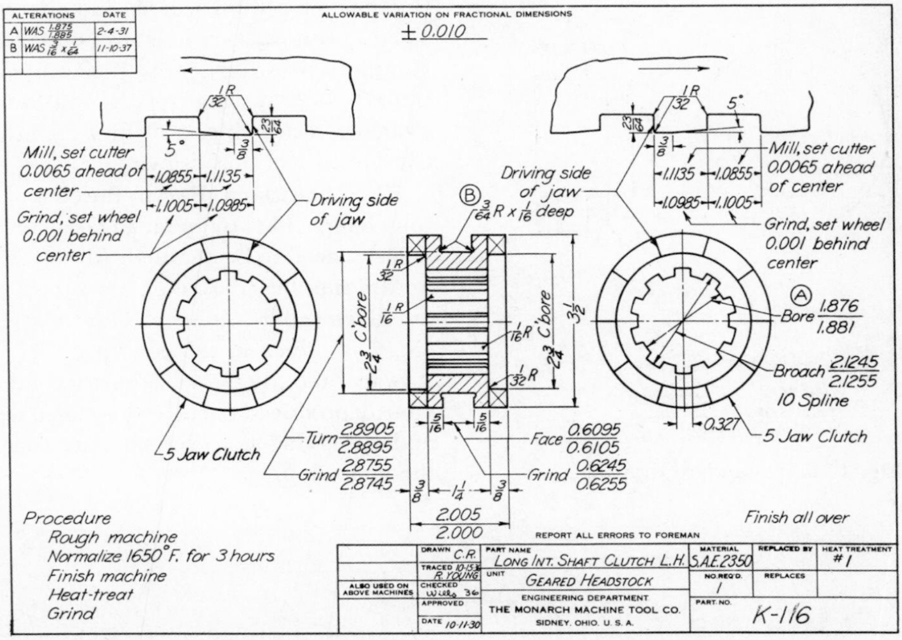

Fig. 12.5. A detail drawing.

details are often grouped together on one sheet, while in modern mechanical practice a separate sheet is used for each part.

If the parts are grouped on one sheet, the detailed pieces should be set, if possible, in the same relative position as on the assembly, and, to facilitate reading, placed as nearly as possible in natural relationship. Parts of the same material or character are usually grouped together, as, for example, forgings on one sheet, castings on another, and parts machined from stock on another. A subtitle must be provided for each part, giving the part number, material, number required for each assembly, etc.

The accepted and best system in mechanical work is to have each piece, no matter how small, on a separate sheet. As described in paragraph 9.3, if the single-drawing system is followed, one drawing will be used by all shops. If the multiple system is used, a separate drawing must be made for each shop; thus there may be a *pattern drawing*, a *casting drawing*, and a *machining drawing*, all for a single cast part. A detail drawing should be a complete unit for the purpose intended and should not be dependent in any way upon any other detail drawing.

12.5. Tabular Drawings. A tabular drawing, either assembly or detail, is one on which the dimension values are replaced with reference letters, an accompanying table on the drawing listing the corresponding dimensions for a series of sizes of the machine or part, thus making one drawing serve for the range covered. Some companies manufacturing parts in a variety of sizes use this tabular system of size description, but a serious danger with it is the possibility of misreading the table. Figure 12.4 illustrates a tabular assembly drawing.

12.6. Standard Drawings. To avoid the difficulties experienced with tabular drawings, some companies are now making a "standard drawing," complete except for the actual figured dimensions. This drawing is reproduced by offset printing or black-and-white reproduction on vellum paper, and the reproductions are dimensioned separately for the various sizes of parts. This method gives a separate complete drawing for each size of part; and when a new size is needed, the drawing is easily and quickly made. Figure 12.6 shows a standard drawing, and Fig. 12.7 the drawing filled in, making a completed working drawing.

12.7. Standard Parts. Purchased or company standard parts may be specified by name and size or by number and, consequently, will not need to be detailed. All standard parts, such as bolts, screws, antifriction bearings, etc., are shown on the assembly drawing and are given a part number. The complete specifications for their purchase are given in the parts list.

Sometimes, however, a part is made by *altering* a standard or previously produced part. In this case a detail drawing is made, showing and specifying the original part with changes and dimensions for the alteration.

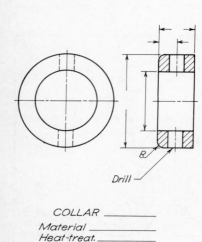

Fig. 12.6. A standard drawing.

12.8. The Bill of Material, or Parts List. This is a tabulated statement, usually placed on a separate sheet in the case of quantity production (as in Prob. 12.2.3) or on the assembly drawing in other cases, as illustrated in Prob. 12.3.12. This table gives the piece number, name, quantity, material, sometimes the stock size of raw material, detail drawing numbers, weight of each piece, etc. A final column is usually left for remarks. The term "bill of material" is usually used in structural and architectural drawing. The term "parts list" more accurately applies in machine-drawing practice. In general, the parts are listed in the order of their importance, with the larger parts first and ending with the standard parts such as screws, pins, etc.

The blank ruling for a bill of material should not be crowded. Lines should never be spaced closer than ¼ in.; ⁵⁄₁₆ or ³⁄₈ in. is better, with the height of the lettering not more than half the space and centered between lines. Instead of being lettered, bills of material are frequently typed on forms printed on thin paper. Intensifying the impression by carbon paper on the back increases the opacity of the typing, and a clearer blueprint will result.

12.9. Set of Drawings. A *complete set* of working drawings consists of detail sheets and assembly sheets, the former giving all necessary information for the manufacture of each of the individual parts which cannot be purchased and the latter showing the parts assembled as a finished unit or machine. The set includes the bill of material or parts list and may also contain special drawings for the purchaser, such as foundation plans or oiling diagrams.

12.10. Making a Working Drawing: Basic Concepts. Although pictorial drawings are used to some extent in special cases, the basis of all working drawings is orthographic projection. Thus, to represent an object completely, at least two views are ordinarily necessary, often more. The only general rule is *to make as many views as are necessary to describe the object clearly—and no more*. Instances may occur in which the third dimension is so evident as to make one view sufficient, as, for example, in the drawing of a shaft or bolt. In other cases, perhaps a half-dozen views might be required to describe a piece completely. Sometimes half, partial, or broken views may be used to advantage.

As previously stated, select for the front view the face showing the largest dimension, preferably the obvious front of the object when in its functioning position, and then decide what other views are necessary. A vertical cylindrical piece, for example, would require only a front and a top view; a horizontal cylindrical piece, only a front and a side view. Determine which side view to use or whether both are needed. The one with the fewest hidden lines should be preferred. In some cases the best representation may be to use *both* side views with all unnecessary dotted lines omitted. See whether an auxiliary view or a note will save one or more other views and whether a section will be better than an exterior view. One state-

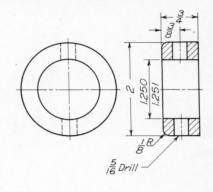

COLLAR   X6
Material   S.A.E. 1020
Heat-treat.   S.A.E. 2
No. Req'd.   50

Fig. 12.7. A filled-in standard drawing.

ment may be made with the force of a rule: *If anything in clearness can be gained by violating a principle of projection, violate it.*

Paragraphs 7.20 to 7.33 give a number of examples of conventions that are in violation of theoretical representation but are in the interest of clearness. The draftsman must remember that his responsibility is to the reader of the drawing and that he is not justified in saving himself any time or trouble at the expense of the drawing by making it less plain or easy to read. The time so saved by the draftsman may be lost to the company a hundredfold in the shop, where the drawing is used not once but repeatedly.

There is a *style* in drawing, just as there is in literature, which indicates itself in one way by ease of reading. Some drawings stand out, while others, which may contain all the information, are difficult to decipher. Although dealing with mechanical thought, there is a place for some artistic sense in mechanical drawing. The number, selection, and disposition of views, the omission of anything unnecessary, ambiguous, or misleading, the size and placement of dimensions and lettering, and the contrast of lines are elements concerned in the style.

In commercial drafting, *accuracy* and *speed* are the two requirements. The drafting room is an expensive department, and time is thus an important element. The draftsman must therefore have a ready knowledge not only of the principles of drawing but of the conventional methods and abbreviations and of any device or system that will save time without sacrificing clearness. See paragraph 12.29.

The usual criticism of the beginner by the employer is the result of the former's lack of appreciation of the necessity for speed.

12.11. Materials Used for Working Drawings. Working drawings go to the shop in the form of blueprints, black-line prints, or other similar forms of reproduction, and the drawings must therefore be made on translucent material, either directly or as tracings. Pencil drawings may be made on tracing paper or on pencil cloth; inked drawings, on tracing paper or on tracing cloth.

Tracing paper is a thin translucent material, commonly called "vellum." Considerable time and expense may be saved by making the original pencil drawing on this material. Excellent prints may be had if the lines are of sufficient blackness and intensity.

Pencil cloth is a transparentized fabric with one or both sides of its surface prepared to take pencil so that the original drawing may be made on it and prints made either from the pencil drawing or after it has been inked. Some of the newer cloths are moisture resistant, others are really waterproof. Pencil cloth is made for pencil drawings, and perfect blueprints can be made from drawings made on it with sharp, hard pencils. Ink lines, however, do not adhere well and have a tendency to chip or rub off in cleaning.

Tracing cloth is a fine-thread fabric sized and transparentized with a starch preparation. The smooth side is considered by the makers as the working side, but most draftsmen prefer to work on the dull side, which will take pencil marks. The cloth should be fastened

FINISHED FLAT–SHEET SIZES

Designation	Width	Length	Designation	Width	Length
A	8½	11	A	9	12
B	11	17	B	12	18
C	17	22	C	18	24
D	22	34	D	24	36
E	34	44	E	36	48
F*	28	40	F*	28	40

* Not a multiple of the basic size. To be used when width of *E* size is not adaptable.

down smoothly over the pencil drawing and its selvage torn off. To remove the traces of grease that sometimes prevent the flow of ink, it should then be dusted with chalk or prepared pounce (a blackboard eraser may be used) and rubbed off with a cloth. Carbon tetrachloride is an effective cleaning agent. Rub a moistened cloth over the surface—any excess will evaporate in a moment.

A *plastic material*, known as Kodatrace,[1] similar to film backing, is now available for both pencil and ink drawings. It is evenly translucent, has a fine matte surface, good lasting qualities, and requires no special storage precautions. Several companies are now making a similar material.

12.12. Drawing Sizes. Drawing paper and cloth are available in rolls of various widths and in standard trimmed sizes. Most drafting rooms use standard sheets, printed with border and title block. The recommended sizes shown in the preceding table, based on multiples of 8½ by 11 in. and 9 by 12 in., permit the filing of prints in a standard letter file.

Figure 12.8 illustrates the most common trimmed sizes. Larger

[1] Eastman Kodak Co., Rochester, N.Y.

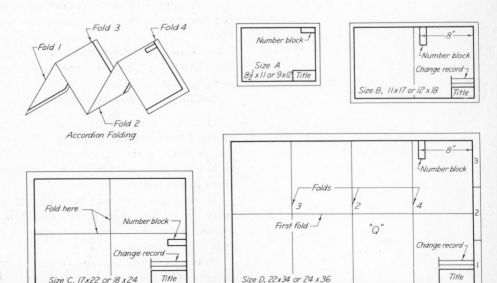

Fig. 12.8. ASA trimmed sizes of paper and cloth.

drawings may be made on rolled stock of standard width, with the length as a multiple of 11 or 12 in., not to exceed 144 in.

12.13. Order of Penciling. After the scheming, inventing, and calculating have been done and the design drawing has been completed, the order of procedure for making the detail drawings is:

1. Select a suitable standard sheet or lay off a sheet to standard size, with the excess paper to the right, as a convenient space for making sketches and calculations, and block out the space for the title.

2. Decide what scale is to be used, choosing one large enough to show all dimensions without crowding, and plan the arrangement of the sheet by making a little preliminary freehand sketch, estimating the space each view will occupy and placing the views to the best advantage for preserving, if possible, a balance in the appearance of the sheet. Be sure to leave sufficient space *between* views for the dimensions.

3. Draw the center lines for each view, and on these "block in" the views by laying off the principal dimensions and outlines, using *light, sharp, accurate* pencil lines. Center lines are drawn for the axes of symmetry of all symmetrical views or parts of views. Thus every cylindrical part should have a center line—the projection of the axis of the piece. Every circle should have two center lines intersecting at its center.

4. Draw the views beginning with the most dominant features and progressing to the subordinate. The different views should be carried on together, projecting a characteristic shape as shown on one view to the other views and *not* finishing one view before starting another. Draw the lines to the final finished weight (wherever possible), using a minimum of construction. *Never* make a drawing lightly and then "heavy" it later.

5. Finish the projections, putting in last the minor details. Check the projections and make sure that all views are complete and correct.

6. Draw all necessary dimension lines; then put in the dimensions.

7. Draw guide lines for the notes, and then letter them.

8. Lay out the title.

9. Check the drawing carefully.

The overrunning lines of the constructive stage should not be erased before tracing or inking. These extensions are often convenient in showing the stopping points. All unnecessary erasing should be avoided as it abrades the surface of the paper so that it catches dirt more readily.

As an aid in stopping tangent arcs in inking, it is desirable to mark the tangent point on the pencil drawing with a short piece of the normal to the curve at the point of tangency. Figure 12.9 illustrates the stages of penciling.

12.14. Order of Inking. To ensure good printing, the ink should be perfectly black and the ruling pens in good condition. Red ink

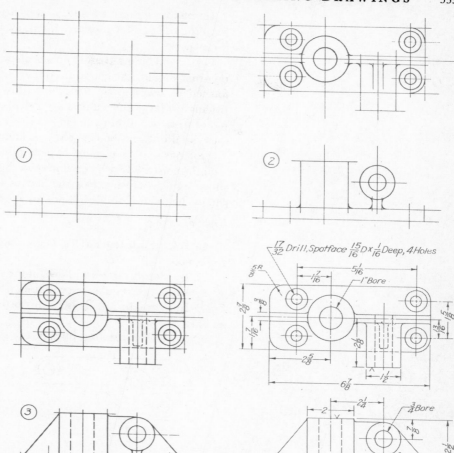

Fig. 12.9. Order of penciling.

should not be used unless it is desired to have some lines inconspicuous on the print. Blue ink will not print well. Sometimes, on maps, diagrams, etc., it is desirable to use colored inks on the tracing to avoid confusion of lines; in such cases, the addition of a little Chinese white will render them sufficiently opaque to print.

Ink lines may be removed from tracing cloth by rubbing with a hard pencil eraser, slipping a triangle under the tracing to give a harder surface. The rubbed surface should afterward be burnished with a burnisher or with the fingernail. In tracing a part that has been section-lined, a piece of white paper may be slipped under the cloth and the section lining done without reference to the section lines underneath.

Tracing cloth is very sensitive to atmospheric variations, often changing overnight so as to require restretching. If a large tracing cannot be finished during the day, some views should be finished and no figure left with only part of its lines traced.

In making a large tracing, it is well to cut off the required piece from the roll and lay it exposed, flat, for a short time before fastening it down.

Water will ruin a tracing on starch-coated cloth, and moist hands or arms should not come in contact with it. The habit should be formed of keeping the hands off drawings. In both drawing and tracing on large sheets, it is a good plan to cut a mask of drawing paper to cover all but the view being worked on. Unfinished drawings should always be covered overnight.

Tracings may be cleaned of pencil marks and dirt by wiping with a cloth moistened with benzine or carbon tetrachloride. To prevent smearing when using this method of cleaning, borders and titles should be printed in an ink not affected by benzine.

Order of Inking

1. Ink all full-line circles, beginning with the smallest, and then circle arcs.

2. Ink dotted circles and arcs in the same order as full-line circles.

3. Ink any irregular curved lines.

4. Ink straight full lines in this order: horizontal, vertical, and inclined.

5. Ink straight dotted lines in the same order.

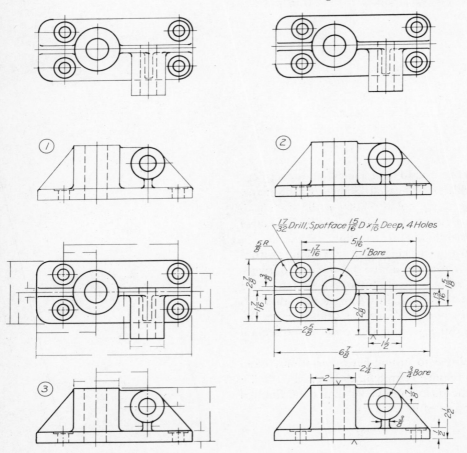

Fig. 12.10. Order of inking.

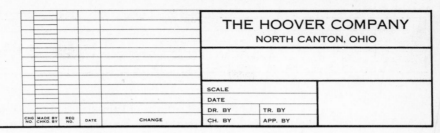

Fig. 12.11. A printed title form.

6. Ink center lines.
7. Ink extension and dimension lines.
8. Ink arrowheads and dimensions.
9. Section-line all areas representing cut surfaces.
10. Letter notes and titles. (On tracings, draw pencil guide lines first.)
11. Ink the border.
12. Check the inked drawing.

Figure 12.10 shows the stages of inking.

12.15. Title Blocks. The title of a working drawing is usually located in the lower right-hand corner of the sheet, the size of the space varying with the amount of information to be given. The spacing and arrangement are designed to provide the information most helpful in a particular line of work.

In general, the title of a machine drawing should contain the following information:

1. Name of company and its location
2. Name of machine or unit
3. Name of part (if a detail drawing)
4. Drawing number
5. Part number (if a detail drawing)
6. Number of parts required (for each assembly)
7. Scale
8. Assembly-drawing number (given on a detail drawing to identify the part in assembly)
9. Drafting-room record: names or initials of draftsman, tracer, checker, approving authority; each with date
10. Material

To these, depending upon the need of the information, may be added:

11. Stock size
12. Heat-treatment
13. Finish
14. Name of purchaser, if special machine
15. Drawing "supersedes" and "superseded by"

Form of Title. Every drafting room has its own standard form for titles. In large offices, the blank form is often printed in type on the tracing paper or cloth. Figures 12.11 and 12.12 are characteristic examples.

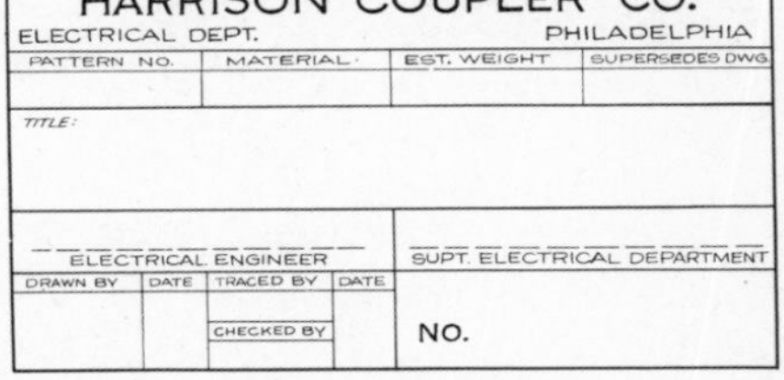

Fig. 12.12. A printed title form.

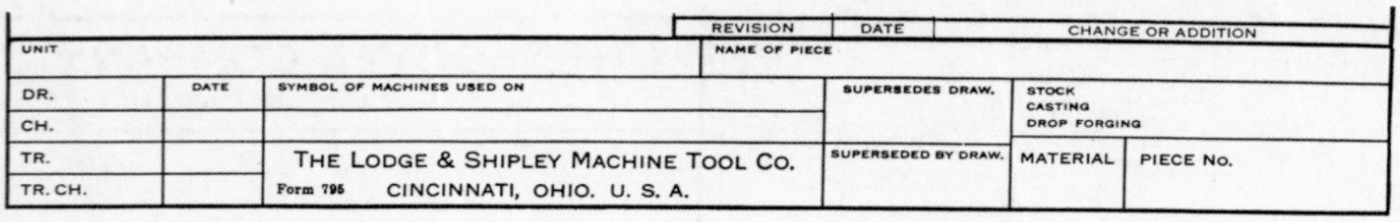

UNIT			REVISION	DATE	CHANGE OR ADDITION		
			NAME OF PIECE				
DR.	DATE	SYMBOL OF MACHINES USED ON		SUPERSEDES DRAW.	STOCK CASTING DROP FORGING		
CH.							
TR.		THE LODGE & SHIPLEY MACHINE TOOL CO.		SUPERSEDED BY DRAW.	MATERIAL	PIECE NO.	
TR. CH.		Form 795 CINCINNATI, OHIO. U. S. A.					

Fig. 12.13. A strip title.

A form of title that is used to some extent is the *record strip*, a strip marked off across either the lower part or right end of the sheet, containing the information required in the title and space for the recording of orders, revisions, changes, etc., that should be noted, with the date, as they occur. Figure 12.13 illustrates one form.

It is sometimes desired to keep the records of orders and other private information on the tracing but not to have them appear on the print. In such cases, a record strip is put outside the border and trimmed off the print before sending it out.

To Letter a Title. The title should be lettered freehand in single-stroke capitals, either vertical or inclined, but not both styles in the same title. Write out the contents on a separate piece of paper; then refer to paragraph 3.17, where full instructions have been given.

12.16. Zoning. As an aid in locating some item on a large drawing, the lower and right borders may be ruled and marked as shown on the *D*-size drawing of Fig. 12.8. Item *Q* would be located in zone *b*2. A separate column in the change-record block is often used to indicate the position of each drawing change.

12.17. Checking. When a working drawing is finished, it must be checked by an experienced person, who, in signing his name to it, becomes responsible for any errors. This is the final "proofreading" and cannot be done by the one who has made the drawing nearly so well as by another person. In small offices, all the work is checked by the chief draftsman, and draftsmen sometimes check each other's work; in large drafting rooms, one or more checkers who devote all their time to this kind of work are employed. All notes, computations, and checking layouts should be preserved for future reference.

Students may gain experience in this work by checking each other's drawings.

To be effective, checking must be done in an absolutely systematic way and with thorough concentration.

12.18. Order of Checking. Each of the following items should be gone through separately. As each dimension or feature is verified, a check mark in colored pencil should be placed on or above it and corrections indicated with a different colored pencil.

1. Put yourself in the position of those who are to read the drawing, and find out whether it is easy to read and tells a straight story. Always do this before checking any individual features, in other words, before you have had time to become accustomed to the contents.

2. See that each piece is correctly designed and illustrated and that all necessary views are shown but none that is not necessary.

3. Check all the dimensions by scaling and, where advisable, by calculation also. Preserve the calculations.

4. See that dimensions for the shop are given as required by the shop and that the shop is not left to do any adding or subtracting in order to get a needed dimension.

5. Check for tolerances. See that they are neither too "fine" nor too "coarse" for the particular conditions of the machine so as neither to increase unnecessarily the cost of production nor, on the other hand, to impair accuracy of operation or duplication.

6. Go over each piece and see that finishes are properly specified.

7. See that every specification of material is correct and that all necessary ones are given.

8. Look out for "interferences." This means that each detail must be checked with the parts that will be adjacent to it in the assembled machine to see that proper clearances have been allowed.

9. When checking for clearances in connection with a mechanical movement, lay out the movement to scale, figure the principal angles of motion, and see that proper clearances are maintained in all positions, drawing small mechanisms to double size or larger.

10. See that all the small details such as screws, bolts, pins, rivets, etc., are standard and that, where possible, stock sizes have been used.

11. Check every feature of the title or record strip and bill of material.

12. Review the drawing in its entirety, adding such explanatory notes as will increase its efficiency.

12.19. Alterations. Once a drawing has been printed and the prints have been released to the shop, any alterations or changes should be recorded on the drawing and new prints issued. If the changes are extensive, the drawing may be *obsoleted* and a new drawing made which *supersedes* the old drawing. Many drawing rooms have "change-record" blocks printed in conjunction with the title, where minor changes are recorded (Fig. 12.11). The change is identified in the record and on the face of the drawing with a letter.

New designs may be changed so often that the alterations cannot be made fast enough to reach the shop when needed. In this case, sketches showing the changes are rapidly made, reproduced, and sent to the shop, where they are fastened to each print of the drawing. These sketches, commonly known as "engineering orders," are later incorporated on the drawing.

Portions of a drawing may be canceled by drawing closely spaced parallel lines, usually at 45°, over the area to be voided.

12.20. Working Sketches. Facility in making, freehand, an orthographic drawing is an essential part of the equipment of every engineer. Such routine men as tracers and detailers may get along with skill and speed in mechanical execution, but the designer must be able to record his ideas freehand. In all inventive mechanical thinking, in all preliminary designing, in all explanation and instructions to draftsmen, freehand sketching is the mode of expression. Its mastery means the mastery of the language, and it is gained only after full proficiency in drawing with instruments is acquired. It is the mastery which the engineer, inventor, designer, chief draftsman, and contractor, with all of whom time is too valuable to spend in mechanical execution, must have.

Working sketches may be made in either orthographic or pictorial form. Chapter 5 gives the fundamentals for orthographic freehand drawings, and Chap. 8 discusses pictorial sketching.

12.21. Kinds of Working Sketches. Working sketches may be divided into two general classes: (1) those made before the structure is built and (2) those made after the structure is built.

In the first class are included the sketches made in connection with the designing of the structure, which may be classified as (1) *scheme* or *idea* sketches, used in studying and developing the arrangement and proportion of parts; (2) *computation sketches*, made in connection with the figured calculations for motion and strength; (3) *executive sketches*, made by the chief engineer, inventor, or consulting engineer, to give instructions for special arrangements or ideas which must be embodied in the design; (4) *design sketches*, used in working up the schemes and ideas into such form that the design drawing can be started; and (5) *detail sketches*, made as substitutes for detail drawings.

The second class includes (1) *detail sketches*, drawn from existing parts, with complete notes and dimensions, from which duplicate parts may be constructed directly or from which working drawings may be made (Fig. 12.14); (2) *assembly sketches*, made from an assembled machine to show the relative positions of the various parts, with center and location dimensions, or sometimes for a simple machine, with complete dimensions and specifications; and (3) *outline* or *diagrammatic sketches*, generally made for the purpose of location:

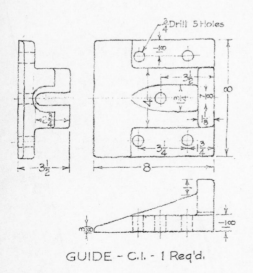

GUIDE - C.I. - 1 Req'd.

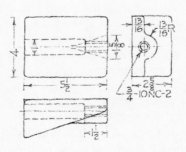

BLOCK - C.I. - 1 Req'd.
$\frac{3}{4}''$ Cap Screw $3\frac{3}{4}''$ Lg. - 1 Req'd.
Washer for Screw - 1 Req'd.

Fig. 12.14. A detail sketch (leveling block).

sometimes, for example, to give the size and location of pulleys and shafting, piping, or wiring, that is, information for use in connection with the setting up of machinery; sometimes to locate a single machine, giving the over-all dimensions, sizes, and center distances for foundation bolts and other necessary information.

12.22. Making a Working Sketch. In making a working sketch, the principles of projection and the rules of practice for working drawings are to be remembered and applied. A systematic order should be followed for both idea sketches and sketches from objects, as listed below:

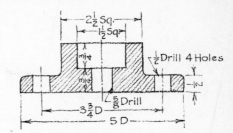

Fig. 12.15. A one-view sketch.

1. Visualize the object.
2. Decide on the treatment, orthographic or pictorial.
3. Determine the view or views.
4. Determine the size of the sketch.
5. Locate the center lines.
6. Block in the main outlines.
7. Complete the detail.
8. Add dimension lines and arrowheads.
9. Put on the dimensions.
10. Letter notes and title, with date.
11. Check the drawing.

Before a good graphical description of an object or idea can be developed, it is essential that the mental image of it be definite and clear. The clearness of the sketch is a direct function of this mental picture. Hence the first step is to concentrate on visualization, leading directly to the second step—determination of the best method of representation. This will probably not be just the same as would be made in a scale drawing. For example, a note in regard to thickness or shape of section will often be used to save a view, Fig. 12.15; thus one view of a piece that is circular in cross section would be sufficient. In other cases, additional part views and extra sections may be sketched rather than complicate the regular views with added lines that might confuse the sketch, although the same lines might be perfectly clear in a measured drawing. The third step is to determine the view (pictorial) or views (orthographic). Draw the object in its functioning position, if possible, but if another position will show the features to better advantage, use it. A machine should, of course, be represented right-side up, in its natural working position. If symmetrical about an axis, often only one-half need be sketched. If a whole view cannot be made on one page, it may be put on two, each part being drawn up to a break line used as a datum line.

The fourth step is to proportion the size of the sketch to the sheet. Have it large enough to show all detail clearly, but allow plenty of room for dimensions, notes, and memorandums. Small parts may be sketched larger than full size. Do not try to crowd all the views on one sheet of paper. Use as many sheets as may be required, but

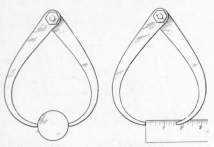

Fig. 12.16. Outside caliper.

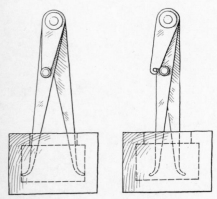

Fig. 12.17. Inside transfer caliper.

name each view, indicating the direction in which it is taken. Sometimes one view alone will require a whole sheet.

In drawing on plain paper, the location of the principal points, centers, etc., should be so judged that the sketches will fit the sheet, and the whole sketch, with as many views, sections, and auxiliary views as are necessary to describe the piece, will be drawn in as nearly correct proportion as the eye can determine, *without taking any measurements.*

12.23. Dimension Lines. After the sketching of a piece is finished, it should be gone over and *dimension lines* for all the dimensions needed for the construction added, drawing extension lines and arrowheads carefully and checking to see that none is omitted.

12.24. Measuring and Dimensioning. Up to this stage, the object has not been handled, and consequently the drawing has been kept clean. The measurements for the dimensions indicated on the drawing may now be added. A flexible rule or steel scale will serve for getting most of the dimensions. Never use a draftsman's scale for measuring castings, as it will be soiled and have its edges marred. The diameter of cylindrical shapes or the distance between outside surfaces may be measured by using outside calipers and scale, Fig. 12.16; and the sizes of holes or internal surfaces, by using inside calipers. Figure 12.17 illustrates the inside transfer caliper, used when a projecting portion prevents removing the ordinary caliper. The outside transfer caliper is used for a similar condition, occurring with an outside measurement. The depth of a hole is easily measured with the depth gage, Fig. 12.18*A*. Screw threads are measured by calipering the body diameter and either counting the number of threads per inch or gaging with a screw-pitch gage, Fig. 12.18*B*. A fillet-and-round gage measures radii by fitting the gage to the circular contour, Fig. 12.18*C*. It is often necessary to lay a straightedge across a surface, as in Fig. 12.19. This type of measurement could be made conveniently with a combination square or with a surface gage. The combination square uses two different heads, the regular 90°-45° head, Fig. 12.20*A*, for a variety of measurements, or the protractor head, Fig. 12.20*B*, for measuring or laying out angles. For accurate measurements, outside or inside micrometer calipers are necessary. The outside type is illustrated in Fig. 12.21. Readings

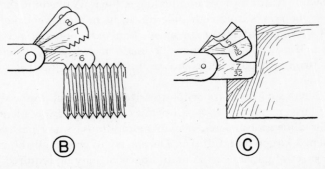

Ⓐ   Ⓑ   Ⓒ

Fig. 12.18. (*A*) Depth gage, (*B*) screw-pitch gage, (*C*) fillet-and-round gage.

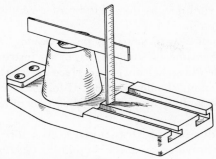

Fig. 12.19. Making a measurement.

to 0.001 in. are easily obtained. Accurate measurements of holes may be made with a telescopic gage in conjunction with an outside micrometer.

A variety of gages made for special purposes, as a wire gage, gage for sheet metal, etc., may be used as occasion demands. With some ingenuity, measurements can often be made with the simpler instruments when special ones are not available.

Always measure from finished surfaces, if possible. Judgment must be exercised in measuring rough castings so as not to record inequalities.

In finding the distance between centers of two holes of the same size, measure from the edge of one to the corresponding edge of the other. Curves are measured by coordinates or offsets, as shown in Fig. 10.39. A curved outline may be recorded by laying a sheet of paper on it and making a rubbing.

Add all remarks and notes that may seem to be of possible value. The title should be written or lettered on the sketch.

Always Date a Sketch. Valuable inventions have been lost through inability to prove priority because the first sketches had not been dated. In commercial work, the draftsman's notebook with sketches and calculations is preserved as a permanent record, and its sketches should be made so as to stand the test of time and be legible after the details of their making have been forgotten.

For gaining skill through practice, sketches should be made entirely freehand. However, in commercial work the engineer often saves time by making a hybrid sketch, drawing circles with the compasses or even with a coin from his pocket, ruling some lines with a pocket scale or a triangle and making some freehand but always keeping a workmanlike quality and good proportion.

Cross-section Paper. Sketches are often made on coordinate paper ruled faintly in $\frac{1}{16}$, $\frac{1}{8}$, or $\frac{1}{4}$ in., used either simply as an aid in drawing straight lines and judging proportions or for drawing to approximate scale by assigning suitable values to the unit spaces. The latter use is more applicable to design sketches than to sketches from the object (Fig. 12.22).

12.25. Checking the Sketch. The final step is to check the sketch. It is a curious fact that, when a beginner omits a dimension, it is

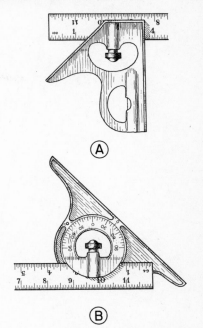

Fig. 12.20. Combination square.

Fig. 12.21. Outside micrometer caliper.

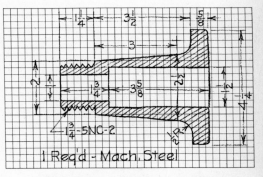

Fig. 12.22. A sketch on coordinate paper.

usually a basic, vital one, as that of the center height of a machine or an over-all length.

Sketches are not always made on paper having a printed title, but essentially the same information as for an instrument drawing should be recorded in some convenient place on the sheet. All notes and special directions should be checked for accuracy along with the drawing proper. In general, follow the order of checking given in paragraph 12.17.

12.26. Reproduction of Drawings. As has already been indicated, working drawings go to the shop in the form of prints made from the original drawings. Several different printing processes are in use, all of which give the best results from tracings inked on tracing cloth or paper. However, quite satisfactory prints may be obtained from pencil drawings on translucent paper when the penciling is done skillfully, with uniform opaque lines. In fact, most of the drawings of industry are not inked; only those of a permanent nature, such as maps, charts, etc., and tracings that must be printed a great many times, are inked.

Blueprints. The simplest and most generally used copying process is the blueprinting process, in which the prints are made by exposing a piece of sensitized paper and a tracing in close surface contact with each other to sunlight or electric light in a printing frame or machine made for the purpose. On exposure to the light, a chemical action takes place, which, when fixed by washing in water, gives a strong blue color. The parts protected from the light by the black lines of the tracing wash out, leaving the white paper.

Vandyke Paper. This is a thin sensitized paper which turns dark brown when exposed to light and properly "fixed." A reversed negative of a tracing may be made on it by exposing it to light with the inked side of the drawing next to the sensitized side of the paper; then this negative can be printed on blueprint paper, giving a positive print with blue lines on white.

BW Prints and Directo Prints. These have black lines on a white ground and are made directly from the original tracing, either in a blueprinting machine (and developed by hand) or in a special machine made for the purpose. They are used extensively when positive prints are desired.

Ozalid Prints. This process is based on the chemical action of light-sensitive diazo compounds. It is a contact method of reproduction in which the exposure is made in either a regular blueprinting machine or an ozalid "whiteprint" machine, and the exposed print is developed dry with ammonia vapors in a developing machine. Standard papers giving black, blue, and maroon lines on a white ground are available. Dry developing has the distinct advantage of giving prints without distortion, and it also makes possible the use of transparent papers, cloth, and foils, which effects savings in drafting, as these transparent replicas can be changed by additions or erasures and prints made from them without altering the original tracing.

Photostat Prints. These are extensively used by large corporations. By this method, a print with white lines on a dark background is made directly from any drawing or tracing, to any desired reduction or enlargement, through the use of a large specially designed camera. This print may be again photostated, giving a brown-black line on a white ground. This method is extremely useful to engineers for drawings to be included in reports and for matching drawings of different scales which may have to be combined into one.

Duplicating Tracings. Tracings having all the qualities of ordinary inked ones are made photographically from pencil drawings by using a sensitized tracing cloth.

Lithoprinting. When a number of copies of a drawing (50 or more) are needed, they may be reproduced by lithoprinting, a simplified form of photolithography, at comparatively small cost.

Copying Methods. Such of them as the mimeograph, ditto machine, and other forms of the hectograph or gelatin pad are often used for small drawings.

12.27. Filing and Storing of Drawings. Drawings are filed in steel or wooden cabinets made for the purpose. Many engineering offices store their drawings in fireproof vaults and remove them only for making alterations or for printing. Photographic copies are sometimes made as a separate permanent record. Drawings are always filed flat or rolled. Prints, however, are folded for filing or mailing. The usual method is the "accordion" fold illustrated in Fig. 12.8. To aid in the filing of accordion-folded prints, a supplementary number block may be added, as shown.

12.28. Individual Fields. The foregoing paragraphs of this chapter have described the usual methods employed in the drafting rooms of industry. However, it must be realized that each major branch of engineering (or divisions within a major branch) will have some special practices. As examples, a civil engineer in sanitary work will deal with drainage, water treatment, etc., while his brother civil engineer in structural work will be concerned with steel, concrete, etc., in fabricating bridges, roadways, etc.

To meet these varied requirements, every engineer must have a basic graphical training, but there must naturally be a corresponding variation in the emphasis placed on some phases of graphical work.

In preparation for aircraft drawing, the requisites are a thorough knowledge of orthographic projection and engineering geometry; an acquaintance with shop practice, including riveted construction and welding; experience in the use of sheet-metal stamped shapes; and, desirably, a facility in using perspective and other pictorial methods. Training in engineering geometry is especially important since more than usual emphasis is placed on the theory, drawing, and dimensioning of warped surfaces. Drawings used in the aircraft industry may be classified under three general divisions: (1) preliminary design drawings, (2) layout drawings, and (3) production drawings.

Agricultural engineers should have a good basic training with attention paid to working drawings of machines and farm buildings.

In preparation for ceramic engineering, emphasis should be placed on mechanical and structural drafting practice.

The study of drawing in preparation for chemical engineering involves all the basic principles considered in this and previous chapters. The chemical engineer should be informed on piping and on the various forms of equipment used in industrial chemistry, such as mixing, grinding, filtering, drying, and conveying machinery.

Civil engineers should be well trained in the making of piping, welding, structural, architectural, map, and topographic drawings.

Electrical engineers need the basic equipment in the language of drawing as do mechanical or other engineers. In its application in their profession, it may be divided into two general classes: working drawings, as of electrical machinery, and diagrammatic or symbolic drawings, such as wiring diagrams, etc. In electrical working drawings, the principles and conventions of this chapter are all applicable. Diagrammatic drawings, using conventional symbols for electrical equipment and connections, form an important class of electrical drawings. Electrical symbols, wiring symbols, and radio symbols are given in the Appendix.

Industrial and mechanical engineers should have a broad training in working-drawing practice, including structural and architectural drawings, and should be thoroughly familiar with drawing practices for gears, cams, welded construction, and jigs and fixtures.

Metallurgical, mining, and petroleum engineers should have a good basic training in engineering drawing and geometry.

It is evident that a welding engineer should be thoroughly familiar with welding-drawing practice, in addition to his basic training.

12.29. "Simplified" Drawing: Economical Drafting Practices. The drafting of any engineering creation is generally considered by management to be an expensive part of the complete operation of producing a finished salable product. Furthermore, the percentage of total cost relegated to research, development, drafting, tooling, factory, labor, and other items of expense can be judged only on the economy of each individual department. Thus the drafting department comes under the same critical scrutiny as any other division of operation. Whatever can be saved in time and expense without injuring the effectiveness and efficiency of the department may be considered as true economy.

This question of thrift has been studied by many executives for years, but W. L. Healy and A. H. Rau,[1] of the General Electric Company, are credited with the first publication recommending and describing the methods by which economies can be effected in the drafting room. There are a number of frugal practices in making the drawings and others that are important only to management. The principles on which economical drafting is based are discussed in the paragraphs following.

[1] "Simplified Drafting Practice," John Wiley & Sons, Inc., New York, 1953.

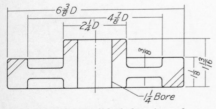

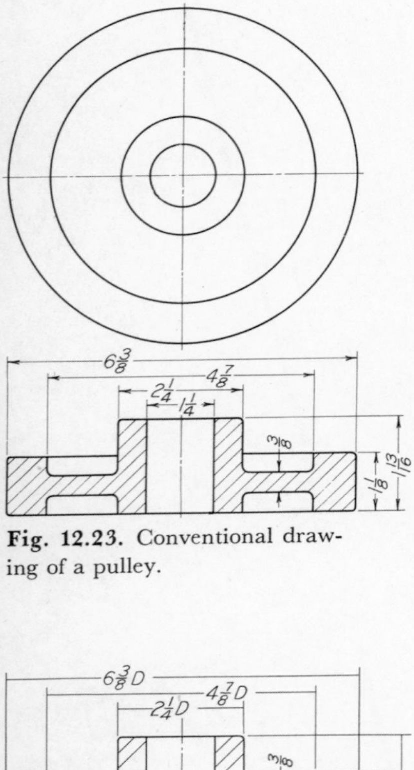

Fig. 12.23. Conventional drawing of a pulley.

Fig. 12.24. Simplified drawing of a pulley.

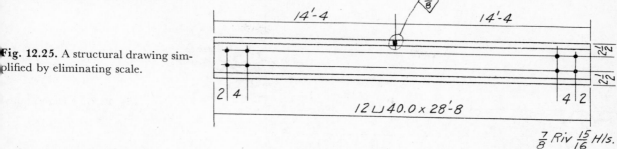

Fig. 12.25. A structural drawing simplified by eliminating scale.

12.30. Unnecessary Views. Any view which is not necessary for the description is a waste of drafting time, paper, reproduction (area and cost), and filing space. Figure 12.23 is a conventional drawing of a pulley in which the top view is used to describe the cylindrical shapes. This pulley *can* be represented economically, as at Fig. 12.24, by eliminating the top view and using the letter *D* on the dimensions of the front view to show that the shapes represented are cylinders. Some drafting economists argue that even the letters *D* are not necessary because the title block will tell that the object is a pulley and therefore a combination of cylinders. Each drafting executive will have to judge the extent to which extra views, letters, etc., can be eliminated without making the interpretation of the drawing obscure or misleading. Nevertheless, the following may be stated with the force of rules: (1) Never draw more views than are necessary for description; (2) examine the object to see whether a view can be eliminated by the use of a descriptive title, note, symbols, letters, or numbers; (3) examine the object to determine whether a word statement might eliminate *all* views (this is usually possible only for very simple parts).

12.31. Unnecessary Scale. The reader of the drawing does not establish distances by scaling the drawing: Most commercial drawings carry a note stating that the drawing is not to be scaled. Some drafting time may be consumed in drawing to scale when it may not be necessary. A good example is shown in Fig. 12.25, a structural detail *not to any scale* at all but just as effective and readable as if drawn carefully and meticulously to scale. The cardinal points are: (1) Do not draw to scale unless necessary for proper layout and readability; (2) do not cautiously draw to scale when approximations will suffice. However, almost everything can be carried to absurdity. Figure 12.26 is an example where the drawing is so far out of scale that the drawing is misleading. Notice that the 2-in. square cannot possibly be larger than the 5-in. circle. However, *if the dimensions on the drawing are followed*, it will be learned that the object wanted is a 5-in.-diameter and 1/4-in.-thick disk with a 2-in. square hole in the center. Thus if the dimensions carry the weight of authority, the drawing is readable. This is, of course, an extreme case and is given here to urge the reader to consider all the possibilities.

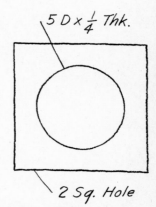

Fig. 12.26. An ambiguous drawing.

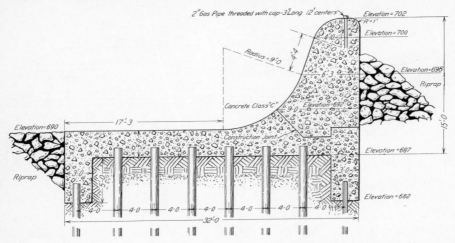

Fig. 12.27. A conventional drawing.

12.32. Unnecessary Lines and Elaboration. Every line made on a drawing costs in drafting time and the company's money. Therefore, any line that accomplishes no useful purpose should be eliminated. This will include extra lines (on any view) which are not necessary for describing the object. Especially, meticulous cross-hatching and embellishment may be omitted without seriously affecting the readability. Compare the two drawings of Figs. 12.27 and 12.28. Painstaking and complete representation of sections such as occur on Fig. 12.27 are a complete waste of time and could be very advantageously simplified as in Fig. 12.28. Incidentally, the drawing of Fig. 12.28 gives more structural information than the detailed representation of Fig. 12.27.

12.33. Arrowless Dimensioning. One saving of time can be made by eliminating unnecessary arrows on dimension lines and leaders, as indicated in Figs. 12.24, 12.25, 12.26, 12.28, and 12.30. To the uninitiated, these drawings appear to be unfinished, but if they are examined carefully and with an open mind, it will be seen that arrows are not really needed and that, economically, the time necessary for placing them on the drawing is a waste.

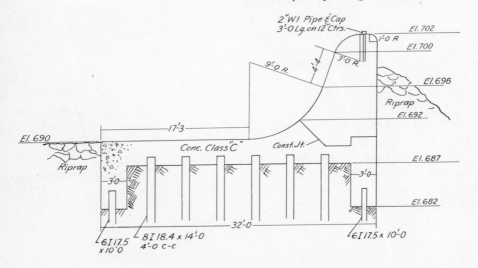

Fig. 12.28. Drawing simplified by elimination of unnecessary lines.

12.34. Simplified Base-line Dimensioning. If the base-line system of dimensioning is used, even the dimension *lines* themselves can be eliminated. As shown in Fig. 12.29, two base lines, one horizontal and the other vertical, are established. The location of base lines may be at the edge of the part, on the center of symmetry, or through some important feature. Distances are then given as shown on the figure, *from* the base lines (corresponding to any coordinate system), to give all information necessary for construction.

12.35. Freehand Drawing. The greatest saving of drafting time can often be realized by taking advantage of the methods described in the previous paragraphs and by making the drawing freehand. Figure 12.30 is an example. Compare Fig. 12.30 with the conventional sketch of Fig. 12.15.

12.36. Mechanical Aids. Much drafting time can be conserved by employing modern aids such as the drafting machine, pencil sharpener and pointer, and an efficient drafting table. Also, for features such as circles, ellipses, boltheads, nuts, and symbols which must be drawn repeatedly, a template will greatly simplify and shorten the time of layout. Figure 12.31 shows several typical templates, at (*A*) and (*B*) the Rapidesign templates for ellipses and

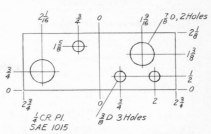

Fig. 12.29. Simplified base-line dimensioning.

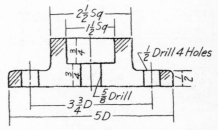

Fig. 12.30. A simplified sketch.

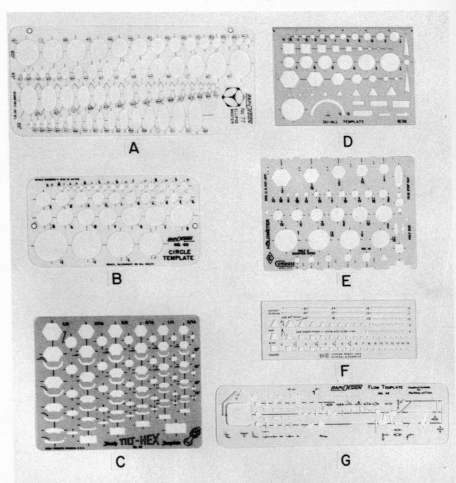

Fig. 12.31. Time-saving templates.

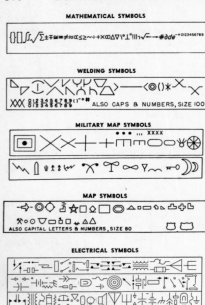

Fig. 12.32. LeRoy symbol templates.

circles and at (*C*) a Tilthex template for boltheads. (*D*) is a Do-all template for a variety of operations. (*E*) is a Holometer for boltheads and nuts, (*F*) is a K & E thread template, and (*G*) is a Rapidesign template for piping symbols.

Several symbol templates are available for use with the LeRoy lettering equipment. A number of these are shown in Fig. 12.32. Figure 12.33 is an example of a symbolic drawing, which can be made in a fraction of the time required for a complete detailed layout.

12.37. Abbreviations. Another economy can result from using abbreviations wherever possible, without affecting the readability of the drawing. American Standard abbreviations are given in the Appendix. Note the extensive use of abbreviations on Figs. 12.24 to 12.30.

PROBLEMS

The first part of any working-drawing problem consists of the selection of views, the choice of suitable scales, and the arrangement of the sheet. In classwork, a preliminary sketch layout should be submitted for approval before the drawing is commenced.

In dimensioning these problems, the principles given in Chap. 10 should be followed carefully. Before applying finish marks, study the problem to determine which surfaces should be so marked. On parts that are to fit accurately, the class of fit is to be assumed or assigned, and limit dimensions are to be figured from the nominal sizes given, using the ASA tables of allowances and tolerances in the Appendix. The illustration for the problem is to be taken as the preliminary sketch or design drawing from which to make the actual working drawings for the shop. Because of restricted space, the illustrations are often crowded; do not, therefore, follow them as examples of good spacing or of the best placing of dimensions. The dimensions used are intended primarily for drawing purposes and are not necessarily those which should be selected for the working drawing.

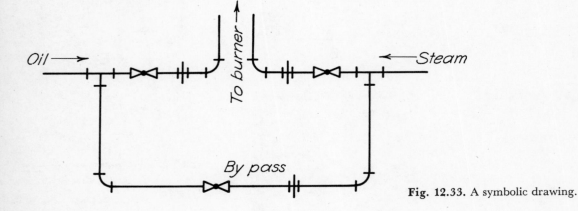

Fig. 12.33. A symbolic drawing.

Group 1. Detail drawings

This group includes problems involving sectional views, auxiliaries, and conventional representation. Several methods of part production will be found: casting, forging, forming of sheet metal, and plastic molding.

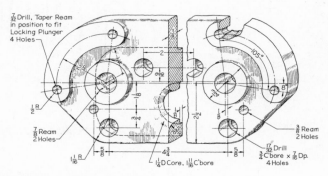

Prob. 12.1.1. Gear-shifter bracket.

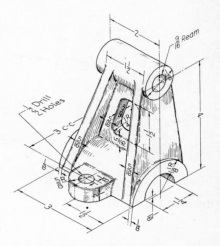

Prob. 12.1.2. Friction-shaft bearing.

12.1.1. Make complete working drawing with necessary sectional views. Cast iron.

12.1.2. Working drawing of friction-shaft bearing. Cast iron.

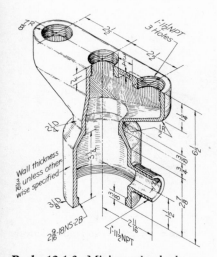

Prob. 12.1.3. Mixing-valve body.

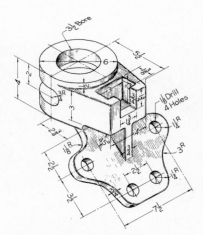

Prob. 12.1.4. Conveyer hanger.

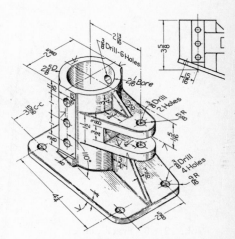

Prob. 12.1.5. Strut base.

12.1.3. Working drawing of mixing-valve body. Cast brass.

12.1.4. Working drawing of conveyer hanger. Determine what views and part views will best describe the piece. Cast steel.

12.1.5. Working drawing of strut base. Determine what views and part views will best describe the piece. Cast aluminum.

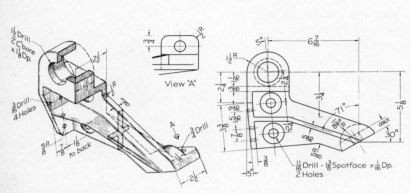

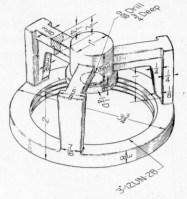

Prob. 12.1.6. Hinge bracket.

Prob. 12.1.7. Valve cage.

12.1.6. Draw given front view. Add part views and auxiliaries to describe the piece best. Cast aluminum.

12.1.7. Working drawing of valve cage. Cast bronze.

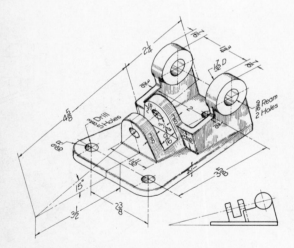

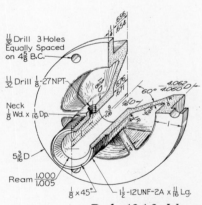

Prob. 12.1.8. Brace plate.

Prob. 12.1.9. Water-pump cover.

12.1.8. Determine what views and part views will best describe the piece. Malleable iron.

12.1.9. Working drawing of water-pump cover. Aluminum alloy die casting.

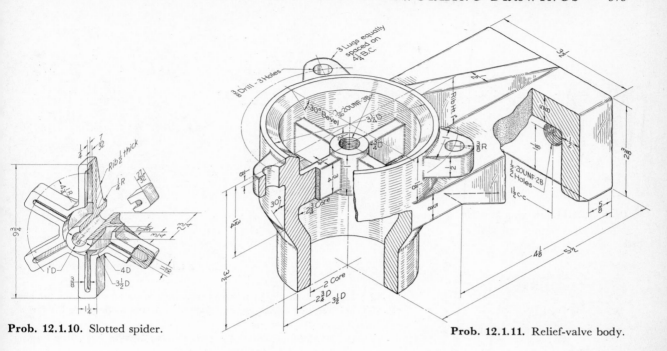

Prob. 12.1.10. Slotted spider.

Prob. 12.1.11. Relief-valve body.

12.1.10. Working drawing of slotted spider. Malleable iron.

12.1.11. Make working drawing of relief-valve body. Cast brass.

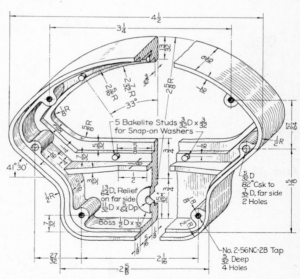

0.062 Stock

Prob. 12.1.12. Breaker.

Prob. 12.1.13. Meter case.

12.1.12. Working drawing of breaker. Steel.

12.1.13. Working drawing of meter case. Molded bakelite.

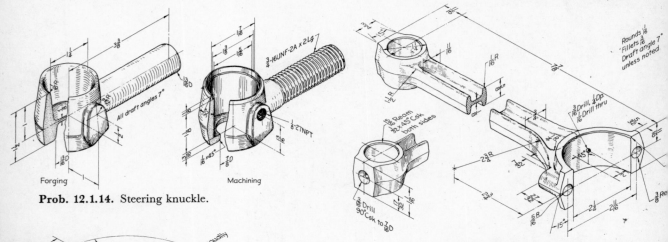

Prob. 12.1.14. Steering knuckle.

Forging

Machining

Prob. 12.1.15. Automotive connecting rod.

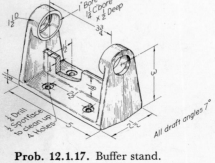

Prob. 12.1.16. Puller body.

12.1.14. (*a*) Make detail working drawings on same sheet, one for *rough* forging and one for *machining;* or (*b*) make one detail drawing for forging and machining. Alloy steel.

12.1.15. Working drawing of automotive connecting rod. Drop forging, alloy steel. Drawings same as Prob. 12.1.14.

12.1.16. Working drawing of puller body. Press forging, steel. Drawings same as Prob. 12.1.14.

12.1.17. Make working drawing of buffer stand. Steel drop forging. Drawings same as Prob. 12.1.14.

12.1.18. Working drawing of torque-tube support. Drop forging, aluminum alloy. Drawings same as Prob. 12.1.14.

Prob. 12.1.17. Buffer stand.

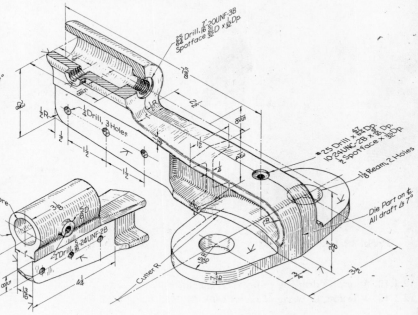

Prob. 12.1.18. Torque-tube support.

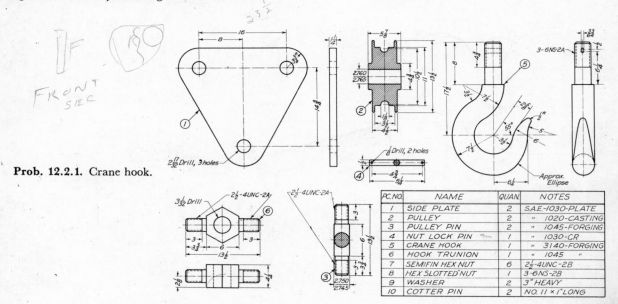

Group 2. An assembly drawing from the details

Prob. 12.2.1. Crane hook.

PC.NO.	NAME	QUAN.	NOTES
1	SIDE PLATE	2	S.A.E.-1030-PLATE
2	PULLEY	2	" 1020-CASTING
3	PULLEY PIN	2	" 1045-FORGING
4	NUT LOCK PIN	1	" 1030-CR
5	CRANE HOOK	1	" 3140-FORGING
6	HOOK TRUNION	1	" 1045 "
7	SEMIFIN HEX NUT	6	2½-4UNC-2B
8	HEX SLOTTED NUT	1	3-6NS-2B
9	WASHER	2	3" HEAVY
10	COTTER PIN	2	NO. 11 × 1"LONG

12.2.1. Make an assembly drawing of the crane hook from details given. Standard parts 7 to 10 are not detailed; see Appendix or handbook for sizes.

12.2.2. Make an assembly drawing, front view in section, of caster.

12.2.2A. Redesign caster for ball-bearing installation.

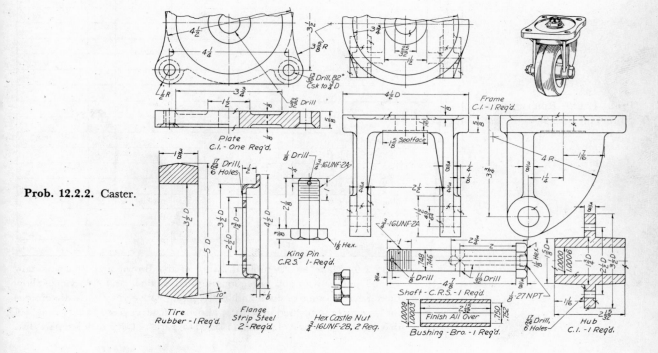

Prob. 12.2.2. Caster.

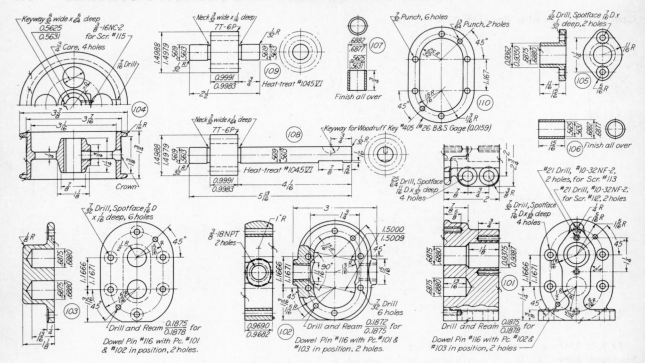

		BROWN AND SHARPE No. 1 ROTARY GEARED PUMP								
		NAME	**MAT.**				**NAME**	**PC. NO.**	
101		Base	1	C.I.						
102		Body	1	C.I.						
103		Cover	1	C.I.						
104		Pulley	1	C.I.						
105		Gland	1	C.I.						
106		Gland Bushing	1	Bro.						
107		Gear Bushing	4	Bro.						
108		Driving Gear	1	S.A.E. #1045	1 9/16	5 7/8				
109		Driven Gear	1	S.A.E. #1045	1 9/16	2 9/16				
110		Gasket	2	Sheet Copper			Body	102	#26 B&S Gage (0.0159)
111		#10-32 x 1 5/8 Slotted Hex. Hd. Mach. Scr. & Nut	4				Cover	103	
112		#10-32 x 1 5/8 Slotted Hex. Hd. Cap Scr.	2				Cover	103	
113		#10-32 x 7/8 Slotted Hex. Hd. Cap Scr.	2				Gland	105	
114		Woodruff Key #405	1				Driving Gear	108	
115		3/8 x 3/8 Headless Set Scr., 3/8-16NC-2	1				Pulley	104	
116		3/16 x 1 7/16 Dowel Pin	2	C.R.S.			Cover	103	
		Packing	To Suit						Garlock Rotopac #239

Prob. 12.2.3. Rotary geared pump and parts list.

12.2.3. Make an assembly drawing of the Brown and Sharpe rotary geared pump, with top view, longitudinal section, and side view. Show direction of rotation of shafts and flow of liquid with arrows. Give dimensions for base holes to be used in setting; also give distance from base to center of driving shaft and size of shaft and key. For parts not detailed, see parts list.

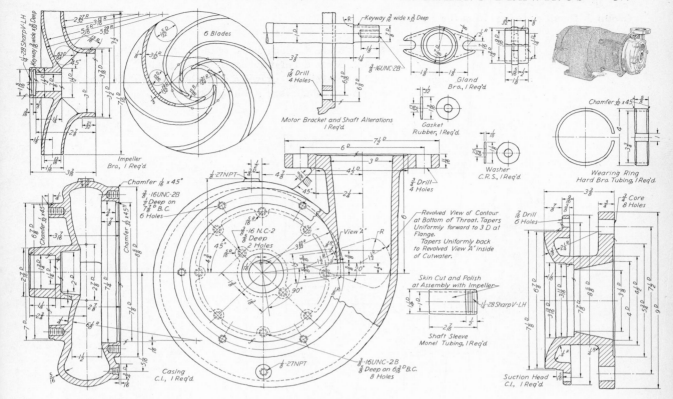

Prob. 12.2.4. Centrifugal pump.

12.2.4. From detail sketches, make assembly and detail drawings of Unipump centrifugal pump, as made by the Weinman Pump Mfg. Co., in which the pump casing is mounted directly on a driving motor, making a compact and efficient design. Cross sections of the volute taken at intervals of 45° should be shown by removed sections, either successive or superimposed, and similar sections should be made through the impeller. At 3,425 rpm this pump delivers 520 gal per min against a head of 160 ft.

The detail drawings should be made up as a set of drawings with each part drawn on a separate sheet. Choose a standard sheet size so that the part may be drawn either full or half size. Dimensioning should be for quantity production with limit dimensions given wherever the function of the parts requires such dimensions. See Chap. 10 for the method of selecting the various fits needed. Drawings of cast parts may be made either in the "single-drawing" or "multiple-drawing" system as described in Chap. 9.

The assembly drawing should show, by dimensions, the relationship between intake and exhaust openings. The sizes of intake and exhaust openings should be given. The mounting flange should also be dimensioned, and the number and size of holes in this flange should be specified.

Complete the set of drawings by making a parts list. See Prob. 12.2.3 for items and style.

Group 3. Detail drawings from the assembly

12.3.1. Make detail drawings of the jig table. Parts, cast iron.

12.3.2. Make detail drawings of the door catch.

12.3.3. Make detail drawings of the belt drive. Pulley and bracket, cast iron; gear and shaft, steel; bushing, bronze.

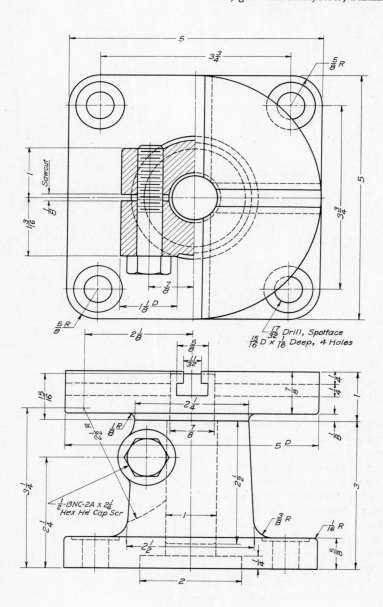

Prob. 12.3.1. Jig table.

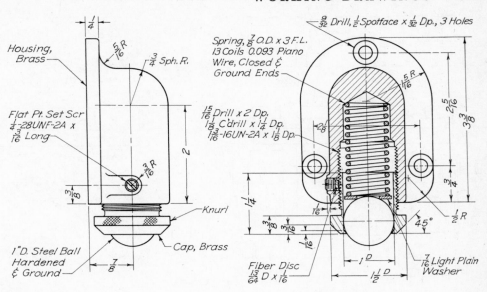

Prob. 12.3.2. Door catch.

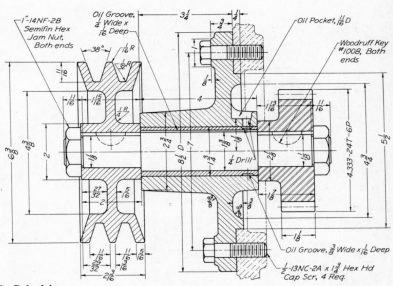

Prob. 12.3.3. Belt drive.

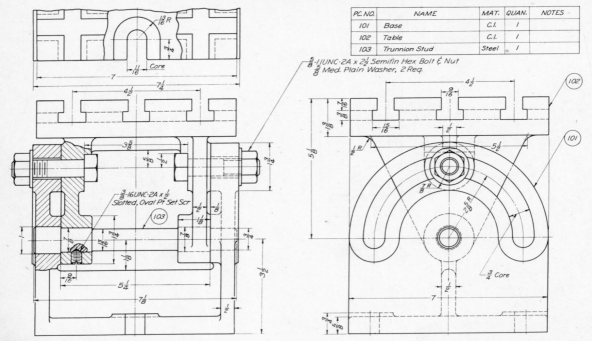

PC. NO.	NAME	MAT.	QUAN.	NOTES
101	Base	C.I.	1	
102	Table	C.I.	1	
103	Trunnion Stud	Steel	1	

Prob. 12.3.4. Swing table.

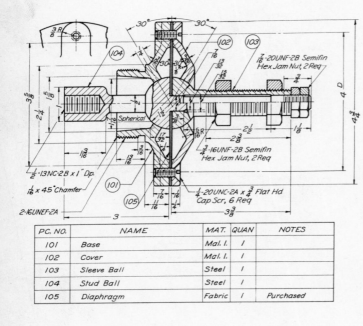

Prob. 12.3.5. Sealed ball joint.

PC. NO.	NAME	MAT.	QUAN	NOTES
101	Base	Mal. I.	1	
102	Cover	Mal. I.	1	
103	Sleeve Ball	Steel	1	
104	Stud Ball	Steel	1	
105	Diaphragm	Fabric	1	Purchased

12.3.4. Make detail drawings of swing table.
12.3.5. Make detail drawings of sealed ball joint.

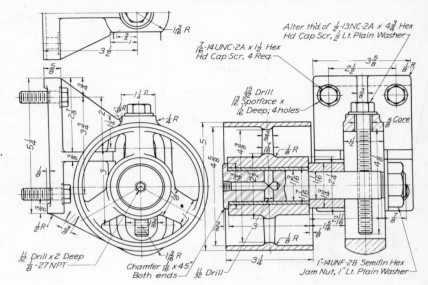

Prob. 12.3.6. Belt tightener.

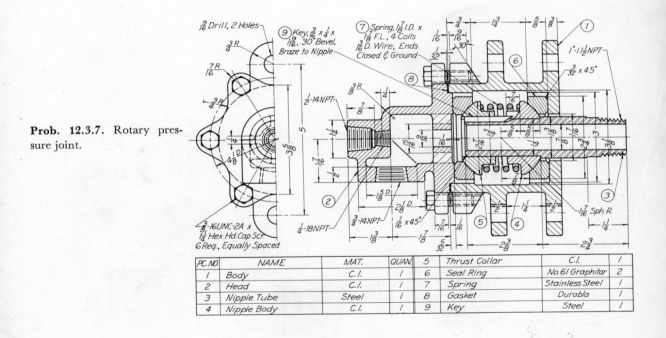

Prob. 12.3.7. Rotary pressure joint.

PC. NO.	NAME	MAT.	QUAN.				
				5	Thrust Collar	C.I.	1
1	Body	C.I.	1	6	Seal Ring	No. 61 Graphitar	2
2	Head	C.I.	1	7	Spring	Stainless Steel	1
3	Nipple Tube	Steel	1	8	Gasket	Durabla	1
4	Nipple Body	C.I.	1	9	Key	Steel	1

12.3.6. Make detail drawings of belt tightener. Bracket, pulley, and collar, cast iron; bushing, bronze; shaft, steel.

12.3.7. Make detail drawings of rotary pressure joint.

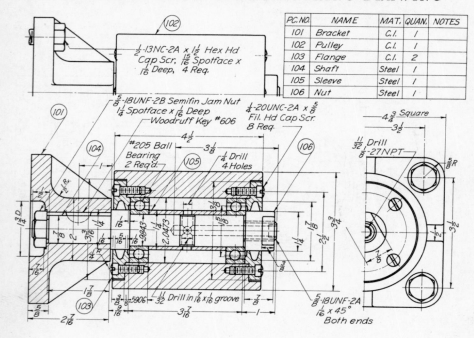

PC. NO.	NAME	MAT.	QUAN.	NOTES
101	Bracket	C.I.	1	
102	Pulley	C.I.	1	
103	Flange	C.I.	2	
104	Shaft	Steel	1	
105	Sleeve	Steel	1	
106	Nut	Steel	1	

Prob. 12.3.8. Ball-bearing idler pulley.

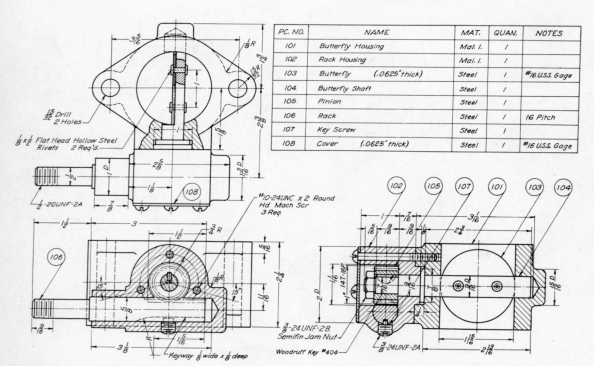

PC. NO.	NAME		MAT.	QUAN.	NOTES
101	Butterfly Housing		Mal. I.	1	
102	Rack Housing		Mal. I.	1	
103	Butterfly	(.0625˝ thick)	Steel	1	#16 U.S.S. Gage
104	Butterfly Shaft		Steel	1	
105	Pinion		Steel	1	
106	Rack		Steel	1	16 Pitch
107	Key Screw		Steel	1	
108	Cover	(.0625˝ thick)	Steel	1	#16 U.S.S. Gage

Prob. 12.3.9. Butterfly valve.

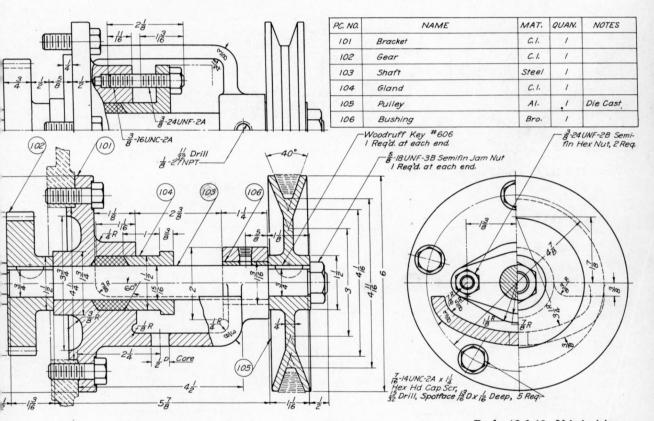

PC. NO.	NAME	MAT.	QUAN.	NOTES
101	Bracket	C. I.	1	
102	Gear	C. I.	1	
103	Shaft	Steel	1	
104	Gland	C. I.	1	
105	Pulley	Al.	1	Die Cast
106	Bushing	Bro.	1	

Prob. 12.3.10. V-belt drive.

12.3.8. Make detail drawings of ball-bearing idler pulley.
12.3.9. Make detail drawings of butterfly valve.
12.3.10. Make detail drawings for V-belt drive.

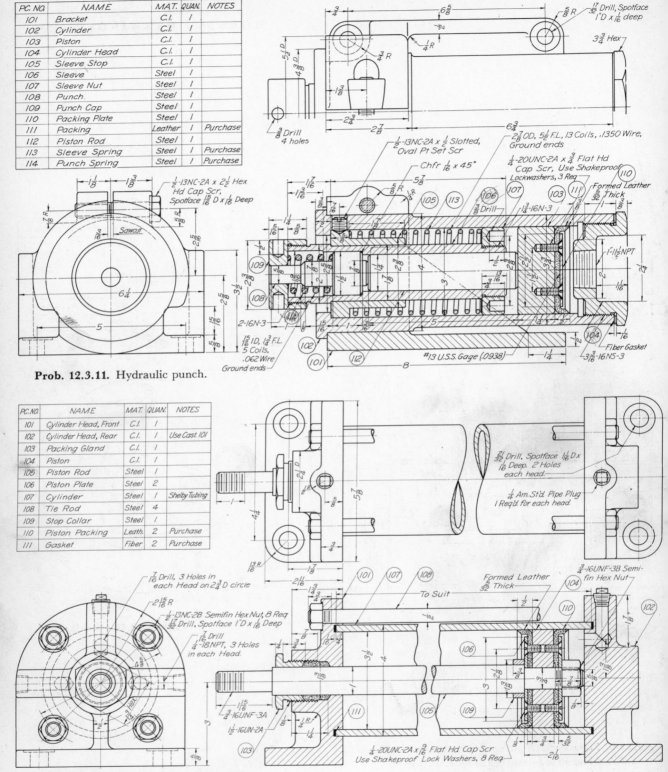

PC. NO.	NAME	MAT.	QUAN.	NOTES
101	Bracket	C.I.	1	
102	Cylinder	C.I.	1	
103	Piston	C.I.	1	
104	Cylinder Head	C.I.	1	
105	Sleeve Stop	C.I.	1	
106	Sleeve	Steel	1	
107	Sleeve Nut	Steel	1	
108	Punch	Steel	1	
109	Punch Cap	Steel	1	
110	Packing Plate	Steel	1	
111	Packing	Leather	1	Purchase
112	Piston Rod	Steel	1	
113	Sleeve Spring	Steel	1	Purchase
114	Punch Spring	Steel	1	Purchase

Prob. 12.3.11. Hydraulic punch.

PC. NO.	NAME	MAT.	QUAN.	NOTES
101	Cylinder Head, Front	C.I.	1	
102	Cylinder Head, Rear	C.I.	1	Use Cast. 101
103	Packing Gland	C.I.	1	
104	Piston	C.I.	1	
105	Piston Rod	Steel	1	
106	Piston Plate	Steel	2	
107	Cylinder	Steel	1	Shelby Tubing
108	Tie Rod	Steel	4	
109	Stop Collar	Steel	1	
110	Piston Packing	Leath.	2	Purchase
111	Gasket	Fiber	2	Purchase

Prob. 12.3.12. Double-acting air cylinder.

MW I
NO COILS
MAT'L

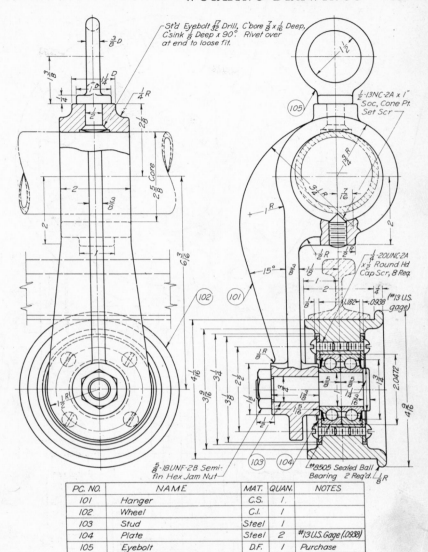

Prob. 12.3.13. Rail-transport hanger.

PC. NO.	NAME	MAT.	QUAN.	NOTES
101	Hanger	C.S.	1	
102	Wheel	C.I.	1	
103	Stud	Steel	1	
104	Plate	Steel	2	#13 U.S. Gage (.0938)
105	Eyebolt	D.F.	1	Purchase

12.3.11. Make detail drawings of hydraulic punch. In action, the punch assembly proper advances until the cap, piece 109, comes against the work. The assembly (piece 106 and attached parts) is then stationary, and the tension of the punch spring (piece 114) holds the work as the punch advances through the work and returns.

12.3.12. Make detail drawings of double-acting air cylinder. Length of stroke to be assigned. Fix length of cylinder to allow for clearance of 1 in. at ends of stroke. Note that pieces 101 and 102 are identical except for the extra machining of the central hole in piece 101 for the shaft, packing, and gland. Make separate drawings for this piece, one for the pattern shop and two for the machine shop.

12.3.13. Make detail drawings of rail-transport hanger. Rail is 10-lb ASCE.

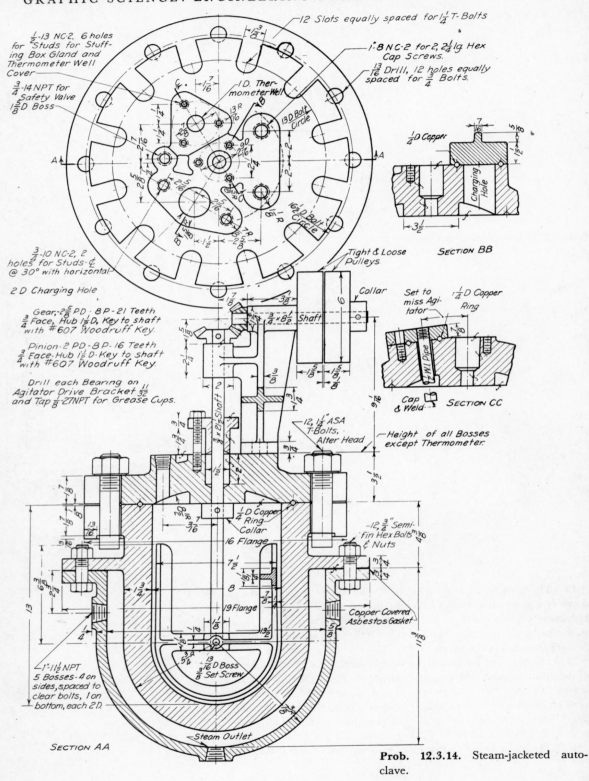

SECTION AA

SECTION BB

SECTION CC

Prob. 12.3.14. Steam-jacketed autoclave.

12.3.14. Make detail drawings for steam-jacketed laboratory autoclave. An autoclave is an apparatus used when chemical action under pressure is required. It may be built with a steam jacket, as in the figure, or without. Stirring devices may or may not be provided, depending on the use. The autoclave shown has a 2-gal capacity and is designed for 800-lb working pressure.

Group 4. A set of drawings from an exploded pictorial

The problems in this group have been arranged for complete exercises in the making of a set of working drawings. Remember that the dimensions given on the pictorial views are to be used only to obtain distances or information needed. In some cases, the data needed for a particular part may have to be obtained from the mating part.

The detail drawings should be made with each part on a separate sheet. Drawings of cast or forged parts may be made either in the single-drawing or the multiple-drawing system described in Chap. 9.

The assembly drawing should include any necessary dimensions, such as number, size, and spacing of mounting holes, that might be required by a purchaser or needed for checking with the machine on which a subassembly is used.

For the style and items to be included in the parts list, see Prob. 12.2.3.

12.4.1. Make a complete set of working drawings for the antivibration mount.

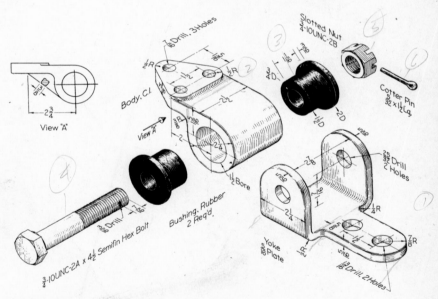

Prob. 12.4.1. Antivibration mount.

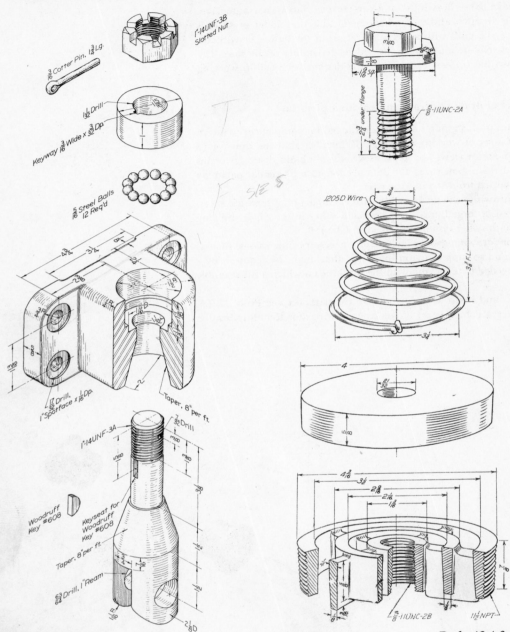

Prob. 12.4.2. Pivot hanger.

Prob. 12.4.3. Pump valve.

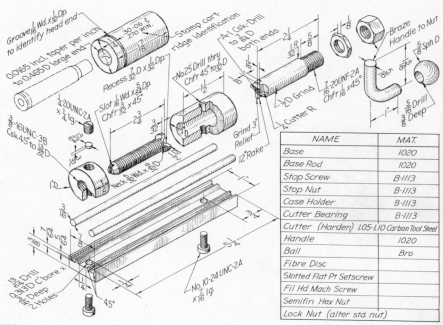

Prob. 12.4.4. Cartridge-case trimmer.

12.4.2. Make a complete set of drawings for pivot hanger, including detail drawings, assembly drawing, and parts list. All parts are steel. This assembly is comprised of a yoke, base, collar, and standard parts.

12.4.3. Make a complete set of drawings for pump valve. The valve seat, stem, and spring are brass; the disk is hard-rubber composition. In operation, pressure of a fluid upward against the disk raises it and allows flow. Pressure downward forces the disk tighter against the seat and prevents flow.

12.4.4. Make a complete set of working drawings for the cartridge-case trimmer. Note that some of the dimensions will have to be obtained from the mating part. A tabular drawing may be made of the case holder, covering holders for various cartridge cases. The dimensions to be tabulated are (a) holder length, (b) diameter, and (c) taper of hole.

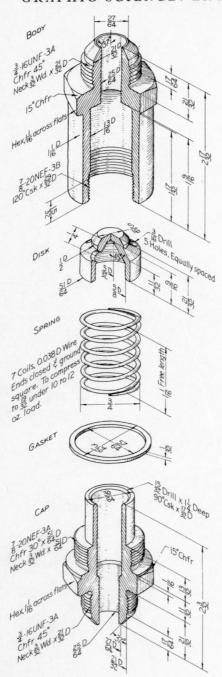

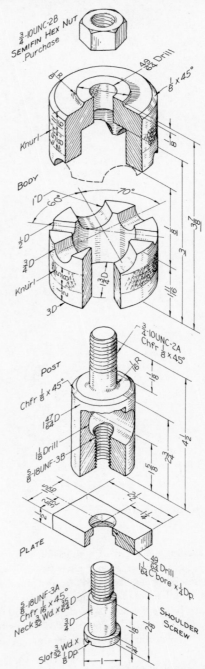

Prob. 12.4.5. Hydraulic check valve.

Prob. 12.4.6. Boring-bar holder.

12.4.5. Make a complete set of working drawings of the hydraulic check valve. Spring is stainless steel; gasket is soft aluminum; all other parts are steel.

12.4.6. Make a complete set of working drawings of the boring-bar holder. All parts are steel. Note that the *body* is made in one piece, then split with a ⅛-in.-wide cut (exaggerated in the picture). The holder may be seen in use in Fig. 9.11.

12.4.6*A.* Design three boring bars (see Fig. 9.11) to fit the boring-bar holder, and make a tabular drawing.

12.4.7. Make a complete set of working drawings of the ratchet wrench.

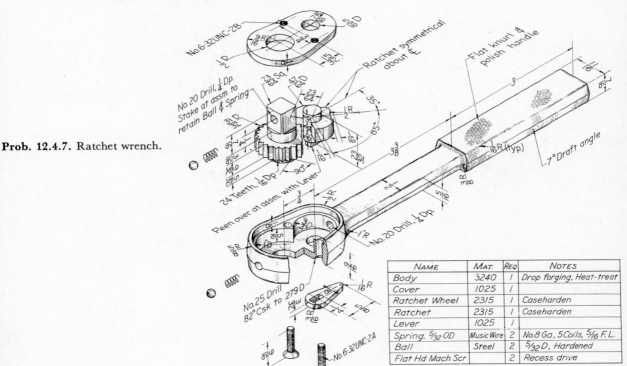

Prob. 12.4.7. Ratchet wrench.

Name	Mat.	Req	Notes
Body	3240	1	Drop forging, Heat-treat
Cover	1025	1	
Ratchet Wheel	2315	1	Caseharden
Ratchet	2315	1	Caseharden
Lever	1025	1	
Spring, 5⁄32 OD	Music Wire	2	No.8 Ga, 5 Coils, 5⁄16 F. L.
Ball	Steel	2	5⁄32 D, Hardened
Flat Hd Mach Scr		2	Recess drive

Group 5. A set of drawings from a pictorial assembly

12.5.1. Make a complete set of working drawings of the high-tension coil mount.

12.5.2. Make a complete set of working drawings of the pipe clamp. The flange is cast steel.

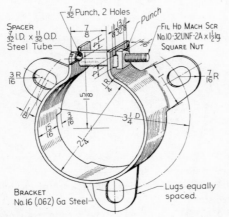

Prob. 12.5.1. High-tension coil mount.

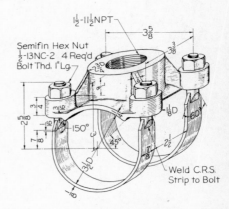

Prob. 12.5.2. Pipe clamp.

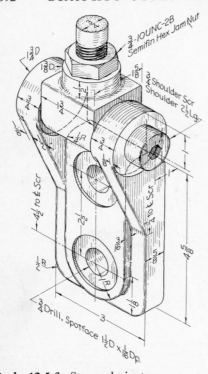

Prob. 12.5.3. Stay-rod pivot.

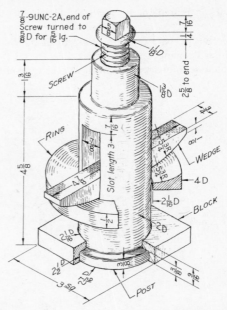

Prob. 12.5.4. Tool post.

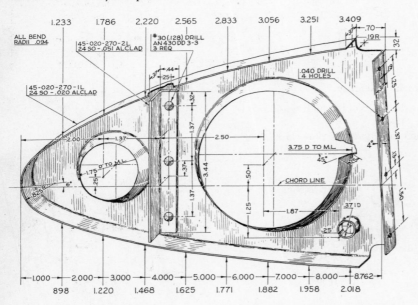

Prob. 12.5.5. Wing-nose rib.

12.5.3. Make a complete set of working drawings of the stay-rod pivot. Parts are malleable iron.

12.5.4. Make a complete set of working drawings of the tool post. All parts are steel.

12.5.5. Make a unit-assembly working drawing of the wing-nose rib.

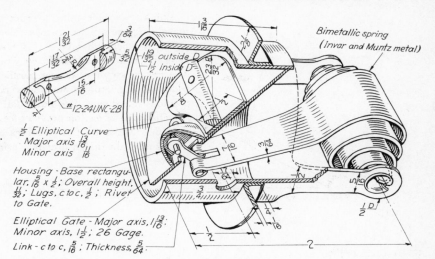

Prob. 12.5.6. Liquid-flow thermostat.

12.5.6. Make assembly and details of liquid-flow thermostat to double size. In detailing the bimetallic spring, use a development to show the shape before coiling. The width changes uniformly from 1½ in. at the base to ⁷⁄₁₆ in. at the end.

Group 6. A set of drawings from the design drawing

In working from a design drawing, most dimensions are obtained by scaling. However, for dimensions where close fits are involved, limits and tolerances will have to be applied to the scaled *basic* size, as explained in Chap. 10. In some of the following problems, appropriate limits have been given on the design drawing.

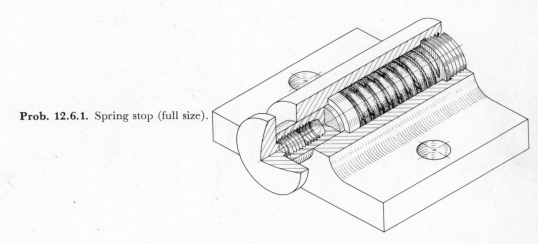

Prob. 12.6.1. Spring stop (full size).

12.6.1. Make a complete set of working drawings from the full-size isometric design drawing. Remember that measurements can be made only on isometric axes. All parts are steel. Spring is of ⁷⁄₁₆-in. outside diameter, 1¼-in. free length; nine coils, 0.062-in. music wire; ground ends.

12.6.2. Saw-hole punch. From design drawing, shown one-half size, make complete set of drawings. Frame is 1035 steel drop forging. Screw is 1025 CRS. Screw handle is 1020 CRS; ends are upset. Punch and die are 1085 HR, heat-treat SAE No. 66. Transfer outer curve of handle from design drawing; draw other curves parallel. Dimension handle curve by giving width across narrowest and widest points and the end radius. Locate these positions lengthwise. Use note "fair curve through points dimensioned." Dimensioning of section provides for the inner curves.

12.6.3. Make a set of drawings of the pulley bracket and support assembly from the design drawing, printed half size.

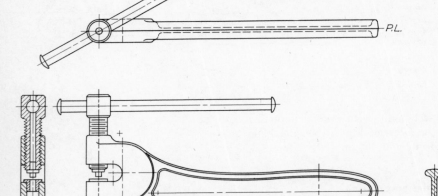

Prob. 12.6.2. Saw-hole punch (½ size).

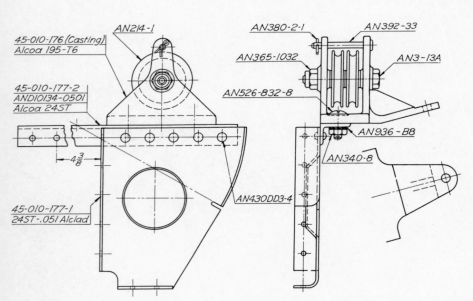

Prob. 12.6.3. Pulley bracket and support (½ size).

12.6.4. Make a unit-assembly working drawing from the design drawing, printed half size. Add parts list.

12.6.4A. Marking machine. From design drawing, shown half size, make

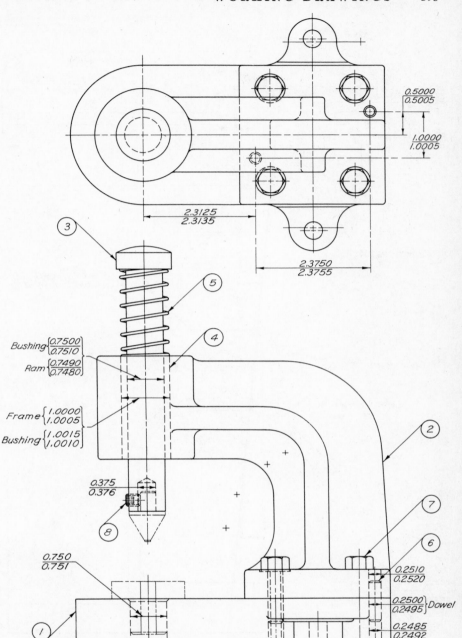

Prob. 12.6.4. Marking machine ($\frac{1}{2}$ size).

complete set of drawings. Base, piece 1, is malleable-iron casting. Frame, piece 2, is cast iron. Ram, piece 3, is 1020 HR; bushing, piece 4, is 1020 cold-drawn tubing; heat-treatment for both is carburize at 1650 to 1700°F, quench direct, temper at 250 to 325°F. Spring, piece 5, is piano wire, No. 20 (0.045) gage, six coils, free length 2 in., heat-treatment is "as received." Marking dies and holders are made up to suit objects to be stamped.

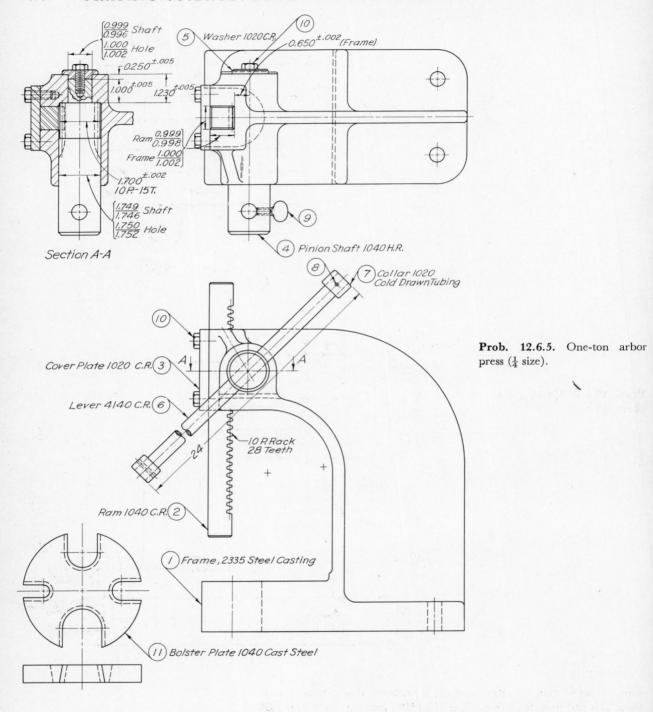

Section A-A

$\frac{0.999}{0.996}$ Shaft

$\frac{1.000}{1.002}$ Hole

0.250 ±.005

1.000 ±.005   1.230 ±.005

Ram $\frac{0.999}{0.998}$

Frame $\frac{1.000}{1.002}$

1.700 ±.002
10 P-15 T.

$\frac{1.749}{1.746}$ Shaft

$\frac{1.750}{1.752}$ Hole

⑤ Washer 1020 C.R.   ⑩

0.650 ±.002 (Frame)

⑨

④ Pinion Shaft 1040 H.R.

⑧   ⑦ Collar 1020 Cold Drawn Tubing

⑩

Cover Plate 1020 C.R. ③   A   A

Lever 4140 C.R. ⑥

10 P. Rack 28 Teeth

2⁴

Ram 1040 C.R. ②

① Frame, 2335 Steel Casting

⑪ Bolster Plate 1040 Cast Steel

Prob. 12.6.5. One-ton arbor press (¼ size).

12.6.5. Arbor press. From design drawing, shown one-quarter size, make complete set of drawings. All necessary information is given on the design drawing.

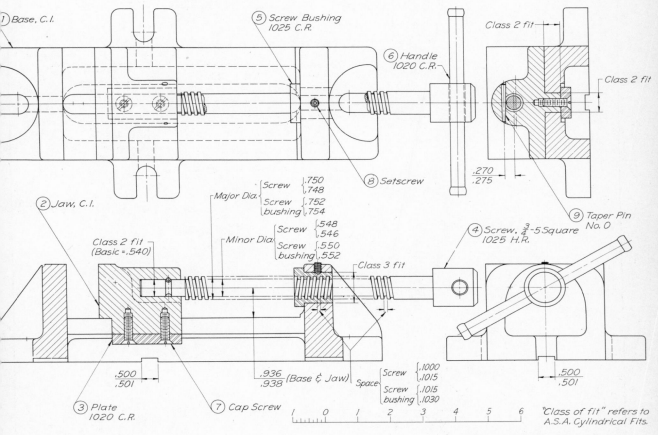

① Base, C.I.

⑤ Screw Bushing
1025 C.R.

⑥ Handle
1020 C.R.

Class 2 fit

Class 2 fit

⑧ Setscrew

$\left\{\begin{array}{ll}\text{Screw} & {.750 \atop .748}\end{array}\right.$

Major Dia. $\left\{\begin{array}{l}\text{Screw} \\ \text{bushing}\end{array}\right. {.752 \atop .754}$

.270
.275

⑨ Taper Pin
No. 0

② Jaw, C.I.

Class 2 fit
(Basic = .540)

Minor Dia. $\left\{\begin{array}{l}\text{Screw} \\ \text{Screw} \\ \text{bushing}\end{array}\right.$ $\begin{array}{l}.548 \\ .546 \\ .550 \\ .552\end{array}$

Class 3 fit

④ Screw, ¾-5 Square
1025 H.R.

.500
.501

.936
.938 (Base & Jaw)

Space $\left\{\begin{array}{l}\text{Screw} \\ \text{Screw} \\ \text{bushing}\end{array}\right.$ $\begin{array}{l}.1000 \\ .1015 \\ .1015 \\ .1030\end{array}$

.500
.501

③ Plate
1020 C.R.

⑦ Cap Screw

1 0 1 2 3 4 5 6

"Class of fit" refers to
A.S.A. Cylindrical Fits.

Prob. 12.6.6. Number 2
flanged vise (⅓ size).

12.6.6. Number 2 flanged vise. From design drawing, make complete
set of drawings, including details, parts list, and assembly. Design drawing
is shown one-third size. All necessary information is given on the design
drawing.

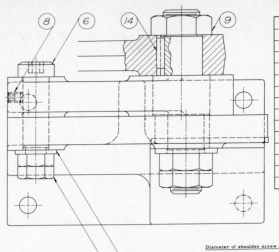

PC. NO.	NAME	MAT.	REQ	NOTES
1	Base	2335	1	Steel Casting
2	Jaw	2335	1	Steel Casting
3	Eccentric	2340 HR	1	
4	Blade	1095 HR	2	
5	Handle	1040	1	Drop Forging
6	Shoulder Screw		1	
7	Flat Head Cap Screw		4	
8	Socket Set Screw		1	Flat Point
9	Semifin Hex Jam Nut		1	
10	Semifin Hex Jam Nut		2	
11	Semifin Hex Jam Nut		2	
12	Cut Washer	1112 CR	1	
13	Cut Washer	1112 CR	1	
14	Key	Key Stock	1	

LIMITS AND TOLERANCES TO BE USED FOR CLOSE FITS

Diameter of shoulder screw and hole in both base and jaw.

Screws (as manufactured): $\frac{0.623}{0.621}$ Hole: $\frac{0.624}{0.626}$

Diameter of eccentric and hole in handle.

Eccentric: $\frac{0.999}{0.997}$ Handle: $\frac{0.999}{1.001}$

Diameter of eccentric and hole in base.

Eccentric: $\frac{1.3745}{1.3740}$ Base: $\frac{1.3750}{1.3755}$

Diameter of eccentric and width of slot in jaw.

Eccentric: $\frac{0.874}{0.872}$ Jaw: $\frac{0.875}{0.877}$

Width of key and keyway in both handle and eccentric.

Key (as purchased stock): $\frac{0.250}{0.249}$ Slot: $\frac{0.250}{0.251}$

Depth of keyway in both handle and eccentric.

$3/32" + 1/64 - 0$

Control of clearance between blades.

Thickness of blade: $\frac{0.1250}{0.1245}$ Dimension "A": $\frac{0.562}{0.561}$

Dimension "B": $\frac{0.812}{0.813}$

Tolerance on shoulder screw and eccentric hole locations.

For base and jaw (two dimensions on each part) use ± 0.002 on scaled values.

Limits for eccentric offset.

Center to center: $\frac{0.248}{0.252}$

Length of handle.

From center of hub to center of ball: 12".

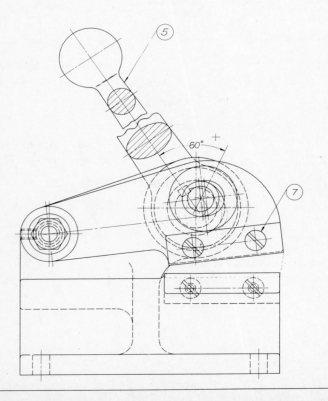

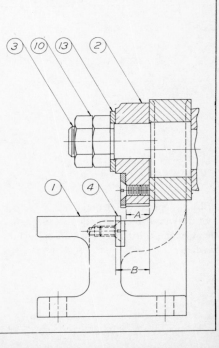

12.6.7. Bench shears. Design drawing is half size. Make a complete set of drawings. For dimensions where close fits are involved, either the decimal limits or the tolerance to be applied to the scaled basic size are given on the design drawing. Heat-treatments should be specified as follows: for base and jaw, "normalize at 1550°F"; for eccentric, "as received"; for blade, "to Rockwell C57-60"; for handle, none. Finish for blades, "grind." Washers are special but may be specified on the parts list by giving inside diameter, outside diameter, and thickness. The key may be specified on the parts list by giving width, thickness, and length.

Group 7. Working sketches

12.7.1. Make a selection of one of the problems in Group 1, and make a detail working sketch.

12.7.2. Make a selection of one of the problems in Group 2, and make an assembly sketch.

12.7.3. Select a single part from one of the assemblies of Groups 3 to 5, and make a working sketch.

12.7.4. Select a single part from one of the Probs. 12.1.1 to 12.4.7, and make a pictorial working sketch.

12.7.5. Make a selection of one of the problems in Group 3, and make detail working sketches.

12.7.6. Make a selection of one of the problems in Group 4 or 5, and make a complete set of working sketches.

Group 8. Economical practices

12.8.1. Select a problem in Group 1, and make a simplified detail drawing.

12.8.2. Select a problem in Group 2, and make a simplified assembly drawing.

12.8.3. Select a problem in Group 4, and make a set of simplified drawings.

12.8.4. Select a problem in either Group 5 or 6, and make a set of simplified drawings.

Prob. 12.6.7. Bench shears, $2\frac{3}{4}$-in. ($\frac{1}{2}$ size).

13

POINT, EDGE, AND NORMAL VIEWS

13.1. Engineering Geometry. Before an object can be described, dimensioned, and specified completely on a working drawing, some preliminary work must often be done in order to determine true relationships between lines or surfaces, to find intersections, to locate elements or tangents, to ascertain clearances, or to decide relationships affecting the design of a single part (or of parts) in a machine or structure. To do this work, one must have a knowledge of points, lines, planes, and curved and warped surfaces combined with a complete understanding of their geometrical properties and combination.

This classification of graphic science can be known as either "engineering geometry" or "descriptive geometry." To solve the basic problems of space, involving points, lines, planes, and surfaces, the orthographic views required are:

1. The normal view of a line
2. The end, or "point," view of a line
3. The edge view of a plane
4. The normal view of a plane

With these available views, together with a knowledge of plane and solid geometry, all problems may be solved involving parallelism, perpendicularity, angularity, clearance, tangency, location, and layout.

Thus this chapter is prerequisite to the chapters following. The four basic views described above and the various ways in which they may be obtained are considered the necessary equipment for problem solution.

13.2. Specification of a Line. (A line may be located in space by specifying two points on it.) If the two points are located in two adjacent orthographic views, the points are fixed in space, and the line passing through these two points, therefore, has its direction in space determined. A line is considered to be infinite in length, and the portion between any two points on it simply specifies a segment. (The space direction (bearing and slope) and *one* point will also locate a line.)

13.3. Normal View of a Line. The term "normal" is mathematically defined as meaning "perpendicular" or "at right angles." Thus the term is here geometrically applied to a view in which the direction of observation is perpendicular to a line or surface. For example, the normal view (true length) of a *horizontal* line will be seen in the top view because the view direction for the top view is taken perpendicular to a horizontal plane containing the horizontal line. Similarly, the front view will be the normal view of any *frontal* line (a line lying in a frontal plane), and the side view is the normal view of any *profile* line (a line lying in a profile plane).

The general case, however, is that where the line is in an oblique position (not parallel to any of the three principal planes of projection). Again, the normal view of such a line is the one observed *in a direction perpendicular to the line.* Figure 13.1 shows in (*A*), (*B*), and (*C*) a line *AB* that is an oblique line. The top and front views ($A_T B_T$ and $A_F B_F$) of Fig. 13.1*A* and *B* show that the line extends from point *A* in a direction downward, to the right, and toward the rear. In Fig. 13.1*C*, *AB* extends from *A* in a direction upward, to the right, and forward. At (*A*) the normal view of the line ($A_A B_A$) has been obtained by making an elevation auxiliary view taken in a direction perpendicular to the line. This line of sight perpendicular to the line may be visualized if one considers that the observer moves around the line, looking in a horizontal direction, until his direction of observation is oriented perpendicular to the line; or one may hold a pencil in the position of the line and observe this simple phenomenon. It should also be observed that, in accordance with the theory of orthographic projection, the observer is theoretically at infinity and all points of the line will be equidistant from the eye. Therefore the true length of the line will be obtained. So in Fig. 13.1*A* the lines of projection for the elevation auxiliary are drawn parallel to the line of sight shown, which is perpendicular to the top view of *AB*. The horizontal reference plane *HRP* is established in the front view through point A_F. The *HRP* for the auxiliary view is located at some convenient distance from $A_T B_T$ and perpendicular to the lines of projection for the auxiliary view. The auxiliary view is then drawn by locating A_A on the reference plane and then by measuring

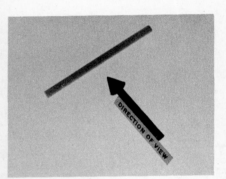

Normal view of line.

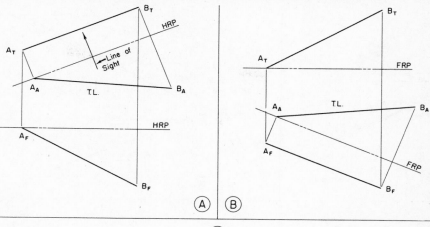

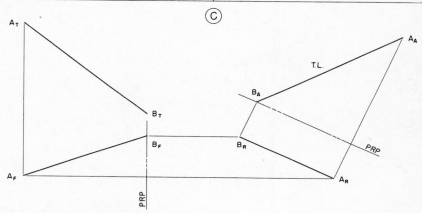

Fig. 13.1. True length of a line by auxiliary view.

the distance in the front view from the reference plane to B_F and transferring this distance to the auxiliary, thus locating B_A.

Figure 13.1B shows a normal view of AB made by employing a right auxiliary view. Observe that this auxiliary, projected in a direction perpendicular to the front view ($A_F B_F$), will have a *viewing direction* perpendicular to line AB. Similarly, Fig. 13.1C shows the normal view of AB obtained by using a rear auxiliary view. As described in Chap. 6, this view must be projected from the side view. Notice also that the viewing direction is perpendicular to line AB.

13.4. Normal View of a Line by Rotation. As explained before in paragraph 13.3, a line in a horizontal plane appears in true length in the top view, a line in a frontal plane appears in true length in the front view, and a line in a profile plane appears in true length in either side view. Therefore, if an *oblique* line is rotated so that it coincides with, or is parallel to, one of the planes of projection, the true length of the line will appear in one of the principal views.

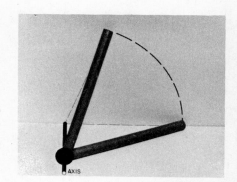

Rotation, normal view.

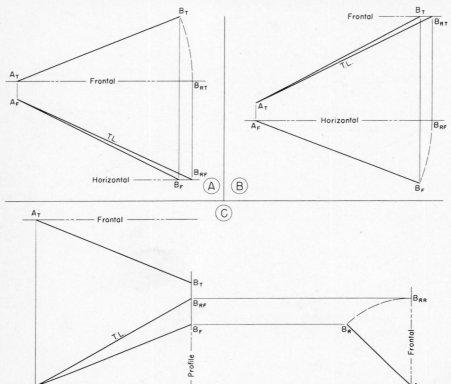

Fig. 13.2. True length of a line by rotated view.

Figure 13.2 shows in (A), (B), and (C) an oblique line AB. In (A) the line has been rotated until it is frontal, thus giving the true length in the front view. The axis of rotation is perpendicular to the horizontal plane and therefore appears as a point in the top view. With center at A_T, an arc is drawn from B_T intersecting a frontal plane through A_T at B_{RT}, the rotated position (in the same frontal plane as A) of B. As B rotates, it must move in a plane *perpendicular* to the axis of rotation; and, in this case, because the axis is perpendicular to the horizontal, B must move in a horizontal plane. Therefore a horizontal plane through B, intersected by projection from B_{RT}, locates the front view B_{RF}, the rotated position of point B. The true length of the line AB is then the distance from A_F (which remained stationary during the rotation) to B_{RF}.

Figure 13.2B shows the same line rotated until it is horizontal. The axis of rotation is the horizontal profile. With center at A_F, an arc from B_F brings B to coincidence with the horizontal plane through A at B_{RF}; point B must move in a frontal plane (perpendicular to the horizontal-profile axis); the intersection of the projector from B_{RF} with the frontal plane through B locates B_{RT}; and the true length of the line is $A_T B_{RT}$.

Figure 13.2C shows a rotation similar to Fig. 13.2B, but here the

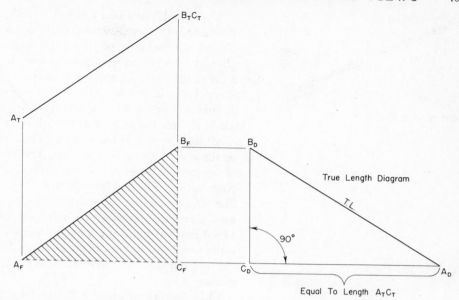

Fig. 13.3. True length of a line by true-length diagram.

rotation is made by using the front and right-side views of a line. In the side view the arc $B_R B_{RR}$ with center at A_R brings B to coincidence with a frontal plane through A; perpendicular to the horizontal-frontal axis through A, point B must move in a profile plane; the intersection of this plane from B_{RR} at B_{RF} locates the rotated position of B; and the true length is $A_F B_{RF}$.

Study each illustration, (A), (B), and (C), of Fig. 13.2, carefully visualizing the position of the axis in each case. Also, note and remember the important point that the *plane* of rotation of a point will be *perpendicular to the axis of rotation*.

13.5. True Length by Diagram. The true length of a line may also be found by a "true-length diagram." This method is not employed in problems where the normal view of a line may be needed to locate some point or element; but where nothing more than the true length is required, for example, in the development of a surface, the use of a true-length diagram is a simple but accurate method. In Fig. 13.3, line AB is an oblique line, which may be considered as the hypotenuse of a right-angled triangle having AC as a horizontal leg and BC as a vertical leg. If the true length of these legs is found and the right angle laid out, the hypotenuse will be determined. A diagram is prepared to one side of the front view (in this case, the right side). The projection of $B_F C_F$ to the diagram transfers the true length of the vertical leg to $B_D C_D$. The true length of the horizontal leg is the distance $A_T C_T$ (the top view of the horizontal leg). Therefore, if this distance is transferred by dividers or compass to the diagram at $C_D A_D$, the distance $B_D A_D$ on the diagram will be the true length of line AB. This method is very useful when a number of true lengths, for example, elements of a cone or cylinder, must be found.

True length of line by true-length diagram.

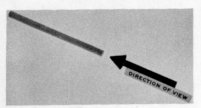

Point view of line.

13.6. End View of a Line. The end, or point, view of a line may be made only after the true-length, or normal, view has been drawn. To get the end view of a line, the direction of observation must be aligned with (or parallel to) the line. In Fig. 13.4*A*, the line *AB* is an oblique line; its normal view has been made as an elevation auxiliary $A_A B_A$. If now an oblique view is made, looking in the direction of (parallel to) $A_A B_A$, the end view will be obtained. The reference plane *RP*, for the oblique view, will be perpendicular to the viewing direction for the oblique view. This reference plane will appear again as an edge in the top view, it will be perpendicular to the rays of projection between the top and auxiliary views, and it is most conveniently placed through $A_T B_T$. Thus in the oblique view, the line *AB* appears on one single projector and on the reference plane and, therefore, appears as a point, the end view of the line. Figure 13.4*B* illustrates the end view obtained by a right auxiliary and oblique view. Study both illustrations of Fig. 13.4 carefully, and note the relationships of viewing direction, projectors, and reference planes.

13.7. Specification of a Plane. As described in paragraph 13.2, a line is located in space by specifying two points on the line. If a plane is passed through a line, the plane may be rotated around the line as an axis and is therefore not fixed immovably in space. To determine the position of a plane definitely, either *three points* or *two intersecting lines* in the plane must be specified. In Fig. 13.5*A*, three points, *A*, *B*, and *C*, specify a plane. Note also that any pair of intersecting lines *AB* and *AC*, *AB* and *BC*, or *BC* and *CA* would specify the same plane. A *pair of parallel lines* will also specify a plane.

13.8. Edge View of a Plane. The edge view of a plane will be obtained when the direction of observation is aligned with some line of the plane. In other words, if an end view of a line of the plane is obtained, the plane will appear in its edge view. The plane of Fig. 13.5*A* is horizontal and therefore contains many horizontal-profile lines that would appear as points in the front view; the plane thus

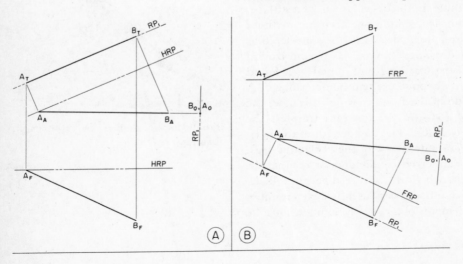

Fig. 13.4. End view of a line.

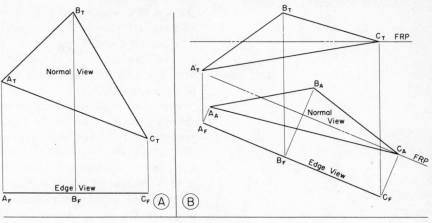

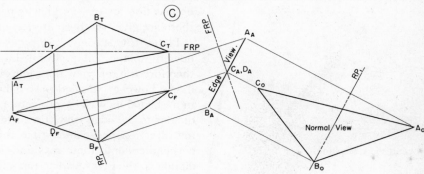

Fig. 13.5. Edge and normal views of a plane.

appears as an edge in the front view. The plane at Fig. 13.5B is positioned so that no lines in it will appear as points in the top view, but horizontal-profile lines will appear as points in the front view, giving the edge view shown. Similarly, a plane containing frontal-profile lines will appear as an edge in the top view, and a plane containing horizontal-frontal lines will appear as an edge in a side view. (A plane positioned as just described is said to *recede* in the view in which the plane appears as an edge. Thus, in Fig. 13.5B, the plane is known as a frontal receding plane.)

The plane of Fig. 13.5C is oblique, and no lines in it, in either the front or the top view, will appear as points. If, however, a line is drawn on the plane in a position so that it appears in true length in one of the views, the end view of the line and the resulting edge view of the plane may be obtained. Line CD of plane ABC in Fig. 13.5C is a frontal line, therefore appearing in true length at $C_F D_F$ in the front view of the plane. A right auxiliary then taken in the direction of $C_F D_F$ will show the point view of CD and the edge view of plane ABC. The frontal reference plane FRP is located for the auxiliary at a convenient distance from the front view and perpendicular to the projector from $C_F D_F$. This reference plane will appear again as an edge in the top view and will be perpendicular to the rays between front and top views; for convenience and simplicity of location, the FRP is taken through $C_T D_T$. Measurements from FRP in

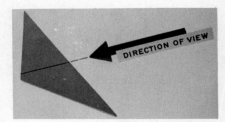

Edge view of plane.

the top view transferred to the rays of projection for points A and B and laid off from FRP in the auxiliary view will locate A_A and B_A. The frontal line CD appears as a point at $C_A D_A$. It should be noted that *all* frontal lines in plane ABC will appear as points in this edge view and that the edges AB, BC, and CA all align on one single line in the edge view.

If a horizontal line is drawn on a plane, an elevation auxiliary taken in the direction of the line will give the edge view; and if a profile line is placed on a plane, either a front or rear auxiliary aligned with the line will give the edge view of the plane. *Never* is more than *one* auxiliary required to obtain the edge view of a plane.

13.9. Normal View of a Plane. The normal view of a plane will be obtained when the viewing direction is perpendicular to the plane. In Fig. 13.5A, the plane ABC is horizontal; the direction of observation for the top view is perpendicular to the horizontal and therefore gives the normal view of plane ABC in the top view.

Plane ABC of Fig. 13.5B appears as an edge in the front view, as does the plane of Fig. 13.5A, but the plane is not horizontal, and therefore the top view does not give the normal view. A right auxiliary, however, aligned perpendicular to the edge view will result in a normal view. The projectors in Fig. 13.5B are drawn perpendicular to the edge view (the front view) thus establishing the viewing direction perpendicular to the edge view. The FRP is located perpendicular to these rays and is located in the top view perpendicular to the rays between top and front views. Measurements then made from the FRP in the top view and transferred to the auxiliary complete the location of A_A, B_A, and C_A, the normal view of plane ABC.

Plane ABC of Fig. 13.5C is oblique. Therefore the edge view will have to be made as described in paragraph 13.8 before the normal view can be constructed. In Fig. 13.5C, the rays of projection for the normal view are drawn perpendicular to the edge view. The reference plane RP_1 is then located perpendicular to these rays. This reference plane, RP_1, will appear again as an edge in the front view and will be perpendicular to the rays of projection from front view to edge view. Measurements then made from RP_1 in the front view and transferred to the oblique view will locate A_O, B_O, and C_O, the normal view of plane ABC.

13.10. Specification of a Plane by "Strike" and "Dip." Instead of the usual specification by either three points or two intersecting lines, as described in paragraph 13.7, the position of a plane may be described by strike and dip. This method is used principally on mining, oil-prospecting, or other geologic maps. The *strike* of a plane is defined as the direction of a horizontal line on the plane. Thus in Fig. 13.6, the line AB, a horizontal line, may be designated as the strike of a plane by specification of its direction as shown in the top view. The direction may be given either as shown or by an azimuth from either magnetic or true north. *Dip* is defined as the true angle of the plane downward from the horizontal; a part of

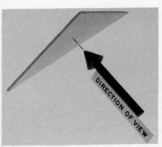

Normal view of plane.

he specification is on which side of the strike line the plane passes
below the horizontal. Therefore, in Fig. 13.6, the small arrow perpendicular to the strike line $A_T B_T$ shows that the plane dips on *that*
side of the strike line, and the accompanying angle of 34° completes
he specification. Thus on a map the location of the strike line, the
elevation of a point on the line, and the dip specification will give
complete information as to the location of the plane relative to other
points on, over, or under the earth's surface.

Strike and dip specification of a plane is not restricted, however,
to geologic maps. The *position* of the plane is much easier to visualize
when strike and dip are given instead of either three points or two
intersecting lines, and for this reason the method may be used advantageously in the solution of problems of a general nature.

13.11. Edge View of a Plane Specified by Strike and Dip.
Specifying the edge view of a plane by the method of strike and dip
is simple because the strike line is a horizontal line on the plane and
the end view of this line is easily determined. In Fig. 13.6, the end
view of strike line AB is $A_A B_A$. The reference plane (*HRP*) through
AB appears as an edge in the auxiliary view, and the true angle of
dip may therefore be laid out in the auxiliary view. Note that the
angle of dip must be laid out *below* the *HRP*, for if a mistake by reversal is made, the plane will not dip on the correct side of the strike
line. Note that the edge view of the plane will be seen in the auxiliary
view since the strike line (a line of the plane) appears as a point in
this view. Also note that an elevation auxiliary *must* be used.

13.12. Normal View of a Plane Specified by Strike and Dip.
To find the normal view of a plane (specified by strike and dip),
three points must be assumed on the plane because the strike and
dip specification does not include located points that may be used
for projection of a normal view. In Fig. 13.7, the strike line BC and
the dip angle of 36° specify the plane. First the edge view of the
plane, as described in paragraph 13.11, is made by making the end
view of AB and laying out the dip angle. Then the two points B and
C (the ends of the strike line) and a third point A may be taken as
three points on the plane. Point A is assumed at any convenient
position in the top view (A_T) and may then be projected to the aux-

Strike and dip.

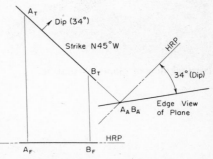

Fig. 13.6. Edge view of a plane specified by strike and dip.

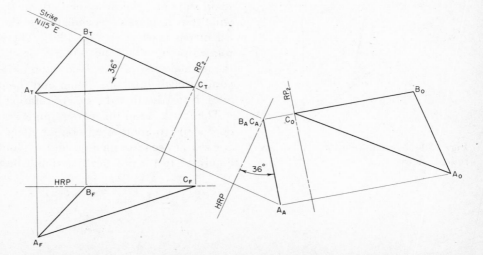

Fig. 13.7. Normal view of a
plane specified by strike and
dip.

iliary, where it will lie on the edge view at A_A. Finally an oblique view, C_O, B_O, and A_O, is established by projecting in a direction perpendicular to the edge view. This is the normal view of triangle ABC on the strike and dip plane. Other assumed triangles similar to ABC would, of course, serve the purpose as well, so that the three points used may be picked purely for purposes of convenience.

13.13. Normal View of a Plane by Rotation. The normal view of a plane may be made by rotating the plane until it comes into coincidence with *one* of the planes of projection. If the plane is rotated until it is horizontal, the normal view will be seen in the top view; if it is rotated to a frontal position, the front view will show the normal view; and if it is rotated to a profile position, either of the side views will show the normal view. The edge view of the plane is not needed as an intermediate step (as in the use of auxiliary views to obtain a normal view) because the plane can be rotated directly to either a horizontal, frontal, or profile position. However, the consideration of an edge view will help to explain the procedure. Therefore, in Fig. 13.8, a plane ABC is shown with an edge view as the front view. If a horizontal-profile axis is placed at point A, this axis will appear as a point in the front view and as a true-length line in the top view. The plane can then be rotated about this axis until it is horizontal. The path of rotation of any point in the plane (in this case) will lie in a frontal plane through the point because frontal planes are perpendicular to the horizontal-profile axis. Therefore the path of rotation of point B will be $B_F B_{RF}$ in the front view and $B_T B_{RT}$ in the top view, and for point C the path of rotation is $C_F C_{RF}$ in the front view and $C_T C_{RT}$ in the top view. Naturally, since the axis is at A, point A does not move. Thus the plane has been rotated to a horizontal position as shown at A_F, B_{RF}, and C_{RF}. The normal view of ABC is then seen in the new top view, A_T, B_{RT}, and C_{RT}.

If the plane is oblique as in Fig. 13.9, a similar procedure may be followed. A horizontal axis BD is located on the plane. This axis will appear as a point in the auxiliary view at $B_A D_A$ because the auxiliary has been made in a direction looking along the axis BD. Therefore the edge view, A_A, B_A, D_A, and C_A, is obtained. In this edge view, the plane can be rotated to a horizontal position at A_{RA}, B_A, D_A, and C_{RA}. During this rotation, the points B and D will remain stationary because they are on the axis, and points A and C will rotate in planes perpendicular to the axis (in this case, the vertical planes marked on Fig. 13.9). Therefore the new position (the rotated position and the new top view) becomes A_{RT}, B_T, and C_{RT}, the normal view of the plane. Study Fig. 13.9 carefully, noting the position of the axis of rotation and the path of each point as it rotates. Note also that the axis of rotation lies in the plane.

The foregoing in this paragraph is a background for an explanation of the rotation of an oblique plane to a normal position by a quick and accurate method and without the use of an edge view. Figure 13.10A is practically a duplicate of Fig. 13.9 but with some

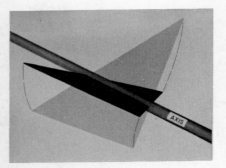

Normal view of plane by rotation.

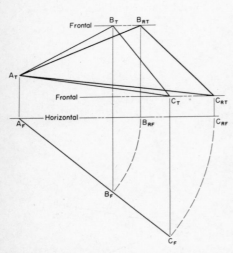

Fig. 13.8. Normal view of a plane by rotated view.

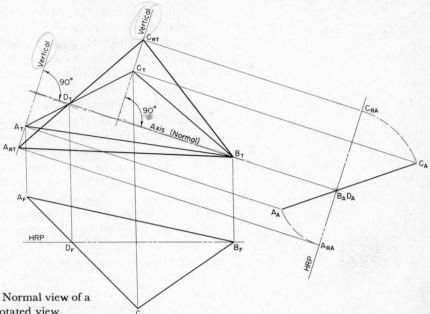

Fig. 13.9. Normal view of a plane by rotated view.

Fig. 13.10. Normal view of a plane by rotated view.

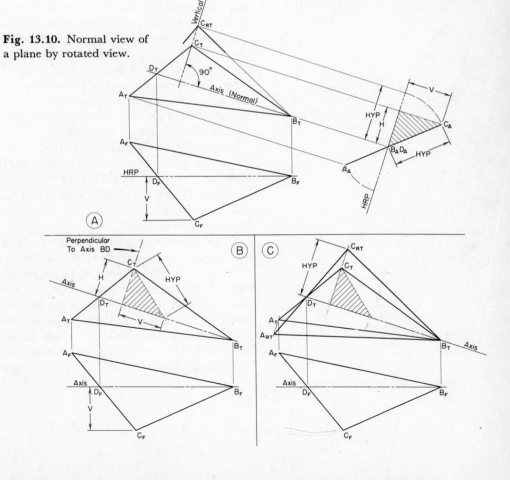

additions for analysis. In the edge view at A_A, $B_A D_A$, and C_A, the crosshatched area represents a right-angled triangle with a vertical leg (V), a horizontal leg (H), and hypotenuse (HYP). The hypotenuse of this triangle is the true distance of point C from the axis BD. To prove this fact, note that axis BD appears as a point in the auxiliary view and that C_A to $B_A D_A$ is then the shortest (true) distance from point to line. We know from plane geometry that, if the two legs of a right-angled triangle can be determined, the hypotenuse will also be determinable. Further, an examination of Fig. 13.10B will show that the vertical leg and the horizontal leg of Fig. 13.10A may be obtained without the edge view of Fig. 13.10A. On Fig. 13.10B, the vertical leg (V) is the vertical distance of point C to the horizontal axis BD (measured in the front view). Also, the horizontal leg (H) is the horizontal *perpendicular* distance (in the top view) from axis BD to point C. Therefore, because point C must rotate in a plane perpendicular to axis BD, the vertical leg may be laid out along the axis as shown from the point where the horizontal leg intersects the axis. The hypotenuse may then be found as marked on Fig. 13.10B.

Finally all the above discussion is brought to completion at Fig. 13.10C, where the simplest and most practical method is shown. First, axis BD is located. Second, the path of rotation for point C is located, perpendicular to the true length of axis BD (in the top view). Third, the vertical leg for point C is taken with dividers or compass from the front view and laid off along axis BD in the top view. Fourth, the hypotenuse is spaced on the dividers or compass from the top view. Fifth, the hypotenuse is laid off from the axis, thus locating point C_{RT}, the revolved position of point C. A similar procedure is followed for point A, and the lines $A_{RT} C_{RT}$, $C_{RT} B_T$, and $B_T A_{RT}$ are drawn. This completes the normal view of plane ABC.

Note that, if desired, the plane may be rotated to a frontal position instead of horizontal. If this is done, the construction in the view where the axis appears in true length will be identical with the top view just discussed, as will be the construction in the accompanying view. To see the relationship, turn Fig. 13.10C upside down so that the former front view is now the top view and the former top view is the front view.

13.14. Methodology. The constructions given in this chapter will be used repeatedly for solving the problems in the chapters following. The student should, therefore, learn so thoroughly all the methods of determining point, edge, and normal views that the constructions may be made without the slightest hesitation. Remember that a firm foundation is the basis for understanding more complicated problems. The explanations in the chapters following assume that the constructions of this chapter are known, that their theory is understood, and that they can be applied with confidence.

PROBLEMS

Group 1. True length of lines

13.1.1. Find, by the use of an elevation auxiliary view, the true length of *AB*. Scale: $1'' = 1'-0''$.

13.1.2. Using the layout of Prob. 13.1.1, determine, by projecting in a frontal direction, the true length of *AB*. Scale: $\frac{3}{8}$ size.

13.1.3. Using the layout of Prob. 13.1.1, determine, in a front auxiliary view, the true length of *AB*. Scale: $\frac{3}{4}'' = 1''$.

Group 2. End view of lines

13.2.1. Using the layout of Prob. 13.1.1, show the end view of *AB* by projecting from an elevation auxiliary view. Identify all reference planes, and label all points.

13.2.2. Using the layout of Prob. 13.1.1, show the end view of *AB* by projecting from a left auxiliary view. Identify all reference planes, and label all points.

13.2.3. Using the layout of Prob. 13.1.1, consider *AB* as the center line of a $3\frac{1}{2}$-in. (nominal size) American Standard pipe. Show the end view of the pipe by projecting from a front auxiliary of the center line *AB*. Scale: $\frac{1}{2}$ size.

Group 3. Edge view of planes

13.3.1. Show the view of *RSP* by projecting parallel to a horizontal line of *RSP*.

13.3.2. Using the layout of Prob. 13.3.1, determine the edge view of *RSP* in a right auxiliary view.

13.3.3. Using the layout of Prob. 13.3.1, draw the view of *RSP* when seen from the rear along a profile line of sight.

Group 4. Normal view of planes

13.4.1. Using the layout of Prob. 13.3.1, draw the normal view of *RSP* by projecting from an elevation auxiliary view of *RSP*. Label all points and identify the reference planes used.

13.4.2. Using the layout of Prob. 13.3.1, determine the true size and shape of *RSP* when projecting from a right auxiliary view of *RSP*. Label all points, and identify the reference planes used.

13.4.3. Using the layout of Prob. 13.3.1, first show the edge view of *RSP* in a rear auxiliary view, and then draw the normal view of *RSP*. Label all points, and identify all reference planes used.

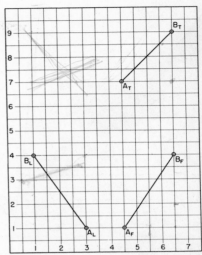

Prob. 13.1.1

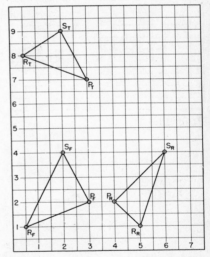

Prob. 13.3.1

13. 3 . 1
4 . 1
7. 1
7. 2

Group 5. Edge view of planes defined by strike and dip

13.5.1. Show the edge view of the plane that strikes as shown through A. The plane dips 45° in a northwesterly direction. Consider north at the top of the plate.

13.5.2. Using the layout of Prob. 13.5.1, determine the edge view of the plane that strikes as shown through point A. The plane dips 60° in a southeasterly direction. Consider north at the top of the plate.

Group 6. Normal view of planes defined by strike and dip

13.6.1. XYZ is an equilateral triangle, which strikes and dips through point X as indicated. Y is to the rear of X. Draw the top and front views of XYZ.

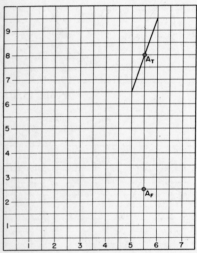

Prob. 13.5.1

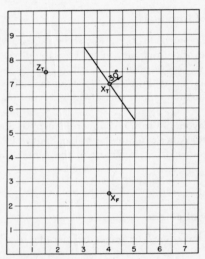

Prob. 13.6.1

13.6.2. *EG* is 2½ in. long and makes an angle of 45° with *EF*. *EF* and *G* lie in the plane that strikes and dips through point *E* as shown. Draw the top and front views of *EF* and *EG*. Scale: full size.

Group 7. Normal view of planes by rotation

13.7.1. Draw the normal view of *LMO* by rotating the plane about a horizontal axis. Solve by using an edge view.

13.7.2. Using the layout of Prob. 13.7.1, draw the normal view of *LMO* by rotating the plane about a frontal axis. Solve by using an edge view.

13.7.3. Using the layout of Prob. 13.7.1, draw the normal view of *LMO* by rotating the plane about a horizontal axis. Solve by using only the views given.

13.7.4. Using the layout of Prob. 13.7.1, draw the normal view of *LMO* by rotating the plane about a frontal axis. Solve by using only the views given.

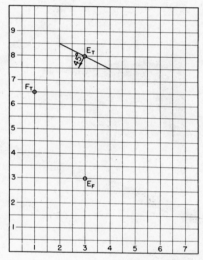

Prob. 13.6.2

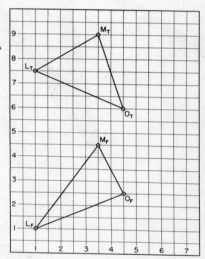

Prob. 13.7.1

14

POINTS AND STRAIGHT LINES

14.1. Modern machines and structures are made up of many complicated elements and surfaces, but the predominating component will probably always be the straight line. This is so because forces act along straight lines, thus dictating the design in many respects; also, manufacturing economy and other practical considerations demand the use of straight-line elements. Repeatedly, many of the complicated surfaces of parts may be made up of straight-line elements. Thus the point and straight line become basic elements of study.

14.2. Fundamental Items. A point which moves in one direction generates a straight line. Any two points of a straight line determine the direction of the line, and the distance between the two points is the length of a segment of the line. The length of a line is indefinite since it may be extended through the two points which determine its direction. The student should have a thorough working knowledge of the various line positions as described in paragraph 4.10 and Fig. 4.25.

14.3. Intersecting Lines. Lines which pass through the same point are intersecting lines. The common point is the point of intersection. A single orthographic view does not give sufficient information to determine whether existing lines do or do not intersect. Ex-

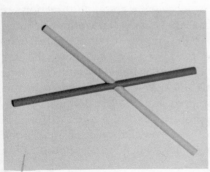

Intersecting lines.

417

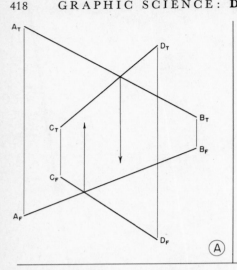

Fig. 14.1. Nonintersecting and intersecting lines.

Skew lines.

Parallel lines.

amination of the front view *only* of Fig. 14.1*A* does not justify the conclusion that *AB* and *CD* intersect, because the crossing of the lines is only the projection in the front view: The top view shows a crossing *not* in projection with the crossing in the front view; therefore there is no common point, and the lines do not intersect. On the other hand, reading both the front and the top views of Fig. 14.1*B*, by following along the projector from E_F, shows that point E lies on both *AB* and *CD*, and the lines therefore intersect. Thus if two views (or more) show the lines to have a common point, the lines intersect. This intersecting-line principle is an important tool for solving many space problems. Points, in various orthographic views, may be located at the intersection of projectors as explained in many of the examples following.

14.4. Skew Lines. Skew lines are those which do not intersect and yet are not parallel. Lines *AB* and *CD* of Fig. 14.1*A* appear to intersect when each view is read separately; but, as explained in paragraph 14.3, the lines do not have a point common to both and therefore are not intersecting lines. Furthermore they do not have a common direction and hence are not parallel lines.

14.5. Parallel Lines. Lines which have a common direction are parallel lines. Different views of parallel lines will not alter or change their direction; consequently parallel lines will remain parallel regardless of the number of views made. Figure 14.2 shows the top, front, and right-side views of two parallel lines *AB* and *CD*. Note that in each view the lines are parallel. This orthographic principle of parallel-line relationship is of great value to the designer. It can be used not only to solve space problems but also to check for projection errors on drawings where the geometric relationships are of a parallel nature, such as those in a parallelogram, opposite sides of a rectangle, etc.

Lines may appear to be parallel in one view and yet not be par-

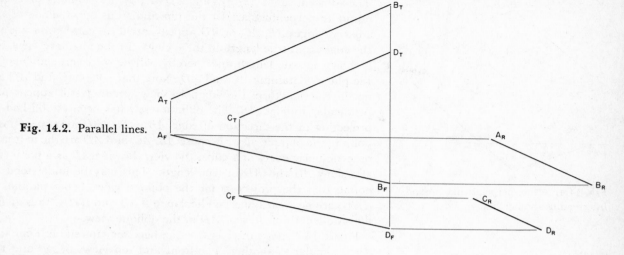

Fig. 14.2. Parallel lines.

allel. Two principal views are *usually* sufficient to determine whether lines are parallel, but, theoretically, it will require either three principal views or two principal views and an auxiliary view. For example, if the lines are both profile, the front and top views will show the lines parallel (actually they *are* in parallel planes) and a side or auxiliary view will clearly show that the lines are either parallel or not parallel.

14.6. Perpendicular Lines. Lines are perpendicular if their directions are 90° with respect to one another. Perpendicular lines may be skew or intersecting. When perpendicular lines are represented on a drawing, they appear perpendicular in those views where *one* or *both* of the lines are shown in true length. Figure 14.3 shows the top, front, auxiliary, and oblique views of a cube in space.

Perpendicular intersecting lines.

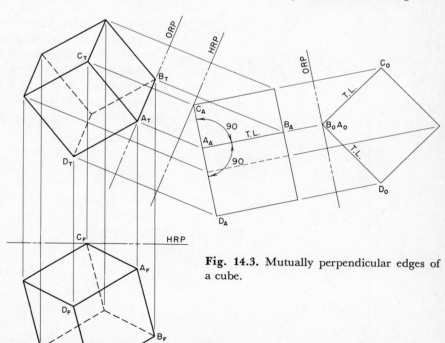

Fig. 14.3. Mutually perpendicular edges of a cube.

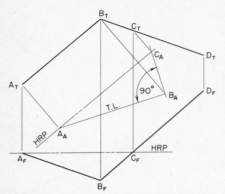

Fig. 14.4. A line perpendicular to and intersecting another line.

Perpendicular lines.

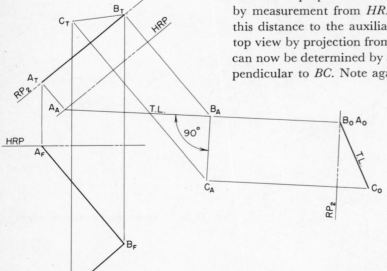

Fig. 14.5. True length of perpendicular.

The adjacent edges AB, AC, and AD are, by the geometry of a cube, mutually perpendicular. In the top and front views, none of the adjacent edges AB, AC, or AD appears at 90° to another, as none of the edges is in true length in these views. In the auxiliary view, AB is shown in true length and thereby will be seen perpendicular to the plane containing AC and AD. Note that edges AC and AD are not in true length in the auxiliary view, yet they still appear perpendicular to edge AB. The oblique view has been established by projecting in the direction of edge AB; AB therefore appears as a point in the oblique view. Because AB, AC, and AD are the mutually perpendicular edges of a cube, the view showing AB as a point will also show AC and AD in true length. This may be understood by noting that the projectors for the oblique view, being parallel to $A_A B_A$, are necessarily perpendicular to $A_A C_A$ and $A_A D_A$, thus giving the true length of AC and AD in the oblique view.

Figure 14.4 shows the construction necessary to establish one line perpendicular to another. The front and top views of AB and the front view (only) of BD were given as initial information. Since neither line appears in true length in either the top or front view, a normal view of one of the lines must be made in order to establish the perpendicular relationship between the two lines. A normal view of AB ($A_A B_A$) is the required view. In this view, the *direction* of BD is drawn perpendicular to AB intersecting the HRP at C. The top view of C is at the intersection of the projectors from C_F and C_A. The top view of BD is then drawn through point C_T, locating D_T by intersection of the projector from the front view.

Frequently, after the direction of a line has been established, it is necessary to determine the true length of a segment of that line. In Fig. 14.5, BC is to be drawn perpendicular to AB, and the length of BC is to be determined. The top and front views of AB and the front view of BC are given initially. As in the problem of Fig. 14.4, a normal view of AB is first made; in this view the *direction* of BC is established perpendicular to AB. C_A is located in the auxiliary view by measurement from HRP in the front view and by transferring this distance to the auxiliary view. Then C may be located in the top view by projection from C_A and from C_F. The true length of BC can now be determined by an oblique view made in a direction perpendicular to BC. Note again how the two perpendicular lines AB

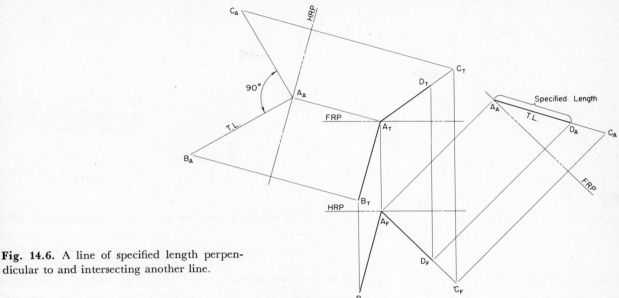

Fig. 14.6. A line of specified length perpendicular to and intersecting another line.

and BC appear in the oblique view: AB appears as a point and BC appears in true length.

In Fig. 14.6, a line of specified length is drawn perpendicular to a given line. The top and front views of AB and the front view of AC are given. AD (to some specified length) is to be drawn perpendicular to AB. D is to be on AC. AC is drawn perpendicular to AB in the normal view (the elevation auxiliary). C_T is located at the intersection of the projectors from C_A and C_F. A projection normal to the front view of AC determines the true length of AC in the right auxiliary view. AD is laid off to the specified length on AC in this view. D is then projected on line AC to the front and top views.

The example shown in Fig. 14.7 has the same requirements as

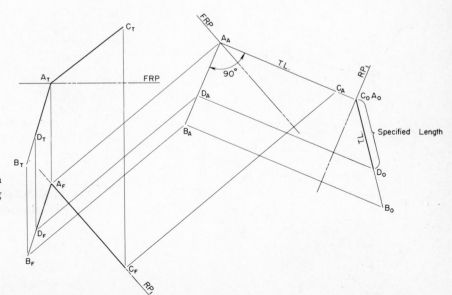

Fig. 14.7. A line of specified length perpendicular to and intersecting another line.

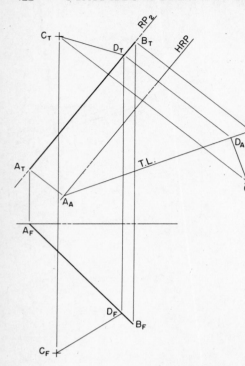

Fig. 14.8. From a point, a line perpendicular to and intersecting another line.

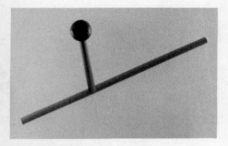

Shortest distance, point to line.

that of Fig. 14.6 but differs in the method of solution. *AD*, of a specified length, is to be established perpendicular to *AC*. *D* is on *AB*. The top and front views of *AC* and the front view of *AB* are given.

AB is drawn perpendicular to the normal view of *AC*, as shown in the right auxiliary view. The projection is now continued from the auxiliary view to the oblique view in a direction parallel to *AC*, thus establishing the end view of *AC* and the normal view of *AB*. A_0D_0, of specified length, is laid off on A_0B_0. *D* on line *AB* is then projected back to the auxiliary and then to front and top views.

14.7. Distance from a Point to a Line. The distance from a point to a line is construed as the shortest distance between the point and the line; the shortest distance is measured along a perpendicular from the point to the line.

Figure 14.8 shows the construction necessary to determine the length of *CD*, the shortest distance from point *C* to line *AB*. Since *AB* is not in true length in either the top or front views, a normal view of *AB* is established in the auxiliary view. A *perpendicular* from point *C* to *AB* can be drawn in the auxiliary view. *CD* is the required distance, but it should be clearly understood that *CD* is not in true length in the auxiliary view. The true length of *CD* must be deter-

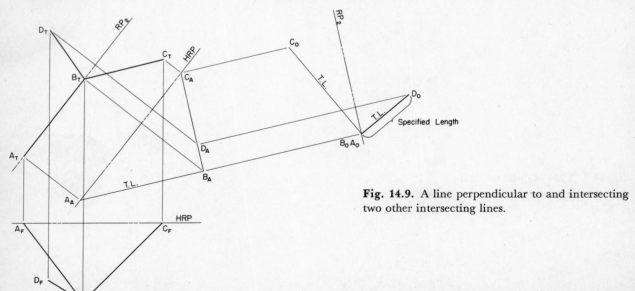

Fig. 14.9. A line perpendicular to and intersecting two other intersecting lines.

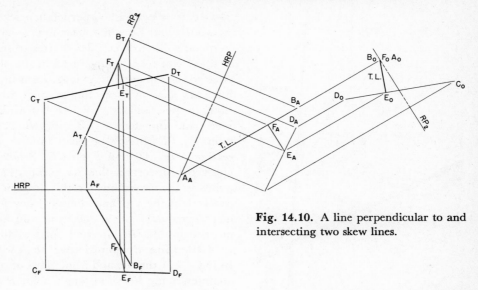

Fig. 14.10. A line perpendicular to and intersecting two skew lines.

mined. A normal view of *CD* is obtained in the oblique view by projecting in the direction of *AB*. This gives the true length of the shortest distance from point *C* to line *AB*.

14.8. Three Mutually Perpendicular Lines. The corner of any rectangular solid is a condition of three mutually perpendicular lines. The representation of three mutually perpendicular lines frequently occurs on engineering drawings. In Fig. 14.9, *AB*, *BD*, and *BC* have been drawn mutually perpendicular to each other, the top and front views of *AB* and the front view of point *C* having been given. *BD* is to be of some specified length with *D* above point *B*.

A normal view of *AB* is first made. In this view, the direction of *BD* and *BC* can be established as perpendicular to *AB*. C_A can now be located on the *HRP*. The top view of *C* can now be located by projection. D_A is somewhere above *B*, as stated in the problem. An oblique view is projected in the direction of *BA*, showing *AB* as a point. *BC* and *BD* will appear in true length in this oblique view. The direction B_OC_O can be determined by projecting C_A to the oblique view and measuring from RP_2. A_OD_O can now be drawn perpendicular to B_OC_O. *D* can now be located in the auxiliary view at the specified distance from *B*. The top and front views of point *D* can then be located by projection and measurement from proper reference planes.

14.9. Common Perpendicular. The shortest distance between two nonintersecting lines is measured along the *one and only* perpendicular that intersects *both* lines. In Fig. 14.10, *FE* has been determined as the shortest distance between lines *AB* and *CD*. *AB* and *CD* are given. *FE* is to be determined. First, an auxiliary A_AB_A, showing the true length of *AB*, is made; then an oblique view, showing the point view of *AB*, is projected. In this view, the shortest distance

Three mutually perpendicular lines.

Common perpendicular.

$F_O E_O$ can be established perpendicular to $D_O C_O$ because AB appears as a point and FE will appear in true length and is therefore drawn perpendicular to CD. The shortest distance FE between lines AB and CD can then be measured in the oblique view. To project FE back to the top and front views, FE is first projected to the elevation auxiliary view by projecting point E, which is on CD, from the oblique to the auxiliary view. AB is normal in the elevation auxiliary view, and therefore $F_A E_A$ is drawn perpendicular to $A_A B_A$ from point E_A. FE can now be located in the top and front views by intersecting F on AB and E on CD. Problems of this type should be checked to ascertain that no mistake has been made in projecting points to the wrong line. In this problem, points F and E should be checked in the top and oblique view for corresponding measurement from RP_2 and in the front and auxiliary view for measurements from the HRP in the front and auxiliary view.

14.10. Line Perpendicular to Two Nonintersecting Lines. In Fig. 14.11 the top and front views of AB and CD are given as two nonintersecting lines. Through point P a line OP is to be located perpendicular to AB and CD with point O and P equidistant from any particular point on AB. The auxiliary and oblique view shows the construction necessary to obtain the solution. The true length of AB has been determined in the right auxiliary view. Point P and line CD are then projected to this view. The direction of OP can be established in this view, but point O cannot be located to satisfy the solution. The direction for the oblique view is taken to show the end view of AB; $O_O P_O$ will appear in true length and can be drawn perpendicular to $C_O D_O$. As O and P must be equidistant from any particular point on AB, point O can be located on the circle arc that passes through point P with AB as a center.

Because the direction of line OP has been established in the auxiliary view as perpendicular to AB, point O can now be projected from the oblique view to the auxiliary view. The top and front views of point O can now be established by projection and measurement from the reference planes, and line OP can be drawn.

14.11. The Angle between Two Intersecting Lines. The angle between two intersecting lines will lie in the plane of the lines and

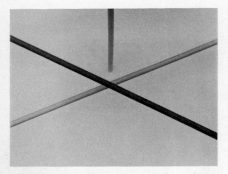

Line perpendicular to two skew lines.

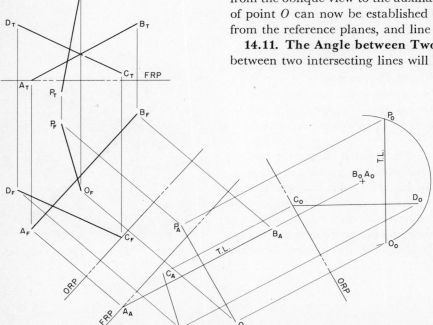

Fig. 14.11. From a point, a line perpendicular to two skew lines.

herefore appears in true size in a view which shows both the true
ength and true relationship of the lines. The required view is thus
a normal view of the plane of the lines, which may be obtained
either by auxiliaries (edge and normal views) or by rotation, as
explained in paragraphs 13.8, 13.9, and 13.13.

Angle between Lines by Edge and Normal Views. Figure 14.12 shows
two intersecting lines, *AB* and *AC*. The angle between these two
lines is to be determined. The two lines *AB* and *AC* may be considered as designating a plane *ABC*. A horizontal line *BD* of the
plane *ABC* appears in true length in the top view, and a view (auxiliary) made to obtain the point view of *BD* gives the edge view
of the plane at $A_A B_A D_A C_A$. A view then made by projecting in a
direction *perpendicular* to the edge view gives the normal view at
$A_O B_O C_O$. In this normal view, the true length and relationship of
both lines, *AB* and *AC*, is shown, and the true angle between
the lines is angle *R*. Incidentally, the angle between *AB* and *BC*
(angle *T*) and the angle between *BC* and *CA* (angle *S*) are also
shown on Fig. 14.12.

Angle between Lines by Rotation. Figure 14.13 duplicates the given
data of Fig. 14.12, but in Fig. 14.13 the normal view of lines *AB* and

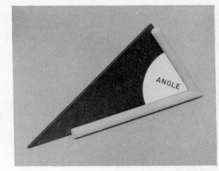

Angle between lines.

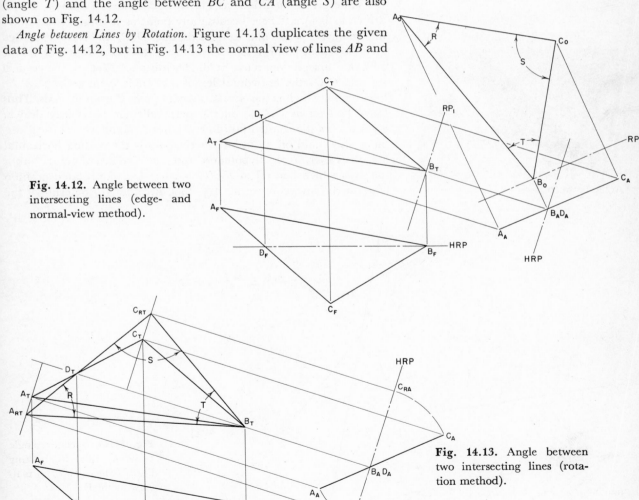

Fig. 14.12. Angle between two
intersecting lines (edge- and
normal-view method).

Fig. 14.13. Angle between
two intersecting lines (rotation method).

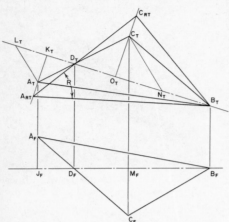

Fig. 14.14. Angle between two intersecting lines (rotation method).

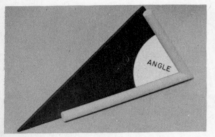

Angle between lines.

AC is obtained by rotation. A horizontal line *BD* of the plane *ABC* serves as an axis of rotation because it appears in true length in the top view at $B_T D_T$. The point view of the axis at $B_A D_A$ gives a "pivot" about which the plane may be *rotated to the horizontal* at $A_{RA} B_{RA} C_{RA}$. The rotation of any point occurs in a plane *perpendicular* to the axis. Thus a perpendicular from C_T (to the axis) and a projection from C_{RA} to the top view locate C_{RT}, the rotated position of *C* in the top view. Similarly, a perpendicular to the axis from A_T and a projection from A_{RA} to the top view locate A_{RT}, the rotated position of *A*. Lines then connecting A_{RT}, C_{RT}, B_T, and A_{RT} form the normal view of *ABC*, and the angle between *AB* and *AC* is angle *R*.

The auxiliary view of Fig. 14.13 and the rotation procedure in that view are not necessary constructions if advantage is taken of the fact that the distance of any point from the axis is the hypotenuse of a triangle having vertical and horizontal legs, as explained previously in paragraph 13.13 and Fig. 13.10. Figure 14.14 shows the same given conditions as Fig. 14.13. A horizontal axis, *BD*, is drawn as before. Then, because any point as it rotates must move in a plane perpendicular to the axis, lines $O_T C_T$ and $K_T A_T$ extended give the *path* of points *C* and *A* as they rotate. Points *B* and *D*, on the axis, of course, do not move at all. The distance $M_F C_F$ is the vertical leg and $C_T O_T$ the horizontal leg of a triangle having $C_T N_T$ as the hypotenuse which is the *actual distance* of point *C* from the axis. Thus $C_T N_T$ laid off at $O_T C_{RT}$, on the perpendicular previously drawn, gives C_{RT} as the rotated position of point *C*. Similarly, vertical distance $A_F J_F$ laid off at $K_T L_T$, where $A_T K_T$ is the mating horizontal leg, gives $L_T A_T$ as the hypotenuse and true distance of point *A* from the axis, which laid off at $K_T A_{RT}$ locates A_{RT}, the rotated position of point *A*. Now, connecting A_{RT}, C_{RT}, B_T, and A_{RT} determines the

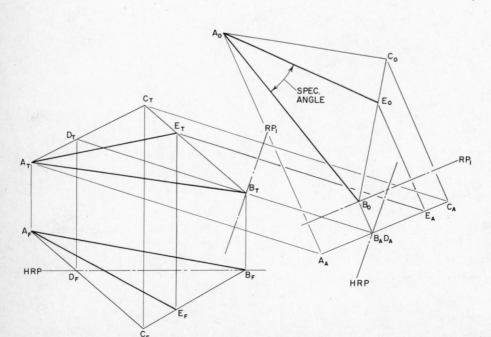

Fig. 14.15. Specified angle between two intersecting lines (edge- and normal-view method).

normal view of *ABC*, and the true angle between *AC* and *AB* is angle *R*. Note that line $A_{RT}C_{RT}$ must pass through point D_T because *D* is on the axis and is also a point on line *AC*.

14.12. Specified Angle between Two Intersecting Lines. If the angle between a pair of intersecting lines is specified, instead of to be determined, the solutions are similar to those of paragraph 14.11, except that the angle will be laid out in a normal view, thus *locating* one of the lines.

Specified Angle by Edge and Normal Views. In Fig. 14.15, *AB* is a given line and *C* a point in the *plane* of line *AE* that is to make a specified angle with *AB*. The normal view of plane *ABC* is thus a view where both *AB* and *AE* appear in true length and therefore a view in which the specified angle may be laid out. In Fig. 14.15, edge and normal views are made as explained before for Fig. 14.12. Then, in the normal view the angle may be laid out and, on Fig. 14.15, is shown at $B_0A_0E_0$. Point *E* has been conveniently located *on* line *BC* and can therefore be easily projected back to E_A (the edge view) and thence to E_T and E_F.

Specified Angle by Rotation. The shortest method, from the standpoint of construction and number of views required, is the rotation method shown in Fig. 14.16. The given information is the same as for Fig. 14.15, but in Fig. 14.16 the normal view of the plane has been determined by rotation. In the normal view, at $A_{RT}E_{RT}$, the line *AE* is drawn at the specified angle to *AB*. To counterrotate the line back to the given views, point *E* must move in a plane *perpendicular* to the axis and thus, in the top view, moves from E_{RT} to E_T on line *BC*. The front view of point *E* may then be found by projection from E_T to E_F. Note also that point *O*, where line *AE* crosses the axis of rotation, will remain fixed. With this fact, a line from A_T through point O_T extended to C_TB_T will determine E_T, *or* this construction will check on the accuracy of location of point E_T by the previously explained construction.

14.13. Angular Relationships: True Length and Point Views. The examples of paragraphs 14.11 and 14.12 present the general case where the two lines, for which an angular relationship is required, are both oblique. This condition may not always prevail. *One* line may appear in true length in one of the views. In such a special case, a view made to obtain the true length of *both* lines gives a simple and direct solution.

Angle between Lines. In Fig. 14.17, line *AB* is vertical and appears as a point in the top view. Line *AC* is oblique. If an elevation auxiliary is made to give the true length of *AC*, as shown in the figure, the true relationship and true length of both lines, *AC* and *AB*, will be obtained in this view (any elevation view will give the true length of *AB*). Also note that the top view of *ABC* is the edge view of the plane of both lines. Therefore, in the elevation auxiliary both lines are normal, and the true angle may be measured.

If one of the lines is in an auxiliary position—as the horizontal

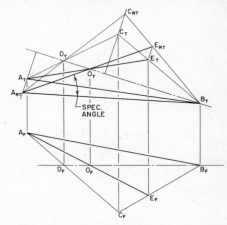

Fig. 14.16. Specified angle between two intersecting lines (rotation method).

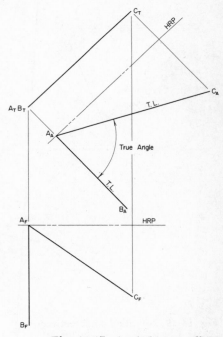

Fig. 14.17. Angle between lines.

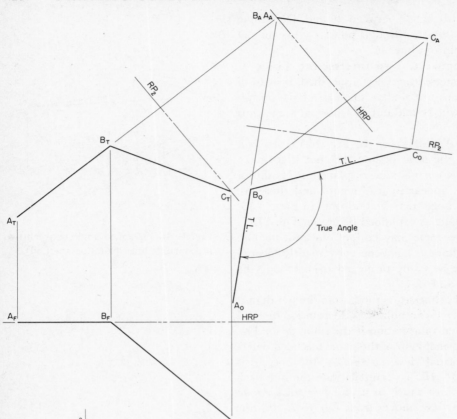

Fig. 14.18. Angle between lines.

Fig. 14.19. Specified angle between lines.

line *AB* of Fig. 14.18—but the other line oblique (line *BC*), then two views will be required. The elevation auxiliary $A_A B_A C_A$ gives the point view of *AB*. The oblique view, $A_O B_O C_O$, taken in a direction perpendicular to *BC*, gives the true length of *BC and of AB*. The true angle may then be measured in the oblique view.

Specified Angle between Lines. In Fig. 14.19, line *AB* and point *C* are given. A line *CD* is to be drawn making a specified angle with *AB* and (of course) intersecting *AB*. The elevation auxiliary taken in a direction perpendicular to the edge view of *ABC* will show the true length of *AB* and, even though not yet drawn, the true length of any line *CD* that intersects *AB* at *D*. Thus in this view, the line *CD* may be laid out at a specified angle with *AB* and the position of *D* determined. Measurement from the *HRP* will then locate point *D* in the front view.

The solution for one oblique line and the other in an auxiliary position (lying in a plane of projection) is given in Fig. 14.20. The auxiliary $A_A B_A C_A$ gives the edge view of the plane of the lines, and the oblique view $A_O B_O C_O$, taken perpendicular to $A_A B_A C_A$, gives the normal view of both lines, where the specified angle may be laid out. The intersection *D* on *AB* may then be carried back to top and front views.

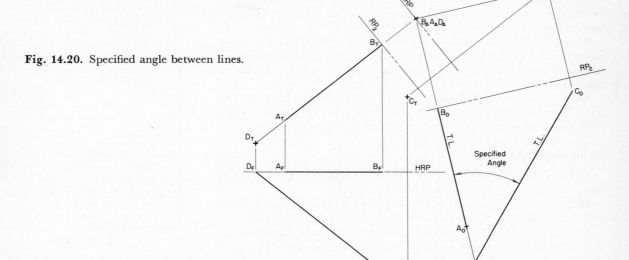

Fig. 14.20. Specified angle between lines.

PROBLEMS

The following problems are shown on a grid with coordinate lines ½ in. apart. The markings at the left and bottom indicate inches. Thus these problems may be plotted in a space 7½ by 10 in. on standard 8½- by 11-in. coordinate paper or on paper prepared for the purpose.

Group 1. True lengths

14.1.1. Find the true length of *AB*. Scale: ½ size.

14.1.2. Find the perimeter of the triangle *ABC*. Scale: full size.

14.1.3. The line *CL* slopes upward from *C* with a 60 per cent grade. Draw the front view of *CL*. Find the distance from *C* to *L*. Scale: 1″ = 50′.

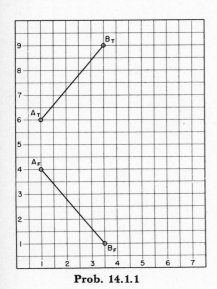

Prob. 14.1.1

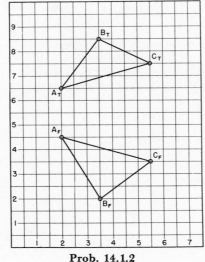

Prob. 14.1.2

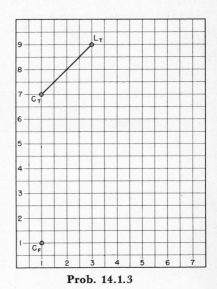

Prob. 14.1.3

14.1.4. Line *AB* is to be established with a bearing of N60°E with a 60 per cent positive grade from *A*. The distance from *A* to *B* is 336 ft. Draw the top and front views of *AB*. Scale: $1'' = 100'$.

14.1.5. A power-line pole is supported by two guy wires. *E* and *D* are the points on the ground where the guy wires are to be attached. Find the length of the guy wires from point *C* on the pole. Disregard lengths for attaching. Scale: $1'' = 10'\text{-}0''$.

14.1.6. Line *OP* is to be established with a grid azimuth of 213°45'. The line slopes down from *P* with a grade of 66⅔ per cent. The length of *OP* is 84 ft. Draw the top and front views of *OP*. Scale: $1'' = 20'$.

Group 2. Points on lines

14.2.1. Point *W* is on *UV* and is 6½ in. from *V* toward *U*. Locate the top, front, and right-side views of point *W*. Scale: ¼ size.

14.2.2. Point *D* is on line *AB*. Point *C* is ½ in. above point *A*. Draw the front view of *CD*. What is the true length of *CD*? Scale: full size.

14.2.3. *AB* is 14 in. long. *B* is to the rear of *A*. *C* is on *AB* and is 4¼ in. in front of *B*. Complete the top, front, and right-side views of *ABC*. Find the true distance from *B* to *C*. Scale: ¼ size.

14.2.4. A series of points on 2-in. centers are to be located along line *AB*. The edge distances of the end points are to be equally spaced from points *A* and *B*. Locate the top and front views of these points. Find the true edge distance of the end points from *A* and *B*. Scale: ½ size.

14.2.5. The line segment *AB* is to be divided into five equal spaces. Locate the top and front views of these divisions. Find the true length of the subdivisions. Scale: ½ size.

14.2.6. Locate in the top and front views the quarter points of line segment *LM*. What is the true distance between the quarter points? Scale: $1'' = 1'\text{-}0''$.

14.2.7. A manufacturing company is to subdivide its outside storage into seven areas. Each area is to have equal frontage along the Elm Street line *CD*. Locate in the top and front views the frontage of each area. Determine the length of frontage of each area. Scale: $1'' = 500'$.

Group 3. Intersecting lines

14.3.1. The horizontal line *CD* intersects the profile line *EF*. Draw the front view of *CD*. What is the true distance from *E* to *D*? Scale: $1'' = 1'\text{-}0''$.

14.3.2. *AB* has a bearing of N60°W and intersects the line *XY* at point *C*. *B* is 3¾ in. below *X*. Complete the top and front views of *AB* and *C*. What is the true length of *BC*? Scale: ½ size.

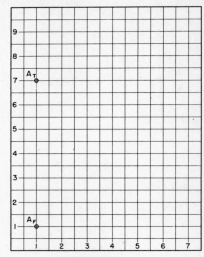

Prob. 14.1.4

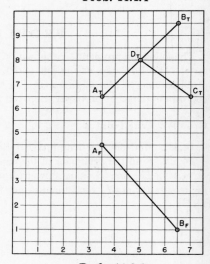

Prob. 14.2.2

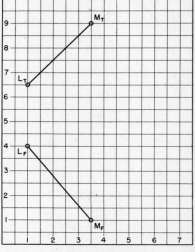

Prob. 14.2.6

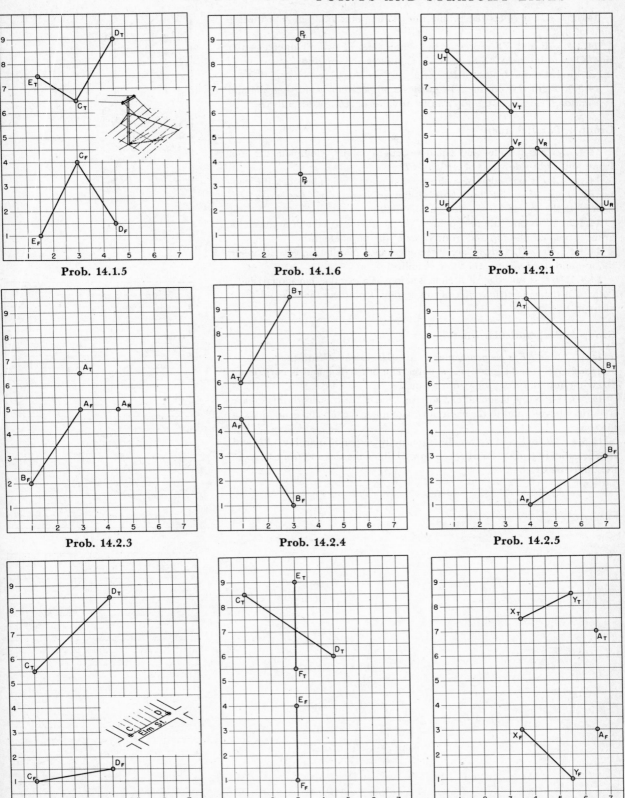

Prob. 14.1.5

Prob. 14.1.6

Prob. 14.2.1

Prob. 14.2.3

Prob. 14.2.4

Prob. 14.2.5

Prob. 14.2.7

Prob. 14.3.1

Prob. 14.3.2

14.3.3. *AC* intersects the profile line *RS* at point *B*. Complete the top view of *ABC*.

14.3.4. *AB* and *XY* represent the center lines of two air ducts. Center line *XY* is to intersect *AB* at point *Z*. Complete the top and front views of *XYZ*. Find the true length of *BZ*. Scale: $\frac{1}{8}'' = 1'\text{-}0''$.

14.3.5. Point *B* is on line *XY*. *AB* has a 40 per cent negative grade and is 3 in. long. Complete the top and front views of *AB*. Scale: full size.

Group 4. Parallel lines

14.4.1. *CD* is parallel and equal in length to *AB*. Complete the top, front, and right-side views of *AB* and *CD*.

14.4.2. *AB* is one edge of a sheet-metal plate. This plate has the geometric shape of a rhombus. One of the adjacent edges lies along *AC*. Complete the top and front views of the plate.

14.4.3. *XY* is one side and point *C* the geometric center of a parallelogram. Complete the top and front views of the parallelogram.

14.4.4. *AB*, *AD*, and *AC* are three edges of a parallelepiped. Complete the top and front views, and show visibility.

14.4.5. *HE* is an edge of a right section of a regular hexagonal shaft. Point *X* is the geometric center of this section. Complete the top and front views of this section.

Group 5. Perpendicular lines

14.5.1. Line *EF* is perpendicular to line *GH*. Locate *GH* in the top view.

14.5.2. *AB* is a diagonal of a square. The other diagonal is horizontal. Draw the top and front views of the square.

14.5.3. *OP* is one diagonal of a square. One of the corners of this square is $1\frac{3}{4}$ in. above *O* and to the right of *O*. Complete the top and front views of the square.

14.5.4. *AB*, *BD*, and *BC* are three mutually perpendicular lines. *BD* and *BC* are equal in length. Point *D* is below *B*. Show the top and front views of the three lines.

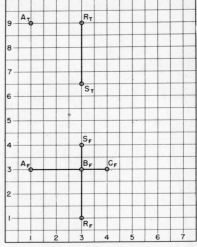

Prob. 14.3.3

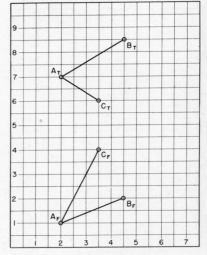

Prob. 14.4.2

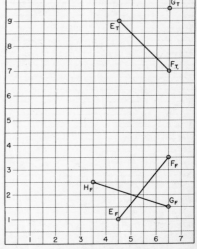

Prob. 14.5.1

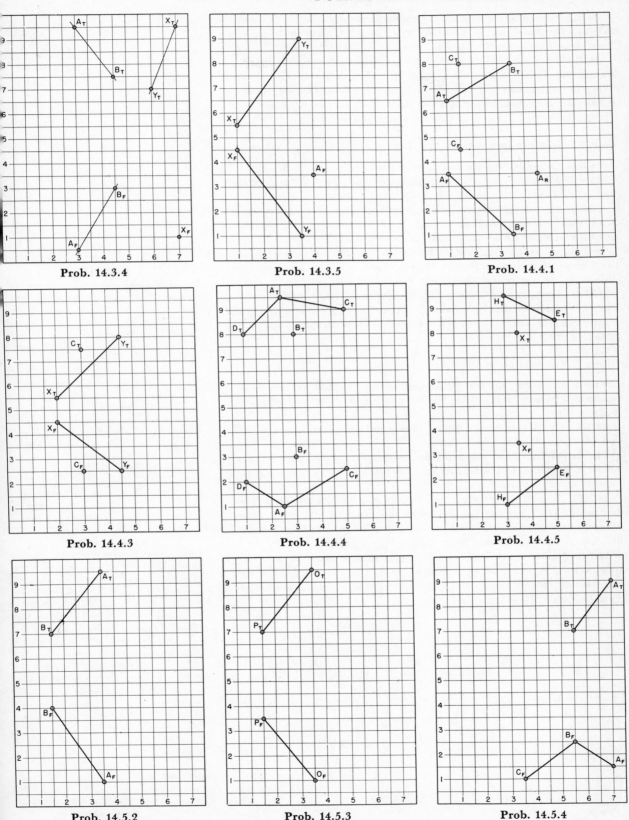

Prob. 14.3.4

Prob. 14.3.5

Prob. 14.4.1

Prob. 14.4.3

Prob. 14.4.4

Prob. 14.4.5

Prob. 14.5.2

Prob. 14.5.3

Prob. 14.5.4

14.5.5. Shown in the sketch is a pictorial kinematic diagram of a slide-crank mechanism. Find the maximum stroke of link 4. Show in the top and front views the limiting positions of center 0,3,4. Scale: $\frac{3}{8}$ size.

14.5.6. Shown in the sketch is a pictorial kinematic drawing of a four-bar mechanism. Link 2 rotates about center line A with a constant velocity. When link 2 becomes perpendicular to link 3, link 4 has reached its maximum velocity. Locate in the top and front views all possible positions of centers 0,2,3 and 0,3,4 as link 4 obtains maximum velocity.

Group 6. Distance from a point to a line

14.6.1. Determine the shortest distance from point E to the line CD.

14.6.2. EF is the base of a triangular steel plate. Find the area of the surface EFG. Scale: $\frac{1}{4}$ size.

14.6.3. Find the diameter of the circular path of point C as it revolves about the center line AB. Scale: $\frac{3}{8}$ size.

14.6.4. AB and EF are the center lines of two pipes. They are to be connected from G on EF using a standard tee (90°) on AB. Draw the top and front views of the connecting-pipe center line. What is the center-line distance of the connecting pipe? Scale: $\frac{1}{2}'' = 1'-0''$.

14.6.5. The spur gear G drives the pinion gear H. Gear G rotates at 200 rpm. X is a point on the pitch diameter of gear G. The speed of a spur gear is inversely proportional to its pitch diameter. What is the rpm of shaft CD? Scale: $\frac{1}{4}$ size.

Group 7. Common perpendicular

14.7.1. Draw the top and front views of the common perpendicular between the lines AB and CD. What is the true length of this perpendicular? Scale: $\frac{1}{2}$ size.

14.7.2. Find the minimum distance between lines AB and CD and AB and CE. Scale: $\frac{1}{4}$ size.

14.7.3. AB and CD are the center lines of two pipes which are to be connected with another pipe using standard tees (90°). Draw the top and front views of this center line.

14.7.4. LM and OP are the center lines of two circular air ducts. The duct with LM as a center line has an outside diameter of 5 in. Is there sufficient clearance to use OP as the center line of a 4-in.-OD duct? What is the clearance or interference? Scale: $\frac{1}{4}$ size.

14.7.5. A cable attached at point R must be secured along line AB. The attachment along AB must be as close to point B as possible, and yet the cable should clear line EF by 12 in. Draw the top and front views of the cable. Scale: $1'' = 1'-0''$.

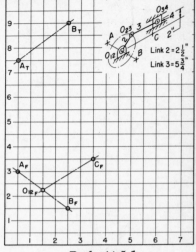

Prob. 14.5.5

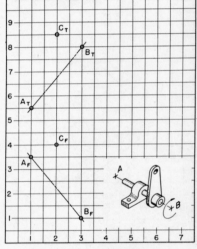

Prob. 14.6.3

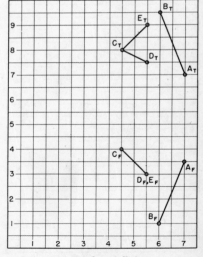

Prob. 14.7.2

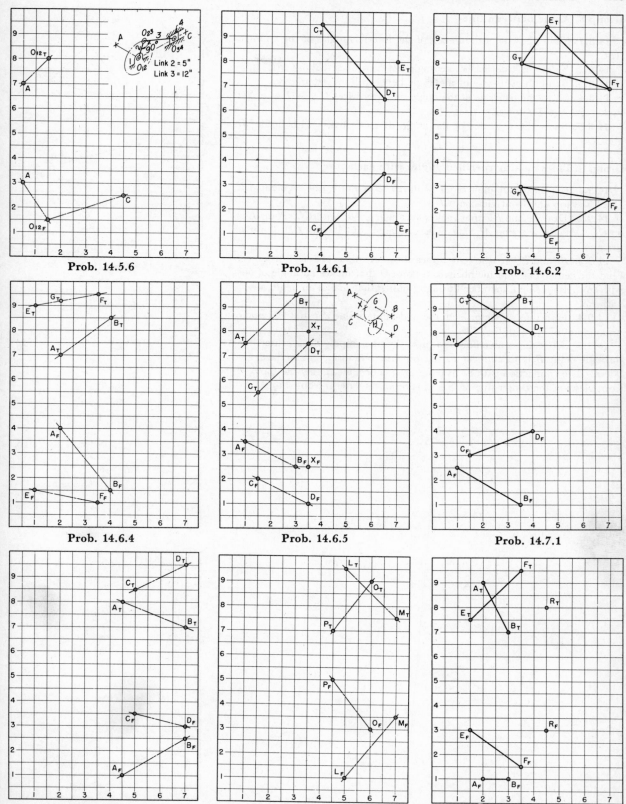

Prob. 14.5.6

Prob. 14.6.1

Prob. 14.6.2

Prob. 14.6.4

Prob. 14.6.5

Prob. 14.7.1

Prob. 14.7.3

Prob. 14.7.4

Prob. 14.7.5

Group 8. Angle between lines

14.8.1. Show the true size of each of the interior angles of the triangle *ABC*.

14.8.2. Show the true size of the angle between lines *AB* and *BC*.

14.8.3. Show the true size of the angle between lines *AB* and *BC*.

14.8.4. Show the true size of the angle that guy wires *LO*, *MO*, and *NO* make with the TV tower.

14.8.5. Show the true size of the angle that *CL* makes with both *ED* and *XP*.

Group 9. Lines making specified angles with each other

14.9.1. *CD* makes an angle of 60° with *AB*. *D* is on the line segment *AB*. Draw the top and front views of *CD*.

14.9.2. Draw a line *BE* that makes an angle of 60° with *CD*. Point *E* is on *CD*. Also draw a line *AF* that makes an angle of 45° with *CD*. Point *F* lies on *CD*.

14.9.3. *RS* and *PQ* are the center lines of two members of a steel structure. Find the center line of a member from point *Q* that makes an angle of 60° with *RS*. Also locate a member through point *P* that makes an angle of 45° with *RS*.

14.9.4. Find the connector from the mid-point of line *AB* that will make an angle of 67½° with line *CD*.

14.9.5. *JK* is the center line of a pipe. Another pipe with a center line through point *P* is to connect to the pipeline *JK*, using a standard 45° lateral. The connection is to be as close to *J* as possible. Draw the top and front views of the center line of that portion of the lateral from *P* to *JK*.

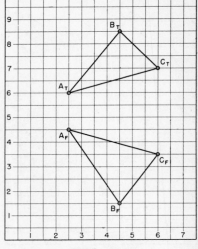

Prob. 14.8.1

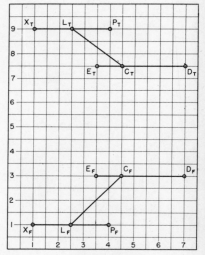

Prob. 14.8.5

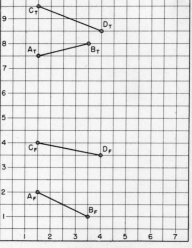

Prob. 14.9.4

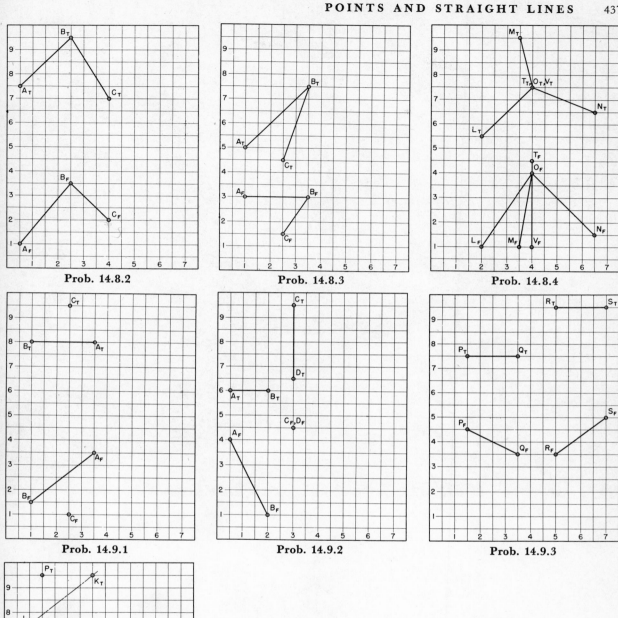

Prob. 14.8.2

Prob. 14.8.3

Prob. 14.8.4

Prob. 14.9.1

Prob. 14.9.2

Prob. 14.9.3

Prob. 14.9.5

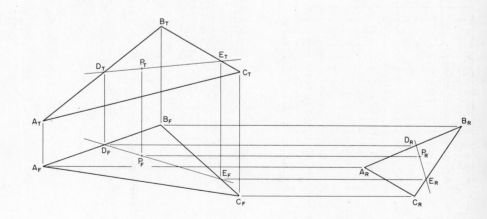

Fig. 15.1. Points and lines in a plane.

15

STRAIGHT LINES AND PLANES

15.1. In the previous chapter, the importance of straight lines as they occur in a variety of engineering problems has been discussed, and the diversity of their relationships has been explained. Straight lines occur often in machines, structures, etc., but probably they will more often be found *in combination with* planes. Consequently the study of straight lines and planes is a continuing investigation of line relationships as they occur with planes and with lines and points in planes. Also discussed here are the relationships of planes to other planes. It is interesting to note that, in the solution of *plane* problems, *lines* are used to establish one plane relative to another. Thus this chapter brings together the elements of engineering geometry, exclusive of curved lines and surfaces, which are treated in the chapters following.

15.2. Points and Lines in a Plane. A point may be established in a plane by locating any convenient line in the plane which passes through the point.

In Fig. 15.1, the top view of P is initially given as a point in plane ABC. To locate the front and right-side views of point P, a line lying in the plane of ABC is drawn through the point. This line intersects AB at D and BC at point E. Both D and E are projected to the front view on AB and BC, respectively. This locates the front view of DE, a line of ABC. Point P is now projected to the front view of line DE. Point P is established in the right-side view by first projecting DE

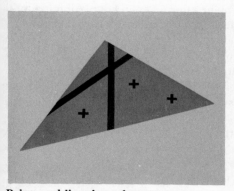

Points and lines in a plane.

439

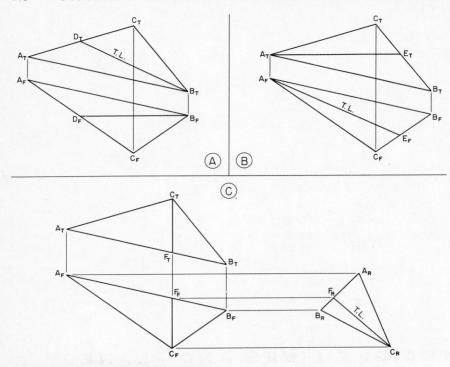

Fig. 15.2. Horizontal, frontal, and profile lines in a plane.

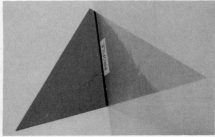

Profile line in a plane.

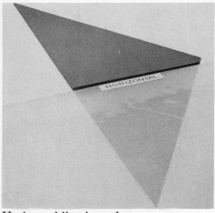

Horizontal line in a plane.

to the right-side view and then projecting P from the front view to the right-side view of DE.

15.3. Horizontal, Frontal, and Profile Lines of an Oblique Plane. Any horizontal line in an oblique plane either lies in, or is parallel to, some horizontal plane. To establish a horizontal line in an oblique plane, the line is first drawn in a view where the horizontal plane appears as an edge, such as the front, side, or any elevation auxiliary view. Similarly, a frontal line is first established in a view where the frontal plane appears as an edge, as the top, side, or any right or left auxiliary view. Likewise, a profile line must first be established in either the top, the front, or the front or rear auxiliary views, where a profile plane appears as an edge. All horizontal lines *in a given plane* are parallel. Similarly, all frontal lines are parallel and all profile lines are parallel.

Figure 15.2*A* shows the top and front views of an oblique plane *ABC*. To establish the horizontal line *BD* in *ABC*, the front view is drawn first. The top view of *BD* is located by projecting *D* to the top view on *AC*. Then *BD* is horizontal and is shown in true length in the top view.

Figure 15.2*B* shows the same plane *ABC*. To establish the frontal line *AE* in the plane *ABC*, the top view is drawn through *A*, intersecting *BC* at *E*. The front view of *AE* is established by projecting *E*, which is on *BC*, to the front view. The line *AE* is in true length in the front view.

In Fig. 15.2*C*, the top, front, and right-side views of the same plane *ABC* are shown. To establish the profile line *CF* in *ABC*, either the front or the top view is first drawn through point *C*, intersecting *AB* at *F*. The right-side view of *CF* is drawn by projecting the front view of *F*, which is on *AB*, to the right-side view. The right-side view shows the profile line *CF* in true length.

15.4. Parallel Relationships of Lines and Planes. *A Line Parallel to a Plane.* A line is parallel to a plane if it is parallel to *any* line of that plane. Parallelism between a line and plane can be easily recognized in a view that shows the plane as an edge because, in this view, *all* lines in the plane appear coincident. However, only *one* line of the plane is needed. Figure 15.3*A* shows the necessary construction to draw *DE* parallel to *ABC*. The top and front views of *ABC*, the top view of *DE*, and the front view of point *D* are initially given. The top view of *CF* is established in *ABC*, parallel to *DE*. The intersection *F* on *AB* is projected to the front view. *CF* is drawn in the front view. Through the front view of point *D*, *DE* is drawn parallel to *CF*, establishing *DE* parallel to *ABC*.

A Plane Parallel to a Line. Figure 15.3*B* shows the construction of a plane *RST* that is parallel to *HG*. The top and front views of *HG* and *RS* and the top view of *RT* are given. Through any point on *RS* (in this example, point *X*), the top and front views of a line are drawn parallel to *HG*. This construction constitutes a plane parallel to *HG*, formed by two intersecting lines: (1) *RS* and (2) the line through *X* parallel to *HG*. Point *Y* in the top view is at the intersection of *RT* and the line through *X*. Point *Y* is projected to the front view on the line through *X*. Then the front view of *RT* may be drawn through point *Y*. Note that plane *RST* now contains a line *XY*, which is parallel to *HG*.

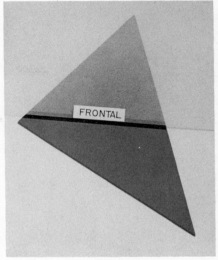

Frontal line in a plane.

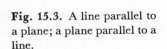

Fig. 15.3. A line parallel to a plane; a plane parallel to a line.

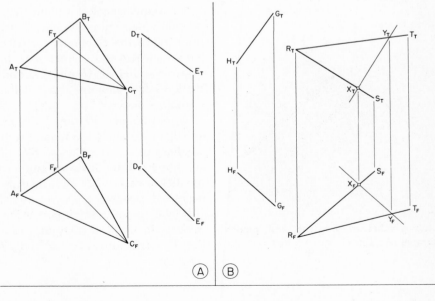

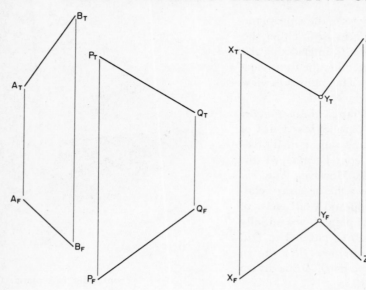

Fig. 15.4. A plane parallel to two skew lines.

Line parallel to a plane and plane parallel to a line.

Similarly, a plane may be established parallel to any two skew lines. For example, having any two skew lines *AB* and *RS* given, two intersecting lines are drawn in the plane, one parallel to *AB* and the other parallel to *RS*. Actually, this is what has been done in Fig. 15.3*B*, but in this case the plane is coincident with one of the skew lines. If the plane is separated from both of the skew lines, Fig. 15.4 will illustrate the procedure. *AB* and *PQ* are the given skew lines, and point *Y* is a point in a plane which is to be made parallel to *AB* and *PQ*. From point *Y*, a line *YX* is drawn parallel (in both views, top and front) to *PQ*; also, *YZ* is drawn parallel to *AB*, thus establishing a plane *YZX* parallel to *AB* and *PQ* because the plane contains a line parallel to each of the given lines.

The requirement of a plane parallel to two skew lines might also include a determination of the distance *from* the plane *to* the skew lines. When this requirement exists, Fig. 15.5 illustrates the method employed. *AB* and *CD* are skew lines. A plane through *P* is to be drawn parallel to *AB* and *CD* and the distance from the plane to the lines determined. *PY* parallel to *CD* and *PT* parallel to *AB* determine a plane *PTY* parallel to *AB* and *CD* and through point *P*. The lines *PT* and *PY* may be made any convenient length. Then if an edge view of *PTY* is made (in this case, by making the elevation auxiliary in the direction of *TZ*, a line of *PTY*) and if *AB* and *CD* are projected to this auxiliary view, *AB*, *CD*, and *PTY* will be parallel to each other and the distances from the lines to the plane measured as shown.

It follows now that it is possible to locate a plane parallel to a pair of skew lines and at a certain distance *from* the skew lines. Again, Fig. 15.5 will illustrate. *AB* and *CD* are given skew lines. The *top* view of *RSQ* is given. The problem is to locate *RSQ* so that it is a specified distance from a position midway between lines *AB* and *CD* and *lower* than *AB* and *CD*. Any plane (in this case, *PTY*) is drawn—as before—parallel to the two skew lines; also, the edge view is made of *PTY* with accompanying lines *AB* and *CD*, as before. The position midway between *AB* and *CD* can now be located in the auxiliary view and the required distance to *RSQ* measured. Projection from the top view of *RSQ* to the line established for the edge view now locates $R_A S_A Q_A$, making it possible then to measure $R_A S_A Q_A$ distances from the reference plane and to transfer these distances to the front view, completing the solution.

In the next paragraph, the construction of a *plane* parallel to a *plane* is discussed but it is interesting to note that, in Figs. 15.4 and 15.5, if the skew lines were *intersecting* lines, they would constitute a plane; then the problems of Figs. 15.4 and 15.5 would be transposed to the problem of a plane parallel to a plane.

Parallel Planes. Two intersecting lines that are parallel to any two lines of a given plane will define a plane parallel to the given plane.

Plane parallel to a plane.

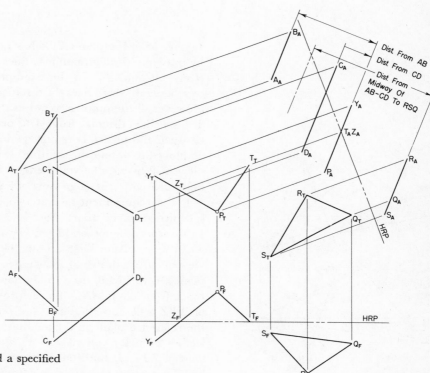

Fig. 15.5. A plane parallel to, and a specified distance from, two skew lines.

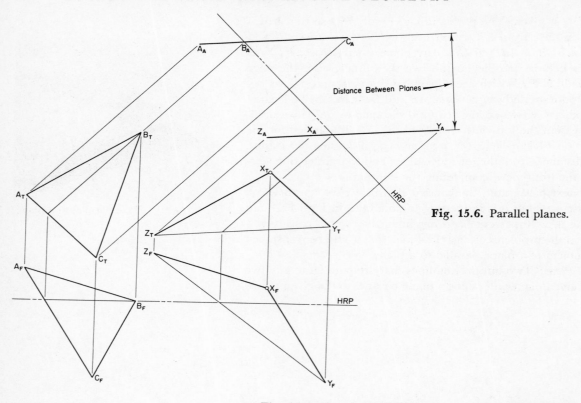

Fig. 15.6. Parallel planes.

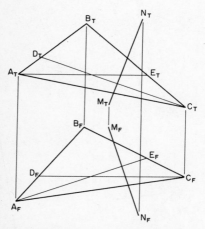

Fig. 15.7. A line perpendicular to a plane.

In Fig. 15.6, the plane XYZ has been constructed parallel to ABC by drawing, through point X, lines XY and XZ parallel to, respectively, AC and AB. In this example, the top and front views of X were known, which fixes the distance between planes ABC and XYZ. However, if the problem requires that the parallel plane be located at a specified distance from ABC or, in this example, if the distance between the planes is required, the auxiliary view shown may be employed to obtain the solution. If the planes are parallel, the edge views will be parallel and the true distance between the planes may be measured in the edge view of both.

If the requirement is that two planes be made parallel and a specified distance apart, Fig. 15.6 will also illustrate the solution. In this case, the top and front views of plane ABC and the top view of XYZ are given. First, an auxiliary view $A_A B_A C_A$ giving the edge view of ABC is drawn as shown. Second, the edge view of the second plane (in this case, XYZ) may now be drawn at the required distance from plane ABC. Third, projection from the given top view of XYZ will now establish $X_A Y_A Z_A$. Fourth, measurements from the reference plane in the auxiliary view for X, Y, and Z and projection from the top view of X, Y, and Z will determine the front view of XYZ. If the front view of XYZ—instead of the top view—had been given, measurements from the reference plane in the front view would establish $X_A Y_A Z_A$ on the edge view; then projection from

he auxiliary and front views would finish the solution by locating the
op view at the intersection of projectors from auxiliary and front
iews.

15.5. A Line Perpendicular to a Plane. A line perpendicular
o a plane is perpendicular to every line in that plane.

A line drawn perpendicular to a *single* line of a given plane would
ot necessarily be perpendicular to that plane because the line could
otate about the single line of the plane; but if a line is drawn *per-
endicular to two nonparallel lines* of a plane, then the perpendicular
lirection of that line with respect to the plane is established.

Figure 15.7 shows MN established through point N' perpendicular
o plane ABC, using the principles of perpendicular-line relation-
hips discussed in paragraph 14.6. The horizontal line CD is estab-
ished in plane ABC and is in true length in the top view. The top
iew of MN, through N, is drawn *perpendicular* to CD. The top view
of M is arbitrarily located on the line for the purposes of this illus-
ration. A frontal line AE is drawn in the top view, and its direction
nd true length are then shown in the front view. The front view of
MN is drawn *perpendicular* to AE. The top view of M is projected to
the front view. Thus line MN has been established perpendicular
o ABC by drawing it *perpendicular* to lines CD and AE, two nonparallel lines of plane ABC.

Problems dealing with oblique planes frequently involve true
lengths of lines in the plane. Become observant, and notice any lines
that may already exist in true length in any given view of an oblique
plane. Also, become competent in placing horizontal, frontal, or
profile lines in an oblique plane. This is a convenient way of establishing lines in true length in any principal view of an oblique plane
and is to be used in establishing the relationship of other lines to
the plane.

15.6. Distance from a Point to a Plane. The distance from a
point to a plane is construed as the shortest distance that can be
measured between the point and the plane; this measurement will
lie on a perpendicular dropped from the point to the plane.

In Fig. 15.8, the shortest distance from point N to the plane ABC
has been determined. An edge view of the plane is first drawn as

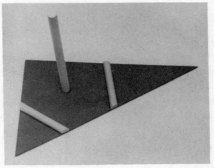

Line perpendicular to a plane and plane
perpendicular to a line.

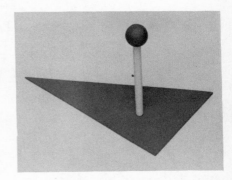

Shortest distance, point to plane.

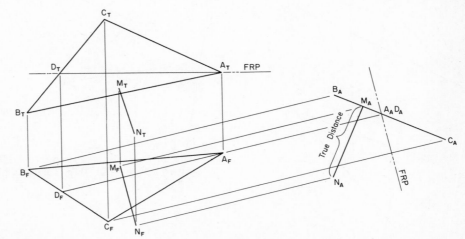

Fig. 15.8. Distance from a point
to a plane.

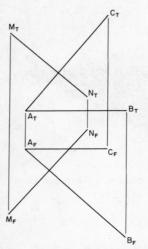

Fig. 15.9. A plane perpendicular to a line.

shown in the right auxiliary view. Point N is located in this view. A line drawn from point N perpendicular to the plane, intersecting the plane at M, is now drawn. MN is in true length in this auxiliary view, the length of which is the distance that N is from the plane. As explained in paragraph 15.5, a line perpendicular to a plane is perpendicular to *all* lines of the plane and will appear at 90° to any true-length line of the plane.

Thus the direction of MN is established in the front view perpendicular to AD, a frontal line of the plane. The front view of M is located by projection. Similarly, the top view of MN may be drawn by establishing the direction perpendicular to a horizontal line of the plane. However, in this case MN in the top view has been located by projection from the front view and measurement from the auxiliary. Note also that, because MN is in true length in the auxiliary view, its direction in the front view must be perpendicular to the rays of projection connecting front and auxiliary views.

A further statement can be made with reference to the graphics shown in the auxiliary view: *If a line is perpendicular to a plane*, it will appear in true length in any view where the plane appears as an edge and will appear at 90° to the edge view.

15.7. A Plane Perpendicular to a Line. A plane perpendicular to a given line can be established by drawing two intersecting lines perpendicular to the given line. This can most readily be accomplished by using lines that appear in true length in one of the views. Therefore, if front and top views are to be drawn, a horizontal and a frontal line will be employed. The problem of Fig. 15.9 will illustrate the procedure. A plane, containing point A, perpendicular to the given line MN is to be drawn. AC, a horizontal line, is in true length in the top view and is therefore drawn perpendicular to MN. Frontal line AB is in true length in the front view and is therefore drawn perpendicular to MN. Then AC and AB are two intersecting lines which form a plane perpendicular to MN. Since this construction conversely satisfies the conditions for perpendicularity given in

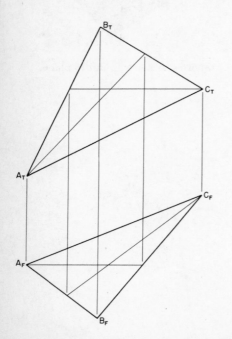

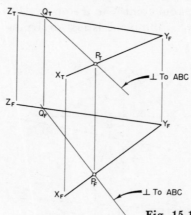

Fig. 15.10. A plane perpendicular to a plane.

paragraph 15.5, the plane *ABC* has been established perpendicular to line *MN*.

15.8. A Plane Perpendicular to a Plane. A plane containing *one* line perpendicular to a given plane will be perpendicular to the given plane. In Fig. 15.10, *XYZ* is to be drawn perpendicular to the given plane *ABC*. The top and front views of *ABC*, the front view of *XYZ*, and the top view of *XY* are initially known. Through any point in plane *XYZ*, such as *P*, a *line* is drawn *perpendicular* to *ABC* as outlined in paragraph 15.5 on drawing a line perpendicular to a plane. Thus $P_F Q_F$ is drawn perpendicular to the *frontal* line of *ABC*, and the top view of the line through *P* is drawn perpendicular to the horizontal line of *ABC*. At this stage of construction, the top and front views of a plane have been established, defined by two intersecting lines, *XY* and the line through *P*; this plane is perpendicular to *ABC* since the line through *P* is perpendicular to *ABC*. The top view of *Z* is located according to the principles of paragraph 15.2, by first projecting Q_F to Q_T *on* the line through point P_T.

15.9. Three Mutually Perpendicular Planes. Two of three mutually perpendicular planes can be drawn perpendicular to each other by the construction given in paragraph 15.8. Then a third perpendicular plane may be found by establishing two intersecting lines through any point of the third plane, each perpendicular to one of the other two planes. In Fig. 15.11, a plane containing the given line *DE* and the front view of point *F* is drawn perpendicular to the given plane *ABC*. A line *EZ* perpendicular to *ABC* through point *E* establishes this plane perpendicular to *ABC* by the principles of paragraph 15.5. The front view of point *Z* is arbitrarily selected and located in the top view of this plane according to the principles of paragraph 15.2. The top view of point *F* is similarly located by projecting the front view of *F* to the top view of *DZ*. Point *G* is a known point of a third plane. Through *G* a line *GK* perpendicular to *ABC* and another line *GH* perpendicular to *DEF*

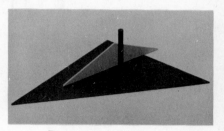

Plane perpendicular to a plane.

Three mutually perpendicular planes.

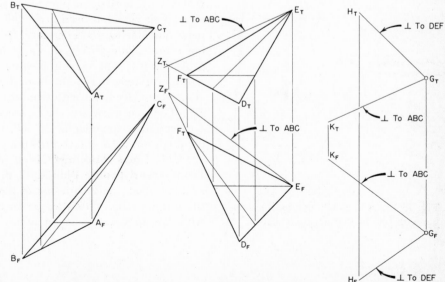

Fig. 15.11. Three mutually perpendicular planes.

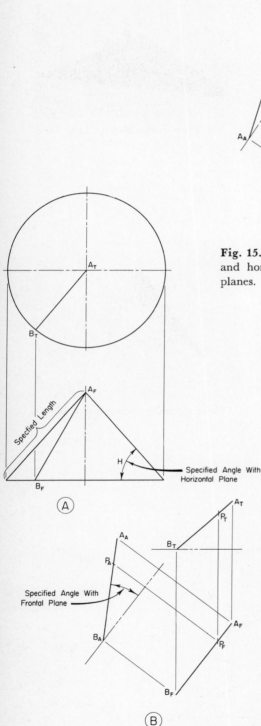

Fig. 15.12. The angle between a line and horizontal, frontal, and profile planes.

Fig. 15.13. A line making a specified angle with one of the principal planes.

establish a plane perpendicular to *ABC* and *DEF*. Thus *ABC*, *DEF*, and *GHK* are three mutually perpendicular planes.

15.10. The Angle between a Line and a Horizontal (*H*), **Frontal** (*F*), **and Profile** (*P*) **Plane.** The true size of the angle between a line and a plane may be seen in any orthographic view which shows the line in true length and the plane as an edge.

The angle between a line and a plane is measured between the given line and the *plane trace* (intersection), on the given plane, formed by a plane passed through the given line and perpendicular to the given plane. The true size of the angle can be seen in an orthographic view which shows the normal view of the passed plane; the normal view of the passed plane will show the given line in true length and the given plane as an edge.

In Fig. 15.12, the true size of angle *H*—the angle that line *AB* makes with horizontal planes—is shown in the elevation auxiliary view. This view has been projected from the top view in a direction perpendicular to *AB*. Therefore, *AB* appears in true length, and the horizontal plane (*HRP*) shows as an edge. The left auxiliary view, projected from the view in a direction perpendicular to *AB*, shows *AB* in true length and the frontal plane as an edge; therefore, the angle that *AB* makes with frontal planes (angle *F*) appears in true size. The rear auxiliary view, projected from the right-side view in a direction perpendicular to *AB*, shows the true size of angle *P*, the angle that *AB* makes with the profile plane.

15.11. Lines Making Given Angles with the Horizontal, Frontal, and Profile Planes. To draw a line through a given point at a specified angle with one of the principal planes of projection, the line may be established as an element of a right circular cone with the apex at the given point. The base of the cone must be parallel to the principal plane and the base angle of the cone equal to the specified angle. If the length of the line is specified, the element length (slant height) of the cone should be made equal to this length. If no other conditions of the problem are specified, then each element of the cone will satisfy the condition of the problem; the number of possible solutions will be infinite.

In Fig. 15.13*A*, *AB* is to be drawn making a specified angle *H* with the horizontal plane. The top-view direction of *AB*, the true length of *AB*, and the front view of *A* are known. A right circular cone is established with the apex at *A*, a base angle equal to the specified angle *H*, and the element length equal to the true length of *AB*. Point *B* is then located on the base of the cone to satisfy the conditions of the problem and from there projected to the top view. In this example, *B* is below and to the left of *A*, but *B* might have been specified to be above *A*.

Figure 15.13*B* shows another solution of a similar problem, using an auxiliary view. The line direction in the front view is specified by $B_F P_F$, and B_T is given. An angle with *frontal* planes is also specified. An auxiliary view *perpendicular* to $A_F B_F$ will show the line in true length. Therefore, projectors from $B_F P_F$ are drawn, a reference plane assumed through *B* (in auxiliary and top views), and the specified angle with frontal planes laid out in the auxiliary view. Point P_A then may be located on the true length of the required line in the auxiliary view. Point *P* may be located in the top view by projection from the front view and measurement from the auxiliary. Finally, the specified length of *AB* may be measured in the auxiliary view and projected to front and top views.

Note in both examples of Fig. 15.13 that a specified angle with a given plane must be laid out in a view showing the true length of the line *and* the edge view of the plane.

To draw a line through a given point making specified angles with *two* of the principal planes, the line may be established as a common element (intersection) of two cones. The apexes of both cones are located at the given point, and their bases are constructed parallel to the respective principal planes. No intersection of the cones is possible unless the sum of the base angles ranges from 0 to 90° inclusive. To facilitate the determination of lines of intersection of the two cones, the element lengths (slant heights) must be made equal. In Fig. 15.14*A*, two right circular cones have been constructed with apexes at the center *C* of a sphere. The element lengths are equal in length to the radius of the sphere, thus placing the circular bases on the surface of the sphere. The bases intersect because they are lines (curved) of a common surface. Lines drawn through the apexes and intersections of the bases are elements of both cones (the straight-line intersection of the cones).

Considering both nappes of each cone, we find the circular bases intersecting at eight different points. Drawing straight-line elements of the cones from the points of intersection on the bases through the apexes gives four straight lines of intersection. These four lines are

Angle between a line and *H*, *F*, or *P* plane and specified angle between an *H*, *F*, or *P* plane.

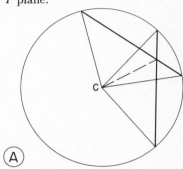

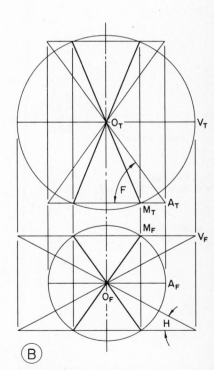

Fig. 15.14. A line making specified angles with two of the principal planes.

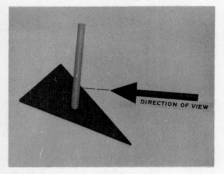

Angle between a line and plane.

all possible solutions of the problem. Further specifications must be added to limit the solution to one line.

In Fig. 15.14B, OM is to be established through the given point O making a specified angle H with the horizontal plane and an angle F with the frontal plane. H plus F is somewhere between 0 and 90°. The front view of a right circular cone with a horizontal base and apex at O is constructed with a base angle equal to H. OV is the true length (in the front view) of any element of this cone. The top view of another right circular cone with apex at O is constructed in the top view with the base angle equal to F. The element length of this cone is made equal in length to OV, the element length of the other cone, to ensure intersection of the bases. M is then located at one of the intersections of the two bases and is, in this case, in front and to the right of point O. The projection of point M to either view should pass through the intersection of the bases; this should be checked for each problem to verify that no mistakes have been made in construction of the cones.

15.12. Angle between a Line and an Oblique Plane: Edge-view Method. As explained in paragraph 15.10, the true angle between a line and a plane will be observed when the edge view of the plane and the true length of the line are obtained in the same view. A convenient method of accomplishing this is to make an edge view of the plane and project the line along with the plane; then, by placing the line on the surface of a cone, the line may be rotated, *without changing the relationship of line and plane*, until the line shows in true length. Then the true length of the line and the edge view of the plane will show the true angle between the two.

Figure 15.15 is an illustration using this cone method for finding

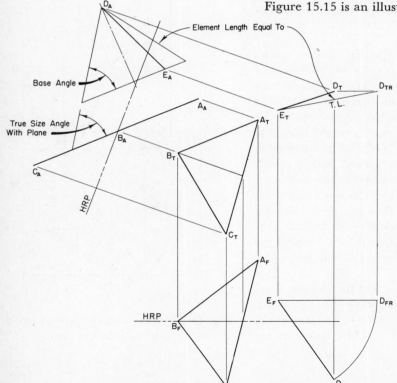

Fig. 15.15. The angle between a line and an oblique plane (edge-view method).

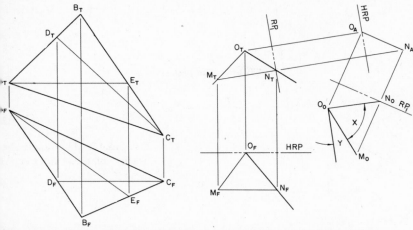

Fig. 15.16. The angle between a line and an oblique plane (complementary-angle method).

the angle between line *DE* and the oblique plane *ABC*. An auxiliary view that shows the edge view of *ABC* is established, and *DE* is projected to this view. A right circular cone using *DE* as an element is constructed with the apex at *D*; then *E* is a point on the circular base. The base is drawn parallel to *ABC*. The limiting element of this cone is determined as the true length of *DE*, obtained by rotation as shown. The true size of the base angle is shown between the limiting element and the base. All elements of a right circular cone make the same angle with the base of the cone. Since the base of the cone is parallel to *ABC*, *DE* makes an angle with *ABC* equal in size to the base angle. The cone can be constructed using point *D* or *E* as the apex and the other point as a point on the base. The base of the cone *must* be constructed parallel to the given oblique plane.

15.13. Angle between a Line and an Oblique Plane: Complementary-angle Method. Another method (as contrasted with the method of paragraph 15.12) of finding the angle between a line and an oblique plane is to select some point on the line and draw from it a perpendicular to the plane; the angle between the line and the perpendicular will be the complement of the angle between the line and plane.

Figure 15.16 shows the above method for finding the true size of angle *Y* between line *NO* and the given oblique plane. From point *O* a line is drawn perpendicular to the plane *ABC*, using the principles given in paragraph 15.5. The included angle formed by the perpendicular and *NO* is the complement of the required angle. A normal view of this angle is now required. A horizontal line drawn through the front view of *N* intersects the perpendicular at *M*, forming the plane *MNO*. An edge view of this plane is shown in the elevation auxiliary view. A normal view of *MNO* is established in the oblique view by projecting perpendicular to the edge view of *MNO*. Angle *X*, the complement of the required angle, is shown in true size in the oblique view. Angle *X* is subtracted graphically from 90°, leaving, as the remainder angle *Y*, the angle that *ON* makes with the plane *ABC*.

Angle between a line and plane.

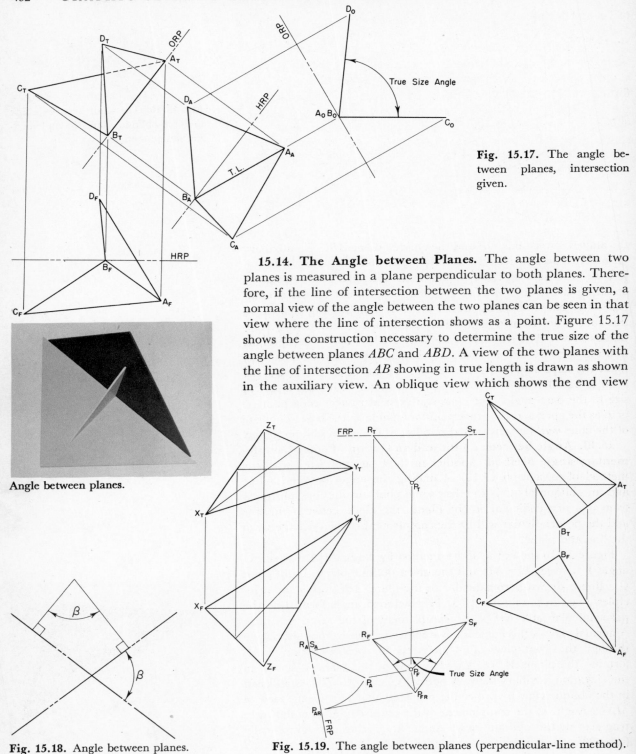

Fig. 15.17. The angle between planes, intersection given.

Angle between planes.

15.14. The Angle between Planes. The angle between two planes is measured in a plane perpendicular to both planes. Therefore, if the line of intersection between the two planes is given, a normal view of the angle between the two planes can be seen in that view where the line of intersection shows as a point. Figure 15.17 shows the construction necessary to determine the true size of the angle between planes *ABC* and *ABD*. A view of the two planes with the line of intersection *AB* showing in true length is drawn as shown in the auxiliary view. An oblique view which shows the end view

Fig. 15.18. Angle between planes.

Fig. 15.19. The angle between planes (perpendicular-line method).

of *AB* and each plane as an edge is established. The true size of the angle is measured in this view.

In case the line of intersection is not given, further advantage may be taken of the opening statement of this section. From any convenient point drop a perpendicular to each plane. These two lines form a plane perpendicular to both given planes. The angle between the perpendiculars is equal to the angle between the two planes. There are *two* angles between a pair of intersecting lines, one the supplement of the other. The *acute* angle is generally accepted as the standard method of specification. This principle is illustrated in Fig. 15.18. In Fig. 15.19, the true size of the angle between planes *XYZ* and *ABC* is to be determined. The top and front views of *P* are established in any convenient position relative to the given planes. From *P* a line *PR* is drawn perpendicular to *XYZ*, and also from *P* a line *PS* is drawn perpendicular to *ABC*, using the principles outlined in paragraph 15.5 on drawing a line perpendicular to a plane. *RS* is conveniently established as a frontal line. The included angle *RPS* is equal to the angle between planes but does not show in true size in either the top or the front view. A normal view of *RPS* is shown using the method of rotation as outlined in paragraph 13.13.

15.15. A Plane Making Specified Angles with Other Planes. The previous paragraphs have stated that the true angle between planes is seen in a view where both planes appear as edges and that this view will be had when the line of intersection of the planes appears as a point. These facts may be applied to locate a plane at a specified angle with another plane.

Specified Angle between an Oblique Plane and a Horizontal, Frontal, or Profile Plane. If the line of intersection of the planes is given, this problem is capable of a single solution; otherwise there will be an infinite number of answers. For example, in Fig. 15.20, the top view of plane *ABC* and the front view of *AB* are given, along with a specification of an angle that this plane is to make with frontal planes. Line *AB* is frontal and is, therefore, the intersection with a frontal plane through *AB*. Consequently, if the auxiliary view, giving the point view of *AB*, is made as shown, the edge view of a frontal plane through *AB* and the edge view of *ABC* will both appear with *AB* as their line of intersection. In this view, then, the specified angle may be laid out. Point *C* then measured from the top view (distance *X*) and located on the auxiliary view completes the location of *ABC* at the specified angle with frontal planes. Point *C* in the front view then lies at the intersection of projectors from the top and auxiliary views.

Specified Angle between Two Oblique Planes. Again, if the line of intersection between the planes is given, the problem is capable of a single

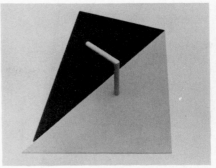

Angle between planes.

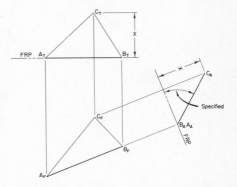

Fig. 15.20. A plane making a specified angle with a frontal plane.

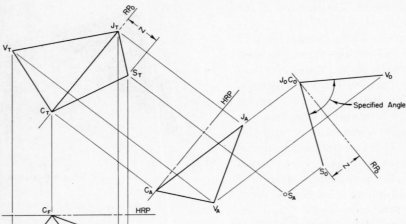

Fig. 15.21. A plane making a specified angle with another plane.

solution. In Fig. 15.21, plane *CJV* is a given oblique plane. The top view of *CJS*, a second plane to be located at a specified angle with *CJV*, is given. The line of intersection is *CJ*. The auxiliary view, perpendicular to *CJ*, gives the true length of *CJ*; the oblique view gives the point view of *CJ* and the edge view of *CJV*. In this view, then, the specified angle may be laid out, thus locating the edge view of *CJS*. Point *S* may now be measured from RP_O in the top view (distance *Z*) and transferred to the oblique view, locating S_O. The auxiliary view of *S* then lies at the intersection of projectors from the top and oblique views at S_A. The front view of *S* is then found by projection from the top view and measurement from *HRP*.

Specified Angle between a Plane and Two of the Three Planes of Projection. Any oblique plane will make *some* angle, which can be determined (paragraph 15.14), with all three planes of projection. If two of the three angles are specified, the plane will be fixed in four possible positions, which can be then restricted to make for a single solution.

An excellent method of determining a plane at specified angles with two of the planes of projection is first to draw a line (paragraph 15.10) making complements of the angles which the plane is to make

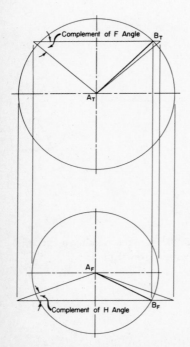

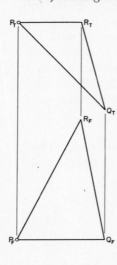

Fig. 15.22. A plane making specified angles with two of the principal planes.

and then to draw a plane perpendicular to the line. The sum of the angles the plane makes with two of the planes of projection must be between 90 and 180°; otherwise the solution is impossible. In Fig. 15.22, a plane making a specified angle H with horizontal planes and a specified angle F with frontal planes is to be determined. The plane is to pass through point P and have a direction in space that dips forward and to the left of P. Therefore, a line perpendicular to this plane has a direction (from any point on the line) downward, rearward, and toward the right. First, determine by subtraction the complements of the angles the plane is to make; then, from any point such as A, draw the required line as described in paragraph 15.10. Second, through point P, draw a plane perpendicular to the line. In Fig. 15.22, the plane PQR is the required plane designated by horizontal line PQ and frontal line PR, which are both perpendicular to AB.

15.16. Shortest Line Intersecting Two Skew Lines: Plane Method. The shortest distance between two skew lines is the perpendicular distance between the parallel planes that contain each of them. This distance is measured in that view which shows the edge view of the planes.

In Fig. 15.23, it is required to find the shortest distance between the two skew lines AB and MN. By using one of the given skew lines AB, a plane ABC is established parallel to MN by drawing a line through B parallel to MN in both top and front views. C is conveniently located by drawing AC horizontal. An edge view of ABC is established in the elevation auxiliary view by projection in the direction of AC. MN is projected to this auxiliary view. Note the appearance of AB and MN in this view. The lines, in space, actually are not parallel, but they appear parallel in this view because the plane containing MN parallel to ABC, if drawn, would appear as an edge in this view. In this view the true length of the shortest distance (common perpendicular) between the skew lines can be measured as the perpendicular distance between the planes.

In general, this would satisfy the requirements of many clearance problems of this type; but if the *location* of the perpendicular is required in addition, one more view will be necessary. An oblique

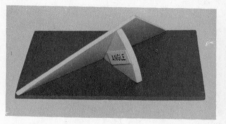

Angle between a plane and H, F, or P plane.

Common perpendicular.

Fig. 15.23. Shortest line intersecting two skew lines (plane method).

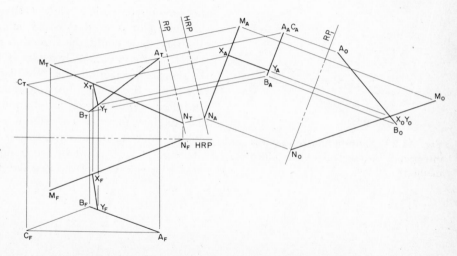

Shortest horizontal line connecting two skew lines.

Shortest profile line connecting two skew lines.

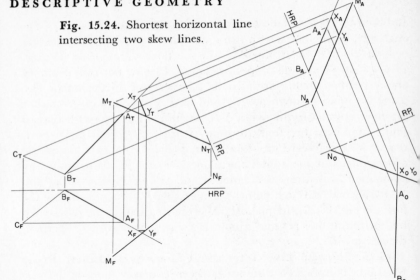

Fig. 15.24. Shortest horizontal line intersecting two skew lines.

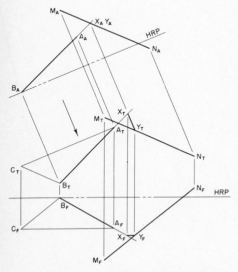

Fig. 15.25. Shortest horizontal line intersecting two skew lines (simplified method).

view is established by projecting in a direction perpendicular to *ABC*. The oblique view shows a normal view of each of the skew lines, and the shortest distance between the two lines must therefore appear as a point in this view. The common perpendicular *XY* between the two skew lines appears as a point at the *apparent* intersection of *MN* and *AB*. *XY* is located in the auxiliary, top, and front views by projecting *X* and *Y* to intersect, respectively, *MN* and *AB*.

15.17. Shortest Horizontal Line Intersecting Two Skew Lines. The true length of the shortest horizontal line intersecting two skew lines is the shortest horizontal distance between the parallel *planes* that contain each of the skew lines.

In Fig. 15.24, it is required to find the line *XY*, the shortest horizontal line intersecting *AB* and *MN*. The plane *ABC* is established in both top and front views parallel to *MN*, similar to the procedure given in paragraph 15.16. *AC* is constructed as a horizontal line. An elevation auxiliary view, projected in the direction of *AC*, establishes the edge view of *ABC*. *MN* is projected to this view. The plane parallel to *ABC* and containing *MN* will appear as an edge in this view. The true length of the shortest distance can be measured in the elevation auxiliary view. Other auxiliary views which would show the planes as edges could be drawn, but only in an elevation auxiliary view could the direction of a *horizontal* line (parallel to the *HRP*) between the two planes be determined. The *location* of the shortest horizontal line, however, cannot be determined in this view. Since the shortest horizontal line appears in true length in the elevation auxiliary view, an oblique view is drawn, projected from the auxiliary view in a direction parallel to the horizontal. This oblique view is, in this case, *another* elevation auxiliary. Therefore, *XY* appears as a point in the oblique view and is located at the *apparent* intersection of the two skew lines *MN* and *AB*. *XY* is projected back to the auxiliary, top, and front views by locating X and Y, respectively, on AB and MN.

Figure 15.25 shows another and shorter method of solving the problem just explained (Fig. 15.24) by employing the following theory: *The shortest horizontal line between two parallel planes is perpendicular to all horizontal lines of both planes.* It follows then that, in order to find the shortest horizontal line between two skew lines, a plane may be passed through one of the skew lines parallel to the other. A view now made looking in a horizontal direction and also *perpendicular* to a horizontal line of this plane will show the shortest horizontal (between the two skew lines) as a *point* at the apparent intersection of the two skew lines.

In Fig. 15.25, ABC is constructed parallel to MN as in Fig. 15.24. From the above principles, an elevation auxiliary view has been projected from the top view in a direction *perpendicular* to AC, a horizontal line of plane ABC, thereby obtaining a view which will show the shortest horizontal line as a point. The auxiliary view of XY is located at the apparent intersection of AB and MN. Then XY is located in the top and front views by projecting X and Y to AB and MN, respectively.

Note that the oblique view of Fig. 15.24 and the elevation auxiliary view of Fig. 15.25 are identical. The projectors for the oblique view of Fig. 15.24 are perpendicular to the projectors between the top and auxiliary view, therefore showing the space dimension of true height in this particular oblique view; consequently, if a view is projected from the top view with projectors parallel (physical relationship on the sheet) to those of the oblique view, the two views will be identical. This same relationship exists in a side view projected from the front view and in a side view in the alternate position.

15.18. Shortest Frontal Line Intersecting Two Skew Lines. The *true length* of the shortest frontal line intersecting two skew lines can be determined as the shortest frontal distance between the parallel planes that contain the two lines.

The location of the shortest frontal line can be determined in that view where the frontal line will show as a point at the apparent intersection of the two skew lines.

In Fig. 15.26, the determination of the shortest frontal line XY

Shortest frontal line connecting two skew lines.

Shortest grade line between two skew lines.

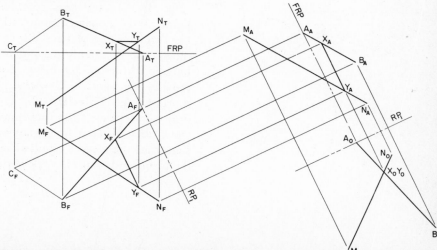

Fig. 15.26. Shortest frontal line intersecting two skew lines.

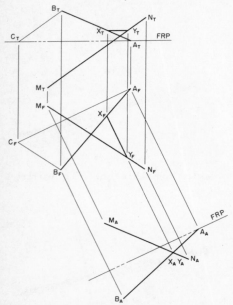

Fig. 15.27. Shortest frontal line intersecting two skew lines (simplified method).

which intersects the skew lines *AB* and *MN* is illustrated. The solution is identical with that of paragraph 15.17 and Fig. 15.24, except that a right auxiliary is used in order to determine the frontal-line direction and the direction of the oblique view. Figure 15.27 shows the shorter solution (similar to Fig. 15.25 for a horizontal line), using a right auxiliary made perpendicular to the frontal line *CA* of the plane *ABC*.

The shortest profile line connecting two skew lines is found by using the principles given in this section and paragraph 15.17, with the exception that either a front or rear auxiliary must be used.

15.19. Shortest Line of Specified Grade Intersecting Two Skew Lines. All shortest lines, *intersecting two skew lines*, that are either horizontal, vertical, or at a specified grade and the common perpendicular will lie in *vertical* planes, which are perpendicular to horizontal lines on parallel planes passed through the two skew lines. Furthermore, all the above shortest lines will intersect a horizontal axis parallel to the parallel planes of the skew lines. These facts may be used advantageously to find any of the shortest lines listed above. For example, assume that the shortest 25 per cent grade connector between two skew lines is required. In Fig. 15.28, a plane *DCE* is passed through one skew line *DC* parallel to *AB*, the other skew line. *DE* is made horizontal, for convenience. The elevation auxiliary shown drawn in the direction of *DE* then gives the edge

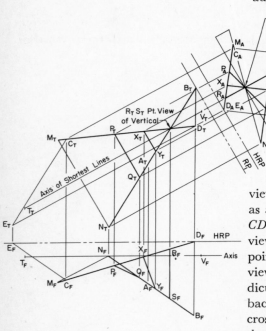

Fig. 15.28. Shortest line of specified grade intersecting two skew lines.

view of *DCE*. The vertical line connecting the two skew lines appears as a point in the top view at the apparent intersection of *AB* and *CD*. This line *RS* is readily located by projection to the auxiliary view. The shortest line (common perpendicular) will appear as a point at the apparent intersection of *AB* and *CD* in the oblique view which shows *AB* and *CD* in true length. The common perpendicular *XY* is readily located in the auxiliary view by projection back from the oblique view. These two shortest lines, *RS* and *XY*, cross in the auxiliary view and locate the point view of the axis of shortest lines. This axis *TV* may then be located in the top and front views. Since all shortest lines pass through *TV* in the auxiliary view, other shortest lines may now be found. The shortest 25 per cent grade connector required in this problem may be laid out at the proper relationship with horizontal planes and passing through

TV in the auxiliary view. (*Grade* is defined as units of vertical rise over 100 units of horizontal run.) The 25 per cent grade line of this problem, *PQ*, located in the auxiliary view may then be projected back to top and front views, where *P* lies on *CD* and *Q* on *AB*. Note that there will be two possible shortest 25 per cent grade connectors, *PQ*, the one just found, and another, *MN*, which rises upward from *TV*, while *PQ* descends from *TV* as both lines progress forward and to the right from *TV*.

Taking advantage of all the facts presented in paragraphs 15.16 and 15.17 and thus far in 15.18, a shorter solution of a problem similar to Fig. 15.28 is possible. In Fig. 15.29, *BN* and *DM* are two skew lines. Assume that the shortest line connector making 15° with the horizontal is wanted. A plane *DCE* parallel to *BN* is passed through *DM*, and *DE* of this plane is made horizontal. Then the elevation auxiliary in the direction of *DE* gives the edge view of *DCE*. Line *BN* is projected to this view. The vertical *RS* appears as a point in the top view and is projected to the auxiliary at $R_A S_A$. *Any* shortest line (as stated before) will lie in a vertical plane perpendicular to horizontal lines of the parallel planes containing the two skew lines and will therefore appear at right angles to *ED* (a horizontal line of *DCE*). One such line, *PQ*, is selected at random, but in a convenient place in the top view at $P_T Q_T$. This line projected to the auxiliary will cross *RS*, the vertical, at *TV*, thus locating the axis of shortest lines. In the auxiliary view, through *TV*, the line $G_A H_A$ making 15° with horizontal planes may then be drawn and projected back to top and front views.

If a line at some angle to the frontal was required (instead of the line of Fig. 15.29 making an angle with horizontal planes), a right or left auxiliary (giving the edge view of a plane through one line parallel to the other) would be employed in place of the elevation auxiliary of Fig. 15.29.

15.20. Shortest Line of Specified Bearing Intersecting Two Skew Lines.
A line of specified bearing means a line having a particular map direction, or "heading." This means that the line will lie in, or be parallel to, a vertical plane whose direction is the specified bearing. There are an infinite number of lines of specified bearing that will intersect two skew lines, but only one shortest line.

The required line may be established parallel to the bearing plane in all views that show the plane as an edge. Also, the length of any shortest line between two skew lines will be seen in a view in which the lines *appear* parallel or, in other words, in a view giving the edge

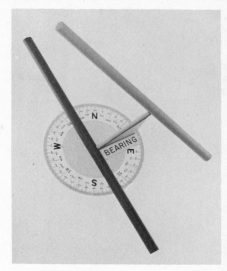

Shortest line of specified bearing between two skew lines.

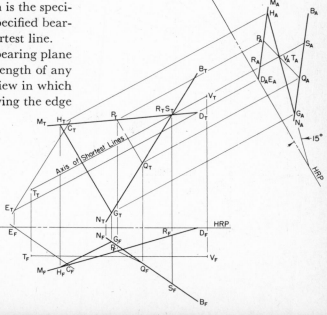

Fig. 15.29. Shortest line of specified grade intersecting two skew lines (simplified method).

view of the parallel planes containing the lines. Therefore, in order to find the shortest line of specified bearing between two skew lines, we must draw a view which simultaneously shows the edge of the bearing plane and the edge views of parallel planes containing the skew lines.

In Fig. 15.30, AB and CD are given skew lines, and plane BP is a plane establishing the *direction* of bearing of a line which will later be determined as the shortest line of this bearing which intersects AB and CD. The line BX, parallel to CD, establishes a plane ABX through AB, parallel to CD. Next, a view made in a direction perpendicular to the bearing plane BP establishes a view in which the bearing plane appears normal. This is the auxiliary view $A_A B_A C_A D_A \ldots$ Any view now projected from the auxiliary view will show the bearing plane as an edge. Furthermore, a view projected parallel to a normal line in plane ABX will also show ABX as an edge. Points X and Y in plane ABX have been located where the bearing plane intersects AB and BX; hence XY is in the bearing plane and will appear normal (where the bearing plane appears normal) in the auxiliary view. An oblique view now made looking in a direction parallel to $X_A Y_A$ will show the edge view of the bearing plane (marked BP in the view) and will show AB and CD parallel to each other (because they lie in parallel planes). In the oblique view any line parallel to BP and intersecting AB and CD will have

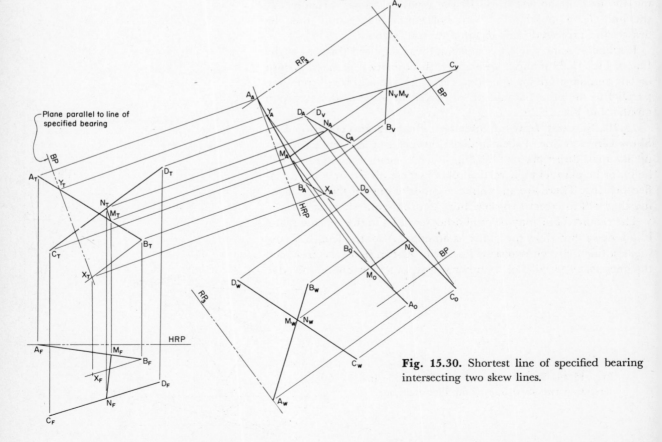

Fig. 15.30. Shortest line of specified bearing intersecting two skew lines.

the proper bearing and meet all specifications of the problem except for the location of the *shortest* line. A view now projected in the direction of the bearing plane BP in the oblique view will again give the edge view of the bearing plane and will, at the crossing of AB and CD, reveal the position of the shortest line of the specified bearing. This is line $M_W N_W$ in the new view, which, projected to the oblique view at $M_O N_O$, shows the line to be parallel to the bearing plane. From $M_O N_O$ the line may then be projected back to all other views.

The shorter and simpler solutions of paragraphs 15.17 to 15.19 may also be applied to the above solution. Note that the view $A_V B_V C_V D_V \ldots$, projected *perpendicular* to $X_A Y_A$, is a view made in exactly the same viewing direction in space as the view $A_W B_W \ldots$. Thus the two extra views, (1) the auxiliary and (2) the oblique view $A_V B_V \ldots$, are the only views needed for a solution.

PROBLEMS

Group 1. Points in planes

15.1.1. Points X, Y, and Z lie in the plane ABC. Draw the top and front views of triangle XYZ.

15.1.2. Find the top view of point S, which lies in the plane PQR.

15.1.3. Lines AC and BD lie in the plane $KLMN$. AC is parallel to KL and is $1'\text{-}6''$ long. C is above A. BD is a horizontal line, and D is $1'\text{-}9''$ to the left of N. Scale: $\tfrac{3}{4}'' = 1'\text{-}0''$. Draw the top and front views of AC and BD.

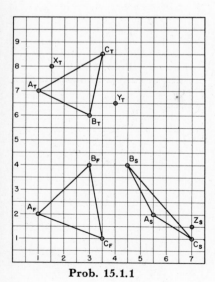

Prob. 15.1.1

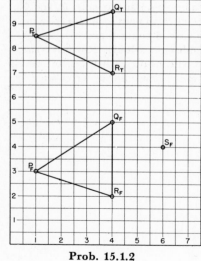

Prob. 15.1.2

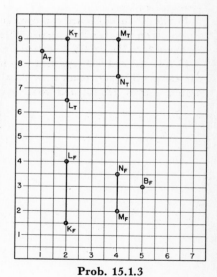

Prob. 15.1.3

15.1.4. *A*, *B*, and *C* are points on the sloping plane surface of a gravity dam. The elevations of these points above the surface of the water below the dam are 224, 203, and 100 ft, respectively. A drain emerges from the surface of the dam at a point 62 ft to the rear and 30 ft to the right of *C*. Scale: 1″ = 50′. How far is the drain above the surface of the water?

15.1.5. A ball rolls downward along a circular path through points 1, 2, and 3 in the plane surface *ABCD*. Draw the top and front views of the point *P* where the ball leaves the surface.

15.1.6. *AB* is a tunnel lying in the ore vein that strikes and dips as shown. Draw the top view of the tunnel.

Group 2. Plane figures

15.2.1. *PQ* is the hypotenuse of a right triangle. The third corner, *R*, lies on line *PS*. Complete the top and front views of the triangle.

15.2.2. *KL* and *KM* are the legs of an isosceles right triangle. *M* is above *K* and 18 in. behind *L*. Scale: ⅛ size. Complete the top and front views of the triangle *KLM*.

15.2.3. *AB* is one diagonal of a rhombus. The third corner, *C*, lies on line *BG*. Draw the top and front views of the rhombus *ABCD*.

15.2.4. *AB* is one side of a regular hexagon lying in the plane *ABM*. The hexagon lies in front of *AB*. Draw the top and front views of the hexagon.

15.2.5. *AB* and *KL* are the bases of two similar isosceles triangles. The altitude of the triangle *KLM* is 2¼ in., and *M* is behind *K*. The vertex, *C*, of triangle *ABC* is above and 1¼ in. behind *A*. Scale: ¾ size. Draw the top and front views of the triangle *ABC*.

Group 3. Lines parallel to planes, planes parallel to lines, and planes parallel to planes

15.3.1. Line *WV* is a portion of the path of the center of a wheel as it rolls across the plane *ABC*. Complete the front view of the path.

15.3.2. *DE* is the center line of a shaft supported by two identical bearings. *FGH* is the plane of the base of these bearings. Complete the front view of the plane.

15.3.3. *DE* and *FG* are two control cables in an airframe. *A*, *B*, and *C* are points on the plane surface of a bulkhead which must maintain constant distances from the cables. Locate the top view of points *B* and *C*.

15.3.4. *AB* and *CD* represent two members in a bridge structure. The shortest possible horizontal catwalk is to be constructed between the two members. Draw the top and front views of the center line of the catwalk.

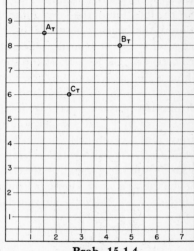

Prob. 15.1.4

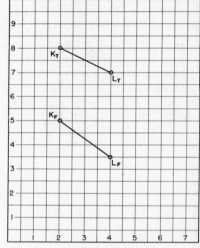

Prob. 15.2.2

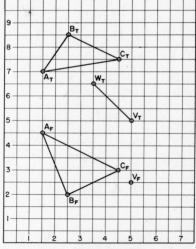

Prob. 15.3.1

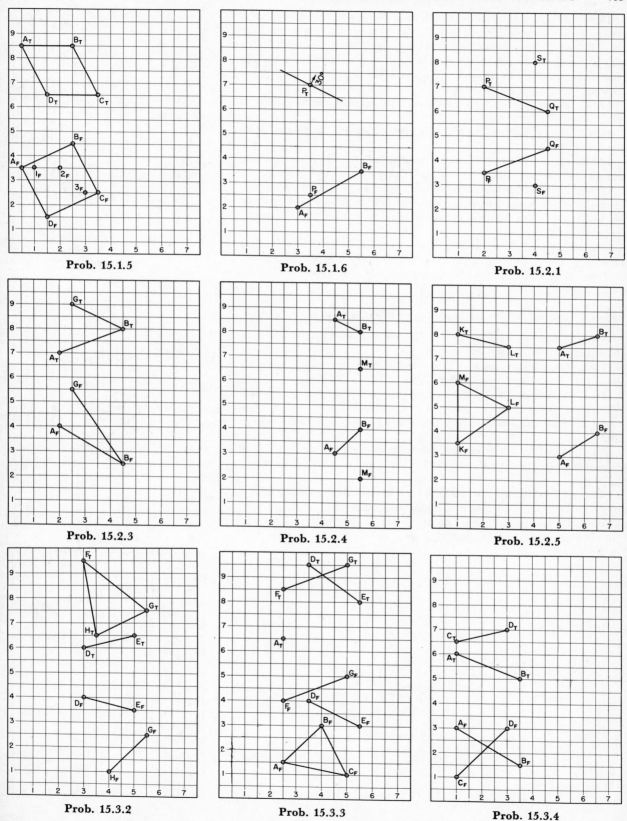

Prob. 15.1.5

Prob. 15.1.6

Prob. 15.2.1

Prob. 15.2.3

Prob. 15.2.4

Prob. 15.2.5

Prob. 15.3.2

Prob. 15.3.3

Prob. 15.3.4

15.3.5. *JK* and *LM* are the center lines of two conduits in an irrigation system. It has been decided to install a bypass connection between these conduits. Maximum hydraulic efficiency requires a 24-in. pipe on a 25 per cent grade. Draw the plan and elevation views of the center line of the bypass so as to use the least amount of pipe. How much pipe is required (center to center)? Scale: 1″ = 30′.

15.3.6. Planes *ABC* and *RST* are parallel. Complete the front view of *ABC*.

15.3.7. Planes *ABC* and *RST* are parallel. Complete the top and front views of *RST*.

15.3.8. Planes *ABC* and *KLM* are parallel. *KLM* is 1¼ in. away from, and generally below, *ABC*. Scale: ⅜ size. Draw the top view of *KLM*.

15.3.9. Plane *ABCD* is a portion of the upper surface of a vein of coal. Plane *KLMN* is a portion of the lower surface of another vein passing nearby. What is the thickness of the material separating the two veins? Scale: 1″ = 20′.

15.3.10. An ore vein strikes and dips as shown at *P*. Another vein, *R*, is parallel to, above, and 40 ft away from, vein *P*. Point *R* is 20 ft above and 60 ft east of *P*. Scale: 1″ = 50′. Draw the top and front views of vein *R* in terms of strike and dip.

Group 4. Line perpendicular to plane and distance from point to plane

15.4.1. Complete the front view of *PO*, a line which is perpendicular to plane *ABC*. Use auxiliary-view method.

15.4.2. Complete the top and front views of *PO*, a line perpendicular to plane *ABC*. Use normal-line relationships.

15.4.3. A point moves in a circular path passing through points *A*, *B*, and *C*. Draw the top and front views of the axis of rotation.

15.4.4. Draw the normal view of the distance from point *P* to the plane *ABC*.

15.4.5. Draw the top, front, and auxiliary views of line *MN*, which is perpendicular to plane *KLM*. *MN* is 72 in. long and *N* is above *M*. Scale: ³⁄₁₆″ = 1′-0″.

15.4.6. A 7-in. diameter wheel rolls in a straight line across the plane surface *RSTU* from point *P* in a direction perpendicular to *RS*. Locate, in the top and front views, the center *C* of the wheel when its line of contact with the plane intersects *UT*. Scale: ¼ size.

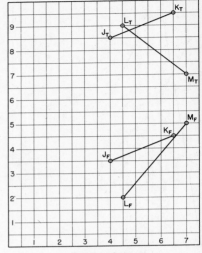

Prob. 15.3.5

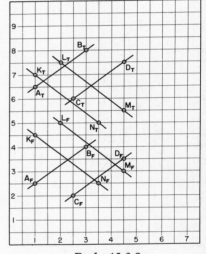

Prob. 15.3.9

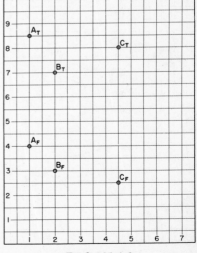

Prob. 15.4.3

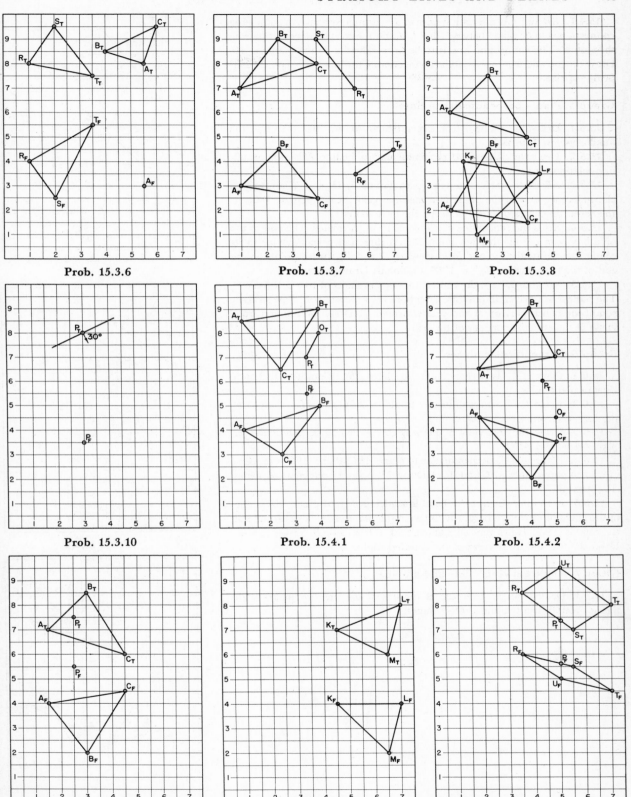

Prob. 15.3.6

Prob. 15.3.7

Prob. 15.3.8

Prob. 15.3.10

Prob. 15.4.1

Prob. 15.4.2

Prob. 15.4.4

Prob. 15.4.5

Prob. 15.4.6

15.4.7. *AB* and *LM* are tubing lines in a hydraulic system. An equalizing connection is to be made between line *LM* and the straight segment passing through *B*. The connecting line is to be perpendicular to the plane of *AB*. Draw the top and front views of the connection. How long is the connection? Scale: ¾ size.

Group 5. Planes perpendicular to lines

15.5.1. Draw the plane *ABC* perpendicular to the line *DA*. Use the auxiliary-view approach.

15.5.2. Draw the plane *JLM* perpendicular to the line *JK*. Use normal-line relationships.

15.5.3. *AB* is the shaft of a spur gear. Points *P*, *O*, and *T* are on the circumference and in the plane of a meshing gear. Scale: ⅜ size. What is the center-to-center distance between the gear shafts?

15.5.4. *AB* is the center line of a pipe of 10 in. diameter. The end of the pipe has been cut off through point *B* in a direction perpendicular to its center line. Draw the top and front views of 12 equally spaced points on the end of the pipe. Scale: 1½″ = 1′-0″. Optional: Draw the curve.

15.5.5. *AB* and *CD* are the center lines of the shafts of two belt pulleys. The pulleys are driven in opposite directions by a crossed belt. One straight run of the belt is horizontal and passes through *P*. Draw the top and front views of the straight portions of the belt.

Group 6. Perpendicular planes

15.6.1. Plane *XYZ* is perpendicular to plane *ABC*. Complete the front view of plane *XYZ*.

15.6.2. Plane *RST* is perpendicular to planes *ABC* and *JKL*. Complete the top and front views of plane *RST*.

15.6.3. Draw the top view of plane *PQR*, which is perpendicular to planes *ABC* and *ABD*.

15.6.4. Plane *ACD* is perpendicular to plane *ABC*. Plane *AFG* is perpendicular to both planes *ABC* and *ACD*. Draw the top and front views of planes *ACD* and *AFG*.

15.6.5. A counterweight for a bascule bridge is a right prism. *AB* is one of the edges of its square base, which lies in the plane *ABK*. The altitude of the weight is 9 ft. It lies generally above and in front of *AB*. Scale: ⅛ size. Draw the top and front views of the counterweight.

Group 7. Angle between a line and a plane

15.7.1. Determine the true size of the angles the line *AB* makes with the horizontal, frontal, and profile planes.

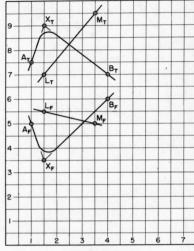

Prob. 15.4.7

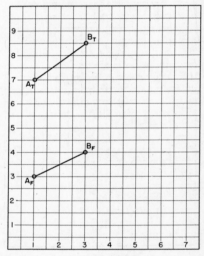

Prob. 15.5.4

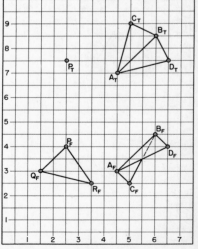

Prob. 15.6.3

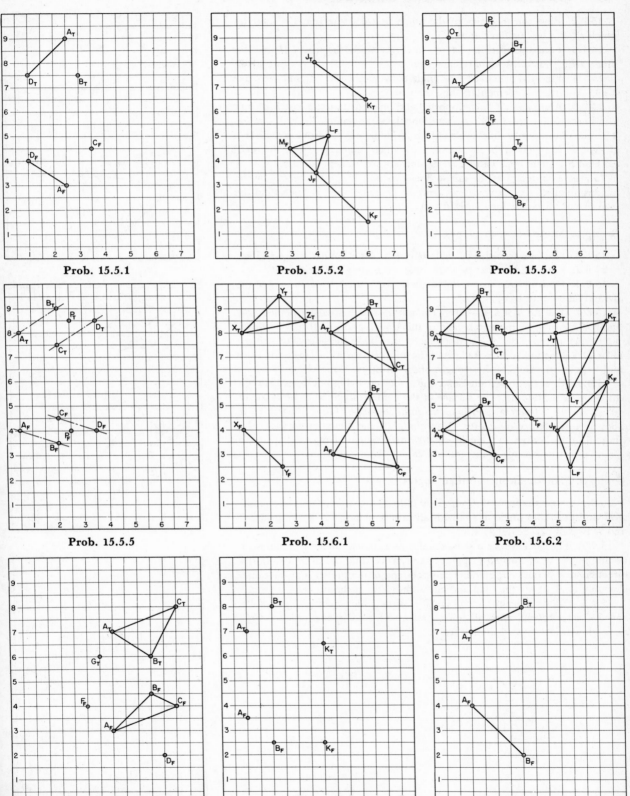

Prob. 15.5.1

Prob. 15.5.2

Prob. 15.5.3

Prob. 15.5.5

Prob. 15.6.1

Prob. 15.6.2

Prob. 15.6.4

Prob. 15.6.5

Prob. 15.7.1

15.7.2. Find the true size of the angle between the line *VW* and the plane *PQR*. Use auxiliary and oblique views only.

15.7.3. Find the true size of the angle between the line *LM* and the plane *DEF*. Use only one auxiliary view.

15.7.4. Find the true size of the angle between the line *PQ* and the plane *KLM*. Use the complementary-line method.

15.7.5. A gin pole, *BT*, is supported and pivoted about its base *B* by four guy lines, which are anchored at ground level at points *W*, *X*, *Y*, and *Z*. The maximum permissible angle of lean of the pole is 45° from the vertical. Draw the plan view of the maximum area which can be served by the vertical load line. The hook can be raised and lowered independently.

15.7.6. The design of the anchorages in Prob. 15.7.5 is affected by the maximum angle that can exist between the pole and the guy lines. Find the true size of this angle for line *WT*.

Group 8. Angle between planes

15.8.1. Find the true size of angle between planes *RSTU* and *STVW*.

15.8.2. Find the true size of angle between planes *ABC* and *DEF*.

15.8.3. Find the true size of the angle between the lateral surfaces of the pyramidal column base.

15.8.4. The sides of a V-shaped trough are represented by planes *ABC* and *ABD*. An 8-in. pipe is to be laid in this trough and is to be covered by a plate lying on top of the pipe and so placed as to make the sides of the trough alike. Draw the top and front views of the joints between the cover and sides and between the sides of the trough. Show visibility. Scale: 1″ = 1′-0″.

15.8.5. *RS* is the lower edge of a chute for conveying packages between the floors of a building. The surface of the chute is inclined at an angle of 40° above the horizontal and is rectangular in shape. The ceiling is 11 ft above the bottom of the chute. Draw the plan and elevation views of the chute from its bottom to the ceiling. How many square feet of material are required for the surface of the chute? Scale: ¼″ = 1′-0″.

Group 9. Planes making specified angles

15.9.1. Draw the top and front views of line *CD*, which lies in the plane *ABC* and makes an angle of 45° with all profile planes. *CD* is 1½ in. long and *D* is above *C*. Scale: ¾ size.

15.9.2. The Buckeye Vein strikes and dips as shown at *B*. A tunnel is to be dug in the vein, starting at point *A* and proceeding uphill in a westerly direction at a 20 per cent grade. The upper end of the tunnel is at the same elevation as *B*. Draw the map and elevation views of the tunnel.

15.9.3. Draw the front view of *ABC*, a plane which makes angles of 40 and 75° respectively, with all horizontal and frontal planes. Plane *ABC* slopes downward toward the left front.

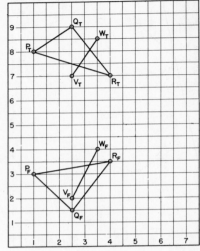

Prob. 15.7.2

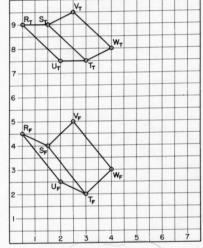

Prob. 15.8.1

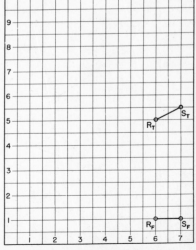

Prob. 15.8.5

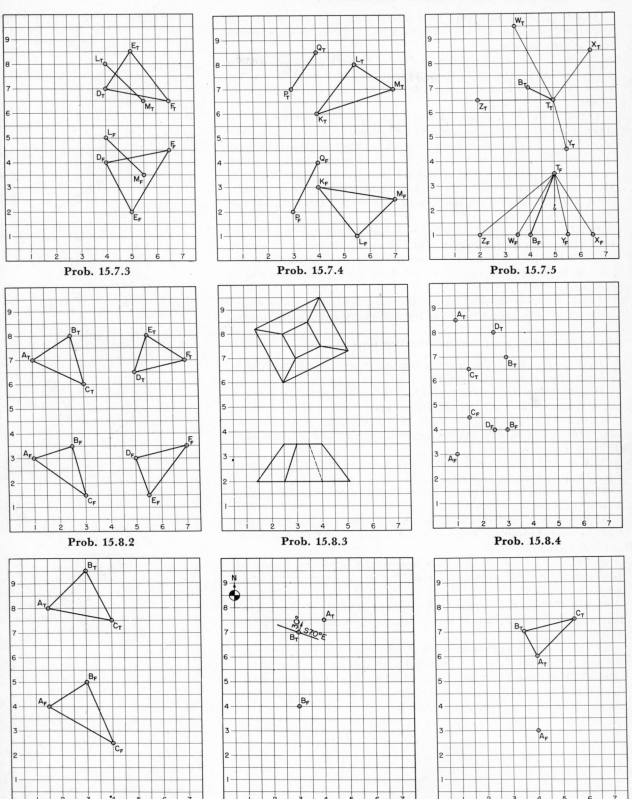

Prob. 15.7.3

Prob. 15.7.4

Prob. 15.7.5

Prob. 15.8.2

Prob. 15.8.3

Prob. 15.8.4

Prob. 15.9.1

Prob. 15.9.2

Prob. 15.9.3

15.9.4. Complete the top and front views of plane *ABC*, which makes an angle of 60° with both the frontal and profile planes. Plane *ABC* slopes downward to the right rear.

15.9.5. The plane *XYZ* makes an angle of 45° with plane *ABC* and an angle of 60° with plane *BCD*. Draw the front view of plane *XYZ*. Use the plane which slopes downward to the left and whose strike line is most nearly profile.

15.9.6. Plane *RSTU* is a portion of a belt conveyer whose direction of travel is indicated. This conveyer is to be unloaded by a rectangular plow blade so as to discharge the material to the right. The blade makes an angle of 45° with the belt and an angle of 75° with a plane that is perpendicular to the belt and parallel to the direction of travel. The top of the blade is 1 ft above the belt. The length of the blade is limited by the edges of the belt. Point *A* is one corner of the blade. Scale: ¼″ = 1′-0″. Draw the top and front views of the blade.

15.9.7. A pencil of light is emitted from source *S* and reflected from an 8- by 12-in. rectangular mirror at point *R* so as to pass through a target at point *T*; the mirror is centered at *R* and has its longer edge parallel to the plane of the light rays. Scale: ¾″ = 1′-0″. Draw the top and front views of the mirror.

15.9.8. Complete the front view of the plane *PQR* which makes angles of 60 and 30° with lines *AB* and *CD*, respectively. *PQR* dips northeasterly.

Group 10. Shortest lines between two skew lines

15.10.1. Draw front, top, and any other necessary views of the shortest horizontal line between the lines *AB* and *CD*.

15.10.2. Using the layout for Prob. 15.10.1, determine the shortest distance between lines *AB* and *CD*. Scale: ¼ size.

15.10.3. Using the layout for Prob. 15.10.1, draw top, front, and any other necessary views of the shortest line connecting *AB* and *CD* that makes 15° with horizontal planes.

15.10.4. Draw front, top, and any other necessary views of the shortest frontal line between the lines *RS* and *TU*.

15.10.5. Using the layout for Prob. 15.10.4, determine the shortest distance between lines *RS* and *TU*.

15.10.6. Using the layout of Prob. 15.10.4, draw top, front, and any other necessary views of the shortest line connecting *RS* and *TU* that makes 10° with frontal planes.

15.10.7. *AB* and *CD* are skew lines. Locate the shortest line, parallel to bearing plane *BP*, that intersects *AB* and *CD*. Use the first method of paragraph 15.20.

15.10.8. *RS* and *TU* are skew lines to be intersected by the shortest line parallel to the bearing plane *BP* shown. Use the first method of paragraph 15.20.

15.10.9. *BP* is the bearing direction of the shortest line *PQ* intersecting *XY* and *MN*. Locate *PQ* by the simplified method of paragraph 15.20.

15.10.10. *PQ* and *RS* are skew lines and *BP* is the bearing *direction* of the shortest line *XY* (of this bearing) that intersects *PQ* and *RS*. Locate *XY* by the simplified method of paragraph 15.20.

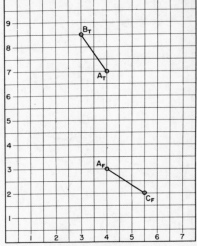

Prob. 15.9.4

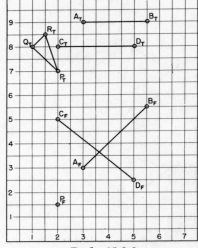

Prob. 15.9.8

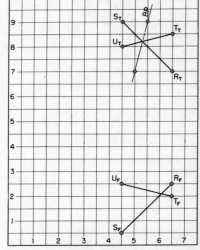

Prob. 15.10.8

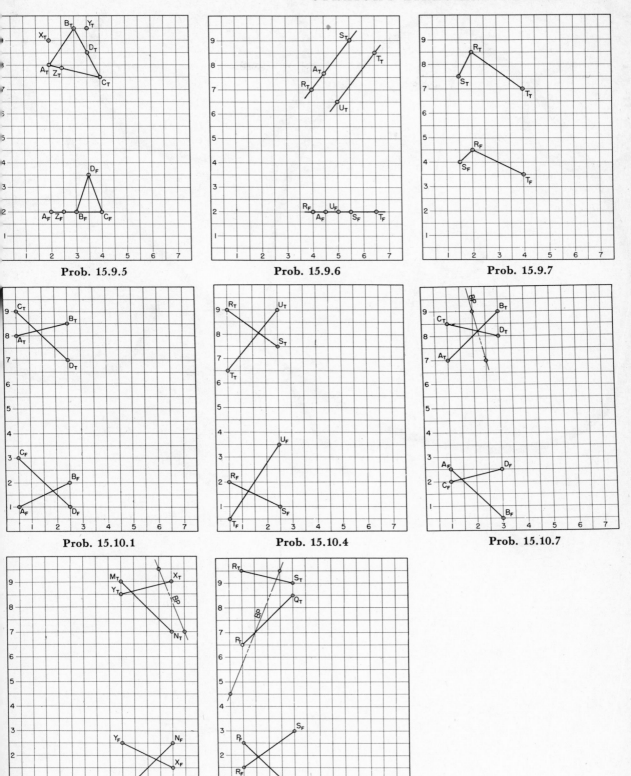

Prob. 15.9.5

Prob. 15.9.6

Prob. 15.9.7

Prob. 15.10.1

Prob. 15.10.4

Prob. 15.10.7

Prob. 15.10.9

Prob. 15.10.10

16

CURVED LINES

16.1. The previous two chapters have dealt with the problems of straight lines and with the problems of straight lines and their relationships to planes. In addition to straight lines and planes, machines and structures will also contain various curves and combinations of straight and curved lines. The trained engineer must therefore be familiar with the mathematical and graphical theory and the practical construction of curves.

16.2. Definitions. *A curved line* is generated by a point moving in a constantly changing direction, according to some mathematical or graphical law. Curved lines may be classified as either single-curved or double-curved.

A *single-curved line* is a curved line having all points of the line in a plane. Single-curved lines are often called plane curves.

A *double-curved line* is a curved line having no four consecutive points in the same plane. Double-curved lines are also known as space curves.

A *tangent* to a curved line is a line, either straight or curved, that passes through two points on the curve that are infinitely close together. Note that this definition of tangency places the tangent in the plane of the curve for single-curved lines and in an instantaneous plane of the curve for double-curved lines.

A *normal* to a single-curved line will be a line in the plane of the curve and perpendicular to a straight line connecting two consecu-

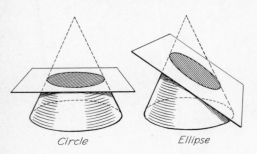
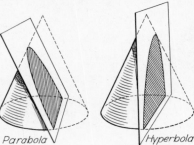

Fig. 16.1. The conic sections.

Circle   *Ellipse*   *Parabola*   *Hyperbola*

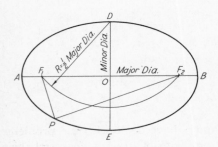

Fig. 16.2. The ellipse: major and minor diameters.

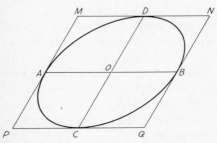

Fig. 16.3. The ellipse: conjugate diameters.

tive points of the curve. A normal to a double-curved line will be a line perpendicular to the instantaneous plane of the curve at the point of contact with the curve. A normal is perpendicular to the tangent at the same point of contact with the curve.

16.3. Plan for Study. Because even the simplest plane curve, the circle, becomes an ellipse when in an oblique position, it is necessary to study the plane curves in simple position before attempting solutions of plane curves in oblique positions. Plane curves, the circle, ellipse, parabola, hyperbola, cycloid, involute, and spiral, are discussed in paragraphs 16.4 to 16.27. Then the space problems of plane curves may be studied. These are given in paragraphs 16.29 to 16.32. Finally, double-curved lines are analyzed in paragraphs 16.33 to 16.36.

16.4. Plane Curves: The Conic Sections. In cutting a right-circular cone (a cone of revolution) by planes at different angles, we obtain four curves called "conic sections," Fig. 16.1. These are the *circle*, cut by a plane perpendicular to the axis; the *ellipse*, cut by a plane making a greater angle with the axis than do the elements; the *parabola*, cut by a plane making the same angle with the axis as do the elements; the *hyperbola*, cut by a plane making a smaller angle than do the elements. These curves are studied mathematically in analytic geometry but may be drawn, without a knowledge of their equations, by knowing something of their characteristics.

16.5. The Circle. The circle and its tangents and normals have been discussed in paragraphs 2.6 to 2.21 as a necessary part of the geometrical constructions for the drawings of solid objects. The mathematical equation of a circle with the origin of rectilinear coordinates at the center of the circle is: $x^2 + y^2 = r^2$, where r is the radius of the circle.

16.6. The Ellipse: Major and Minor Diameters (Fig. 16.2). An ellipse is the plane curve generated by a point moving so that the sum of its distances from two fixed points (F_1 and F_2), called "focuses," is a constant equal to the major axis,[1] or *major diameter, AB*.

[1] The terms "major axis" and "minor axis" are traditional terms. However, because of the confusion between these and the mathematical X and Y axes and the central axis (axis of rotation), the terms "major diameter" and "minor diameter" will be used in this discussion.

The minor axis, or *minor diameter*, *DE* is the line through the center perpendicular to the major diameter. The focuses may be determined by cutting the major diameter with an arc having its center at an end of the minor diameter and a radius equal to one-half the major diameter.

Aside from the circle, the ellipse is met with in practice much more often than any of the other conics, and draftsmen should be able to construct it readily; hence several methods are given for its construction, both as a true ellipse and as an approximate curve made by circle arcs. In the great majority of cases when this curve is required, its major and minor diameters are known.

The mathematical equation of an ellipse with the origin of rectilinear coordinates at the center of the ellipse is $x^2/a^2 + y^2/b^2 = 1$, where a is the intercept on the X axis and b is the intercept on the Y axis.

16.7. The Ellipse: Conjugate Diameters (Fig. 16.3). Any line through the center of an ellipse may serve as *one* of a pair of conjugate diameters. A property of conjugate diameters is that each is parallel to the tangents to the curve at the extremities of the other. *AB* and *CD* are a pair of conjugate diameters having *AB* parallel to the tangents *MN* and *PQ* and *CD* parallel to the tangents *MP* and *NQ*. A given ellipse may have an unlimited number of pairs of conjugate diameters. Also, either one of a pair of conjugate diameters bisects all the chords parallel to the other.

To Determine the Major and Minor Diameters of a Given Ellipse, a Pair of Conjugate Diameters Being Given: First Method (Fig. 16.4). The conjugate diameters *CN* and *JG* are given. With a center *O* and radius *OJ*, draw a semicircle intersecting the ellipse at *P*. The major and minor diameters will be parallel to the chords *GP* and *JP*, respectively.

Second Method When the Curve Is Not Given (Fig. 16.5). The conjugate diameters *CN* and *JG* are given. With a center *O* and radius *OJ*, describe a circle and draw the diameter *QR* at right angles to *JG*. Bisect the angle *QCR*. The major diameter will be parallel to this bisector and equal in length to *CR* + *CQ*. The length of the minor diameter will be *CR* − *CQ*.

16.8. Ellipse: Pin-and-string Method. This well-known method, sometimes called the "gardener's ellipse," is often used for large work and is based on the definition of the ellipse. Drive pins at the points *D*, F_1, and F_2, Fig. 16.2, and tie an inelastic thread or cord tightly around the three pins. If the pin *D* is removed and a marking point moved in the loop, keeping the cord taut, it will describe a true ellipse.

16.9. Ellipse: Trammel Method for Major and Minor Diameters. *First Method* (Fig. 16.6). On the straight edge of a strip of paper, thin cardboard, or sheet of celluloid, mark the distance *ao* equal to one-half the major diameter and *do* equal to one-half the minor diameter. If the strip is moved, keeping *a* on the minor di-

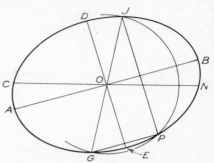

Fig. 16.4. Determination of major and minor diameters from conjugate diameters.

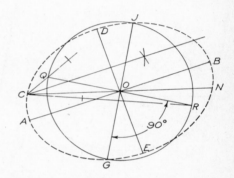

Fig. 16.5. Determination of major and minor diameters from conjugate diameters.

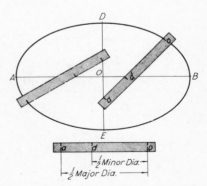

Fig. 16.6. Ellipse by trammel (first method).

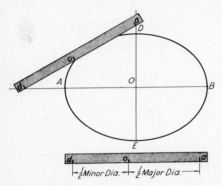

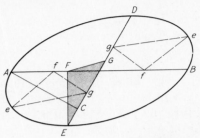

Fig. 16.8. Ellipse by triangle trammel (conjugate diameters).

Fig. 16.7. Ellipse by trammel (second method).

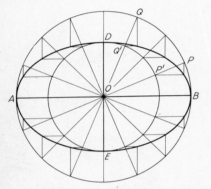

Fig. 16.9. Ellipse by concentric-circle method.

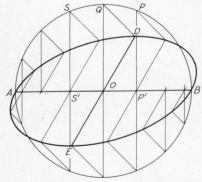

Fig. 16.10. Ellipse by circle method (conjugate diameters).

ameter and *d* on the major diameter, *o* will give points on the ellipse. This method will be found very convenient as no construction is required, but for accurate results great care must be taken to keep the points *a* and *d* exactly on the major and minor diameters.

Second Method (*Fig.* 16.7). On some suitable material—as in the first method—mark the distance *do* equal to one-half the minor diameter and *oa* equal to one-half the major diameter. If this strip is moved, keeping *a* on the minor diameter and *d* on the major diameter, *o* will give points on the ellipse. This arrangement is preferred where the ratio between the major and minor diameters is small.

16.10. Ellipse: Triangle Trammel for Conjugate Diameters (**Fig. 16.8**). The conjugate diameters *AB* and *DE* are given. Erect the perpendicular *AC* to the diameter *ED* and lay off distance *AC* from *E* to locate point *G*. Erect the perpendicular *EF* to the diameter *AB*. Transfer to a piece of paper, thin cardboard, or sheet of celluloid, and cut out the triangle *EFG*. If this triangle is moved, keeping *f* on *AB* and *g* on *ED*, *e* will give points on the ellipse. Extreme care must be used to keep points *f* and *g* on the conjugate diameters.

16.11. Ellipse: Concentric-circle Method for Major and Minor Diameters (**Fig. 16.9**). This is perhaps the most accurate method for determining points on the curve. On the two principal diameters, which intersect at *O*, describe circles. From a number of points on the outer circle, as *P* and *Q*, draw radii *OP*, *OQ*, etc., intersecting the inner circle at *P′*, *Q′*, etc. From *P* and *Q* draw lines parallel to *OD*, and from *P′* and *Q′* draw lines parallel to *OB*. The intersection of the lines through *P* and *P′* gives one point on the ellipse, the intersection of the lines through *Q* and *Q′* another point, and so on. For accuracy, the points should be taken closer together toward the major diameter. The process may be repeated in each of the four quadrants and the curve sketched in lightly freehand; or one quadrant only may be constructed and the remaining three repeated by marking the french curve.

16.12. Ellipse: Circle Method for Conjugate Diameters (**Fig. 16.10**). The conjugate diameters *AB* and *DE* are given. On the

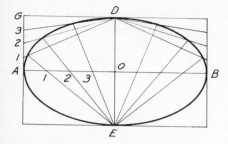

Fig. 16.11. Ellipse by parallelogram method.

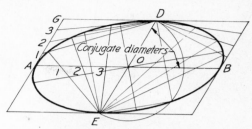

Fig. 16.12. Ellipse by parallelogram method (conjugate diameters).

conjugate diameter *AB*, describe a circle; then from a number of points, as *P*, *Q*, and *S*, draw perpendiculars *QO* to the diameter *AB*. From *S* and *P*, etc., draw lines parallel to *QD*, and from *S'* and *P'* draw lines parallel to *OD*. The intersection of the lines through *P* and *P'* gives one point on the ellipse, the intersection of the lines through *S* and *S'* another point, and so on.

16.13. Ellipse: Parallelogram Method (Figs. 16.11 and 16.12). This method may be used either with the major and minor diameters or with any pair of conjugate diameters. On the given diameters construct a parallelogram. Divide *AO* into any number of equal parts and *AG* into the same number of equal parts, numbering points from *A*. Through these points draw lines from *D* and *E*, as shown. Their intersections will be points on the curve.

16.14. To Draw a Tangent to an Ellipse. *At a Point P on the Curve (Fig. 16.13).* Draw lines from the point to the focuses. The line bisecting the exterior angle of these focal radii is the required tangent.

Parallel to a Given Line GH (Fig. 16.13). Draw F_1E perpendicular to *GH*. With F_2 as the center and a radius *AB*, draw an arc cutting F_1E at *K*. The line F_1K cuts the ellipse at the required point of tangency *T*, and the required tangent passes through *T* parallel to *GH*.

From a Point Outside (Fig. 16.14). Find the focuses F_1 and F_2. With given point *P* and a radius PF_2, draw the arc RF_2Q. With F_1 as the center and a radius *AB*, strike an arc cutting this arc at *Q* and *R*. Connect QF_1 and RF_1. The intersections of these lines with the ellipse at T_1 and T_2 will be the tangent points of tangents to the ellipse from *P*.

Concentric-circle Method. When the ellipse has been drawn by the concentric-circle method, Fig. 16.15 a tangent at any point *H* may be drawn by drawing a line perpendicular to *AB* from the point to the outer circle at *K* and drawing the auxiliary tangent *KL* to the outer circle, cutting the major diameter at *L*. From *L* draw the required tangent *LH*.

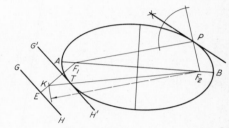

Fig. 16.13. Tangents to an ellipse.

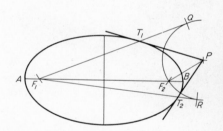

Fig. 16.14. Tangents to an ellipse from an outside point.

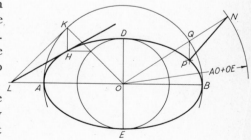

Fig. 16.15. Tangent and normal to an ellipse.

Application of circles and arcs.

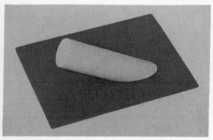

Application of the ellipse (intersection).

16.15. To Draw a Normal to an Ellipse (Fig. 16.15). From point *P* on the curve, project a parallel to the minor diameter to intersect the major diameter circle at *Q*. Draw *OQ* extended to intersect (at *N*) an arc with center at *O* and radius *AO* + *OE*. *NP* is the required normal.

Or, normals may be drawn perpendicular to the tangents of Figs. 16.13 and 16.14.

16.16. Approximate Four-centered Ellipse (Fig. 16.16). Join *A* and *D*. Lay off *DF* equal to *AO* − *DO*. Bisect *AF* by a perpendicular crossing *AO* at *G* and intersecting *DE* produced (if necessary) at *H*. Make *OG'* equal to *OG* and *OH'* equal to *OH*. Then *G*, *G'*, *H*, and *H'* will be centers for four tangent circle arcs forming a curve approximating the shape of an ellipse.

Another method is shown in Fig. 16.17. This should be used only when the minor diameter is at least two-thirds the length of the major diameter.

16.17. Approximate Eight-centered Ellipse (Fig. 16.18). When a closer approximation is desired, the eight-centered ellipse, the upper half of which is known in masonry as the "five-centered arch," may be constructed. Draw the rectangle *AFDO*. Draw the diagonal *AD* and the line from *F* perpendicular to it, intersecting the extension of the minor diameter at *H*. Lay off *OK* equal to *OD*, and, on *AK* as a diameter, draw a semicircle intersecting the extension of the minor diameter at *L*. Make *OM* equal to *LD*. With a center *H* and radius *HM*, draw the arc *MN*. From *A*, along *AB*, lay off *AQ* equal to *OL*. With *P* as the center and a radius *PQ*, draw an arc intersecting *MN* at *N*; then *P*, *N*, and *H* are centers for one-quarter of the eight-centered approximate ellipse.

It should be noted that an ellipse is changing its radius of curvature at every successive point and that these approximations are therefore not ellipses, but simply curves of the same general shape and, incidentally, not nearly so pleasing in appearance.

16.18. Any Noncircular Curve. This may be approximated by

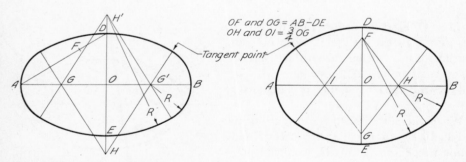

Fig. 16.16. Four-centered approximate ellipse.

Fig. 16.17. Four-centered approximate ellipse.

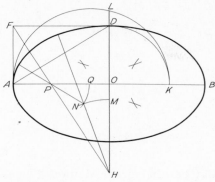

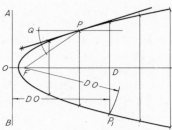

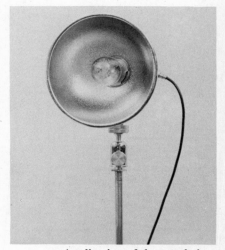

Fig. 16.19. A curve constructed with circle arcs.

Fig. 16.18. Eight-centered approximate ellipse.

Fig. 16.20. Parabola.

tangent circle arcs as follows: Select a center by trial, draw as much of an arc as will practically coincide with the curve, and then, changing the center and radius, draw the next portion, remembering always that, *if arcs are to be tangent, their centers must lie on the common normal at the point of tangency.* Draftsmen sometimes prefer to ink curves in this way rather than to use irregular curves. Figure 16.19 illustrates the construction.

16.19. The Parabola. The parabola is a plane curve generated by a point so moving that its distance from a fixed point, called the "focus," is always equal to its distance from a straight line, called the "directrix." Among its practical applications are included searchlights, parabolic reflectors, some loudspeakers, road sections, and certain bridge arches.

The mathematical equation for a parabola with the origin of rectilinear coordinates at the intercept of the curve with the X axis and the focus on the axis is $y^2 = 2px$, where p is twice the distance from the origin to the focus.

When the focus F and the directrix AB are given, Fig. 16.20, draw the axis through F perpendicular to AB. Through any point D on the axis, draw a line parallel to AB. With the distance DO as radius and F as a center, draw an arc intersecting the line, thus locating a point P on the curve. Repeat the operation as many times as needed.

To Draw a Tangent at Any Point P. Draw PQ parallel to the axis and bisect the angle FPQ.

Application of the parabola.

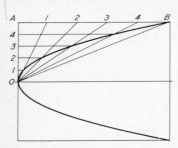

Fig. 16.21. Parabola by parallelogram method.

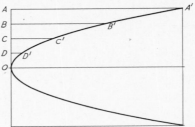

Fig. 16.22. Parabola by offset method.

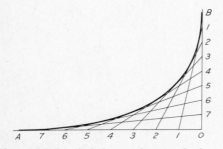

Application of the hyperbola (intersection).

Fig. 16.23. Parabola by envelope method.

16.20. Parabola: Parallelogram Method. Usually when a parabola is required, the dimensions of the enclosing rectangle, that is, the width and depth of the parabola (or span and rise), are given, as in Fig. 16.21. Divide OA and AB into the same number of equal parts. From the divisions on AB, draw lines converging at O. The intersections of these with the lines from the corresponding divisions on OA that are drawn parallel to the axis will be points on the curve.

16.21. Parabola: Offset Method. Given the enclosing rectangle, the parabola, Fig. 16.22, may be plotted by computing the offsets from the line OA. These offsets vary in length as the square of their distances from O. Thus if OA is divided into four parts, DD' will be $\frac{1}{16}$ of AA'; CC', since it is twice as far from O as DD' is, will be $\frac{4}{16}$ of AA'; and BB', $\frac{9}{16}$. If OA had been divided into five parts, the relations would be $\frac{1}{25}$, $\frac{4}{25}$, $\frac{9}{25}$, and $\frac{16}{25}$, the denominator in each case being the square of the number of divisions. This method is the one generally used by civil engineers in drawing parabolic arches.

16.22. Parabolic Envelope (Fig. 16.23). This method of drawing a pleasing curve is often used in machine design. Divide OA and OB into the same number of equal parts. Number the divisions from O and B and connect corresponding numbers. The tangent curve will be a portion of a parabola—but a parabola whose axis is not parallel to either ordinate.

16.23. The Hyperbola. It is a plane curve generated by a point moving so that the difference of its distances from two fixed points, called the "focuses," is a constant. (Compare this definition with that of the ellipse.)

The mathematical equation for a hyperbola with the center at the origin of rectilinear coordinates and the focuses on the X axis is $x^2/a^2 - y^2/b^2 = 1$, where a is the distance from the center to the X intercept and b is the corresponding Y value of the asymptotes.

To Draw a Hyperbola When the Focuses F_1F_2 and the Transverse Axis AB (Constant Difference) Are Given (Fig. 16.24). With F_1 and F_2 as centers and any radius greater than F_1B, as F_1P, draw arcs. With the same centers and radius $F_1P - AB$, strike arcs intersecting these arcs, giving points on the curve.

To Draw a Tangent at Any Point P. Bisect the angle F_1PF_2.

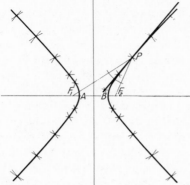

Fig. 16.24. Hyperbola.

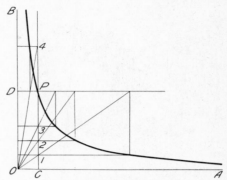

Fig. 16.25. Equilateral hyperbola.

16.24. Equilateral Hyperbola. The case of the hyperbola of commonest practical interest to the engineer is the equilateral, or rectangular, hyperbola referred to its asymptotes. With it the law $PV = c$, connecting the varying pressure and volume of a portion of steam or gas, can be graphically presented.

To Draw the Equilateral Hyperbola (*Fig.* 16.25). Let OA and OB be the asymptotes of the curve and P any point on it (this might be the point of cutoff on an indicator diagram). Draw PC and PD. Mark any points 1, 2, 3, etc., on PC, and through these points draw a system of lines parallel to OA and a second system through the same points converging to O. From the intersections of these lines of the second system with PD extended, draw perpendiculars to OA. The intersections of these perpendiculars with the corresponding lines of the first system give points on the curve.

16.25. Cycloidal Curves. A cycloid is the curve generated by the motion of a point on the circumference of a circle rolled in a plane along a straight line. If the circle is rolled on the outside of another circle, the curve generated is called an "epicycloid"; if rolled on the inside, it is called a "hypocycloid." These curves are used in drawing the cycloid system of gear teeth.

The mathematical equation of a cycloid (parametric form) is $x = r\theta - r \sin \theta$, $y = r - r \cos \theta$, where r is the radius of a moving point and θ is the turned angle about the center from zero position.

To Draw a Cycloid (*Fig.* 16.26). Divide the rolling circle into a convenient number of parts (say, eight), and, using these divisions, lay off on the tangent AB the rectified length of the circumference. Draw through C the line of centers CD, and project the division points up to this line by perpendiculars to AB. About these points as centers, draw circles representing different positions of the rolling circle, and project in order the division points of the original circle across to these circles. The intersections thus determined will be points on the curve. The epicycloid and hypocycloid may be drawn similarly, as illustrated in Fig. 16.27.

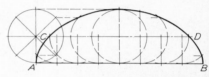

Fig. 16.26. Cycloid.

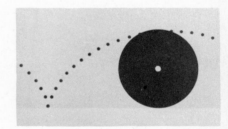

Formation of a cycloid.

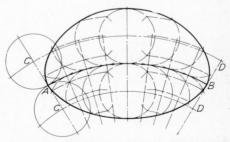

Fig. 16.27. Epicycloid and hypocycloid.

Application of the involute.

16.26. The Involute. An involute is the spiral curve traced by a point on a taut cord unwinding from around a polygon or circle. Thus the involute of any polygon may be drawn by extending its sides, as in Fig. 16.28, and, with the corners of the polygon as successive centers, drawing arcs terminating on the extended sides.

The equation of the involute of a circle (parametric form) is $x = r (\sin \theta - \theta \cos \theta)$, $y = r (\cos \theta + \theta \sin \theta)$, where r is the radius of the circle and θ is the turned angle for the tangent point.

In drawing a spiral in design, as, for example, of bent ironwork, the easiest way is to draw it as the involute of a square.

A circle may be conceived of as a polygon of an infinite number of sides. Thus to draw the involute of a circle, Fig. 16.29, divide it into a convenient number of parts, draw tangents at these points, lay off on these tangents the rectified lengths of the arcs from the point of tangency to the starting point, and connect the points by a smooth curve. The involute of the circle is the basis for the involute system of gearing.

16.27. The Spiral of Archimedes. The spiral of Archimedes is the plane curve generated by a point moving uniformly along a straight line while the line revolves about a fixed point with uniform angular velocity.

To Draw a Spiral of Archimedes That Makes One Turn in a Given Circle (Fig. 16.30). Divide the circle into a number of equal parts, drawing the radii and numbering them. Divide the radius 0-8 into the same number of equal parts, numbering from the center. With 0 as a center, draw concentric arcs intersecting the radii of corresponding numbers, and draw a smooth curve through these intersections. The Archimedean spiral is the curve of the heart cam used for converting uniform rotary motion into uniform reciprocal motion.

The mathematical equation is $p = a\theta$ (polar form).

16.28. Other Plane Curves. The foregoing paragraphs discuss common plane curves occurring frequently in scientific work. Other curves, whenever needed, may be found in any good textbook of

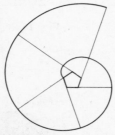

Fig. 16.28. Involute of a pentagon.

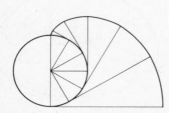

Fig. 16.29. Involute of a circle.

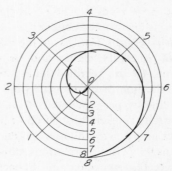

Fig. 16.30. Spiral of Archimedes.

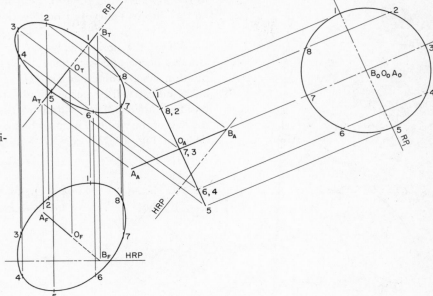

Fig. 16.31. Circle in oblique position by plotted points.

analytic geometry and calculus. Typical of the curves that may be met with are the *catenary, cardioid, sine curve, cosine curve, logarithmic spiral, reciprocal (hyperbolic) spiral, parabolic spiral, logarithmic curve, exponential curve,* and curves of *velocity* and *acceleration.*

16.29. Plane Curves in Space. A plane curve may, of course, lie in a horizontal, frontal, or profile plane, in which case the normal view of the curve will appear in one of the principal views. If the curve is in an auxiliary or oblique plane, extra construction will be necessary before the principal views of the curve can be drawn. With the exception of a circle in an oblique position, when the diameters of an ellipse may be located by special projective methods (paragraph 16.30), a normal view of the curve is required.

16.30. A Circle in an Oblique Position. In designating the position of a circle in space, either the position of the central axis (axis of rotation) will have to be given, *or* the plane of the circle defined. In Fig. 16.31, the axis *AB* of a circle with center at *O* has been located. The diameter of the circle is given. The axis *AB* is oblique; therefore, an auxiliary view will be required to get the normal view. If now the end view of axis *AB* is made as at $B_O O_O A_O$, the *plane* of the circle will appear normal because the plane of the circle must be perpendicular to the axis of rotation. In this oblique view, the circle may then be drawn. In the auxiliary view, the axis appears in true length, and therefore the plane of the circle, perpendicular to the axis, will appear as an edge. Thus points, for example, 1 to 8 in Fig. 16.31, located on the circle in the oblique view (end view of axis) may be projected to the auxiliary view, where they are located on the edge view of the circle. Next, these points may be projected

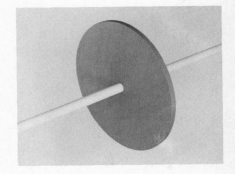

Circle in oblique position.

to the top view and then to the front view, thus determining points on the elliptical curves through which smooth curves may be drawn.

The above problem can also be solved, without bringing points back from the normal view, by locating the major and minor diameters needed for each view. In *any* view of a circle in an oblique position where the circle appears as an ellipse, the major diameter of the ellipse will be perpendicular to the axis of the circle, and the minor diameter of the ellipse will coincide (on the drawing) with the axis of the circle. This may be proved by examining the auxiliary views of Fig. 16.32. Axis *AB* and the diameter of the circle with

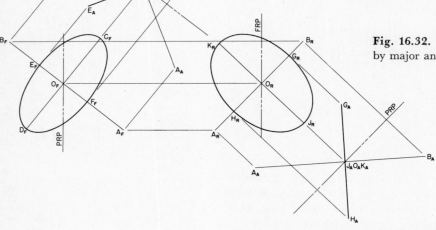

Fig. 16.32. Circle in oblique position by major and minor diameters.

center at *O* are given. The rear auxiliary view, projected from the right-side view, gives the true length of axis *AB*. From *O*, perpendicular to A_AB_A, the plane of the circle and the diameter *GH* may then be laid out at G_AH_A. One diameter of the circle appears as a point at J_AK_A. Projection of this diameter back to the side view shows *JK* in true length in the side view. Because this diameter is in true length, it has not been foreshortened and is therefore the major diameter of the ellipse in this, the side view. Note that *JK* is perpendicular to the circle axis *AB* in the side view. Diameter *GH* is in true length at G_AH_A in the rear auxiliary. Its position in the side view will therefore be perpendicular to the rays of projection between side view and rear auxiliary, and, as this diameter contains point *O* (the center), *GH* must appear in coincidence with the axis *AB*. Because *GH* is the perpendicular bisector of *JK*, the major diameter, it is the minor diameter. Also, *GH* is the diameter foreshortened to the greatest degree, proving again that it is the minor diameter. Thus, having established the major and minor diameters for the ellipse, we can draw the curve by either the concentric-circle or trammel method to complete the view. The front view of Fig. 16.32 may be established in a similar way by employing the right auxiliary shown and determining the major diameter *CD* and the minor diameter *EF*.

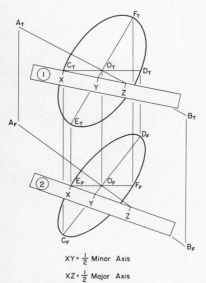

$XY = \frac{1}{2}$ Minor Axis

$XZ = \frac{1}{2}$ Major Axis

Fig. 16.33. Circle in oblique position by simplified method (trammel).

16.31. A Circle in an Oblique Position: Simplified Method. If advantage is taken of the facts just presented in paragraph 16.30

and, in addition, a knowledge of the trammel method is applied, a circle in an oblique position may be drawn without the necessity of extra views. In Fig. 16.33, the rotation axis AB, the center, and the diameter of the circle are given. It has been shown in paragraph 16.30 that the major diameter in each view will be perpendicular to the axis of rotation and equal in length to the diameter of the circle. Therefore, the major diameters, $E_T F_T$ for the top view and $C_F D_F$ for the front view of Fig. 16.37, can be drawn. The major diameter $E_T F_T$ is in true length in the top view and will therefore be a horizontal line $E_F F_F$ in the front view. This gives two points, E_F and F_F, in the front view that are on the elliptical curve. Then by employing a trammel (2 in Fig. 16.33) with point x as the plotting end, distance xz is marked off equal to one-half the major diameter. Now with point x located at point F_F and point z on the minor diameter (extended), a mark at point y, where the trammel intersects the major diameter, will give distance xy equal to one-half the minor diameter. The trammel may then be moved as described in paragraph 16.9 to plot points on the curve. The top view is drawn similarly, employing major diameter $E_T F_T$, points C_T and D_T (either one) on the curve, and trammel 1, shown.

An equivalent construction may be made by using the concentric-circle method shown in Fig. 16.34, in place of the trammel method of Fig. 16.33. In Fig. 16.34, as before in Fig. 16.33, the axis AB, the center O, and the diameter of the circle are given. The major diameter $E_T F_T$ in the top view and $C_F D_F$ in the front view and the projection of these diameters to the other view, $E_F F_F$ in the front view and $C_T D_T$ in the top view, are projected, giving points on the curve in each view, as described for the trammel method. Then, to draw the top view, the major-diameter circle for the ellipse is drawn and point C_T projected (perpendicular to the major diameter) to the circle at C_{MT}. This is the revolved position of point C on the ellipse to its original position on the major-diameter circle. If then the radial line $C_{MT}O_T$ is drawn and a projector perpendicular to the minor diameter (also perpendicular to $A_T B_T$) drawn to intersect the radial line at C_{NT}, the distance $C_{NT}O_T$ is the length of one-half the minor diameter. The minor-diameter circle then drawn, as shown, completes the construction necessary to plot the curve by the concentric-circle method of paragraph 16.11. Construction for the front view is similar, as indicated on the figure.

16.32. Any Plane Curve in an Oblique Position. If the position of the plane in which a plane curve lies is known and the orientation of the plane curve on its plane is also fixed, the curve may be laid out and drawn in any required view. The plane of the curve will probably occur as the surface of some object and is therefore fixed in space. The curve on the plane may occur as a geometrical shape, produced either by design requirements or by some necessary structural feature or, in some cases, by an intersection of some surface with the plane. Because of the numerous possibilities, the plane curve may be either a geometrical shape or some general curve not governed by mathematical laws.

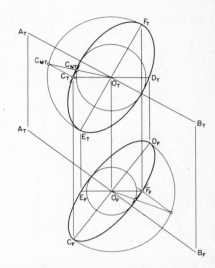

Fig. 16.34. Circle in oblique position by simplified method (concentric-circle).

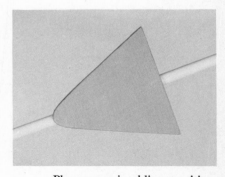

Plane curve in oblique position.

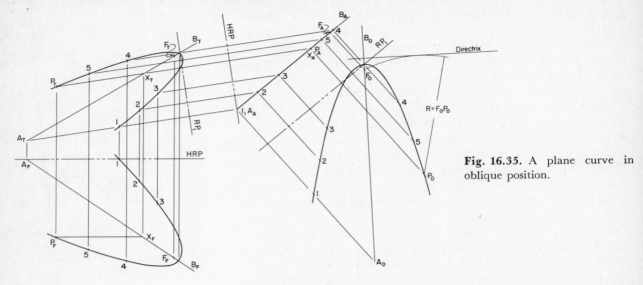

Fig. 16.35. A plane curve in oblique position.

In paragraphs 5.8 and 5.9, the circle on an oblique plane, an ellipse on an oblique plane (produced by intersection with a cylinder), and the projection of a general curve on a plane have been discussed. Also, in Chap. 18, the intersections of various surfaces with planes are shown. In paragraphs 16.30 and 16.31, the circle in oblique position was given. Note in every case that, if the plane is known or can be determined, the curve can then be located *on* the plane. The normal view of the plane will be required in order to lay out the curve.

The principles just presented may be illustrated by Fig. 16.35, in which line AB is the central axis of a parabola. Point F on AB is the focus of the parabola and point P is a point on the curve. This information fixes the curve and the plane of the curve: First, by considering that ABP is the plane of the curved line, PX in plane ABP is drawn horizontal. Then an elevation auxiliary in the direction of $X_T P_T$ will give the edge view of the plane at $B_A F_A X_A P_A A_A$. An oblique view now made perpendicular to the edge view gives the normal view of the plane, and $A_O B_O F_O$ and P_O are required points in this view. The directrix of the parabola will be perpendicular to axis AB and may be located by drawing an arc with center at P through F_O as shown. The directrix is then tangent to this arc. Now that the axis, the focus, and the directrix are located, the curve may be drawn in the oblique view. Points now located on the curve (1 to 5, as shown) may be projected to the edge view and thence to the top and front views, completing the views required.

Any other geometrical curve may be drawn as described for the parabola of Fig. 16.35 if enough information is available to orient the plane and curve. For example, if the curve is an ellipse, the plane and either the position of the major diameter and minor diameter *or* the major diameter and a point on the curve must be known.

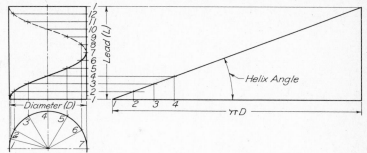

Fig. 16.36. Cylindrical helix and its development.

Nongeometrical curves may be laid out in the normal view if their true configuration is known.

16.33. Double-curved Lines. The scarcity of geometrical double-curved lines, by comparison with the numerous single-curved lines, is surprising. There are only two double-curved lines, the cylindrical and the conical helix, much used in engineering work. Double-curved lines will, however, often occur as the lines of intersection between two curved solids or surfaces. These lines are not geometric but are double-curved lines of general form. It will be interesting to note the double-curved lines of intersection in the figures of Chap. 18.

16.34. The Helix. The helix is a space curve generated by a point moving uniformly along a straight line while the line revolves uniformly about another line as an axis. If the moving line is parallel to the axis, it will generate a cylinder. The word "helix" alone always means a cylindrical helix. If the moving line intersects the axis at an angle less than 90° it will generate a cone, and the curve made by the point moving on it will be a "conical helix." The distance parallel to the axis through which the point advances in one revolution is called the "lead." When the angle becomes 90°, the helix degenerates into the Archimedean spiral.

16.35. To Draw a Cylindrical Helix (Fig. 16.36). Draw the two views of the cylinder, and measure the lead along one of the contour elements. Divide this lead into a number of equal parts (say, 12) and the circle of the front view into the same number. Number the divisions on the top view starting at point 1 and the divisions on the front view starting at the front view of point 1. When the generating point has moved one-twelfth of the distance around the cylinder, it has also advanced one-twelfth of the lead; when halfway around the cylinder, it will have advanced one-half the lead. Thus points on the top view of the helix may be found by projecting the front views of the elements, which are points on the circular front view of the helix, to intersect lines drawn across from the corresponding divisions of the lead. If the cylinder is developed, the helix will appear on the development as a straight line inclined to the base at an angle, called the "helix angle," whose tangent is $L/\pi D$, where L is the lead and D the diameter.

Application of the helix.

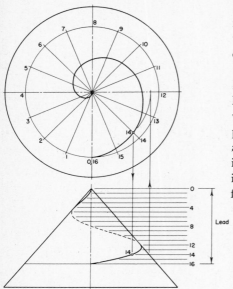

Fig. 16.37. Conical helix.

16.36. To Draw a Conical Helix. The conical helix, Fig. 16.37, is drawn by first making two views of the right-circular cone on which the helix will be generated. Then lay out uniform angular divisions in the view showing the end view of the axis (in Fig. 16.37, the top view) and divide the lead into the same number of parts. Points may now be plotted on the curve. Each plotted point will lie on a circle cut from the cone by a plane dividing the lead and will also lie on the angular-division line. Thus, for example, to plot point 14, the circle diameter obtained from the front view is drawn as shown in the top view. Point 14 in the top view then lies at the intersection of this circle and radial-division line 14. The front view is then located by projection from the top view to plane 14 in the front view.

PROBLEMS

To be of value both as drawing exercises and as solutions, geometrical problems should be worked very accurately. The pencil must be kept extremely sharp, and comparatively light lines must be used. A point should be located by two intersecting lines, and the length of a line should be indicated by short dashes across the line.

Group 1. Plane curves

16.1.1. The conjugate diameters of an ellipse measure 3 and 4 in., the angle between them being 60°. Construct the major and minor diameters of this ellipse by the second method of paragraph 16.7, and draw the ellipse by one of the methods in the following paragraphs.

16.1.2. Using the method of the pin and string described in paragraph 16.8, draw an ellipse having a major diameter of 6 in. and a minor diameter of $4\frac{1}{4}$ in.

16.1.3. Draw an ellipse having a major diameter of $4\frac{1}{2}$ in. and a minor diameter of 3 in., using the trammel method as explained in paragraph 16.9, first method.

16.1.4. Draw an ellipse having a major diameter of $4\frac{1}{2}$ in. and a minor diameter of 4 in., using the trammel method as explained in paragraph 16.9, second method.

16.1.5. Draw an ellipse having a major diameter of $4\frac{5}{8}$ in. and a minor diameter of $1\frac{1}{2}$ in., using the concentric-circle method as explained in paragraph 16.11.

16.1.6. Draw an ellipse on a major diameter of 4 in. One point on the ellipse is $1\frac{1}{2}$ in. to the left of the minor diameter and $\frac{7}{8}$ in. above the major diameter.

16.1.7. Draw an ellipse whose minor diameter is $2\frac{3}{16}$ in. and distance between focuses is $3\frac{1}{4}$ in. Draw a tangent at a point $1\frac{3}{8}$ in. to the right of the minor diameter.

16.1.8. Draw an ellipse whose major diameter is 4 in. A tangent to the ellipse intersects the minor diameter $1\frac{3}{4}$ in. from the center, at an angle of 60°.

16.1.9. Draw a five-centered arch with a span of 5 in. and a rise of 2 in. Refer to paragraph 16.17.

16.1.10. Draw an ellipse having conjugate diameters of 4¾ in. and 2¾ in. making an angle of 75° with each other. Determine the major and minor diameters.

16.1.11. Draw the major and minor diameters for an ellipse having a pair of conjugate diameters 60° apart, one horizontal and 6¼ in. long, the other 3¼ in. long.

16.1.12. Draw an ellipse having a pair of conjugate diameters, one making 15° with the horizontal and 6 in. long, the other making 60° with the first diameter and 2½ in. long, using the circle method as explained in paragraph 16.12.

16.1.13. Draw an ellipse having a pair of conjugate diameters 60° apart, one horizontal and 6 in. long, the other 4 in. long, using the triangle-trammel method as explained in paragraph 16.10.

16.1.14. Draw an ellipse having a pair of conjugate diameters 45° apart, one making 15° with the horizontal and 6 in. long, the other 3 in. long, using the triangle-trammel method as explained in paragraph 16.10.

16.1.15. Draw a parabola, axis vertical, in a rectangle 4 by 2 in.

16.1.16. Draw a parabolic arch, with 6-in. span and a 2½-in. rise, by the offset method, dividing the half span into eight equal parts.

16.1.17. Draw an equilateral hyperbola passing through a point P, ½ in. from OB and 2½ in. from OA. (Reference letters correspond to Fig. 16.25.)

16.1.18. Draw two turns of the involute of a pentagon whose circumscribed circle is ½ in. in diameter.

16.1.19. Draw one-half turn of the involute of a circle 3¼ in. in diameter whose center is 1 in. from the left edge of space. Compute the length of the last tangent and compare with the measured length.

16.1.20. Draw a spiral of Archimedes making one turn in a circle 4 in. in diameter.

16.1.21. Draw the cycloid formed by a rolling circle 2 in. in diameter. Use 12 divisions.

16.1.22. Draw the epicycloid formed by a 2-in.-diameter circle rolling on a 15-in.-diameter directing circle. Use 12 divisions.

16.1.23. Draw the hypocycloid formed by a 2-in.-diameter circle rolling inside a 15-in.-diameter directing circle. Use 12 divisions.

Group 2. Circle in oblique position

16.2.1. AB is the axis and C the center of a circle of 2 in. diameter. Draw top, front, elevation auxiliary, and normal views by plotting points on the circle. Refer to paragraph 16.30. Scale: full size.

16.2.2. AB is the axis and C the center of a circle of 3½ in. diameter. Draw the top and front views by locating major and minor diameters of the elliptical representation for each view. Refer to paragraph 16.30. Scale: ½ size.

16.2.3. AB is the axis and C the center of a circle of 16 in. diameter. Draw top and front views by the trammel method of paragraph 16.31. Scale: ¼ size.

16.2.4. AB is the axis and C the center of a circle of 15 in. diameter. Draw top and front views by the concentric-circle method of paragraph 16.31. Scale: ¼ size.

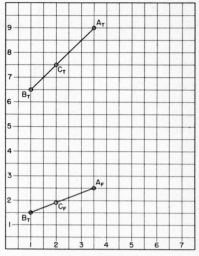

Prob. 16.2.1

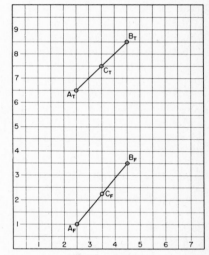

Prob. 16.2.2

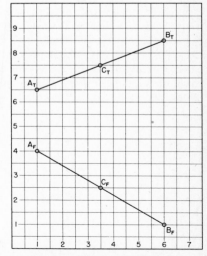

Probs. 16.2.3 and 16.2.4

16.2.5. AB is the axis, C the center, and P a point on the circumference of a circle. Draw top, front, and any other necessary views of the circle. Scale: full size.

Group 3. Plane curves in oblique position

16.3.1. ABC is the plane and C the center of an ellipse whose major diameter is horizontal and $2\frac{1}{2}$ in. long and whose minor diameter is $1\frac{3}{4}$ in. Draw top, front, and other necessary views of the ellipse. Scale: full size.

16.3.2. Using the layout for Prob. 16.2.1., AB is the axis of an elliptical cylinder with a right section at point C. The elliptical section has the major diameter frontal and $2\frac{3}{4}$ in. long. The minor diameter is 2 in. Draw top, front, and other necessary views of the right section and the limiting-element lines. Scale: full size.

16.3.3. AB is the axis of a parabola with focus at point B. Point P is a point on the parabola. Draw front, top, and other necessary views.

Group 4. The circle

16.4.1. AB is the axis and B is the center of a circle of $2\frac{1}{2}$ in. diameter. Draw the top and front views of the circle. Scale: full size.

16.4.2. LM is the axis and L is the center of a 6-in.-diameter circle. Draw the top and front views of the circle. Scale: $\frac{3}{8}$ size.

16.4.3. AB is the major diameter of the elliptical top view of a circle. The major diameter of the elliptical front view of the circle lies along line ST. Draw the top and front views of the circle.

16.4.4. P is a point on the circumference of a circle whose axis is AB. Draw the top and front views of the circle.

16.4.5. A, B, and C are points on the circumference and in the plane of the crown of a belt pulley. Draw the top and front views of the crown and its axis.

Group 5. The ellipse

16.5.1. F_1 and F_2 are the foci of an ellipse whose major diameter is 4 in. long. The plane of the ellipse makes a 30° angle with the frontal plane. Scale: $\frac{3}{4}$ size. Draw the top and front views of the ellipse.

16.5.2. Draw the top, front, and normal views of the conic section cut from the cone V by the plane whose edge view is CD.

16.5.3. RS is the center line of a $1\frac{1}{2}$-in.-diameter drill which passes through the plane $ABCD$. Using conjugate diameters, draw the top and front views of the hole in the plane. Scale: $\frac{3}{4}$ size.

16.5.4. The plan and elevation views of a portion of a wall are shown. An arched opening is to be made in this wall as indicated. The arch is to be of semielliptical shape. The ends of the major diameter of the semi-ellipse are at A and B. P is a point on the arch. Complete the elevation view of the opening.

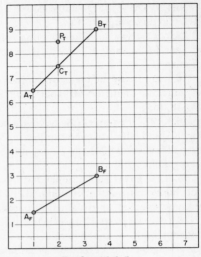

Prob. 16.2.5

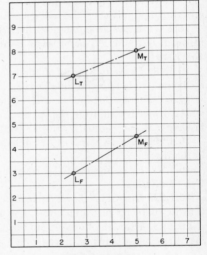

Prob. 16.4.2

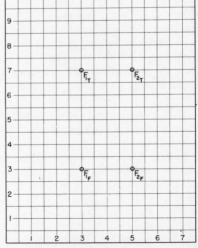

Prob. 16.5.1

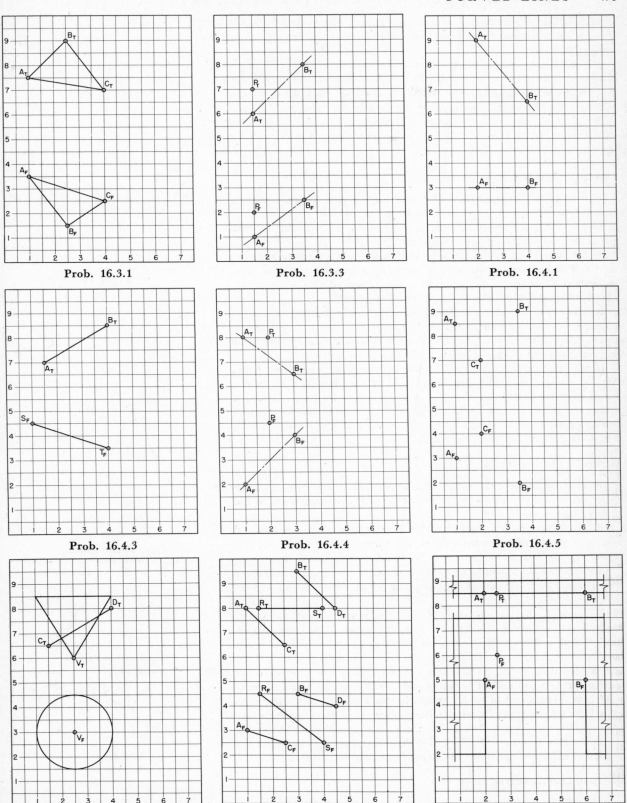

Prob. 16.3.1

Prob. 16.3.3

Prob. 16.4.1

Prob. 16.4.3

Prob. 16.4.4

Prob. 16.4.5

Prob. 16.5.2

Prob. 16.5.3

Prob. 16.5.4

16.5.5. Line *PQ* is tangent to an ellipse whose diameters are *AB* and *CD*. *P* is on the curve and directly above the right-hand focus. Draw the front view of line *PQ*.

16.5.6. *V* is the vertex of an oblique cone. Its circular base is $3\frac{1}{2}$ in. in diameter, is centered at *B*, and lies in the plane *ABC*. Draw the top and front views of the cone, showing visibility. The base ends of the contour elements are to be located by a precise method. Scale: $\frac{1}{2}$ size.

16.5.7. *L*, *C*, and *M* are points on a semielliptical spring. *C* is one end of the minor diameter which is 3 ft 6 in. long. Draw the front view of the spring. Scale: $\frac{3}{4}'' = 1' - 0''$.

Group 6. The parabola

16.6.1. *XY* is the directrix and *F* is the focus of a frontal parabola. Draw the front view of the parabola as far as the line *CD*.

16.6.2. Draw the top, front, and normal views of the parabola cut from the cone *V* by the plane that contains the line *AB*.

16.6.3. One of the cables of a suspension bridge is anchored to its towers at *A* and *B*. The loaded cable closely assumes the shape of a parabola with its focus at *F*. Determine the sag at the center measured with respect to the chord *AB*. Scale: $1'' = 50'$. Optional: Draw the curve.

16.6.4. *GH* is the tube of a 105-mm howitzer which is firing at a target on the mountain side represented by the plane *TUV*. The highest point on the parabolic trajectory of the shell is at *X*. Find the map and elevation views of the point of impact of the shell. Neglect air resistance.

16.6.5. The superstructure of the Rio Blanco bridge near Vera Cruz, Mexico, consists essentially of two arches leaning against each other in a manner similar to that shown in the pictorial sketch. In this problem, the arches are parabolic and are in contact at their vertices. The vertex and two other points on one of the arches are shown orthographically at *V*, *A*, and *B*. Draw the plan view of the arch.

Group 7. The hyperbola

16.7.1. Given the foci F_1 and F_2 and the vertices V_1 and V_2 of a frontal hyperbola, draw the front view of both branches, extending them to the limiting lines L_1 and L_2.

16.7.2. F_1 and F_2 are the foci of the normal view of a hyperbola. *P* is a point on one of its branches. Draw the normal view of both branches of the hyperbola. Extend the view to the limits of the graph field.

16.7.3. Draw the top and normal views of both branches of the hyperbola which is cut from the cone *V* by the plane whose edge view appears as line *ST*.

16.7.4. *M* is the map location of a 4.2-in. mortar whose maximum range is approximately 2,500 yards. Friendly listening posts are located at *A*, *B*, and *C*. Reports from enemy mortars located generally to the north have been detected by the listening posts. There is a difference of 1.09 sec between the time when a given report is heard at *A* and the time when the same report is heard at *B*. The corresponding difference for posts *B* and *C* is 3.82 sec. The speed of sound under the conditions of this problem is 1,100 ft per sec. All points involved in this problem are at the same elevation. Scale: $1'' = 1,000$ yards. Locate all the enemy positions which are in range of the weapon at *M*. (*Hint.* The listening posts may be regarded as the foci of hyperbolas which pass through the enemy positions.)

Group 8. Double-curved lines

16.8.1. Draw one turn of a right-hand cylindrical helix having a cylinder diameter of 3 in. and a lead of 4 in. Scale: full size.

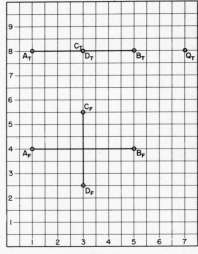

Prob. 16.5.5

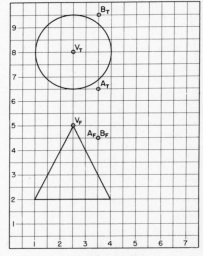

Prob. 16.6.2

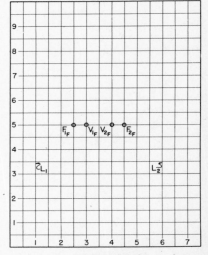

Prob. 16.7.1

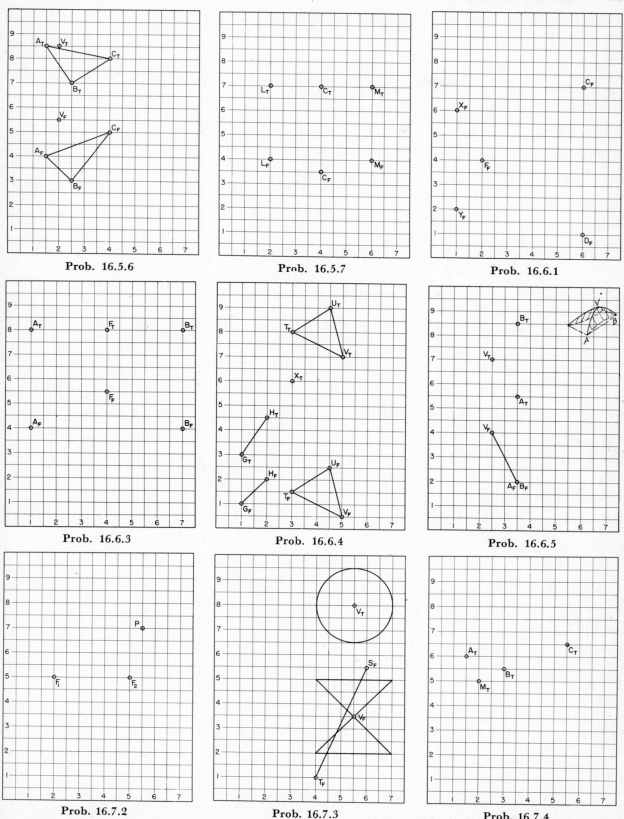

Prob. 16.5.6

Prob. 16.5.7

Prob. 16.6.1

Prob. 16.6.3

Prob. 16.6.4

Prob. 16.6.5

Prob. 16.7.2

Prob. 16.7.3

Prob. 16.7.4

16.8.2. Draw one turn of a left-hand cylindrical helix having a cylinder diameter of 4 in. and a lead of 3 in. Locate a point on the helix 270° from point of beginning.

16.8.3. Draw one turn of a left-hand conical helix. The cone base is 3 in. in diameter, the altitude 4 in. The lead is 3 in., starting at the cone base.

16.8.4. Draw one turn of a right-hand conical helix starting at the apex of a cone whose elements make an angle of 40° with the axis. The lead is 3 in.

Group 9. The involute

16.9.1. Draw one complete turn of the involute of the circle about *C*. Start at point *P* and proceed counterclockwise. Use at least 16 points.

16.9.2. *P* is a point on the involute of circle *A*. The involute unwinds clockwise. Draw the curve from its origin to the limit of the graph field.

16.9.3. *A* and *B* are the centers of two 20° involute spur gears. The direction of rotation of the driving gear *B* is indicated. Their pitch circles are tangent at the pitch point *P*. The profile of the gear teeth is an involute of the base circle. The base circles of both gears are tangent to the line of action. The tooth profile between the base and root circles is a radial line. Draw the contacting profiles of the two teeth which are touching (one profile on each gear). These profiles both pass through point *P*. Scale: full size.

Group 10. The cycloid

16.10.1. Draw one lobe of the cycloid generated by point *A* on circle *C* as the circle rolls along line *AB*. The origin of the curve is at *A*.

16.10.2. *ABCD* is a chute, of cycloidal profile, which is designed so as to permit objects to slide or roll from elevation *AB* to elevation *LM* in the shortest possible time. The chute terminates at its tangent line in the horizontal plane through *LM*. Complete the top and front views of the chute.

16.10.3. The arrangement and critical dimensions of the cycloidal impellers of a blower are shown in the design sketch. Draw the front view of the entire upper half of the left-hand impeller. Scale: ¼ size.

Group 11. The helix

16.11.1. Draw the front view of the helix which lies on the cylinder about axis *AB*. The lead is 4 in. and the curve rises counterclockwise from point *P*. The upper end of the helix is at elevation *A*. Scale: full size.

16.11.2. The tangent of the helix angle of the helix on the cylinder about axis *CD* is 0.4. The helix starts at point *P* and rises clockwise. The upper end of the helix is at elevation *C*. Draw the front view of the helix.

16.11.3. *P*, *Q*, and *R* are points on the helix that rises counterclockwise around the cylinder whose axis is *LM*. Find the front view of point *R*.

16.11.4. *RT* is the axis of a right-hand double-flight helicoidal screw conveyer whose pitch is 12 in. *P* is a point on the outer edge of one of the flights. Draw the top view of the outer edge of each flight through the axial distance *RT*. Scale: ⅛ size.

16.11.5. *AB* is the axis and the free height of a compression coil spring of five complete turns. The helix *angle*, when the spring is fully compressed, is two-thirds of the helix *angle* at free height. The bottom of the spring is fixed at elevation *B*. Find the elevation of the top of the spring when it is fully compressed.

16.11.6. *AB* is the axis of two concentric cylinders. On the smaller cylinder, there is a helix which rises clockwise from *P* and has a lead of 2 in. *PT* is a line which moves continually tangent to the helix on the smaller cylinder. Draw the front view of one turn of the helix traced on the larger cylinder by point *T*. Scale: full size.

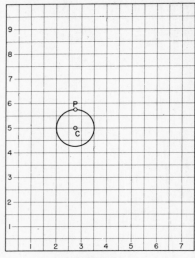

Prob. 16.9.1

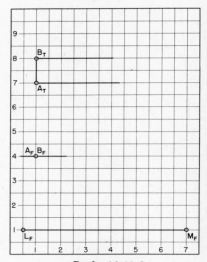

Prob. 16.10.2

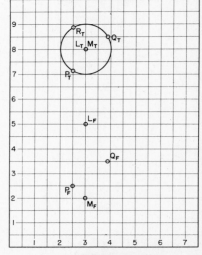

Prob. 16.11.3

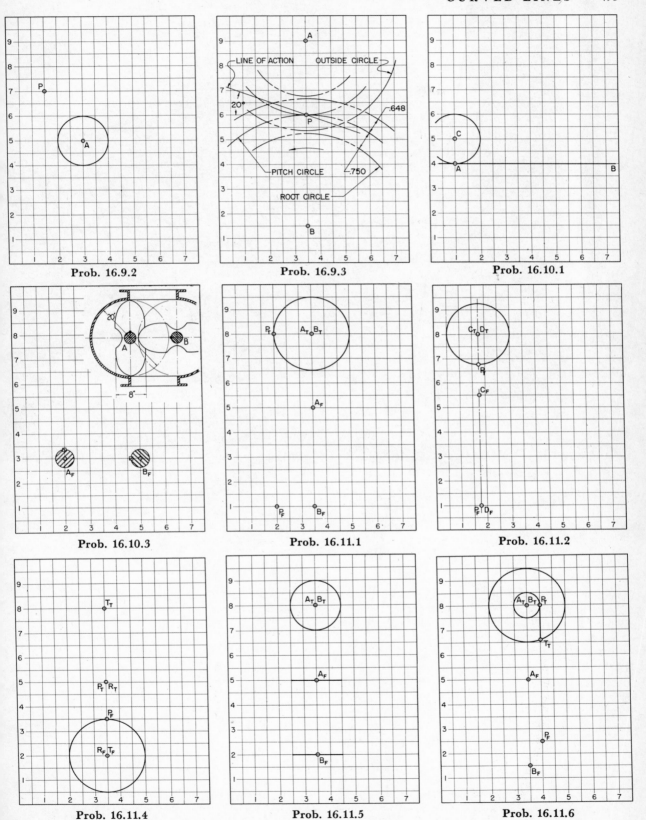

Prob. 16.9.2

Prob. 16.9.3

Prob. 16.10.1

Prob. 16.10.3

Prob. 16.11.1

Prob. 16.11.2

Prob. 16.11.4

Prob. 16.11.5

Prob. 16.11.6

17

CURVED AND WARPED SURFACES

17.1. In all science and engineering, but particularly in the mechanical phases of engineering, curved surfaces will frequently occur. Geometrically, shafts, bolts, rivets, and pipes are cylinders; hoppers, tanks, ducts, and discharge devices frequently occur as cones or portions of cones; transitions and blends often are oblique cones or convolutes; and we all observe in everyday life the double-curved and warped surfaces of automobile bodies, ship hulls, and aircraft fuselages and wings. Nevertheless, a knowledge of curved surfaces is important in the nonmechanical fields. In physics and other sciences, the theories of light, heat, sound, etc., will involve the cylinder, cone, paraboloid, and other surfaces. As a class, surfaces probably have a greater and more varied application than any other single portion of engineering geometry.

17.2. Classification of Surfaces. A surface may be considered to be generated by a line, called the "generatrix," which moves according to some law. Surfaces may thus be divided into two general classes: (1) those which can be generated by a moving *straight* line and (2) those which can be generated only by a moving *curved* line. The first are called *ruled surfaces;* the second, *double-curved surfaces.* Any position of the generatrix is called an *element* of the surface.

Ruled surfaces may be divided into (1) the plane, (2) single-curved surfaces, and (3) warped surfaces.

The plane may be generated by a straight line moving so as to

497

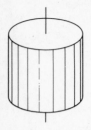

RIGHT CYLINDER

OBLIQUE CYLINDER

CYLINDER, GEN. FORM

Fig. 17.1. Cylinders.

touch two other intersecting or parallel straight lines or a plane curve *or* a point and a straight line.

Single-curved surfaces have their elements either parallel or intersecting. In this class are the *cylinder*, the *cone*, and a third surface, the *convolute*, in which only consecutive elements intersect.

Warped surfaces have no two consecutive elements either parallel or intersecting. There is a great variety of warped surfaces. The surface of a screw thread and that of an airplane wing are two examples.

Double-curved surfaces are generated by a curved line moving according to some law. The commonest forms are surfaces of revolution, made by revolving a curve about an axis in the same plane, as the sphere, torus or ring, ellipsoid, paraboloid, hyperboloid, etc.

17.3. Single-curved Surfaces. A single-curved surface, as the name implies, is a surface having curvature in one direction only. A single-curved surface may be generated by a straight-line generatrix moving (1) parallel to itself and intersecting a curved directrix not coplanar with the line (cylinder) or (2) so that consecutive elements intersect each other and intersect two curved-line directrices (convolute) or (3) in contact with a point directrix and a curved directrix not coplanar with the point (cone).

17.4. Cylinders. A cylinder, Fig. 17.1, is a single-curved surface generated by the motion of a straight-line generatrix remaining parallel to itself and constantly intersecting a curved directrix. The various positions of the generatrix are elements of the surface. It is a *right* cylinder when the elements are perpendicular to the bases, an *oblique* cylinder when they are not. A truncated cylinder is that portion which lies between one of its bases and a cutting plane that cuts all the elements. The axis is the line joining the centers of the bases. Cylinders and cones do not necessarily have closed base surfaces.

A cylinder may be represented by drawing two views, usually (1) a view showing the end of the axis and (2) a view showing the true length of the axis, Fig. 17.2A. This is the simplest possible position. The cylinder might be located in space as at *B*, where the axis is frontal. In this case, right sections for bases at *A* and *B* will appear as edges in the front view, and either (1) projection to the top view will determine major and minor diameters—as explained in paragraph 16.30—to plot the elliptical curves or (2) the end view shown may be employed to plot points on the curves. If the axis is oblique, as at *C*, either a true-length view or a true-length view and an end view of the axis may be made and the cylinder then laid out in these views, as described for case *B*. Another way is to lay out the base curves by treating them as circles in oblique position, using one of the methods of paragraph 16.31.

A point on the surface of a cylinder is located by realizing the fact that a point must lie on an element of the cylinder. Thus, in Fig. 17.2, if point *P* is known in either the top or front view, the ad-

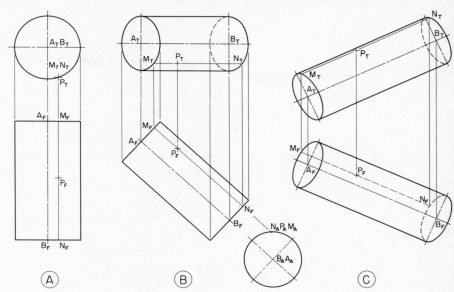

Fig. 17.2. Representation of cylinders.

jacent view (top or front) may be determined by projecting point *P* to the element of the cylinder on which it lies.

17.5. Cones. A cone, Fig. 17.3, is a single-curved surface generated by the movement, along a curved directrix, of a straight-line generatrix, one point of which is fixed and not coplanar with the directrix. The directrix is the base, and the fixed point (point directrix) is the vertex of the cone. Each position of the generatrix is an element of the surface. The axis is a line connecting the vertex and the center of the base. The altitude is a perpendicular dropped from the vertex to the base. A cone is *right* if the axis and altitude coincide; it is *oblique* if they do not coincide. A truncated cone is that portion lying between the base and a cutting plane which cuts all the elements. The frustum of a cone is that portion lying between the base and a cutting plane parallel to the base which cuts all the elements.

A cone may be determined by the position and shape of a base

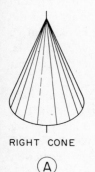

RIGHT CONE

Ⓐ

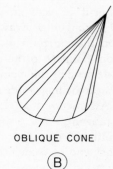

OBLIQUE CONE

Ⓑ

CONE, GEN. FORM

Ⓒ

Fig. 17.3. Cones.

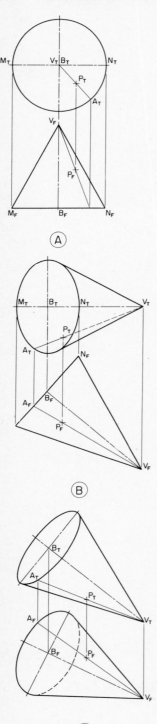

Fig. 17.4. Representation of cones.

curve and the position of the apex. Figure 17.4*A* is the simplest position, with the end (top view) and the true length (front view) of the axis. In Fig. 17.4*B*, the front view shows the base as an edge. The right-circular base in this view may be drawn perpendicular to the axis and then projection made to the top view to locate the diameters of the ellipse, as explained in paragraph 16.30. At *C*, the axis is oblique; the base may be determined by the simplified methods of paragraph 16.31, or, if preferred, a true-length and end view of the axis will make possible the location of points in the end view to project back to the top and front views and locate the base curves.

Any point on a cone lies on some element of the cone. Figure 17.4*A* to *C* shows a point *P* assumed to have been located in one of the views and then projected to the other view by locating the point on an element of the cone through the point.

17.6. Convolutes. The term "convolute" is derived from the Latin *volvere*, "to roll." This mathematically and graphically means "to form by a rolling element." Specifically, the rolling element is either a tangent plane or a line. Thus any surface formed by the location of elements produced by tangency of a line or plane may be termed a convolute. There are two forms, *conical* and *helical*, in general use (Fig. 17.5).

17.7. The Conical Convolute. The conical convolute commonly known as the "convolute transition," Fig. 17.5*A*, is generated by a straight-line generatrix in contact with two curved-line directrices, the generatrix moving so as to lie always in a plane tangent to the curved-line directrices. *Adjacent* elements, infinitely close together, will be planar and will intersect. The surface will revert to a right-circular cone when both directrices are circular right sections and are coaxial. Note in Fig. 17.4*A* that a series of planes, tangent to the cone, would produce elements at the lines of tangency.

Figure 17.6 illustrates the construction of a conical convolute. The pictorial view at (*A*) shows how an element of the surface is located. Any plane placed against both base curves will, of course, contact both curves and form a line connecting the points of contact. This line will be an element of the surface. *In* the plane contacting the base curves, there will be tangents to the base curves, lines *PQ* and *OQ* on the figure. Thus if an element, say, through point *P* on the lower base is wanted, a tangent is drawn emanating from point *P*. Then *Q* is located on this tangent *at the intersection of base planes.* Finally, a tangent from point *Q* to the upper base and the tangent point *O* located will determine the element *OP*.

Figure 17.6*B* shows the orthographic construction when the base planes are parallel. Assume that an element through point *Y* is wanted. From *Y_T* a tangent *YR* is drawn. The base planes, being parallel, intersect at infinity; therefore, a tangent *XS* parallel to *YR* will locate *X*, the other end of element *YX*. Note the construction shown for accurate location of the tangent points. A number of elements similar to YX, evenly spaced around either base, will complete the representation.

Figure 17.6C illustrates the construction when the base planes intersect at a finite distance. Any tangents to the base curves will, of course, lie in the plane of the curves. The intersection of the base planes at C_F is projected to the top view, where the line of intersection appears as a true-length line. Any pair of tangents to both base curves will intersect on this line. It follows then that a tangent constructed to the ellipse at point B and extended to C_T locates the intersection of a tangent to the upper base curve. From C_T, then, a line drawn to the upper base curve is the tangent line, and the tangent point A, then determined by the method of paragraph 16.14, completes the location of element AB. Other elements, similar to AB, are then located to complete the representation.

17.8. The Helical Convolute. The helical convolute is a surface generated by a straight-line generatrix moving so as to be tangent always to a helix. From a given diameter of the generating cylinder and the lead, the helix is plotted; then tangents to the helix will locate elements of the helical convolute. In Fig. 17.7, the axis of the surface is centered at O. The top view is the end, and the front view the true length of the axis. In the top view, the smaller circle is the diameter of the generating cylinder for the helix. In this case, the circumference has been divided into six parts; therefore, the lead divided into six parts will locate positions, along the axis, of the generating point, and projection from the top view will then locate points on the helical curve in the front view, as described in paragraph 16.35. Or if the helix angle is drawn as shown on Fig. 17.7, by projecting the lead from the front view and laying out the circumference, sixth points of the circumference may be projected to the developed helix at A_D, B_D, C_D, etc., and then to the front view.

Tangents to the helical curve may now be determined by first drawing them in the top view, tangent to the circle representing the generating cylinder at A_T-1_T, B_T-2_T, C_T-3_T, etc. The outer circle through 1, 2, 3, etc., is the given outer limit for the convolute. Tan-

CONVOLUTE

(A)

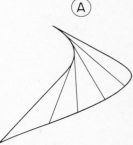

HELICAL CONVOLUTE

(B)

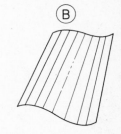

CONVOLUTE, GEN. FORM

(C)

Fig. 17.5. Convolutes.

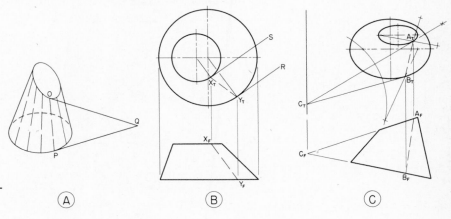

Fig. 17.6. Representation of conical convolutes.

(A)   (B)   (C)

gent A-1 is frontal and will appear in true length in the front view. Also, the tangent at point A will appear *parallel to the helix angle*. Thus, A_F-1_F drawn parallel to $A_D B_D \ldots A_D$ establishes one element of the convolute surface. *Any* tangent (element) of the convolute will have the same directional relationship to the axis. In other words, if tangent B-2 were rotated around the axis O until B-2 is frontal, then B-2 would be parallel, in the front view, to the developed helix $A_D B_D \ldots A_D$. Further, the difference between the inner point B and the outer point 2, *measured parallel to the axis*, will be identical for any of the tangents. To locate any tangent then, say, E-5, this constant distance (in this case constant height difference Z) is measured for frontal tangent A-1; next, the projector for point 5 on tangent E-5 is drawn to the front view; third, constant distance Z is measured as shown, locating point 5. All the other tangent elements, B-2, C-3, etc., are of course located in the same way. Smooth curves through the points for both helixes complete the representation.

17.9 Tangents to Single-curved Surfaces. The convolutes are constructed of tangents, and the necessity of constructing any tangent line or plane (other than the ones used in generating the surface) is rare. On the other hand, some problem involving a cylinder or cone may require a tangent line or plane to be located. A tangent has been defined as a line that passes through two consecutive points of a curve that are infinitely close together. When this conception is applied to a *surface*, it follows then that a line passing through two consecutive points of the surface will be tangent to the surface. Cylinders and cones contain an unlimited number of possible base curves or sections: for the cylinder, the circle, ellipse, and straight line, and for the cone, the straight line, circle, ellipse, parabola, and hyperbola. A line tangent to *any* one of these possible base curves or sections will be tangent to the surface. Also, any line tangent to a surface will lie in a plane that is tangent to the surface. Note particularly that an *element* of a cylinder or a cone is also a tangent of the surface.

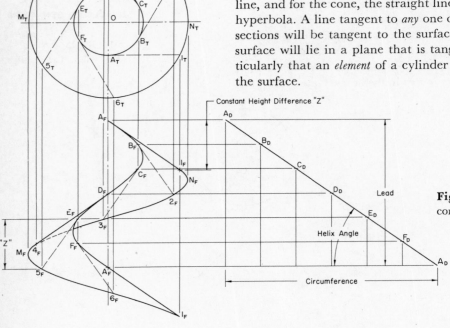

Fig. 17.7. Representation of helical convolute.

Tangents to a Cone. In Fig. 17.8, a plane containing point O, tangent to the cone, is required. Through point O, a plane is passed parallel to the base plane (horizontal). This plane cuts from the cone the circle shown; a tangent OP to this circle then establishes a line tangent to the cone. The element of the cone through P is then drawn at VX. The plane tangent to the cone is then PXO or VPO, established by an element and a tangent to a base curve of the cone. Any line in this tangent plane will be a line tangent to the cone. Thus QO, PO, RO, and XO are line tangents.

Tangents to a Cylinder. Figure 17.9 illustrates lines and planes tangent to a cylinder. The cylinder is right circular. Therefore, the end view will show the edge view of any plane tangent to the cylinder. For a tangent plane containing point O, the point is located in the end view at O_A and the tangent $O_A R_A$ drawn. R lies on an element of the cone. Thus any other point on the same element, such as Q, will now determine a plane ORQ tangent to the cylinder.

The problem can also be solved without the end view. Assume a tangent plane containing point P, on the cylinder, is wanted. Through point P in the front view, a section parallel to the bases is drawn. This section will be a circle, as shown in the top view. Then a tangent from point P and the element through P will determine the tangent plane. Point O in this case may be assumed in any convenient place on the tangent through P.

Any line tangent to the cylinder will lie in the tangent plane. Thus OR, OP, OS, and OQ are lines tangent to the cylinder through point O.

17.10. Double-curved Surfaces. Engineering structures and mechanical parts often are made up of, or employ, surfaces that are completely curved. Examples of surfaces of this type are the streamlined surfaces of aircraft and automobile bodies, boat and ship hulls, parabolic and ellipsoid reflectors, and many others. Because no straight-line element can be drawn on a completely curved surface, it is said to be double-curved.

The generating curve may be either a geometrical curve or a curve of general form, and the generating curve may be controlled in various ways; moreover, the generating curve may be either constant or variable. The variety of forms is therefore unlimited.

17.11. Classification. Double-curved surfaces may be classified as follows:

Surfaces of revolution are surfaces generated by revolving a curved-line generatrix about a straight line as an axis. If the generatrix lies in the same plane as the axis, the surface generated will conform to the curve of the generatrix.

Surfaces of general form are surfaces generated by moving a constant or variable curved-line generatrix along a noncircular curved path.

17.12. Surfaces of Revolution. A surface of revolution may be formed by employing any curve as a generating line. Geometrical curves, however, usually one of the conics, are most common, as

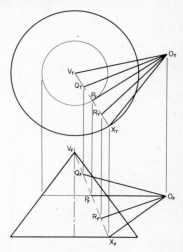

Fig. 17.8. Tangents to a cone.

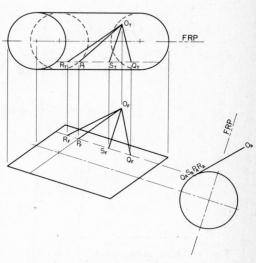

Fig. 17.9. Tangents to a cylinder.

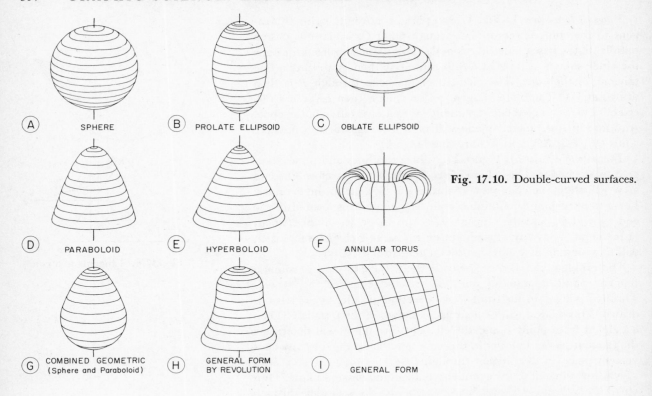

Fig. 17.10. Double-curved surfaces.

(A) SPHERE (B) PROLATE ELLIPSOID (C) OBLATE ELLIPSOID

(D) PARABOLOID (E) HYPERBOLOID (F) ANNULAR TORUS

(G) COMBINED GEOMETRIC (Sphere and Paraboloid) (H) GENERAL FORM BY REVOLUTION (I) GENERAL FORM

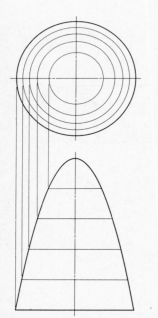

Fig. 17.11. Representation of a double-curved surface (simple position).

illustrated pictorially in Fig. 17.10. At (A) is shown a sphere, generated by revolving a circle around one of its diameters. Figure 17.10B illustrates a prolate ellipsoid generated by revolving an ellipse about its major diameter. (C) is an oblate ellipsoid formed by revolving an ellipse about its minor diameter. The paraboloid at (D) is generated by revolving a parabola about its central axis. This is the surface of parabolic reflectors. The hyperboloid (E) is formed by revolving a hyperbola about its central axis. The hyperboloid of revolution may also be formed by revolving a straight line around an axis, as described in paragraph 17.30, and in this form is a warped surface. It is interesting to note that the hyperboloid is the only warped surface that is also a surface of revolution. (F) is a torus, formed by revolving a circle around an axis which is not a diameter of the circle. If the axis lies within the circle a closed torus will be formed; if the axis is outside the circle, an annular torus is made. Any curve, either open or closed, may be employed to form a torus. Odd curves are often used in architecture to form a decorative torus on columns or on circular moldings.

Geometric curves may, of course, be combined to form a surface of revolution. An example is shown at (G). Furthermore, any nongeometric curve may be rotated about an axis, producing a surface of revolution as, for example, the bell-shaped surface at (H). The completely general form of a double-curved surface is indicated at

(*I*). This might be a portion of an automobile body, airplane fuselage, or ship hull.

17.13. Representation. Because a surface of revolution is generated by the revolution of a line around an axis, it is necessary to have one view showing the axis as a point and another view showing the axis in true length. In most cases, the surface will be drawn in a simple position, where top and front or front and side views will be the point and true length of axis views. However, when the surface is in some auxiliary or oblique position, one or more extra views must be made. Figure 17.11 shows a paraboloid in a simple position. The front view shows the true length; and the top view, the end view of the axis. The outline of the front view will be the true shape of the parabola and the top view will be a circle showing the base diameter. Sections of the surface perpendicular to the axis are circular. Therefore, if planes of circular sections are located in the front view and then projected to, and drawn as circles in, the top view (as shown on Fig. 17.11), these circular sections will be circular elements of the surface.

When the surface of revolution is in an auxiliary position as in Fig. 17.12 or in an oblique position such as Fig. 17.13, the method of tangent spheres is a most convenient method of drawing the outline. Circles representing spheres are drawn tangent to the surface outline in a view where the true length of the axis shows the true surface outline. Then if these sphere centers are projected to the axis in any other view and the circles representing the spheres drawn in that view, the outline of the view will be a curve tangent to the circles. In Fig. 17.12, the axis is horizontal. Circles are drawn in the top view tangent to the true surface outline, using any convenient series of centers such as 1, 2, 3, as shown. The circle centers are then pro-

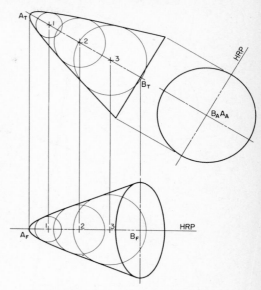

Fig. 17.12. Representation of a double-curved surface (tangent-sphere method).

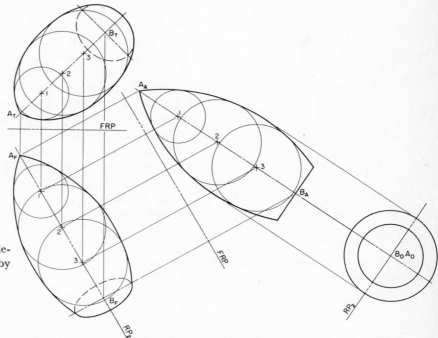

Fig. 17.13. Representation of a double-curved surface (auxiliary position) by tangent-sphere method.

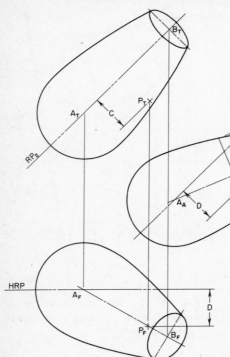

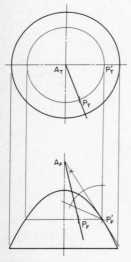

Fig. 17.14. Location of a point on a double-curved surface.

Fig. 17.15. Line tangent to a double-curved surface.

jected to the front view of the axis, and the circles (diameters identical to the top view) are then drawn in the front view. A curve drawn *tangent* to these circles gives the front-view outline. The ellipse representing the base may be drawn as described in paragraph 16.31. The end view of the axis and accompanying base circle may be drawn if desired.

For an oblique position such as Fig. 17.13, an auxiliary view showing the true length of the axis must be made and the true surface outline laid out. Then tangent spheres in the auxiliary view may be projected to the other views, as shown, to complete the representation. The oblique view showing the axis as a point may be drawn, if desired, although it is not necessary to the representation. The outline of the base will be elliptical and may be drawn as described in paragraph 16.31.

17.14. Location of a Point on a Surface of Revolution. The specifications for the location of a point on a surface of revolution must in some way be referred to the axis of the surface, for if it is not, the problem becomes one of finding where a line intersects the surface. In Fig. 17.14, the point P has been specified as somewhere on a plane at distance D below A (one end of the axis) and at a distance Q from the base of the surface containing point B, the other end of the axis. First, in the auxiliary view showing the true length of the axis AB, the distances D and Q may be laid out and the point P located, as shown at P_A. Second, the circle of the surface upon which P_A lies is drawn in the oblique view showing the end view of axis AB. Third, point P may be located in the oblique view because it must lie on the circle and be in projection with P_A. Finally, the top view may then be located by projection from P_A and by measurement of distance C from RP_2.

The front view of P may then be found by projection from the top view to the horizontal plane on which point P was originally specified.

Many variations of the specification for the location of point P are possible. As an example, point P may be specified on some vertical, horizontal, or profile plane and at some distance from either end of the axis. Another possible specification is to locate the point on a particular circle of the surface and at some distance from one end of the axis with, in addition, a plane specification on which the point must lie.

17.15. A Line or Plane Tangent to a Surface of Revolution. A line tangent to a surface of revolution must lie in a plane tangent to the surface at the same point. Thus a line tangent, unless special conditions prevail, is best found by first finding or locating a plane tangent. Special conditions of line tangency are illustrated by Figs. 17.15 and 17.16. In Fig. 17.15, a tangent is drawn through point P so that the tangent intersects the axis. If the point P is revolved about the axis until it falls on a limiting element of the surface at P', a tangent to the true generating curve of the surface will pass through the axis, as shown. The intersection with the axis will not move under counterrevolution, and thus the tangent through point P will be a line drawn through points A and P.

Figure 17.16 illustrates a tangent to a circular section of a surface of revolution. The tangent must lie in a plane perpendicular to the axis, as shown by the front view, and be tangent to the circular section, as shown on the top view.

Lines tangent in any position other than those described and illustrated by Figs. 17.15 and 17.16 are not easily found because a section of the surface cut by a plane through the line and normal to the surface must be made. However, a *line tangent* drawn in a *plane tangent* is a direct and straightforward solution. Figure 17.17 illustrates a surface of revolution with its axis in an oblique position to which a plane and line tangent are to be drawn at point P. Two tangent lines through point P will determine a plane tangent. On the true-length view of the axis, a tangent VT through point P and intersecting the axis is laid out by the method of Fig. 17.15. On the end view of the axis, a tangent RS through point P (tangent to a

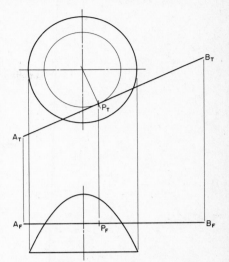

Fig. 17.16. Line tangent to a double-curved surface.

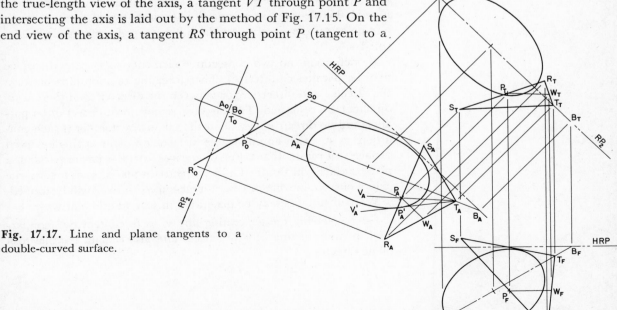

Fig. 17.17. Line and plane tangents to a double-curved surface.

circular section) is laid out by the method of Fig. 17.16. The plane *RST* made from these two tangent lines is then the required tangent plane at point *P*.

Any line through point *P* in plane *RST* will be a line tangent to the surface of revolution. Line *PW* is shown in Fig. 17.17 as an example of a horizontal line through point *P* and tangent to the ellipsoidal surface.

17.16. Warped Surfaces. The major portion of all surfaces used in making up machines and structures will be found to consist of the simpler forms such as planes, prisms, pyramids, cylinders, and cones. Occasionally, however, a surface is required to form a smooth connection, or "blend," between two planes or similar simple surfaces. The surface required to make such a transition must usually be formed by a generating line with a constantly changing direction, and the surface is then said to be "warped."

17.17. Definitions and Classification. *A warped surface* is a surface generated by a straight line moving so that no two consecutive positions are parallel or lie in the same plane. The line and plane elements used in generating warped surfaces are given in the definitions following:

The *generatrix* is a straight line moving so as to form the required surface.

The *directrices* are the straight or curved lines that the generatrix continuously contacts.

The *director* is that plane to which the generatrix is constantly parallel.

An *axis* is a center line around which a generatrix may revolve; *or* an axis is a line around which a surface is symmetrical.

The *elements* are straight lines shown on the surface, indicating different plotted positions of the generatrix.

Warped surfaces may be classified as *ruled surfaces* because they are generated by the motion of a straight line. The hyperboloids may be double-ruled as it is possible to draw two elements through any point on the surface. All the other warped surfaces are single-ruled.

By definition, no two consecutive elements on a warped surface may be parallel or intersect. Therefore, the relationships between the director and directrices or between the directrices (if there is no director) are restricted. The directrices may not intersect or be parallel, and no directrix may lie in the plane director; for if such conditions exist, either an impossible surface or a plane or single-curved surface will result. If two line directrices intersect or are parallel, a plane surface will result. If a line directrix is placed so as to form the axis of curved line directrices, a single-curved surface will be formed.

Warped surfaces may be generated in several different ways:

(1) By moving the generating line so as to contact two nonparallel, nonintersecting line directrices and also remain parallel to a plane director.

(2) By moving the generating line so as to follow a space-curve directrix and also remain at a constant angle to a line directrix.

(3) By moving the generating line so as to contact three nonparallel, nonintersecting line directrices.

Warped surfaces may be classified according to their family grouping; the following outline also gives the method of generation in each case:

I. Single-ruled surfaces
    A. Cylindrical forms
        1. *Cylindroid*, generated by two curved directrices and a plane director
        2. *Cow's horn*, generated by two curved directrices and one straight directrix
    B. Conical forms
        1. *Right conoid and oblique conoid*, generated by a curved directrix, a straight directrix, and a plane director
        2. *Warped cone*, generated by two curved directrices and a straight directrix
    C. Helicoidal forms
        1. *Cylindrical helicoid (right or oblique)*, generated by a cylindrical helix and a generatrix having a constant angle with a straight directrix
        2. *Conical helicoid (right or oblique)*, generated by a conical helix and a generatrix having a constant angle with a straight directrix
    D. General forms: *Ruled surfaces of airfoils and streamlined shapes*
II. Double-ruled surfaces
    A. Circular form: *Hyperboloid of revolution*, generated by a straight generatrix revolving about a straight nonparallel, nonperpendicular directrix
    B. Elliptical form: *Elliptical hyperboloid*, generated by a straight generatrix moving in contact with three straight directrices
    C. Parabolic form: *Parabolic hyperboloid*, generated by a straight generatrix moving in contact with two straight directrices and parallel to a plane director

17.18. Single-ruled Surfaces: Cylindrical Forms. The cylindrical forms of warped surfaces make a transition between two cylindrical surfaces, either right or oblique. These warped surfaces are often used in vaulted ceilings or arched passageways and where cylindrical flumes or ducts change in size or direction.

17.19. The Cylindroid. A cylindroid is a warped surface formed by a generatrix moving parallel to a plane director and in contact with two curved directrices. Figure 17.18*A* shows the surface pictorially.

The cylindroid shown in Fig. 17.18*B* has a plane director appearing as an edge in the top view. The front curved directrix *AB* is circular. The rear curved directrix *CD* is elliptical. The projected size of the curved directrices perpendicular to the plane director

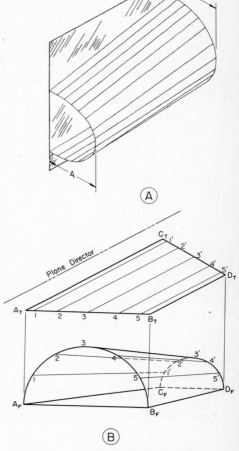

Fig. 17.18. Cylindroid.

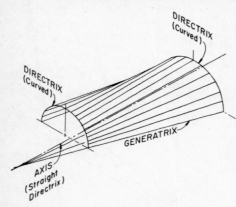

Fig. 17.19. Cow's horn.

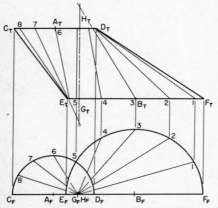

Fig. 17.20. Construction of cow's horn.

must be identical; for if they are not the same, some position of the generatrix (parallel to the plane director) will not intersect both directrices. This is shown by dimension A on the pictorial illustration. Successive positions of the generatrix, 1-1', 2-2', etc., are drawn parallel to the edge view of the plane director and then projected to the front view.

If a cylindroid is to be drawn in an oblique position or if the plane director is an oblique plane, an auxiliary view showing the edge of the plane director will have to be drawn, in which view the generatrix positions may be shown and then projected back to the principal views.

17.20. The Cow's Horn. The cow's horn is a warped surface generated by a line moving in contact with two curved directrices and intersecting a third straight directrix employed as an axis. Figure 17.19 shows the surface pictorially and identifies the directrices and generatrix.

The common cow's horn is usually designed with circular directrices although it may be made with ellipses. The cow's horn should not be confused with the sometimes similar warped cone, because the cow's horn has its axis placed in a position so that one central element of the surface intersects the axis at infinity whereas the warped cone has its axis through the center of each base.

Figure 17.20 shows the construction of a typical cow's horn. The two curved directrices (in this case circles) are CD with center A and EF with center B. The axis is GH, located on the line of centers. The elements (positions of the generatrix) are first drawn in the front view so as to intersect both directrices and the axis. The elements, 1, 2, etc., are then projected to the top view. Element 5 will intersect the axis at infinity.

Note that some of the elements will intersect the axis on one end of the surface, and others will intersect on the opposite end. The elements do not intersect the axis at a common point.

17.21. Single-ruled Surfaces: Conical Forms. Conical-form

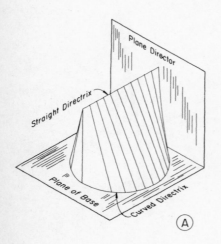

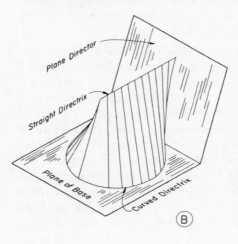

Fig. 17.21. Right and oblique conoids.

warped surfaces are used to make a transition between two curved surfaces or from a curved surface (usually a cylinder) to a plane. They are, in a practical way, found approximated in the surfaces of some jets and nozzles and on some bits and forming tools. One common use is for the transition between a curved and flat ceiling. As the surfaces are not easily developable, they are not so common as similar transitions formed by plane surfaces and portions of oblique cones.

17.22. The Conoid. A conoid is a warped surface formed by a generatrix moving parallel to a plane director and in contact with a curved directrix and a straight directrix. If the straight directrix is perpendicular to the plane director, the surface is a right conoid; if not perpendicular, the surface is an oblique conoid. Figure 17.21*A* illustrates a right conoid, and Fig. 17.21*B* an oblique conoid.

17.23. The Right Conoid. In the typical right conoid in Fig. 17.22*A*, the line *AB* is the straight-line directrix and the circular base is the curved directrix. The plane director is, in this case, a vertical plane and perpendicular to the horizontal-line directrix *AB*, thus satisfying the conditions necessary to obtain a right conoid. Positions of the generatrix will be parallel to the edge view of the plane director. The intersections of the generatrix thus are easily obtained in the top view and are then projected to the front view.

Note that the length of the straight directrix must be the same as the distance across the base perpendicular to the plane director. If those distances were not identical, the generatrix could not remain parallel to the plane director and intersect both line directrices.

A right conoid may, of course, be in an oblique position in space instead of the regular position shown in Fig. 17.22*A*. The problem, however, may be solved by making an auxiliary view to get the edge view of the plane director and, in this view, setting up positions of the generatrix and then projecting the intersections back to the principal views.

17.24. The Oblique Conoid. Figure 17.22*B* illustrates a typical oblique conoid. The plane director in this case shows as an edge in the front view. The straight directrix *AB* is an oblique line, therefore satisfying the conditions for an oblique conoid. Successive positions of the generatrix are drawn parallel to the edge view of the plane director and then projected to the top view.

Note that the projected length of the straight directrix must be the same as the *projected* size of the curved directrix in a direction perpendicular to the plane director.

An oblique conoid in an oblique position in space may be drawn as described in paragraph 17.23.

17.25. The Warped Cone. The warped cone is a warped surface formed by a generatrix moving in contact with two curved directrices and intersecting a third directrix located as a central axis.

The definitions of the warped cone and the cow's horn are similar.

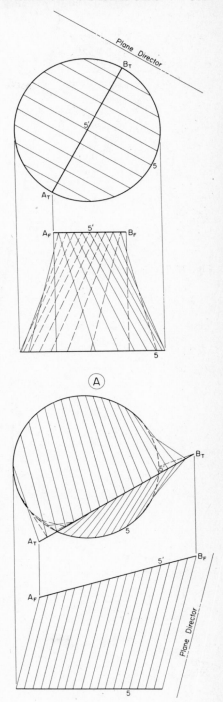

Fig. 17.22. Construction of right and oblique conoids.

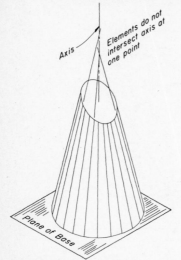

Fig. 17.23. Warped cone.

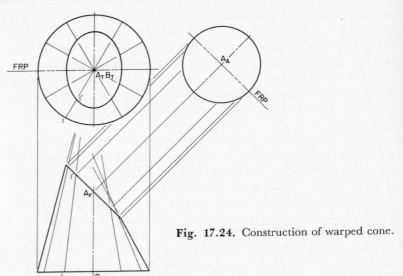

Fig. 17.24. Construction of warped cone.

This similarity is, however, only superficial: The axis of a warped cone is central, whereas in the cow's horn it is not; the elements of a warped cone all intersect the axis on one end, whereas the elements of a cow's horn intersect half on one end and half on the other; also, the form of a warped cone is conical, and the cow's horn is cylindrical. Figure 17.23 pictorially represents a typical warped cone.

Figure 17.24 is an orthographic drawing of a warped cone. In this case, the lower base is circular, with center at *B*. The upper base is also circular, but with center at *A*. The axis *AB* is located so as to pass through the center of both bases. The surface will be a warped cone instead of a right cone because the upper base is not a section of a right cone.

Elements of the surface are located by dividing the base into a convenient number of parts and drawing elements to intersect the upper base and the axis. In this case the elements must first be drawn in the top view where the axis appears as a point and then projected from the top view to the front view to complete the representation of the surface. In any case where the axis does not appear as a point in one of the regular views, a point view must be made before the elements can be drawn. The elements may be extended to the axis in the front view if desired; and if they are so extended, the intersections will be at different points, proving that the surface is warped instead of the surface of a right or oblique cone.

17.26. Single-ruled Surfaces: Helicoidal Forms. Helicoidal surfaces are warped surfaces in which one of the directrices is a helix. These surfaces are very common as they are present on screw threads, coil springs, twist drills, spiral chutes, and other similar elements or structures.

17.27. Cylindrical Helicoids. A cylindrical helicoid is a warped surface formed by a generatrix having a constant angle with a

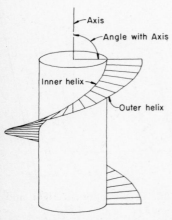

Fig. 17.25. Cylindrical helicoid.

straight directrix and moving in contact with a cylindrical helix (curved directrix). If the angle with the axis is 90° (generatrix perpendicular to the axis), the surface will be a right helicoid. If the angle is other than 90°, the surface will be an oblique helicoid. Figure 17.25 is a pictorial drawing of a cylindrical helicoid.

Figure 17.26 shows the construction of a cylindrical right helicoid. The straight directrix is *AB*. The generatrix *CD* is perpendicular to the axis *AB*. The space curve *DD'* is a cylindrical helix. Positions of the generatrix are first located in the top view by dividing the enclosing cylinder into a convenient number of equal parts. These points are then connected to the axis *AB*, thus intersecting the inner cylinder and producing successive positions of the generatrix, 1, 2, 3, etc. The helix and positions of the generatrix may then be drawn. The lead of the helix, laid out as shown, is divided into the same number of equal parts used in dividing the enclosing cylinder. This procedure is necessary since a helix is defined as a point moving at a constant rate around an axis and at the same time moving at a constant rate parallel to the axis. Dividing the lead (distance traveled parallel to the axis in one revolution) into equal parts locates a series of planes upon which successive positions of the generatrix will lie. Positions of the generatrix may then be plotted in the front view by projecting the top view position to the proper plane in front view.

An oblique cylindrical helicoid is identical to a right cylindrical helicoid except that the acute angle of the generatrix with the axis is less than 90°. The inner end of the generatrix therefore starts at a different level than the outer end, as shown by the front view of Fig. 17.27. The lead for each helix is laid out and divided individually into the same number of equal parts as the top view. The front view may then be completed by projecting successive positions of the inner and outer ends of the generatrix to the proper plane position, as indicated in Fig. 17.27.

Any oblique helicoidal surface must have the generatrix at some angle to the axis, but the generatrix need not intersect the axis. Figure 17.28 shows an oblique cylindrical helicoid in which the

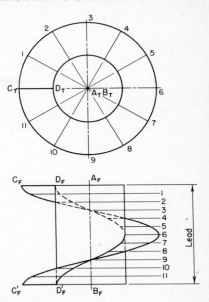

Fig. 17.26. Construction of cylindrical right helicoid.

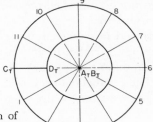

Fig. 17.27. Construction of cylindrical oblique helicoid.

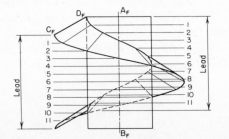

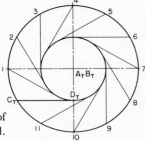

Fig. 17.28. Construction of cylindrical oblique helicoid.

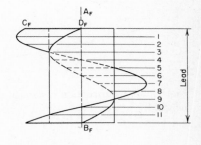

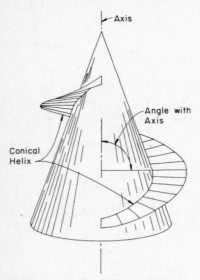

Fig. 17.29. Conical helicoid.

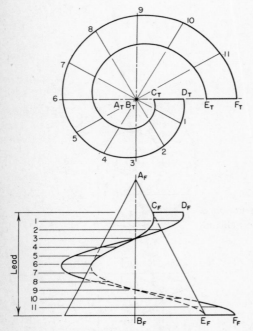

Fig. 17.30. Construction of conical right helicoid.

generatrix *DE* does not intersect the axis. Note that the method of layout is identical to Fig. 17.27 except for the difference in relative position of the generatrix. Also note that the elements, in this case, are horizontal.

17.28. Conical Helicoids. A conical helix is a space curve defined as a point moving at a uniform rate around an axis and at the same time moving at a uniform rate along the axis and on the surface of a cone. Figure 17.29 illustrates the surface pictorially. Figure 17.30 illustrates the construction of a conical right helicoid. The axis is *AB*, and generatrix *CD* is perpendicular to it. The generatrix positions are to be plotted for each $\frac{1}{12}$ of one complete rotation. Thus the top view is divided into 12 parts by drawing lines through the axis at increments of 30°. The lead is also divided into 12 equal parts. The helix (which represents movement on the cone surface of the point *C*) is plotted by first locating circular sections of the cone on which plotted positions of point *C* will lie. In Fig. 17.30, these circular sections are cut by planes 1, 2, 3, etc. On these circles, at successive positions of the lead, are found the several points representing the helical movement of point *C*. For example, on plane 1 of the lead and position 1 of the top view is found the first point, and at plane 2 and position 2 of the top view is found the second point. Note that the points in the top view lie on the circle cut by planes 1, 2, 3, etc. After the top view has been drawn, the points may be projected to the front view. The generatrix *CD* will appear the same length in the top view for all positions and may now be drawn, locating the outer helix from the inner helix. Then, to complete the front view, positions of point *D* are projected to the proper lead plane. The visibility is then determined and the curves drawn in.

A conical oblique helicoid is drawn in a similar manner with, of course, the exception that the generatrix will be drawn at an angle to the axis.

17.29. Double-ruled Surfaces: The Hyperboloids. All double-ruled warped surfaces may be classed as hyperboloids because the principal contour of the surface is hyperbolic. However, in most cases other conic sections, circles, ellipses, and parabolas may also be cut from the surface by properly selected planes. The hyperboloids may be designed in either circular, elliptical, or parabolic form. The elliptical form is rather limited in practical uses, but the circular form is common and important because of its application in hypoid gearing. The parabolic form is often used as the transition surface for ducts, dams, retaining walls, bridges, and other concrete structures.

All the hyperboloids, circular, elliptical, or parabolic, are basically generated by a straight generatrix moving so as to be in contact with three nonparallel, nonintersecting directrices. However, the circular form, called the "hyperboloid of revolution," must have the directrices located so that their relationship to a central axis is the same for all three directrices, and the parabolic form must have all three directrices in parallel planes. Thus it is evident that the elliptical form is the general case and that the circular and parabolic forms are special arrangements. Conversely, the directrices for an elliptical hyperboloid must be carefully chosen or the circular or parabolic form may be generated.

The directrices for any hyperboloid will be elements of the surface for the second generation. Therefore, any *three* elements of one generation may be taken as directrices for the second generation. Every element of the first generation will intersect every element of the second generation, proving that both generations form the same surface.

Figure 17.31 shows pictorially the three nonparallel, nonintersecting directrices for a hyperboloid. The elements are positions of the generatrix intersecting all three directrices. Note that elements of the second generation must have as their directrices *three* elements of the first generation.

Figure 17.32 is an orthographic drawing of a hyperboloid, illustrating the method of location for elements that intersect all three directrices. The directrices are lines *AB*, *CD*, and *EF*. If the end view of one of the directrices is obtained, all elements in that view must, in order to intersect that directrix, pass through the directrix where it appears as a point. In Fig. 17.32, directrix *CD* is horizontal, and therefore an elevation auxiliary taken in the direction of $C_T D_T$ will show *CD* as a point. Directrices *AB* and *EF* are projected to this view. Then any straight line through $C_A D_A$ intersecting *AB* and *CD* (line 2-6, etc.) will be an element of the surface. The elements may then be projected back to the top view and to the front view. If the second generation is desired, elements *F*-1, 3-5, and *B*-4 may be taken as directrices and an end view of one of these directrices employed, as described for the first generation, to give elements for the second generation. Although the surface just described is an elliptical hyperboloid, this example gives the basic theory necessary to a complete understanding of the generation of all the hyperboloids.

The explanations following for the circular, elliptical, and parabolic hyperboloids are the useful and practical methods.

17.30. The Circular Hyperboloid. This hyperboloid is often called the hyperboloid of revolution because, as the cross section perpendicular to the axis must be circular, it may be generated by a single generatrix revolving about an axis.

Figure 17.33 is the representation of a circular hyperboloid. The generatrix, *AB*, having a fixed relationship (nonparallel and nonintersecting) to the axis, will describe circles on any plane perpendicular to the axis. The smallest circle described is known as the "gore circle." The simplest and most direct construction is first to locate and draw two circles representing the circular path of points on the generatrix at the extremities of the surface parallel to the axis. Next, draw the gore circle in the top view. All positions of the generatrix must contact the gore circle and the two extremity circles

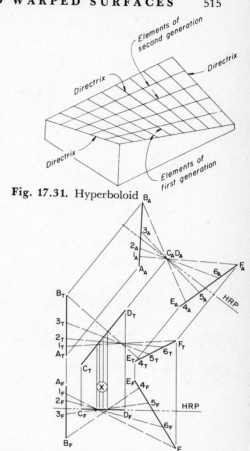

Fig. 17.31. Hyperboloid

Fig. 17.32. Construction of hyperboloid.

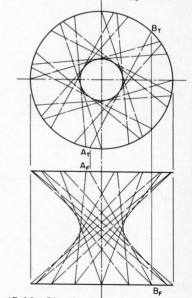

Fig. 17.33. Circular hyperboloid.

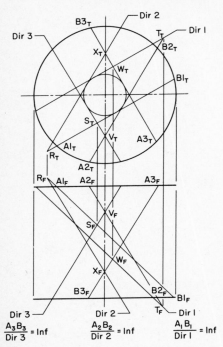

Fig. 17.34. Elements and directrices of circular hyperboloid.

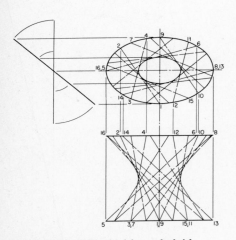

Fig. 17.35. Elliptical hyperboloid.

and thus are drawn tangent to the gore circle in the top view and crossing the two extremity circles. For convenience, one extremity circle may be divided into a number of equal parts, thus producing evenly spaced elements of the representation.

The elements located in the top view are then projected down to the front view from their intersection with the two extremity circles.

Following the basic theory of the hyperboloids as described in paragraph 17.27, it is interesting to note that elements of one generation will be directrices for the second generation. Figure 17.34 shows three elements of one generation taken as directrices and marked Dir. 1, Dir. 2, and Dir. 3. Three elements of the second generation, A_1B_1, A_2B_2, A_3B_3, intersect all three directrices. As an example in reading the drawing of Fig. 17.34, Dir. 1 intersects A_1B_1 at infinity, A_2B_2 at T, and A_3B_3 at W. Similarly, A_1B_1 intersects Dir. 1 at infinity, Dir. 2 at R, and Dir. 3 at S.

17.31. The Elliptical Hyperboloid. The general hyperboloid form is the elliptical hyperboloid, as described in paragraph 17.29. However, in order to control the elliptical shape wanted, the layout should be made by locating two ellipses representing the path of points on the generatrix in planes perpendicular to the axis. In Fig. 17.35, two ellipses representing the extremities of the surface have been drawn by revolving circles, as shown, to obtain the required minor diameters. Positions of the generatrix are found by drawing the gore ellipse and drawing the generatrix positions tangent to the gore ellipse. Thus, in Fig. 17.35, elements 1-2, 3-4, 5-6, etc., are positions of the generatrix of the required surface. The second generation may be made by reversing the direction of the generatrix relative to the axis.

Figure 17.36 shows that the elliptical hyperboloid may be formed by a generatrix in contact with three straight-line directrices. A_1B_1, A_2B_2, and A_3B_3 are elements of one generation. Three elements of the opposite generation are taken as directrices and are marked Dir. 1, Dir. 2, and Dir. 3. Note that Dir. 1 intersects A_1B_1 at infinity, A_2B_2 at T, and A_3B_3 at W. Similarly, A_1B_1 intersects Dir. 1 at infinity, Dir. 2 at R, and Dir. 3 at S.

17.32. The Parabolic Hyperboloid. The parabolic hyperboloid is one of the most common and useful of all for the warped surfaces of ducts, dams, and retaining walls and in bridges and culverts. It is also often found in the external surfaces of castings and forgings of mechanical parts. The name "hyperbolic paraboloid" has been generally accepted for this warped surface. However, it is apparent from the classification in paragraph 17.27 that the term parabolic hyperboloid is more accurate and logical. Figure 17.37 illustrates the surface pictorially.

Definition. The parabolic hyperboloid is the surface formed by a generating line moving parallel to a plane director and in contact with two straight nonintersecting, nonparallel directrices.

Figure 17.38 illustrates the general case: The lines *AB* and *CD* are the two directrices and form the two limiting ends of the surface. The generatrix will constantly contact lines *AB* and *CD* and be parallel to a plane director. Because lines *AB* and *CD* are nonintersecting and nonparallel and are also of different length, the plane director will be an oblique plane that must be parallel to the two limiting positions *AD* and *BC* of the generatrix. To locate the plane director, a *point view* of one position of the generatrix may be obtained, and a second position of the generatrix carried into this point view will then indicate the direction for the edge view of the plane director. In Fig. 17.38, the generatrix position *BC* has been selected for the point view. The auxiliary view of *BC* is $B_A C_A$ and shows the true length of *BC*. *AD* is carried into this view. The point view of *BC* is $B_O C_O$ and the generatrix position *AD* is carried from the first auxiliary to the view showing the point view of *BC*. *AD* is shown in this view at $A_O D_O$. The line *AD* is not in true length in this view, but a receding plane passed parallel to *AD* will also be parallel to *BC*. This plane will be the necessary plane director and is marked on the figure. All positions of the generatrix will be parallel to the plane director and may now be drawn. They are indicated in the point view of *BC* by 1-3 and 2-4. The generatrix positions may now be carried back to the auxiliary view and then to the principal views. Note that 1-3 and 2-4 divide the directrix lines *AB* and *CD* into equal parts but that successive positions of the generatrix are nonparallel and nonintersecting. The plotted positions of the generatrix form elements of the parabolic hyperboloid.

The surface just discussed may be said to be in an oblique position because the positions of the directrix and plane director are oblique. Often, however, the directrices may be oblique but the plane director either horizontal, frontal, or profile, thus simplifying the solution

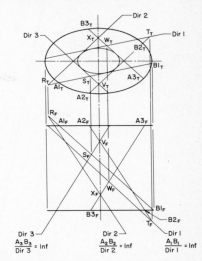

Fig. 17.36. Elements and directrices of elliptical hyperboloid.

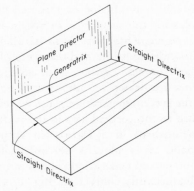

Fig. 17.37. Parabolic hyperboloid.

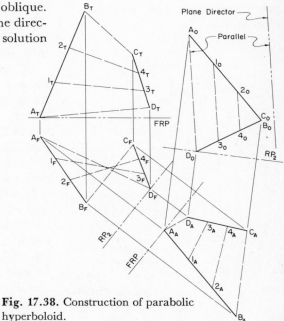

Fig. 17.38. Construction of parabolic hyperboloid.

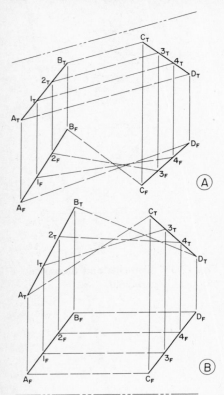

Fig. 17.39. (*A*) Parabolic hyperboloid with vertical plane director. (*B*) Parabolic hyperboloid with horizontal plane director.

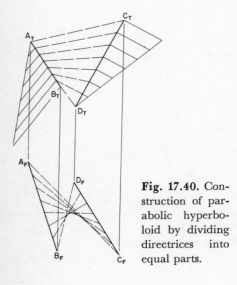

Fig. 17.40. Construction of parabolic hyperboloid by dividing directrices into equal parts.

and the position of the surface in space. Figure 17.39 shows at (*A*) a parabolic hyperboloid with a vertical plane director, at (*B*) one with a horizontal plane director. Note in each case that the projected lengths of the directrices perpendicular to the plane director must be the same.

If it is not necessary in a practical case to locate the plane director, any parabolic hyperboloid may be drawn in the principal views by dividing the directrices into equal parts and then connecting these points with lines to show successive positions of the generatrix. Note that in Fig. 17.38 the positions of the generatrix, 1-3 and 2-4, divide both directrices *AB* and *CD* into equal parts. Figure 17.40 shows a method (based on the above fact) for drawing the principal views. Here the top view is selected for dividing the lines. Note that here is employed the familiar scale method of drawing a perpendicular from one end of the line and orienting a scale with convenient divisions so that points located may be projected back as perpendiculars to the line. Thus *AB* and *CD* have been equally divided and the generatrix positions drawn in the top view and then projected to the front view. If, after this method has been used to draw the principal views, the position of the plane director is required, it may be found by proceeding as in Fig. 17.38.

Figure 17.41 illustrates the fact that a parabolic hyperboloid may be formed by a generatrix in contact with three straight-line directrices. As stated before, the three directrices must lie in parallel planes. In Fig. 17.41, *AB* and *CD* are taken as two of the directrices. A point view is made of directrix *CD*, and directrix *AB* is carried to the point view. Then if a third directrix, for example, *EF*, is drawn parallel to *AB*, all three directrices will lie in parallel planes. The third directrix *EF* is carried back to the principal views, and it is evident from these views that all the elements intersect all three directrices.

The parabolic hyperboloid may also be constructed by drawing the two limiting parabolas for the surface as shown in Fig. 17.42. As explained before, all the elements must lie in parallel planes so that it is necessary (in this case) to locate and draw the plane director. In Fig. 17.43, the plane director appears as an edge in the front view, and all the elements are drawn parallel to it. The plane director and elements for the second generation must be reversed but have the same relationship to the vertical axis of the surface.

17.33. Element Relationships of a Parabolic Hyperboloid. Any element of a parabolic hyperboloid is not only a line about which the generatrix of the second generation rotates but also a line which the generatrix will constantly contact. In Fig. 17.43, a parabolic hyperboloid is drawn in a simple position with the plane director frontal. Every position of the generatrix, 1-2, 3-4, etc., contacts line *AB*, one element (second generation) of the surface. Note, incidentally, that the element *AB* becomes the third straight-line directrix of Fig. 17.41. If the parabolic hyperboloid is in an ob-

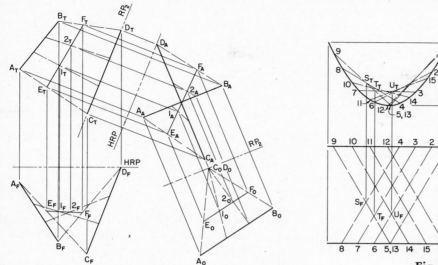

Fig. 17.41. Three straight-line directrices of parabolic hyperboloid.

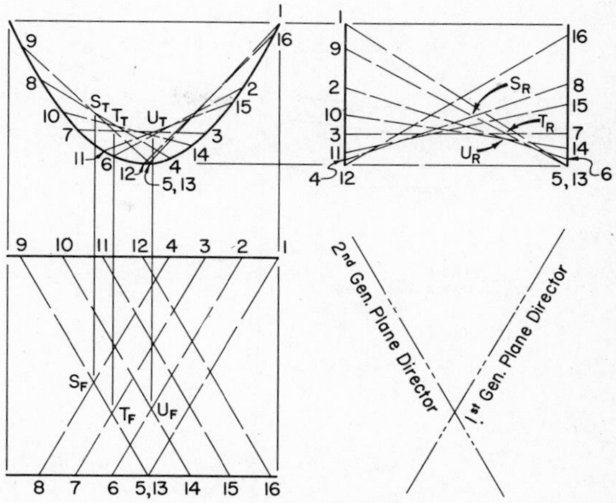

Fig. 17.42. Parabolic hyperboloid constructed by limiting parabolas.

lique position, a special element may be located by setting up a plane through one line director parallel to the other line director, as shown by plane *DEF* of Fig. 17.44. An edge view of the plane *DEF* then results in a view in which the two line directors appear as seen at $A_A B_A$ and $C_A D_A$ of Fig. 17.44. In this view, all positions of the generatrix will pass through a common point $X_A Y_A$, the point view of the special element. The point view of the element at $X_A Y_A$ may be found by drawing, in the top view, the vertical position of the generatrix 5-6 and projecting it to the auxiliary view and then setting up any element such as 1-2 in the auxiliary view. All elements of the surface are perpendicular to XY. Therefore, 1-2 may be located at any convenient place in the top view, perpendicular to XY, and then projected to the auxiliary view. These two positions, 5-6 and 1-2, of the generatrix determine the point view $X_A Y_A$, from which $X_T Y_T$ and $X_F Y_F$ may be located. Note that the plane director in this case will be a vertical plane and will appear as an edge in the top view parallel to 1-2, 3-4, etc., and that the auxiliary view will be the normal view of the plane director. The element just described is the basis for locating all shortest lines intersecting two skew lines as discussed in paragraphs 15.16 to 15.20. Note that this is a special case of the parabolic hyperboloid in which the plane director is *parallel* to a group of shortest lines of the surface. Elements of the surface *do not* divide the directrices equally, as in 17.40, 17.43, and 17.45.

As indicated above, there are an infinite number of elements, and any element of one generation may be taken as the third line directrix for the second generation. Therefore, a point view of *any* element will locate a third line directrix for the other generation. Also, by obtaining the point view of an element, the position of the plane

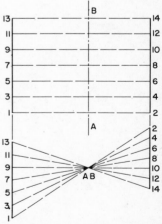

Fig. 17.43. Parabolic hyperboloid with frontal plane director.

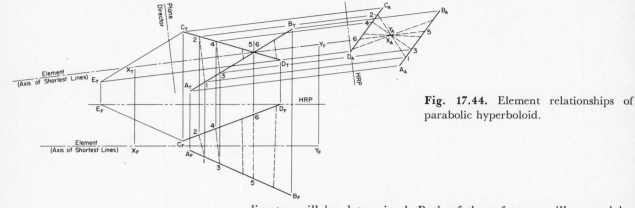

Fig. 17.44. Element relationships of parabolic hyperboloid.

director will be determined. Both of these facts are illustrated by Fig. 17.45. The top and front views of a parabolic hyperboloid have been drawn by dividing *AB* and *CD* equally for one generation and *BC* and *AD* for the second generation. Then an element 7-8 is selected at random for the true-length and point view at the left side of the figure. Note in the point view of 7-8 that *AB*, *CD*, 7-8, 9-10, and 11-12 all appear parallel to each other and that the plane director will therefore appear as an edge in this view. Element 5-6 of the second generation has been selected for a point view at the right side of the figure. Here *BC*, 5-6, 3-4, 1-2, and *AD* all appear parallel, and the plane director for the second generation can be established. Thus we conclude that any element will be the third line directrix of the opposite generation and that the point view of any element will give a view in which the edge view of the plane director of that generation (of which the element is a member) will appear.

17.34. The Axis of Symmetry of a Parabolic Hyperboloid. The axis of symmetry, or "central axis," of a parabolic hyperboloid is a line about which the surface is coextensive and proportional; the surface "balances" about its central axis. The axis of symmetry may be found by locating the *shortest* line of each generation and then erecting a perpendicular at the intersection of the shortest lines. However, before this is possible, *the surface itself must be symmetrical.* No central axis can exist for *any* surface that is asymmetrical.

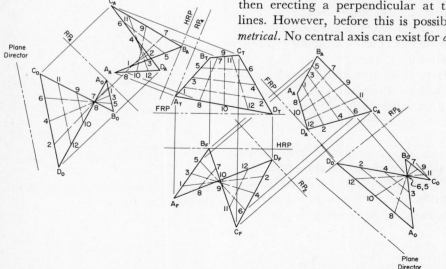

Fig. 17.45. Element relationships of parabolic hyperboloid (two generations).

A symmetrical parabolic hyperboloid is one in which the surface progresses in a uniform manner on opposite sides of the axis. Therefore, the axis must intersect *an element of the surface that is symmetrical to the directrices*. Furthermore, the only possible line symmetrical to two skew line directrices is the *common perpendicular* of the directrices. Therefore, if the surface is made so that it is symmetrical about the common perpendicular between each pair of directrices for the two generations, the surface will be symmetrical and an axis can be located.

Figure 17.46 will illustrate the determination of a symmetrical parabolic hyperboloid and the location of its central axis. Lines AD and BC are taken as directrices of the first generation. The surface will be symmetrical about the common perpendicular PQ, which has been located by the method of paragraph 15.16. In the oblique view, PQ appears as a point at P_oQ_o, and both directrices, AD and BC, appear in true length. An axis symmetrical to AD and BC will show in true length and will be the bisector of the angle between A_oD_o and B_oC_o. This axis, MN, must also be symmetrical to directrices for the second generation. Therefore, two directrices, R_oS_o and T_oU_o, are drawn equidistant from the point view of PQ at P_oQ_o and parallel to M_oN_o. The directrices RS and TU will thus have a common perpendicular GH, which intersects PQ at M. The axis must, of course, also be symmetrical to the directrices RS and TU. This symmetry is shown by the view at $R_{oo}S_{oo}T_{oo}U_{oo}$, which is made in a direction to give the true length of RS and TU. All lines may now be projected back to the top and front views. Note, in the oblique and second oblique views, that axis MN is perpendicular to the common perpendicular for each pair of directrices. The plane director for each generation is shown on the figure. Also note that, in each case, the plane director is parallel to the directrices of the opposite generation and also parallel to the central axis.

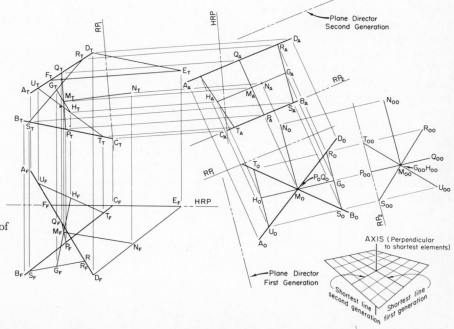

Fig. 17.46. Axis of symmetry of parabolic hyperboloid.

PROBLEMS

Group 1. The cylinder

17.1.1. *AB* is the axis of a cylinder whose circular right section is 2 in. in diameter. The base at *B* is frontal; the base at *A* is horizontal. Draw the top and front views of the cylinder, showing visibility. Scale: ¾ size.

17.1.2. *AB* is the axis of a cylinder whose circular right section is 4 in. in diameter. The bases are frontal and contain points *A* and *B*. Draw the top and front views of the cylinder, showing visibility. Scale: ⅜ size.

17.1.3. *CD* is the axis of a cylinder of circular right section. Its circular base about point *D* is shown. Draw the conjugate diameters of the elliptical front view of the base about *D*. One of these diameters is frontal.

Optional. Complete the views.

17.1.4. Draw a view which shows the true shape of the right section of the cylinder *LM*.

17.1.5. The axis, *AB*, and contour elements of a cylindrical surface are shown. Find the top view of *P*, a point on the rearward portion of the surface.

17.1.6. Planes *POT* and *LMN* are tangent to cylinder *AB*. Complete the top view of plane *POT* and the front and right-side views of plane *LMN*.

17.1.7. Draw the top view of plane *PLM*, which is tangent to the upper surface of the cylinder *CD*. Draw the front view of plane *PQR*, which is tangent to the lower surface of cylinder *CD*.

17.1.8. *UV* is the axis of a pulley around which a belt passes. *TL* is the line of contact between one run of the belt and the pulley. The belt passes through a frontal partition whose edge view appears as line *FP*. The belt may be considered as a plane. Draw the top and front views of the slot where this run of the belt passes through the partition.

Group 2. The cone

17.2.1. *VC* is the axis of a right-circular cone. The base is 3 in. in diameter and is centered about *C*. Draw the top and front views of the cone, showing visibility. Scale: full size.

17.2.2. *A* is the vertex and *AB* is the axis of a cone. The right section about *B* is a circle of 6 in. diameter. The base is frontal and contains *B*. Draw the top and front views of the major and minor diameters of the elliptical base. Scale: ⅜ size.

Optional. Draw the curve and complete the views.

17.2.3. Centered at *A* and *B* are two circular bases cut from an oblique cone. Find the top and front views of the vertex of the cone. Find the true length of the longest element on the surface of the cone between the bases *A* and *B*.

17.2.4. *VA* is the axis of a right-circular cone. Its base is 6 in. in diameter and contains point *A*. Another right-circular cone, whose axis is *VD*, is tangent to cone *VA* along the upper frontal element of cone *VA*. The vertex angle of cone *VD* is 50°, and its base contains point *D*. The cones have equal slant heights. Draw the top and front views of the axis of cone *VD*. Scale: half ize.

Optional. Complete the views of the cones.

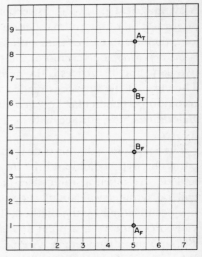

Prob. 17.1.1

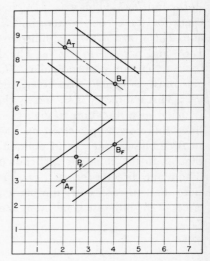

Prob. 17.1.5

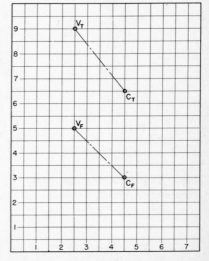

Prob. 17.2.1

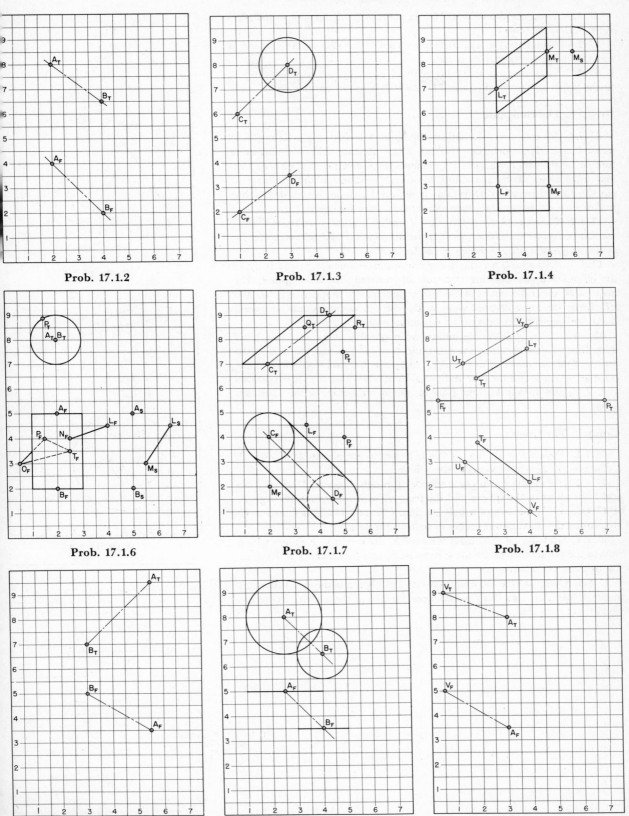

Prob. 17.1.2

Prob. 17.1.3

Prob. 17.1.4

Prob. 17.1.6

Prob. 17.1.7

Prob. 17.1.8

Prob. 17.2.2

Prob. 17.2.3

Prob. 17.2.4

17.2.5. Draw the top view of *PQR*, a plane which is tangent to the rearward surface of cone *V*.

17.2.6. Complete the top and front views of *RST*, a plane which is tangent to the lower surface of cone *V*.

17.2.7. Draw the top and front views of *EFG*, a plane which is tangent to the upper surface of the cone *VC*. Point *E* is on the surface of the cone.

Group 3. The convolute

17.3.1. *XY* is the axis of a helical convolute. The directing helix begins at point *P* and rises clockwise. Its lead is the distance *XY*. The surface is limited by the outer cylinder. Its elements slope downward. Draw the top and front views of the convolute, between elevations *X* and *Y*, using 12 equally spaced elements. Draw the involute intersection which the surface makes with the horizontal plane through *X*. Show visibility.

17.3.2. The two pipe openings at *A* and *B* are to be connected by a conical-convolute transition piece. Draw the top and front views of the five elements whose ends are shown in the front view.

17.3.3. *AB* and *CD* are the major and minor diameters, respectively, of the elliptical upper opening of a conical-convolute transition piece. The major and minor diameters of the lower openings are, respectively, *GH* and *EF*. Draw the top and front views of the contour elements and four additional well-spaced elements of the convolute surface.

17.3.4. *AB* and *CD* are the minor and major diameters, respectively, of the elliptical end of a conical-convolute transition piece. Point *E* is the center of the circular end of the piece. Draw the top and front views of the contour elements and the four additional elements whose ends are indicated at 1, 2, 3, and 4. Points 1 and 2 are on the upper surface of the transition piece.

Group 4. The sphere

17.4.1. Two plane sections through a sphere are shown at *C* and *D*. Draw the top and front views of the sphere.

17.4.2. *A* and *B* are two plane sections through a sphere. Draw the top and front views of the sphere and the front view of the section through *B*.

17.4.3. *XY* is the axis of a ball bearing. One of its balls is shown at *C*. Determine the maximum number of balls in the bearing.

17.4.4. Find the top and front views of *X*, the center of a sphere which rests in the pocket formed by the spheres *A*, *B*, and *C*. Sphere *X* is the same size as the given spheres.

17.4.5. Complete the top and front views of *PQR*, a plane that is tangent to the sphere about *S*. *P* is on the upper surface of the sphere. Show the visibility of the plane.

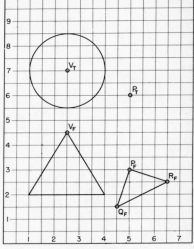

Prob. 17.2.5

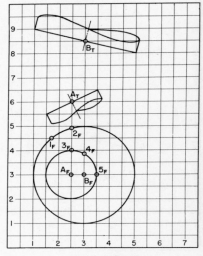

Prob. 17.3.2

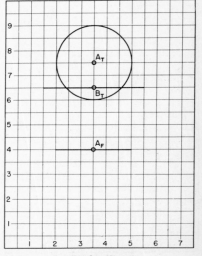

Prob. 17.4.2

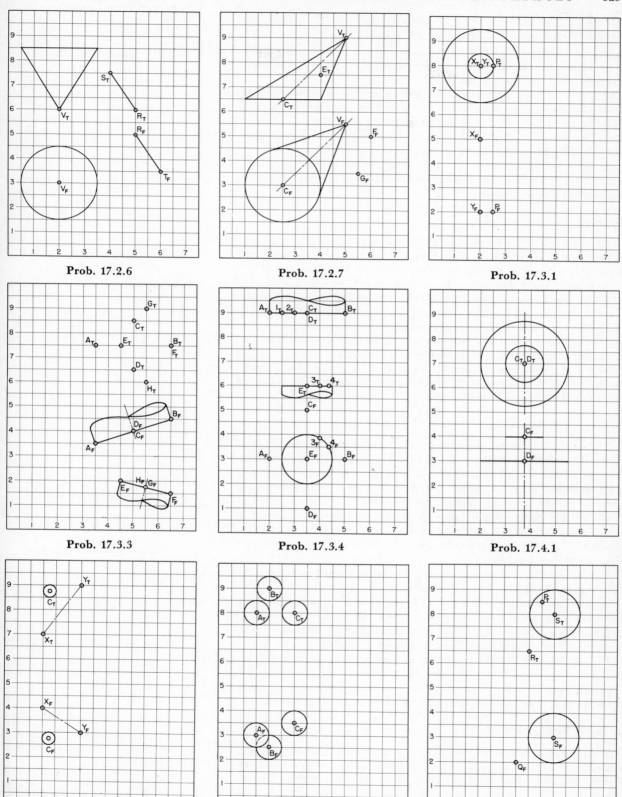

Prob. 17.2.6

Prob. 17.2.7

Prob. 17.3.1

Prob. 17.3.3

Prob. 17.3.4

Prob. 17.4.1

Prob. 17.4.3

Prob. 17.4.4

Prob. 17.4.5

Group 5. The ellipsoid

17.5.1. *AB* is the major diameter of a prolate ellipsoid. Its minor diameter is one-third the length of the major diameter. Draw the top and front views of the ellipsoid. Draw the view of the ellipsoid in which its major diameter will appear as a point.

17.5.2. The lower portion of a cylindrical water tank is shown in the front view. The bottom of the tank is half of an ellipsoid which fits smoothly onto the rest of the tank. The lowest point on the bottom is 4 ft below *T*. Draw the top, front, and right-side views of the tank bottom. Scale: ¼″ = 1′-0″. Is the tank bottom oblate or prolate?

17.5.3. Point *P* represents a pulley through which a taut rope passes. The rope is attached to swivels which are anchored at *A* and *B*. Draw the top and front views of the locus of point *P*.

Group 6. The paraboloid

17.6.1. *XY* is the directrix and *F* is the focus of the generatrix of a parabolic mirror. The axial length of the mirror is 4 in. Draw the top, front, and half right-side views of the mirror. Scale: half size.

17.6.2. *XY* is the directrix and *F* is the focus of a generating parabola. Draw the top, front, and half right-side views of the surface created by the parabola as it revolves about its directrix. The height of the surface is *XY*.

17.6.3. Point *F* is the focus of a parabola whose directrix lies along line *AB*. Draw the top and front views of the paraboloid generated by this parabola. The axial length of the surface is 1½ in. Scale: full size.

17.6.4. *XY* is the directrix and *F* is the focus of the generatrix of a paraboloid. Plane *RST* is tangent to the paraboloid at *T*, which is on the upper portion of the surface. Draw the top and front views of plane *RST*.

Group 7. The hyperboloid

17.7.1. *AB* is the conjugate axis, *F*₁ and *F*₂ are the focuses, and *T*₁ and *T*₂ are the ends of the transverse axis of a frontal hyperbola. This hyperbola is the generatrix of a hyperboloid of revolution of one sheet. The altitude of the hyperboloid is *AB*. Draw the top and front views of 12 equally spaced elements of each generation of the hyperboloid.

17.7.2. The ellipses whose diameters are *AB* and *CD* with centers at *O* and *T* are the bases of an elliptical hyperboloid. The gore ellipse has diameters *EF* and *GH*. Draw the top and front views of six equally spaced elements of each generation.

17.7.3. *ABCD* is one wing of the projection-screen structure for an outdoor automobile theater. It is desired to cover this surface with sheet metal, thus forming a parabolic hyperboloid. Draw the plan, front-elevation, and side-elevation views of nine horizontal and seven profile elements, equally spaced, which represent the locations of the supporting members. These elements are in addition to the boundary elements shown.

17.7.4. *AB* and *CD* are the boundaries of a parabolic hyperboloid. (*a*) Draw the top and front views of eight elements of each generation. (*b*) Using *AB* and *CD* as directrices, draw the view of the surface which shows the edge view of the plane director and the elements parallel thereto.

Group 8. The cylindroid

17.8.1. The semiellipses centered at *A* and *B* are the directrices of a cylindroid whose plane director is frontal. Draw the top and front views of 10 elements, the ends of which are equally spaced around the front view of ellipse *B*.

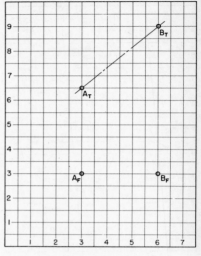

Prob. 17.5.1

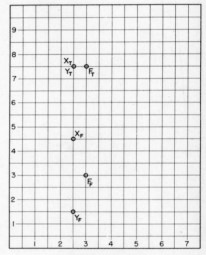

Prob. 17.6.2

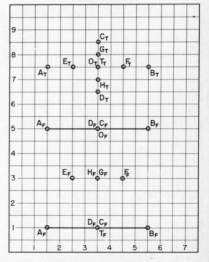

Prob. 17.7.2

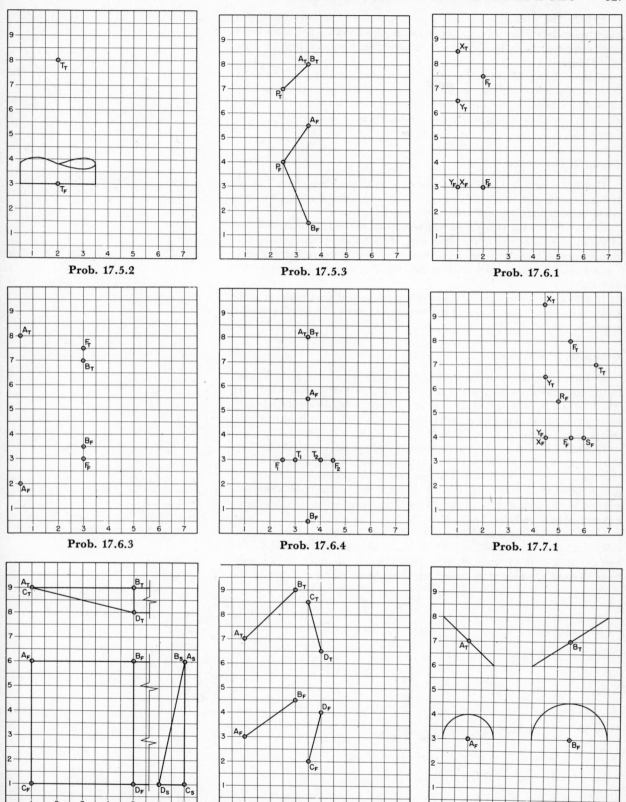

Prob. 17.5.2

Prob. 17.5.3

Prob. 17.6.1

Prob. 17.6.3

Prob. 17.6.4

Prob. 17.7.1

Prob. 17.7.3

Prob. 17.7.4

Prob. 17.8.1

17.8.2. The semiellipses centered at C and D are the directrices of a cylindroid whose plane director is horizontal. Draw the top and front views of 10 elements, the ends of which are equally spaced around the front view of the ellipses.

17.8.3. Curves AB and CD are the directrices of a cylindroid. The plane director appears as an edge in the front view and is parallel to the line of tangency between the two curves. Draw the top and front views of 10 elements, the ends of which are equally spaced around the front view of curve AB.

Group 9. The conoid

17.9.1. Circle C and line AB are the directrices of a right conoid. Draw the top, front, and right-side views of the conoid, employing 10 elements whose intersections with AB are equally spaced.

17.9.2. BC is a bowstring truss which supports the end of the arched roof of a warehouse. The roof of the office wing of the building terminates in the straight line AD. Draw the plan and elevation views of the positions of nine equally spaced joists which support the conoidal surface connecting AD and BC.

17.9.3. Line AB and circle C are the directrices of an oblique conoid. Draw the top and front views of the conoid, employing 12 equally spaced elements.

Group 10. The helicoid

17.10.1. CD is the center line of the 2-in.-diameter shaft of a right-hand right-helicoidal screw conveyer. The outside diameter of the screw is 10 in. The lead is 8 in. The first element of the surface is AB. Draw the top and front views of one turn of the conveyer, employing 16 equally spaced elements. Show visibility. Scale: ⅜ size.

17.10.2. CD is the axis of a right-hand oblique helicoidal chute. The chute is attached to a column of 1 ft diameter. The outside diameter of the chute is 2 ft, and its lead is 6 ft. The elements slope upward from the center and make an angle of 60° with the axis. Starting with element AB, draw the top and front views of one-half turn of the chute, using eight equally spaced elements. Show visibility. Scale: $1'' = 1'\text{-}0''$.

17.10.3. CD is the axis of an earth auger bit. The blade of the bit is a right-hand right-conical helicoid. The design cone is given. The lead is one-half the altitude of the cone. Starting with element AB, draw the top and front views of one turn of the auger bit blade. Show visibility.

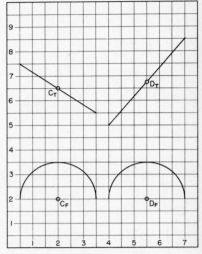

Prob. 17.8.2

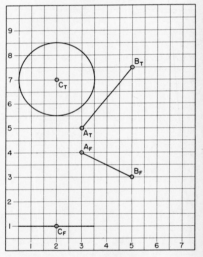

Prob. 17.9.3

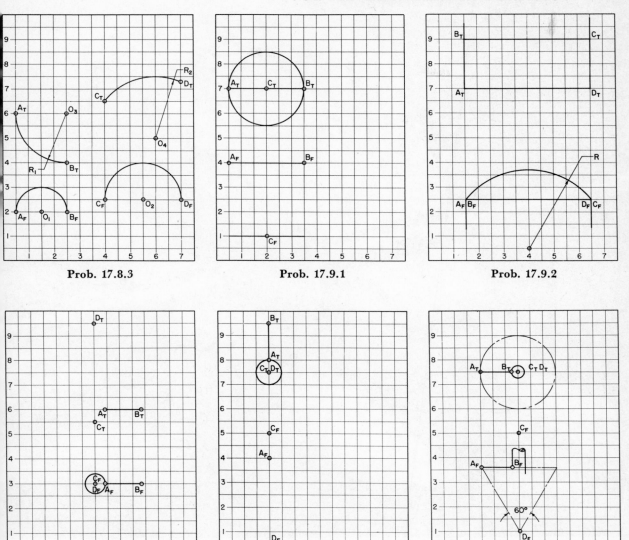

Prob. 17.8.3 Prob. 17.9.1 Prob. 17.9.2

Prob. 17.10.1 Prob. 17.10.2 Prob. 17.10.3

18

INTERSECTIONS AND DEVELOPMENTS

18.1. In the making of orthographic drawings, there is the repeated necessity to represent the *lines of intersection* between the various surfaces of a wide variety of objects. Nearly every line on a drawing is a line of intersection, generally the intersection of two planes, giving a straight line, or of a cylinder and a plane, giving a circle or an ellipse. The term "intersection of surfaces" refers, however, to the more complicated lines that occur when geometrical surfaces such as planes, cylinders, cones, and ellipsoids intersect each other. These lines of intersection may be shown by one of two basic methods: (1) *conventional intersections*, usually used to represent a fillet, round, or runout, as explained in paragraph 7.29 and shown in Fig. 7.34, or (2) *plotted intersections*, employed when an intersection must be located accurately for purposes of dimensioning or for development of the surfaces. In sheet-metal combinations the intersection *must* be found before the piece can be developed. In this chapter we are concerned solely with the methods of projecting plotted intersections and with the procedures employed in the development of surfaces.

18.2. Intersections of Plane Surfaces. The intersection of a line and a plane is a *point* common to both. The intersection of two planes is a *line* common to both. After mastering the graphical methods of these intersections (paragraphs 18.3 to 18.6), the student may apply the principles learned to finding the line of intersection between

531

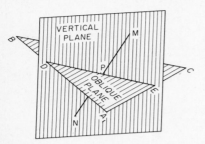

Fig. 18.1. Intersection of a line and a plane.

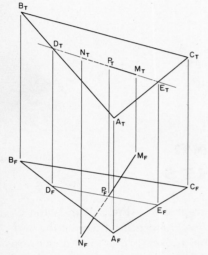

Fig. 18.2. Construction for finding the intersection of a line and a plane.

objects made up of plane surfaces (prisms and pyramids, paragraphs 18.7 to 18.9). The method of solution for the intersection of other polyhedrons should follow logically from the examples given.

18.3. Intersection of a Line and a Plane. The intersection of a line and a plane is a point common to both. A given line will intersect all lines of the plane which pass through the point of intersection. The intersection therefore can readily be determined by locating a *line of the plane* which intersects the given line.

The pictorial example of Fig. 18.1 illustrates the theory of finding the intersection P of line MN with an oblique plane ABC. To find a line of ABC which intersects MN, a vertical plane containing MN is passed through ABC, thereby establishing DE as the straight-line intersection between the vertical plane and ABC. DE and MN are nonparallel lines of a common plane (vertical plane) and therefore must intersect; their common point is point P. Since point P is on line DE, it is a point in plane ABC. Therefore, P is a point common to plane ABC and the given line MN.

Figure 18.2 illustrates the orthographic procedure of finding the point of intersection of a line MN and an oblique plane ABC. A vertical plane, which appears as an edge in the top view, is passed through MN, cutting the top view of AB at D and the top view of AC at E. DE is the line of intersection of the vertical plane and ABC. DE is located in the front view by projecting points D and E to the front view on AB and AC, respectively. The intersection of MN and DE, point P, is located in the front view where MN intersects DE (DE and MN both lie in the same vertical plane). Point P is projected to the top view on MN, completing the top and front views of point P, the intersection of line MN, and the oblique plane ABC. An identical solution may be had by using a receding plane through the *front* view of line MN. The intersection of receding plane and given plane is then projected to the top view, where the intersection with line MN locates point P.

When the edge view of the plane is given, the point of intersection of the line and plane is apparent in that edge view.

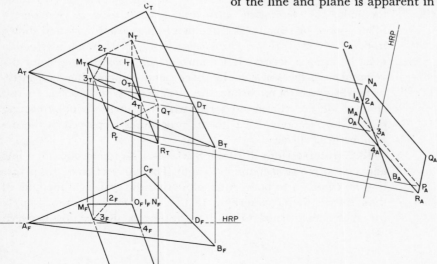

Fig. 18.3. Intersection of several lines and a plane.

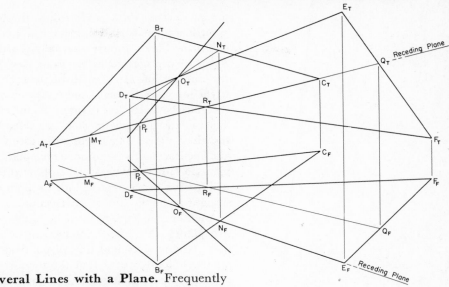

Fig. 18.4. Intersection of two planes.

18.4. Intersection of Several Lines with a Plane. Frequently problems occur which require the intersection of many lines with a plane. Figure 18.3 is an example of such a problem, requiring the determination of the intersection of the oblique plane *ABC* and the parallelepiped *MNOPQR*. The problem is solved by determining the intersection of the edges of the parallelepiped with the given plane and drawing the consecutive lines of intersection on the parallelepiped between the points determined. The solution illustrated in Fig. 18.3 first requires that an edge view of the plane be established as shown in the elevation auxiliary view. The parallelepiped is projected to the auxiliary view. The auxiliary view clearly shows where the plane *ABC* cuts through the parallelepiped, as at points 1 to 4 on lines *NO*, *MN*, *MP*, and *OR*, respectively. The numbered points are projected back to the top and front views and the consecutive lines of intersection drawn in both views.

The points of intersection 1 to 4 could have been determined by the procedure outlined in paragraph 18.3, but the time required for the necessary construction would be excessive compared to the edge-view method just described.

18.5. Intersection of Planes. The intersection of two planes is a straight line. To determine the location and direction of the line of intersection, it is necessary to determine two points on this line. The points are necessarily common to both planes. In Fig. 18.4, the line of intersection between planes *ABC* and *DEF* is to be established by locating points *O* and *P*, two points common to both planes, by the procedure outlined in paragraph 18.3. *O* is the intersection of *DE* and plane *ABD*. A front receding plane is passed through the front view of *DE*, cutting *AC* at *M* and *BC* at *N*. *MN* is the line of intersection between the front receding plane and *ABC*. *MN* is then located in the top view, intersecting *DE* at point *O*, which is the intersection of *DE* and *ABC*. *O* is located in the front view by projecting O from the top view onto the front view of DE. Similarly, a vertical plane is passed through AC, cutting DF at R and EF at Q. RQ is the line of intersection between the vertical plane and DEF. RQ is then projected to the front view, intersecting AC at point P, the intersection of AC with plane DEF. Point P is then projected to the top view. Points O and P are common to both planes and must therefore be on the line of intersection between planes ABC and DEF. The top and front views of OP are extended to any desired length, as the given planes are indefinite in extent. As a check on correctness and accuracy of the solution, a *third* point may be located. A receding plane in either view may be employed to do this; of course, for the solution to be correct, all three points must align on the same straight line—the line of intersection.

Another conception may be used to find the intersection of two planes: Any plane intersecting a second plane will intersect that plane in a straight line all points of which are common to both planes. It follows then that the two given planes may be cut by a receding plane, giving a line of intersection of the receding plane and *each* of the given planes. These two lines of intersection will intersect at a point which is common to both given planes, thus giving one point on the line of intersection of the given planes. This operation repeated with a second receding plane will give a second point, thus determining the line of intersection of given planes. Therefore, in Fig. 18.5, the receding plane in the top view will cut RS from plane PTY and WU from CJV. The intersection of RS and WU in the front view at O_F is then projected to the top view, where O_T lies on the receding plane used.

Similarly, the receding plane in the front view will cut PF from plane PTY and CE from plane CJV. The intersection of PF and CE in the top view at N_T is then projected to the front view, where N_F lies on the receding plane used. Thus O and N are common to planes PTY and CJV and determine the line of intersection.

This method would be employed whenever the triangles represent-

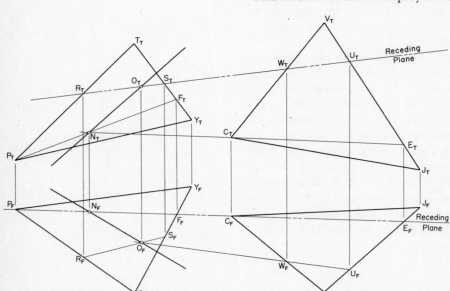

Fig. 18.5. Intersection of two planes.

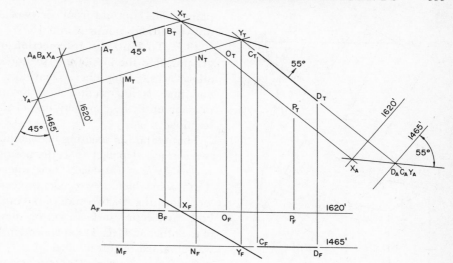

Fig. 18.6. Intersection of two planes (strike and dip).

ing the planes do not conveniently cross as they do in Fig. 18.4. Also, later, in the solution of problems involving curved surfaces, cutting planes will be chosen to pass through two surfaces but will not necessarily be placed at any particular edge or element of either surface.

18.6. Intersection of Planes When Strike and Dip Are Given. A point common to two planes can be located at the intersection of two strike lines, one in each plane, provided the lines are at the same elevation. Two such points will determine the direction and location of the straight-line intersection between the two planes.

In Fig. 18.6, the plane on the left is defined in both the top and front views by the strike AB and the 45° angle of dip. Note the elevation of AB at 1,620 ft. The plane on the right is defined by the strike CD and the 55° angle of dip. Note the elevation of CD at 1,465 ft.

In the elevation auxiliary view, projected from the top view in the direction of CD, CD appears as a point; and the plane will necessarily appear as an edge, drawn 55° below the horizontal as prescribed by the angle of dip. At an elevation of 1,620 ft (the same elevation as AB) a horizontal line OP is drawn in the elevation auxiliary view. The top view of OP is drawn parallel to CD, extended to intersect the top view of AB at X. AB and OP are two horizontal lines at the same level or elevation. The front view of X is located at the 1,620-ft level. Point X is common to both planes and is a point on the line of intersection of the two planes.

In the elevation auxiliary view projected in the direction of AB, the edge view of the plane is determined and drawn 45° below the horizontal as presented. At an elevation of 1,465 ft (same elevation as CD), a horizontal line MN is located in the plane. MN is projected to the top view and drawn parallel to AB, extended to intersect the top view of CD at Y. CD and MN are two horizontal lines at the same level, or elevation. X and Y are two points common to both planes and are on the line of intersection between the two

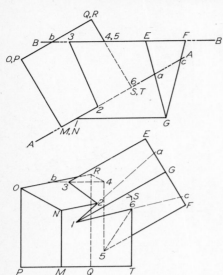

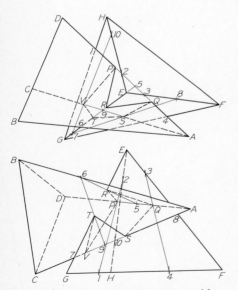

Fig. 18.7. Intersection of two prisms.

Fig. 18.8. Intersection of two pyramids.

planes. The top and front views of the line of intersection are now drawn through points X and Y.

18.7. To Find the Intersection of Two Prisms (Fig. 18.7). In general, find the line of intersection of a surface on one prism with all surfaces on the other. Then take a surface adjacent to the first, and find its intersection with the other prism. Continue in this manner until the complete line of intersection of the prisms is determined.

The method of locating end points on the line of intersection of two surfaces depends upon the position of the surfaces, as follows:

Both Surfaces Receding. Their intersection appears as a point in the view in which they recede. Project the intersection to an adjacent view, locating the two ends of the intersection on the edges of one or both intersecting surfaces so that they will lie within the boundaries of the other surface. The intersection 4-5 of surfaces $QRST$ and EF-3 was obtained in this manner.

One Surface Receding, the Other Oblique. An edge of the oblique surface may appear to pierce the receding surface in a view in which these conditions exist. If, in an adjacent view, the piercing point lies on the edge of the oblique surface and within the boundaries of the other surface, then it is an end point on the intersection of the surfaces. Point 5, lying on edge F-5 of the oblique surface FG-1-5 and the surface $QRST$, is located in the top view in this manner. Point 1 was similarly established. Point 6, lying on edge ST, is found by passing a vertical plane AA through edge ST. Plane AA cuts line 1-c from plane GF-5-1 giving point 6 where line 1-c crosses ST.

Both Surfaces Oblique. Find the piercing point of an edge of one surface with the other surface, as follows: Pass a receding plane through an edge of one surface. Find the line of intersection of the receding plane and the other surface as explained above. The piercing point of the edge and surface is located where the line of intersection, just found, and the edge intersect. Repeat this operation to establish the other end of the line of intersection of the surfaces. Point 3, on the line of intersection 2-3 of the oblique surfaces $NORS$ and EG-1-3, was found in this manner by passing the receding plane BB through edge E-3 finding the intersection b-4 of the surfaces, and then locating point 3 at the intersection of b-4 and E-3.

18.8. To Find the Intersection of Two Pyramids. In general, find where one edge on one pyramid pierces a surface of the other pyramid. Then find where a second edge pierces, and so on. To complete the line of intersection the piercing points of the edges of the second pyramid with surfaces of the first will probably also have to be found. Figure 18.8 illustrates the method. Find where edge AD pierces plane EHG by assuming a vertical cutting plane through edge AD. This plane cuts line 1-2 from plane EHG, and the piercing point is point P, located first on the front view and then projected to the top view. Next, find where AD pierces plane EFG by using a vertical cutting plane through *AD*. This plane cuts line 3-4 from plane *EFG*, and the piercing point is point *Q*.

Having a point *P* on plane *EHG* and point *Q* on plane *EFG*, the piercing point of edge *EG* with plane *ABD* will have to be found in order to draw lines of intersection. A vertical plane through *EG* cuts line 5-6 from plane *ABD*, and the intersection is point *R* on edge *EG*. Thus edges of the "first" pyramid pierce surfaces of the "second," and edges of the second pierce surfaces of the first. Continue in this manner until the complete line of intersection *PRQSTV* has been found.

The use of a vertical cutting plane to obtain the piercing points is perhaps the simplest method and the easiest to visualize. Nevertheless, it should be noted that a plane receding either from the frontal or profile plane could also be used. As an example of the use of a plane receding from the frontal, consider that such a plane has been passed through line *CA* in the front view. This plane cuts line 7-8 from plane *EFG*, and the point of intersection is *S* on line *CA*. The use of a plane receding from the profile would be basically the same but would, of course, require a side view.

18.9. To Find the Line of Intersection between a Prism and a Pyramid (Fig. 18.9). The method, basically, is the same as for two pyramids. Thus a vertical plane through edge *G* cuts line 1-2 from surface *AED*, and a vertical plane through edge *K* cuts line 3-4 from surface *AED*, giving the two piercing points *P* and *Q* on surface *AED*. A vertical plane through edge *AE* cuts elements 7 and 8 from the prism and gives piercing points *R* and *T*. Continue in this manner until the complete line of intersection *PQSTVR* is found.

18.10. Intersections of Curved Surfaces. The line of intersection of two curved surfaces, as was the case for plane surfaces, is a line all points of which are common to both surfaces. There may be more than one "line" of intersection between two curved surfaces. For example, a small pipe which passes completely through a larger pipe will intersect the larger pipe in two lines, one line as it enters and another as it leaves.

The line of intersection of any two surfaces may be found by either one of the following methods:

Selected-line Method. Select a sufficient number of lines of one surface. Find the point where each of these lines pierces the other surface. A line joining these piercing points will be the line of intersection of the two surfaces. This method was used in paragraph 18.5 to find the line of intersection of two plane surfaces.

Cutting-plane Method. Pass a sufficient number of cutting planes through each of the given surfaces simultaneously. Each plane will "cut" a line from each of the given surfaces. These lines will intersect either in a point or points common to the two given surfaces. A line connecting these points will be the line of intersection of the given surfaces. This method was also used in paragraph 18.5 to find the line of intersection of two plane surfaces.

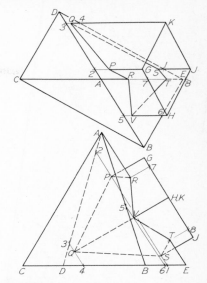

Fig. 18.9. Intersection of a pyramid and a prism.

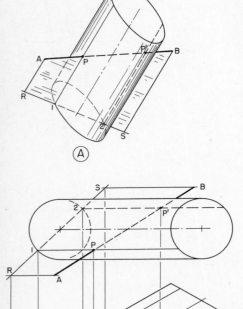

Fig. 18.10. Intersection of a line and a cylinder.

Cutting-sphere Method. In finding the line of intersection between two double-curved surfaces, sometimes a plane will cut circles from one of the surfaces but parabolas, hyperbolas, etc., from the other surface. In such cases, it may be possible to use a cutting sphere, thus obtaining circles from both surfaces and simplifying the solution.

In attacking any problem of surface intersection, always examine the problem carefully to discover the simplest lines possible to cut from each surface.

In applying any of the general methods outlined above, exercise care or the solution of the problem may become more complicated than necessary. In applying the selected-line method, for example, lines from one surface should be selected by giving primary consideration to the method that will be used to find where these lines pierce the other surface. In applying the cutting-plane method, planes should be selected that will cut *simple* lines (either straight lines or circles) from each of the given surfaces.

For purposes of analyzing the problems of geometric curved-surface intersection, curved surfaces may be divided into two classes: (1) single-curved surfaces of revolution and (2) double-curved surfaces of revolution.

18.11. Intersection of a Single-curved Surface and a Line. In paragraph 18.3, directions were given for finding the point of intersection between a line and plane. Basically, the same method is used to find the intersection of a line and a single-curved surface. If a cutting plane is passed through the line and the intersection of the cutting plane with the single-curved surface found, this intersection will cross the line in points common to the line, the cutting plane, and the single-curved surface. The cutting plane is preferably passed through the single-curved surface so that it will cut a straight line. This means that, for a cone, the plane will be passed through the apex or, for a cylinder, parallel to the axis.

18.12. Intersection of a Cylinder and a Line. The problem of finding the intersection of a cylinder and a line is illustrated pictorially in Fig. 18.10*A*. A plane passed parallel to the axis of a cylinder will cut straight-line elements from the cylinder. Therefore, in Fig. 18.10*A*, lines from *A* and *B* parallel to the cylinder axis will determine a plane that contains *AB* and is also parallel to the cylinder axis. These lines intersect the base plane of the cylinder at *R*

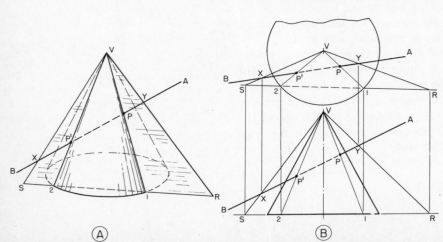

Fig. 18.11. Intersection of a line and a cone.

and S. Points 1 and 2, where RS cuts the base curve, determine the ends of two elements of the cylinder in plane $ABRS$. The intersections of AB and the elements at P and P' are then points which are common to the line AB, the cutting plane, and the cylinder.

Figure 18.10B illustrates the orthographic solution. From A and B, lines are drawn parallel to the cylinder axis to intersect the base plane at R and S. The line RS then cuts the base curve at 1 and 2, thus locating elements of the cylinder. The elements intersect AB at P and P', the piercing points.

18.13. Intersection of a Cone and a Line. Figure 18.11A illustrates pictorially the problem of finding the points where a line pierces a cone. A cutting plane, VXY, containing the given line AB and passing through the apex, V, of the cone, is selected. A plane passing through the apex of a cone will intersect the cone in straight lines. The lines of intersection of the cutting plane and the cone are lines V-1 and V-2. These lines are determined by finding the line of intersection, RS, between the cutting plane and the base plane of the cone and then finding the points 1 and 2 where this line crosses the base curve. Line AB intersects both lines V-1 and V-2, establishing the points P and P' where line AB pierces the cone.

The orthographic solution is illustrated in Fig. 18.11B. Convenient points X and Y on line AB are selected so that plane VXY (a plane containing the apex of the cone and line AB), extended, will intersect the base plane of the cone in the line RS. In the top view, RS cuts the base curve at 1 and 2, thus locating elements V-1 and V-2 *in* cutting plane and *on* the surface of the cone. V-1 and V-2 then intersect BA at P and P', the piercing points of line AB and the cone.

If the line and cone are both oblique as in Fig. 18.12, an extra

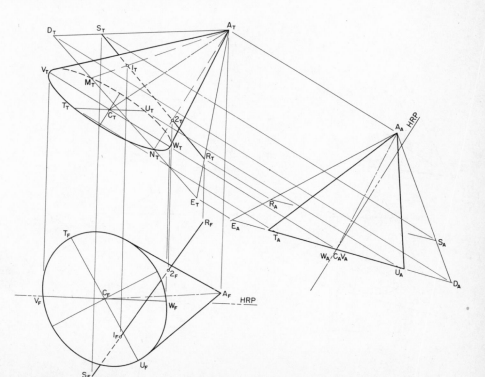

Fig. 18.12. Intersection of a line and a cone (oblique position).

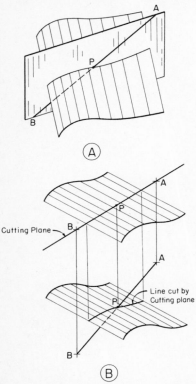

Fig. 18.13. Intersection of a line and a ruled surface.

view will assist in getting an accurate solution. If either the major and minor *or* the conjugate diameters of the cone's base are given, these diameters may be employed to get the edge view of the base. In Fig. 18.12, the major and minor diameters are given for each elliptical representation in top and front views of the base. The base is circular but not a right section of the cone, and the cone is therefore oblique. The top-view major diameter *VW* is a horizontal line and is in true length. An auxiliary view then made as a point view of *VW* will give the edge view of the base, and having the point view at $V_A A_A$, *any* other point in the plane of the base allows completion of the edge view of the base in the auxiliary view. *TU*, the front-view major diameter, may be employed for this purpose. *TU* is frontal and may therefore be located in the top view. Then projection from *T* and *U* to the auxiliary and measurement from the front view locate a point in the auxiliary through which the edge view of the base may be drawn. Now through *RS* in the auxiliary a plane *ARS* will pass through the apex of the cone and contain line *RS*. *AR* and *AS*, extended to the base plane, locate a line of plane *ARS* in the *base plane* of the cone at $E_A D_A$. This line *ED*, projected back to *AR* and *AS* (extended) in the top view, will reveal the points *M* and *N* where plane *ARS* intersects the base curve. Thus two elements, *MA* and *NA*, are cut from the cone. These elements intersect *RS* at points 1 and 2, the piercing points of *RS* with the cone. The front view of points 1 and 2 may be found by projecting 1 and 2 to *RS* in the front view. The location of elements *MA* and *NA* in the front view is not necessary to the solution, but their projection to the front view allows checking for accuracy. Note in Fig. 18.12 that the top view and auxiliary have the same relationship to the solution as do the top and front views of Fig. 18.11.

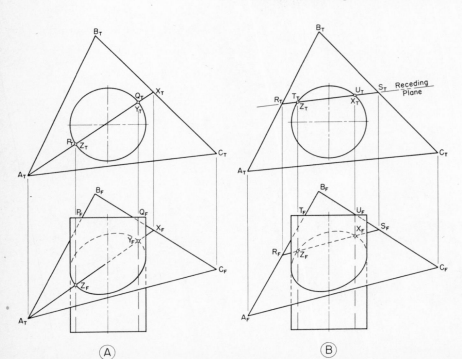

Fig. 18.14. Intersection of a plane and a cylinder.

18.14. Intersection of Any Single-curved (Ruled) Surface and a Line. The problem of finding the piercing point of a line and any ruled surface is illustrated pictorially in Fig. 18.13A. A plane passed through the line will cut a line (often curved) from the surface. This line of intersection between cutting plane and surface may be located by finding where the cutting plane intersects elements of the surface. Then where the given line intersects the *surface intersection* of the cutting plane is a point common to the given line and surface. Figure 18.13B shows the orthographic construction. A receding plane in the top view through *AB* cuts elements of the surface. These points of intersection on the elements may then be projected to the front view, locating the front view of the line of intersection between cutting plane and ruled surface. The intersection at *P* is then a point common to the given line and ruled surface. The above method is useful in finding the piercing point of a line and either a geometrical ruled surface, such as one of the hyperboloids, or a ruled (or single-curved) surface of general form.

18.15. Intersection of a Single-curved Surface and a Plane. In the solution of these problems, either the selected-line or the cutting-plane method may be used. However, the selected-line method is usually used when the edge view of the plane is given or a rearrangement of views can easily be made in which the plane will show as an edge. The cutting plane is usually used in all other cases. A straight line or circle can always be cut from a single-curved surface by a cutting plane.

18.16. Intersection of a Cylinder and a Plane. Figure 18.14 illustrates both the selected-line and the cutting-plane method of finding the intersection of a cylinder and plane. At *A*, a selected line of the plane, such as *AX*, is seen to intersect the cylinder in the top view where the cylindrical surface appears as an edge. Therefore, element *P* of the cylinder will contain point *Z*, one point on the line of intersection. A number of selected lines of the plane will give points to plot the complete curve of intersection. Note that line *AX* also intersects the cylinder at point *Y*, on element *Q*.

At Fig. 18.14B, a vertical cutting plane is shown. This plane, parallel to the cylinder axis, will cut elements of the cylinder at *T* and *U* and will also cut a line *RS* from the plane *ABC*. Points *Z* and *X* are then points common to cutting plane, given plane, and cylinder and are two points on the line of intersection sought. A series of planes similar to the one shown will give other points to complete the line of intersection.

18.17. Intersection of a Cone and a Plane. Figure 18.15A illustrates pictorially the determination of the line of intersection between a cone and a plane by the selected-line method. Lines (elements) of the cone, such as *V*-1, *V*-2, etc., will respectively intersect the plane at *a*, *b*, etc. If the edge view of the plane appears in one of the views, as in 18.15B, the solution is quite simple. Selected elements of the cone, *V*-1, *V*-2, etc., are drawn in both views. These

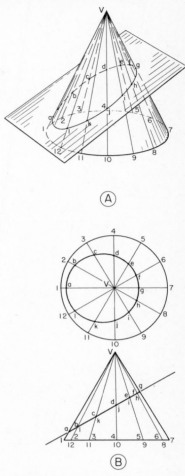

Fig. 18.15. Intersection of a plane and a cone.

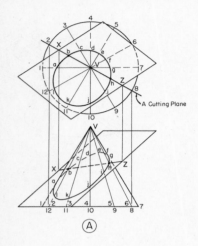

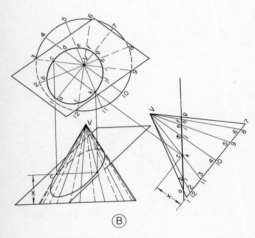

Fig. 18.16. Intersection of a plane and a cone.

elements are seen to intersect the plane in the front view at *a*, *b*, etc. Projection of these points to the top view then gives points through which a smooth curve is drawn to complete the solution. The edge view of the plane (within the confines of the cone) is, of course, the intersection in the front view.

If the plane intersecting the cone is oblique, as in Fig. 18.16, the cutting-plane method would probably be preferred because of the simplicity of the solution. Any plane passed through the apex of the cone will cut straight lines from the cone. Therefore, in Fig. 18.16*A*, if vertical cutting planes are employed, all passing through *V*, the apex, these planes will cut lines such as *V*-2 and *V*-8 from the cone. At the same time, such a cutting plane will cut *XZ* from the plane. *XZ* then intersects *V*-2 at *b* and *V*-8 at *h*, giving two points on the line of intersection. A series of planes thus passed and points found will complete the solution.

Even though the above plane method is simple and requires only the given views for solution, one *might* prefer to draw an extra view (auxiliary), as at Fig. 18.16*B*, where, by projecting parallel to a horizontal line of the plane, *the plane appears as an edge*. In this event, selected lines of the cone are seen to intersect the plane in the auxiliary view (where the plane appears as an edge), and the solution becomes basically the same as in Fig. 18.15*B*. In addition, of course, points located first in the auxiliary view and then in the top view will have to be found in the front view by projection from the top view and measurement from the auxiliary, indicated by distance *X* on the figure.

18.18. Intersection of Two Ruled Surfaces. In determining the line of intersection of two ruled surfaces either the selected-line or the cutting-plane method may be used. However, when the selected-line method is used, cutting planes will have to be employed to find the points where the selected lines pierce the other surface. Therefore, no matter which analysis is applied, the construction involved will be the same as if the cutting-plane analysis had been applied. As a result, problems involving the intersection of ruled surfaces should be solved using the cutting-plane analysis. Planes are se-

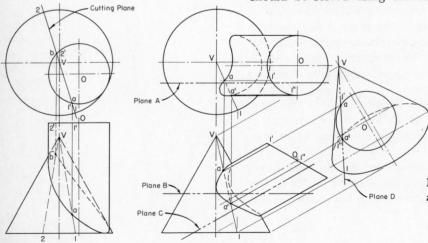

Fig. 18.17. Intersection of a cylinder and a cone.

lected, when possible, to cut straight lines from each of the given ruled surfaces simultaneously.

18.19. Intersection of a Cylinder and a Cone. Figure 18.17*A* illustrates the determination of the line of intersection of a cone and a cylinder by the cutting-plane method. The axes of both surfaces of Fig. 18.17*A* are vertical. Therefore, any vertical plane that passes through the apex of the cone will cut straight-line elements from the cone, and these vertical planes will also cut elements from the cylinder. One such cutting plane is shown on the figure. This plane cuts elements *V*-1 and *V*-2 from the cone and at the same time cuts elements 1′ and 2′ from the cylinder. Element *V*-1 of the cone intersects element 1′ of the cylinder and element *V*-2 of the cone intersects element 2′ of the cylinder, thus locating two points on the line of intersection. A number of vertical planes thus employed will give points to locate the curve in the front view. The line of intersection in the top view is, of course, the circle shown, the end view of the cylinder.

It should be noted that the problem of Fig. 18.17*A* may also be solved by cutting both surfaces with horizontal planes, thus obtaining a circle from each surface. The intersections of circles may be found in the top view and then be projected to the front view.

Figure 18.17*B* illustrates the determination of the line of intersection for another cone-and-cylinder combination. In the views given (top and front), it can be seen that no suitable cutting plane can be employed to determine the line of intersection *if simple lines are to be cut from each surface*. Planes parallel to plane *A* will cut straight lines from the cylinder but a hyperbola from the cone. Planes parallel to plane *B* will cut circles from the cone but ellipses from the cylinder. Planes parallel to plane *C* will cut straight lines from the cylinder but ellipses from the cone. It is now evident that some other method may give an easier solution. The auxiliary view shown, giving the end view of the cylinder, offers the advantage that planes may be passed through the apex of the cone and also parallel to the cylinder axis without burdensome extra construction. One such plane is shown, which cuts a line *V*-1 from the cone and which also cuts elements 1′ and 1″ from the cylinder. These elements intersect at *a* and *a*′ (first located in the front view), giving two points on the line of intersection. Additional planes similar to the one illustrated will determine other points to complete the intersection.

18.20. Intersection of Two Cones. Figure 18.18 illustrates another variation of the intersection of single-curved surfaces—this time for two cones. Employing only top and front views (given), no series of planes either horizontal, frontal, profile, or receding in any view will cut simple lines from the surfaces. Yet, as shown in Fig. 18.17 and explained in paragraph 18.14, if a plane is passed through the apex of a cone it will cut straight-line elements from the cone. It follows then that, if a plane is passed through the apexes of *both* cones, straight-line elements will be cut from both cones. Therefore,

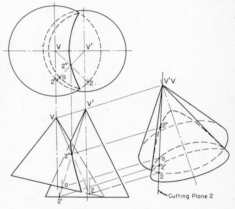

Fig. 18.18. Intersection of two cones.

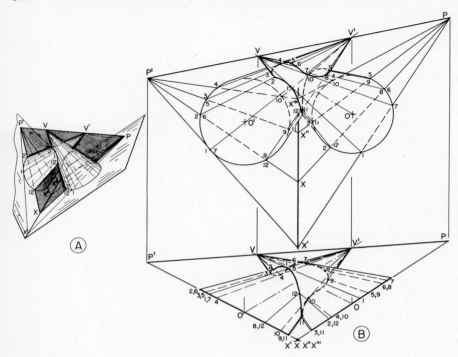

Fig. 18.19. Intersection of two cones.

a plane passed through a line connecting the apex points of both cones should give a relatively simple solution.

A point view of the line connecting the apex points of the cones of Fig. 18.18 is had in the auxiliary view shown at $V'V$ and, having the *point view of a line through which a plane is passed*, gives the edge view of the plane. One such plane (2) is shown, which cuts an element V-2 from one cone and an element V'-$2'$ from the other. These two elements intersect at $2''$, giving one point on the line of intersection of the cones. A series of planes passed as described will give other points to plot the complete line of intersection.

Two Cones, Edge Views of Bases Given. In Fig. 18.18, the edge views of the bases of both cones appear in the front view, but when the point view of the line connecting the apexes is made, in this new view the base curves must be plotted. Depending, to some extent, on the position of the cones, a better solution might be to pass planes through the apexes of both cones, determining where these planes intersect the base planes of the cones. Figure 18.19A illustrates the principle pictorially. Line V-V' connecting the apex points is extended to P and P', where the line intersects the base planes. Then a point such as X, chosen on the line of intersection of the base planes, will make a plane $PP'X$ which contains a line $P'X$ cutting the base curve of one cone and a line PX cutting the base curve of the other. Elements of each cone thus located (by cutting the base curves) will intersect in four points on the line of intersection.

The orthographic drawing at Fig. 18.19B will illustrate the details of construction. Apex line V-V' is extended to intersect the base planes at P and P'. The line of intersection of the base planes appears as a point in the front view and as a line in the top view. A point X selected on the base-plane intersection in the top view produces $P'X$, points 2 and 8 on the base of the left cone, and PX and points 6 and 12 on the right cone. These elements, $2\text{-}V'$, $8\text{-}V'$, $6\text{-}V$, and $12\text{-}V$, intersect at 2, 6, 8, and 12 in the cutting plane and on both cones. Elements $2\text{-}V'$, $8\text{-}V'$, $6\text{-}V$, and $12\text{-}V$ then located in the front view allow projection of 2, 6, 8, and 12 to the front view. Other points are located by shifting the plane to another position, such as $PP'X'$ and $PP'X''$. In the illustration, elements cut from each cone by each cutting plane are numbered alike so that identically numbered elements intersect at a point designated by the number. This method of determining the line of intersection of two cones is sometimes called "the swinging-plane method."

18.21. Intersection of Two Cylinders. Figure 18.20 illustrates pictorially at A and orthographically at B the determination of the line of intersection of two cylinders. As explained before, a plane passed *parallel to the axis* of a cylinder will cut straight-line elements from the cylinder. Logic then dictates that a plane parallel to the axes of *two* cylinders will cut straight-line elements from both. Following the theory of paragraph 15.4 (drawing a plane parallel to two skew lines) in Fig. 18.20A, line XS is made parallel to one cylinder axis and line XR parallel to the other cylinder axis. RS is located so that it will be *in the plane of the bases of both cylinders*. Thus a line parallel to RS will cut the base curves of both cylinders and locate points, such as 1 through 7—shown—which will fix the location of elements of each cylinder which lie in the same plane and will therefore determine points on the line of intersection. The details of projection are shown in Fig. 18.20B. First, for the method to be applied, *both cylinder bases must lie in the same plane*, preferably horizontal, frontal, or profile. If the original views do not include bases in one plane, they can be made so by finding the cylinder intersections with a common plane, as explained in paragraph 18.16.

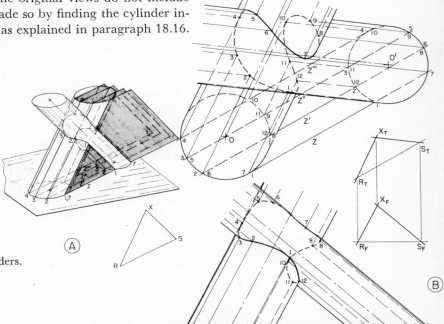

Fig. 18.20. Intersection of two cylinders.

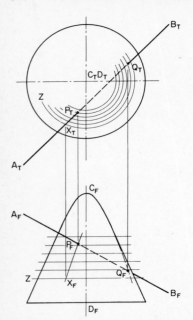

Fig. 18.21. Intersection of a double-curved surface (hyperboloid) and a line.

In this case, the bases are in a horizontal plane. Second, a plane must be established parallel to both cylinder axes. This construction is shown at XRS, where point X has been assumed at any convenient place, and then by drawing XR parallel to the left cylinder and XS parallel to the right cylinder. RS is made horizontal *because the bases are horizontal*, thus producing a line of intersection RS of plane XRS with a horizontal plane. The *direction* of $R_T S_T$ will fix the direction of the intersection with horizontal planes of *any* plane parallel to both cylinders. Lines Z, Z', Z'', and Z''' drawn parallel to RS are therefore the intersections of planes parallel to both cylinders with the horizontal base plane of the cylinders. Third, the horizontal intersection of any plane passed as described will cut the base curves of the cylinders. For example, plane Z' cuts the base of the left cylinder at points 2 and 8 and the base of the right cylinder at 6 and 12. The elements of the cylinders then emanate from these points and intersect in four points, 2, 6, 8, and 12, which are points on the line of intersection. The top view is drawn first, and then the elements and points are projected down to the front view. The numbering system of Fig. 18.20 is similar to the one just described for Fig. 18.19. Notice in this case that 2 and 12, cut by plane Z', are on the bottom side of the cylinders and that points 6 and 8 are on the upper side. Note also that plane Z is the foremost plane that will cut both cylinders and that Z''' is the rearmost. Except for a plane tangent to one of the cylinders, four points on the line of intersection are obtained by each cutting plane. The visibility is determined by inspection after the line of intersection is plotted.

18.22. Intersection of Double-curved Surfaces of Revolution. Double-curved surfaces of revolution present problems somewhat more complicated than do single-curved surfaces because straight lines cannot be cut from a double-curved surface. However, the geometric double-curved surfaces, the ellipsoid, paraboloid, etc., are surfaces of revolution and circles may therefore be cut by planes perpendicular to the axis of revolution.

18.23. Intersection of a Surface of Revolution and a Line. Because no straight line can be drawn on a surface of revolution, any plane passed through the surface will be a curve. In finding the points of intersection of a line and a surface of revolution, it is necessary to pass a plane through the line. The curve resulting from the intersection of the cutting plane and the surface of revolution will then intersect the line to locate the points of intersection of line and surface.

Figure 18.21 illustrates the intersection of an oblique line AB and a surface of revolution (hyperboloid). A vertical cutting plane is passed through the line AB. To find the intersection of the cutting plane and the surface of revolution, a number of horizontal planes are passed through both. Plane Z, for example, cuts a circle from the surface of revolution. This circle in the top view is seen to intersect the edge view of the cutting plane at point X_T. Point X_F then projected from the top view locates one point on one curve of intersection between the vertical plane through *AB* and the hyperboloid. Other points so located will plot the curves, shown in the front view, which intersect the line *AB* at P_F and Q_F, the points of intersection of *AB* and the hyperboloid.

18.24. Intersection of a Double-curved Surface and a Plane.

Figure 18.22 shows a double-curved surface of revolution (a paraboloid) to be intersected by the plane *ABC*. The axis of the paraboloid is vertical. Horizontal planes are perpendicular to the vertical axis and will therefore cut circles from the double-curved surface. Horizontal planes will cut straight lines from the plane. For example, a horizontal plane through point *c* on line *BC* will cut a horizontal line from plane *ABC*. The top view of the horizontal line through *c* is found by projection as shown. The horizontal plane *c* also cuts a circle from the paraboloid. This circle appears as an edge in the front view and also appears in its true diameter. The circle is then drawn in the top view. The line in plane *ABC* and the circle then intersect at two points 3 and 3′, located first in the top view and then projected to the front view. A series of planes through *a*, *b*, *c*, *d*, etc., will give points to plot the intersection.

The problem could also have been solved by employing the auxiliary view shown, where the axis of the double-curved surface appears in true length and the plane appears as an edge. Horizontal planes located in the auxiliary view will cut circles from the double-curved surface and will show the intersections of the passed plane and *ABC* as points. These intersections are projected to the top view (on the circle cut from the double-curved surface) and then located in the front view by projection from the top view and measurement from the auxiliary.

If the axis of the double-curved surface is in an oblique position instead of vertical, two extra views will be required: (1) an auxiliary view giving the true length and (2) an oblique view giving the point

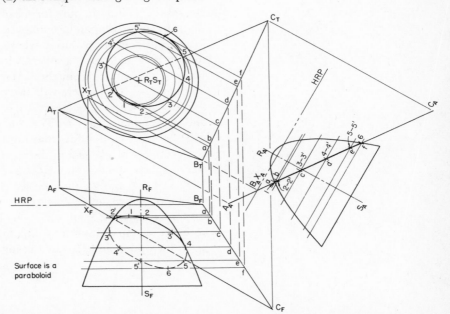

Fig. 18.22. Intersection of a double-curved surface (paraboloid) and a plane.

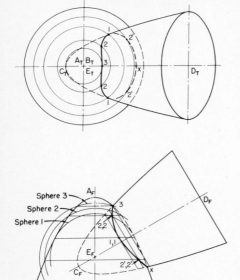

Fig. 18.23. Intersection of two double-curved surfaces (sphere method).

view of the axis of the paraboloid. The plane, ABC, is projected into these views. Thus the auxiliary and oblique views will have the same relationship as the top and front views of Fig. 18.22. The problem is then solved in auxiliary and oblique views, and the line of intersection is then projected back to top and front views.

18.25. Intersection of Two Double-curved Surfaces of Revolution. As explained before, the simplest line that can be cut from a double-curved surface of revolution is a circle. Also, if the axes of two double-curved surfaces are at an angle to each other, a circle could be obtained from one surface but a curve would be cut from the other, producing a difficult solution. An alternate, and better, method may be applied *if* the axes of the surfaces intersect. A sphere with its center at the intersection of the axes will cut circles from both surfaces.

Figure 18.23 illustrates the sphere method of finding the line of intersection between a paraboloid and hyperboloid. The axes of the two surfaces intersect at point E. In the front view (where both axes appear in true length), with center at E_F, a circle is drawn representing a sphere as, for example, the circle marked "sphere 2" on the figure. This sphere will intersect the surface having axis AB by producing a circle, which appears as an edge, perpendicular to axis AB. Also, the same sphere will intersect the surface having axis CD by producing a circle which appears as an edge perpendicular to axis CD. These two edge views intersect at 2 and 2 in the front view. These points 2 are common to the sphere and both double-curved surfaces. To get the top view, points 2 lie on the circle cut from the surface having axis AB. The size of the sphere is altered to get more points. In Fig. 18.23, sphere 1 is the smallest sphere used because one smaller will not cut one of the surfaces. Sphere 3 is the largest that will give points on the line of intersection.

It is possible of course, and even probable, that the axes of two double-curved surfaces of revolution may not intersect. In this event, the sphere method in pure form cannot be applied; but, with alterations, the principle can be employed. Figure 18.24 shows two double-curved surfaces of revolution whose axes do not intersect. The intersection is to be found. A sphere with center arbitrarily located at O will cut two circles from the surface having axis AB, as indicated on the figure. This sphere will also cut a curve from the surface with axis CD, which may be found by passing planes through the sphere and perpendicular to CD. The end view of the axis of surface CD will show the circles cut from both sphere and surface CD as true circles and will also show the intersections 1, 2, 3, 4, 3', and 2', where sphere and surface CD have common points. These points, 1, 2, 3, 4, 3', and 2', then projected back to the front view locate the curve shown, which intersects the circles cut from surface AB at points X, Z, Z', and X', which are then points common to both double-curved surfaces. The top views of points X and X' then lie on the upper circle cut by the sphere from surface AB, and points

Z and Z' lie on the lower circle. A sufficient number of points to complete the line of intersection may be found by repeating the process, starting each time with a different size of sphere.

The above method may seem to be somewhat complicated, but compared with other methods it is not. For instance, if both surfaces were simply cut by horizontal planes, circles would be cut from surface AB, but the curve cut from CD would have to be plotted in the top view by finding intersections of right sections of CD with the original cutting plane, a tedious process if done with all. Note in Fig. 18.24 that the cutting planes passed perpendicular to CD and the resulting circles (right sections of CD) in the end view will remain constant throughout the completion of the solution.

18.26. Developments. In many different kinds of construction, full-size patterns of some or all of the faces of an object are required, as in stonecutting a template or pattern giving the shape of an irregular face or in sheet-metal work a pattern to which a sheet may be cut so that when rolled, folded, or formed it will make the object.

The complete surface laid out in a plane is called the "development" of the surface.

Surfaces about which a thin sheet of flexible material (as paper or tin) can be wrapped smoothly are said to be developable; these include objects made up of planes and single-curved surfaces only. Warped and double-curved surfaces are nondevelopable; and when patterns are required for their construction, they can be made only by methods that are approximate, but, assisted by the ductility or pliability of the material, giving the required form. Thus while a ball cannot be wrapped smoothly, a two-piece pattern developed approximately and cut from leather may be stretched and sewed on in a smooth cover, or a flat disk of metal may be die-stamped, formed, or spun to a hemispherical or other required shape.

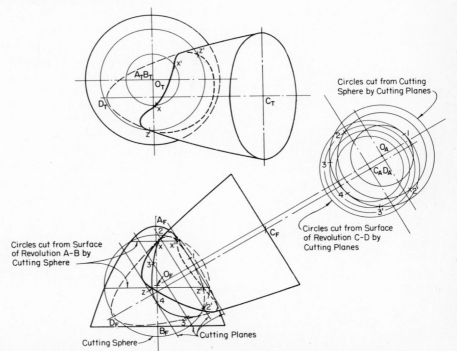

Fig. 18.24. Intersection of two double-curved surfaces, axes not intersecting.

Circles cut from Surface of Revolution A-B by Cutting Sphere

Circles cut from Cutting Sphere by Cutting Planes

Circles cut from Surface of Revolution C-D by Cutting Planes

Cutting Sphere

Cutting Planes

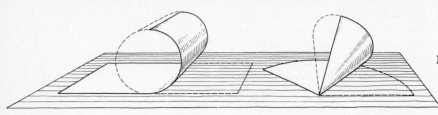

Fig. 18.25. Theory of development.

18.27. Basic Considerations. We have learned the method of finding the true size of a plane surface by projecting it on an auxiliary plane. If the true size of all the plane faces of an object are found and joined in order at their common edges so that all faces lie in a common plane, the result will be the developed surface. Usually this may be done to the best advantage by finding the true length of the edges.

The development of a right cylinder is evidently a rectangle whose width is the altitude and length the rectified circumference (Fig. 18.25); and the development of a right-circular cone is a circular sector with a radius equal to the slant height of the cone and an arc equal in length to the circumference of its base (Fig. 18.25).

As illustrated in Fig. 18.25, developments are drawn with the inside face up. This is primarily the result of working to inside rather than outside dimensions of ducts. This procedure also facilitates the use of fold lines, identified by punch marks at each end, along which the metal is folded in forming the object.

In the laying out of real sheet-metal designs, an allowance must be made for seams and lap and, in heavy sheets, for the thickness and crowding of the metal; there is also the consideration of the commercial sizes of material as well as the question of economy in cutting, in all of which some practical shop knowledge is necessary. Figure 18.41 and paragraph 18.39 illustrate and explain the usage of some of the more common joints, although the developments in this chapter will be confined to the principles alone.

18.28. To Develop a Truncated Hexagonal Prism (Fig. 18.26). First draw two projections of the prism: (1) a normal view of a right. section (a section or cut obtained by a plane perpendicular to the

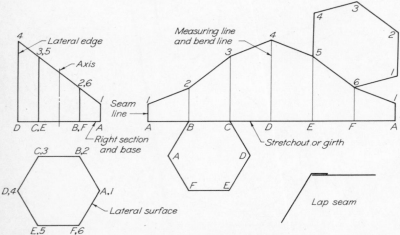

Fig. 18.26. Development of prism.

axis) and (2) a normal view of the lateral edges. The base *ABCDEF* is a right section shown in true size in the bottom view. Lay off on line *AA* of the development the perimeter of the base. This line is called by sheet-metal workers the "stretchout" or "girth" line. At points *A*, *B*, *C*, etc., erect perpendiculars called "measuring lines" or "bend lines," representing the lateral edges along which the pattern is folded to form the prism. Lay off on each of these its length *A*-1, *B*-2, *C*-3, etc., as given on the front view. Connect the points 1, 2, 3, etc., in succession, to complete the development of the lateral surfaces. Note on the pattern that the inside of the lateral faces is toward the observer. For the development of the entire surface in one piece, attach the true sizes of the upper end and the base as shown, finding the true size of the upper end by an auxiliary view as described in paragraph 6.7. For economy of solder or rivets and time, it is customary to make the seam on the shortest edge or surface. In seaming along the intersection of surfaces whose dihedral angle is other than 90°, as is the case here, the lap seam lends itself to convenient assembling. The flat lock could be used if the seam were made on one of the lateral faces.

18.29. To Develop a Truncated Right Pyramid (Fig. 18.27). Draw the projections of the pyramid which show (1) a normal view of the base or right section and (2) a normal view of the axis. Lay out the pattern for the pyramid, and then superimpose the pattern of the truncation.

Since this is a portion of a right regular pyramid, the lateral edges are all of equal length. The lateral edges *OA* and *OD* are parallel to the frontal plane and consequently show in their true length on the front view. With center O_1, taken at any convenient place, and a radius $O_F A_F$, draw an arc which is the stretchout of the pattern. On it step off the six equal sides of the hexagonal base, obtained from the top view, and connect these points successively with each other and with the vertex O_1, thus forming the pattern for the pyramid.

The intersection of the cutting plane and lateral surfaces is developed by laying off the true length of the intercept of each lateral

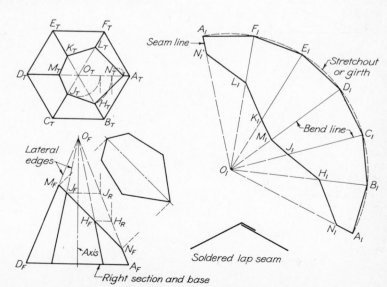

Fig. 18.27. Development of pyramid.

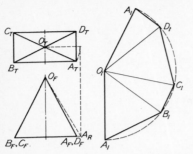

Fig. 18.28. Development of pyramid.

edge on the corresponding line of the development. The true length of each of these intercepts, such as OH and OJ, is found by rotating it about the axis of the pyramid until they coincide with $O_F A_F$, as explained in paragraph 13.4. The path of any point, as H, will be projected on the front view as a horizontal line. To obtain the development of the entire surface of the truncated pyramid, attach the base; also find the true size of the cut face and attach it on a common line.

The lap seam is suggested for use here for the same reason that was advanced in paragraph 18.28.

The right-rectangular pyramid, Fig. 18.28, is developed in a similar way, but as the edge OA is not parallel to the plane of projection, it must be rotated to $O_F A_R$ to obtain its true length.

18.30. To Develop an Oblique Pyramid (Fig. 18.29). Since the lateral edges are unequal in length, the true length of each must be found separately by rotating it parallel to the frontal plane. With O_1 taken at any convenient place, lay off the seam line $O_1 A_1$ equal to $O_F A_R$. With A_1 as center and radius $A_1 B_1$ equal to the true length of AB, describe an arc. With O_1 as center and radius $O_1 B_1$ equal to $O_F B_R$, describe a second arc intersecting the first in vertex B_1. Connect the vertices O_1, A_1, and B_1, thus forming the pattern for the lateral surface OAB. Similarly, lay out the patterns for the remaining three lateral surfaces, joining them on their common edges. The stretchout is equal to the summation of the base edges. If the complete development is required, attach the base on a common line. The lap seam is suggested as the most suitable for the given conditions.

18.31. To Develop a Truncated Right Cylinder (Fig. 18.30). The development of a cylinder is similar to the development of a prism. Draw two projections of the cylinder: (1) a normal view of

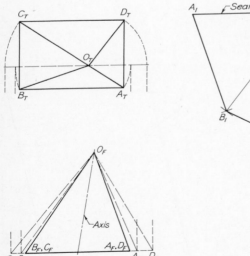

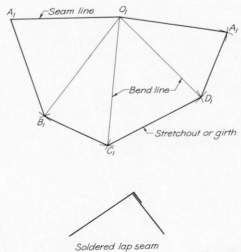

Fig. 18.29. Development of oblique pyramid.

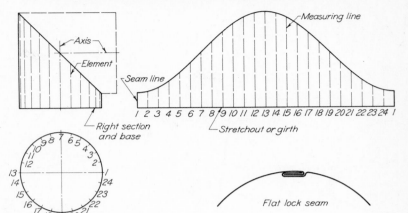

Fig. 18.30. Development of cylinder.

a right section and (2) a normal view of the elements. In rolling the cylinder out on a tangent plane, the base or right section, being perpendicular to the axis, will develop into a straight line. For convenience in drawing, divide the normal view of the base, here shown in the bottom view, into a number of equal parts by points that represent elements. These divisions should be spaced so that the chordal distances closely enough approximate the arc to make the stretchout practically equal to the periphery of the base or right section. Project these elements to the front view. Draw the stretchout and measuring lines as in Fig. 18.26, the cylinder now being treated as a many-sided prism. Transfer the lengths of the elements in order, either by projection or with dividers, and join the points thus found by a smooth curve, sketching it in freehand very lightly before fitting the french curve to it. This development might be the pattern of one-half of a two-piece elbow. Three-piece, four-piece, or five-piece elbows may be drawn similarly, as illustrated in Fig. 18.31. As the base is symmetrical, only one-half of it need be drawn. In these cases, the intermediate pieces, as B, C, and D, are developed on a stretchout line formed by laying off the perimeter of a right section. If the right section is taken through the middle of the piece, the stretchout line becomes the center line of the development.

Evidently any elbow could be cut from a single sheet without

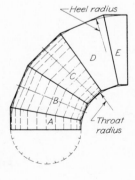

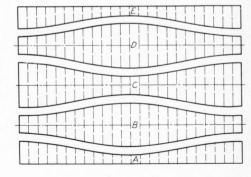

Fig. 18.31. Development of elbow (cylinders).

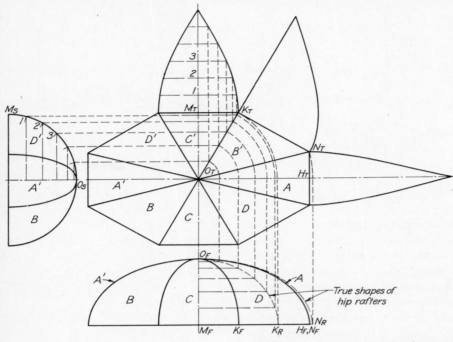

Fig. 18.32. Development of dome (cylinders).

waste if the seams were made alternately on the long and short sides. The flat lock seam is recommended for Figs. 18.30 and 18.31, although other types could be used.

The octagonal dome, Fig. 18.32, illustrates an application of the development of cylinders. Each piece is a portion of a cylinder. The elements are parallel to the base of the dome and show in their true lengths in the top view. The true length of the stretchout line for sections A and A' shows in the front view at $O_F H_F$. By considering $O_T H_T$ as the edge of a plane cutting a right section, the problem is identical with the preceding problem.

Similarly, the stretchout line for sections B, B', D, and D' shows in true length at $O_F K_R$ in the front view, and for section C and C' at $O_S M_S$ in the side view.

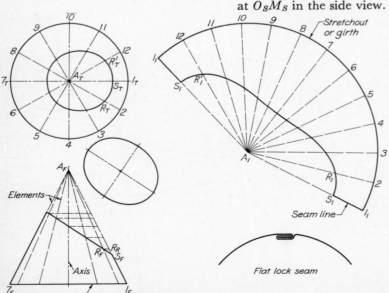

Fig. 18.33. Development of cone.

The true shape of hip rafter ON is found by rotating it until it is parallel to the frontal plane, as at $O_F N_R$, in the same manner as in finding the true length of any line. A sufficient number of points should be taken to give a smooth curve.

18.32. To Develop a Truncated Right-circular Cone (Fig. 18.33). Draw the projections of the cone which will show (1) a normal view of the base or right section and (2) a normal view of the axis. First develop the surface of the complete cone and then superimpose the pattern for the truncation.

Divide the top view of the base into a sufficient number of equal parts so that the sum of the resulting chordal distances will closely approximate the periphery of the base. Project these points to the front view, and draw front views of the elements through them. With center A_1 and a radius equal to the slant height A_F-1_F, which is the true length of all the elements, draw an arc, which is the stretchout, and lay off on it the chordal divisions of the base, obtained from the top view. Connect these points 1_1, 2, 3, etc., with A-1, thus forming the pattern for the cone. Find the true length of each element from vertex to cutting plane by rotating it to coincide with the contour element A-1, and lay off this distance on the corresponding line of the development. Draw a smooth curve through these points. The flat lock seam along element S-1 is recommended, although other types could be employed. The pattern for the cut surface is obtained from the auxiliary view.

18.33. Triangulation. Nondevelopable surfaces are developed approximately by assuming them to be made of narrow sections of developable surfaces. The commonest and best method for approximate development is that of triangulation, that is, the surface is assumed to be made up of a large number of triangular strips, or plane triangles with very short bases. This method is used for all warped surfaces and also for oblique cones. Oblique cones are single-curved surfaces and thus are theoretically capable of true development, but they can be developed much more easily and accurately by triangulation.

The principle is extremely simple. It consists merely in dividing the surface into triangles, finding the true lengths of the sides of each, and constructing them one at a time, joining these triangles on their common sides.

18.34. To Develop an Oblique Cone (Fig. 18.34). An oblique

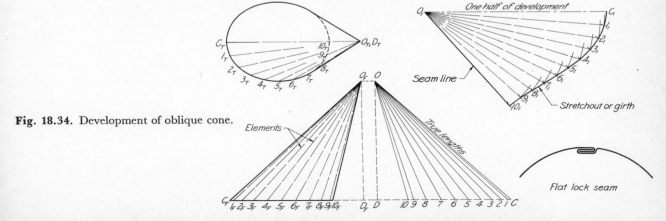

Fig. 18.34. Development of oblique cone.

cone differs from a cone of revolution in that the elements have different lengths. The development of the right-circular cone is, practically, made up of a number of equal triangles which meet at the vertex and whose sides are elements and whose bases are the chords of short arcs of the base of the cone. In the oblique cone, each triangle must be found separately.

Draw two views of the cone showing (1) a normal view of the base and (2) a normal view of the altitude. Divide the true size of the base, here shown in the top view, into a sufficient number of equal parts so that the sum of the chordal distances will closely approximate the length of the base curve. Project these points to the front view of the base. Through these points and the vertex, draw the elements in each view. Since this cone is symmetrical about a frontal plane through the vertex, the elements are shown only on the front half of it. Also, only one-half of the development is drawn. With the seam on the shortest element, the element OC will be the center line of the development and may be drawn directly at O_1C_1, as its true length is given at O_FC_F. Find the true length of the elements by rotating them until parallel to the frontal plane or by constructing a "true-length diagram." The true length of any element would be the hypotenuse of a triangle, one leg being the length of the projected element as seen in the top view and the other leg being equal to the altitude of the cone. Thus to make the diagram, draw the leg OD coinciding with or parallel to O_FD_F. At D and perpendicular to OD, draw the other leg, on which lay off the lengths D-1, D-2, etc., equal to D_T-1_T, D_T-2_T, etc., respectively. Distances from O to points on the base of the diagram are the true lengths of the elements.

Construct the pattern for the front half of the cone as follows: With O_1 as center and radius O-1, draw an arc. With C_1 as center and radius C_T-1_T, draw a second arc intersecting the first at 1_1; then O_1-1_1 will be the developed position of the element O-1. With 1_1 as center and radius 1_T-2_T, draw an arc intersecting a second arc with O_1 as center and radius O-2, thus locating 2_1. Continue this

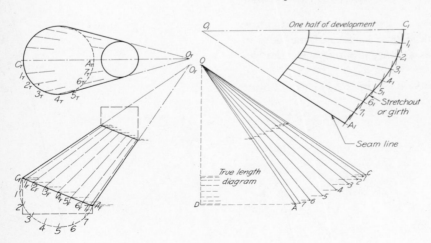

Fig. 18.35. Development of transition (oblique cone).

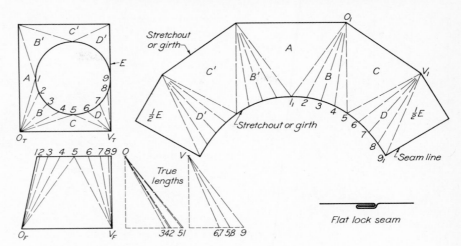

Fig. 18.36. Development of transition (planes and oblique cones).

procedure until all the elements have been transferred to the development. Connect the points C_1, 1_1, 2_1, etc., with a smooth curve, the stretchout line, to complete the development. The flat lock seam is recommended for joining the ends of the pattern to form the cone.

18.35. A Conical Connection between Two Parallel Cylindrical Pipes of Different Diameters. This is shown in Fig. 18.35. The method used in drawing the pattern is an application of the development of an oblique cone. One-half of the elliptical base is shown in true size in an auxiliary view, here attached to the front view. Find the true size of the base from its major and minor diameters, divide it into a number of equal parts so that the sum of these chordal distances closely approximates the periphery of the curve, and project these points to the front and top views. Draw the elements in each view through these points, and find the vertex O by extending the contour elements until they intersect. The true length of each element is found by using the vertical distance between its ends as the vertical leg of the diagram and its horizontal projection as the other leg. As each true length from vertex to base is found, project the upper end of the intercept horizontally across from the front view to the true length of the corresponding element to find the true length of the intercept. The development is drawn by laying out each triangle in turn, from vertex to base, as in paragraph 18.34, starting on the center line O_1C_1 and then measuring on each element its intercept length. Draw smooth curves through these points to complete the pattern. Join the ends of the development with a flat lock seam to form the connection.

18.36. Transition Pieces. They are used to connect pipes or openings of different shapes of cross section. Figure 18.36, showing a transition piece for connecting a round pipe and a rectangular pipe, is typical. These are always developed by triangulation. The piece shown in Fig. 18.36 is, evidently, made up of four triangular planes whose bases are the sides of the rectangle and four parts of

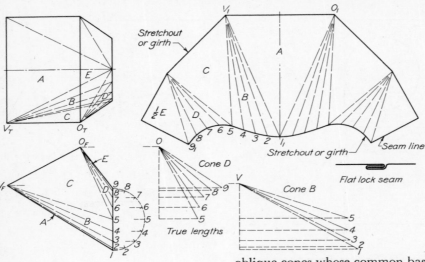

Fig. 18.37. Development of transition (planes and oblique cones).

oblique cones whose common bases are arcs of the circle and whose vertices are at the corners of the rectangle. To develop it, make a true-length diagram as in Fig. 18.34. The true length of O-1 being found, all the sides of triangle A will be known. Attach the development of cones B and B', then those of triangles C and C', and so on.

Figure 18.37 is another transition piece joining a rectangular to a circular pipe whose axes are nonparallel. By using a partial right-side view of the round opening, the divisions of the bases of the oblique cones can be found (as the object is symmetrical, one-half only of the opening need be divided). The true lengths of the elements are obtained as in Fig. 18.35.

With the seam line the center line of the plane E in Figs. 18.36 and 18.37, the flat lock is recommended for joining the ends of the development.

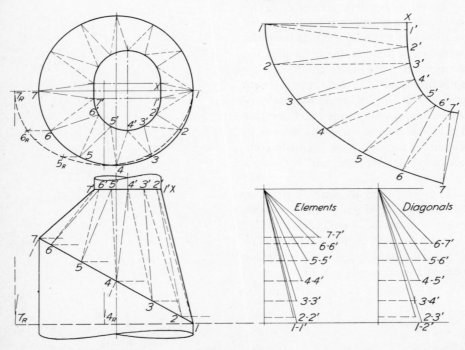

Fig. 18.38. Development of transition (warped surface).

18.37. Triangulation of Warped Surfaces. The approximate development of a warped surface is made by dividing it into a number of narrow quadrilaterals and then splitting each of these quadrilaterals into two triangles by a diagonal, which is assumed to be a straight line, although really a curve. Figure 18.38 shows a warped transition piece to connect an ovular (upper) pipe with a right-circular cylindrical pipe (lower). Find the true size of one-half the elliptical base by rotating it until horizontal about an axis through, when its true shape appears on the top view. The major diameter is $1\text{-}7_R$, and the minor diameter through 4_R will equal the diameter of the lower pipe. Divide the semiellipse into a sufficient number of equal parts, and project these to the top and front views. Divide the top semicircle into the same number of equal parts, and connect similar points on each end, thus dividing the surface into approximate quadrilaterals. Cut each into two triangles by a diagonal. On true-length diagrams find the lengths of the elements and the diagonals, and draw the development by constructing the true sizes of the triangles in regular order. The flat lock seam is recommended for joining the ends of the development.

18.38. To Develop a Sphere. The sphere may be taken as typical of double-curved surfaces, which can be developed only approximately. It may be cut into a number of equal meridian sections, or lumes, as in Fig. 18.39, and these may be considered to be sections of cylinders. One of these sections, developed as the cylinder in Fig. 18.39, will give a pattern for the others.

Another method is to cut the sphere into horizontal sections, or zones, each of which may be taken as the frustum of a cone whose vertex is at the intersection of the extended chords (Fig. 18.40).

18.39. Joints, Connectors, and Hems. There are numerous joints used in seaming sheet-metal ducts and in connecting one duct to another. Figure 18.41 illustrates some of the more common types, which may be formed by hand on a break or by special seaming machines. No attempt to dimension the various seams and connections has been made here because of the variation in sizes for different gages of metal and in the forming machines of manufacturers.

Hemming is used in finishing the raw edges of the end of the duct. In wire hemming, an extra allowance of about $2\frac{1}{2}$ times the diameter of the wire is made for wrapping around the wire. In flat hemming, the end of the duct is bent over either once or twice to relieve the sharp edge of the metal.

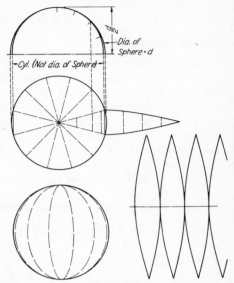

Fig. 18.39. Development of sphere (gore method).

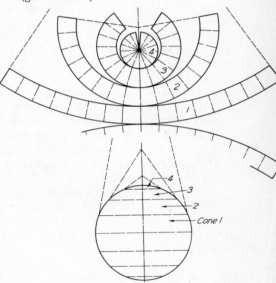

Fig. 18.40. Development of sphere (zone method).

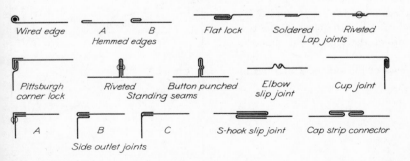

Wired edge   Hemmed edges A   B   Flat lock   Soldered   Riveted
Lap joints

Pittsburgh corner lock   Riveted   Button punched   Elbow slip joint   Cup joint
Standing seams

A   B   C   S-hook slip joint   Cap strip connector
Side outlet joints

Fig. 18.41. Joints and finished edges.

PROBLEMS

INTERSECTIONS

In the study of intersections, a purely theoretical approach may be used without any reference whatever to practical utility where the lines, planes, and surfaces form pipes, ducts, or other real objects. On the other hand, some may prefer to teach the subject by applying the theory on useful objects. For these reasons, the problems following on intersections are given first from the standpoint of pure theory (Groups 1 to 4) and then from a more practical standpoint (Groups 5 to 8). Note that, in Groups 5 to 8, even though the surfaces are geometrical, they are the ducts, hoppers, transitions, etc., that will often be found in practical work.

Group 1. Intersection of lines and planes

18.1.1. Locate the top and front views of *P*, the point where the line *JK* pierces the plane *EFG*.

18.1.2. Find the true distance from point *P* to the plane *RST*, using the given views only.

18.1.3. A control cable, *AB*, passes through the surfaces *KLM*, *LMN*, and *LNO* of reinforcing webs in an airframe. Draw the top and front views of the points where the cable passes through the webs. Show the visibility of the cable in both views.

18.1.4. The entrances to three vertical mine shafts on a mountainside are shown at *R*, *S*, and *T*. These shafts give access to the ore vein that strikes and dips as shown at *P*. Scale: $1'' = 100'$. Find the depths of the shafts.

18.1.5. Two electrical distributing cables, *AB* and *CD*, are to be connected to a power source at *P* using the shortest possible single connecting line. Draw the top and front views of the connecting line.

18.1.6. An outside storage bin discharges through the pyramidal hopper *VABCD* which passes through a roof, a portion of which is shown by points *WXYZ*. Draw the plan and elevation views of the roof opening which fits snugly around the hopper.

18.1.7. *AB* is the axis of a pipe of circular cross section. This pipe enters the side of a tank, a portion of whose surface is indicated by points *K*, *L*, and *M*. Draw the top and front views of 10 well-distributed points on the edge of the tank opening which fits snugly around the pipe.

Optional. Draw the curve.

Group 2. Intersection of planes

18.2.1. Find the line of intersection between the planes *ABC* and *DEF*. Show visibility.

18.2.2. Find the line of intersection between the planes *MNO* and *RST*.

18.2.3. Find the intersection of the three planes *ABC*, *JKL*, and *RST*.

18.2.4. Find the line of intersection and complete the views of the two hollow sheet-metal shapes shown. The top of the right-hand shape is enclosed.

18.2.5. Draw the map and elevation views of the tunnel which lies in both veins *W* and *V*.

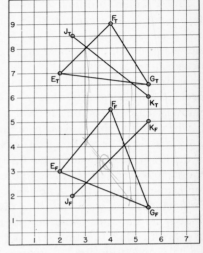

Prob. 18.1.1

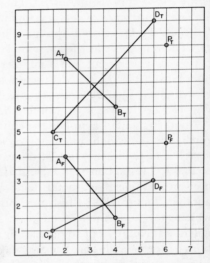

Prob. 18.1.5

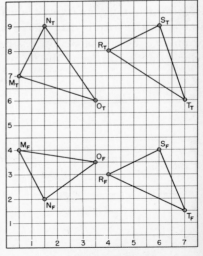

Prob. 18.2.2

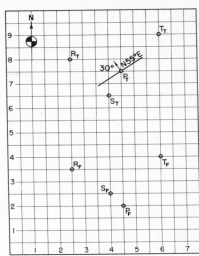

Prob. 18.1.2

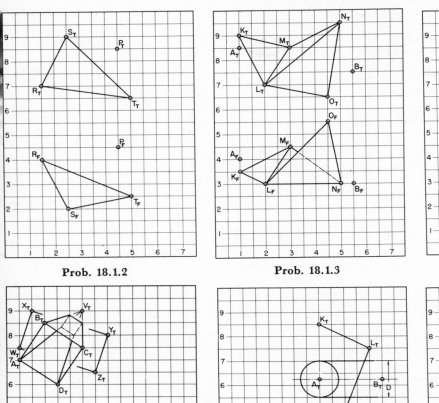

Prob. 18.1.3

Prob. 18.1.4

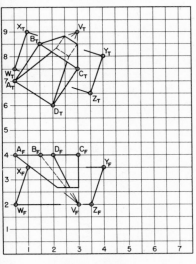

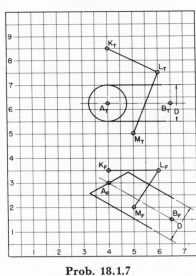

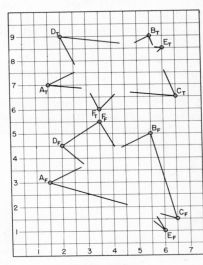

Prob. 18.1.6

Prob. 18.1.7

Prob. 18.2.1

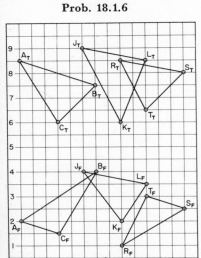

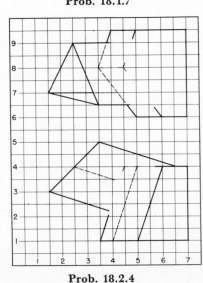

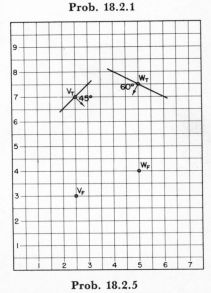

Prob. 18.2.3

Prob. 18.2.4

Prob. 18.2.5

Group 3. Intersections of single-curved surfaces

18.3.1. Find the points X and Z where line AB pierces the 2-in.-diameter right-circular cylinder OP. Find the points R and S where line CD pierces this cylinder.

18.3.2. Find the points X and Z where line AB pierces the 2-in.-diameter right-circular cylinder OP.

18.3.3. Draw the top view of the line of intersection between plane A and the 2-in.-diameter right-circular cylinder OP. Draw the front view of the line of intersection between plane B and this cylinder.

18.3.4. Draw the top and front views of the line of intersection between plane ABC and the 2-in.-diameter right-circular cylinder OP. Complete the cylinder and show visibility.

18.3.5. Find the point P where line AB pierces the surface of the cylindroid $XZX'Z'$. XZ and $X'Z'$ are the curved-line directrices of the cylindroid. Its plane director is the vertical plane director shown.

18.3.6 and 18.3.7. Find the points X and Z where line AB pierces the cone VO. Show visibility of line AB.

18.3.8. (*a*) Draw the front view of the line of intersection between plane A and cone VO. (*b*) Draw the top view of the line of intersection between plane B and cone VO. (*c*) Draw the top view of the line of intersection between plane C and cone VO. (*d*) What is the name of the conic section cut by each of the planes?

18.3.9. Draw the front view of the line of intersection between plane A and cone VO. Draw the top view of the line of intersection between plane B and cone VO.

18.3.10. Draw the top and front views of the line of intersection between plane ABC and cone VO. Complete the cone and show visibility.

18.3.11 to 18.3.13. Complete the views of cylinders AB and CD, showing their line of intersection.

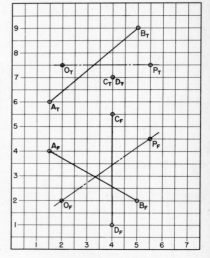

Prob. 18.3.1

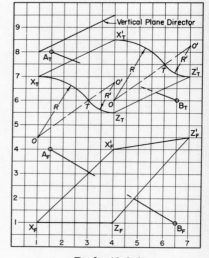

Prob. 18.3.5

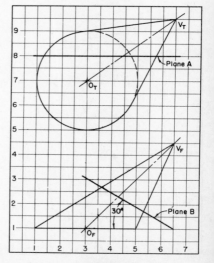

Prob. 18.3.9

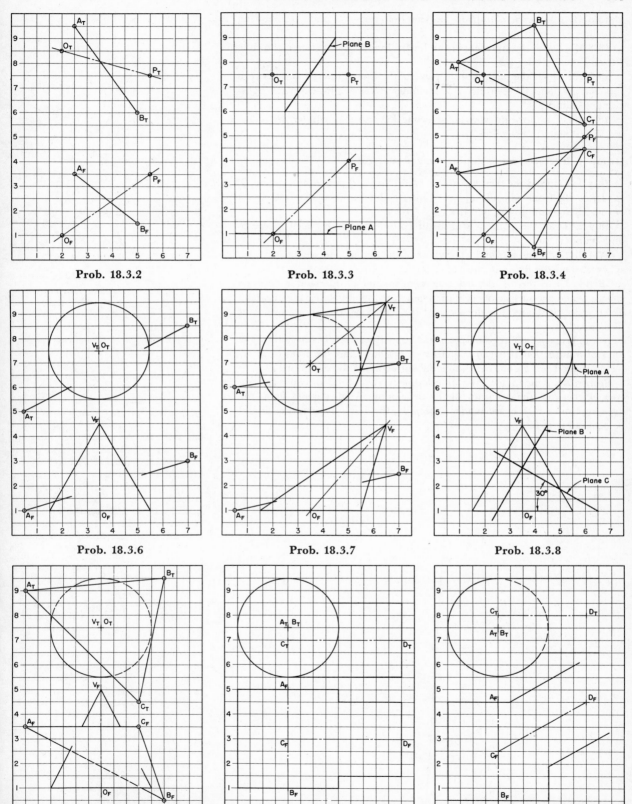

Prob. 18.3.2

Prob. 18.3.3

Prob. 18.3.4

Prob. 18.3.6

Prob. 18.3.7

Prob. 18.3.8

Prob. 18.3.10

Prob. 18.3.11

Prob. 18.3.12

18.3.14 to 18.3.16. Complete the views of cones *VO* and *XP*, showing their line of intersection.

18.3.17. Draw the top view of the line of intersection between the cone *VO* and the cylinder *AB*.

18.3.18. Draw the top and front views of the line of intersection between the cone *VO* and the cylinder *AB*. Cylinder *AB* is a 3-in.-diameter right-circular cylinder.

18.3.19. Complete the views of the cone *VO* and the cylinder *AB*, showing their line of intersection.

Group 4. Intersections of double-curved surfaces

18.4.1. (*a*) Find the points *X* and *Z* where line *AB* pierces the sphere *O*. (*b*) Draw the front view of the line of intersection between sphere *O* and a vertical plane containing line *AB*.

18.4.2. Draw the front view of the line of intersection between sphere *O* and cylinder *AB*.

18.4.3. Draw the top and front views of the line of intersection between sphere *O* and the lower portion of cone *VO*.

18.4.4. Draw the top and front views of the line of intersection between sphere *O* and the surface of revolution generated by revolving the parabola about axis *AB*. Point *A* is the focus of the parabola; the line shown is its directrix.

Not only may the foregoing problems be used for exercises in finding the lines of intersection between various surfaces but, after the lines of intersection have been found, the individual surfaces may be developed.

Problems intended for later development should be drawn very accurately because the accuracy of the development will depend upon the drawing from which it was made. Especially, the line of intersection should be accurately found.

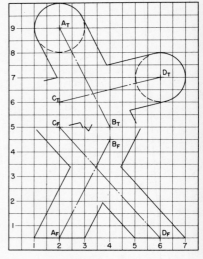

Prob. 18.3.13

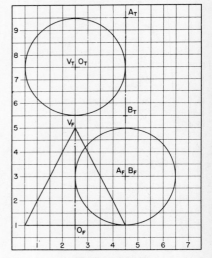

Prob. 18.3.17

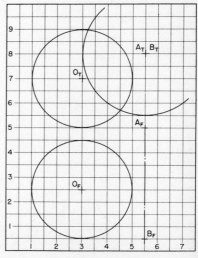

Prob. 18.4.2

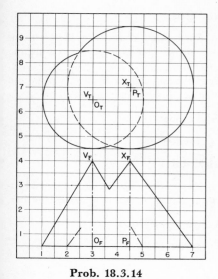

Prob. 18.3.14

Prob. 18.3.15

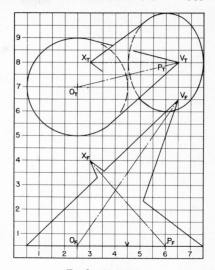

Prob. 18.3.16

Prob. 18.3.18

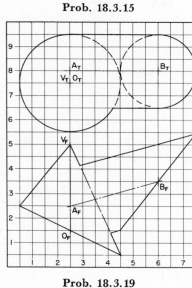

Prob. 18.3.19

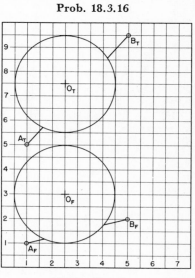

Prob. 18.4.1

Prob. 18.4.3

Prob. 18.4.4

Group 5. Intersections of prismatic ducts

18.5.1 to 18.5.3. Find the line of intersection, considering the prisms a pipes opening into each other. Use particular care in indicating visible and invisible portions of the line of intersection.

18.5.4 to 18.5.6. Find the line of intersection, indicating visible and invisible parts and considering prisms as pipes opening into each other.

Group 6. Intersections of pyramidal objects

18.6.1 to 18.6.5. Find the lines of intersection.

Group 7. Intersections of cylindrical ducts

18.7.1 to 18.7.3. Find the line of intersection, indicating visible and invisible portions and considering cylinders as pipes opening into each other.

Group 8. Intersections of conical objects and ducts

18.8.1 to 18.8.11. Find the line of intersection.

DEVELOPMENTS

Selections from the following problems may be made and the figures

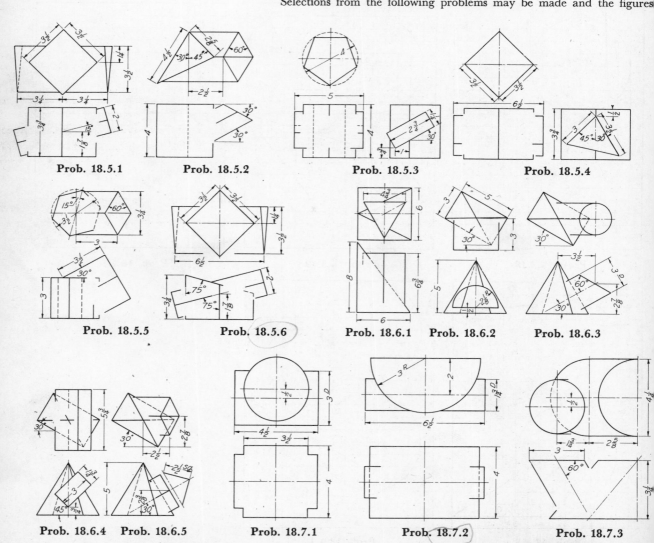

Prob. 18.5.1   Prob. 18.5.2   Prob. 18.5.3   Prob. 18.5.4

Prob. 18.5.5   Prob. 18.5.6   Prob. 18.6.1   Prob. 18.6.2   Prob. 18.6.3

Prob. 18.6.4   Prob. 18.6.5   Prob. 18.7.1   Prob. 18.7.2   Prob. 18.7.3

constructed accurately in pencil without inking. Any practical problem can be resolved into some combination of the "type solids," and the exercises given illustrate the principles involved in the various combinations.

An added interest in developments may be found by working problems on suitable paper, allowing for fastenings and lap, and cutting them out. It is recommended that at least one or two models be constructed in this way.

In sheet-metal shops, development problems, unless very complicated, are usually laid out directly on the metal.

The following problems may be drawn on 8½- by 11-in. or 11- by 17-in. sheets. Assume the objects to be made of thin metal with open ends unless otherwise specified.

Group 9. Prisms

18.9.1 to 18.9.6. Develop lateral surfaces of the prisms.

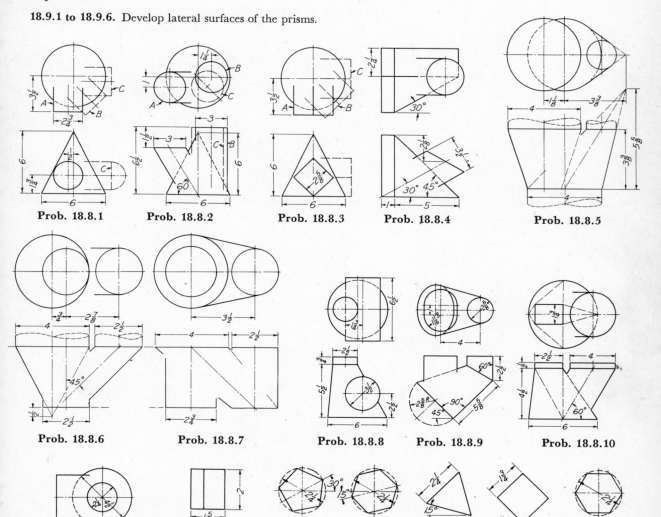

Prob. 18.8.1   Prob. 18.8.2   Prob. 18.8.3   Prob. 18.8.4   Prob. 18.8.5

Prob. 18.8.6   Prob. 18.8.7   Prob. 18.8.8   Prob. 18.8.9   Prob. 18.8.10

Probs. 18.8.11   18.9.1   18.9.2   18.9.3   18.9.4   18.9.5   18.9.6

Group 10. Pyramids

18.10.1 to 18.10.3. Develop lateral surfaces of the hoppers.
18.10.4 and 18.10.5. Develop lateral surfaces of the pyramids.

Group 11. Cylinders

18.11.1 to 18.11.7. Develop lateral surfaces of the cylinders.

Group 12. Combinations of prisms and cylinders

18.12.1 to 18.12.3. Develop lateral surfaces.

Group 13. Cones

18.13.1 to 18.13.5. Develop lateral surfaces.

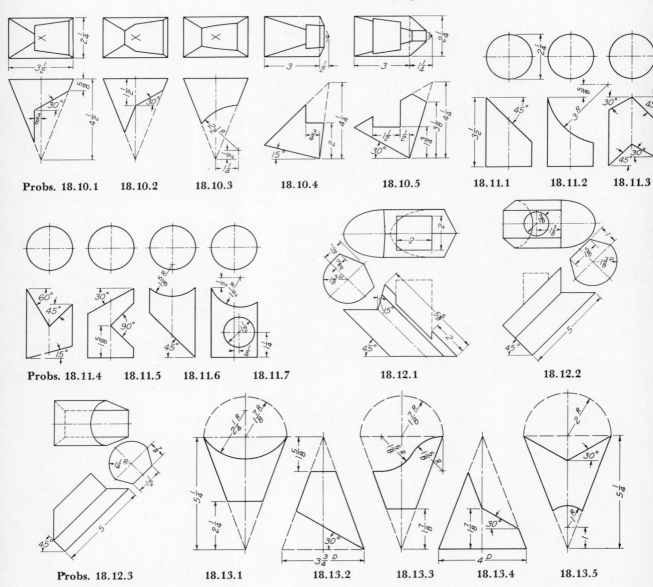

Probs. 18.10.1   18.10.2   18.10.3   18.10.4   18.10.5   18.11.1   18.11.2   18.11.3

Probs. 18.11.4   18.11.5   18.11.6   18.11.7   18.12.1   18.12.2

Probs. 18.12.3   18.13.1   18.13.2   18.13.3   18.13.4   18.13.5

Group 14. Combinations of surfaces

18.14.1 to 18.14.4. Develop lateral surfaces of the objects.

Group 15. Cones and transition pieces

18.15.1 to 18.15.8. Develop lateral surfaces of the objects (one-half in Probs. 18.15.1, 18.15.2, 18.15.4, 18.15.5, and 18.15.7).

Group 16. Furnace-pipe fittings

18.16.1 to 18.16.8. Develop surfaces, and make paper models.

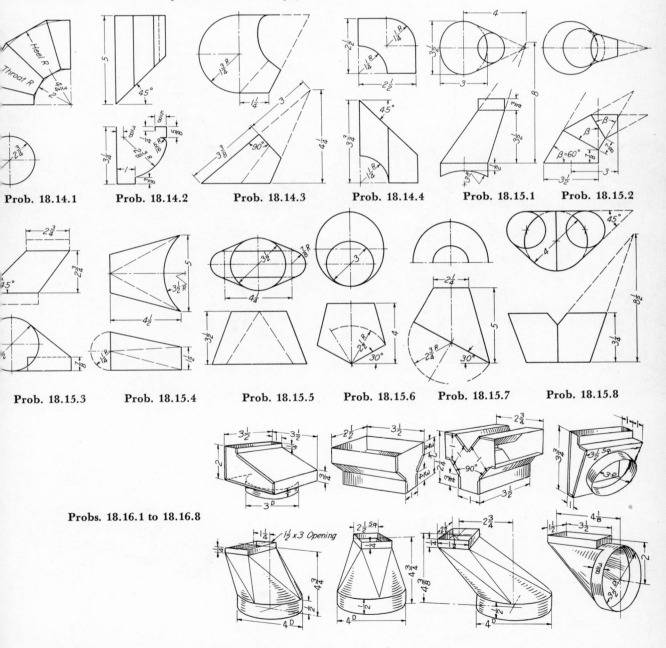

Prob. 18.14.1   Prob. 18.14.2   Prob. 18.14.3   Prob. 18.14.4   Prob. 18.15.1   Prob. 18.15.2

Prob. 18.15.3   Prob. 18.15.4   Prob. 18.15.5   Prob. 18.15.6   Prob. 18.15.7   Prob. 18.15.8

Probs. 18.16.1 to 18.16.8

Fig. 19.1. Illustration of scalar and vector quantities.

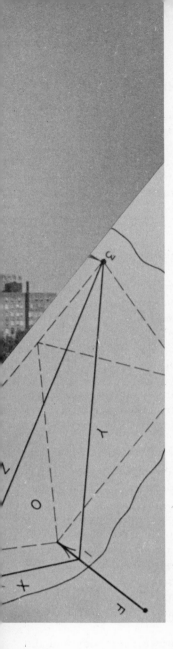

19

VECTOR GEOMETRY

19.1. Many engineering problems involve only simple measurable quantities such as volume, mass, and temperature, which may have their *magnitude* represented either by a single real number or by a linear distance and are therefore called "scalar" quantities. Often, however, there will be quantities such as velocity, acceleration, force, or displacement which have *magnitude*, *direction*, and a point of application or *position*. Because of these additional properties, such quantities cannot be represented by a single numerical value and are called "vector" quantities.

Figure 19.1 will assist in showing the difference between scalar and vector quantities. Any mass, such as the weight shown in the figure, will have its magnitude represented by a single number (ounces, pounds, etc.) and is therefore a scalar quantity. But if this mass is now placed on a beam supported as shown, the weight becomes a *force* (directed downward by gravity), which bears on the beam at the point of application or position of the weight. Thus we now have a vector quantity, a force, having magnitude, direction, and position.

The typical analysis of vector problems can also be illustrated by Fig. 19.1. The weight, placed as shown, will produce a force directed to the beam, which in turn produces forces downward at each end of the beam where the supports are placed. In order for the beam to remain in equilibrium, the supports must resist the downward pressure by equal and opposite forces. If the weight is centrally located, the force on each support will be equal; if the weight is off center as shown, one support receives more force than the other.

571

To find the force on each support is a typical problem of vector analysis.

Vector problems may be solved equationally, but these methods are sometimes more complicated and laborious than graphical methods, which are simple and direct and, furthermore, aid greatly in visualization and analysis of any problem.

19.2. Definitions. Other necessary items, such as resultants and components, will be defined later, but at the outset it is necessary to define the fundamentals.

A *scalar quantity* is a quantity having magnitude only and has its measure described by a single number or by a linear distance. Examples are volume (cubic feet), temperature (degrees), mass (pounds), and pressure (pounds per square inch).

A *vector quantity* is a quantity having magnitude, direction, and position and is described by a specification of all three details. The position, in some cases, may be either general or so obvious that description may not be vital to the solution; in other cases, position is very important. In all cases, magnitude and direction must be given. Force, velocity, acceleration, and displacement are examples of vector quantities.

A *force* is the action of one body on another body. A force, therefore, never exists alone. Forces always occur in pairs, one acting on a body and the body then resisting the action, so that to every action there is an equal and opposite reaction.

A *vector* is the graphical representation of a vector quantity. It consists of a straight line whose length, to scale, represents the magnitude and whose direction and position are fixed by orthographic views.

A *line of action* is a direction along which a vector quantity acts.

An *origin* is either the point of application of a vector quantity or the intersection of the lines of action of two or more vector quantities.

A *free vector* is a vector representing magnitude and direction only and may be drawn anywhere in the plane of the vector quantity.

A *localized vector* is a vector showing magnitude, direction, and position and must be laid out along the line of action of the vector quantity.

A *space diagram* is a drawing which represents the body and the action lines of all the vector quantities (Fig. 19.7).

A *vector diagram* is a drawing containing free vectors (magnitude and direction only) which represent the forces on a body (Fig. 19.7).

As this discussion goes forward, and the above terms are mentioned, the student is urged to reread the definitions.

19.3. Classification of Force Systems. Any number of forces, considered as a group, constitute a force system.

A *coplanar system* is one in which all the forces lie in the same plane, Fig. 19.2*A* and *C*.

A *noncoplanar system* is one in which the forces do not lie in a common plane, Fig. 19.2*B* and *D*.

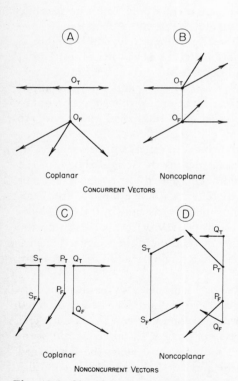

Fig. 19.2. Classification of vector quantities.

A *concurrent system* is one in which two or more forces have their line of action through a common point, Fig. 19.2*A* and *B*.

A *nonconcurrent system* is one in which the lines of action do not intersect as a common point, Fig. 19.2*C* and *D*.

Thus systems may be: coplanar and concurrent, coplanar and nonconcurrent, noncoplanar and concurrent, noncoplanar and nonconcurrent.

A *parallel system* is one in which all the forces are parallel. This system is not necessarily coplanar.

A *nonparallel system* is one in which the forces are not parallel and may be either coplanar or noncoplanar.

A *collinear system* is one in which all forces have the same line of action.

19.4. The Graphical Vector. To lay out a vector, as stated in the definition, the position, direction, and magnitude must be known. The position is located on an orthographic drawing of the structure or machine involved. Assume that a simple beam of a structure is to be loaded at its center with a weight of 1,750 lb. Figure 19.3 shows the beam laid out to scale. The vector is then drawn at the beam's center, the point of application or *position* of the force. The direction of the force is downward (force of gravity) so that the arrowhead may be placed on the direction line, as shown. The length of the vector is proportional to the magnitude and the vector scale used in Fig. 19.3 is 1 in. = 100 lb. Naturally, the vector scale will have no relationship whatever to the space scale for the orthographic drawing because one scale is in terms of weight (pounds) and the other in distance (feet).

In this case, the space diagram and vector are superimposed. This is to show that position, direction, and magnitude of the force are represented by the vector. Later, the vector diagram will be separated from the space diagram.

19.5. Resultants. A resultant is a vector quantity which will replace two or more vector quantities and have the same action. Any system of *concurrent* vectors and also any system of *coplanar nonconcurrent* vectors can be added geometrically to give a single vector that will have the same effect as the original system. The process of finding a resultant is called *composition*. Resultants are determined by applying either the parallelogram or triangle laws, the principles of which may be employed to form a vector polygon.

19.6. The Parallelogram Law. *Two concurrent nonparallel vectors, acting either away from (Fig. 19.4A) or toward (Fig. 19.4B) their origin will have a resultant which is the diagonal of a parallelogram constructed on the two vectors.* Note in Fig. 19.4*A* that the resultant acts in a direction away from the origin and in Fig. 19.4*B* in a direction toward the origin. Proof of the validity of this law may be had experimentally.

In Fig. 19.4*A* and *B*, the original vectors *V*1 and *V*2 and the resultants *R* are all in true length in the front view. In Fig. 19.4*C*, however,

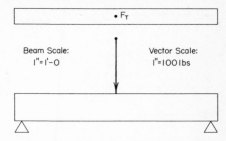

Fig. 19.3. Space diagram and vector.

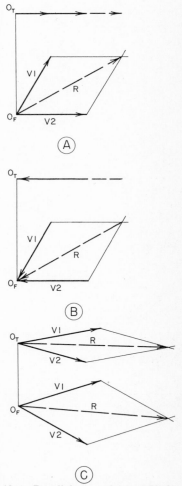

Fig. 19.4. Parallelogram law applied.

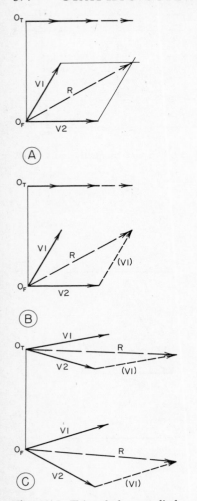

(A)

(B)

(C)

Fig. 19.5. Triangle law applied.

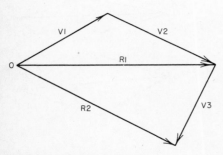

Fig. 19.6. Vector polygon.

vectors $V1$ and $V2$ are in oblique positions and, therefore, not in true length in either view. Nevertheless, the parallelogram law can be applied to find the resultant of Fig. 19.4C. The parallelogram is drawn as before by making the sides parallel, in both views, to $V1$ and $V2$. The resultant, R, is the diagonal as before but is an oblique line. A true length view of R will then give the magnitude of the resultant.

19.7. The Triangle Law. *Two concurrent nonparallel vectors acting either toward or away from their origin may be drawn as two sides of a triangle, and the third side will be the resultant.* Figure 19.5A is a copy of the vector parallelogram of Fig. 19.4A. Note that $V1$ could be moved to an alternate position on the opposite side, and the resultant would be the same as indicated in Fig. 19.5B. Also, note that $V2$ could be moved to the top of the parallelogram, with $V1$ remaining in the original position, and a different triangle obtained, but with the same resultant. Thus the triangle construction is a simplification of the parallelogram.

Figure 19.5C shows how the vector triangle can be used to find the resultant when the two concurrent vectors do not appear in true length in the given views. A line parallel to, and of the same length as, $V1$ is drawn from the end of $V2$, giving the resultant R from O to the end of $V1$ in the new position. The true length of R will give the magnitude of the resultant. Compare Figs. 19.5C and 19.4C.

In the above constructions, $V1$ becomes a free vector because it can be (and is) moved away from its line of action.

Note in Fig. 19.5A and B that, if R is replaced by a vector in the opposite direction, the resultant of $V1$, $V2$, and R will be zero. This is evidence of the validity of the construction.

If vectors are collinear, both the vector polygon and vector triangle will degenerate into a straight line, and the vectors are directly additive or subtractive, whichever the case may be.

19.8. The Vector Polygon. When three or more coplanar vectors exist, the vector triangle is expanded into a vector polygon. To prove this statement, in Fig. 19.6, three vectors $V1$, $V2$, and $V3$ have been laid out in successive order with the origin of $V2$ at the end of $V1$ and the origin of $V3$ at the end of $V2$. Then $R2$ is the resultant of $V1$, $V2$, and $V3$. To prove the construction, $V1$ and $V2$ form a vector triangle with $R1$ as the resultant; then $R1$ and $V3$ form a second vector triangle with $R2$ as the resultant; and because $R1$ is the resultant of $V1$ and $V2$, the resultant of $V1$, $V2$, and $V3$ is $R2$. Any number of vectors may be composed in this way to find the resultant of the system. The paragraphs following will illustrate the use of a vector polygon for concurrent coplanar and noncoplanar forces.

19.9. Concurrent Coplanar Forces. Figure 19.7A is the space diagram for three coplanar forces, $F1$, $F2$, and $F3$, concurrent at point O. These forces are to be composed into a resultant. The vector diagram at (B) is made by selecting an origin O at any convenient place on the paper and then drawing the vectors parallel

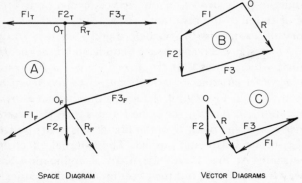

Space Diagram · Vector Diagrams

Fig. 19.7. Resultant of concurrent coplanar forces.

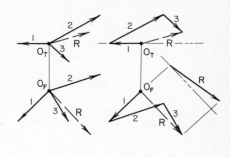

Space Diagram · Vector Diagram

Fig. 19.8. Resultant of concurrent non-coplanar forces.

to the directions established by the space diagram, making the length of the vectors to scale, representing the magnitude of each. Any successive order may be chosen, but care must be taken to maintain the given direction of each vector. Thus at (B), F1, F2, and F3 are laid out in that order and R, the resultant, is the line necessary to close the diagram. The magnitude of R is found by scaling the line. At (C), the order starting from O is F2, F3, and F1. Note that R, the resultant, has the same direction and length as in diagram (B). The resultant can then be transferred to the space diagram, where it will be concurrent at O with the original forces, which it replaces, and will be parallel to R on the vector diagram.

Vectors F1, F2, and F3 on the vector diagram are free vectors because they have been moved away from a definite line of action in order to determine the resultant. Note, however, that when the resultant is placed back on the space diagram it becomes the representation of a vector quantity which has magnitude, direction, and position and is now a localized vector.

19.10. Concurrent Noncoplanar Forces. Any two concurrent forces will be coplanar, but three or more *may or may not* be coplanar. The space diagram of Fig. 19.8 shows three forces, 1, 2, and 3, that are not coplanar but are concurrent at O. The vector diagram for these forces will be similar to Fig. 19.7, but because the forces are noncoplanar and therefore cannot all appear in true length in one view, the polygon becomes a *space* polygon requiring two views. To make the diagram, a point O is selected. Next, vector 1 is drawn parallel to force direction 1 on the space diagram. The length of vector 1 is made (to some convenient scale) equal in length to the magnitude of force 1. Then, vectors 2 and 3 are drawn by laying out their direction, drawing a true-length view and on it measuring the magnitude, and then projecting to top and front views R, the resultant, is the line necessary to close the diagram. The magnitude of R is found by determining its true length as shown by the auxiliary view. R may be transferred back to the space diagram by

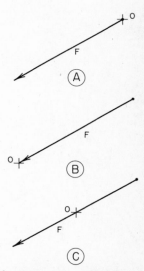

Fig. 19.9. Transmissibility.

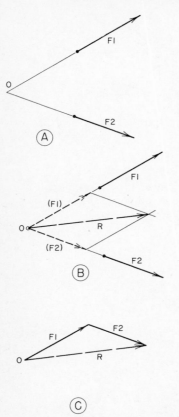

Fig. 19.10. Transmissibility applied.

drawing it parallel in both views to R on the vector diagram. This locates the line of action of the resultant.

19.11. Theory of Transmissibility. Before going on to a study of nonconcurrent forces, it will be necessary to understand the theory of transmissibility, which states that *the external effect of a force on a rigid body is unchanged for all points of application along the line of action.* To explain this theory, in Fig. 19.9A, a force is directed *away from* a point of application, O. At (B), the same force is directed *toward* point O. In other words, the point O in the first case is being pulled upon and in the second it is being pushed. The external effect on the body is the same. At Fig. 19.9C, the point of application has been moved away from point O, but the effect on O is still identical. Thus we conclude that a vector, representing a force, may be moved along the line of action without changing the external effect.

For future reference, however, it should be noted that the *internal* effect on a body may not be the same. Stress and deformation may be greatly influenced by the point of application.

19.12. Nonconcurrent Coplanar Forces. *Line-of-action Method.* The theory of transmissibility may be employed to find the resultant of nonconcurrent coplanar forces. As shown in Fig. 19.10A, if two vectors are coplanar and nonparallel, their lines of action will intersect, and by the theory of transmissibility, this intersection may then be considered as the origin of the forces. Therefore, if the vectors of Fig. 19.10A are moved along the lines of action to the origin, as shown at Fig. 19.10B, the resultant can be found by the parallelogram method. As illustrated at (C), the resultant may also be found by using a vector triangle.

The foregoing principles may be applied to find the resultant of three or more nonconcurrent coplanar vectors. In Fig. 19.11, three forces are represented by vectors $V1$, $V2$, and $V3$. At (A), the lines of action of $V1$ and $V2$ have been extended to their intersection at P_1, the point through which $V1$ and $V2$ both act. $V1$ and $V2$ are then moved with their bases at P_1 and the resultant $R1$ found by the parallelogram method. As shown at (B), the resultant $R1$ and vector $V3$ act through point P_2, the intersection of the lines of action of $R1$ and $V3$. If now $R1$ and $V3$ are moved with their bases at P_2, the resultant $R2$ may be found. This is the resultant of all three forces,

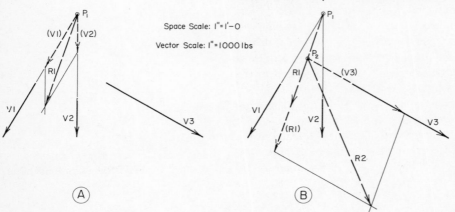

Space Scale: 1"=1'-0

Vector Scale: 1"=1000 lbs

Fig. 19.11. Resultant of coplanar nonconcurrent forces (line-of-action method).

and its magnitude, direction, and position are now determined. In this solution, the space and vector diagrams are superimposed. An identical solution could have been accomplished by first finding the resultant of $V2$ and $V3$ and then finding the final resultant with $V1$.

19.13. Components. Before proceeding to other solutions, it will be necessary to define and study components. *A component is one of the two or more forces into which a single force may be converted.* Collectively, the components will have the same action as the original force. The process of determining components of a force is called *resolution.* Figure 19.12 will illustrate the fundamentals. $V1$ is an original force represented by a vector. $C1$ and $C2$ are components of $V1$. The conception of components is actually the reverse of the triangle law for a resultant because if $C1$ and $C2$ were original vectors, then $V1$ is the resultant. It should also be noted that $C3$ and $C4$ are components of $V1$. The number of components into which a single force may be resolved is infinite.

If the directions of the lines of action of two components are known, a vector diagram may be made to find the magnitude of both components. In Fig. 19.13, the space diagram shows a force V. The directions of two components $C1$ and $C2$ are also known. Therefore, in the vector diagram, $C1$ and $C2$ are drawn parallel (to $C1$ and $C2$ on the space diagram) from the two ends of $V1$. These lines will intersect at O, now giving the magnitude of $C1$ and $C2$.

19.14. Nonconcurrent Coplanar Forces. *Component-polygon Method.* The space diagram of Fig. 19.14 shows two nonconcurrent coplanar forces, $F1$ and $F2$, for which the magnitude, direction, and position of the resultant are to be found. First, a vector diagram is made by drawing $F1$ and $F2$ parallel to the space directions and making their length equal to their magnitude, according to the vector scale. This now gives the magnitude and direction of the resultant R. The *position* of the resultant must now be found. Any point O may be selected (convenience is the criterion) and lines drawn from O to points 1, 2, and 3, the intersection of the vectors. These lines O-1, O-2, and O-3 may now be considered as components $C1$ and $C2$ of $F1$, $C2$ and $C3$ of $F2$, and $C1$ and $C3$ of R. The component $C2$ is a common component of $F1$ and $F2$, and for $F1$ acts in a direction from O to 2; for $F2$ it acts in a direction from 2 to O. Therefore, the action

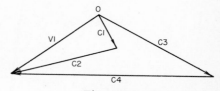

Fig. 19.12. Components.

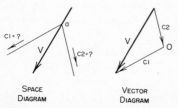

SPACE DIAGRAM

VECTOR DIAGRAM

Fig. 19.14. Resultant determined by component polygon.

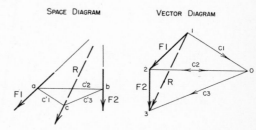

Fig. 19.13. Component magnitudes determined by known directions.

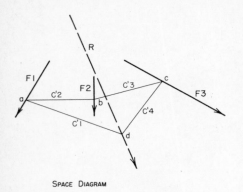

SPACE DIAGRAM

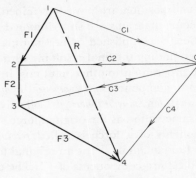

Fig. 19.15. Resultant determined by component polygon.

VECTOR DIAGRAM
(COMPONENT POLYGON)

of C2 is zero because of equal and opposite forces. The position of the resultant can now be located by drawing the components C1, C2, and C3 on the space diagram. The component C2 cancels out between forces F1 and F2 and has no action on the resultant. Therefore C'2 is drawn parallel to C2 giving the line ab on the space diagram. C1 is a component of both F1 and R. A line C'1 is therefore drawn from a on F1, parallel to C1. Also, C3 is a component of F2 and R. A line C'3 is therefore drawn from b parallel to C3. These lines, C'1 and C'3, then intersect at c which is a point through which the resultant R acts. It will make no difference where, on F1 and F2, the line C'2 is drawn to start the construction on the space diagram. As C'2 varies in position, a different point c will be obtained, but it will be on the line of action of R. Thus the magnitude, direction, and position of R have now been determined.

Figure 19.15 illustrates a similar case but for three forces. The vector diagram of the forces and a group of components concurrent at some point O are arranged as in the previous example. This time, however, there will be two common (equal and opposite) components, C2 and C3. These are drawn on the space diagram first, making C'2 parallel to C2, locating ab connecting F1 and F2. Then, from b on F2, C'3 is drawn parallel to C3, locating c on F3. Now C'1 from a parallel to C1 and C'4 from c parallel to C4 locate d, a point through which R acts. On the theory of transmissibility, any point d through which R acts will have the same external effect on the body of the material.

The component method just described is especially useful when the forces are almost parallel, causing the intersection of their lines of action to be beyond the limits of the drawing. If the forces are parallel, it is the only practical method.

19.15. Parallel Nonconcurrent Coplanar Forces. As explained in paragraph 19.3, when concurrent forces are parallel, they will be collinear (act along the same line) and are, therefore, directly additive or subtractive. For nonconcurrent parallel forces, the lines of action will not be the same so that extra construction is necessary to find the position of the resultant. The component-polygon method is best because the line-of-action method involves the use of components and, for several forces, becomes somewhat laborious and confusing.

In Fig. 19.16, the space diagram shows three parallel forces of different magnitude. Since the forces are parallel, the vector triangle degenerates into a straight line, as shown. The resultant will be the summation of the three vectors $F1$, $F2$, and $F3$ and will lie along the straight line of the three vectors. To find the position of the resultant, a point O is selected at random and components $C1$, $C2$, $C3$, and $C4$ drawn (as in Fig. 19.15). The rest of the construction is the same as described in paragraph 19.14. Note again that components $C2$ and $C3$ are each common components of two forces and $C'2$ and $C'3$ are thus the connecting lines between forces $F1$ and $F2$ and $F2$ and $F3$ on the space diagram.

19.16. Coplanar Forces in Auxiliary and Oblique Positions.
It is evident from the foregoing chapters of this book that the various points, lines, and planes of modern machines and structures do not always occur in simple positions or relationships. Consequently, the stresses introduced on machine parts and elements of structures will often be in auxiliary or oblique planes. This apparent complication, however, is not serious since the normal view of such planes may be easily obtained, where the forces will appear in their true relationship. This normal view then becomes the space diagram for forces, and from it a component polygon may be made to determine a resultant. The resultant may then be located on the space diagram.

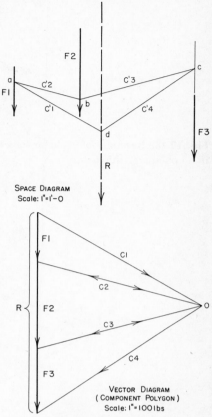

Fig. 19.16. Resultant of parallel coplanar forces.

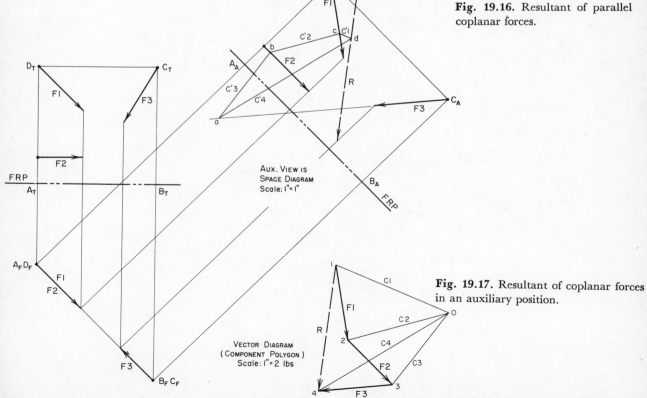

Fig. 19.17. Resultant of coplanar forces in an auxiliary position.

In Fig. 19.17, forces $F1$, $F2$, and $F3$ lie in plane $ABCD$, a plane in an auxiliary position. The right auxiliary shown is a normal view of all the force directions, gives their true relationship, and becomes the space diagram. The vector diagram and determination of the resultant's position, magnitude, and direction are identical to the description given in paragraph 19.14.

Figure 19.18 is a similar case except that the forces lie in an oblique plane. After the normal view of the plane of the forces has been found, the solution is again the same as in paragraph 19.14.

Fig. 19.18. Resultant of coplanar forces in an oblique position.

19.17. Resolution of Coplanar Concurrent Forces. In paragraph 19.13, it was shown how a vector could be resolved into two components concurrent with the vector by constructing a vector triangle with sides parallel to the components desired. Nevertheless, certain conditions must be met before the problem has only *one* answer. If the direction and magnitude of a vector are considered as *two* conditions, then $N - 2$ conditions must be known before the

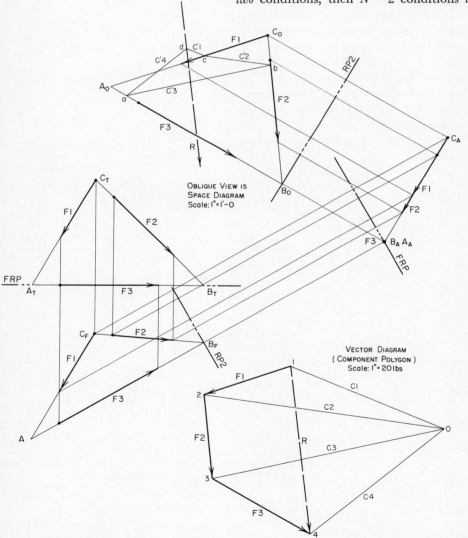

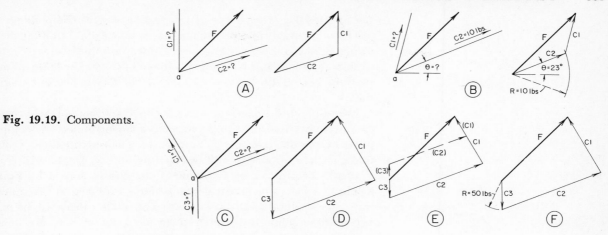

Fig. 19.19. Components.

problem has a single solution. For example, in Fig. 19.19A, the directions of two desired components are known. *Six* conditions are involved, the magnitude and direction of the vector F and the magnitudes and directions of both components. *Four* conditions are known, the magnitude and direction of F and the directions of the components. Therefore, the limit of $N - 2$ is satisfied, and the problem can be solved on the vector diagram by laying out the directions of both components. In Fig. 19.19B, again six conditions are involved, but this time the direction of one component and the magnitude of the other give a total of four known conditions. The problem is then solved as shown by laying out the direction of one component and the magnitude of the other. In Fig. 19.19C, the directions of three desired components are known; thus eight conditions are involved (two conditions for four vectors), but only five (four directions and one magnitude) are known. The problem will have an infinite num-

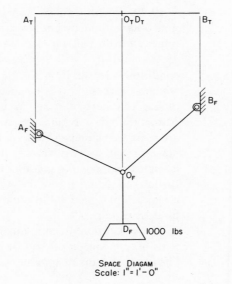

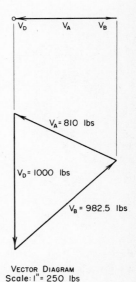

Fig. 19.20. Resolution of forces in equilibrium.

SPACE DIAGAM
Scale: 1" = 1' - 0"

VECTOR DIAGRAM
Scale: 1" = 250 lbs

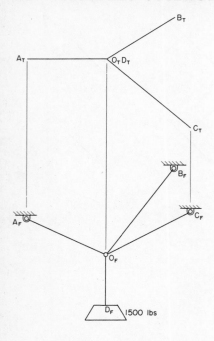

SPACE DIAGRAM
Scale: 1" = 1'- 0"

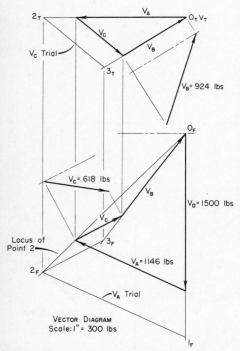

VECTOR DIAGRAM
Scale: 1" = 300 lbs

Fig. 19.21. Resolution by point view of a known force.

ber of answers, as shown at (*D*), by *assuming* three components, or at (*E*), where two other possible solutions are shown; but if the magnitude of one component had been known, as indicated at (*F*), the problem has only one solution: Component *C3* can be laid out, and then the known directions of *C1* and *C2* will determine their magnitude.

Even though the conditions stated above are met, a single vector cannot be resolved into *nonconcurrent* components unless the components are parallel (concurrent at infinity). The resolution of a vector into parallel components will be discussed in paragraph 19.22.

19.18. Resolution of Coplanar Concurrent Forces in Equilibrium. When concurrent coplanar forces are placed in equilibrium, the resultant of all forces must be zero; also, there will be only two possible components for a given force, for if there are more, equilibrium will be upset and the components become indeterminate. For example, in the space diagram of Fig. 19.20, a weight is supported by two members *AO* and *BO*. If a third support *in the plane* of *AO* and *BO* is added, one support will share more load than it should and the determination of stress in the supports is impossible. Thus the *N − 2* conditions mentioned previously must be maintained.

To find the forces in members *AO* and *BO*, in the vector diagram, V_D is laid off vertically to scale and equal to the magnitude of the force (1,000 lb). Then V_B parallel to *OB* and V_A parallel to *OA* will intersect, determining the two components of V_D. These are the forces in *OA* and *OB*. For the system to remain in equilibrium, the direction of V_B must be upward and to the right and that of V_A must be upward and to the left. Note that these directions of force make V_A and V_B in *opposition* to V_D, thus placing the whole system in balance. In the vector diagram, the front view shows all forces in true length.

19.19. Resolution of Noncoplanar Concurrent Forces. When noncoplanar concurrent forces are placed in equilibrium, three component forces will be *required* to maintain equilibrium, and thus *N − 3* conditions will be necessary. One might be asked why *N − 2* conditions are the limit for coplanar and *N − 3* the limit for noncoplanar forces. This is because more than *two* components for coplanar and more than *three* for noncoplanar forces are indeterminate. Also, if there is only one component, the forces will be collinear—*two* are required to make the forces coplanar, and *three* are required for a noncoplanar system. Note in the space diagram of Fig. 19.21 that, if a fourth supporting member is added, one member will take more (or less) load and throw the system out of balance. Remember that a rigid four-legged table often requires a wedge under one leg to prevent tilting.

The resolution of components for noncoplanar concurrent systems may be accomplished by either obtaining a point view of any one of the vectors or making an edge view of two unknown vectors.

19.20. Resolution by a Point View. To resolve a force into three noncoplanar concurrent forces (components), at least *one* view should be made in which one force appears as a point and the other three appear either in true length or foreshortened. If *both* views of the vector diagram show all four vectors foreshortened or in true length, the determination can only be made by trial-and-error methods, which are tedious and time-consuming. The point view of *any* one of the vectors will give a straightforward solution.

Resolution by the Point View of a Known Quantity. Figure 19.21 shows by the space diagram that a weight is supported by three members, OA, OB, and OC. The weight gives vector V_D, which appears as a point in the top view and in true length in the front view of the vector diagram. The directions of all the vectors can now be established in both views. Any order may be selected, and in this case V_B is laid off from the base of V_D and, of course, must be parallel in both views to OB. Then V_A is drawn from the tip of V_D, parallel in both views to OA. The vector V_C may now be laid off in both views, parallel to OC, but its actual location cannot be found before some extra construction. Therefore, V_C is drawn first as line 2-3 in the top view, which is then projected to the front view. This trial line would place V_A as line 2-1 in the front view, and V_A *must* emanate from the tip of V_D. Thus it is necessary now to *move* the V_C line until the polygon of vectors can be closed. Point 3 of the trial line will move along the directional line for V_B, and point 2 will have a locus that is a line connecting point 2 and O (the base of V_D). To prove this relationship, draw several trial lines for V_C. Finally, then, where the directional line for V_A crosses the "locus of points 2" in the front view determines the end of V_A and one end of V_C, and V_C then drawn parallel to OC closes the polygon. The true length of vectors will now give the magnitudes needed. V_A is in true length in the front view and may be scaled there. The left auxiliary shown gives the true length of V_C. The elevation auxiliary shown gives the true length of V_B.

Resolution by the Point View of an Unknown Quantity. In any particular problem, one of the forces, known or unknown, may appear as a point. There is also the possibility that *none* of the forces will appear as a point in the views given, and therefore the point view of one force will have to be made before laying out the vector diagram. A system of this type is shown in Fig. 19.22. The direction of OA, however, is frontal, and the left auxiliary view shown will give the point view of OA. The diagram will employ views *projectively matching* the front and auxiliary views of the space diagram. To start the vector diagram, the known force in the direction of OD must first be located. Therefore, some point O' for the diagram is selected and $O'D'$ laid out parallel to front and auxiliary views. Then a true length view of $O'D'$ (shown here projected from the front view of $O'D'$) gives a view in which the magnitude of the force in OD may be laid out. Next, in the auxiliary view, where V_A (the vector repre-

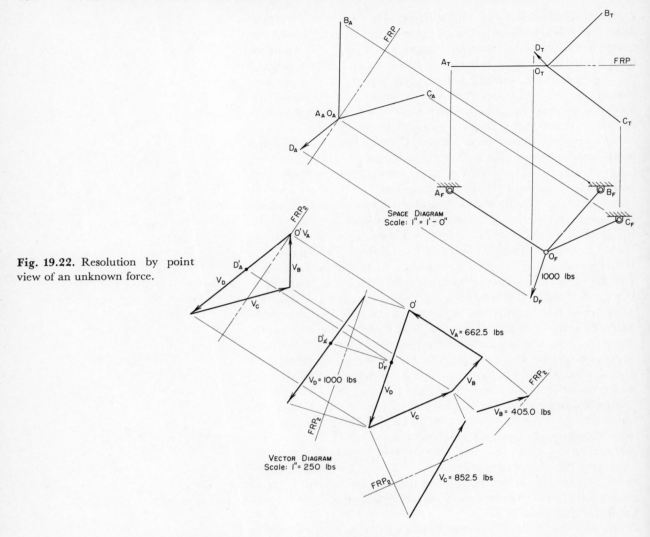

Fig. 19.22. Resolution by point view of an unknown force.

sentation of the force in OA) appears as a point, the directions of V_B, parallel to OB, and V_C, parallel to OC, will make a closed vector polygon. Now, projection of the intersection of V_C and V_B (in the auxiliary view) to the front view and the *directions* of V_A, V_B, and V_C in the front view make possible the completion of the polygon in the front view. Finally, the separate auxiliaries for V_B and V_C give the magnitude of these forces, and because V_A is frontal, it can be scaled in the front view. Note that the directional arrows on the vectors place the system in equilibrium because V_C, V_B, and V_A *oppose* (act in reverse direction to) V_D.

19.21. Resolution by the Edge View of the Plane of Two Unknown Quantities. Whether or not some force directions are in true length or appear as points in the given views, resolution can always be had by making the edge view of the plane of two of the un-

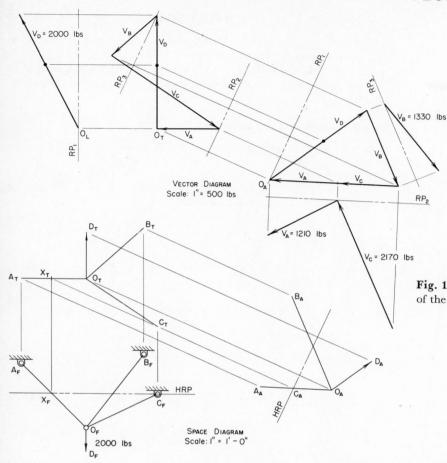

Fig. 19.23. Resolution by edge view of the plane of two unknown forces.

knowns. In Fig. 19.23, the plane of OC and OA has been selected for the edge view. Thus the view made looking in the direction of CX, a horizontal line of plane OAC, gives the edge view in the elevation auxiliary shown. The vector diagram may now be started by selecting a point O and locating the known force vector V_D parallel to OD in top and auxiliary views. In the true length view for V_D, the magnitude of V_D is measured and then projected back to top and auxiliary views. Next, the vectors can be partially located in the auxiliary view by drawing V_B parallel to $O_A B_A$ and a line for V_A and V_C parallel to $O_A C_A A_A$. Going now to the top view, V_B can be established in direction by drawing it parallel to $O_T B_T$. Projection of the intersection of V_B and $V_A C_A$ in the auxiliary, to the top view, locates the end of V_B. Having V_B established in both views, V_A parallel to $O_T A_T$ and V_C parallel to $O_T C_T$ complete the top view of the vector polygon. Finally, projection of the intersection of V_C and V_A in the top view, to the auxiliary view, determines V_C and V_A in the auxiliary view. True lengths of V_A, V_B, and V_C, as shown, then give the needed magnitudes.

PROBLEMS

Selections from the following problems may be made and the figures constructed to any desired scale on 8½- by 11-in. or 11- by 17-in. drawing sheets. The direction and position of all given vectors are indicated in the problem illustrations; the magnitudes of the vectors are stated in the problems listed below.

Group 1. Resultants and components

Determine the magnitude, position, and direction of the resultant of the given force system.

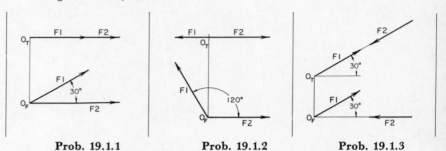

Prob. 19.1.1   Prob. 19.1.2   Prob. 19.1.3

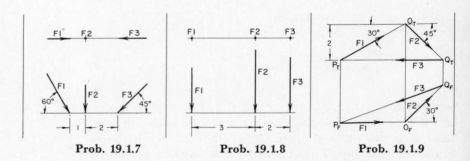

Prob. 19.1.7   Prob. 19.1.8   Prob. 19.1.9

19.1.1. $F1 = 250$ lb, $F2 = 300$ lb.
19.1.2. $F1 = 250$ lb, $F2 = 200$ lb.
19.1.3. $F1 = 190$ lb, $F2 = 170$ lb.
19.1.4. $F1 = 300$ lb, $F2 = 350$ lb.
19.1.5. $F1 = 200$ lb, $F2 = 250$ lb, $F3 = 170$ lb.
19.1.6. $F1 = 200$ lb, $F2 = 200$ lb, $F3 = 250$ lb.
19.1.7. $F1 = 160$ lb, $F2 = 100$ lb, $F3 = 150$ lb.
19.1.8. $F1 = 160$ lb, $F2 = 220$ lb, $F3 = 200$ lb.
19.1.9. $F1 = 170$ lb, $F2 = 160$ lb, $F3 = 170$ lb.
Resolve the given force into the components indicated.
19.1.10. $F = 220$ lb.
19.1.11. $F = 210$ lb, $C1 = 240$ lb.

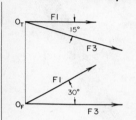

Prob. 19.1.4

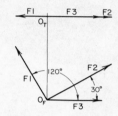

Prob. 19.1.5

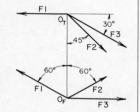

Prob. 19.1.6

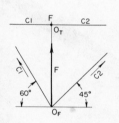

Prob. 19.1.10

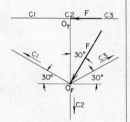

Prob. 19.1.11

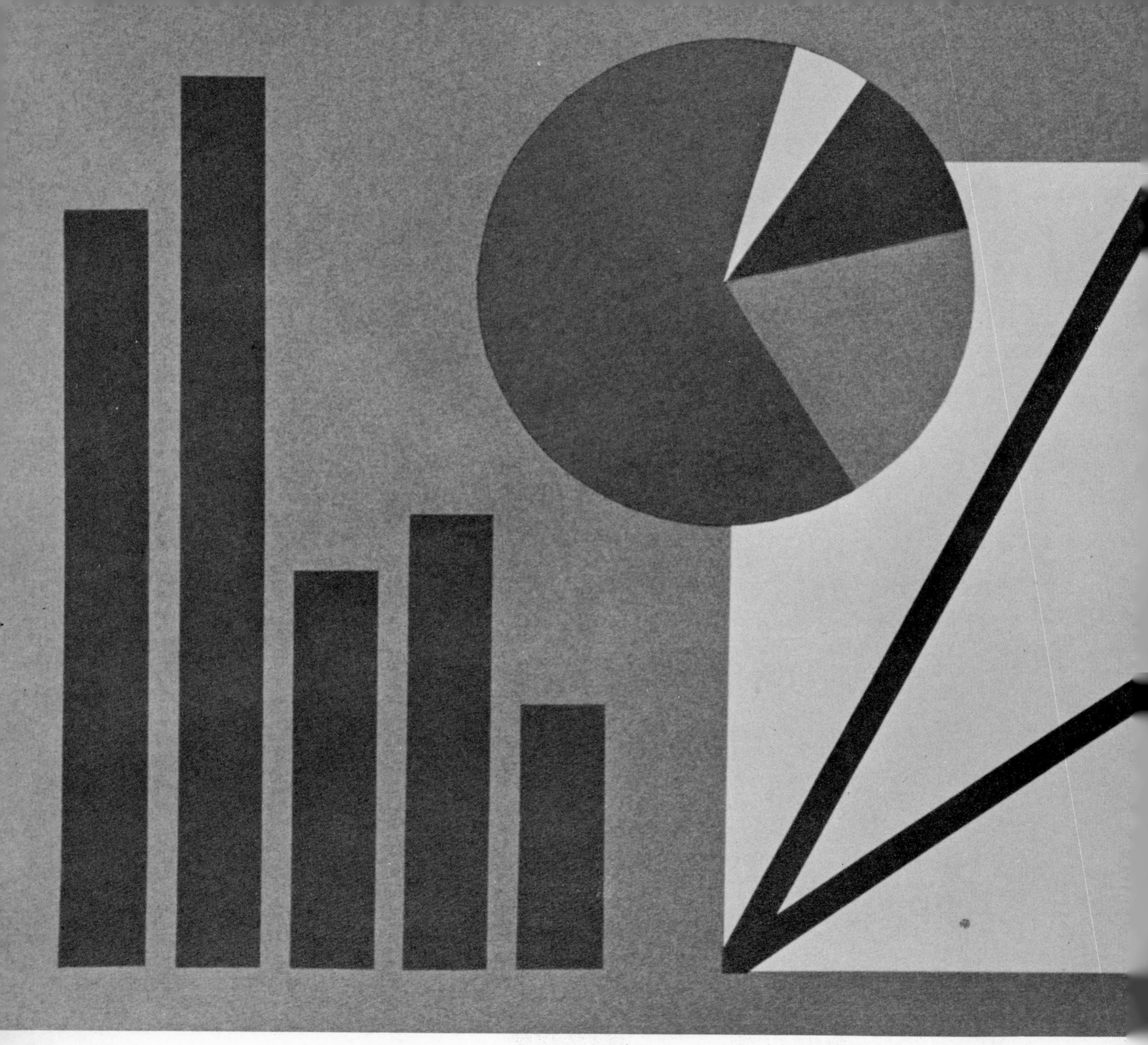

20

CHARTS, GRAPHS,
AND DIAGRAMS

20.1. This chapter is given as an introduction to the use of graphical methods in tabulating data for analysis, solving problems, and presenting facts. It will indicate to the prospective engineer the uses and value of this application of graphics and suggest his further study of the subject.

For the purposes of presenting a series of quantitative facts quickly, the graphical chart is an excellent method. When properly constructed, charts, graphs, and diagrams constitute a powerful tool for computation, analysis of engineering data, and the presentation of statistics for comparison or prediction.

20.2. Classification. Charts, graphs, and diagrams may be divided roughly into two classes: (1) those used for purely technical purposes and (2) those used for popular appeal in advertising or the presentation of information. The engineer is concerned mainly with the first class, but he should have some acquaintance with the preparation and the influential possibilities of the second class. The aim here is to give a short study of the types with which engineers and those in allied professions should be familiar.

It is assumed that the reader is familiar with the use of rectangular coordinates and that the meaning of such terms as "axes," "ordinates," "abscissas," "coordinates," "variables," etc., is understood.

20.3. Rectilinear Charts. As the greater part of chart work in experimental engineering is done on rectilinear graph paper, the

589

student should become familiar with this form of chart early in his course. The rectilinear chart is made on a sheet ruled with equispaced horizontal lines crossing equispaced vertical lines. The spacing is optional, but one commercial graph paper is divided into squares of $\frac{1}{20}$ in., with every fifth line heavier, to aid in plotting and reading. Sheets are printed with various other rulings, as 4, 6, 8, 10, 12, and 16 divisions per inch.

It is universal practice to use the upper right-hand quadrant for plotting experimental-data curves, making the lower left-hand corner the origin. In case both positive and negative values of a function are to be plotted, as with many mathematical curves, it is necessary to place the origin so as to include all desired values.

Figure 20.1 shows a usual form of rectilinear chart, such as might be made for inclusion in a written report.

20.4. Drawing the Curve. In drawing graphs from experimental data, it is often a question whether the curve should pass through all the points plotted or strike a mean between them. In general, observed data not backed up by definite theory or mathematical law are shown by connecting the points plotted with straight lines, as in Fig. 20.2A. An empirical relationship between curve and plotted points may be used, as at (B), when, in the opinion of the engineer, the curve should exactly follow some points and go to one side of others. Consistency of observation is indicated at (C), in which case the curve should closely follow a true theoretical curve.

20.5. Titles and Notation. The title is a very important part of a chart, and its wording should be studied until it is clear and concise. In every case, it should contain sufficient description to tell what the chart is, the source or authority, the name of the observer, and the date. Approved practice places the title at the top of the sheet, arranged in phrases symmetrically about a center line. If placed within the ruled space, a border line or box should set it out from the sheet. Each sheet of curves should have a title; and when more than one curve is shown on a sheet, the different curves should be drawn so as to be easily distinguishable, by varying the

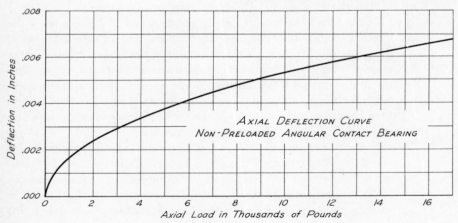

Fig. 20.1. A rectilinear chart.

character of the lines, using full, dotted, and dot-and-dash lines, with a tabular key for identification, or by lettering the names of the curves directly along them. When the charts are not intended for reproduction, inks of different colors may be used.

20.6. To Draw a Chart. In drawing a coordinate chart the general order is (1) compute and assemble all data; (2) determine size and kind of chart best adapted and whether printed or plain paper should be used; (3) determine, from the limits of the data, the scales for abscissas and ordinates to give the best effect to the resulting curve; (4) lay off the independent variable (often *time*) on the horizontal, or *X*, axis and the dependent variable on the vertical, or *Y*, axis; (5) plot points from the data and pencil the curves; (6) ink the curve; (7) compose and letter title and coordinates.

The construction of a graphical chart requires good draftsmanship, especially for the lettering, but in engineering and scientific work the primary considerations are judgment in the proper selection of coordinates, accuracy in plotting points and drawing the graph, and an understanding of the functions and limitations of the resulting chart.

When the chart is drawn on a printed form, to be blueprinted, the curve may be drawn on the reverse side of the paper, enabling erasures to be made without injuring the ruled surface.

Green is becoming the standard color for printed forms. Blue will not print or photograph, and red is trying on the eyes.

If the curve is for purposes of computation, it should be drawn with a fine accurate line. If for demonstration, it should be fairly heavy, for contrast and effect.

The following rules are adapted from ASA Y15 (formerly Z15):

STANDARDS FOR GRAPHIC PRESENTATIONS

1. A graph should be free of all lines and lettering that are not essential to the reader's clear understanding of its message.

2. All lettering and numbers on a graph should be placed so as to be easily read from the bottom and from the right-hand side of the graph, not the left-hand side.

3. Standard abbreviations should be used where space is limited as, for example, in denoting the unit of measurement in scale captions.

4. The range of scales should be chosen so as to ensure effective and efficient use of the coordinate area in attaining the objective of the chart.

5. The zero line should be included if visual comparison of plotted magnitudes is desired.

6. When it is desired to show whether the rate of change of the dependent variable is increasing, constant, or decreasing, a logarithmic vertical scale should be used in conjunction with an arithmetic horizontal scale.

7. The horizontal (independent variable) scale values should usually increase from left to right and the vertical (dependent variable) scale values from bottom to top.

8. Scale values and scale captions should be placed outside the grid area, normally at the bottom for the horizontal scale and at the left side for the

Fig. 20.2. Methods of drawing curves.

vertical scale. On wide graphs it may be desirable to repeat the vertical scale at the right side.

9. For arithmetic scales, the scale numbers shown on the graph and the space between coordinate rulings should preferably correspond to 1, 2, or 5 units of measurement, multiplied or divided by 1, 10, 100, etc.

10. The use of many digits in scale numbers should be avoided.

11. The scale caption should indicate both the variable measured and the unit of measurement. For example: EXPOSURE TIME IN DAYS.

12. Coordinate rulings should be limited in number to those necessary to guide the eye in making a reading to the desired degree of approximation. Closely spaced coordinate rulings are appropriate for computation charts but not for graphs intended primarily to show relationship.

13. Curves should preferably be represented by solid lines.

14. When more than one curve is presented on a graph, relative emphasis or differentiation of the curves may be secured by using different types of line, that is, solid, dashed, dotted, etc., or by different widths of line. A solid line is recommended for the most important curve.

15. The observed points should preferably be designated by circles.

16. Circles, squares, and triangles should be used rather than crosses or filled-in symbols to differentiate observed points of several curves on a graph.

17. Curves should, if practicable, be designated by brief labels placed close to the curves (horizontally or along the curves) rather than by letters, numbers, or other devices requiring a key.

18. If a key is used, it should preferably be placed within the grid in an isolated position, and enclosed by a light line border—grid lines, if convenient.

19. The title should be as clear and concise as possible. Explanatory material, if necessary to ensure clearness, should be added as a subtitle.

20. Scale captions, designations, curves, and blank spaces should, so far as practicable, be arranged to give a sense of balance around vertical and horizontal axes.

21. The appearance and the effectiveness of a graph depend in large measure on the relative widths of line used for its component parts. The widest line should be used for the principal curve. If several curves are presented on the same graph, the line width used for the curves should be less than that used when a single curve is presented.

22. A simple style of lettering, such as the gothic with its uniform line width and no serifs, should in general be used.

20.7. Logarithmic Scales. A very important type of chart is that in which the divisions, instead of being equally spaced, are made proportional to the logarithms of the numbers at the margin instead of to the numbers themselves. When ruled logarithmically in one direction with equal spacing at right angles, it is called "semilogarithmic."

Logarithmic spacing may be done directly from the graduations on one of the scales of a slide rule. Logarithmic paper is sold in various combinations of ruling. It may be had in one, two, three, or more cycles; or multiples of 10, also in part-cycle and split-cycle form. In using logarithmic paper, interpolations should be made logarithmically, for arithmetical interpolation with coarse divisions might lead to considerable error.

20.8. Semilogarithmic Chart. This chart has equal spacing on one axis, usually the X axis, and logarithmic spacing on the other axis. Owing to a property by virtue of which the slope of the curve at any point is an exact measure of the rate of increase or decrease in the data plotted, it is frequently called a "ratio chart." Often called the "rate-of-change" chart as distinguished from the rectilinear, or "amount-of-change," chart, it is extremely useful in statistical work as it shows at a glance the rate at which a variable changes. By the use of this chart it is possible to predict a trend, such as the future increase of a business, growth of population, etc.

In choosing between rectilinear ruling and semilogarithmic ruling, the important point to consider is whether the chart is to represent *numerical* increases and decreases or *percentage* increases and decreases. In many cases, it is desired to emphasize the percentage, or rate, change, not the numerical change; hence a semilogarithmic chart should be used.

An example of the use of the semilogarithmic chart is illustrated in Fig. 20.3. This curve was drawn from data compiled for the *World Almanac*. The dash line shows the actual production by years, and the full line is the trend curve, the extension of which predicts future production.

20.9. Logarithmic Charts. With both abscissas and ordinates spaced logarithmically, these are used more for the solution of problems than for presenting facts. A property which distinguishes the logarithmic chart and accounts for its usefulness in so many cases is that the graphs of all algebraic equations representing multiplication, division, roots, and powers are straight lines. If the equation $x^2y = 16$ were plotted on ordinary rectangular coordinates, the resulting curve would be a hyperbola of the third degree with the x and y axes as asymptotes. By taking the logarithms of both sides of the given equation, it becomes $2 \log x + \log y = \log 16$. The

Fig. 20.3. A semilogarithmic chart.

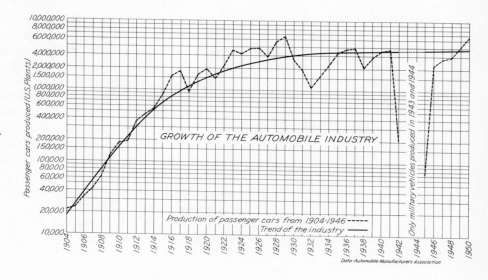

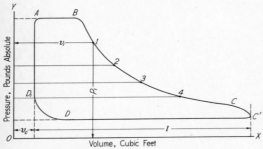

Fig. 20.4. Indicator diagram.

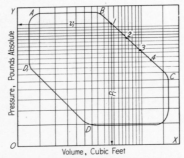

Fig. 20.5. Indicator diagram on logarithmic paper.

AMPLIFIER POWER OUTPUT REQUIRED TO COVER VARIOUS DISTANCES AS COMPARED TO THE SURROUNDING NOISE LEVEL

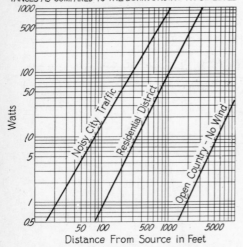

Fig. 20.6. Multiple-cycle ruling.

equation now has the slope intercept form $y = mx + b$ and, if so desired, could be plotted on rectangular coordinates by substituting the logarithms of the variables. Obviously, it is easier to use logarithmic coordinates and plot the points directly than to take the logarithms of the variables and plot them on rectangular coordinates.

A feature of the logarithmic chart which makes it valuable for the study of many problems is that the exponent in the equation may be determined by measuring the slope of the graph. An inspection of the foregoing equations will show that the slope m, as given by the slope intercept form, is -2. The value of this exponent may be determined by direct measurement of the slope, using a uniformly graduated scale.

Figures 20.4 and 20.5 show an example of the use of a logarithmic chart in studying steam-engine performance. When the indicator card, Fig. 20.4, is plotted on logarithmic paper it takes the form shown in Fig. 20.5. The hyperbolas of a perfect card become straight lines, deviations from which indicate faults.

Figure 20.6 illustrates the use of multiple-cycle paper.

20.10. Polar Chart. The use of polar coordinate paper for representing intensity of illumination, intensity of heat, polar forms of curves, etc., is common. Figure 20.7 shows a candle-power distribution curve for an ordinary Mazda B lamp and Fig. 20.8 the curve for a certain type of reflector. The candle power in any given direction is determined by reading off the distance from the origin to the curve. Use of these curves enables the determination of the foot-candle intensity at any point.

20.11. Trilinear Chart. The trilinear chart, or "triaxial diagram," as it is sometimes called, affords a valuable means of studying the properties of chemical compounds consisting of three elements, alloys of three metals or compounds, and mixtures containing three variables. The chart has the form of an equilateral triangle, the altitude of which represents 100 per cent of each of the three constituents. Figure 20.9, showing the ultimate tensile strength of copper-tin-zinc alloys, is a typical example of its application. The usefulness of such diagrams depends upon the geometrical principle that the sum of the perpendiculars to the sides from any point within an equilateral triangle is a constant and is equal to the altitude.

20.12. Choice of Type and Presentation. The function of a chart is to reveal facts. It may be entirely misleading if a wrong choice of paper or coordinates is taken. The growth of an operation plotted on a rectilinear chart might, for example, entirely mislead an owner analyzing the trend of his business, while if plotted on a semilogarithmic chart, it would give a true picture of conditions. Intentionally misleading charts have been used many times in advertising matter, the commonest form being the chart with a greatly exaggerated vertical scale. Naturally, in engineering work the facts must be presented honestly and with scientific accuracy.

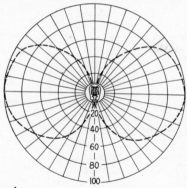

Fig. 20.7. A polar chart.

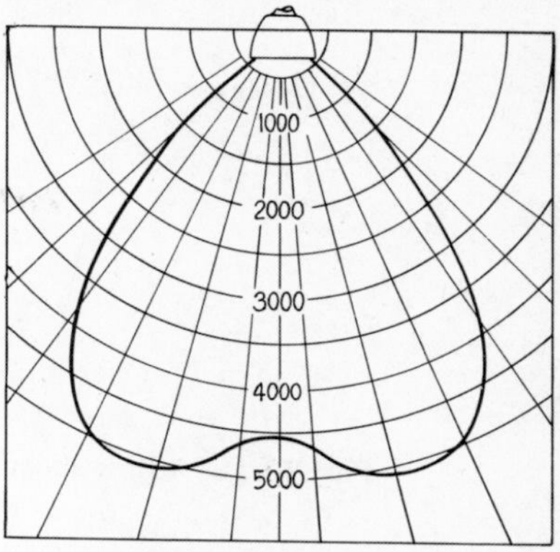

Fig. 20.8. A polar chart.

20.13. Classification Charts, Route Charts, and Flow Sheets.
The uses to which these three classes of charts may be put are widely different; but their underlying principles are similar, and they have thus been grouped together for convenience.

A *classification chart*, as illustrated in Fig. 20.10, is intended to show the subdivisions of a whole and the interrelation of its parts to each other. Such a chart often takes the place of a written outline since it gives a better visualization of the facts than words alone would convey. A common application is an organization chart of a corporation or business. It is customary to enclose the names of the divisions in rectangles, although circles or other shapes may be used. The rectangle has the advantage of being more convenient for lettering, while the circle may be drawn more quickly and possesses a greater popular appeal. Often a combination of both is used.

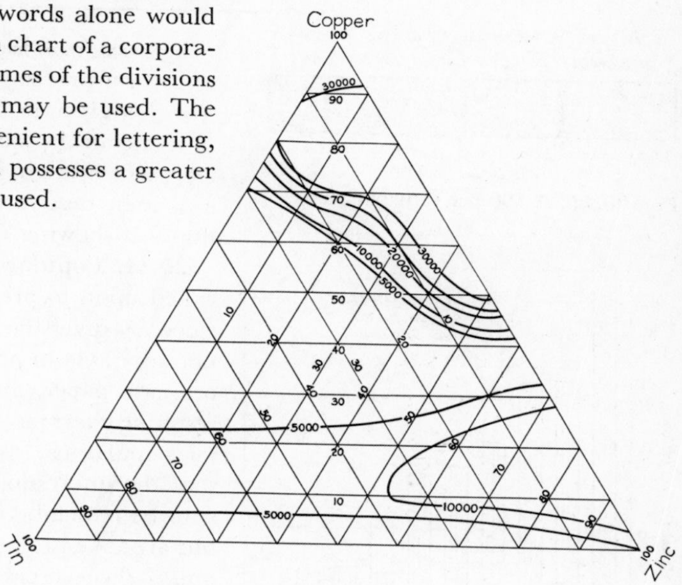

Fig. 20.9. A trilinear chart.

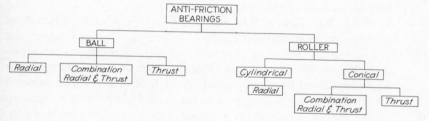

Fig. 20.10. A classification chart.

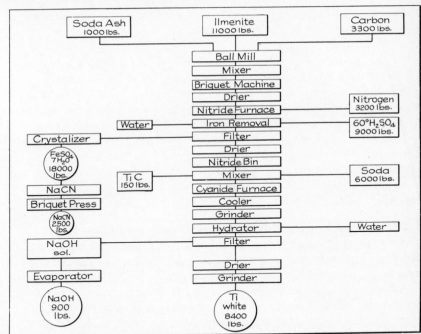

Fig. 20.11. A flow sheet.

WEIGHT PERCENTAGE ANALYSIS FOR AN
INTERNALLY BRACED CABIN MONOPLANE

| 26.4% | 22.4% | 33.1% | 15.6% |

Wing Group | Body Group Power Plant | Fixed
                 Tail Group 2.5%   Equip.

Fig. 20.12. A 100 per cent bar chart.

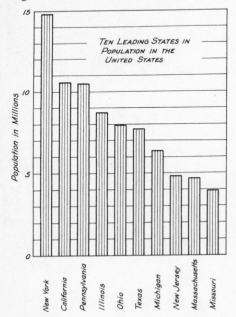

Fig. 20.13. A multiple-bar chart.

The *route chart* is used mainly for the purpose of showing the various steps in a process, either of manufacturing or other business. The *flow sheet* given in Fig. 20.11 is an example of a route chart applied to a chemical process. Charts of this type show in a dynamic way facts which might require considerable study to comprehend from a written description. A different form of route chart is that of Fig. 9.1, showing the course of a drawing through the shops.

20.14. Popular Charts. Engineers and draftsmen are frequently called upon to prepare charts and diagrams which will be understood by diversified and nontechnical readers. In many cases, it is not advisable to present the facts by means of curves drawn on coordinate paper, although for the sake of greater effectiveness the resulting chart may suffer somewhat in accuracy. In preparing charts for popular use, particular care must be taken to make them so that the impression produced will be both quick and accurate. It is to be remembered that such charts are seldom studied critically but are taken in at a glance; hence the method of presentation requires the exercise of careful judgment and the application of a certain amount of psychology.

20.15. Bar Charts. The bar chart is a very easily understood type for the nontechnical reader. One of its simplest forms is the 100 *per cent bar* for showing the relations of the constituents to a given total. Figure 20.12 is an example of this form of chart. The different segments should be crosshatched, shaded, or distinguished in some effective manner, the percentage represented placed on the diagram or directly opposite, and the meaning of each segment clearly stated. These bars may be placed either vertically or horizontally, the vertical position giving an advantage for lettering and the horizontal position an advantage in readability, as the eye judges horizontal distances readily.

Figure 20.13 is an example of a *multiple-bar chart*, in which the length of each bar is proportional to the magnitude of the quantity represented. Means should be provided for reading numerical values represented by the bars. If it is necessary to give the exact value represented by the individual bars, these values should not be lettered at the ends of the bars since the apparent length would be increased. This type is made both horizontally, with the description at the base, and vertically. The vertical form is sometimes called the "pipe-organ chart." When vertical bars are drawn close together so as to touch along the sides, the diagram is called a "staircase chart." This is made oftener as the "staircase curve," a line plotted on coordinate paper representing the profile of the tops of the bars.

A *compound-bar chart* is made when it is desired to show two or more components in each bar. It is really a set of 100 per cent bars of different lengths set together either in pipe-organ or horizontal form.

20.16. Pie Charts. The "pie diagram," or 100 per cent circle, Fig. 20.14, is much inferior to the bar chart but is used constantly because of its insistent popular appeal. It is a simple form of chart and, with the exception of the lettering, is easily constructed. It may be regarded as a 100 per cent bar bent into circular form. The circumference of the circle is divided into 100 parts, and sectors are used to represent percentages of the total. To be effective, this diagram must be carefully lettered and the percentages marked on the sectors or at the circumference opposite the sectors. For contrast, it is best to crosshatch or shade the individual sectors. If the original drawing is to be displayed, the sectors may be colored and the diagram supplied with a key showing the meaning of each color. In every case, the percentage notation should be placed where it can be read without removing the eyes from the diagram.

20.17. Strata and Volume Diagrams. The use of strata and volume diagrams has been very common although they are usually the most deceptive of the graphic methods of representation. Figure 20.15 is a strata chart showing a change in amounts over a period of time. The area between the curves is shaded to emphasize each variable represented. However, in reading it should be remembered that the areas *between* curves have no significance.

20.18. Pictorial Charts. Pictorial charts were formerly much used for comparisons, such as costs, populations, standing armies, livestock, and various products. It was customary to represent the data by human or other figures whose heights were proportional to the numerical values or by silhouettes of the animals or products concerned whose heights or sometimes areas were proportional. Since volumes vary as the cubes of the linear dimensions, such charts are grossly misleading. For such comparisons, bar charts or charts such as Fig. 20.16, where the diameter of the column is constant, should be used.

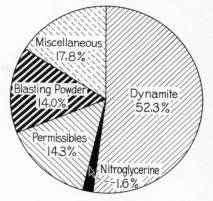

Fig. 20.14. A pie chart.

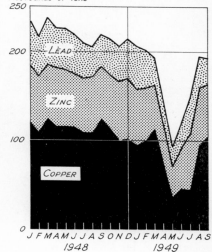

Fig. 20.15. A strata chart.

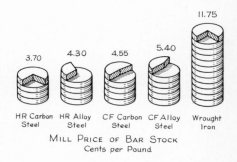

Fig. 20.16. A pictorial chart.

20.19. Charts for Reproduction. Charts for reproduction by the zinc-etching process should be carefully penciled to about twice the size of the required cut. In inking, first ink circles around plotted points; second, ink the curves with strong lines. A border pen is useful for heavy lines, and a LeRoy pen (in socket holder) may be used to advantage, particularly for dotted lines. Third, ink the title box and all lettering; fourth, ink the coordinates with fine black lines, putting in only as many as are necessary for easy reading and breaking them wherever they interfere with title or lettering or where they cross plotted points.

20.20. Charts for Display. Large charts for demonstration purposes are sometimes required. These may be drawn on sheets 22 by 28 in. or 28 by 44 in. known as "printer's blanks." The quickest way to make them is with the show-card colors and single-stroke sign-writer's brushes. Large bar charts may be made with strips of black adhesive tape. Lettering may be done with the brush or with gummed letters.

PROBLEMS

The following problems are given as suggestive of various types for both technical and popular presentation.

20.1.1. In a tension test of a machine-steel bar the following data were obtained:

Applied load, lbs per sq in.	Elongation per in. of length
0	0
3,000	0.00011
5,000	0.00018
10,000	0.00033
15,000	0.00051
20,000	0.00067
25,000	0.00083
30,000	0.00099
35,000	0.00115
40,000	0.00134
42,000	0.00142

Plot the foregoing data on rectangular coordinates, using the elongation as the independent variable and the applied load as the dependent variable.

20.1.2. A test of the corrosive effect of 5 per cent sulfuric acid, both air-free and air-saturated, on 70 per cent nickel 30 per cent copper alloy (Monel) over a temperature range from 20 to 120°C resulted in the data tabulated below. Plot this data on rectangular coordinates with corrosion rate as ordinate versus temperature as abscissa.

| Temp., °C | Corrosion rate, MDD (mg per sq dm per day) | |
	Acid sat. with air	Acid air-free, sat. with N_2
20	195	35
30	240	45
40	315	50
50	425	63
60	565	70
70	670	74
80	725	72
83	715	70
85	700	68
92	580	57
95	470	42
101	60	12

20.1.3. In testing a small 1-kw transformer for efficiency at various loads, the following data were obtained: Watts delivered: 948, 728, 458, 252, 000. Losses: 73, 62, 53, 49, 47.

Plot curves on rectangular coordinate paper showing the relation between percentage of load and efficiency, using watts delivered as the independent variable and remembering that efficiency = output ÷ (output + losses).

20.1.4. The following data were obtained from a test of an automobile engine:

Rpm	Length of run, min	Fuel per run, lb	Bhp
1,006	11.08	1.0	5.5
1,001	4.25	0.5	8.5
997	7.53	1.0	13.0
1,000	5.77	1.0	16.3
1,002	2.38	0.5	21.1

Plot curves on rectangular coordinate paper, showing the relation between fuel used per brake horsepower-hour and brake horsepower developed. Show also the relation between thermal efficiency and brake horsepower developed, assuming the heat value of the gasoline to be 19,000 Btu per lb.

20.1.5. During the year 1950, the consumption of wood pulp by various grades in the United States was as follows:

Grade of pulp	Consumption in paper and board manufacture, tons
Sulfate	8,380,864
Sulfite	3,331,668
Groundwood	2,483,980
Defibrated, exploded, etc.	971,912
Soda	564,355
All other	754,331
Total (all grades)	16,487,110

Show these facts by means of a 100 per cent bar, a pie diagram, and a multiple-bar chart.

20.1.6. Put the data of Fig. 20.14 into 100 per cent bar form.

20.1.7. Put the data of Fig. 20.12 into pie-chart form.

20.1.8. A test of the resistance of alloy steels to high-temperature steam resulted in the data tabulated below. Represent the results of the test graphically by means of a multiple-bar chart.

CORROSION OF STEEL BARS IN CONTACT WITH STEAM AT 1100°F FOR 2,000 Hr

Steel	Average penetration, in.
SAE 1010	0.001700
1.25 Cr-Mo	0.001169
4.6 Cr-Mo	0.000956
9 Cr 1.22 Mo	0.000694
12 Cr	0.000045
18-8-Cb	0.000012

20.1.9. From the data below, plot curves showing the "thinking distance" and "braking distance." From these curves, plot the sum curve "total distance." Title "Automobile Minimum Travel Distances When Stopping—Average Driver."

Mph	Ft per sec	Thinking distance, ft	Braking distance, ft
20	29	22	18
30	44	33	40
40	59	44	71
50	74	55	111
60	88	66	160
70	103	77	218

20.1.10. Make a semilogarithmic chart showing the comparative rate of growth of the five largest American cities from 1880 to 1950. Data for this chart are given below:

POPULATION

City	1880	1890	1900	1910
New York, N.Y.	1,911,698	2,507,414	3,437,202	4,766,883
Chicago, Ill.	503,185	1,099,850	1,698,575	2,185,283
Philadelphia, Pa.	847,170	1,046,964	1,293,697	1,549,008
Los Angeles, Calif.	11,181	50,395	102,479	319,198
Detroit, Mich.	116,340	205,876	285,704	465,766

City	1920	1930	1940	1950
New York, N.Y.	5,620,048	6,930,446	7,454,995	7,835,099
Chicago, Ill.	2,701,705	3,376,438	3,396,808	3,606,436
Philadelphia, Pa.	1,823,779	1,950,961	1,931,334	2,064,794
Los Angeles, Calif.	576,673	1,238,048	1,504,277	1,957,692
Detroit, Mich.	993,678	1,568,662	1,623,452	1,838,517

20.1.11. On polar coordinate paper, plot a curve for the first set of data given below as a solid line (Fig. 20.8) and a curve for the second set as a broken line (Fig. 20.7). The lower end of the vertical center line is to be taken as the zero-degree line. The curves will be symmetrical about this line, two points being plotted for each angle, one to the left and one to the right. Mark the candle power along this center line also.

Angle, °	(1) Mazda lamp and porcelain enameled reflector, candle power	(2) Type S-1 sun lamp, candle power	Angle, °	(1) Mazda lamp and porcelain enameled reflector, candle power	(2) Type S-1 sun lamp, candle power
0	600	1,000	50	785	130
5	655	925	55	740	120
10	695	790	60	640	0
15	725	640	65	485	—
20	760	460	70	330	—
25	800	350	75	200	—
30	815	260	80	90	—
35	825	205	85	25	—
40	830	170	90	0	—
45	815	150			

20.1.12. On trilinear coordinate paper plot the data below. Complete the chart, identifying the curves and lettering the title below the coordinate lines (Fig. 20.9).

FREEZING POINTS OF SOLUTIONS OF GLYCEROL AND METHANOL IN WATER

Water	Weight, per cent Methanol	Glycerol	Freezing points, °F	Water	Weight, per cent Methanol	Glycerol	Freezing points, °F
86	14	0	+14	55	0	45	− 4
82	8	10	+14	54	28	18	−40
78	6	16	+14	53	47	0	−58
76	24		− 4	52	10	38	−22
74	2	24	+14	50	20	30	−40
71	17	12	− 4	47	31	22	−58
70	0	30	+14	45	0	55	−22
68	32	0	−22	42	7	51	−40
65	10	25	− 4	39	12	49	−58
62	23	15	−22	37	0	63	−40
60	40	0	−40	36	8	56	−58
58	5	37	− 4	33	0	67	−58
57	17	26	−22				

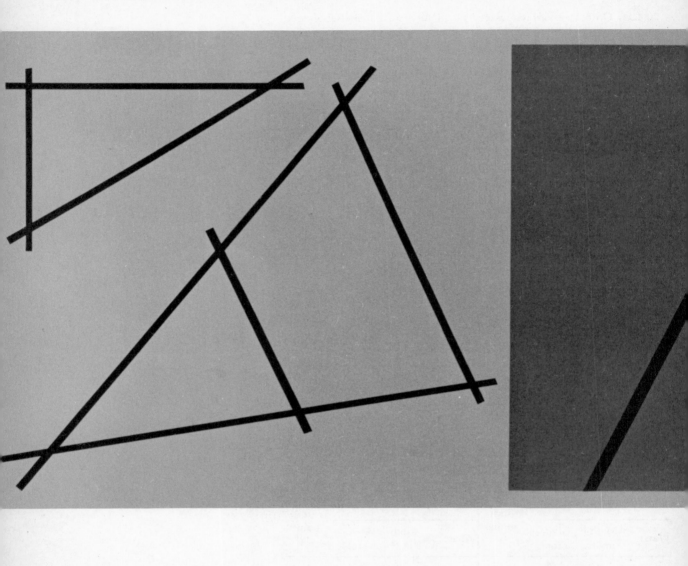

21

GRAPHICAL SOLUTIONS

21.1. In almost every phase of engineering endeavor, there is the necessity of making calculations in the research, in the preliminary and final design of products, and in the operation, adjustment, and stabilization of manufacturing processes. In all these activities, algebraic methods may be employed. Nevertheless, graphical methods will in many cases (and especially when recurring calculations of the same nature must be made) reduce the time involved, minimize the occurrence of errors, and give a visual conception of the relationship of variables.

At the outset, it must be said that one can add, subtract, multiply, divide, calculate powers and roots, etc., quite as easily graphically as algebraically. Further, whenever a mathematician, scientist, or engineer needs to visualize the relationship of variable quantities, the accepted method and the first move toward understanding will be to make a rectilinear plot of the associated items. These items may be either from experimental data or from a mathematical equation. One has only to glance through a text on analytic geometry to realize the value of plotting a relationship on rectilinear or other coordinates.

From the foregoing, it should be evident that the rectilinear chart (described previously in Chap. 20) is a very basic and powerful tool. The following paragraphs will show how rectilinear, oblique, and logarithmic plots may be employed to solve arithmetic and algebraic problems.

603

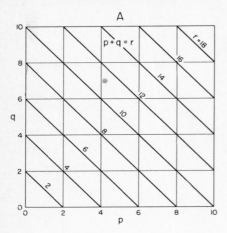

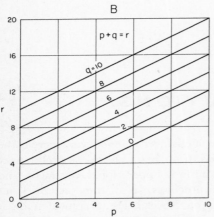

Fig. 21.1. Addition and subtraction.

21.2. Graphical Accuracy. The accuracy of any graphical solution will depend principally on the size of the chart, graph, or diagram used and on the care and precision with which it is drawn. To make a comparison, a slide rule is a series of graphical scales, arranged for multiplication, etc. The scales are very carefully and accurately divided by the manufacturer on precision machines made for the purpose. A draftsman cannot hope to plot points on a graph or locate lines on a chart to compare with the accuracy of a slide-rule scale. Nevertheless, if the accuracy, say, of a 10-in. slide rule would be sufficient for a certain type of calculation, a chart of possibly two or three times the size of the slide rule, prepared with light carefully drawn lines, will have a comparable accuracy. Also, in many cases, the complete logarithmic-cycle length (again comparing with the slide rule) would not be needed so that the increased size would not be difficult to obtain.

Problems where absolute numerical accuracy is needed are seldom solved either on a slide rule or graphical chart. For example, calculation of money owed is figured to the penny. But in a wide variety of problems involving capacity, mechanical or electrical efficiency, rate, velocity, acceleration, etc., a tolerance is allowable, and a graphical chart can be made with readable accuracy well within the tolerance.

The cardinal points, then, in preparing a graphical chart are:

1. Determine some reasonable tolerance for the answer.
2. Design the size of the chart so that the tolerance is attainable.
3. Lay out the scales or lines with care, being especially precise where there may be critical points or difficult intersections.
4. Draw the chart with light, crisp lines, being very careful to keep straight lines straight and to have curves pass through all plotted points on the curve.
5. Check the chart for accuracy at selected points.

21.3. Graphical Addition and Subtraction. An equation stating the relationship of three variables may be represented on rectangular coordinates as a family of straight or curved lines. Two of the variables will plot as coordinates along the axes, and the third as parameters.[1] When the function is either addition or subtraction, the family of lines (parameters) will be straight and parallel to each other. This may be demonstrated by plotting an equation such as $p + q = r$, as shown in Fig. 21.1A. If one of the variables (p) is plotted on the X axis and the other (q) on the Y axis, the sum of the two will be represented by a series of parameters (r). To make the plot, one may take arbitrary values of p and q and plot the parameter r for these values. Thus $p = 4$ and $q = 6$ locate $r = 10$ at the intersection of coordinates. Also, $p = 8$ and $q = 2$ give $r = 10$, another point on the parameter $r = 10$. A third point for $r = 10$ will show

[1] The term "parameter" is here used in the graphical sense that a parameter is a *line* of constant value representing the locus of a mathematical constant.

that the parameter is a straight line. It is now noticed that the parameter $r = 10$ connects $p = 10$ on the X axis with $q = 10$ on the Y axis. Therefore, all parameters will pass through their own value on X and Y axes and may now be drawn in without further plotting of points. To prove this fact, note that the intercepts on the X axis of the parameters will all be for $q = 0$, and on the Y axis for $p = 0$.

The same chart may be used for subtraction by simply rewriting the equation $p + q = r$ in the form $p = r - q$ or $q = r - p$. For subtraction, then, one coordinate and the parameters are used as the two variables for which the sum is wanted. For $r - q = p$, the sum will then be read on the X axis.

A chart such as Fig. 21.1B employs the parameters for one of the variables for which the sum, with another variable, is wanted. In this case, for $p + q = r$, values of p are plotted on the X axis, values of q are the parameters, and the sum r is plotted on the Y axis. Again, as in Fig. 21.1A, two or three random values of p and q (or p and r, solving for q) may be selected and points on the parameter plotted. Then, noticing that the parameter passes through its own value on the Y axis, all parameters may then be drawn in and their value marked.

To use Fig. 21.1B for subtraction, the equation may be rewritten to $r - q = p$. Then the coordinate line for a value of r, intersecting the parameter line for a value of q, locates the coordinate line on which the sum p will be read.

Plots such as Fig. 21.1A and B are often called "network charts."

21.4. Addition and Subtraction of Three or More Variables. Network charts may be combined in various ways to add or subtract three or more variables. Figure 21.2 will illustrate the basic method of combination. A chart such as Fig. 21.1, as described, will handle the relationship of three variables; but when a fourth is added, the limitations of the chart are exceeded. Therefore, for the equation $p + q + r = s$ of Fig. 21.2, an adjustment in the equation must be made. If the equation is split by the introduction of a term

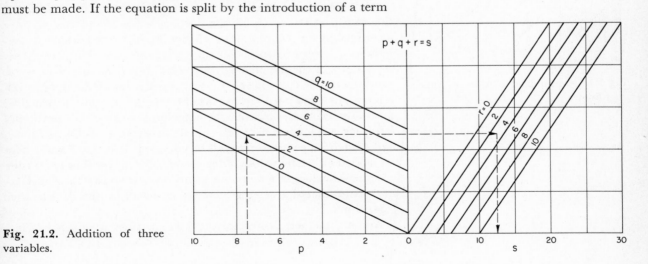

Fig. 21.2. Addition of three variables.

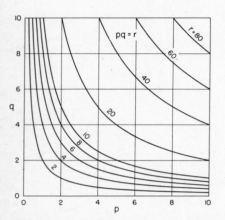

Fig. 21.3. Multiplication on rectilinear coordinates.

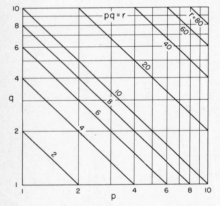

Fig. 21.4. Multiplication on logarithmic coordinates.

y, equal to the sum of two of the variables, two parallel-line network charts will result. Thus, for $p + q + r = s$, the equation is rewritten to $p + q = y$ and $y + r = s$, resulting in the two charts shown in Fig. 21.2.

Because values of y for both equations must be equal, the two charts are placed side by side. Values of y need not be calibrated on the completed chart but will be needed in making the chart. First, values of p are laid off on the X axis (in this case, from right to left). Next, temporary values of y are laid off on the Y axis, and the parameters representing values of q are plotted and drawn, as in Fig. 21.1B. Then, using y values and values of s (on the X axis), parameters are drawn for values of r. In using the chart, y values are simply projected across from the left side of the chart to the right, as shown by the dotted line, where $p = 7.5$, $q = 2$, $r = 3$, and then the sum $s = 12.5$.

A similar chart may be made for subtraction of one or two of the variables, either $p + q - r = s$ or $p - q - r = s$. In the first case, the left side of the chart would remain the same and the right side would take the form of Fig. 21.1B but, probably, reoriented so that both plus and minus values could be obtained. Note, in Fig. 21.1B, that the parameters progress from 0, the opposite direction from the parameters on the right side of Fig. 21.2, so that, in Fig. 21.1B, $r - q = p$; and the chart could then be employed as the right side of Fig. 21.2 but for subtraction. For $p - q - r = s$, both sides of the chart would be altered, the left side now taking the form of the right side of Fig. 21.2.

If more than three variables are to be added or subtracted, other terms such as y will have to be introduced and the equation rewritten. For example, for four terms, the equation $p + q + r + s = t$ would be rewritten to $p + q = y$, $y + r = z$, and $z + s = t$, thus obtaining data to plot three separate charts relating three variables, which could then be combined into a composite chart.

21.5. Graphical Multiplication and Division. The multiplication of two variables to obtain a third, $pq = r$, when plotted on uniform rectangular coordinates with the product r as parameter, results in a series of hyperbolic curves, as shown in Fig. 21.3. The asymptotes of the hyperbolas will be the X and Y axes. This is, of course, a usable chart for $pq = r$, but the plotting of the hyperbolas is laborious—and not nearly so accurate as the plotting of straight-line parameters. If, however, the equation is written in logarithmic form, $\log p + \log q = \log r$, the equation becomes one of addition, and straight-line parameters will be obtained. Values of p and q can be plotted either by values of $\log p$ and $\log q$ on rectilinear coordinates or as values of p and q on logarithmic coordinates, as in Fig. 21.4. Note that the spacing of the parameters in Fig. 21.4 is also logarithmic.

Another method of multiplying two variables is shown in Fig.

21.5A. If one of the variables, in this case, q, is plotted as a series of parameters on uniform rectangular coordinates, the product is then one of the coordinate values, and the parameters will be straight lines. The construction of the chart will be indicated by a study of Fig. 21.5A.

The concurrent straight lines of Fig. 21.5A, representing the equation $pq = r$, may be plotted on oblique coordinates as shown in Fig. 21.5B. In this case, the coordinates of p are the oblique lines, q is represented as parameters, and the coordinates of r are rectangular. It is also possible to make both coordinates of p and r oblique, although there would be little reason for doing so.

Division of variables may be accomplished by rewriting the equation and employing the chart accordingly. In Fig. 21.5A, if the equation $pq = r$ is rewritten to $q = r/p$ then values of r and p on the chart intersect to locate the quotient q.

21.6. Multiplication of Three Variables. Three variables may be multiplied to obtain a fourth by combining two concurrent-line network charts. In Fig. 21.6, the equation of four variables $pqr = s$ is rewritten, by the introduction of a term y, as two equations of three variables, $pq = y$ and $yr = s$. This results in two charts, similar to Fig. 21.5A, combined to represent $pqr = s$, as shown in Fig. 21.6. The left side of the chart is the representation of $pq = y$. The uncalibrated y scales of both halves run vertically. Thus y values carried over by horizontal projection now intersect values of r (parameters). A vertical projection now locates the coordinate value of s. The dotted line on Fig. 21.6 indicates values of $p = 8.5$, $q = 8$, $r = 10$, and the product $s = 680$. Each half of the chart is plotted separately, the left half for $pq = y$ and the right half for $yr = s$. The origin of both charts, at the center on the X axis, will of course be zero for all values.

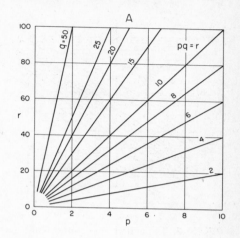

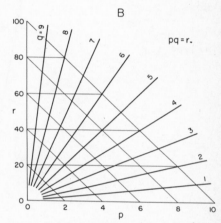

Fig. 21.5. Multiplication (A) with parameters representing a variable and (B) on oblique coordinates.

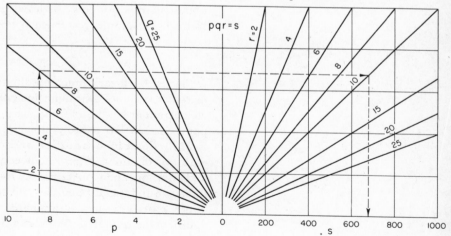

Fig. 21.6. Multiplication of three variables.

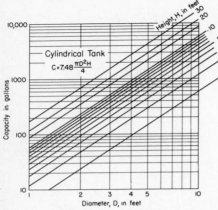

Fig. 21.7. Capacities of cylindrical tanks.

A practical example of the multiplication of three variables is given in Fig. 21.7, where the capacities of cylindrical tanks are determined by the equation

$$C = 7.48 \, \frac{\pi D^2 H}{4}$$

where C = capacity, gal
   7.48 = gal per cu ft
   D = diameter, ft
   H = height, ft

Combining constants, the equation is

$$C = 5.88 D^2 H$$

and in logarithmic form, it is

$$\log C = \log 5.88 + 2 \log D + \log H$$

Instead of determining logarithms of the variables and plotting on uniform coordinates, it will be more convenient to plot on logarithmic coordinates. Therefore, in Fig. 21.7, capacity (C) is graduated from 10 to 10,000 on the Y axis and diameter (D) on the X axis. Height (H) will then be a series of straight-line parameters. The constant 5.88 applies only to shift the parameters. To plot the parameter, for example, of $H = 2$, assume a diameter (D) of 10. Then $C = 5.88 \times 100 \times 2 = 1,176$, one point on parameter $H = 2$. A second point for $H = 2$ when $D = 2$ gives $C = 5.875 \times 4 \times 2 = 47.0$. A line now connecting points $D = 10$ and $C = 1,175$ and $D = 2$ and $C = 47.0$ locates the parameter $H = 2$. The other parameters may be plotted in the same manner, but it will be noticed that the parameters are spaced logarithmically. Thus if $H = 1$ and $H = 10$ are located, the other parameters may be located by dividing the distance between $H = 1$ and $H = 10$ logarithmically.

21.7. Powers and Roots. A network chart may be employed to obtain powers or roots by drawing parameters for the powers or roots. For example, $y = x^a$ when rewritten in logarithmic form becomes

$$\log y = a \log x$$

Plotted on logarithmic coordinates for both x and y, the power or root a becomes a straight-line parameter with positive slope and concurrent at $x = 1$ and $y = 1$. Because of the concurrency, only one point need be located to plot each parameter.

21.8. Combined Addition and Multiplication. Network charts may be combined to represent equations involving both addition and multiplication of terms. As an example, exhaust systems installed in industrial plants for the collection and removal of dusts, fumes, mists, or other contaminants may include canopy hoods. The approximate quantity of air that must be exhausted from a canopy hood, without flanges, to produce a desired capture velocity at a point of fume or dust origin is given by the equation

$$Q = V(10x^2 + A)$$

where Q = quantity of air, cu ft per min
  V = air-capture velocity, at point of capture, ft per min
  X = distance from face of hood to point of capture on center line of hood, ft
  A = area of hood opening, sq ft

If x is expressed in inches, the equation becomes

$$Q = V(^{10}\!/_{144}x^2 + A)$$

or

$$= V(0.0694x^2 + A)$$

Now, by the introduction of a term y, where y replaces $0.0694x^2 + A$, two equations will be obtained:

$$y = 0.0694x^2 + A$$

and

$$Q = Vy \quad \text{or} \quad y = \frac{Q}{V}$$

Two charts can now be prepared, as in Fig. 21.8, with identical y scales (uncalibrated) oriented so that they run vertically and adjacent to one another.

The left half of the chart for $0.0694x^2 + A = y$ will have the x scale plotted as a power scale (squares). To plot a scale of squares, $x = 1$ is plotted at one unit, $x = 2$ at four units, $x = 3$ at nine units, and so on. This is necessary since the function of x is x^2. When x is plotted as a power scale, the parameters for A will then be straight and the y scale will be uniform. In order to plot the parameters for A, a temporary y scale is set up on the vertical axis. For the right half of the chart, representing $y = Q/V$, the standard multiplication form as in Fig. 21.5A is employed—this time for division. With Q plotted on uniform coordinates on the horizontal axis and with y on the vertical axis, V then becomes a series of parameters concurrent at

$$Q = 0, y = 0$$

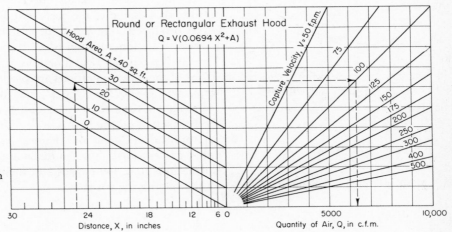

Fig. 21.8. Combined addition and multiplication.

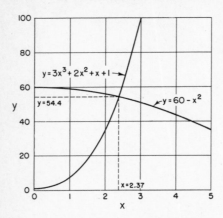

Fig. 21.9. Solution of simultaneous equations.

A test line is shown on the chart. For a distance of 25 in. from a hood of 20 sq in., a volume of air of 6,300 cu ft per min will be required to maintain a capture velocity of 100 ft per min. The possibilities for use of the chart should now be evident. For instance, if the quantity Q is known and the capture velocity V is decided, the size of the hood A and distance from the hood x can now be designed, etc.

21.9. Simultaneous Equations. Any single equation relating two variables will be satisfied by an indefinite number of pairs of the variables; but if two equations relating two variables are available, there will be a definite number of pairs of the variables that will satisfy both equations. The number of solutions will depend upon the form of the equations and whether or not minus values are considered.

The solution of simultaneous equations can be and often is done algebraically; but in cases where the data are empirical (and no mathematical equation can be written), the algebra fails completely. Also, in many cases where the equations are complicated—especially when they are in cubical, logarithmic, or power form—the algebraic solution may be very complicated and time-consuming. For these reasons and because of the advantage of having a graphical record of the relationship, it may be desirable to solve the problem graphically.

Figure 21.9 shows the solution of a pair of simultaneous equations by graphical means. Each equation is plotted separately as shown. The single point (in this case) where the curves coincide will be a point common to the locus of both equations and will therefore give x and y values that will satisfy both equations. The values of x and y obtained by graphical means may not perfectly satisfy the equation; but if a tolerance, as explained in paragraph 21.2, is applicable for the conditions, the graphical method will be quite satisfactory.

21.10. Addition and Subtraction of Functions. It is often necessary to add (or subtract) two or more functions of a variable quantity. For example, in determining total cost of a product, raw material, labor, tooling, factory overhead, etc., all combine to make up the total. Some of the costs may be constant for the number of pieces produced; others may be variable. The locus of the total-cost curve will be the addition of all the individual functions. Thus in Fig. 21.10, having two functions $y_1 = 20 - 0.24x$ and $y_2 = 10 + 0.01x^2$, if these two equations are plotted as shown, the graph of the total, $y_3 = 30 - 0.24x + 0.01x^2$, may be had by graphically adding the y value of each curve at a number of values of x, as indicated by the brackets A on the figure.

Graphical addition of functions (on uniform rectilinear coordinates, as described) has the distinct advantage over mathematical calculations that, for purposes of analysis, a true representation of all the relationships is shown.

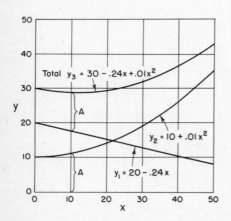

Fig. 21.10. Addition of functions.

PROBLEMS

Prepare network charts to represent the equations in Groups 1, 2, and 3. Where the range of a variable is not indicated, limiting values are to be determined by substitution in the equation. Coordinate scales are to be appropriately graduated and calibrated, and each is to have a legend indicating the quantity represented and the unit of measurement. Network lines are to be similarly identified. Each chart is to have a descriptive title that includes the chart equation.

Group 1. Addition and subtraction

21.1.1. Equation. $2p + q = r$ $\begin{aligned} 0 &< p < 10 \\ 0 &< q < 25 \\ 0 &< r < 40 \end{aligned}$

21.1.2. Equation. $3p + q = 50 - r$ $\begin{aligned} 0 &< p < 10 \\ 0 &< q < 20 \\ 0 &< r < 45 \end{aligned}$

21.1.3. Air flow.

$$TP = SP + VP$$

where TP = total pressure, in. water
SP = static pressure, 0 to 10 in. water
VP = velocity pressure, 0 to 2.5 in. water

21.1.4. Pressure conversion.

$$P_A = P_G + 0.49B$$

where P_A = absolute pressure, lb per sq in.
P_G = gage pressure, 0 to 25 lb per sq in.
B = barometric pressure, 28 to 32 in. mercury

21.1.5. Insulation. $T_M = \dfrac{T_H - T_C}{2}$

where T_M = arithmetic mean of temperature, °F
T_H = temperature, hot side, 200 to 1200°F
T_C = temperature, cold side, 80 to 200°F

21.1.6. Tube swaging.

$$L = 4.08(D_1 - D_2) + 0.13$$

where L = length of runout, 0 to 5 in.
D_1 = outside diameter of tube before swaging, $\frac{1}{4}$ to 4 in.
D_2 = outside diameter of tube after swaging, $\frac{3}{16}$ to 3 in.

Group 2. Multiplication and division

21.2.1. Equation. $2pq = r$ $\begin{aligned} 0 &< p < 10 \\ 0 &< q < 10 \\ 0 &< r < 50 \end{aligned}$

21.2.2. Equation. $\dfrac{pq}{2} = r - 10$ $\begin{aligned} 0 &< p < 10 \\ 0 &< q < 20 \\ 0 &< r < 50 \end{aligned}$

21.2.3. Ohm's law. $I = \dfrac{E}{R}$

where I = current, 0 to 10 amp
    E = voltage, 0 to 120 volts
    R = resistance, 1 to 20 ohms

21.2.4. Sharp-crested submerged rectangular weir.

$$Q = 3.33BH^{1.5}$$

where Q = discharge, cu ft water per sec
    B = width, 1 to 10 ft
    H = head above sill, 0.5 to 2 ft

21.2.5. Dry air. $D = \dfrac{P}{0.754(T + 460)}$

where D = density, lb per cu ft
    P = absolute pressure, 16 to 30 in. mercury
    T = temperature, −40 to 180°F

21.2.6. Air ducts.

$$D = 1.075\sqrt{WH}$$

where D = diameter of equivalent round duct, in.
    W = width of rectangular duct, 10 to 100 in.
    H = height of rectangular duct, 5 to 50 in.

Group 3. Combined networks

21.3.1. Equation.

$$2p + q = r + s$$

$0 < p < 10$
$0 < q < 40$
$0 < r < 30$
$0 < s < 20$

21.3.2. Equation.

$$pq = r + 4s$$

$0 < p < 10$
$0 < q < 10$
$0 < r < 40$
$0 < s < 5$

21.3.3. Equation.

$$pq = rs^2$$

$1 < p < 10$
$1 < q < 15$
$1 < r < 10$
$1 < s < 4$

21.3.4. Joggle in sheet-metal flange.

$$A = 0.27(4.3D + R + T)$$

where A = joggle-relief encroachment, in.
    D = joggle depth, 0 to 0.5 in.
    R = flange-bend radius, 0 to 1.0 in.
    T = sheet-metal thickness, 0 to 0.20 in.

21.3.5. Spherical pressure vessel. $S = \dfrac{PD}{4T}$

where S = circumferential stress, lb per sq in.
    P = internal pressure, 0 to 250 lb per sq in.
    D = internal diameter, 5 to 25 in.
    T = shell thickness, 0.2 to 1.0 in.

21.3.6. Pipe insulation. $B = \dfrac{0.38L}{DT}$

where B = applied cost, dollars per board ft

    L = applied cost, 0.50 to 10.00 dollars per lin ft

    D = outside diameter of insulation, 3 to 20 in.

    T = thickness of insulation, 1 to 5 in.

21.3.7. Moist air.

$$D = 1.326 \left(\frac{B - 0.38W}{T + 460} \right)$$

where D = density, lb per cu ft

    B = barometric pressure, 28 to 32 in. mercury

    W = water-vapor pressure, 0 to 3 in. mercury

    T = temperature, 40 to 140°F

21.3.8. Sheet-metal bend.

$$B = A(0.0175R + 0.0078T)$$

where B = bend allowance, in.

    A = angle through which sheet metal is bent, 0 to 120°

    R = bend radius, 0 to 2.0 in.

    T = sheet-metal thickness, 0 to 0.25 in.

Group 4. Roots of equations

21.4.1. Solve graphically for the roots of the quadratic equation

$$x^2 - 4.2x + 2.5 = 0$$

21.4.2. Solve graphically for the roots of the equation

$$0.25x^2 - 1.85x^{0.7} + 1 = 0$$

21.4.3. Solve graphically for the square root of 7.55. (*Hint.* Solve for the roots of the equation $x^2 - 7.55 = 0$.)

Group 5. Simultaneous equations

21.5.1. Solve simultaneously, by graphic means, the two equations

$$y = 0.5x^2 \qquad y = x + 1.7$$

21.5.2. Solve simultaneously, by graphic means, the two equations

$$y = e^x \qquad y = 10 - 0.4x$$

Group 6. Addition of functions

21.6.1. Plot graphically the equation $y = e^x + x^{2.5}$ for values of x from 0 to 5. Values of e^x and $x^{2.5}$ are given in the table for various values of x.

21.6.2. The annual fixed costs for insulating a certain steam-pipe installation can be expressed as $C_F = 35S + 40$ in dollars per year, where S is the thickness of insulation in inches. The annual cost of heat lost from the installation can be expressed as $C_H = 105/S$ in dollars per year. Plot the total annual cost $C_F + C_H$ for values of S from 0 to 6 in., and determine the optimum thickness of insulation.

21.6.3. A quantity, A, is equal to the sum of two components, B and C, which vary with time, T. Values of B and C, measured experimentally at various time values, are given in the table. Determine graphically the maximum value of A and the time at which it occurs.

x	e^x		x	$x^{2.5}$
0	1.00		0	0
0.8	2.23		1.0	1.00
1.6	4.95		2.0	5.65
2.6	13.5		2.5	9.86
3.2	24.5		3.0	15.6
3.9	49.4		3.5	22.9
4.4	81.5		4.0	32.0
4.8	121.5		4.5	43.0
5.0	148.4		5.0	53.0

T	B		T	C
0	3.0		0	4.4
1.5	1.6		2.0	5.8
2.8	1.1		3.8	6.8
3.5	1.2		5.0	7.0
4.6	1.6		6.0	6.8
6.5	2.4		7.2	6.5
8.0	3.1		8.6	5.4
10.0	4.0		10.0	4.2

22

FUNCTIONAL SCALES

22.1. The scale is a fundamental element of the graphic language. In the previous chapters, the types and uses of standard drafting scales have been given, and their employment in problems of ortho-graphic-projection drawing, pictorial drawing, dimensioning and working drawings, engineering geometry, and vector geometry and for charts, graphs, and diagrams has been discussed. In fact, the engineer, architect, and others use graphical scales repeatedly and extensively in the layout of drawings and in the measurement of distances resulting from some graphical construction. But the full importance of graphical scales is realized only when the many other uses of them are known.

In the previous chapter, on graphical solutions, when values representing a variable quantity were laid off on X or Y axes, the representation is actually a graphical scale which shows numerical values of a variable quantity. The engineer's slide rule, a general-purpose instrument, and the many special-purpose calculators used in the design and selection of industrial equipment are made up entirely of graphical scales. Every chart, graph, or diagram will be constructed by using a scale or scales and may have one or more scales as a component part. Many devices in common daily use, such as the clock, thermometer, radio dial, etc., employ scales for measurement or for adjustment.

For the construction of nomographic charts in Chap. 23, a knowledge of graphical scales is absolutely necessary.

615

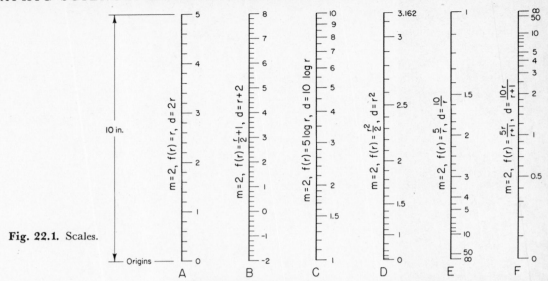

Fig. 22.1. Scales.

22.2. Definition. A scale may be defined as a straight or curved line on which is located a series of marks corresponding to values of a variable quantity. The straight or curved line is known as the *stem*. The marks are *graduations* and correspond graphically to values of the function of the variable quantity represented. Some of the graduations will be identified by numerical values, *calibrations*, which either increase or decrease along the stem. All scales have a beginning point, or *origin*, from which all other points (graduations) are located. Distances measured away from the origin in the direction which is considered to be positive make distances negative from the origin in the opposite direction.

Figure 22.1 shows several examples of scales on which the stem, graduations, and calibrations may be identified.

22.3. Classification. Based on the function of the variable quantity represented and subsequently on the manner in which the scale is constructed, scales may be classified as either uniform or nonuniform.

A *uniform scale* is one representing a linear function and will therefore have graduations that are evenly spaced. The numerical values corresponding to the graduations will increase or decrease by equal increments. The distance from the origin to each graduation is proportional to the value represented. Figure 22.1*A* and *B* shows uniform scales.

A *nonuniform* scale is one representing any nonlinear function and will therefore have graduations that are unevenly spaced, which *represent* equal increments of numerical value. Moreover, numerical values corresponding to the graduations will often increase or decrease by unequal increments. The distance from the origin to each graduation is *not* proportional to the value represented, but is related to the *function of the variable*. Figure 22.1*C* to *F* shows nonuniform scales. Study these scales carefully.

22.4. The Scale Equation. A function of a variable quantity is a mathematical expression which has a definite value or set of values for each specific value of the quantity. Thus the expressions $2r + 1$, $\log r$, r^2, $\sin r$, $1/r$, etc., are functions of the variable r.

A straight scale may be graduated by the equation

$$d = mf(r)$$

where d is a distance on the scale from the origin, representing a specific value of a variable r. All finite distances on the scale stem correspond to some value of the variable. A multiplying factor, or modulus, m is a constant introduced to control the needed or necessary length of the scale. $f(r)$ is a function of a variable r.

Distance (d) along the scale, measured from the origin (as can be seen from the scale equation), is the product of modulus times function. This distance, for any particular value of r, the variable, may be measured in any convenient units, usually centimeters or inches. Various values of the variable are chosen, inserted in the equation, and plotted (measured) along the stem of the scale, thus locating graduations. A convenient way to accomplish the work is to make a table for needed values:

Values r	Function $f(r) = 2r - 1$	Modulus m	Distance d
1	1	2	2
2	3	2	6
3	5	2	10
4	7	2	14
⋮	⋮	⋮	⋮

Modulus (m) is simply a constant *introduced into the equation* to control the length of scale required to represent a given range of values of the variable. Modulus may be defined as the increment of scale length corresponding to a unit change *in the value of the scale function.*[1] Thus, in the preceding table, if the modulus is changed to a value of unity, distances along the scale would then be 1, 3, 5, and 7 for values of r of 1, 2, 3, and 4. A modulus of 3 would give distances of 3, 9, 15, and 21. We see, then, that the modulus will control the distance, along the scale, of the graduations representing values of r and will, therefore, for a particular set of values, control the length of the scale.

Range (R) is the difference between extreme (maximum and minimum) values of the scale function. For values of r in the preceding table from 1 to 4 for the function $2r - 1$, the range is, then,

$$R = (2 \times 4 - 1) - (2 \times 1 - 1) = 6$$

Thus we see that, without a modulus or multiplying factor, the

---

[1] Modulus is a constant in the scale *equation* and is *not* a multiplier in the scale proper, except by application through the scale equation. In the opinion of this author, any consideration of "scale modulus" will serve only to make for confusion.

range of the scale would be the *length* in whatever units are used for measurement.

Length (L) of a scale is the product of the scale range R and the modulus m. Therefore, in the previous example for a range of 1 to 4 for the function $2r - 1$ and a modulus of 2, the length is

$$L = mR \qquad \text{or} \qquad L = 2 \times 6 = 12$$

Scale length, modulus, and range are, of course, unchangeably related to each other by the equation $L = mR$. Therefore, for a certain specified range, an *assumed modulus* will determine the scale length or an *assumed length* will determine the modulus. For example, in a scale representing the function $\log r$, to be calibrated with values of r from 2 to 10, the range is

$$R = \log 10 - \log 2 = 0.699 \text{ units}$$

Assuming a modulus for this logarithmic scale of 10 in. per unit, the length of scale is

$$L = 10 \times 0.669 = 6.99 \text{ in.}$$

Assuming a scale length of 4 in., the modulus then is

$$m = \frac{L}{R} = \frac{4}{0.669} = 5.964$$

which is the length of one logarithmic cycle.

As will be seen later, in Chap. 23 on nomography, in some cases the scale length may be decided for convenience or reasonable size and the modulus then calculated, or in other cases the modulus (necessary or assumed) will determine the scale length.

The origin of a scale either may or may not appear on the actual scale. The origin is the point where the value of the function is zero. Therefore for the functions r^2, $2r$, etc., where, if the variable is zero, the function is also zero, the origin is at $r = 0$. For a logarithmic scale, however, when $r = 1$, $\log r = 0$, and the origin is therefore at the graduation $r = 1$.

For a scale function of, say, $d = 2r$, for a range of 6 to 16, the scale will begin with the value of $r = 6$, and the origin will not appear on the scale.

Notice that the function has no bearing whatever on whether or not the origin will appear on the scale; the range is the only determining factor.

Several examples of functional scales are shown in Fig. 22.1. It will be advantageous for the student to note and calculate or check distance d, modulus m, range R, length L, and *origin* in every case. Also note that only portions of the scales are shown and that they could be extended either in a positive or negative direction to cover a wider range of values.

22.5. To Graduate and Calibrate a Scale. In general, a scale is graduated by substitution of a number of values of the variable quantity into the scale equation; the several solutions of the equation then give distances along the stem to locate scale graduations. The following example will explain the procedure:

Assume a scale function of $f(r) = r/2 + 1$ for a scale of 10 in. in length, representing values of r from -2 to $+8$, as in Fig. 22.1B. The range is, then,

$$R = f(r)_{max} - f(r)_{min} = \left(\frac{8}{2} + 1\right) - \left(\frac{-2}{2} + 1\right) = 5.0$$

The modulus is

$$m = \frac{L}{R} = \frac{10}{5} = 2$$

The scale equation then becomes

$$d = 2\left(\frac{r}{2} + 1\right)$$

Assuming that graduations are needed for each 0.2 of the variable, substitution in the equation may now be made to locate the graduations. A convenient way to do this is to prepare a table of calculations, as follows:

SCALE EQUATION $d = 2\left(\frac{r}{2} + 1\right)$

r	$r/2 + 1$	$= f(r)$	$m = 2$	$= d$
-2.0	$-2/2 + 1$	0	2	0
-1.8	$-1.8/2 + 1$	0.1	2	0.2
$\vdots$	$\vdots$	$\vdots$	$\vdots$	$\vdots$
0	$0/2 + 1$	1	2	2.0
$\vdots$	$\vdots$	$\vdots$	$\vdots$	$\vdots$
0.2	$0.2/2 + 1$	1.1	2	2.2
0.4	$0.4/2 + 1$	1.2	2	2.4
$\vdots$	$\vdots$	$\vdots$	$\vdots$	$\vdots$
2	$2/2 + 1$	2	2	4
$\vdots$	$\vdots$	$\vdots$	$\vdots$	$\vdots$
8	$8/2 + 1$	5	2	10.0

Distances from the table, in inches, then laid off on the scale stem will locate all graduations. The calibrations may then be located in the most convenient manner for reading the scale.

Note in this case that the origin of the scale is at $r = -2$, where the value of the function $r/2 + 1$ is zero.

The above table of calculations could have been simplified by combining constants in the scale equation. Thus $d = 2(r/2 + 1)$, simplified to $d = r + 2$, gives a table as follows:

SCALE EQUATION $d = r + 2$

r	$r + 2$	$= d$
-2	$-2 + 2$	0
-1.8	$-1.8 + 2$	0.2
$\vdots$	$\vdots$	$\vdots$
0	$0 + 2$	2
$\vdots$	$\vdots$	$\vdots$

A

B

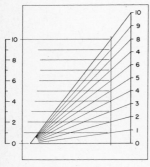

C

Fig. 22.2. Graphical graduation of scales.

The previous table, however, was given to indicate the fundamental operations and to show how modulus is employed.

This is the fundamental method of scale layout. The procedure is the same no matter what the function and (subsequently) the scale equation.

Further examples will help in demonstrating the basic facts presented thus far.

The function for scale c of Fig. 22.1 is $5 \log r$. The scale length is 10 in. The variable is calibrated from $r = 0$ to $r = 10$. Therefore,

$$R = f(r)_{max} - f(r)_{min} = 5 \log 10 - 5 \log 1 = 5 - 0 = 5$$

also,

$$m = \frac{L}{R} = \frac{10}{5} = 2$$

Then

$$d = 2 \times 5 \log r = 10 \log r$$

A table for calculations will show:

SCALE EQUATION $d = 10 \log r$

r	$\log r$	$10 \log r$
1	0	0
2	0.30103	3.0103
$\vdots$	$\vdots$	$\vdots$
5	0.69897	6.9897
$\vdots$	$\vdots$	$\vdots$
10	1.0000	10.0000

It is now evident from the table that the scale may be plotted by using a 10-in. logarithmic cycle, for $10 \log 1 = 0$ and $10 \log 10 = 10$.

In some cases, especially in the construction of nomographic charts (Chap. 23), it may be necessary to start with a known modulus m and *then* determine either the scale length or the range from the relationship $m = L/R$. In Fig. 22.1D, assume that $m = 2$ and $L = 10$ in. are previously determined. Then

$$R = \frac{L}{M} = \frac{10}{2} = 5$$

also,

$$R = f(r)_{max} - f(r)_{min} \quad \text{and} \quad f(r) = \frac{r^2}{2}$$

Therefore, if the scale is to start at the origin, where $f(r) = 0$,

$$R = f(r)_{max} - 0 \quad \text{and} \quad 5 = \left(\frac{r^2}{2}\right)_{max}$$

Then

$$r^2{}_{max} = 10 \quad \text{and} \quad r_{max} = 3.162$$

Now that the maximum value on the scale has been calculated, all necessary items are known. The scale may be plotted as described before by calculating the position of the necessary graduations.

Good technique and extreme accuracy are essential in scale layout. Scale construction involves initially a decision as to which points are to be marked, that is, the degree of subdivision. Points are marked with fine lines, $\frac{1}{16}$ to $\frac{3}{16}$ in. in length, at right angles to the stem, principal graduations having longer marks to distinguish them. Graduations should, in general, not be closer together than $\frac{1}{16}$ in. It is also necessary to determine which of the graduations are to be calibrated. It is desirable that numerical values run in systematic fashion. Sufficient values must be provided to ensure ready identification of all points on the stem. The manner of subdivision should not change between calibrated graduations, and the beginning and end of the scale should be identified by numerical value.

22.6. Graphical Methods of Graduating a Scale. It is not always necessary to graduate a scale as described in paragraph 22.5. A scale representing any linear (first-degree) function will plot with uniformly spaced graduations. Therefore, for any uniform scale, if the length and range are known, the stem can be divided graphically into equal parts to locate the graduations. In some cases, as indicated in Fig. 22.2*A*, the graduations may match the divisions on a standard machine-divided engineer's scale of decimal parts, and the graduations thus can be laid off directly. In other cases, where the divisions of some standard scale do not match the needed number of uniform parts, a standard scale may still be employed as at Fig. 22.2*B*. This is the familiar method of dividing a line into a number of equal parts. A uniform *modulus chart*, Fig. 22.2*C*, may also be used. This is a chart made by drawing rays from points on a uniformly divided line to a concurrent point, as shown. Then uniform divisions on a line of any length may be had by locating a line of the needed length that intersects the rays, as indicated by the example on Fig. 22.2*C*.

A *modulus chart* may also be used to divide a logarithmic scale. An example of such a chart is shown in Fig. 22.3. In this case, a logarithmic scale with rays from the graduations to a concurrent point may be used in the manner explained for Fig. 22.2*C*, to locate graduations on a logarithmic scale of any length. Actually, in one respect, a logarithmic scale is uniform because cycles are of equal length, and they repeat.

Modulus charts may also be prepared for power (or root) scales by employing the desired scale in place of the logarithmic scale of Fig. 22.3.

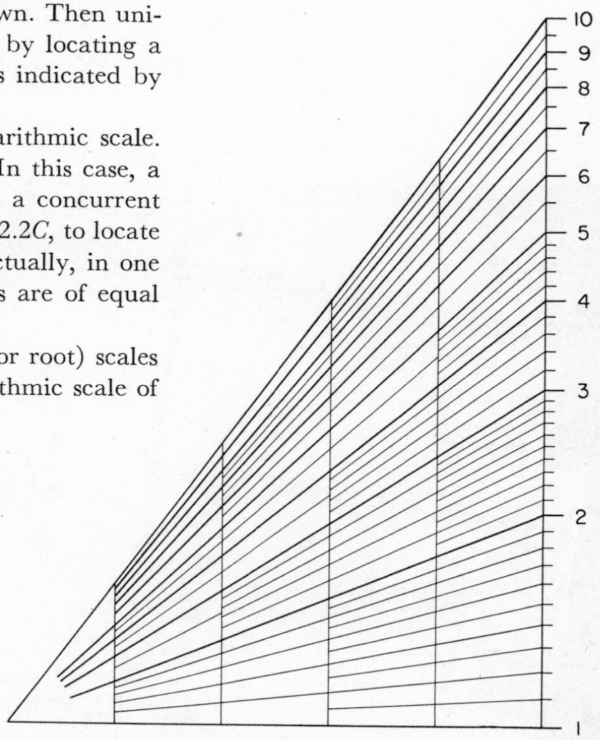

Fig. 22.3. A logarithmic modulus chart.

22.7. Parallel Scales. Parallel scales provide graphic counterparts of many algebraic processes. With fixed scales, mathematical equalities may be represented. When one or more of the scales is made so that it can be moved relative to another scale or scales, addition and subtraction, multiplication and division, the determination of powers and roots, and combinations of these processes can be accomplished.

22.8. Equalities. A mathematical equality is an expression in which the function of one variable is equal to the function of another variable. Mathematically, $f(v) = f(g)$. Therefore, if an equation can be solved for one variable in terms of the other—in other words, all terms containing each one of the variables placed on opposite sides of the equation—the relationship may be represented graphically by constructing a scale for each variable on opposite sides of the same stem. To demonstrate this, take two standard drafting scales, one fractional (sixteenths) and the other decimal (tenths), and place them side by side as in Fig. 22.4. This, graphically, will provide a method of converting from fractional parts of an inch to decimal parts. Any equivalent of some fraction may be read on the decimal scale, and, conversely, any equivalent of a decimal may be read on the fractional scale. Scales thus arranged represent a mathematical equality and are called *conversion scales.*

To show this mathematical equality, the two functions may be equated to each other. Let F be the value of the fraction in sixteenths and D the decimal value in tenths. The equation would then be

$$f(F) = f(D)$$

and, by proportion,

$$\frac{F}{16} = \frac{D}{10} \qquad \text{or} \qquad F = 1.6D$$

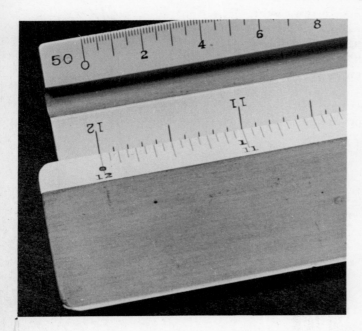

Fig. 22.4. Illustration of equality (conversion scales).

The origin of both scales will be at the same point because, when $f(F)$ is zero, $f(D)$ is also zero.

The length of both scales may be taken as 1 in., considering that this length then repeats.

Therefore, for the F scale,

$$f(F) = F$$
$$L = 1 \text{ in.} \qquad R = f(F)_{max} - f(F)_{min} = 16 - 0 = 16$$
$$m = \frac{L}{R} = \frac{1}{16} = 0.0625$$

For the D scale,

$$f(D) = 1.6D$$
$$L = 1 \text{ in.} \qquad R = f(D)_{max} - f(D)_{min} = 1.6 \times 10 - 1.6 \times 0 = 16$$
$$m = \frac{L}{R} = \frac{1}{16} = 0.0625$$

It is now seen that the modulus (m) for both scale *equations* is identical. Equationally, this means that $mf(F) = mf(D)$. Note that no equality could otherwise exist. This will always be necessary if the scales are to be an equality relationship on the same stem. Also note that the ranges for both functions are identical.

The scale equation for F is

$$d = 0.0625F$$

and for the D scale,

$$d = 0.0625 \times 1.6D = 0.1D$$

A table for each scale would show:

F SCALE			D SCALE	
F	$d = 0.0625F$		D	$d = 0.1D$
1	0.0625		1	0.1
2	0.1250		2	0.2
3	0.1875		3	0.3
⋮	⋮		⋮	⋮
16	1.0000		10	1.0

The student is urged to put two drafting scales together as suggested and to study the relationships of the divisions on each. Then reread whatever portions of this paragraph are necessary to firmly fix the following important points: (1) The mathematical equality is $f(F) = f(D)$. (2) The origin, mathematically and on the two scales, is at the same point. (3) The modulus is identical for both functions.

An example of the construction of a pair of conversion scales may be illustrated by Fig. 22.5. The equation relating the variables is $p = 2q + 4$. The functions are, then,

$$f(p) = p \qquad f(q) = 2q + 4$$

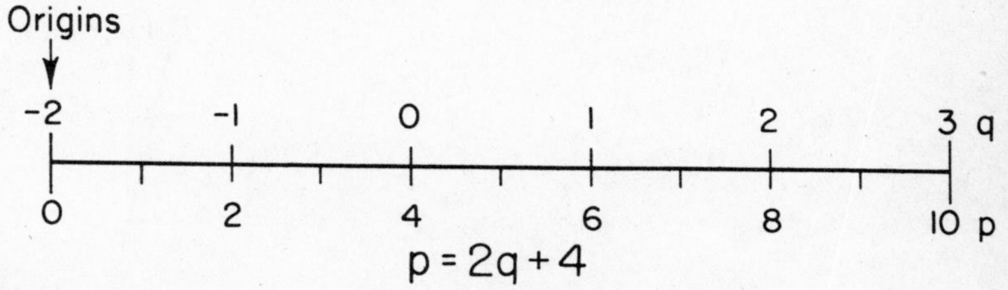

Fig. 22.5. Conversion scales (uniform).

Assume the scale length to be 10 in. The values of p vary from 0 to 10. The maximum and minimum values of the q scale can then be calculated.

$$q = \frac{p - 4}{2}$$

$$q_{max} = \frac{10 - 4}{2} = 3 \qquad q_{min} = \frac{0 - 4}{2} = -2$$

Then, for the p scale, $f(p) = p$:

$$L = 10 \qquad R = 10 - 0 = 10$$

$$m = \frac{L}{R} = \frac{10}{10} = 1$$

For the q scale, $f(q) = 2q + 4$:

$$L = 10 \qquad R = 2 \times 3 + 4 - (2 \times -2 + 4) = 10$$

$$m = \frac{L}{R} = \frac{10}{10} = 1$$

The scale equations are, then,

$$d_p = p \qquad d_q = 2q + 4$$

Tables for each are:

p SCALE				q SCALE	
p	$d_p = p$	p	$d_p = p$	q	$d_q = 2q + 4$
0	0	6	6	-2	0
1	1	7	7	-1	2
2	2	8	8	0	4
3	3	9	9	1	6
4	4	10	10	2	8
5	5			3	10

Measurements then made, in inches, from an origin (in this case at the left) will locate distances along the stem for the graduations of both scales.

Another example is shown in Fig. 22.6. The equation is $p = 4q^2$, and in logarithmic form is $\log p = 2 \log q + \log 4$. Therefore,

$$f(p) = \log p$$
and
$$f(q) = 2 \log q + \log 4$$

Assume the length of the scales to be 10 in. Also assume that values of p are to vary from 1 to 10. The maximum and minimum values of the q scale can then be calculated.

$$\log q = \frac{\log p - \log 4}{2}$$

$$\log q_{max} = \frac{1 - 0.60206}{2} = 0.19897$$

$$\log q_{min} = \frac{0 - 0.60206}{2} = -0.30103$$

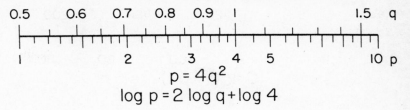

Fig. 22.6. Conversion scales (logarithmic).

$$p = 4q^2$$
$$\log p = 2 \log q + \log 4$$

Then, for the p scale, $f(p) = \log p$:

$$L = 10 \qquad R = \log 10 - \log 1 = 1 - 0 = 1$$
$$m = \frac{L}{R} = \frac{10}{1} = 10$$

and for the q scale, $f(q) = 2 \log q + \log 4$:

$$L = 10$$
$$R = 2 \times 0.19897 + 0.60206 - (2 \times -0.30103 + 0.60206)$$
$$= 1 - 0 = 1$$
$$m = \frac{10}{1} = 10$$

Thus we see again that the modulus of both functions will be identical. The modulus for a logarithmic function will be the length of one logarithmic cycle. This is so because the difference in logarithmic value for one cycle is unity.

The scale equations are, for the p scale,

$$d_p = 10 \log p$$

and for the q scale,

$$d_q = 10(2 \log q + \log 4)$$
$$d_q = 20 \log q + 10 \log 4$$

Now, we see that a 20-in. logarithmic cycle will be used to graduate the q scale. However, in order to orient the scales properly, the origins must match. The origin on either scale is where the function is zero. Therefore, for the p scale,

$$f(p) = \log p$$

Origin, for p, is $f(p) = 0$; therefore

$$\log p = 0 \qquad p = 1$$

For the q scale,

$$20 \log q + 10 \log 4 = 0$$
$$\log q = \frac{-10 \log 4}{20} = \frac{-10 \times 0.60206}{20}$$
$$= -0.30103 \qquad \text{also} \qquad 9.69897 - 10$$
$$q = 0.5$$

Thus a 20-in. logarithmic cycle beginning at 0.5 for the q scale and a 10-in. logarithmic cycle beginning at 1.0 for the p scale will be used to graduate the scales.

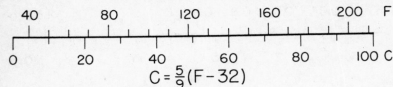

Fig. 22.7. Conversion scales (temperature, degrees centigrade to degrees Fahrenheit).

$$C = \frac{5}{9}(F - 32)$$

Another example will assist in establishing the facts of scale construction and of graphical and mathematical equalities. Figure 22.7 is a conversion scale for the familiar centigrade-to-Fahrenheit temperature conversion. The equation relating the variables is $°C = \frac{5}{9}(°F - 32)$. Assume a scale length of 10 in., and assume that the centigrade scale is to be graduated from 0 to 100°. Then, for the C scale,

$$f(C) = C$$
$$L = 10 \text{ in.} \qquad R = 100 - 0 = 100$$
$$m = \frac{10}{100} = 0.1$$
$$d_C = 0.1C$$

and for the F scale,

$$f(F) = \frac{5}{9}(F - 32)$$
$$L = 10 \text{ in.}$$
$$F_{\max} = \frac{9}{5} \times 100 + 32 = 212 \qquad F_{\min} = \frac{9}{5} \times 0 + 32 = 32$$
$$R = f(F)_{\max} - f(F)_{\min} = \frac{5}{9}(212 - 32) - \frac{5}{9}(32 - 32) = 100 - 0 = 100$$
$$m = \frac{10}{100} = 0.1$$
$$d_F = 0.1 \times \frac{5}{9}(F - 32) = 0.0556(F - 32)$$

Tables can now be made to plot both scales:

C SCALE		D SCALE	
C	$d_C = 0.1C$	F	$d_F = 0.0556(F - 32)$
0	0	32	0
1	0.1	33	0.0556
2	0.2	34	0.1112
3	0.3	⋮	⋮
⋮	⋮	40	0.4448
10	1.0	⋮	⋮
⋮	⋮	120	4.8928
50	5.0	160	7.1168
⋮	⋮	⋮	⋮
100	10.0	200	9.3408
		⋮	⋮
		212	10.00

It will be noticed that both scales are uniformly divided. Therefore, if preferred, the two scales can be prepared by graphically

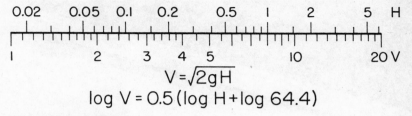

Fig. 22.8. Conversion scales (velocity, head in feet to feet per second).

$$V = \sqrt{2gH}$$
$$\log V = 0.5(\log H + \log 64.4)$$

dividing the C scale into 100 parts and the F scale into 180 parts.

The equation of Fig. 22.8 converts velocity head of a liquid, H, in feet, to velocity in feet per second. The quantity g is acceleration due to gravity (32 ft per sec²). In this case, the equation is converted to logarithmic form, and the procedure for laying out the scales would be as described for Fig. 22.6. Because $f(V) = 2 \log V$ and $f(H) = 0.5 (\log H + \log 64.4)$, both V and H scales will be logarithmic. There are cases, however, when one of the scales cannot be logarithmic because of the conditions under which the chart must be used. Figure 22.9 illustrates a case where one scale must be uniform.

The velocity of air in the ducts of heating, ventilating, and exhaust systems is often indicated by pitot-tube readings, which measure velocity pressure as the difference between total and static pressure. The manometer tube, inclined for greater accuracy, provides readings in inches of water (gage). A conversion scale affixed to the tube to allow velocity readings to be made directly in feet per minute requires a uniform velocity-pressure scale. The equation for the relationship, shown in Fig. 22.9, for air at standard conditions (70°F, 29.92 in. mercury, and 13.33 cu ft per lb) is $P = (V/4{,}005)^2$.

The velocity-pressure scale P is to be 6 in. long and is to vary from 0 to 1.0. Therefore,

$$f(P) = P$$
$$R = 1 - 0 = 1$$
$$m = \tfrac{6}{1} = 6$$

The scale equation is then $d_p = 6P$.

As explained for the examples of Figs. 22.5 to 22.7, the modulus of both functions must be the same. Therefore, the scale equation for V is $d_V = 6(V/4{,}005)^2$.

Substitution of values of V, from 0 to 4,000, in this equation will give distances to plot the V scale. A typical distance for $V = 3{,}400$ is shown on the V scale. The calculation is

$$d_V = 6\left(\frac{3{,}400}{4{,}005}\right)^2 = 6 \times 0.849^2 = 6 \times 0.721 = 4.32$$

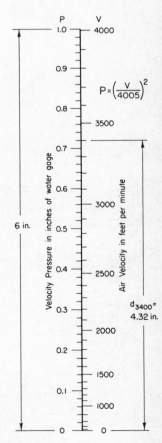

Fig. 22.9. Conversion scales (one scale necessarily uniform).

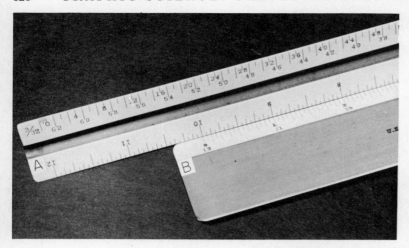

Fig. 22.10. Illustration of sliding scales.

22.9. Sliding Scales. If one of a pair of scales is made so that it can be moved relative to the other scale, the graphical counterpart of addition, subtraction, multiplication, division, and combinations of these processes can be accomplished. This is the principle upon which all slide rules are based.

To demonstrate the use of sliding scales, take a pair of standard drafting scales, as indicated in Fig. 22.10, and place them as shown with the origin (zero) of one scale (B) indexed (mated) with some division of the other scale (A). Then some distance on scale B will match a graduation on scale A, and the reading here will be the difference of the two distances selected. Addition would be just the reverse of the above procedure.

The principles just presented are shown graphically in Fig. 22.11. At (A) a pair of scales have been laid out with their origins in coincidence. This is the arrangement for equality, as explained in paragraph 22.8. Now, if one scale is made movable as at (B), distances on the scales representing values of a variable may be added or subtracted. In Fig. 22.11B, one scale has been laid out on both the upper and lower portions of the body of the rule, for the distances a and c shown. The scale for distance b has its origin shown by the arrow. Thus a distance a, added to distance b, now has its sum, distance c, on the upper scale. These distances represent numerical values of a variable, and $a + b = c$. For subtraction, $c - b = a$.

By adding another scale on the slide (replacing the index of Fig. 22.11B), as shown in Fig. 22.11C, four factors may be handled by equating the sum of two distances to the sum of two others. Thus in Fig. 22.11C, it can be seen that $a - c = d - b$, from which, algebraically, we have $a + b = c + d$.

Study the illustrations carefully, noting in each case the relationships of distances added or subtracted.

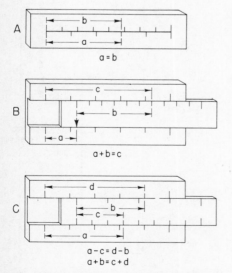

Fig. 22.11. Sliding scales for addition and subtraction.

22.10. Construction of Slide Charts for Addition and Subtraction. Slide charts for addition and subtraction employ two fixed scales and a slide with a third scale and index arrow to solve equations of the form $f(p) + f(q) = f(r)$. All scale equations have the same modulus. The three scale origins and the index arrow orient all scales and for this reason are usually aligned as in Fig. 22.12.

The example of Fig. 22.12 is for addition of three functions where $f(p) = p$, $f(q) = 2q$, $f(r) = r - 4$, and $f(p) + f(q) = f(r)$. Assume the length of the scales to be 10 in. and that p is to vary from 0 to 10. Then, for the p scale,

$$f(p) = p$$
$$L = 10 \qquad R = 10 - 1 = 10$$
$$m = {}^{10}\!/_{10} = 1$$
$$d_p = p$$

The modulus of all scale equations must be the same. Therefore, the scale equation for the q scale is

$$d_q = 2q$$

and for the r scale,

$$d_r = r - 4$$

The origin for any scale is the point at which the function is zero. Therefore, the origin for p is

$$f(p) = p = 0$$

For q the origin is

$$f(q) = 2q = 0$$

and for r,

$$f(r) = r - 4 = 0 \qquad \text{and} \qquad r = 4$$

All scales are now oriented with their origins in alignment and the scales graduated as described in paragraph 22.5. An example of a typical solution of $p + 2q = r - 4$ is shown in Fig. 22.12B.

The order of scales on the slide chart is not necessarily that shown in Fig. 22.12. Scale positions on the chart of Fig. 22.13A are altered from those of Fig. 22.11B by inversion of the slide. Addition of two distances, a and b, to obtain a third distance, c, is still possible. In addition, scale origins and index arrow need not be aligned. Thus in Fig. 22.13B, the offset, e, between the scale measurements, a and

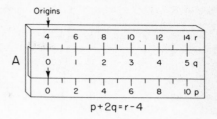
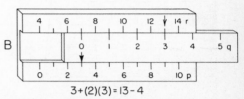

Fig. 22.12. Sliding scales for addition of three functions.

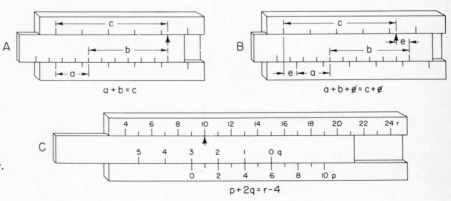

Fig. 22.13. Location of index arrow.

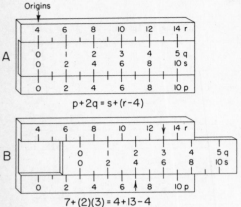

Fig. 22.14. Sliding scales for four functions.

c, is compensated for by a shift in the position of the index arrow. Therefore, in the design of the slide chart of Fig. 22.13C, for the equation $p + 2q = r - 4$ the three scales are conveniently positioned in the horizontal direction and the index arrow located by a trial solution. All three scale equations have identical moduli. Note, for example, that in Fig. 22.13C $p = 4$ and $q = 1$ and also $p = 6$ and $q = 0$ satisfy the equation.

Slide charts of the type illustrated in Fig. 22.14 employ two fixed scales and a slide with two scales to solve equations of the form $f(p) + f(q) = f(r) + f(s)$. Again, all scales will have the same modulus, and in this case, the origins are aligned. Figure 22.14 illustrates a slide chart made for the equation $p + 2q = s + r - 4$. A sample solution is shown at (B). The scales would be constructed in the manner described for Fig. 22.12.

A practical example of a slide chart for addition is shown in Fig. 22.15. The minimum thread depth for tapped holes in aluminum is given by the expression $C = 2D + 4/n$, where C is the thread depth in inches, D equals the major diameter of thread, and n is the number of threads per inch. Note that this chart is of the form of Fig. 22.11B with the exception that the pitch scale (n) increases in value from right to left. This is because the function of n is reciprocal, $4/n$. The apparent complication of this chart is superficial and is caused only by the complication of numerical values, not by chart form. When analyzed from the standpoint of Fig. 22.11B, where $a + b = c$, and Fig. 22.15, $2D + 4/n = C$, the real simplicity will be evident.

22.11. Construction of Slide Charts for Multiplication and Division. When an expression for multiplication, for example, $pq = r$, is written in logarithmic form, the equation becomes that of addition, $\log p + \log q = \log r$. It is evident, then, that, when the logarithms of numbers are added, the numbers are multiplied. It therefore follows that, if the logarithms are plotted on graphical scales, the addition of scale distances will multiply the values on the scales.

The construction of graphical scales for multiplication is therefore the same as for addition, as described in paragraph 22.10, with the exception that the scales must be made logarithmic. This is the method of construction for all standard slide rules.

Figure 22.16 illustrates a slide chart made for the expression $pq^2 = 0.2r$. When this expression is written logarithmically, it becomes

$$\log p + 2 \log q = \log r - \log 5$$

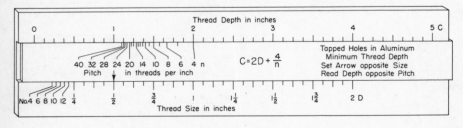

Fig. 22.15. A slide chart for minimum thread depth.

The slide chart will have to add the logarithms, and therefore the mathematical expression of the scales will be $f(p) + f(q) = f(r)$. The logarithmic equation may then be divided into

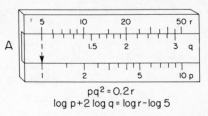

$$f(p) = \log p$$
$$f(q) = 2 \log q$$
$$f(r) = \log r - \log 5$$

As before, the length of the scale and the variation of the quantity must be assumed for one variable. Assume that p is to vary from 1 to 10 and that the scale length is 10 in.

Then for the p scale,

$$f(p) = \log p$$
$$L = 10 \qquad R = \log 10 - \log 1 = 1$$
$$m = {}^{10}\!/_1 = 10$$
$$d_p = 10 \log p$$

Therefore, a 10-in. logarithmic cycle will be used to plot the p scale.

The modulus of all scale equations must be the same, giving for the q scale

$$f(q) = 2 \log q$$
$$d_q = 10 \times 2 \log q$$
$$= 20 \log q$$

A 20-in. logarithmic cycle will be used to plot the q scale.

For the r scale,

$$f(r) = \log r - \log 5$$
$$d_r = 10(\log r - \log 5)$$
$$= 10 \log r - 10 \log 5$$

A 10-in. logarithmic cycle will be used to plot the r scale.

The origins are where the functions are zero:

$$f(p) = \log p = 0 \qquad \text{and} \qquad p = 1$$
$$f(q) = 2 \log q = 0 \qquad \text{and} \qquad q = 0$$
$$f(r) = \log r - \log 5 = 0$$
$$\log r = \log 5 \qquad \text{and} \qquad r = 5$$

Now all the scales may be oriented with their origins in alignment, and the scales may be plotted as described in paragraph 22.5.

A sample calculation is shown in Fig. 22.16B, where $p = 2$, $q = 2$, and $r = 40$, giving proof that $2 \times 2^2 = 0.2 \times 40$.

As described before for addition, if the index is replaced by a fourth scale so that there are two scales on the body and two on the slide, expressions of the form $f(p) + f(q) = f(r) + f(s)$ may be solved. In Fig. 22.17, the logarithmic expression is

$$\log p + 2 \log q = \log s + \log r - \log 5$$

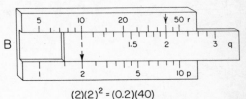

pq² = 0.2r
log p + 2 log q = log r − log 5

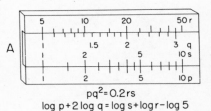

(2)(2)² = (0.2)(40)

Fig. 22.16. Sliding scales for multiplication.

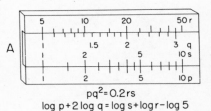

pq² = 0.2rs
log p + 2 log q = log s + log r − log 5

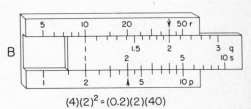

(4)(2)² = (0.2)(2)(40)

Fig. 22.17. Sliding scales for multiplication of four functions.

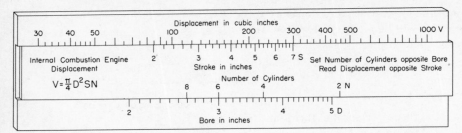

Fig. 22.18. A slide chart for displacement of an internal-combustion engine.

which, divided into functions, is

$$f(p) = \log p$$
$$f(q) = 2 \log q$$
$$f(s) = \log s$$
$$f(r) = \log r - \log 5$$

The construction of this slide chart will be identical with that of Fig. 22.16, except that the additional s scale must be oriented and constructed. A sample solution of $pq^2 = 0.2rs$ is shown in Fig. 22.17B, where $p = 4$, $q = 2$, $r = 40$, and $s = 2$.

A practical example of a four-scale slide chart for multiplication is shown in Fig. 22.18, where the formula for the displacement of an internal-combustion engine is

$$V = \frac{\pi D^2 SN}{4}$$

where V = displacement, cu in.

S = stroke, in.

N = number of cylinders

D = bore of cylinders

By combining constants in the equation, we obtain

$$V = 0.7854 D^2 SN$$

Then, by transposing terms to get two variables on each side of the equation, we obtain

$$D^2 S = \frac{V}{0.7854N}$$

This equation written logarithmically gives

$$2 \log D + \log S = \log V - \log N - \log 0.7854$$

And we now have the equation in the form of the chart of Fig. 22.17. All scales can then be calculated, oriented, and plotted as described for Fig. 22.16. Note again that all scale equations must have the same modulus and must have their origins properly mated. In this case, the D scale will have a logarithmic cycle length twice that of the others because of the coefficient 2 in the equation.

PROBLEMS

Group 1

Plot straight functional scales, calibrated with appropriate values of the variable r and approximately 10 in. in length, to represent the following:

22.1.1. $f(r) = 6.5r$, $0 < r < 10$.
22.1.2. $f(r) = 0.4r^3 - 20$, $0 < r < 5$.
22.1.3. $f(r) = 8/r$, $1 < r < 50$.
22.1.4. $f(r) = 1 - \log r$, $1 < r < 10$.
22.1.5. $f(r) = r/(r-1)$, $2 < r < 20$.
22.1.6. $f(r) = r(r-1)$, $1 < r < 4$.

Group 2

Plot adjacent scales (conversion scale) to represent the following equations. Where the range of a variable is not indicated, limiting values are to be determined by substitution in the equation. Each scale is to be appropriately graduated and calibrated and is to bear a legend indicating the quantity represented and the unit of measurement. The chart is to have a descriptive title that includes the chart equation.

22.2.1. Pressure conversion.

$$P = 0.434H$$

where P = pressure, lb per sq in.
  H = head, 0 to 50 ft water

22.2.2. Flow conversion.

$$W = 500Q$$

where W = weight of water, lb per hr
  Q = volume of water, 0 to 50 gal per min

22.2.3. Fuel oil.

$$H = 18,300 + 40G$$

where H = heating value, Btu per lb
  G = API gravity, 10 to 34°

22.2.4. Low-pressure steam.

$$H = 1,050 + 0.473T$$

where H = heat content above water at 32°F, Btu per lb
  T = temperature, 200 to 500°F

22.2.5. Concrete.

$$S_{28} = S_7 + 30\sqrt{S_7}$$

where S_{28} = probable 28-day strength, lb per sq in.
  S_7 = 7-day test strength, 1,000 to 3,000 lb per sq in.

22.2.6. Heavy liquids, liquors, and acids.

$$B = 145 - \frac{145}{S}$$

where B = Baumé gravity, °
  S = specific gravity 60/60°F, 1.00 to 1.60.

22.2.7. Round brass bar stock.

$$W = 2.92D^2$$

where W = weight, lb per ft
D = diameter, 0 to 6 in.

22.2.8. Simple pendulum.

$$T = 2\pi \sqrt{\frac{L}{g}}$$

where T = period of oscillation, sec
L = centroidal distance, 0 to 10 ft
g = acceleration due to gravity, 32.2 ft per sec^2

22.2.9. Sharp-crested 90° V-notch weir.

$$Q = 2.5H^{2.5}$$

where Q = discharge (water), cu ft per sec
H = head above sill, 0.5 to 2.0 ft

22.2.10. Standard annealed copper wire.

$$L = \frac{3,000}{(10)S/10}$$

where L = breaking load, lb
S = wire size, 0 to 16 AWG

Group 3

Plot slide charts for solving the following equations. Each scale is to be appropriately graduated and calibrated and is to bear a legend indicating the quantity represented and the unit of measurement. The chart should have a descriptive title that includes the chart equation and instructions for operating the chart. Blanks may be prepared from heavy cardboard or wood and the scales affixed thereto.

22.3.1. Equation.

$$3p + q = r - 10 \qquad \begin{array}{c} 0 < p < 5 \\ 0 < q < 10 \\ 10 < r < 30 \end{array}$$

22.3.2. Lead storage cell.

$$E = 1.850 + 0.917(G - G_w)$$

where E = terminal voltage, 2.04 to 2.14 volts
G = specific gravity of electrolyte, 1.18 to 1.32
G_w = specific gravity of water at cell temperature, 0.98 to 1.00

22.3.3. Gear drive.

$$C = \frac{D_G + D_P}{2}$$

where C = center distance, 2 to 15 in.
D_G = gear-pitch diameter, 2 to 20 in.
D_P = pinion-pitch diameter, 2 to 10 in.

22.3.4. Equation.

$$p^2q = 0.5r \qquad \begin{array}{c} 1 < p < 5 \\ 1 < q < 50 \\ 2 < r < 200 \end{array}$$

22.3.5. Automobile.

$$S = VT$$

where S = distance traveled, 20 to 500 mi
       V = average speed, 20 to 60 mph
       T = elapsed time, 1 to 10 hr

22.3.6. Round air duct.

$$V = \frac{183Q}{D^2}$$

where V = average duct velocity, 1,000 to 6,000 ft per min
      Q = volume of air, 200 to 20,000 ft per min
      D = duct diameter, 4 to 40 in.

Group 4

Plot slide charts for solving the following equations. Each scale is to be appropriately graduated and calibrated and is to bear a legend indicating the quantity represented and the unit of measurement. The chart should have a descriptive title that includes the chart equation and instructions for operating the chart. Blanks may be prepared from heavy cardboard or wood and the scales affixed thereto.

22.4.1. Equation.

$$3p + q = r + 0.4s$$

$0 < p < 3$
$0 < q < 10$
$0 < r < 10$
$0 < s < 25$

22.4.2. Fuel combustion.

$$W = 11.5C + 4.3(8H - O)$$

where W = theoretical combustion (air), 5 to 15 lb per lb fuel
     C = weight of carbon, 0.40 to 0.95 lb per lb fuel
     H = weight of hydrogen, 0 to 0.15 lb per lb fuel
     O = weight of oxygen, 0 to 0.40 lb per lb fuel

22.4.3. Belt drive.

$$L = 1.57(D_1 + D_2) + 2C$$

where L = approximate length of belt, 25 to 200 in.
    D_1 = pitch diameter, large sheave, 2 to 48 in.
    D_2 = pitch diameter, small sheave, 2 to 24 in.
     C = center distance, 10 to 60 in.

22.4.4. Equation.

$$pq = 0.5rs^2$$

$1 < p < 10$
$1 < q < 10$
$2 < r < 20$
$1 < s < 3$

22.4.5. Cylindrical tank.

$$S = \frac{PD}{2T}$$

where S = circumferential stress, 200 to 20,000 lb per sq in.
     P = internal pressure, 10 to 250 lb per sq in.
     D = internal diameter, 6 to 36 in.
     T = wall thickness, 0.2 to 1.0 in.

22.4.6. Water pump.

$$B = \frac{QH}{39.6E}$$

where B = brake horsepower, 0.1 to 10
     Q = discharge, 10 to 200 gal per min
     H = head, 20 to 100 ft water
     E = efficiency, 40 to 80 per cent

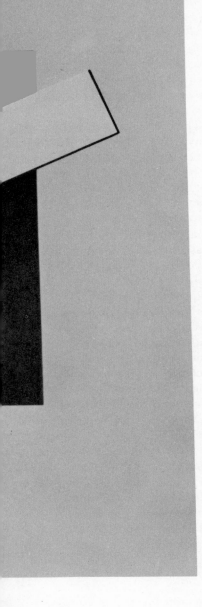

23

NOMOGRAPHY

23.1. Definition and Fundamental Considerations. The term "nomograph," literally a "written or graphic law," from the Greek *nomos*, law, and *graphos*, write, might properly be applied to any type of chart or graph. A nomograph, however, is usually defined as a particular type of chart composed of graduated scales and making use of simple graphic procedures for the solution of equations. These charts are also called "alignment" charts.

A nomographic conversion chart for an equation relating two variable quantities consists of two scales and a pivot point. A nomograph for an equation relating three variables consists of three scales. In each case, the solution of the equation can be effected by the drawing of a straight "tie line," or "join," to connect the scales. The basic two- and three-variable nomographs can be combined to give charts capable of representing relationships involving four or more variables.

The nomograph resembles the engineer's slide rule, which is also an arrangement of scales. The slide rule, however, is a general-purpose instrument for carrying out basic mathematical operations found in all types of problems, while a nomograph must be designed to fit a specific equation and is applicable only to that equation.

23.2. Advantages of the Nomograph. The gamut of engineering calculations ranges in difficulty from the extremely simple to the very complicated; in time consumed, from practically instantaneous to almost endless; and in frequency, from single determinations to operations that must be performed over and over again.

637

Of all calculations, the ones which must be often repeated are, as a class, the most irritating and monotonous and are, therefore, more susceptible to accidental error. In such circumstances, a nomograph can be very valuable since it (1) aids greatly in reducing the time needed for each determination, (2) helps to reduce the number of errors that may occur, and (3) has the advantage that a lower level of mathematical competence is required on the part of the person doing the work. Any one of these advantages may justify the time and expense involved in preparing the chart.

23.3. Construction Methods. The construction of a nomograph to represent a specific equation may follow any one of three slightly differing procedures, depending upon the form of the equation and the extent to which it is desired to become involved with theoretical considerations. In the case of certain equations involving simple addition or multiplication of terms, the nomograph can be constructed by laying out two scales of suitable form along parallel straight stems. Each scale is graduated in terms of one of the variables from the equation. The equation is solved mathematically to obtain sets of corresponding values of the three variables. Points on the third scale, which may be straight or curved, are then located graphically by the intersection of appropriate tie lines.

A second procedure differentiates between charts of different form, that is, parallel scales, concurrent scales, zee chart, etc., associating each with a particular type of equation. Each chart *form* is analyzed geometrically to establish rules for locating and graduating the scales. This method appears in practically all texts on nomography.

A third procedure involves writing the chart equation as a vanishing third-order determinant of special form. The elements of the determinant provide functions of each variable which enable the scales to be plotted in a coordinate system.

The design and construction of a nomograph require the expenditure of a certain amount of time and effort. The limitations on accuracy which are inherent in all graphic methods must be considered. Care must be employed in locating and graduating the scales in order to get the best possible accuracy obtainable.

23.4. Parallel-scale Conversion Chart. A relationship between two variable quantities can often be expressed by a conversion equation of the form

$$f_1(p) = f_2(q) \tag{1}$$

where $f_1(p)$ and $f_2(q)$ are each an algebraic function of a single variable. An equation of this type may be represented by a nomographic chart composed of two parallel straight scales and a pivot point. Each scale is calibrated with values of one of the variables. The unknown value of one of the variables corresponding to a specific value of the other is indicated by a straight line passing through the pivot and connecting the two scales.

The construction of a conversion chart is shown diagrammatically in Fig. 23.1. Two vertical scales, a p scale with a modulus m_1 and a q scale with a modulus m_2, are located a convenient distance apart. The two scales run in opposite directions from a base line joining their origins and are graduated according to the scale equations

$$d_p = m_1 f_1(p) \qquad d_q = m_2 f_2(q)$$

A straight line may be drawn to connect any two values, p^{*}[1] and q^*, on the two scales. The distance c on the p scale is equal to the product of the scale modulus and the value of the scale function,

$$c = m_1 f_1(p^*)$$

and, similarly, on the q scale,

$$e = m_2 f_2(q^*)$$

The tie line connecting p^* and q^* intersects the base line at point P to form two similar triangles in which corresponding sides and altitudes are in the same ratio, $c/e = a/b$. Substituting equivalent values for c and e,

$$\frac{m_1 f_1(p^*)}{m_2 f_2(q^*)} = \frac{a}{b}$$

whence $bm_1 f_1(p^*) = am_2 f_2(q^*)$. In order that this equation reduce to the original chart equation (1), the coefficients of the two terms must be equal:

$$bm_1 = am_2 \qquad \text{or} \qquad \frac{a}{b} = \frac{m_1}{m_2} \qquad (2)$$

Thus the pivot-point locations must be such that the distances a and b are in the same ratio as the moduli of the two scales.

It is often the case that scale origins are not to be included within the range of plotted scale values. Any tie line joining corresponding values of p and q may serve as a base line for the chart. The pivot point may be located on the base line by evaluating the a and b distances or by drawing a second tie line.

The conversion chart shown in Fig. 23.2 makes it possible to convert API gravity readings for light petroleum products to equivalent specific gravities. The conversion formula is

$$\text{Sp. gr.} = \frac{141.5}{°\text{API} + 131.5}$$

The term on the left side of the equation serves as the function of the uniform specific-gravity scale. Construction of the scale may be summarized as follows:

Function: sp. gr.
Range: $1.0 - 0.6 = 0.4$
Modulus: Assume 10
Length: $10 \times 0.4 = 4$ in.
Equation: $d_{\text{sp. gr.}} = 10$ sp. gr.

with positive scale *distance* increasing up the stem.

[1] In this chapter, an asterisked symbol represents a specific value of the variable.

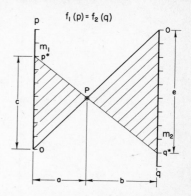

Fig. 23.1. A parallel-scale conversion chart.

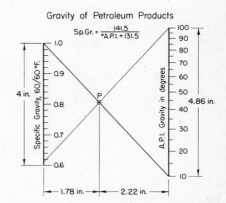

Fig. 23.2. A conversion chart (specific gravity to degrees API).

The expression on the right side of the equation is the function for the nonuniform API gravity scale. Construction of the scale may be summarized as follows:

Function: $\dfrac{141.5}{°\text{API} + 131.5}$

Range: $\dfrac{141.5}{10 + 131.5} - \dfrac{141.5}{100 + 131.5} = 1.0 - 0.611 = 0.389$

Modulus: Assume 12.5

Length: $12.5 \times 0.389 = 4.86$ in.

Equation: $d_{\text{API}} = 12.5 \dfrac{141.5}{°\text{API} + 131.5}$

with positive scale *distance* increasing down the stem. This is because of the reciprocal form of the function for degrees API (the origin is where $°\text{API} = \infty$).

The two scales are located parallel to one another and (arbitrarily) 4 in. apart. A specific gravity of 1.0 is equivalent to an API reading of 10°, and the straight line joining these values serves as a base line. The pivot point P is located on the base line by solving for distances a and b.

$$\frac{a}{b} = \frac{m_{\text{sp.gr.}}}{m_{\text{API}}} \qquad \text{or} \qquad \frac{a}{4 - a} = \frac{10}{12.5}$$

whence $a = 1.78$ in. and $b = 2.22$ in.

A second tie line indicates that an API reading of 100° is equivalent to a specific gravity of 0.611. This line may be used in place of distances a and b to locate the pivot point.

23.5. Parallel-scale Nomographs. Relationships between three variable quantities are often of such a nature that they can be expressed by equations of the form

$$f_1(p) + f_2(q) = f_3(r) \tag{3}$$

where $f_1(p)$, $f_2(q)$, and $f_3(r)$ are each an algebraic function of a single variable. This type of relationship may be represented by a nomographic chart of three parallel straight scales. Each scale is calibrated with values of one of the variables, and the scales are so located and graduated that a straight line cuts them at values of p, q, and r which satisfy the equation. The unknown value of any one of the variables may be determined by drawing a tie line to connect known values of the other two.

The construction of a parallel-scale chart is shown diagrammatically in Fig. 23.3. Two vertical scales, the p scale with a modulus m_1 and the q scale with a modulus m_2, are located at a suitable distance apart. The scales are graduated according to the scale equations

$$d_p = m_1 f_1(p) \qquad d_q = m_2 f_2(q)$$

A vertical scale for r is next located between the p and q scales at a distance a from the p scale and a distance b from the q scale. The

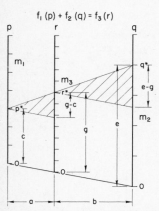

Fig. 23.3. Construction of parallel-scale chart.

origin of the r scale is located on a straight base line joining the origins of the p and q scales. The three points of origin satisfy the chart equation since, by definition, the origin of a scale is the point representing the zero value of the scale *function* and $0 + 0 = 0$.

Any straight line connects three values, p^*, q^*, and r^*, on the three scales. The distance c on the p scale is equal to the product of the scale modulus and the value of the scale function:

$$c = m_1 f_1(p^*)$$

and, similarly, on the q and r scales:

$$e = m_2 f_2(q^*) \qquad g = m_3 f_3(r^*)$$

Lines parallel to the base line form two similar triangles in which corresponding sides and altitudes are in the same ratio,

$$\frac{g - c}{e - g} = \frac{a}{b}$$

Substituting equivalent values for c, e, and g,

$$\frac{m_3 f_3(r^*) - m_1 f_1(p^*)}{m_2 f_2(q^*) - m_3 f_3(r^*)} = \frac{a}{b}$$

whence, collecting terms,

$$m_1 f_1(p^*) + \frac{a}{b} m_2 f_2(q^*) = \left(1 + \frac{a}{b}\right) m_3 f_3(r^*)$$

In order that this equation reduce to the original chart equation (3), the coefficients of the three terms must be equal:

$$m_1 = \frac{a}{b} m_2 = \left(1 + \frac{a}{b}\right) m_3$$

If the first two coefficients are equal, then

$$\frac{a}{b} = \frac{m_1}{m_2} \tag{4}$$

Thus *the location of the center scale must be such that the distances a and b are in the same ratio as the moduli of the two outside scales.* This is the first rule for the construction of the parallel-scale nomograph.

If the first and third coefficients are equal, then

$$m_1 = \left(1 + \frac{a}{b}\right) m_3 = \left(1 + \frac{m_1}{m_2}\right) m_3 \qquad \text{and} \qquad m_3 = \frac{m_1 m_2}{m_1 + m_2} \tag{5}$$

Thus *the center-scale modulus must equal the product of the two outside-scale moduli divided by their sum.* This is the second rule for the construction of the parallel-scale nomograph.

It is not necessary that the straight line connecting the scale origins be used as a base line for the vertical location of the r scale on its stem. In many cases, it is not desired to include the scale origins in the ranges of scale values. Any straight tie line joining values of p, q, and r that satisfy the chart equation may serve as a base line.

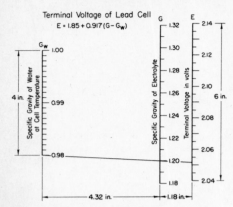

Fig. 23.4. A parallel-scale chart (for terminal voltage of lead cell).

The open-circuit voltage of the lead cell of a storage battery varies with the strength of the electrolyte and the temperature. The voltage may be determined by the formula

$$E = 1.85 + 0.917(G - G_w)$$

where E = terminal voltage, volts
       G = specific gravity of the electrolyte
       G_w = specific gravity of water at the cell temperature

The relationship may be represented by a parallel-scale nomograph. Construction of the chart, shown in Fig. 23.4, may be summarized as follows:

1. Chart equation from the above formula:

$$G_w + 1.09E = G + 2.02$$

2. Specific-gravity-of-water (G_w) scale:
   Function: G_w
   Range: $1.00 - 0.98 = 0.02$
   Length: Assume 4 in.

   Modulus: $\dfrac{4}{0.02} = 200$

   Equation: $d_{G_w} = 200G_w$

3. Terminal-voltage (E) scale:
   Function: $1.09E$
   Range: $1.09(2.14 - 2.04) = 0.109$
   Length: Assume 6 in.

   Modulus: $\dfrac{6}{0.109} = 55$

   Equation: $d_E = 55 \times 109E = 60E$

4. Specific-gravity-of-electrolyte (G) scale:
   Chart width: Assume 5.5 in.

   Scale spacing: $\dfrac{a}{b} = \dfrac{200}{55}$; and $a = 4.32$ in., $b = 1.18$ in.

   Function: $G + 2.02$
   Range: $1.32 + 2.02 - (1.18 + 2.02) = 0.14$

   Modulus: $\dfrac{200 \times 55}{200 + 55} = 43.1$

   Length: $43.1 \times 0.14 = 6.04$ in.
   Equation: $d_G = 43.1(G + 2.02) = 43.1G + 87.1$

5. Base line connects $G_w = 0.98$, $G = 1.20$, and $E = 2.052$.

An equation in three variables often involves the multiplication of two terms to obtain a third. The equation $f_1(p)f_2(q) = f_3(r)$ may be written in logarithmic form as

$$\log f_1(p) + \log f_2(q) = \log f_3(r)$$

and represented by a nomograph of three parallel logarithmic scales.

Both round and rectangular air ducts are used in industrial and home heating-and-ventilating systems. The formula for determining the diameter of a round duct equivalent in terms of air-carrying capacity to a rectangular duct is

$$D = 1.075\sqrt{WH}$$

where D = diameter of round duct, in.
$\quad\quad W$ = width of rectangular duct, in.
$\quad\quad H$ = height of rectangular duct, in.

Construction of the chart in Fig. 23.5 to represent the above relationship may be summarized as follows:

1. Chart equation from the above formula:

$$0.5 \log W + 0.5 \log H = \log D - \log 1.075$$

2. Width (W) scale:
   Function: $0.5 \log W$
   Range: $0.5 \log 100 - 0.5 \log 10 = 0.5$
   Length: Assume 6 in.

   Modulus: $\dfrac{6}{0.5} = 12$

   Equation: $d_W = 12 \times 0.5 \log W = 6 \log W$. (A 6-in. logarithmic cycle is used in graduating the scale.)

3. Height (H) scale:
   Function: $0.5 \log H$
   Range: $0.5 \log 50 - 0.5 \log 5 = 0.5$
   Length: Assume 6 in.

   Modulus: $\dfrac{6}{0.5} = 12$

   Equation: $d_H = 12 \times 0.5 \log H = 6 \log H$. (A 6-in. logarithmic cycle is used in graduating the scale.)

4. Diameter (D) scale:
   Chart width: Assume 5.4 in.

   Scale spacing: $\dfrac{a}{b} = \dfrac{12}{12}$; and $a = 2.7$ in., $b = 2.7$ in.

   Function: $\log D - \log 1.075$
   Range: $\log 80 - \log 1.075 - (\log 7 - \log 1.075) = 1.058$

   Modulus: $\dfrac{12 \times 12}{12 + 12} = 6$

   Length: $6 \times 1.058 = 6.35$ in.
   Equation: $d_D = 6(\log D - \log 1.075) = 6 \log D - 0.186$. (A 6-in. logarithmic cycle is used in graduating the scale.)

5. Base line connects $W = 10$, $H = 10$, and $D = 10.75$.

23.6. Concurrent-scale Nomograph. A relationship between three variables that can be expressed by an equation of the form

$$\frac{1}{f_1(p)} + \frac{1}{f_2(q)} = \frac{1}{f_3(r)} \tag{6}$$

may be represented by a nomographic chart of three concurrent

Equivalent Round and Rectangular Air Ducts

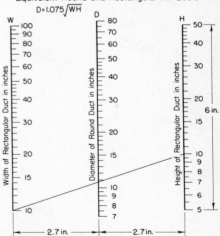

Fig. 23.5. A parallel-scale chart (for equivalent air ducts).

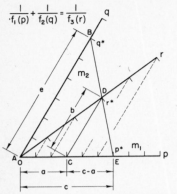

Fig. 23.6. Construction of concurrent-scale chart.

straight scales. The origins of all three scales lie at the point of concurrence.

The construction of a concurrent-scale chart is shown diagrammatically in Fig. 23.6. Two intersecting scales, the p scale with a modulus m_1 and the q scale with a modulus m_2, are located so as to form a convenient angle with one another. The scales are graduated according to the equations

$$d_p = m_1 f_1(p) \qquad d_q = m_2 f_2(q)$$

The r scale is located intermediate to the p and q scales.

Any straight tie line drawn across the three scales connects the three values p^*, q^*, and r^*. The distance c on the p scale is equal to the product of the scale modulus and the value of the scale function,

$$c = m_1 f_1(p^*)$$

and, similarly, on the q scale,

$$e = m_2 f_2(q^*)$$

A straight line through point r^* and parallel to the q scale forms triangle CDE. The tie line and the p and q scales form triangle ABE. Corresponding sides of the similar triangles ABE and CDE are in the same ratio,

$$\frac{c}{e} = \frac{c-a}{b} \qquad \text{whence} \qquad \frac{a}{c} + \frac{b}{e} = 1$$

Substituting equivalent values for c and e and $f_3(r^*)/f_3(r^*)$ for 1,

$$\frac{a}{m_1 f_1(p^*)} + \frac{b}{m_2 f_2(q^*)} = \frac{f_3(r^*)}{f_3(r^*)}$$

In order that this equation reduce to the original chart equations (6), the coefficients of the three terms must be equal:

$$\frac{a}{m_1} = \frac{b}{m_2} = f_3(r^*)$$

If the first two coefficients are equal, then

$$\frac{a}{b} = \frac{m_1}{m_2} \qquad\qquad (7)$$

Thus the center scale must be so located that the offsets a and b for any point on the scale are in the same ratio as the moduli of the two outside scales. *This is the first rule for the construction of the concurrent-scale nomograph.*

If the first and third coefficients are equal, then

$$\frac{a}{m_1} = f_3(r^*) \qquad \text{and} \qquad a = m_1 f_3(r^*) \qquad (8)$$

Thus the r scale may be graduated by projectors parallel to the q scale drawn from a temporary scale laid out on, and having the same modulus as, the p scale. The equation of the temporary scale is

$$d_t = m_1 f_3(r)$$

The temporary scale and projectors are a construction only and do not form a part of the completed chart. *The use of the temporary scale in the above manner may be said to be the second rule for the construction of the concurrent-scale nomograph.*

It should be pointed out that the p and q scales are interchangeable. The temporary scale may, therefore, if it is so desired, be laid out on the q scale, using the q scale modulus m_2. The projectors are then drawn parallel to the p scale in order to locate the r-scale graduations.

Rays of light parallel to the optical axis of a thin convex lens converge at the principal focus of the lens. The focal length can be determined on an optical bench by focusing the image of a brightly illuminated object, such as fine crosshairs, on a screen. Distances from the center of the lens to image, object, and principal focus are related by the formula

$$\frac{1}{L_I} + \frac{1}{L_O} = \frac{1}{F}$$

where L_I = image distance, in.
       L_O = object distance, in.
       F = principal focal length, in.

A nomograph for determining the principal focal length of a lens is shown in Fig. 23.7. Construction of the chart may be summarized as follows:

1. Image-distance (L_I) scale:
    Function: L_I
    Range: $20 - 0 = 20$
    Length: Assume 6 in.
    Modulus: $\frac{6}{20} = 0.30$
    Equation: $d_{L_I} = 0.30 L_I$
2. Object-distance (L_O) scale:
    Function: L_O
    Range: $40 - 0 = 40$
    Length: Assume 6 in.
    Modulus: $\frac{6}{40} = 0.15$
    Equation: $d_{L_O} = 0.15 L_O$
3. Principal-focal-length (F) scale:
    Function: F

    Scale spacing: Assume $a = 4.5$ in., $\dfrac{a}{b} = \dfrac{0.30}{0.15}$, and $b = 2.25$ in.

    Temporary scale modulus: $m_{L_I} = 0.30$
    Temporary scale equation: $d_t = 0.30 F$

Temporary scale graduations are located along the L_I-scale stem and are transferred to the F scale by means of projectors parallel to the L_O scale.

23.7. Parallel- and Transverse-scale Nomograph. It has been

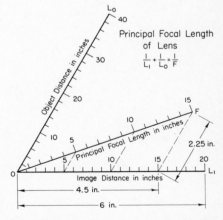

Fig. 23.7. A concurrent-scale chart (for focal length of lens).

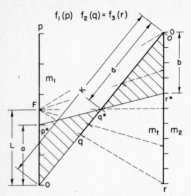

Fig. 23.8. Construction of zee chart.

shown (Fig. 23.5) that the relationship in which one term is equal to the product of two others, that is,

$$f_1(p)f_2(q) = f_3(r) \tag{9}$$

may be represented by a nomograph of three parallel straight logarithmic scales. This equation may also be represented by a nomograph of two parallel scales and a third transverse scale. The parallel scales run in opposite directions from a base line joining their origins. The diagonal scale extending along the base line may represent values of either p or q. Its origin coincides with the origin of the r scale.

The construction of the "zee," or "en," chart, as it is often called, is shown diagrammatically in Fig. 23.8. Two vertical scales, the p scale with a modulus m_1 and the r scale with a modulus m_2, are located a convenient distance apart. The scales are graduated according to the scale equations

$$d_p = m_1 f_1(p) \qquad d_r = m_2 f_3(r)$$

so as to run in opposite directions from a base line. The q scale lies along the base line with its origin at the origin of the r scale. The base line is inclined at an angle so as to provide a chart of rectangular proportions and make for sharp intersections between the scales and tie lines drawn across them.

Any straight line connects three values p^*, q^*, and r^* on the three scales.

The distance a on the p scale is equal to the product of the scale modulus and the value of the scale function,

$$a = m_1 f_1(p^*)$$

and, similarly, on the r scale,

$$b = m_2 f_3(r^*)$$

Corresponding sides of the similar triangles formed by the base line and tie line are in the same ratio,

$$\frac{a}{b} = \frac{K - d}{d}$$

where K = length of transverse scale intermediate to p and r scales
   d = distance from its origin to graduation q^*
Substituting equivalent values for a and b,

$$\frac{m_1 f_1(p^*)}{_2 f m_3(r^*)} = \frac{K - d}{d} \qquad \text{and} \qquad f_1(p^*) \frac{m_1 d}{m_2(K - d)} = f_3(r^*)$$

In order that this equation be equivalent to the original chart equation (9),

$$\frac{m_1 d}{m_2(K - d)} = f_2(q^*)$$

whence, solving for d,

$$d = \frac{K f_2(q^*)}{m_1/m_2 + f_2(q^*)}$$

The scale equation giving the distance from the origin to any point on the q scale is therefore

$$d_q = \frac{Kf_2(q)}{m_1/m_2 + f_2(q)} \tag{10}$$

Scale distances for graduating the scale may be obtained by substituting specific values of q in Eq. (10). This process is complicated by the fact that the scale does not have a constant modulus. Since the ratio m_1/m_2 is always positive, the length K represents all positive values of the function $f_2(q)$ from zero to infinity. There is a rapid convergence of value at the seldom-used upper end of the scale.

A more convenient method for graduating the transverse scale involves projection from a temporary scale on the stem of the r scale to a focus F located on the stem of the p scale. The equation of the temporary scale is

$$d_t = m_t f_2(q)$$

and the distance L, locating the focus, is related to the temporary scale modulus m_t by the equation

$$\frac{L}{m_t} = \frac{m_1}{m_2}$$

In some cases, a more precise location of the graduations of the transverse scale may be effected through the use of a different focus and temporary scale for different portions of the transverse scale. The temporary scale and projectors are a construction only and do not form a part of the completed chart.

The location of the transverse scale depends upon the position of the origins of the parallel scales. It is not always desired to include these origins within the ranges of scale values. In such cases, transverse-scale location may be determined from similar triangle ratios.

Engine brake horsepower is given by the formula

$$BHP = \frac{2\pi NT}{33,000}$$

where BHP = brake horsepower
N = engine speed, rpm
T = braking torque, lb-ft

A nomograph for the above relationship is shown in Fig. 23.9. Construction of the chart may be summarized as follows:

1. Chart equation from the above formula:

$$NT = 5,250 BHP$$

2. Speed (N) scale:
Function: N
Range: $5,000 - 0 = 5,000$
Length: Assume 6.25 in.
Modulus: $\dfrac{6.25}{5,000} = 0.00125$

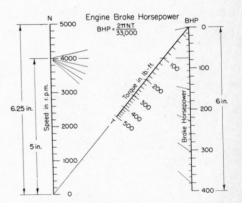

Fig. 23.9. A zee chart (for engine brake horsepower).

Equation: $d_N = 0.00125N$

3. Brake horsepower (*BHP*) scale:
Function: $5,250BHP$
Range: $5,250(400 - 0) = 2,100,000$
Length: Assume 6 in.

Modulus: $\dfrac{6}{2,100,000} = 0.00000286$

Equation: $d_{BHP} = 0.00000286 \times 5,250BHP = 0.015BHP$

4. Torque (*T*) scale:
Function: T
Range: $500 - 0 = 500$
Location of focus: Assume $L = 5$ in.

Temporary scale modulus: $\dfrac{5}{m_t} = \dfrac{0.00125}{0.00000286}$; and $m_t = 0.0114$

Temporary scale length: $0.0114 \times 500 = 5.70$ in.
Temporary scale equation: $d_t = 0.0114T$

The temporary scale is laid out on the stem of the *BHP* scale and transferred to the *T* scale by projectors converging at the focus.

23.8. Chart Layout. The preceding discussion deals with the preparation of certain of the basic types of nomograph. In each case, chart layout is based on rules which result from a geometric analysis of the chart form. Chart construction may be capable of simplification once a chart form is identified as representing a particular type of equation. Two scales of suitable type and modulus may be laid out along properly located stems. Corresponding values of the variables are obtained by repeated substitutions in the chart equation. Pivot points or points on a third scale are then obtained from the intersections of appropriate tie lines.

The use of tie lines to locate a pivot point on a conversion chart or a third scale on a nomograph is illustrated in Fig. 23.10. Three examples are shown. In constructing the conversion chart at (*A*) for the equation $2p = r$, the two scales are first located parallel to one another and at a suitable distance apart. The scales are graduated to any convenient, but not necessarily the same, length. Since the equation contains only linear functions of p and r, the scales are uniform. They may be subdivided by any of the graphic methods for dividing a line into equal parts. A value of p is substituted into the equation, the corresponding value of r determined, and a tie line drawn to connect these values on the scales. The process is repeated to obtain a second tie line. The intersection of the tie lines is the locus of point P, the pivot. A third tie line may be used to check the accuracy of the location.

The p and r scales of the nomographs in Fig. 23.10*B* and *C* may be located and subdivided in the same manner as in Fig. 23.10*A*. The q scale is then plotted, a point at a time, by assigning a specific numerical value to q and then using the same procedure that was used to locate the pivot on the conversion chart at (*A*). The scale

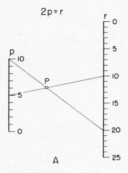

$2p = r$

A

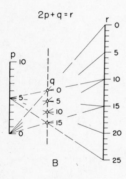

$2p + q = r$

B

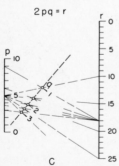

$2pq = r$

C

Fig. 23.10. Graphical method of chart construction.

is completed by drawing a line or stem through the series of plotted q values. Since the equation in example (B) involves only addition of terms, the q scale is uniform and parallel to the p and r scales. In example (C), on the other hand, where multiplication is involved, the q scale is nonuniform and is not parallel to the other two.

The graphic method for locating pivot points or scales produces an accurate and usable chart and, in many cases, reduces the time and effort involved in preparation. Nevertheless, a fundamental understanding of chart form is necessary, or else the third scale may evolve as an unusable curve or as a scale too short for practical use. The parallel scales first drawn must be properly designed. Plotting one of these as a uniform scale when it should be nonuniform to satisfy the chart equation would result in tie-line intersections that could not be checked out by a third tie line. The procedure is best employed when the chart equation is of simple, readily solved form and the general arrangement and subdivision of scales are evident.

23.9. Combined Nomographs. A relationship involving four variable quantities may be such that it can be represented by a chart composed of two three-variable nomographs. The nomographs are combined by arranging them so that a scale of one is superimposed upon an identically constructed scale of the other. The coinciding scales are ungraduated since the common stem serves only as a pivot, or "turning scale," at which the two tie lines across the component nomographs intersect.

An equation of the form

$$f_1(p) + f_2(q) = f_3(r) + f_4(s)$$

for example, may be represented by a nomographic chart composed of two parallel-scale nomographs. The four-variable equation is rewritten as two three-variable equations through the introduction of a quantity Q. If Q is evaluated in terms of p and q so that

$$Q = f_1(p) + f_2(q)$$

then

$$f_3(r) + f_4(s) = Q$$

Each of these equations may be represented by a three-scale nomograph, one relating p, q, and Q and the other relating Q, r, and s.

Another procedure would be to express Q in terms of p and r so that

$$Q = f_3(r) - f_1(p)$$

in which case

$$f_1(p) + Q = f_3(r) \quad \text{and} \quad f_2(q) = Q + f_4(s)$$

Here again, each equation may be represented by a three-scale nomograph. Different combinations and arrangements of the scales are obtained depending upon the way in which Q is introduced into the relationship. It might be desirable, for example, to arrange the terms so that the Q scale is an outside rather than a center scale on each nomograph. In any case, the two nomographs are constructed with identical Q scales and placed side by side so that the Q scale of one coincides with the Q scale of the other. In operation, a tie line joining values of two of the variables, say, p^* and q^* on one of the nomographs, locates a specific value of Q. This Q value and a value of a third variable, say, r^*, then locate a second tie line on the other nomograph, which determines the corresponding value of the fourth variable, s^*. The Q-scale origin, modulus, and range are pertinent to the design of both nomographs and must be determined. Numerical values of Q, however, are not used in solving the equation; and so the pivot scale representing Q is not graduated.

The smoke point of a kerosene or diesel fuel is measured as the height in millimeters of a flame that can be maintained without smoking when the fuel is burned in a standard lamp. Smoke point may be evaluated from the hydrocarbon content of the fuel through the use of the following formula:

$$S = 0.48P + 0.32N + 0.20A$$

where S = smoke-point flame height, mm
$\quad\quad P$ = paraffinic-hydrocarbon content, per cent
$\quad\quad N$ = naphthenic-hydrocarbon content, per cent
$\quad\quad A$ = aromatic-hydrocarbon content, per cent

The formula may be replaced by *two* three-variable equations,

$$0.32N - Q = -0.48P \quad\quad \text{and} \quad\quad S - Q = 0.20A$$

and represented by the nomographic chart shown in Fig. 23.11. Construction of the chart may be summarized as follows:

1. Naphthenic-hydrocarbon-content (N) scale:
   Function: $0.32N$
   Range: $0.32(25 - 0) = 8.0$
   Length: Assume 5 in.
   Modulus: $\dfrac{5}{8.0} = 0.625$
   Equation: $d_N = 0.625 \times 0.32N = 0.20N$

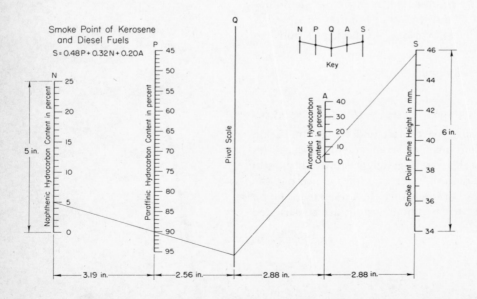

Fig. 23.11. Combined parallel-scale charts.

2. Pivot (Q) scale:
   Function: $-Q$
   Modulus: Assume 0.500
   Equation: $d_Q = -0.500Q$
3. Paraffinic-hydrocarbon-content (P) scale:
   Chart width: Assume 5.75 in.
   Scale spacing: $\dfrac{a}{b} = \dfrac{0.625}{0.500}$; and $a = 3.19$ in., $b = 2.56$ in.
   Function: $-0.48P$
   Range: $-0.48(45 - 95) = 24$
   Modulus: $\dfrac{0.625 \times 0.500}{0.625 + 0.500} = 0.278$
   Length: $0.278 \times 24 = 6.67$ in.
   Equation: $d_P = 0.278 \times -0.48P = -0.133P$
4. When $N = 5$ and $P = 90$, $Q = 44.8$; and the base line for the left side of the chart, representing the first of the three-variable equations, connects these three values.
5. Smoke-point (S) scale:
   Function: S
   Range: $46 - 34 = 12$
   Length: Assume 6 in.
   Modulus: $\%_{2} = 0.500$
   Equation: $d_s = 0.500S$
6. Aromatic-hydrocarbon-content (A) scale:
   Chart width: Assume 5.75 in.
   Scale spacing: $\dfrac{a}{b} = \dfrac{0.500}{0.500}$; and $a = b = 2.88$
   Function: $0.20A$
   Range: $0.20(40 - 0) = 8$
   Modulus: $\dfrac{0.500 \times 0.500}{0.500 + 0.500} = 0.250$
   Length: $0.250 \times 8 = 2$ in.
   Equation: $d_A = 0.250 \times 0.20A = 0.050A$
7. When $Q = 44.8$ and $A = 5$, $S = 45.8$; and the base line for the right side of the chart, representing the second of the three-variable equations, connects these three values.

A key is provided to indicate the correct manner for locating the tie lines on the chart. The tie lines must intersect at the pivot scale. The value of any one of the variables may be determined by locating the tie lines connecting the given values of the other three.

An equation in four variables that can be expressed in the form

$$\frac{f_1(p)}{f_2(q)} = \frac{f_3(r)}{f_4(s)}$$

may be represented by a nomographic chart which combines two three-variable zee charts about a common transverse scale. The chart so formed consists of one graduated scale for each of the four

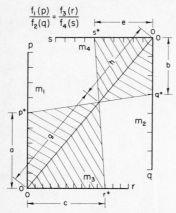

Fig. 23.12. Construction of combined zee chart.

variables plus an ungraduated transverse pivot scale. If a set of four values of the variables is to satisfy the equation, the straight tie line joining the values of p and q must intersect the tie line joining the values of r and s at a point on the pivot scale.

The construction of the double zee chart is shown diagrammatically in Fig. 23.12. Two vertical scales, the p scale with a modulus m_1 and the q scale with a modulus m_2, are located a convenient distance apart. The scales are graduated according to the scale equations

$$d_p = m_1 f_1(p) \qquad d_q = m_2 f_2(q)$$

so as to run in opposite directions from an inclined base line. Two horizontal scales, the r scale with a modulus m_3 and the s scale with a modulus m_4, are graduated according to the scale equations

$$d_r = m_3 f_3(r) \qquad d_s = m_4 f_4(s)$$

so as to run in opposite directions from the same inclined base line. The p and r scales have a common origin, and the q and s scales have a common origin.

Any two tie lines, intersecting at a point on the base line, connect four values, p^*, q^*, r^*, and s^*, on the four scales. The distance a on the p scale is equal to the product of the scale modulus and the value of the scale function,

$$a = m_1 f_1(p^*)$$

and, similarly, on the q, r, and s scales,

$$b = m_2 f_2(q^*)$$
$$c = m_3 f_3(r^*)$$
$$e = m_4 f_4(s^*)$$

In the similar triangles formed by each tie line and the base line, corresponding sides are in the same ratio,

$$a/b = g/h = c/e$$

Substituting equivalent values for a, b, c, and e,

$$\frac{m_1 f_1(p^*)}{m_2 f_2(q^*)} = \frac{m_3 f_3(r^*)}{m_4 f_4(s^*)}$$

In order that this equation reduce to the original chart equation,

$$m_1/m_2 = m_3/m_4$$

This equation provides the relationship between the scale moduli of the four scales.

Automobile speed is related to engine speed, over-all gear ratio, and tire diameter by the formula

$$V = \frac{DN}{336R}$$

where V = automobile speed, mph
   D = tire diameter, in.
   N = engine speed, rpm
   R = over-all gear ratio

The relationship may be represented by the nomographic chart of Fig. 23.13. Construction of the chart may be summarized as follows:

1. Chart equation from the above formula:

$$\frac{N}{336V} = \frac{R}{D}$$

2. Engine-speed (N) scale:
   Function: N
   Range: $5,000 - 0 = 5,000$
   Length: Assume 6.25 in.
   Modulus: $\dfrac{6.25}{5,000} = 0.00125$
   Equation: $d_N = 0.00125N$

3. Automobile-speed (V) scale:
   Function: $336V$
   Range: $336(100 - 0) = 33,600$
   Length: Assume 6.25 in.
   Modulus: $\dfrac{6.25}{33,600} = 0.000186$
   Equation: $d_V = 0.000186 \times 336V = 0.0625V$

4. Tire-diameter (D) scale:
   Function: D
   Range: $40 - 20 = 20$
   Length: Assume 1.20 in.
   Modulus: $\dfrac{1.20}{20} = 0.060$
   Equation: $d_D = 0.060D$

5. Over-all-gear-ratio (R) scale:
   Function: R
   Range: $12 - 2 = 10$
   Modulus: $\dfrac{0.00125}{0.000186} = \dfrac{m_R}{0.060}$; and $m_R = 0.403$
   Length: $0.403 \times 10 = 4.03$
   Equation: $d_R = 0.403R$

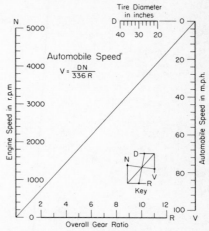

Fig. 23.13. A combined zee chart (for automobile speed).

A key is provided to indicate the correct manner for locating the tie lines on the chart. The tie lines must intersect at the transverse pivot scale.

Other combinations of three-scale nomographs to represent equations in four variables are possible. The process of combining basic nomographs may be expanded to cover the representation of equations in five or more variables. As the form of the chart becomes more complex, however, it becomes more cumbersome to use, and its value as a means of solving an equation diminishes.

PROBLEMS

Prepare nomographic charts to represent the following equations. Where the range of a variable is not indicated, limiting values are to be determined by substitution in the equation. Each scale is to be appropriately graduated and calibrated and is to bear a legend indicating the quantity represented and the unit of measurement. Each chart is to have a descriptive title that includes the chart equation.

Group 1. Conversion charts

23.1.1. Power conversion.

$$HP = 0.746KW$$

where HP = horsepower
KW = electric power, 0 to 100 kw

23.1.2. Wrought-aluminum alloys.

$$T = 575B$$

where T = approximate tensile strength, lb per sq in.
B = Brinell hardness, 20 to 120

23.1.3. Moist air.

$$S = 0.238 + 0.48H$$

where S = humid heat, Btu per lb per °F
H = humidity, 0 to 0.15 lb water vapor per lb dry air

23.1.4. Viscosity conversion.

$$K = 0.22S - \frac{180}{S}$$

where K = kinematic viscosity, centistokes
S = Saybolt Universal viscosity, 30 to 60 sec

23.1.5. Round steel bar stock.

$$W = 2.67D^2$$

where W = weight, lb per ft of length
D = diameter, 0 to 6 in.

23.1.6. Uniformly loaded shaft.

$$f = 211.4 \sqrt{\frac{1}{d}}$$

where f = fundamental frequency of transverse vibration, cycles per min
d = static deflection, 0.01 to 1 in.

Group 2. Parallel-scale nomographs

23.2.1. Roll crusher.

$$F = 0.04D + X$$

where F = maximum feed particle size, in.
D = diameter of rolls, 18 to 72 in.
X = distance between roll faces, 0.25 to 2.5 in.

23.2.2. Gear drive.

$$C = \frac{D_W + D_G}{2}$$

where C = center distance, in.
D_W = worm pitch diameter, 1 to 6 in.
D_G = gear pitch diameter, 5 to 30 in.

23.2.3. Tapped holes in cast iron.

$$T = 1.5D + \frac{4}{P}$$

where T = thread depth, in.
D = nominal thread diameter, $\frac{1}{4}$ to 3 in.
P = pitch, 4 to 32 threads per in.

23.2.4. Falling body.

$$h = h_0 - \frac{gt^2}{2}$$

where h = height, ft
h_0 = initial height, 0 to 500 ft
t = elapsed time, 0 to 5 sec
g = acceleration due to gravity, 32.2 ft per sec^2

23.2.5. Bronze bearing stock.

$$W = 3.72 \frac{\pi}{4} (D_o{}^2 - D_i{}^2)$$

where W = weight, 0 to 120 lb per ft of length
D_o = outside diameter, 1 to 8 in.
D_i = inside diameter, $\frac{1}{2}$ to 6 in.

23.2.6. Ohm's law.

$$E = IR$$

where E = electromotive force, volts
I = current, 1 to 15 amp
R = resistance, 1 to 10 ohms

23.2.7. Roller bearing.

$$L = \frac{60SH}{10^6}$$

where L = minimum life, millions of revolutions
S = speed, 100 to 10,000 rpm
H = minimum life, 1,000 to 20,000 hr

23.2.8. Cylindrical storage tank.

$$C = 7.48 \frac{\pi}{4} D^2 H$$

where C = capacity, gal
D = diameter, 1 to 10 ft
H = height, 1 to 30 ft

Group 3. Concurrent-scale nomographs

23.3.1. Resistances in parallel.

$$\frac{I}{R} = \frac{1}{R_1} + \frac{1}{R_2}$$

where R = equivalent resistance, ohms
R_1 = resistance, 0 to 25 ohms
R_2 = resistance, 0 to 25 ohms

23.3.2. Capacitors in series.

$$\frac{1}{C} = \frac{1}{C_1} + \frac{1}{C_2}$$

where C = equivalent capacitance, μf
C_1 = capacitance, 0 to 500 μf
C_2 = capacitance, 0 to 1,000 μf

Group 4. Parallel- and transverse-scale nomographs

23.4.1. Spur gear.

$$N = PD$$

where N = number of teeth, 0 to 250
P = pitch diameter, 0 to 25 in.
D = diametral pitch, 3 to 30 teeth per in.

23.4.2. Roller chain sprocket.

$$N = \frac{4D}{P} + 5$$

where N = minimum number of teeth, 5 to 55
D = bore diameter, 0.25 to 3 in.
P = chain pitch, 0.25 to 1 in.

23.4.3. Rectangular beam.

$$I = \frac{BH^3}{12}$$

where I = moment of inertia, in.[4]
B = beam-section breadth, 0 to 12 in.
H = beam-section height, 0 to 20 in.

23.4.4. Roller bearing.

$$L = \frac{C}{P} 3.33$$

where L = minimum life, millions of revolutions
C = dynamic capacity, 0 to 100,000 lb
P = applied load, 0 to 25,000 lb

Group 5. Combined nomographs

23.5.1. Fuel combustion.

$$W = 11.5C + 4.3(8H - O)$$

where W = theoretical combustion air, 5 to 15 lb per lb fuel
C = weight of carbon, 0.40 to 0.95 lb per lb fuel
H = weight of hydrogen, 0 to 0.15 lb per lb fuel
O = weight of oxygen, 0 to 0.40 lb per lb fuel

23.5.2. Moist air.

$$d = \frac{B - 0.38w}{0.754(T + 460)}$$

where d = density, 0.06 to 0.08 lb per cu ft
B = barometer reading, 27 to 31 in. mercury
w = water-vapor pressure, 0 to 1.5 in. mercury
T = temperature, 40 to 120°F

23.5.3. Coil spring.

$$S = 2.55 \frac{PD}{d^3}$$

where S = torsional stress, 0 to 120,000 lb per sq in.
P = applied load, 0 to 350 lb
D = mean coil diameter, 0.5 to 3 in.
d = wire diameter, 0.1 to 0.3 in.

23.5.4. Physical pendulum

$$I = \frac{g}{4\pi^2} WLT^2$$

where I = moment of inertia, 0 to 40,000 lb-ft[2]
W = weight, 100 to 2,000 lb
L = centroidal distance, 0 to 15 ft
T = period of oscillation, 0 to 5 sec
g = acceleration due to gravity, 32.2 ft per sec[2]

+ 8.	3.33	1.15	46.7	0.9890	0.14781
+ 9.	3.41	1.07	50.2	0.9874	0.15816
+10.7	3.13	1.35	39.8	0.9826	0.1857
+12.0	.13	1.35	39.8	0.9781	0.2079
+13.7	3. 0	1.28	42.0	0.9715	0.2368
+15.0	3.1	1.38	39.0	0.9657	0.258
+20.0	3.00	.48	36.3	0.9379	. 0
+26.0	2.82	6	32.4	0.898	0.4384
+31.5	2.67	1.	29.7	0. 8	0.5225
+40.0	2.63	1.85	29	0.7660	0.6428
+50.0	2.58			0.6428	0.7660
+53.8	2.	2.05	26.2	0.5906	0.8070
+55.	.68	1.80	29.9	763	0.8192
.0	3.02	1.46	36.8	0.54	0.8387
+59.0	3.60	0.88	61.1	0.5150	0.8572
+60.5	4.02	0.46	116.9	0.4924	0.87
+61.0	4.21	0.27	199.1	0.4848	0.8746
+61.1	4.29	0.19	282.9	0.4833	0.8755
+61.2	4.35	0.13	413.5	0.4818	0.8763

2	0.9
6	7.9
1	7.4
9	
8	9.9
7	10.1
1	12.4
1	14.2
3	15.5
3	18.7
2	21.7
5	21.1
2	24.5
0	30.9
5	52.4
5	101.7
7	247.7
2	362.4

24

EMPIRICAL EQUATIONS

24.1. The engineer continually works with physical quantities and is vitally concerned with the manner in which quantities vary with respect to one another. In the work of research and development, in the design of machinery and equipment, and in the functioning of processes and operation of plants, it may be necessary to determine relationships between variable quantities through tests or observations. Controlled changes may be brought about in one variable with corresponding changes measured in another variable. As a continuous operation proceeds, simultaneous readings of the variables are often made through the use of automatic recording devices. Results of a test are recorded as a set of tabulated values of the variables. This experimental procedure is used extensively in research, both basic and practical.

Experimental data may represent a relationship in which quantities vary according to some known mathematical law, in which case it is possible to determine the algebraic equation that associates the variables. The graphical and analytical procedures of resolving an equation from experimental data are known as *empirical methods*.

24.2. Graphic Representation of Data. After data have been obtained from an experiment, the relationship of variables can be studied. In some of the more simple cases, examination of the numerical values alone may suffice to reveal the desired information concerning the changes taking place. However, in most cases, it is necessary to examine the data graphically.

657

A relationship may be given in graphic form by plotting the data on uniform rectangular coordinates, as indicated in Fig. 24.1. The fact that a smooth line can be drawn so as to pass either through or very near the plotted points indicates the possibility that the relationship may be expressed mathematically by an algebraic equation.

Accuracy. Because an equation is to be determined, if possible, from the plot of the data, accuracy in the location of points and, later, in the drawing of a line through the points is essential. In general, the considerations for accuracy given in Chap. 21 should be followed. The first requisite is to make the plot *large* enough so that accuracy *can* be attained. Printed cross-sectional paper is available in rolls of 20-in. width and in cut sheets up to 16 by 20 in. in size (Fig. 24.1).

Coordinate Divisions and Scales. It is much easier to use cross-sectional paper divided in *tenths*. The divided units may be inches or centimeters, chosen according to necessary size of the plot and decimal places of values of observed data. The scale used can then be easily adjusted to suit, using 1, 2, 5, 10, or 20 (or more) smallest divisions per unit. The paper employed in Fig. 24.1 is divided into tenths of an inch.

Coordinate Axes. It is common practice to plot the independent variable as abscissa (X axis) and the dependent variable as ordinate (Y axis).

Plotted Points. The plotted point is best recorded as a pair of light, sharp, intersecting lines at right angles to each other. This method

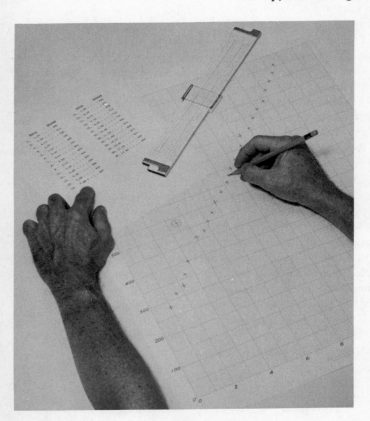

Fig. 24.1. Plotting the data.

is more accurate than either "dots" or circles. See Fig. 24.1 and other illustrations in this chapter.

24.3. Representative Lines. The purpose of drawing a line through a series of plotted points is to obtain a single linear representation that will account for and minimize experimental error. Later, an equation of the line will be derived. Therefore, it is mandatory that the *line* drawn through a series of plotted points be *representative of the data.*

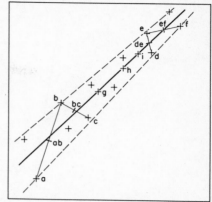

Fig. 24.2. Graphical aids for location of representative line.

Considering that there are errors in reading the instruments used in conducting the experiment but that these errors tend to "balance out" by being over in one case and under in another, the representative line should strike an average between the plotted points.

In many cases, the observed data will so closely fit a straight line that the line can be drawn purely "by eye." However, in other cases where the errors of observation are greater, it may be difficult to "guess" at the position of a representative line and be reasonably sure that the line is the best that can be obtained. The graphic aids illustrated in Fig. 24.2 may then be employed to advantage. First, it is a help to draw an *envelope* of the data (the two dotted lines of Fig. 24.2), which encloses *all* the plotted points. Certainly the representative line must fall somewhere near the middle of the envelope if there are both plus and minus errors in the data. Also, points may have an average struck between them to aid in fixing the position of the "best" line. In Fig. 24.2, the mid-point *ab*, between points *a* and *b*, is an average between *a* and *b*, and the final line should come close to this point. Other average points, *bc* between *b* and *c* and *ed* between *e* and *d*, will give a series of "average points" through which the representative line should pass or come *very* close to. Note that averages between points such as *g*, *h*, and *i* will fall on the line. In addition, it should be noted that this method is really a method of *selected* averages because the average of two points such as *a* and *c*, both of which evidently contain *minus* errors, or points such as *b* and *e*, which contain *plus* errors, is not considered. A very good representative line may be obtained in this way, especially if the plot is *large* enough to distinguish variations between the plotted points easily.

It is interesting to note here that errors in observed data that are *all* plus or minus, caused by an instrument out of adjustment and therefore reading consistently high or low, will not show up in the plot but must be rectified before the experiment is performed. Also, occasionally, there will be a "wild" point in a plot, shown by the encircled point of Fig. 24.1, which falls some distance from the line indicated by all other points. Obviously, such a point is in error because of misreading an instrument, a reading made at the wrong time, or a mistake in recording the reading and therefore should be eliminated.

Note again that, to get the best representative line, it is necessary to *make the plot of data large.*

There are numerical methods of evaluation that will fit a straight line to plotted points. These methods involve consideration of the residuals (deviations) of plotted points from the calculated line. If the ordinate of a point is y_o and the calculated ordinate of the straight line at the same value of x is y_c, then the residual is $R = y_o - y_c$. The method of averages provides the equation of a straight line for which the algebraic sum of the residuals approaches zero. The method of least squares provides the equation of a straight line for which the sum of the squares—and therefore the sum of the absolute values of the residuals—is a minimum. These methods are interesting, mathematically, and they work; but it has been shown again and again that they are much more involved and laborious than the graphical methods and are seldom more appropriate for engineering purposes than is a line obtained graphically on a large plot of data. For these reasons, the numerical methods are not to be discussed here.

Remember that *no* method will produce accurate results from inaccurate data; and if the data are accurate, the graphical methods will do an admirable job.

24.4. Empirical Equations. Since errors may be present in the original observations and also because drafting inaccuracies may be involved in plotting points and drawing a representative line, a derived equation will represent the relationship only approximately and *within the range of the test data*. The derived equation is therefore called an "empirical" equation to distinguish it from theoretically derived formulas expressing physical, chemical, or other laws.

If the plotted points appear to lie in or very nearly in a straight line, a linear, or first-degree, equation, $y = a + bx$, where a and b are constants, may be assumed. If, on the other hand, the points deviate systematically from a straight line, an empirical equation involving power, exponential or periodic terms, or combinations thereof is indicated.

The procedure for determining whether or not an equation of particular form may properly represent a set of data involves, in the case of power and exponential curves, the process of "rectification." Either the values are plotted directly on some type of functional coordinates or suitable *functions* of the values are plotted on uniform coordinates to obtain a straight- or very nearly straight-line relationship. The exact procedure varies according to the form of the equation and the number of constants to be evaluated. Once rectification indicates that the correct equation form has been selected, numerical constants are solved for by graphic or other analytical methods.

24.5. Linear Equations. *Slope-intercept Method.* The observed data may plot on uniform coordinates as a straight line, and the equation of the line will, therefore, be of the form $y = a + bx$. This is the familiar slope-intercept equation, where a is the y intercept and b is the slope of the line.

Figure 24.3 will illustrate the graphical procedure and determination of the equation from observed data recorded in an experiment.

Checking automatic recorder.

These data are plotted as shown in the figure, using light, sharp intersecting lines for the location of points. Then the best straight line representative of the data is drawn through as many of the points as possible but striking an *average* between points not on the line.

The y intercept of this representative line will be the value of a in the equation and may be measured directly from the y scale. In this case, the value is 5.0. To complete the equation, the slope b is needed. If the scales used for x and y are identical, the slope can be measured directly from the line by drawing a horizontal and vertical from two selected points on the line to represent a tangent and then measuring and calculating the *value* of the tangent. However, this requires more graphical construction and is therefore, probably, not so accurate as selecting two points and then obtaining x and y values to calculate the tangent. In any case, when x and y scales are *not* identical, this method *must* be used. Thus in Fig. 24.3, having selected two points on the line (shown by the dashed lines extending to the axes), one point will have values of $x_1 y_1$ and the other $x_2 y_2$. The tangent is then $(y_2 - y_1)/(x_2 - x_1)$ or, in this case,

$$\frac{43.5 - 13.8}{35.0 - 8} = \frac{29.7}{27} = 1.1$$

The equation of the line has therefore been determined as

$$y = 5 + 1.1x$$

24.6. Linear Equations. *Method of Selected Points.* The equation of a straight line on uniform coordinates may be evaluated by reading coordinates of two selected points on the line (x_1, y_1) and (x_2, y_2) and substituting in the equation

$$\frac{y - y_1}{x - x_1} = \frac{y_2 - y_1}{x_2 - x_1} \tag{1}$$

Equation (1) is simply a statement of the fact that the slope of a straight line is everywhere constant and sets up a proportion between corresponding changes in x and y values.

From the graph of Fig. 24.3, coordinates of two selected points are

$$x_1 = 8 \qquad x_2 = 35.0$$
$$y_1 = 13.8 \qquad y_2 = 43.5$$

Substituting in Eq. (1),

$$\frac{y - 13.8}{x - 8.0} = \frac{43.5 - 13.8}{35.0 - 8.0}$$

whence

$$\frac{y - 13.8}{x - 8.0} = 1.1$$

and

$$y = 5.0 + 1.1x$$

It should be noted that the coefficient 1.1 is the slope of the line

$$b = \frac{y_2 - y_1}{x_2 - x_1}$$

and that the constant term 5.0 is the ordinate-axis intercept a.

x	y	x	y
6	12.0	25	33.0
10	15.5	34	41.5
20	27.0	39	48.0

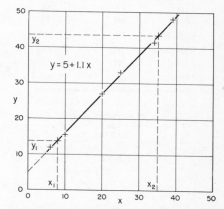

Fig. 24.3. Determination of empirical equation (first degree).

Alloy	Brinell hardness	Tensile strength
2S-0	23	13,000
3S-0	28	16,000
4S-0	45	26,000
14S-0	45	27,000
17S-0	45	26,000
24S-0	47	27,000
52S-0	45	27,000
53S-0	26	16,000
61S-0	30	18,000
75S-0	60	33,000

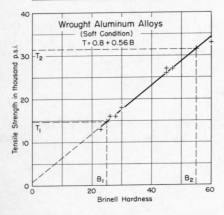

Fig. 24.4. Determination of empirical equation (first degree).

Figure 24.4 and the attendant table show a practical example of the determination of an equation by the method of selected points. Brinell hardness and tensile strength of a number of wrought-aluminum alloys in the soft or annealed condition are tabulated opposite. These data are plotted on uniform rectangular coordinates in Fig. 24.4, and a representative straight line is drawn through the points. Coordinates of two selected points on the line are

$$B_1 = 25 \qquad B_2 = 55$$
$$T_1 = 14.7 \qquad T_2 = 31.5$$

Writing the equation of the straight line,

$$\frac{T - 14.7}{B - 25} = \frac{31.5 - 14.7}{55 - 25}$$

whence

$$T = 0.8 + 0.56B$$

where T is tensile strength in thousands of pounds per square inch.

It seems reasonable now to make a comparison between the slope-intercept method and the method of selected points. In the slope-intercept method, the y-intercept value may be read from the graph, but the slope will have to be obtained by a pair of selected points; in the method of selected points, the equation is determined solely from the selected points. Also, in many cases, the y intercept *will not* appear on the graph. For these reasons and because the method of selected points works equally well for power and exponential equations, the method of selected points is recommended and will be used in all examples following.

24.7. Equations of Power Relationships. The power relationship occurs frequently in nature. Formulas for the distance-time relationship of a falling body, the period of a simple pendulum, and the velocity of free discharge of water from an orifice are examples of power relationships.

The power equation $y = ax^b$, in which one quantity varies directly as some power of another, plots on the uniform rectangular coordinates of Fig. 24.5A as a family of parabolic and hyperbolic curves passing through the point $(1,a)$. When the exponent b is equal to unity, the curve is a straight line through the origin. For other positive values of b, the curves are parabolic, symmetrical with respect

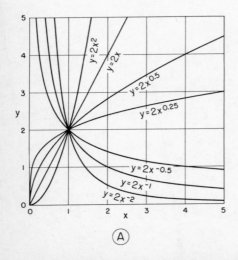

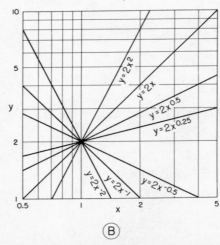

Fig. 24.5. Plots of power equations.

to the Y axis for values of b greater than 1 and the X axis for values of b less than 1. Negative values of b result in hyperbolic curves having the coordinate axes as asymptotes, one variable decreasing as the other increases. When placed in logarithmic form, the equation becomes $\log y = \log a + b \log x$, in which $\log y$ and $\log x$ are variable and $\log a$ and b are constant terms. Hence, curves of this type may be rectified either by plotting the logarithms of x and y on uniform rectangular coordinates or by plotting y versus x directly on logarithmic coordinates as in Fig. 24.5B.

An example of data giving a power equation is shown in Fig. 24.6, where a test resulted in tabulated values of two variables, as shown.

These data plot on uniform coordinates as a curved line but, when plotted on logarithmic coordinates as in Fig. 24.6, rectify to a straight line.

A representative straight line is then drawn through the points. Coordinates of two selected points on the line are

$$x_1 = 2.5 \qquad x_2 = 55.0$$
$$y_1 = 3.8 \qquad y_2 = 26.5$$

Writing the equation of the straight line (from the equation of selected points, paragraph 24.6),

$$\frac{\log y - \log 3.8}{\log x - \log 2.5} = \frac{\log 26.5 - \log 3.8}{\log 55.0 - \log 2.5}$$

whence $\qquad \log y = 0.330 + 0.628 \log x$

and $\qquad y = 2.14 x^{0.628}$

It is noted that the coefficient 2.14 is the ordinate-axis intercept obtained by extending the line to $x = 1$ and that the exponent 0.628 is the slope of the rectified curve.

The y intercept occurs at the coordinate line $x = 1$ since $\log 1 = 0$. The value 1 is therefore the origin of the logarithmic scale.

A practical example of data giving a power equation is shown in Fig. 24.7, where maximum sizes of particles passing U.S. Standard sieves of different mesh are tabulated as shown.

These data are plotted on logarithmic coordinates in Fig. 24.7 and a representative straight line drawn through the points. Coordinates of two selected points on the line are:

$$N_1 = 25 \qquad N_2 = 250$$
$$D_1 = 660 \qquad D_2 = 57$$

Writing the equation of the straight line,

$$\frac{\log D - \log 660}{\log N - \log 25} = \frac{\log 57 - \log 660}{\log 250 - \log 25}$$

whence $\qquad \log D = 4.307 - 1.064 \log N$

and $\qquad D = \dfrac{20{,}300}{N^{1.064}}$

Note that the reciprocal form of the equation is produced by the negative slope of the line of Fig. 24.7.

x	y	x	y
1.75	3.0	20.5	13.5
3.2	4.7	35.0	21.0
8.0	7.7	72.0	31.0

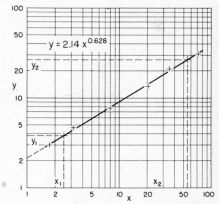

Fig. 24.6. Determination of empirical equation (power).

Mesh No.	Max. particle size, μ
20	840
40	420
60	250
80	177
100	149
140	105
200	74
325	44

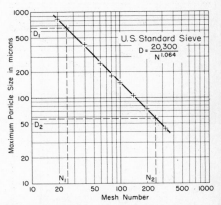

Fig. 24.7. Determination of empirical equation (power).

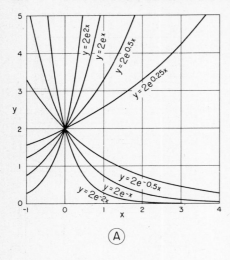

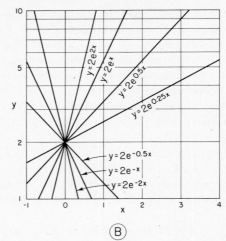

(A)   (B)

Fig. 24.8. Plots of exponential equations.

x	y	x	y
0.6	3.4	3.1	18.0
1.4	5.6	3.8	33.0
2.0	8.8	4.8	60.0

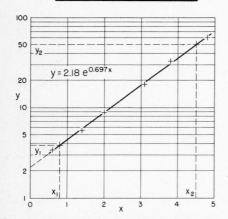

Fig. 24.9. Determination of empirical equation (exponential).

24.8. Equations of Exponential Relationships. In nature many quantities increase or decrease at a rate that is proportional to the amount present at any time. As time varies arithmetically by a constant difference, the quantity changes geometrically by a constant factor. Examples of exponential relationships involving time change are found in formulas for transient currents in an inductive electric circuit, the decay of natural radioactivity, and the increase in a sum of money at compound interest. Variables other than time may be involved. The intensity of light passing through a transparent or translucent substance varies exponentially with the thickness of the material.

The exponential equation $y = ae^{bx}$ or $y = a10^{bx}$ plots on the uniform rectangular coordinates of Fig. 24.8A as a family of curves passing through the point $(0,a)$ and having the X axis as asymptote. When placed in logarithmic form, the equation $y = ae^{bx}$ becomes $\ln y = \ln a + bx \ln e = \ln a + bx$, in which $\ln y$ and x are variable and $\ln a$ and b are constant terms. Similarly, the equation $y = a10^{bx}$ becomes $\log y = \log a + bx \log 10 = \log a + bx$, in which $\log y$ and x are variable and $\log a$ and b are constant terms. Hence, curves of this type may be rectified either by plotting $\ln y$ or $\log y$ versus x on uniform rectangular coordinates or by plotting y versus x directly on semilogarithmic coordinates in which the y scale is logarithmic and the x scale uniform, as shown in Fig. 24.8B.

An example of data giving an exponential equation is shown in Fig. 24.9, where a test resulted in tabulated values of two variables.

These data plot on uniform coordinates as a curved line. However, when the data are plotted on semilogarithmic coordinates, as in Fig. 24.9, with a logarithmic y scale and a uniform x scale, a representative straight line may be drawn through the points. Coordinates of two selected points on the line are

$$x_1 = 0.8 \qquad x_2 = 4.5$$
$$y_1 = 3.8 \qquad y_2 = 50.0$$

Writing the equation of the straight line,

$$\frac{\ln y - \ln 3.8}{x - 0.8} = \frac{\ln 50.0 - \ln 3.8}{4.5 - 0.8}$$

whence $\qquad \ln y = 0.777 + 0.697x$

and $\qquad y = 2.18 e^{0.697x}$

It is noted that the coefficient 2.18 is the ordinate-axis intercept obtained by extending the line to $x = 0$ and that the value 0.697 is the slope of the rectified curve.

A practical example of data yielding an exponential equation is shown in Fig. 24.10 with tabulated data for breaking loads of standard hard-drawn copper wire.

These data are plotted on semilogarithmic coordinates in Fig. 24.10 and a representative line drawn through the points. Coordinates of two selected points on the line are

$$G_1 = 2.9 \qquad G_2 = 13.3$$
$$P_1 = 2,500 \qquad P_2 = 250$$

Writing the equation of the straight line,

$$\frac{\log P - \log 2,500}{G - 2.9} = \frac{\log 250 - \log 2,500}{13.3 - 2.9}$$

whence $\qquad \log P = 3.677 - 0.096G$

and $\qquad P = \dfrac{4,750}{10^{0.096G}}$

The reciprocal form of the equation conforms with the negative slope of the representative line of Fig. 24.10.

Gage No.	Breaking load, lb
2	3,000
4	1,980
6	1,280
8	830
10	530
12	340
14	215
16	135

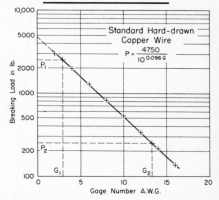

Fig. 24.10. Determination of empirical equation (exponential).

PROBLEMS

Group 1. Linear equations

24.1.1. Measurement of the electrical resistance of a 1-ft length of No. 0 *AWG* standard annealed copper wire at various temperatures resulted in the data tabulated below:

Temperature T, °C	Resistance R, μohms	Temperature T, °C	Resistance R, μohms
14.0	96.00	36.5	105.00
19.2	97.76	40.1	105.75
25.0	100.50	45.0	108.20
30.0	102.14	52.0	110.60

Plotting the data on uniform rectangular coordinates with resistance as ordinate and temperature as abscissa, evaluate the constants a and b in the linear equation $R = a + bT$ relating the variables.

24.1.2. Thermal conductivities of a bonded-asbestos-fiber insulating material at various mean temperatures are tabulated below:

Mean temperature (hot to cold surface) T, °F	Thermal conductivity K, Btu/hr-sq ft-°F temp diff-in. thickness	Mean temperature (hot to cold surface) T, °F	Thermal conductivity K, Btu/hr-sq ft-°F temp diff-in. thickness
100	0.365	460	0.563
200	0.415	600	0.628
320	0.470	730	0.688
400	0.520	900	0.780

Plotting the data on uniform rectangular coordinates with thermal conductivity as ordinate and mean temperature as abscissa, evaluate the constants a and b in the linear equation $K = a + bT$ relating the variables.

24.1.3. Corrosion tests on specimens of pure magnesium resulted in values for weight increase in pure oxygen at 525°C tabulated below:

Elapsed time T, hr	Weight increase W, mg/sq cm	Elapsed time T, hr	Weight increase W, mg/sq cm
0	0	11.5	1.00
2.0	0.17	20.0	1.68
4.0	0.36	24.1	2.09
8.2	0.65	30.0	2.57

Plotting the data on uniform rectangular coordinates with weight increase as ordinate and elapsed time as abscissa, evaluate the constant a in the linear equation $W = aT$ relating the variables.

Group 2. Power equations

24.2.1. Approximate rates of discharge of water under various heads of fall through a 1,000-ft length of 4-in. pipe having an average number of bends and fittings are tabulated below:

Head of fall H, ft	Discharge Q, gal/min	Head of fall H, ft	Discharge Q, gal/min
1	35.8	20	159.7
2	50.6	25	178.9
4	71.6	30	195.8
6	87.7	40	225.8
9	107.5	50	252.2
12	123.7	75	309.8
16	142.9	100	357.9

Plotting the data on logarithmic coordinates with discharge as ordinate and head as abscissa, evaluate the constants a and b in the power equation $Q = aH^b$ relating the variables.

24.2.2. Spark-gap break-down voltages for smooth spherical electrodes 25 cm in diameter and in clean dry air at 25°C and 760 mm are tabulated below for various gap lengths:

Gap length L, cm	Peak voltage V, kv	Gap length L, cm	Peak voltage V, kv
5	0.16	45	1.49
10	0.32	50	1.66
15	0.48	60	2.01
20	0.64	70	2.37
25	0.81	80	2.74
30	0.98	90	3.11
35	1.15	100	3.49
40	1.32		

Plotting the data on logarithmic coordinates with voltage as ordinate and gap length as abscissa, evaluate the constants a and b in the power equation $V = aL^b$ relating the variables.

24.2.3. Steam tables give the specific volume of saturated steam at various absolute pressures as tabulated below:

Absolute pressure P, lb/sq in.	Specific volume V, cu ft/lb	Absolute pressure P, lb/sq in.	Specific volume V, cu ft/lb
1	333.6	14.7	26.80
2	173.73	20	20.089
3	118.71	25	16.303
5	73.52	30	13.746
10	38.42	40	10.498

Plotting the data on logarithmic coordinates with specific volume as ordinate and absolute pressure as abscissa, evaluate the constants a and b in the power equation $V = aP^b$ relating the variables.

24.2.4. Heat losses from horizontal bare-iron hot-water pipes at 180°F to still ambient air at 75°F are tabulated below:

Pipe size D, in.	Heat loss H, Btu/lin ft-24 hr	Pipe size D, in.	Heat loss H, Btu/lin ft-24 hr
1	1,896	5	8,020
1¼	2,398	6	9,530
1½	2,746	8	12,442
2	3,430	10	15,528
2½	4,140	12	18,418
3	5,054	14	20,140
3½	5,771	16	23,088
4	6,493	18	25,998
4½	7,211		

Plotting the data on logarithmic coordinates with heat loss as ordinate and pipe size as abscissa, evaluate the constants a and b in the power equation $H = aD^b$ relating the variables.

24.2.5. Capacities of horizontal conveyer belts, carrying materials of 50-lb per cu ft density at 200-ft per min speed and running on standard 20° troughing idlers, are tabulated below:

Belt width W, in.	Capacity C, short tons (2,000 lb)/hr	Belt width W, in.	Capacity C, short tons (2,000 lb)/hr
12	29	42	406
18	68	48	550
24	125	54	716
30	200	60	900
36	290		

Plotting the data on logarithmic coordinates with capacity as ordinate and width as abscissa, evaluate the constants a and b in the power equation $C = aW^b$ relating the variables.

Group 3. Exponential equations

24.3.1. Creep-strength tests of a high-chromium (23 to 27 per cent) ferritic steel used in high-temperature service resulted in the stress values, to produce a 1 per cent deformation in 10,000 hr at various temperatures, tabulated below:

Temperature T, °F	Stress S, lb/sq in.
1,000	6,450
1,100	2,700
1,200	1,250
1,300	570
1,400	270

Plotting the data on semilogarithmic coordinates with stress as ordinate on a logarithmic scale and temperature as abscissa on a uniform scale, evaluate the constants a and b in the exponential equation $S = a10^{bT}$ relating the variables.

24.3.2. Solubility tables give the data tabulated below for the solubility of anhydrous potassium alum in water:

Temperature T, °C	Solubility S, g K_2SO_4 $Al_2(SO_4)_3$/100 g H_2O for saturated solution
0	3.0
10	4.0
20	5.9
30	8.39
40	11.70
50	17.00
60	24.75

Plotting the data on semilogarithmic coordinates with solubility as ordinate on a logarithmic scale and temperature as abscissa on a uniform scale, evaluate the constants a and b in the exponential equation $S = ae^{bT}$ relating the variables.

24.3.3. Breaking loads for standard annealed copper wire are tabulated below:

Wire size G, AWG	Breaking load L, lb	Wire size G, AWG	Breaking load L, lb
0	2,980	8	480
1	2,430	9	380
2	1,930	10	314
3	1,530	11	249
4	1,210	12	197
5	962	13	156
6	762	14	124
7	605		

Plotting the data on semilogarithmic coordinates with breaking load as ordinate on a logarithmic scale and wire size as abscissa on a uniform scale, evaluate the constants a and b in the exponential equation $L = a10^{bG}$ relating the variables.

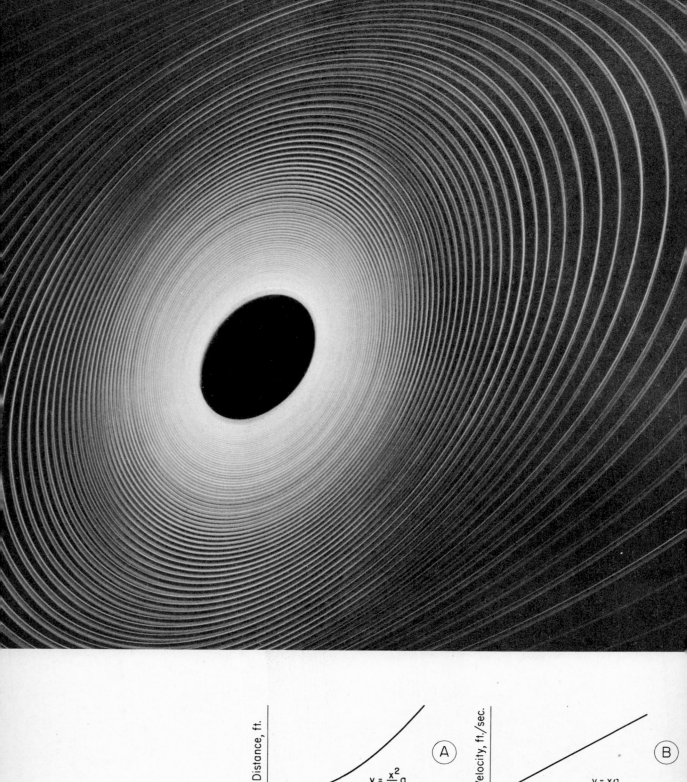

Fig. 25.1. Derived curves.

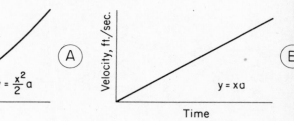

25

GRAPHIC CALCULUS

25.1. In the previous chapter, on empirical equations, it has been shown that the engineer is vitally concerned with the relationship of variable quantities. It was also pointed out that a relationship may be of any order, from a linear, or first-degree, equation to power and exponential types. There are, of course, more complicated forms. The determination of a *relationship*, however, may not complete all the information required for engineering purposes. In any case, it may be necessary to know the *rate of change* of the variables, that is, how fast or how much a change is caused in one variable as the result of a change in the other variable. For a first-degree equation, the rate of change of the variables is constant. For other equations, either the rate of change may be uniform or it may vary according to a mathematical relationship. Moreover, rates of change for other situations may follow some mathematical law or, on the other hand, they may not.

Figure 25.1 illustrates an equational relationship in which a body is moving under constant acceleration. The time-distance curve A has an equation of $y = (x^2/2)a$, where y is distance, x is time, and a is the constant acceleration. By calculus, the first derivative will be $y = xa$, which is velocity, shown by curve B to change at a uniform rate. This is the *rate* of change of the distance-time relationship. The second derivative of $y = (x^2/2)a$ is $y = a$ (or the first derivative of $y = xa$ is $y = a$), the rate of change of the velocity

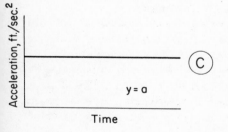

671

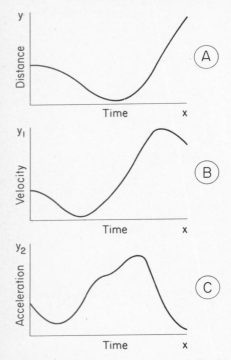

Fig. 25.2. Derived curves.

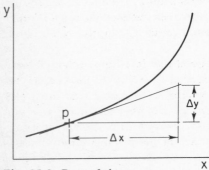

Fig. 25.3. Rate of change.

(curve B), which is shown in curve C to be a constant, the acceleration, equal to a. The third derivative (the derivative of $y = a$, the acceleration) will be zero ($y = 0$). Thus we see that a derivative gives the rate of change of a relationship of *next higher order*. Conversely, if the series is started with the acceleration, $y = a$, the curve of next higher order, the velocity, $y = xa$, is the integral of $y = a$. Also, the distance-time curve $y = (x^2/2)a$ is the second integral of $y = a$ (or the first integral of $y = xa$). Therefore, an integral gives the *summation* for a relationship of lower order.

In many cases, the rate of change of a relationship will not be constant nor will it vary according to any known mathematical law. In Fig. 25.2, a body is shown to be moving according to some changing velocity and acceleration. The first derivative, curve B, which has been produced by graphical methods, shows that the velocity does not change at any easily determinable mathematical rate. Also, the second derivative, the acceleration, curve C, follows a similar pattern for rate of change. Even though the possibility is remote that mathematical equations can be written in this case, the curves show how the rates vary and provide a means of finding the value of the rate of change at any particular point on the curves. Thus the graphic counterpart of mathematical integration and differentiation becomes a *family* of curves on which all necessary relationships and rates of change may be determined. The engineer is often faced with problems similar to the foregoing example, where tabulated data representing a relationship are so complex that either no mathematical equation can be found or the computations become extremely difficult. In such cases, the operations of integration and differentiation, that is, of determining a related curve of next higher or lower degree, can be performed quickly and accurately by graphical methods.

25.2. Rate of Change. *The value of the derivative at any point of a curve is equal to the slope of the line drawn tangent to the curve at that point.* The solution of this mathematical problem led Leibnitz and Newton, independently of each other, to the discovery of the differential calculus. Graphically, the statement means that, if *at any point on a curve* (as, for example, point p of Fig. 25.3) *a tangent is drawn, the value of the tangent, $\Delta y/\Delta x$, is the rate of change at point p.* The application of this theorem to a series of points on a curve is fundamental to both graphic and symbolic calculus.

25.3. Laws of Graphic Calculus. The methods of graphic calculus are based upon two laws of derived curves.

First Law. The slope at any point of a given curve relating two variables is numerically equal to the ordinate at the corresponding point of the derived curve of next lower degree (derivative curve). This law is illustrated in Fig. 25.4, where the slope at $x = 1$ of the curve of higher degree (y_1 versus x) is the tangent of the angle θ, or $\Delta y_1/\Delta x$. This slope is numerically equal to the ordinate a of the derivative curve (y_2 versus x) at the same point, $x = 1$. The slope reaches a maximum value *b* at $x = 2.6$, becomes zero at $x = 5.3$, and then takes on negative values, reaching the value $-c$ at $x = 6$. Notice that the derivative curve (y_2 versus x) is plotted to *twice* the scale of the given curve (y_1 versus x). Also, on the given curve (y_1 versus x), the y_1 scale is *half* that of the x scale.

Second Law. The area bounded by a given curve, any two ordinates, and the X axis is numerically equal to the difference between the two corresponding ordinates of the curve of next higher degree (integral curve). This law is illustrated in Fig. 25.5. The area under the curve of lower degree (y_2 versus x) over the interval from $x = 1$ to $x = 1.8$ is numerically equal to *a*, the *increase* in the value of y_1 *over the same interval*. Similarly, the area of the interval from $x = 1.8$ to $x = 2.6$ is numerically equal to *b*. The total ordinate of the curve of higher degree represents, at any given value of *x*, the *cumulative* area under the curve of lower degree up to that point. Thus it is noted that y_1 reaches a maximum value at $x = 5.3$; then from $x = 5.3$ to $x = 6$, it decreases in value by the increment *c* as the area under the curve y_2 versus *x* becomes negative in sign.

Because slopes (tangents) are generally more difficult to measure or compare than are areas, the latter are preferred as the basis for graphic methods of calculus.

25.4. Equivalent Areas. In applying the *second law*, the area under the curve, for a number of vertical strips, is required. The area under the curve is found and used as an equivalent area, explained by Fig. 25.6, where at (*A*) the real area under a curve is shown and at (*B*) an equivalent rectangular area. If the two small almost triangular areas indicated at (*B*) are made *equal*, one area is additive and the other subtractive to make the rectangular area *identical in value* to the area under the curve. This is easily accomplished by locating a horizontal line which cuts the curve between the two ordinates so as to form a pair of equal "triangular" areas. The horizontal line is located graphically by using a triangle or transparent-blade T square so that both areas under consideration can be seen. When the triangular areas under consideration are small, the eye is quite sensitive to differences and a very good approximation of the position of the mean ordinate is obtained. Also, when the two triangular areas are of approximately the same *shape*, judgment of the two areas is simplified. For example, the two areas of Fig. 25.7*A* are not of the same shape because the curve changes more rapidly on one end than at the other; but if, as at (*B*), the vertical strip is made narrower (in this case, half of the previous strip), the difference in curvature is not so pronounced, the areas are smaller, and very good approximations can be made. Thus we may say with the force of a rule that, *where the curvature is noticeably unequal, narrower strips should be used*.

It is advisable to make the charts for graphic calculus *large*. It is difficult to obtain accuracy in *any* graphical construction when the plot of data is not of sufficient size to get results within the range of

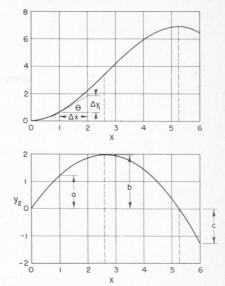

Fig. 25.4. Illustration of slope law.

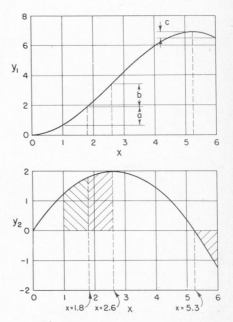

Fig. 25.5. Illustration of area law.

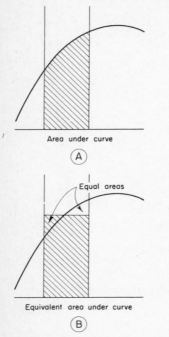

Area under curve

(A)

Equal areas

Equivalent area under curve

(B)

Fig. 25.6. Equivalent area of a strip.

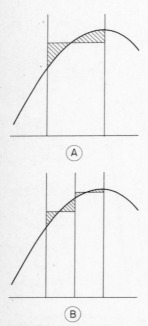

(A)

(B)

Fig. 25.7. Width of strip adjusted to obtain greater accuracy.

accuracy of the experimental data. Standard graph paper is available in cut sheets up to 16 by 20 in.

25.5. Graphic Integration. *Chordal Method.* Of all the known methods for graphic integration, the chordal method is outstanding in that it is as accurate as any, it does not require extra equipment, such as a mirror for locating tangents, and the construction is simple and direct.

The given curve of lower order, representing a relationship between y_2 and x, is plotted on rectangular coordinates as shown in Fig. 25.8. Ordinates are then drawn to divide the chart area into a series of vertical strips. The number and spacing of the ordinates are determined by the shape of the curve: If the curvature either is sharp or reverses itself, the ordinates should be close together; conversely, where the curve is relatively flat, they may be spaced farther apart. On Fig. 25.8, the attempt has been made to locate the vertical strips so that mean ordinate distances can be accurately located.

Next, *mean ordinate heights* for the several strips are determined as described in paragraph 25.4. Thus, as illustrated by Fig. 25.9, the area under the curve in each strip has now been equated to the product of the mean ordinate times the width of the strip. For example, the area under curve pq is equal to the area of the rectangle whose upper boundary is rw, and in similar fashion, all mean ordinate heights have been determined on Fig. 25.8.

Now the height of the mean ordinate of each strip is projected to a vertical line, which, in this case, is the Y axis. A focus F (described in detail in paragraph 25.6) is located on the X axis (extended), and rays are drawn from the focus to the projected heights of the mean ordinates for each strip (illustrated in both Figs. 25.8 and 25.9).

The integral curve can now be started. It is best to draw the integral curve above the given curve as in Fig. 25.8—even a separate piece of paper may be used if desired. The chart is started by laying out the axes y_1 and x in projection with the lower chart so that the same vertical strips on the given curve may be drawn for the integral curve.

Points on the integral curve (y_1 versus x) are located by starting at the origin and drawing a straight line across each strip *parallel* to the corresponding ray below, for example, ab parallel to Fr and then bc parallel to Fs, and so on until all points, a, b, c, etc., have been found. A smooth curve through the points is the integral curve.

25.6. Focal Distance and Scales for the Chordal Method. The focal distance K (on Fig. 25.8) is related to the scales for x, y_1, and y_2 by the formula

$$K = m_x \frac{m_{y_2}}{m_{y_1}}$$

where m_x = modulus for the x scale

m_{y_1} = modulus for the y scale of integral curve

m_{y_2} = modulus of the y scale of the given curve

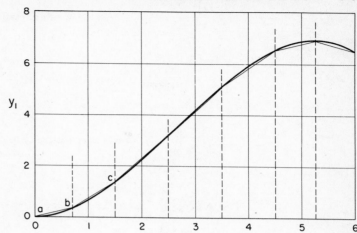

Fig. 25.8. Graphical integration. chordal method.

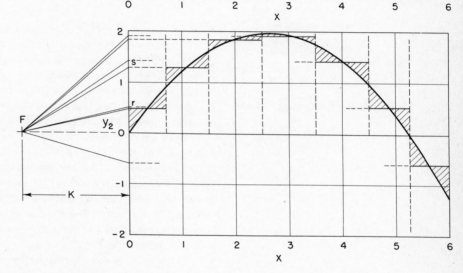

In Fig. 25.9, the area under curve pq of the plot y_2 versus x is the product of the numerical value of the mean ordinate and the numerical value of strip width:

$$\text{Area} = \frac{pr}{m_{y_2}} \frac{rw}{m_x}$$

In the plot y_1 versus x, the numerical value of the y_1 ordinate at point b is

$$y_1^* = \frac{bd}{m_{y_1}}$$

If $y_1^* = \text{area}$, then

$$\frac{bd}{m_{y_1}} = \frac{pr}{m_{y_2}} \frac{rw}{m_x}$$

whence

$$\frac{m_x m_{y_2}}{m_{y_1}} = \frac{pr}{bd} \frac{rw}{bd} \qquad (1)$$

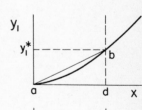

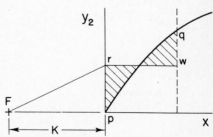

Fig. 25.9. Theory of chordal method.

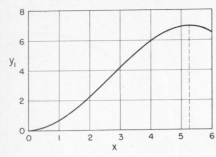

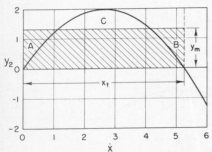

Fig. 25.10. Total (equivalent) area under curve.

From similar triangles Frp and abd,

$$\frac{K}{pr} = \frac{ad}{bd} = \frac{rw}{bd} \qquad (2)$$

From (2), we get

$$K = \frac{pr\ rw}{bd} \qquad (3)$$

whence, from (1) and (3),

$$K = \frac{m_x m_{y_2}}{m_{y_1}}$$

In Fig. 25.8, the scale of y_2 is twice that of y_1. Therefore,

$$K = m_x \tfrac{2}{1} \qquad \text{or} \qquad K = 2m_x$$

In other words, distance K is equal to two units of the x scale. Thus if both scales y_2 and y_1 are decided upon, the distance K may be determined. On the other hand, if a distance K is assumed, the y_1 scale may then be calculated.

The y_1-scale modulus m_{y_1} of the integral curve must normally be smaller than the modulus m_{y_2} of the given curve in order to keep the integral curve within reasonable proportions. The maximum value of y_1 may be estimated by remembering that the maximum value will be equal, *numerically*, to the *total* area under the curve. This total is the summation of all the individual areas in the strips and can be had by actually making the summation, but an easier way is indicated in Fig. 25.10, where a rectangular equivalent area is arranged so that areas $A + B$ balance area C. The product of the y *mean ordinate* y_m and the total x value x_t then gives the maximum y_1 ordinate value. On Fig. 25.10, $y_m = 1.25$ (approximately), and $x_t = 5.3$; the product is 6.6 (approximately). The scale for y_1 can then be selected for good proportions of the integral curve and the K distance calculated to conform.

25.7. Graphic Differentiation. *Chordal Method.* The integral curve y_1 versus x of Fig. 25.8 may be taken as a given curve, and y_2 versus x, the lower curve, then becomes the derivative curve of y_1 versus x. The chordal method just described is *reversible* and can be employed as readily as before to plot the derivative curve. The steps are performed one by one in opposite order. First, chords of the given curve are drawn across each vertical strip. Then, a focus and the axes for the derivative curve are located, using a larger scale for the derivative curve. Next, rays from the focus, *parallel* to the chords, determine mean ordinates on the lower curve. A smooth line drawn across the horizontal mean ordinate lines so as to balance out the triangular areas added on and cut off in each vertical strip then gives the derivative curve.

The above method of drawing a derivative curve is quite satisfactory for most cases, but sometimes it is somewhat difficult to draw a smooth curve to balance the areas on the lower curve. Also, for the best results and easiest solution, the chords of the given curve should be chosen carefully. Fortunately, however, for critical problems, some extra constructions may be made to aid in balancing the areas on the derivative chart. The first law states that the slope at any given point of the given curve will be numerically equal to the ordinate at the corresponding point of the derived curve. Also, from Fig. 25.9, it is readily seen that points p and q on the lower curve and a and b on the upper curve are points *on* the curves. By employing the above facts, graphical derivation may be accomplished simply and with accurate results. In Fig. 25.11A, a given curve with chord ab is shown, along with the derived curve prq. From the chordal method of paragraphs 25.5 and 25.6, it is known that a and b are points on the given curve for which p and q are corresponding points on the derived curve. There is also a y mean height y_m for the area under the derived curve, and at the point r where the y mean height crosses the curve, a tangent t may be drawn on the given curve. From the first law, the slope at point t is equal to the ordinate value at r, and from the figure, it is seen that the ordinate value of r will be equal to y_m. Therefore, if a tangent *point* can be accurately located on the given curve to meet the above conditions, a definite point r can be found on the derived curve. From elementary geometry, it is known that for a circle arc, as shown at Fig. 25.11B, a tangent and a series of parallel chords will all have a radial line that is the perpendicular bisector of the chords. Thus if the given curve is divided into portions which closely approach *arcs*, the perpendicular bisectors of the chords will locate tangent points and, by projection to the derived curve, locate points on the curve. This is illustrated at Fig. 25.11C, where the given curve has been divided into segments and vertical strips have been determined by chords ab, bc, and cd. These chords have been chosen so that each portion of the curve is closely symmetrical about the perpendicular bisector of its chord. Note that where the curve is relatively flat the chord may be longer than where the curvature changes rapidly. The perpendicular bisectors of the chords then locate tangent points t_1 for ab, t_2 for bc, and t_3 for cd. These tangent points then projected down to the derived curve chart will locate points r_1, r_2, and r_3 *on the mean ordinate height lines.*

It is obvious that no curve, unless it is actually a circle arc, can have perfect symmetry about a chord. Nevertheless, if the chords are carefully chosen and made reasonably short, the conditions for a circle arc are approached so closely that the error is negligible. As a matter of fact, the whole system of calculus is based on methods of *limits* where a series of values of a variable approach a definite constant value. Thus the graphical procedure here described follows the philosophy of calculus.

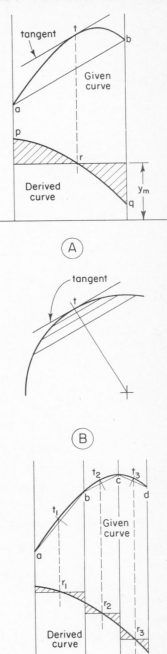

Fig. 25.11. Chords of given curve located to obtain derived curve.

Figure 25.12 illustrates the determination of a derivative curve, based on the foregoing methods. The given curve, y_1 versus x, is plotted on uniform rectangular coordinates as shown. A series of chords, *ab*, *bc*, *cd*, etc., is drawn as described for Fig. 25.11*C* so that the chords cut the curve to produce close symmetry of the curve about the chord. The derivative chart is then started by determining a scale and focal distance K. Reversing the process described for integration, the maximum ordinate of y_1 versus x is 6.7 (approximately). From the second law, this value represents the total value of the area under the derivative curve, up to the corresponding value of x for $y_{1,\max}$, in this case, $x = 5.3$. Therefore, $6.7/5.3 = 1.26$ (approximately), the y mean value of the area up to $x = 5.3$. If the same scale of y_1 versus x is used for the derived curve, the total height will be only about one-third that of the given curve. Thus an increase in scale is desirable. If the y_2 versus x scale is to be three times that of y_1 versus x, then

$$K = \frac{m_x m_{y_2}}{m_{y_1}} = m_x \frac{3}{1}$$

or
$$= 3m_x$$

The K distance is then laid off equal to three times one unit of x, locating F, the focus. Lines now drawn from the focus parallel to

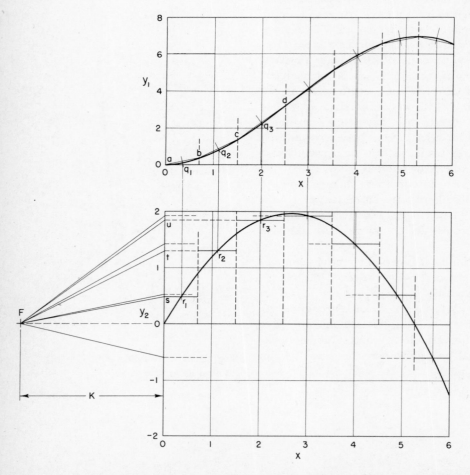

Fig. 25.12. Graphical differentiation, chordal method.

the chords on y_1 versus x, for example, Fs parallel to ab, Ft parallel to bc, and Fu parallel to cd, determine points s, t, u, etc., on the ordinate of y_2 versus x for projection to the strips, giving y mean heights for the strips. The strips on both curves are formed by the intersections of the chords on y_1 versus x. Perpendicular bisectors of the chords on y_1 versus x will locate tangent points q_1, q_2, q_3, etc., which, projected down to y_2 versus x, locate points r_1, r_2, r_3, etc., on the y mean height lines of the strips. A smooth curve through r_1, r_2, r_3, etc., is the derivative curve. As a check, it should be noticed that the derivative curve should balance the additive and subtractive areas from the y mean area in each strip.

25.8. Other Methods of Graphical Integration and Differentiation. There are a number of other graphical methods for integration and differentiation based either on the use of tangents or on a combination of graphical and mathematical procedures. However, these methods all have one or more serious faults and will, therefore, not be described. Any method depending upon the drawing of a tangent to a curve is inaccurate because of the difficulty in drawing an accurate tangent. Any combination of graphics and mathematics can be used only when the curve is parabolic or of a geometrical shape that allows the application of mathematical formulas.

25.9. Constant of Integration. The graphical methods will integrate a given curve and the algebraic methods will integrate an expression, but neither method will orient numerical values of an integral with a corresponding value of the given curve or expression. In all the graphic examples shown thus far, the curves have started at the origin of uniform rectangular coordinates where the constant of integration relating the curves is zero. This condition, however, may not always be the case. To explain, assume that an integral curve is to be determined that passes through $x = 1$ and $y = 4$ from a given curve having a slope of $2x$. Mathematically, this means that the curve to be determined will be the integral of $y = 2x$.

Since the slope at any point is dy/dx, by hypothesis,

$$\frac{dy}{dx} = 2x \qquad \text{and} \qquad dy = 2x\,dx$$

Integrating,

$$y = 2\int x\,dx$$

or

$$= x^2 + C \tag{1}$$

where C is the constant of integration. The curve must pass through the point $x = 1$ and $y = 4$. Therefore, to satisfy Eq. (1),

$$4 = 1 + C \qquad \text{and} \qquad C = 3$$

Graphically, as shown in Fig. 25.13, the curve (straight line) of $y = 2x$ is plotted at y_2 versus x as shown. This is the given curve for which the integral curve is needed. In this case, a K distance of three units of x has been selected, thus making the scale of y_1, the

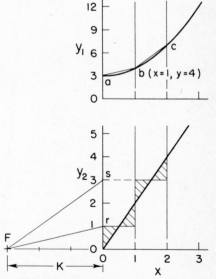

Fig. 25.13. Constant of integration.

integral chart, one-third of the scale for y_2. Then y mean areas are drawn for the strips on y_2 versus x, between $x = 0$, $X = 1$, and $x = 2$. Now focal lines Fr and Fs can be used to get chords on the integral curve. Remembering that the curve must pass through $x = 1$ and $y = 4$, point b (at these values) is located on the integral curve. Then chord ba parallel to Fr and chord bc parallel to Fs give points through which the integral curve may be drawn. It is seen now that the y intercept occurs at $y = 3$, the value of the constant of integration when $x = 0$, satisfying the equation $y = x^2 + C$. Thus the constant of integration simply moves the curve up or down on the Y axis. In other words, if some other values of x and y had been given, the constant of integration would be changed, but the integration would be identical.

In any practical case, the constant of integration is usually determinable by knowing either the relationship of given and integral values of a variable or by knowing *one point* on the integral curve.

It is also valuable to note that a constant does not affect the process of differentiation. Remember that, according to the first law, the *slope* of a given curve gives the ordinate height on the derivative curve and that the second law concurs by stating that the *difference* in ordinate value of a given curve gives the area under the derived curve.

25.10. Example of Graphical Integration. Sometimes in a practical problem an instantaneous rate of change can be determined accurately through the use of measuring instruments or by calculation, but because of the nature of the problem, the *rate-of-change* curve will not follow known or readily determined mathematical law. Therefore, the graphical method of integration is either the *only* or the *easiest* solution. For example, a small conservation dam is known, from a survey of the pool contour and bed, to contain 8,000,000 gal of water when full. Head, in feet of water behind the dam, is easily determined by direct measurement. Flow (gallons per hour) out of a drain pipe may be determined by calculation from head of water and pipe size. Nevertheless, because of the uneven contour of both the pool outline and bed, as the pool is drained, there is no simple relationship for rate of flow versus time. However, by graphical integration of the rate-of-flow curve (determined by a test), the number of gallons drained out may be determined, thus giving information to show (1) remaining capacity of the pool at any particular head, (2) flow rate for any particular head, and (3) time required to drain a given quantity of water from the pool. The data on the opposite page have been obtained from a test.

These data plotted on uniform rectangular coordinates on the lower chart of Fig. 25.14 give the rate-of-flow curve of H and GPH versus T. (Head and flow rate are directly related.) The integral of this rate curve will give the summation of the rate or, in this case, gallons capacity versus time. The head (H) corresponding to quantity at full stage and at lower stages has also been shown on the integral chart. Note that capacity at full stage is the constant of integration in this case and must be plotted first in making the integral curve. The integral curve is plotted as shown on Fig. 25.14 and described in paragraph 25.5.

To use the chart, assume that at head a it is desired to drain y_1 gal from the pool. The time required is then T_1. The rate of flow at the beginning and end of the drain period can be read from c and d on the lower chart. The capacity to hold additional water coming down from the supply stream after this drain period is then y_2 on the integral chart. As another example, assume at head a that the pool is drained for a time of T_1. Then y_1 gal have been taken out. Thus this chart of given and integral curves becomes the operating guide for the conservation and flood-prevention dam.

25.11. Example of Graphical Differentiation. Many devices of science and engineering move with some varying rate of velocity and acceleration. Sometimes these varying rates are known to follow mathematical laws, but in other cases, it may be necessary to verify

DRAIN RATES

Time T, hr	Head H, ft	GPH, gal/hr
0	30	205,000
4	29.4	203,000
8	28.6	200,000
12	27.4	198,600
16	25.8	190,000
20	23.4	180,000
24	20	167,000

Capacity at full stage: 8,000,000 gal
Head at full stage: 30.0 ft

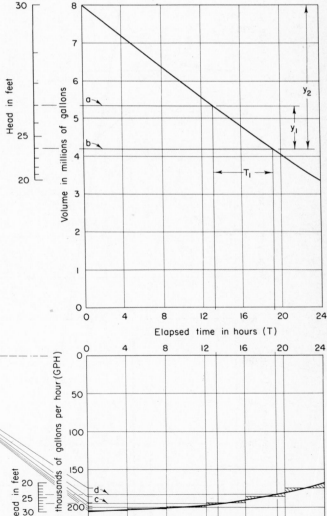

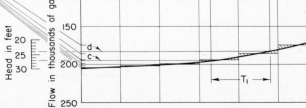

Fig. 25.14. Example of graphical integration.

an assumed law, determine a law, or represent the rates of change (if no known mathematical relationship fits the data). In any case, the graphical method of differentiation will apply. For example, the movement of missiles and rockets may be closely estimated by mathematical means if the fundamentals such as gross weight, fuel capacity, burning rate of fuel, and engine thrust are known; but the actual *performance* may not follow the calculations exactly because of unforeseen variations caused either by unknown design characteristics or other imperfect aspects. Through the use of tracking devices, both

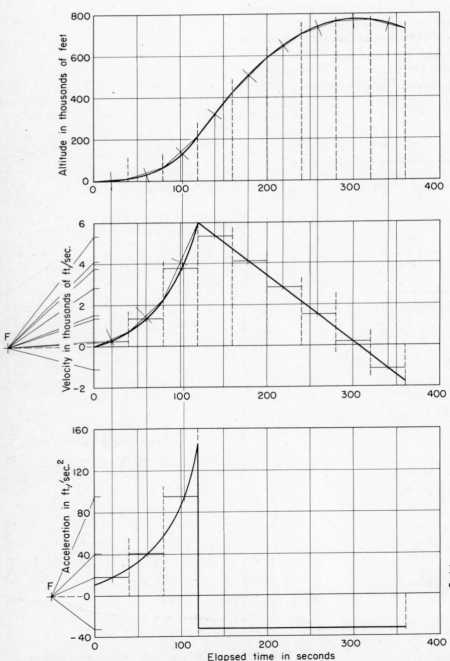

Fig. 25.15. Example of graphical differentiation.

optical and radar, and also by including instruments in the rocket itself, such as a recording altimeter, data of flight may be obtained.

Figure 25.15 illustrates a case where a rocket, having a gross weight of 15,000 lb and engine thrust of 20,000 lb at sea level and a fuel-burning period of 120-sec duration, has been fired vertically from ground level. The data for altitude are plotted against time in the upper curve of Fig. 25.14. The rocket will accelerate until burn-out of the fuel, then coast to its zenith, and finally fall as a free body. For guidance in future designing, not only should the rates of velocity and acceleration be determined but the important *maximum* acceleration is needed. All necessary information can be found by drawing the velocity and acceleration curves.

The velocity curve is the first derivative and is constructed as described in paragraph 25.7. Note that the focal distance (K of Fig. 25.15) has been chosen to keep the velocity curve at a height consistent with the height of the given (original-data) curve. Maximum velocity occurs at burnout.

The acceleration curve will be the derivative of the velocity curve (the second derivative of the given-data curve). This is again plotted as described in paragraph 25.7. This curve shows that the acceleration is at a maximum at burnout, reduces *very* sharply from 146 ft per sec^2 to -32.2 ft per sec^2, and then is constant. Thus all needed information has been obtained by graphical methods, regardless of whether equations are possible to determine.

PROBLEMS

Group 1. Graphic differentiation

25.1.1. Plot the following points, and draw a smooth curve through them. Construct the derivative curve.

x	y	x	y
0	1.0	5	5.6
1	2.2	6	6.1
2	3.3	7	6.5
3	4.2	8	6.8
4	5.0	9	7.0

25.1.2. Plot the following points, and draw a smooth curve through them. Construct the curve giving the rate of change of y with respect to x. Determine the value of x at which the value of y is a maximum.

x	y	x	y
0	0	270	75
40	19	332	80
90	38	410	81
173	60	450	80
220	69	500	76

25.1.3. The position of a body sliding down an inclined surface is measured at half-second intervals. Distance traveled S, in feet, is tabulated below against elapsed time T, in seconds. Plot the distance-versus-time curve, and construct the curve giving the velocity of the body at any instant.

T, sec	S, ft	T, sec	S, ft
0	0	3.0	2.17
0.5	0.06	3.5	2.92
1.0	0.25	4.0	3.88
1.5	0.54	4.5	4.83
2.0	0.98	5.0	6.00
2.5	1.49		

25.1.4. Measurements of the temperature θ, in degrees Fahrenheit, of a cooling body are tabulated below for values of elapsed time T, in minutes. Draw the derivative curve giving the rate of cooling at any time.

T, min	θ, °F	T, min	θ, °F
0	184	7	121
1	171	10	107
2	159	15	90
3	149	20	79
5	134		

25.1.5. An automobile accelerates from a standstill to a speed of 75 ft per sec in 30 sec. Values of the speed V, in feet per second, are given below at 5-sec intervals of elapsed time T, in seconds. Plot the acceleration-versus-time curve.

T, sec	V, ft/sec
0	0
5	23.1
10	37.5
15	49.0
20	58.8
25	67.3
30	75.0

25.1.6. The population of the state of Ohio (U.S. Census) over the period from 1800 to 1950 is given below. Construct the curve showing the rate of population increase.

Year	Population	Year	Population
1800	45,365	1880	3,198,062
1810	230,760	1890	3,672,329
1820	581,434	1900	4,157,545
1830	937,903	1910	4,767,121
1840	1,519,467	1920	5,759,394
1850	1,980,329	1930	6,646,697
1860	2,339,511	1940	6,907,612
1870	2,665,260	1950	7,946,627

25.1.7. The work done by the explosion of a mixture of 1 cu ft of a fuel gas and X cu ft of air is given by the empirical formula $W = 85X - 3.1X^2$. For what value of X is the maximum work obtained? Solve graphically.

25.1.8. Annual costs C, in dollars (return on investment plus cost of heat lost), for various thicknesses T, in inches, of insulation for a piping system are tabulated below. Plot the given data, construct the derivative curve, and determine the thickness of insulation for which the cost is a minimum.

T, in.	C, $
1	275
2	174
3	165
4	190
5	225
6	260

Group 2. Graphic integration

25.2.1. Plot the following points, and draw a smooth curve through them. Construct the integral curve.

x	y	x	y
0	0	5	4.20
1	1.50	6	4.65
2	2.41	7	5.10
3	3.10	8	5.55
4	3.69	9	6.00

25.2.2. Determine graphically the value of π. (*Hint.* Construct a semi-circle of 6-in. radius upon the X axis as diameter. Draw the integral curve. Divide the total area under the semicircle by 18.)

25.2.3. Determine graphically the value of ln 10. (*Hint.* Plot the curve representing the equation $y = 1/x$, and integrate graphically from $x = 1$ to $x = 10$.)

25.2.4. One pound of superheated steam is allowed to expand against a piston, isothermally at 400°F, from a pressure of 200 to a pressure of 40 lb per sq in. gage. Volumes V, in cubic inches, occupied by the steam at various pressures P, in pounds per square inch gage, are tabulated below. Plot the pressure-versus-volume curve, and integrate it graphically to determine the work done on the piston. (*Hint.* Work = $\int P \, dV$.)

V, cu in.	P, lb/sq in. gage	V, cu in.	P, lb/sq in. gage
3,770	200	7,400	100
4,200	180	9,030	80
4,730	160	11,530	60
5,390	140	15,870	40
6,240	120		

25.2.5. The specific heat of water at atmospheric pressure C, in British thermal units per pound per degree Fahrenheit, is tabulated below against temperature T, in degrees Fahrenheit. Plot the tabulated points, and draw a smooth curve through them. Integrate graphically to obtain the amount of heat required to raise the temperature of 1 lb of water from freezing to boiling. [*Hint.* Heat $= \int C \, dT = 180 + \int (C - 1) \, dT$.]

T, °F	C, Btu/lb-°F	T, °F	C, Btu/lb-°F
32	1.0080	140	1.0001
50	1.0019	158	1.0013
68	0.9995	176	1.0029
86	0.9987	194	1.0050
104	0.9987	212	1.0076
122	0.9992		

25.2.6. A plate cam, sliding with uniform motion, is to elevate a follower during a 3-sec time interval. The cam length is 6 in. Velocities V, in inches per second, to be imparted to the follower are tabulated below against values of elapsed time T, in seconds. Plot the velocity-versus-time curve for the follower. Integrate graphically to obtain the distance-versus-time curve, and tabulate offsets at $\frac{1}{2}$-in. intervals for machining the cam.

T, sec	V, in./sec	T, sec	V, in./sec
0	0	1.70	0.665
0.30	0.21	2.00	0.59
0.50	0.34	2.30	0.455
0.75	0.48	2.50	0.34
1.10	0.62	2.75	0.175
1.25	0.655	3.00	0
1.50	0.68		

25.2.7. Soundings D, in feet, taken at points located at distances S, in feet, from one bank of a stream are tabulated below. Draw the integral curve to determine the cross-sectional area of the stream.

S, ft	D, ft	S, ft	D, ft
0	0	30	6.3
6	2.2	36	4.4
12	3.0	42	2.0
18	4.0	47.2	0
24	5.6		

25.2.8. An object starting from rest accelerates uniformly to a velocity of 24 ft per sec in 6 sec time, travels at constant velocity for 7.2 sec time, and then decelerates uniformly to a standstill in 4.8 sec time. Plot the acceleration-versus-time, the velocity-versus-time, and the distance-versus-time curves to describe the motion.

GLOSSARY

OF TECHNICAL TERMS

Part 1. Shop terms

anneal (*v.*) To soften a metal piece and remove internal stresses by heating to its critical temperature and allowing to cool very slowly.

arc-weld (*v.*) To weld by electric-arc process.

bore (*v.*) To enlarge a hole with a boring tool, as in a lathe or boring mill. Distinguished from *drill*.

boss (*n.*) A projection of circular cross section, as on a casting or forging.

braze (*v.*) To join by the use of hard solder.

broach (*v.*) To finish the inside of a hole to a shape usually other than round. (*n.*) A tool with serrated edges pushed or pulled through a hole to enlarge it to a required shape.

buff (*v.*) To polish with abrasive on a cloth wheel or other soft carrier.

burnish (*v.*) To smooth or polish by a rolling or sliding tool under pressure.

bushing (*n.*) A removable sleeve or liner for a bearing; also a guide for a tool in a jig or fixture.

Boss

Bushing

carburize (*v.*) To prepare a low-carbon steel for heat-treatment by packing in a box with car-bonizing material, such as wood charcoal, and heating to about 2000°F for several hours, then allowing to cool slowly.

caseharden (*v.*) To harden the surface of carburized steel by heating to critical temperature and quenching, as in an oil or lead bath.

castellate (*v.*) To form into a shape resembling a castle battle-ment, as castellated nut. Often applied to a shaft with multiple integral keys milled on it.

chamfer (*v.*) To bevel a sharp ex-ternal edge. (*n.*) A beveled edge.

chase (*v.*) To cut threads in a lathe, as distinguished from cut-ting threads with a die. (*n.*) A slot or groove.

chill (*v.*) To harden the surface of cast iron by sudden cooling against a metal mold.

chip (*v.*) To cut or clean with a chisel.

coin (*v.*) To stamp and form a metal piece in one operation, usually with a surface design.

cold-work (*v.*) To deform metal

Chamfer

687

stock by hammering, forming, drawing, etc., while the metal is at ordinary room temperature.

color-harden (*v.*)   To caseharden to a very shallow depth, chiefly for appearance.

core (*v.*)   To form the hollow part of a casting, using a solid form made of sand, shaped in a core box, baked, and placed in the mold. After cooling, the core is easily broken up, leaving the casting hollow.

Counterbore

counterbore (*v.*)   To enlarge a hole to a given depth. (*n.*) 1. The cylindrical enlargement of the end of a drilled or bored hole. 2. A cutting tool for counterboring, having a piloted end of the size of the drilled hole.

Countersink

countersink (*v.*)   To form a depression to fit the conical head of a screw or the thickness of a plate so that the face will be level with the surface. (*n.*) A conical tool for countersinking.

crown (*n.*)   Angular or rounded contour, as on the face of a pulley.

die (*n.*)   1. One of a pair of hardened metal blocks for forming, impressing, or cutting out a desired shape. 2 (thread). A tool for cutting external threads. Opposite of *tap*.

die casting (*n.*)   A very accurate and smooth casting made by pouring a molten alloy (or composition, as Bakelite) usually under pressure into a metal mold or die. Distinguished from a casting made in sand.

die stamping (*n.*)   A piece, usually of sheet metal, formed or cut out by a die.

draw (*v.*)   1. To form by a distorting or stretching process. 2. To temper steel by gradual or intermittent quenching.

drill (*v.*)   To sink a hole with a drill, usually a twist drill. (*n.*) A

pointed cutting tool rotated under pressure.

drop forging (*n.*)   A wrought piece formed hot between dies under a drop hammer, or by pressure.

face (*v.*)   To machine a flat surface perpendicular to the axis of rotation on a lathe. Distinguished from *turn*.

feather (*n.*)   A flat sliding key, usually fastened to the hub.

fettle (*v.*)   To remove fins and smooth the corners on unfired ceramic products.

file (*v.*)   To finish or trim with a file.

fillet (*n.*)   A rounded filling of the internal angle between two surfaces.

fin (*n.*)   A thin projecting rib. Also, excess ridge of material.

Fillet

fit (*n.*)   The kind of contact between two machined surfaces. 1. *Drive, force,* or *press:* When the shaft is slightly larger than the hole and must be forced in with sledge or power press. 2. *Shrink:* When the shaft is slightly larger than the hole, the piece containing the hole is heated, thereby expanding the hole sufficiently to slip over the shaft. On cooling, the shaft will be seized firmly if the fit allowances have been correctly proportioned. 3. *Running* or *sliding:* When sufficient allowance has been made between sizes of shaft and hole to allow free running without seizing or heating. 4. *Wringing:* When the allowance is smaller than a running fit and the shaft will enter the hole by twisting it by hand.

flange (*n.*)   A projecting rim or edge for fastening or stiffening.

forge (*v.*)   To shape metal while hot and plastic by a hammering or forcing process either by hand or by machine.

galvanize (*v.*)   To treat with a

Flange

bath of lead and zinc to prevent rusting.

graduate (*v.*)   To divide a scale or dial into regular spaces.

grind (*v.*)   To finish or polish a surface by means of an abrasive wheel.

harden (*v.*)   To heat hardenable steel above the critical temperature and quench in a bath.

hot-work (*v.*)   To deform metal stock by hammering, forming, drawing, etc., while the metal is heated to a plastic state.

Kerf

kerf (*n.*)   The channel or groove cut by a saw or other tool.

key (*n.*)   A small block or wedge inserted between shaft and hub to prevent circumferential movement.

Keyway

keyway, key seat (*n.*)   A groove or slot cut to fit a key. A key fits into a key seat and slides in a keyway.

knurl (*v.*)   To roughen or indent a turned surface, as a knob or handle.

Key Seat

lap (*n.*)   A piece of soft metal, wood, or leather charged with abrasive material, used for obtaining an accurate finish. (*v.*) To finish by lapping.

Lug

lug (*n.*)   A projecting "ear," usually rectangular in cross section. Distinguished from *boss*.

malleable casting (*n.*)   An ordinary casting toughened by annealing. Applicable to small castings with uniform metal thicknesses.

mill (*v.*)   To machine with rotating toothed cutters on a milling machine.

Neck

neck (*v.*)   To cut a groove around a shaft, usually near the end or at a change in diameter. (*n.*) A portion reduced in diameter between the ends of a shaft.

normalize (*v.*)   To remove internal stresses by heating a metal piece to its critical temperature and allowing to cool very slowly.

pack-harden (*v.*)   To carburize and caseharden.

pad (*n.*)   A shallow projection. Distinguished from *boss* by shape or size.

Pad

peen (*v.*)   To stretch, rivet, or clinch over by strokes with the peen of a hammer. (*n.*) The end of a hammer head opposite the face, as *ball peen*.

pickle (*v.*)   To clean castings or forgings in a hot weak sulfuric acid bath.

plane (*v.*)   To machine work on a planer having a fixed tool and reciprocating bed.

planish (*v.*)   To finish sheet metal by hammering with polished-faced hammers.

plate (*v.*)   The electrochemical coating of a metal piece with a different metal.

polish (*v.*)   To make smooth or lustrous by friction with a very fine abrasive.

profile (*v.*)   To machine an outline with a rotary cutter usually controlled by a master cam or die.

punch (*v.*)   To perforate by pressing a nonrotating tool through the work.

ream (*v.*)   To finish a drilled or punched hole very accurately with a rotating fluted tool of the required diameter.

relief (*n.*)   The amount one plane surface of a piece is set below or above another plane, usually for clearance or for economy in machining.

rivet (*v.*)   1. To fasten with rivets. 2. To batter or upset the headless end of a pin used as a permanent fastening.

round (*n.*)   A rounded exterior corner between two surfaces. Compare with *fillet*.

Round

sandblast (*v.*)   To clean castings or forgings by means of sand driven through a nozzle by compressed air.

shape (*v.*) To machine with a shaper, a machine tool differing from a planer in that the work is stationary and the tool reciprocating.

shear (*v.*) To cut off sheet or bar metal between two blades.

sherardize (*v.*) To galvanize with zinc by a dry heating process.

shim (*n.*) A thin spacer of sheet metal used for adjusting.

shoulder (*n.*) A plane surface on a shaft, normal to the axis and formed by a difference in diameter.

spin (*v.*) To shape sheet metal by forcing it against a form as it revolves.

Spline

spline (*n.*) A long keyway. Sometimes also a flat key.

spot-face (*v.*) To finish a round spot on a rough surface, usually around a drilled hole, to give a good seat to a screw or bolthead, cut, usually $\frac{1}{16}$ in. deep, by a rotating milling cutter.

Spot-face

spot-weld (*v.*) To weld in spots by means of the heat of resistance to an electric current. Not applicable to sheet copper or brass.

steel casting (*n.*) Material used in machine construction. It is ordinary cast iron into which varying amounts of scrap steel have been added in the melting.

swage (*v.*) To shape metal by hammering or pressure with the aid of a form or anvil called a "swage block."

sweat (*v.*) To join metal pieces by clamping together with solder between and applying heat.

tack-weld (*v.*) To join at the edge by welding in short intermittent sections.

tap (*v.*) To cut threads in a hole with a rotating tool called a "tap," having threads on it and fluted to give cutting edges.

temper (*v.*) To change the physical characteristics of hardened

steel by reheating to a temperature below the critical point and allowing to cool.

template, templet (*n.*) A flat pattern for laying out shapes, location of holes, etc.

trepan (*v.*) To cut an outside annular groove around a hole.

tumble (*v.*) To clean, smooth, or polish castings or forgings in a rotating barrel or drum by friction with each other, assisted by added mediums, as scraps, "jacks," balls, sawdust, etc.

turn (*v.*) To machine on a lathe. Distinguished from *face*.

undercut (*v.*) To cut, leaving an overhanging edge. (*n.*) A cut having inwardly sloping sides.

upset (*v.*) To forge a larger diameter or shoulder on a bar.

weld (*v.*) To join two pieces by heating them to the fusing point and pressing or hammering together.

Trepan

Undercut

Part 2. Structural terms

bar Square or round rod; also flat steel up to 6 in. in width.

batten plate A small plate used to hold two parts in their proper position when made up as one member.

batter A deviation from the vertical in upright members.

bay The distance between two trusses or transverse bents.

beam A horizontal member forming part of the frame of a building or structure.

bearing plate A steel plate, usually at the base of a column, used to distribute a load over a larger area.

bent A vertical framework usually consisting of a truss or beam supported at the ends on columns.

brace A diagonal member used to stiffen a framework.

buckle plate A flat plate with

dished depression pressed into it to give transverse strength.

built-up member A member built from standard shapes to give one single stronger member.

camber Slight upward curve given to trusses and girders to avoid effect of sag.

cantilever A beam, girder, or truss overhanging one or both supports.

chord The principal member of a truss on either the top or bottom.

clearance Rivet driving clearance is distance from center of rivet to obstruction. Erection clearance is amount of space left between members for ease in assembly.

clevis U-shaped shackle for connecting a rod to a pin.

clip angle A small angle used for fastening various members together.

column A vertical compression member.

cope To cut out top or bottom of flanges and web so that one member will frame into another.

coping A projecting top course of concrete or stone.

counters Diagonal members in a truss to provide for reversal of shear due to live load.

cover plate A plate used in building up flanges, in a built-up member, to give greater strength and area or for protection.

crimp To offset the end of a stiffener to fit over the leg of an angle.

diagonals Diagonal members used for stiffening and wind bracing.

dowel An iron or wooden pin extending into, but not through, two timbers to connect them.

driftpin A tapered steel pin used to bring rivet holes fair in assembling steel work.

edge distance The distance from center of rivet to edge of plate or flange.

fabricate To cut, punch, and subassemble members in the shop.

fillers Either plate or ring fills used to take up space in riveting two members where a gusset is not used.

flange The projecting portion of a beam, channel, or column.

gage line The center line for rivet holes.

gin pole A guyed mast with block at the top for hoisting.

girder A horizontal member, either single or built up, acting as a principal beam.

girt A beam usually bolted to columns to support the side covering or serve as window lintels.

gusset plate A plate used to connect various members, such as in a truss.

hip The intersection between two sloping surfaces forming an exterior angle.

knee brace A corner brace used to prevent angular movement.

lacing or lattice bars Bars used diagonally to space and stiffen two parallel members, such as in a built-up column.

laterals Members used to prevent lateral deflection.

lintel A horizontal member used to carry a wall over an opening.

louvers Metal slats either movable or fixed, as in a monitor ventilator.

monitor ventilator A framework that carries fixed or movable louvers at the top of the roof.

panel The space between adjacent floor supports or purlins in a roof.

pitch Center distance between rivets parallel to axis of member. Also, for roofs, the ratio of rise to span.

plate Flat steel over 6 in. in width and $\frac{1}{4}$ in. or more in thickness.

purlins Horizontal members extending between trusses, used as beams for supporting the roof.

rafters Beams or truss members supporting the purlins.

sag ties Tie rods between purlins in the plane of the roof to carry the component of the roof load parallel to the roof.

separator Either a cast-iron spacer or wrought-iron pipe on a bolt for the purpose of holding members a fixed distance apart.

sheet Flat steel over 6 in. in width and less than ¼ in. in thickness.

shim A thin piece of wood or steel placed under a member to bring it to a desired elevation.

sleeve nut A long nut with right and left threads for connecting two rods to make an adjustable member.

span Distance between centers of supports of a truss, beam, or girder.

splice A longitudinal connection between the parts of a continuous member.

stiffener Angle, plate, or channel riveted to a member to prevent buckling.

stringer A longitudinal member used to support loads directly.

strut A compression member in a framework.

truss A rigid framework for carrying loads, formed in a series of triangles.

turnbuckle A coupling, threaded right and left or swiveled on one end, for adjustably connecting two rods.

valley The intersection between two sloping surfaces, forming a reentrant angle.

web The part of a channel, I beam, or girder between the flanges.

Part 3. Architectural terms

apron The finished board placed against the wall surface, immediately below a window stool.

ashlar Thin, squared, and dressed stone facing of a masonry wall.

backing The inner portion of a wall; that which is used behind the facing.

batten A strip of wood used for nailing across two other pieces of wood to hold them together and cover a crack.

batter boards Boards set up at the corners of a proposed building from which the lines marking off the walls are stretched.

bearing wall A wall that supports loads other than its own weight.

bond The joining together of building materials to ensure solidity.

bridging The braces or system of bracing used between joists or other structural members to stiffen them and to distribute the load.

centering A substructure of temporary nature, usually of timber or planks, on which a masonry arch or vault is built.

coffer An ornamental panel deeply recessed, usually in a dome or portico ceiling.

corbel A bracket formed on a wall by building out successive courses of masonry.

curtain wall A wall that carries no building load other than its own weight.

fenestration The arrangement and proportioning of window and door openings.

flashing The sheet metal built into the joints of a wall, or covering the valleys, ridges, and hips of a roof for the purpose of preventing leakage.

footing A course or series of courses projecting at the base of a wall for the purpose of distributing the load from above over a greater area, thereby preventing excessive settlement.

furring The application of thin wood, metal, or other building material to a wall, beam, ceiling, or the like to level a surface for lathing, boarding, etc., or to make an air space within a wall.

glazing The act of furnishing or fitting with glass.

ground Strips of wood, flush with the plastering, to which moldings, etc., are attached. Grounds are usually installed first and the plastering floated flush with them.

grout A thin mortar used for filling up spaces where heavier mortar will not penetrate.

head The horizontal piece forming the top of a wall opening, as a door or window.

hip The intersection of two roof surfaces, which form on the plan an external angle.

jamb The vertical piece forming the side of a wall opening.

lintel The horizontal structural member that supports the wall over an opening.

millwork The finish woodwork, machined and in some cases partly assembled at the mill.

miter To match together, as two pieces of molding, on a line bisecting the angle of junction.

mullion A vertical division of a window opening.

muntin The thin members that separate the individual lights of glass in a window frame.

party wall A division wall common to two adjacent pieces of property.

plate A horizontal member that carries other structural members; usually the top timber of a wall that carries the roof trusses or rafters directly.

rail A horizontal piece in a frame or paneling.

return The continuation in a different direction, most often at right angles, of the face of a building or any member, as a colonnade or molding; applied to the shorter in contradistinction to the longer.

reveal The side of a wall opening; the whole thickness of the wall; the jamb.

riser The upright piece of a step, from tread to tread.

saddle A small double-sloping roof to carry water away from behind chimneys, etc.

scratch coat The first coat in plastering, roughened by scratching or scoring so that the next coat may firmly adhere to it.

screeds A strip of plaster of the thickness proposed for the work, applied to the wall at intervals of 4 or 5 ft, to serve as guides.

shoring A prop, as a timber, placed against the side of a structure; a prop placed beneath anything, as a beam, to prevent sinking or sagging.

sill The horizontal piece, as a timber, which forms the lowest member of a frame.

sleepers The timbers laid on a firm foundation to carry and secure the superstructure.

soffit The underside of subordinate parts and members of buildings, such as staircases, beams, arches, etc.

stile A vertical piece in a frame or paneling.

stool The narrow shelf fitted on the inside of a window against the actual sill.

threshold The stone, wood, or metal piece which lies directly under a door.

trap A water seal in a sewage system to prevent sewer gas from entering the building.

tread The upper horizontal piece of a step, on which the foot is placed.

valley The intersection of two roof surfaces which form, on the plan, a reentrant angle.

BIBLIOGRAPHY

OF ALLIED SUBJECTS

The following classified list is given to supplement this book, whose scope as a general treatise on graphic science permits only the mention or brief explanation of some subjects.

Aeronautical drafting and design

Anderson, Newton H.: "Aircraft Layout and Detail Design," McGraw-Hill, New York, 1946.

Apalategui, J. J., and J. J. Adams: "Aircraft Analytic Geometry," McGraw-Hill, New York, 1944.

Davis, D. J., and C. H. Goen: "Aircraft Mechanical Drawing," McGraw-Hill, New York, 1944.

Katz, H. H.: "Aircraft Drafting," Macmillan, New York, 1946.

Leavell, S., and S. Bungay: "Aircraft Production Standards," McGraw-Hill, New York, 1943.

Liston, Joseph: "Powerplants for Aircraft," McGraw-Hill, New York, 1953.

Svensen, C. L.: "A Manual of Aircraft Drafting," Van Nostrand, Princeton, N.J., 1942.

Tharratt, George: "Aircraft Production Illustration," McGraw-Hill, New York, 1944.

Architectural drawing

Crane, T.: "Architectural Construction," Wiley, New York, 1956.

Kenney, Joseph E., and John P. McGrail: "Architectural Drawing for the Building Trades," McGraw-Hill, New York, 1949.

Morgan, Sherley W.: "Architectural Drawing," McGraw-Hill, New York, 1950.

Ramsey, C. G., and H. R. Sleeper: "Architectural Graphic Standards," Wiley, New York, 1956.

Saylor, H. H.: "Dictionary of Architecture," Wiley, New York, 1952.

Sleeper, H. R.: "Architectural Specifications," Wiley, New York, 1940.
694

Descriptive geometry   Bradley, H. C., and E. H. Uhler: "Descriptive Geometry for Engineers,"
International Textbook, Scranton, Pa., 1943.

Grant, Hiram E.: "Practical Descriptive Geometry," McGraw-Hill, New
York, 1952.

Higbee, F. G.: "Drawing-board Geometry," Wiley, New York, 1938.

Hood, George J.: "Geometry of Engineering Drawing," McGraw-Hill,
New York, 1946.

Johnson, L. O. and I. Wladaver: "Elements of Descriptive Geometry,"
Prentice-Hall, Englewood Cliffs, N.J., 1953.

Paré, E. G., R. O. Loving, and I. L. Hill: "Descriptive Geometry," Macmillan, New York, 1952.

Rowe, C. E.: "Engineering Descriptive Geometry," Van Nostrand, Princeton, N.J., 1953.

Shupe, Hollie W., and Paul E. Machovina: "A Manual of Engineering
Geometry and Graphics for Students and Draftsmen," McGraw-Hill,
New York, 1956.

Street, W. E.: "Technical Descriptive Geometry," Van Nostrand, Princeton, N.J., 1946.

Warner, Frank M.: "Applied Descriptive Geometry with Drafting-room
Problems," McGraw-Hill, New York, 1954.

Watts, Earle P., and John T. Rule: "Descriptive Geometry," Prentice-Hall,
Englewood Cliffs, N.J., 1946.

Wellman, B. Leighton: "Technical Descriptive Geometry," McGraw-Hill,
New York, 1957.

Drawing-instrument catalogues   Theo. Alteneder and Sons, Philadelphia.

Eugene Dietzgen Co., Chicago.

Grammercy Guild Group, Inc., New York.

Keuffel & Esser Co., Hoboken, N.J.

The Frederick Post Co., Chicago.

V and E Manufacturing Co., Pasadena, Calif.

Engineering drawing   French, Thomas E., and Charles J. Vierck: "A Manual of Engineering
Drawing for Students and Draftsmen, 8th ed., McGraw-Hill, New York,
1953.

Giesecke, F. E., A. Mitchell, and H. C. Spencer: "Technical Drawing,"
Macmillan, New York, 1940.

Healy, W. L., and A. H. Rau: "Simplified Drafting Practice," Wiley, New
York, 1953.

Hoelscher, R. P., and C. H. Springer: "Engineering Drawing and Geometry," Wiley, New York, 1956.

Luzadder, W. J.: "Graphics for Engineers," Prentice-Hall, Englewood
Cliffs, N.J., 1957.

Zozzora, Frank: "Engineering Drawing," McGraw-Hill, New York, 1953.

Engineering-drawing problem sheets   Higbee, F. G., and J. M. Russ: "Engineering Drawing Problems," $8\frac{1}{2} \times 11$
in., Wiley, New York, 1955.

Levens, A. S., and A. E. Edstrom: "Problems in Engineering Drawing,
Series IV," $8\frac{1}{2} \times 11$ in., McGraw-Hill, New York, 1953.

Vierck, Charles J., Charles D. Cooper, and Paul E. Machovina: "Engineering Drawing Problems, Series Two," 11×17 in., McGraw-Hill,
New York, 1953.

Vierck, Charles J., Charles D. Cooper, and Paul E. Machovina: "Engineering Drawing—Basic Problems, Series A," 8½ × 11 in., McGraw-Hill, New York, 1953.

Vierck, Charles J., and R. I. Hang: "Graphic Science Problems," 11 × 11¼ in., McGraw-Hill, New York, 1958.

Graphical solutions

Davis, D. S.: "Empirical Equations and Nomography," McGraw-Hill, New York, 1943.

Douglass, Raymond D., and Douglas P. Adams: "Elements of Nomography," McGraw-Hill, New York, 1947.

Hoelscher, R. P., J. Norman Arnold, and S. H. Pierce: "Graphic Aids in Engineering Computation," McGraw-Hill, New York, 1952.

Kulmann, C. Albert: "Nomographic Charts," McGraw-Hill, New York, 1951.

Levens, A. S.: "Nomography," Wiley, New York, 1948.

Levens, A. S.: "Graphics in Engineering and Science," Wiley, New York, 1954.

Lipka, J.: "Graphical and Mechanical Computation," Wiley, New York, 1918.

Rule, John T., and Earle P. Watts: "Engineering Graphics," McGraw-Hill, New York, 1951.

Handbooks

A great many handbooks, with tables, formulas, and information, are published for the different branches of the engineering profession, and draftsmen keep the ones pertaining to their particular line at hand for ready reference. Attention is called, however, to the danger of using handbook formulas and figures without understanding the principles upon which they are based. "Handbook designer" is a term of reproach applied not without reason to one who depends wholly upon these aids without knowing their theory or limitations.

Among the best known of these reference books are the following, alphabetized by *title:*

Colvin, Fred H., and Frank A. Stanley: "American Machinists' Handbook," McGraw-Hill, New York, 1948.

Perry, John H.: "Chemical Engineers' Handbook," McGraw-Hill, New York, 1950.

Urquhart, L. C.: "Civil Engineering Handbook," McGraw-Hill, New York, 1950.

"Cutting of Metals," American Society of Mechanical Engineers, New York, 1945.

"Definitions of Occupational Specialties in Engineering," American Society of Mechanical Engineers, New York, 1952.

"Design Data and Methods—Applied Mechanics," American Society of Mechanical Engineers, New York, 1953.

"Dynamics of Automatic Controls," American Society of Mechanical Engineers, New York, 1948.

"Engineering Tables," American Society of Mechanical Engineers, New York, 1956.

"Frequency Response," American Society of Mechanical Engineers, New York, 1956.

O'Rourke, Charles Edward: "General Engineering Handbook," McGraw-Hill, New York, 1940.

"Glossary of Terms in Nuclear Science and Technology," American Society of Mechanical Engineers, New York, 1957.

"Machinery's Handbook," The Industrial Press, New York, 1956.

"Manual on Cutting Metals," American Society of Mechanical Engineers, New York, 1952.

"Manual of Standard Practice for Detailing Reinforced Concrete Structures," American Concrete Institute, Detroit, Mich., 1956.

Marks, Lionel S.: "Mechanical Engineers' Handbook," McGraw-Hill, New York, 1951.

Kent, William: "Mechanical Engineers Handbook," Wiley, New York, 1950.

"Metals Engineering—Design," American Society of Mechanical Engineers, New York, 1953.

"Metals Properties," American Society of Mechanical Engineers, New York, 1954.

"Operation and Flow Process Charts," American Society of Mechanical Engineers, New York, 1947.

Walker, J. H., S. Crocker, and J. R. Allen: "Piping Handbook," McGraw-Hill, New York, 1945.

"Plant Layout Templates and Models," American Society of Mechanical Engineers, New York, 1949.

"Riveted Joints," American Society of Mechanical Engineers, New York, 1945.

"SAE Handbook," Society of Automotive Engineers, New York, yearly.

"Shock and Vibration Instrumentation," American Society of Mechanical Engineers, New York, 1956.

Knowlton, Archer E.: "Standard Handbook for Electrical Engineers," McGraw-Hill, New York, 1949.

"Steel Castings Handbook," Steel Founders Society of America, Cleveland, Ohio, 1956.

"Steel Construction," American Institute of Steel Construction, Inc., New York, 1956.

"Structural Shop Drafting," American Institute of Steel Construction, Inc., New York, 1950.

Wilson, Frank W.: "Tool Engineers' Handbook," McGraw-Hill, New York, 1949.

Illustration   Hoelscher, Randolph Philip, Clifford Harry Springer, and Richard F. Pohle: "Industrial Production Illustration," McGraw-Hill, New York, 1946.

Tharratt, George: "Aircraft Production Illustration," McGraw-Hill, New York, 1944.

Treacy, John: "Production Illustration," Wiley, New York, 1945.

Kinematics and machine design   Albert, C. D.: "Machine Design Drawing Room Problems," Wiley, New York, 1951.

Black, Paul H.: "Machine Design," McGraw-Hill, New York, 1955.

Faires, V. M.: "Design of Machine Elements," Macmillan, New York, 1947.

Guillet, G. L.: "Kinematics of Machines," Wiley, New York, 1950.

Ham, C. W., and E. J. Crane: "Mechanics of Machinery," McGraw-Hill, New York, 1948.

Hyland, P. H., and J. B. Kommers: "Machine Design," McGraw-Hill, New York, 1943.

Keown, Robert McArdle, and Virgil Moring Faires: "Mechanism," McGraw-Hill, New York, 1939.

Prageman, I. H.: "Mechanism," International Textbook, Scranton, Pa., 1943.

Sahag, L. M.: "Kinematics of Machines," Ronald, New York, 1948.

Schwamb, Peter, and others: "Elements of Mechanism," Wiley, New York, 1954.

Sloane, A.: "Engineering Kinematics," Macmillan, New York, 1947.

Vallance, Alex, and Venton L. Doughtie: "Design of Machine Members," McGraw-Hill, New York, 1951.

Lettering   French, Thomas E., and W. D. Turnbull: "Lessons in Lettering," McGraw-Hill, New York, 1950.

Svensen, C. L.: "The Art of Lettering," Van Nostrand, Princeton, N.J., 1947.

Map and topographic drawing   Sloane, Roscoe C., and John M. Montz: "Elements of Topographic Drawing," McGraw-Hill, New York, 1943.

Perspective   Lawson, Philip J.: "Practical Perspective Drawing," McGraw-Hill, New York, 1943.

Lubschez, B.: "Perspective," Van Nostrand, Princeton, N.J., 1926.

Piping   See Handbooks, as well as the following:

"Catalogue," Crane & Co., Chicago.

"Catalogue," Walworth Company, Boston.

Crocker, Sabin: "Piping Handbook," McGraw-Hill, New York, 1954.

Plum, S.: "Plumbing Practice and Design," Wiley, New York, 1943.

Shop practice and tools   See Handbooks, as well as the following:

Benedict, Otis J., Jr.: "Manual of Foundry and Pattern Shop Practice," McGraw-Hill, New York, 1947.

Boston, O. W.: "Metal Processing," Wiley, New York, 1951.

Burghardt, Henry D., and Aaron Axelrod: "Machine Tool Operation," McGraw-Hill, New York, 1953.

Campbell, James S., Jr.: "Casting and Forming Processes in Manufacturing," McGraw-Hill, New York, 1950.

Colvin, Fred H., and Lucian L. Haas: "Jigs and Fixtures," McGraw-Hill, New York, 1948.

Doe, E. W.: "Foundry Work," Wiley, New York, 1951.

Hine, Charles R.: "Machine Tools for Engineers," McGraw-Hill, New York, 1950.

Schaller, Gilbert S.: "Engineering Manufacturing Methods," McGraw-Hill, New York, 1953.

Slide rule   Cajori, F.: "A History of the Logarithmic Slide Rule," Engineering News Publishing Co., New York, 1910.

Machovina, Paul E.: "A Manual for the Slide Rule," McGraw-Hill, New York, 1950.

Structural drawing and design See Handbooks, as well as the following:

Bishop, C. T.: "Structural Drafting," Wiley, New York, 1941.

Shedd and Vawter: "Theory of Simple Structures," Wiley, New York, 1941.

Urquhart, L. C., and C. E. O'Rourke: "Design of Steel Structures," McGraw-Hill, New York, 1930.

Urquhart, Leonard C., Charles Edward O'Rourke, and George Winter: "Design of Concrete Structures," McGraw-Hill, New York, 1954.

AMERICAN STANDARDS

The ASA is working continually on standardization projects. Of its many publications, the following Standards having to do with the subjects in this book are available at the time of this printing. A complete list of American Standards will be sent by the Association on application to its offices, 29 West 39th Street, New York.

American Standard safety codes Code for pressure piping, B31.1—1955

Gas-transmission and distribution piping systems, B31.1.8—1955

Jacks, B30.1—1952

Mechanical power-transmission apparatus, B15.1—1953

Scheme for identification of piping systems, A13.1—1956

ASME boiler and pressure-vessel codes Material specifications, 1956–7

Power boilers, 1956–7

Welding qualifications, 1956–7

Bolts, nuts, rivets, and screws Hexagonal- and slotted-head cap screws, square-head setscrews, slotted headless setscrews, B18.6.2—1956

High-strength, high-temperature internal wrenching bolts, B18.8—1950

Large rivets, B18.4—1957

Plow bolts, B18.9—1950

Round-head bolts, B18.5—1952

Slotted- and recessed-head wood screws, B18.6.1—1956

Small solid rivets, B18.1—1955

Socket-head cap screws and socket setscrews, B18.3—1954

Square and hexagonal bolts and nuts and lag bolts, B18.2—1955

Track bolts and nuts, B18.10—1952

Drafting, charts, and symbols Abbreviations for scientific and engineering terms, Z10.1—1941

Abbreviations for use on drawings, Z32.13—1950

Drawings and drafting-room practice, Z14.1—1946

Graphical symbols for heating, ventilating, and air conditioning, Z32.2.4—1949

Graphical symbols for heat-power apparatus, Z32.2.6—1950

Graphical symbols for pipe fittings, valves, and piping, Z32.2.3—1953

Graphical symbols for plumbing, Y32.4—1955

Graphical symbols for railway use, Z32.2.5—1950

Graphical symbols for welding and instructions for their use, Z32.2.1—1949

A guide for preparing technical illustrations for publications and projections, 1954

Letter symbols for acoustics, Y10.11—1953

Letter symbols for aeronautical sciences, Y10.7—1954

Letter symbols for chemical engineering, Y10.12—1955

Letter symbols for heat and thermodynamics, including heat flow, Z10.4—1943

Letter symbols for hydraulics, Z10.2—1942

Letter symbols for mechanics of solid bodies, Z10.3—1948

Letter symbols for meteorology, Y10.10—1953

Letter symbols for physics, Z10.6—1948

Letter symbols for radio, Y10.9—1953

Letter symbols for structural analysis, Z10.8—1949

Time series charts, Z15.2—1947

Gearde sign, dimensions, and inspection

Design for fine-pitch worm gearing, B6.9—1956

Fine-pitch straight bevel gears, B6.8—1950

Gear nomenclature, B6.10—1954

Gear tolerances and inspection, B6.6—1946

Inspection of fine-pitch gears, B6.11—1956

Letter symbols for gear engineering, B6.5—1954

Nomenclature for gear-tooth wear and failure, B6.12—1954

Spur-gear tooth form, B6.1—1932

System for straight bevel gears, B6.13—1955

Twenty-degree involute fine-pitch system for spur and helical gears, B6.7—1956

Miscellaneous standards

Indicating pressure and vacuum gages, B40.1—1953

Lock washers, B27.1—1950

Plain washers, B27.2—1953

Preferred thickness for uncoated, thin, flat metals, B32.1—1952

Shaft coupling, B49.1—1947

Surface roughness, waviness, and lay, B46.1—1955

Woodruff keys, keyslots, and cutters, B17f—1955

Pipe, pipe fittings, and threads

Brass fittings for flared copper tubes, A40.2—1936

Brass or bronze flanges and flanged fittings—150 and 300 lb, B16.24—1953

Brass or bronze screwed fittings—125 lb, B16.15—1952

Brass or bronze screwed fittings—250 lb, B16.17—1953

Butt-welding ends, B16.25—1955

Cast-brass solder-joint drainage fittings, B16.23—1955

Cast-brass solder-joint fittings, B16.18—1950

CI pipe flanges and flanged fittings, 25-psi, B16b2—1931; class 125, B16.1—1948; class 250, B16b—1944; 800-lb hydraulic pressure, B16b1—1952; class 300-lb refrigerant, B16.16—1952

CI screwed drainage fittings, B16.12—1953

CI screwed fittings, 125- and 250-lb, B16.4—1953

CI soil pipe and fittings, A40.1—1935

Face-to-face dimensions of ferrous flanged and welding end valves, B16.10—1947

Ferrous plugs, bushings, and locknuts with pipe threads, B16.14—1953

Malleable-iron screwed fittings, 150-lb, B16.3—1951

Malleable-iron screwed fittings, 300-lb, B16.19—1951

National plumbing code, A40.8—1955

Nonmetallic gaskets for pipe flanges, B16.21—1951

Pipe threads, B2.1—1945

Ring-joint gaskets and grooves for steel pipe flanges, B16.20—1956

Stainless-steel pipe, B36.19—1957

Steel butt-welding fittings, B16.9—1951

Steel pipe flanges and flanged fittings, 150-, 300-, 400-, 600-, 900-, 1,500-, and 2,500-lb, B16.5—1953

Steel-socket welding fittings, B16.11—1952

Threaded cast-iron pipe for drainage, vent, and waste services, A40.5—1943

Wrought-copper and wrought-bronze solder-joint fittings, B16.22—1951

Wrought-steel and wrought-iron pipe, B36.10—1950

Small tools and machine-tool elements

Acme screw threads, B1.5—1952

Buttress screw threads, B1.9—1953

Chucks and chuck jaws, B5.8—1954

Hose-coupling screw threads, B33.1—1947

Involute serrations, B5.26—1950

Involute splines, B5.15—1950

Jig bushings, B5.6—1949

Knurling, B5.30—1953

Machine tapers, B5.10—1953

Milling cutters, B5.3—1950

Nomenclature, definitions, and letter symbols for screw threads, B1.7—1953

Preferred limits and fits for cylindrical parts, B4.1—1955

Reamers, B5.14—1949

Screw thread gages and gaging, B1.2—1951

Stub Acme screw threads, B1.8—1952

Taps—cut and ground threads, B5.4—1948

T slots and their bolts, nuts, tongues, and cutters, B5.1—1949

Twist drills, B5.12—1950

Unified and American screw threads standard, B1.1—1951

Standards under development

Abbreviations—for use in text

Drafting standards manual—size and format, line conventions, lettering and sectioning, projections, pictorial drawings, dimensions and notes, castings, die castings, forgings, gears, splines and serrations, helical and flat springs, hydraulic and pneumatic diagrams, metal stampings, plastics, schematic wiring and diagrams, screw threads, structural drafting

Fluid meters—theory and application

Gears—inspection of coarse-pitch spur and helical gears

Screws and screw threads—microscope-objective threads, surveying-instrument mounting threads, national miniature screw threads, "trial" class 5 interference-fit thread

Small tools—inserted-blade milling-cutter bodies, driving and spindle ends for portable electric tools

Symbols—miscellaneous

Washers—precision

PUBLICATIONS OF NATIONAL SOCIETIES

The national engineering organizations publish a wide variety of manuals, standards, handbooks, and pamphlets. Because these publications are so varied and extensive, they cannot be individually listed here but may be obtained directly from the publishing societies. The following is a selected list of American organizations:

Air Conditioning and Refrigerating Machinery Association, Southern Bldg., Washington 5, D.C.

Aircraft Industries Association of America, Inc., 610 Shoreham Bldg., Washington 5, D.C.

American Association for the Advancement of Science (AAAS), 1515 Massachusetts Ave. NW, Washington 5, D.C.

American Association of Engineers (AAE), 8 South Michigan Ave., Chicago, Ill.

American Association of Petroleum Geologists, Inc. (AAPG), P.O. Box 979, Tulsa, Okla.

American Association of University Professors, 1155 16th St. NW, Washington 6, D.C.

American Ceramic Society (ACerS), 2525 North High St., Columbus 2, Ohio

American Chemical Society (ACS), ACS Bldg., 1155 16th St. NW, Washington 6, D.C.

American Concrete Institute (ACI), New Center Bldg., Detroit 2, Mich.

American Concrete Pipe Association, 228 North LaSalle St., Chicago 1, Ill.

American Gas Association (AGA), 420 Lexington Ave., New York 17, N.Y.

American Institute of Chemical Engineers (AIChE), 50 East 41st St., New York 17, N.Y.

American Institute of Consulting Engineers (AICE), 75 West St., New York, N.Y.

American Institute of Electrical Engineers (AIEE), 33 West 39th St., New York 18, N.Y.

American Institute of Mining and Metallurgical Engineers, Inc. (AIME), 29 West 39th St., New York, N.Y.

American Institute of Steel Construction, Inc. (AISC), 101 Park Ave., New York, N.Y.

American Mining Congress, 309 Munsey Bldg., Washington 4, D.C.

American Petroleum Institute (API), Rm. 2040, 50 West 50th St., New York, N.Y.

American Society for Engineering Education (ASEE), University of Illinois, Urbana, Ill.

American Society for Metals (ASM), 7301 Euclid Ave., Cleveland, Ohio

American Society for Quality Control (ASQC), 305 East 43d St., New York 17, N.Y.

American Society for Testing Materials (ASTM), 260 South Broad St., Philadelphia, Pa.

American Society of Agricultural Engineers (ASAE), St. Joseph, Mich.

American Society of Civil Engineers (ASCE), 33 West 39th St., New York, N.Y.

American Society of Heating and Ventilating Engineers (ASHVE), 51 Madison Ave., New York 10, N.Y.

American Society of Lubricating Engineers, Rm. 1708, 343 South Dearborn St., Chicago, Ill.

American Society of Mechanical Engineers (ASME), 29 West 39th St., New York, N.Y.

American Society of Photogrammetry, P.O. Box 18, Benjamin Franklin Station, Washington 4, D.C.

American Society of Refrigerating Engineers, 40 West 40th St., New York, N.Y.

American Society of Safety Engineers: National Safety Council Engineering Section, 20 North Wacker Dr., Chicago 6, Ill.

American Society of Tool Engineers (ASTE), 1666 Penobscot Bldg., Detroit 26, Mich.

American Standards Association (ASA), 70 East 45th St., New York 17, N.Y.

American Welding Society (AWS), 33 West 39th St., New York, N.Y.

The Asphalt Institute, 801 Second Ave., New York 17, N.Y.

Association of Iron and Steel Engineers (AISE), 1010 Empire Bldg., Pittsburgh, Pa.

The Electrochemical Society, Inc., 3000 Broadway, New York 27, N.Y.

Federation of American Scientists (FAS), 1749 L St. NW, Washington, D.C.

Highway Research Board, 2101 Constitution Ave., Washington 25, D.C.

Illuminating Engineering Society, 51 Madison Ave., New York 10, N.Y.

Industrial Management Society (IMS), 175 West Adams St., Chicago, Ill.

Industrial Research Institute, Inc., 60 East 42d St., New York 17, N.Y.

Institute of the Aeronautical Sciences (IAS), 2 East 64 St., New York, N.Y.

The Institute of Ceramic Engineers, 2525 North High St., Columbus, Ohio

The Institute of Radio Engineers, Inc. (IRE), 1 East 79th St., New York 21, N.Y.

Mining and Metallurgical Society of America (MMSA), Columbia University School of Mines, New York 27, N.Y.

National Aeronautic Association (NAA), 1025 Connecticut Ave., NW, Washington, D.C.

National Council of Professional Industrial Engineers, 1166 East 61st St., Chicago 37, Ill.

National Society of Professional Engineers (NSPE), 1359 Connecticut Ave. NW, Washington 6, D.C.

Society of Automotive Engineers, Inc. (SAE), 29 West 39th St., New York 18, N.Y.

APPENDIX

LOGARITHMS OF NUMBERS

10	0	1	2	3	4	5	6	7	8	9
10	0000	0043	0086	0128	0170	0212	0253	0294	0334	0374
11	0414	0453	0492	0531	0569	0607	0645	0682	0719	0755
12	0792	0828	0864	0899	0934	0969	1004	1038	1072	1106
13	1139	1173	1206	1239	1271	1303	1335	1367	1399	1430
14	1461	1492	1523	1553	1584	1614	1644	1673	1703	1732
15	1761	1790	1818	1847	1875	1903	1931	1959	1987	2014
16	2041	2068	2095	2122	2148	2175	2201	2227	2253	2279
17	2304	2330	2355	2380	2405	2430	2455	2480	2504	2529
18	2553	2577	2601	2625	2648	2672	2695	2718	2742	2765
19	2788	2810	2833	2856	2878	2900	2923	2945	2967	2989
20	3010	3032	3054	3075	3096	3118	3139	3160	3181	3201
21	3222	3243	3263	3284	3304	3324	3345	3365	3385	3404
22	3424	3444	3464	3483	3502	3522	3541	3560	3579	3598
23	3617	3636	3655	3674	3692	3711	3729	3747	3766	3784
24	3802	3820	3838	3856	3874	3892	3909	3927	3945	3962
25	3979	3997	4014	4031	4048	4065	4082	4099	4116	4133
26	4150	4166	4183	4200	4216	4232	4249	4265	4281	4298
27	4314	4330	4346	4362	4378	4393	4409	4425	4440	4456
28	4472	4487	4502	4518	4533	4548	4564	4579	4594	4609
29	4624	4639	4654	4669	4683	4698	4713	4728	4742	4757
30	4771	4786	4800	4814	4829	4843	4857	4871	4886	4900
31	4914	4928	4942	4955	4969	4983	4997	5011	5024	5038
32	5051	5065	5079	5092	5105	5119	5132	5145	5159	5172
33	5185	5198	5211	5224	5237	5250	5263	5276	5289	5302
34	5315	5328	5340	5353	5366	5378	5391	5403	5416	5428
35	5441	5453	5465	5478	5490	5502	5514	5527	5539	5551
36	5563	5575	5587	5599	5611	5623	5635	5647	5658	5670
37	5682	5694	5705	5717	5729	5740	5752	5763	5775	5786
38	5798	5809	5821	5832	5843	5855	5866	5877	5888	5899
39	5911	5922	5933	5944	5955	5966	5977	5988	5999	6010
40	6021	6031	6042	6053	6054	6075	6085	6096	6107	6117
41	6128	6138	6149	6160	6170	6180	6191	6201	6212	6222
42	6232	6243	6253	6263	6274	6284	6294	6304	6314	6325
43	6335	6345	6355	6365	6375	6385	6395	6405	6415	6425
44	6435	6444	6454	6464	6474	6484	6493	6503	6513	6522
45	6532	6542	6551	6561	6571	6580	6590	6599	6609	6618
46	6628	6637	6646	6656	6665	6675	6684	6693	6702	6712
47	6721	6730	6739	6749	6758	6767	6776	6785	6794	6803
48	6812	6821	6830	6839	6848	6857	6866	6875	6884	6893
49	6902	6911	6920	6928	6937	6946	6955	6964	6972	6981
50	6990	6998	7007	7016	7024	7033	7042	7050	7059	7067
51	7076	7084	7093	7101	7110	7118	7126	7135	7143	7152
52	7160	7168	7177	7185	7193	7202	7210	7218	7226	7235
53	7243	7251	7259	7267	7275	7284	7292	7300	7308	7316
54	7324	7332	7340	7348	7356	7364	7372	7380	7388	7396

LOGARITHMS OF NUMBERS (*Cont.*)

55	0	1	2	3	4	5	6	7	8	9
55	7404	7412	7419	7427	7435	7443	7451	7459	7466	7474
56	7482	7490	7497	7505	7513	7520	7528	7536	7543	7551
57	7559	7566	7574	7582	7589	7597	7604	7612	7619	7627
58	7634	7642	7649	7657	7664	7672	7679	7686	7694	7701
59	7709	7716	7723	7731	7738	7745	7752	7760	7767	7774
60	7782	7789	7796	7803	7810	7818	7825	7832	7839	7846
61	7853	7860	7868	7875	7882	7889	7896	7903	7910	7917
62	7924	7931	7938	7945	7952	7959	7966	7973	7980	7987
63	7993	8000	8007	8014	8021	8028	8035	8041	8048	8055
64	8062	8069	8075	8082	8089	8096	8102	8109	8116	8122
65	8129	8136	8142	8149	8156	8162	8169	8176	8182	8189
66	8195	8202	8209	8215	8222	8228	8235	8241	8248	8254
67	8261	8267	8274	8280	8287	8293	8299	8306	8312	8319
68	8325	8331	8338	8344	8351	8357	8363	8370	8376	8382
69	8388	8395	8401	8407	8414	8420	8426	8432	8439	8445
70	8451	8457	8463	8470	8476	8482	8488	8494	8500	8506
71	8513	8519	8525	8531	8537	8543	8549	8555	8561	8567
72	8573	8579	8585	8591	8597	8603	8609	8615	8621	8627
73	8633	8639	8645	8651	8657	8663	8669	8675	8681	8686
74	8692	8698	8704	8710	8716	8722	8727	8733	8739	8745
75	8751	8756	8762	8768	8774	8779	8785	8791	8797	8802
76	8808	8814	8820	8825	8831	8837	8842	8848	8854	8859
77	8865	8871	8876	8882	8887	8893	8899	8904	8910	8915
78	8921	8927	8932	8938	8943	8949	8954	8960	8965	8971
79	8976	8982	8987	8993	8998	9004	9009	9015	9020	9025
80	9031	9036	9042	9047	9053	9058	9063	9069	9074	9079
81	9085	9090	9096	9101	9106	9112	9117	9122	9128	9133
82	9138	9143	9149	9154	9159	9165	9170	9175	9180	9186
83	9191	9196	9201	9206	9212	9217	9222	9227	9232	9238
84	9243	9248	9253	9258	9263	9269	9274	9279	9284	9289
85	9294	9299	9304	9309	9315	9320	9325	9330	9335	9340
86	9345	9350	9355	9360	9365	9370	9375	9380	9385	9390
87	9395	9400	9405	9410	9415	9420	9425	9430	9435	9440
88	9445	9450	9455	9460	9465	9469	9474	9479	9484	9489
89	9494	9499	9504	9509	9513	9518	9523	9528	9533	9538
90	9542	9547	9552	9557	9562	9566	9571	9576	9581	9586
91	9590	9595	9600	9605	9609	9614	9619	9624	9628	9633
92	9638	9643	9647	9652	9657	9661	9666	9671	9675	9680
93	9685	9689	9694	9699	9703	9708	9713	9717	9722	9727
94	9731	9736	9741	9745	9750	9754	9759	9763	9768	9773
95	9777	9782	9786	9791	9795	9800	9805	9809	9814	9818
96	9823	9827	9832	9836	9841	9845	9850	9854	9859	9863
97	9868	9872	9877	9881	9886	9890	9894	9899	9903	9908
98	9912	9917	9921	9926	9930	9934	9939	9943	9948	9952
99	9956	9961	9965	9969	9974	9978	9983	9987	9991	9996

TRIGONOMETRIC FUNCTIONS

Angle	Sine		Cosine		Tangent		Cotangent		Angle
	Nat.	Log.	Nat.	Log.	Nat.	Log.	Nat.	Log.	
0° 00′	.0000	∞	1.0000	0.0000	.0000	∞	∞	∞	90° 00′
10	.0029	7.4637	1.0000	0000	.0029	7.4637	343.77	2.5363	50
20	.0058	7648	1.0000	0000	.0058	7648	171.89	2352	40
30	.0087	9408	1.0000	0000	.0087	9409	114.59	0591	30
40	.0116	8.0658	.9999	0000	.0116	8.0658	85.940	1.9342	20
50	.0145	1627	.9999	0000	.0145	1627	68.750	8373	10
1° 00′	.0175	8.2419	.9998	9.9999	.0175	8.2419	57.290	1.7581	89° 00′
10	.0204	3088	.9998	9999	.0204	3089	49.104	6911	50
20	.0233	3668	.9997	9999	.0233	3669	42.964	6331	40
30	.0262	4179	.9997	9999	.0262	4181	38.188	5819	30
40	.0291	4637	.9996	9998	.0291	4638	34.368	5362	20
50	.0320	5050	.9995	9998	.0320	5053	31.242	4947	10
2° 00′	.0349	8.5428	.9994	9.9997	.0349	8.5431	28.636	1.4569	88° 00′
10	.0378	5776	.9993	9997	.0378	5779	26.432	4221	50
20	.0407	6097	.9992	9996	.0407	6101	24.542	3899	40
30	.0436	6397	.9990	9996	.0437	6401	22.904	3599	30
40	.0465	6677	.9989	9995	.0466	6682	21.470	3318	20
50	.0494	6940	.9988	9995	.0495	6945	20.206	3055	10
3° 00′	.0523	8.7188	.9986	9.9994	.0524	8.7194	19.081	1.2806	87° 00′
10	.0552	7423	.9985	9993	.0553	7429	18.075	2571	50
20	.0581	7645	.9983	9993	.0582	7652	17.169	2348	40
30	.0610	7857	.9981	9992	.0612	7865	16.350	2135	30
40	.0640	8059	.9980	9991	.0641	8067	15.605	1933	20
50	.0669	8251	.9978	9990	.0670	8261	14.924	1739	10
4° 00′	.0698	8.8436	.9976	9.9989	.0699	8.8446	14.301	1.1554	86° 00′
10	.0727	8613	.9974	9989	.0729	8624	13.727	1376	50
20	.0756	8783	.9971	9988	.0758	8795	13.197	1205	40
30	.0785	8946	.9969	9987	.0787	8960	12.706	1040	30
40	.0814	9104	.9967	9986	.0816	9118	12.251	0882	20
50	.0843	9256	.9964	9985	.0846	9272	11.826	0728	10
5° 00′	.0872	8.9403	.9962	9.9983	.0875	8.9420	11.430	1.0580	85° 00′
10	.0901	9545	.9959	9982	.0904	9563	11.059	0437	50
20	.0929	9682	.9957	9981	.0934	9701	10.712	0299	40
30	.0958	9816	.9954	9980	.0963	9836	10.385	0164	30
40	.0987	9945	.9951	9979	.0992	9966	10.078	0034	20
50	.1016	9.0070	.9948	9977	.1022	9.0093	9.7882	0.9907	10
6° 00′	.1045	9.0192	.9945	9.9976	.1051	9.0216	9.5144	0.9784	84° 00′
10	.1074	0311	.9942	9975	.1080	0336	9.2553	9664	50
20	.1103	0426	.9939	9973	.1110	0453	9.0098	9547	40
30	.1132	0539	.9936	9972	.1139	0567	8.7769	9433	30
40	.1161	0648	.9932	9971	.1169	0678	8.5555	9322	20
50	.1190	0755	.9929	9969	.1198	0786	8.3450	9214	10
7° 00′	.1219	9.0859	.9925	9.9968	.1228	9.0891	8.1443	0.9109	83° 00′
10	.1248	0961	.9922	9966	.1257	0995	7.9530	9005	50
20	.1276	1060	.9918	9964	.1287	1096	7.7704	8904	40
	Nat.	Log.	Nat.	Log.	Nat.	Log.	Nat.	Log.	
Angle	Cosine		Sine		Cotangent		Tangent		Angle

TRIGONOMETRIC FUNCTIONS (*Cont.*)

Angle	Sine		Cosine		Tangent		Cotangent		Angle
	Nat.	Log.	Nat.	Log.	Nat.	Log.	Nat.	Log.	
30	.1305	1157	.9914	9963	.1317	1194	7.5958	8806	30
40	.1334	1252	.9911	9961	.1346	1291	7.4287	8709	20
50	.1363	1345	.9907	9959	.1376	1385	7.2687	8615	10
8° 00′	.1392	9.1436	.9903	9.9958	.1405	9.1478	7.1154	0.8522	82° 00′
10	.1421	1525	.9899	9956	.1435	1569	6.9682	8431	50
20	.1449	1612	.9894	9954	.1465	1658	6.8269	8342	40
30	.1478	1697	.9890	9952	.1495	1745	6.6912	8255	30
40	.1507	1781	.9886	9950	.1524	1831	6.5606	8169	20
50	.1536	1863	.9881	9948	.1554	1915	6.4348	8085	10
9° 00′	.1564	9.1943	.9877	9.9946	.1584	9.1997	6.3138	0.8003	81° 00′
10	.1593	2022	.9872	9944	.1614	2078	6.1970	7922	50
20	.1622	2100	.9868	9942	.1644	2158	6.0844	7842	40
30	.1650	2176	.9863	9940	.1673	2236	5.9758	7764	30
40	.1679	2251	.9858	9938	.1703	2313	5.8708	7687	20
50	.1708	2324	.9853	9936	.1733	2389	5.7694	7611	10
10° 00′	.1736	9.2397	.9848	9.9934	.1763	9.2463	5.6713	0.7537	80° 00′
10	.1765	2468	.9843	9931	.1793	2536	5.5764	7464	50
20	.1794	2538	.9838	9929	.1823	2609	5.4845	7391	40
30	.1822	2606	.9833	9927	.1853	2680	5.3955	7320	30
40	.1851	2674	.9827	9924	.1883	2750	5.3093	7250	20
50	.1880	2740	.9822	9922	.1914	2819	5.2257	7181	10
11° 00′	.1908	9.2806	.9816	9.9919	.1944	9.2887	5.1446	0.7113	79° 00′
10	.1937	2870	.9811	9917	.1974	2953	5.0658	7047	50
20	.1965	2934	.9805	9914	.2004	3020	4.9894	6980	40
30	.1994	2997	.9799	9912	.2035	3085	4.9152	6915	30
40	.2022	3058	.9793	9909	.2065	3149	4.8430	6851	20
50	.2051	3119	.9787	9907	.2095	3212	4.7729	6788	10
12° 00′	.2079	9.3179	.9781	9.9904	.2126	9.3275	4.7046	0.6725	78° 00′
10	.2108	3238	.9775	9901	.2156	3336	4.6382	6664	50
20	.2136	3296	.9769	9899	.2186	3397	4.5736	6603	40
30	.2164	3353	.9763	9896	.2217	3458	4.5107	6542	30
40	.2193	3410	.9757	9893	.2247	3517	4.4494	6483	20
50	.2221	3466	.9750	9890	.2278	3576	4.3897	6424	10
13° 00′	.2250	9.3521	.9744	9.9887	.2309	9.3634	4.3315	0.6366	77° 00′
10	.2278	3575	.9737	9884	.2339	3691	4.2747	6309	50
20	.2306	3629	.9730	9881	.2370	3748	4.2193	6252	40
30	.2334	3682	.9724	9878	.2401	3804	4.1653	6196	30
40	.2363	3734	.9717	9875	.2432	3859	4.1126	6141	20
50	.2391	3786	.9710	9872	.2462	3914	4.0611	6086	10
14° 00′	.2419	9.3837	.9703	9.9869	.2493	9.3968	4.0108	0.6032	76° 00′
10	.2447	3887	.9696	9866	.2524	4021	3.9617	5979	50
20	.2476	3937	.9689	9863	.2555	4074	3.9136	5926	40
30	.2504	3986	.9681	9859	.2586	4127	3.8667	5873	30
40	.2532	4035	.9674	9856	.2617	4178	3.8208	5822	20
50	.2560	4083	.9667	9853	.2648	4230	3.7760	5770	10
	Nat.	Log.	Nat.	Log.	Nat.	Log.	Nat.	Log.	
Angle	Cosine		Sine		Cotangent		Tangent		Angle

TRIGONOMETRIC FUNCTIONS (*Cont.*)

Angle	Sine		Cosine		Tangent		Cotangent		Angle
	Nat.	Log.	Nat.	Log.	Nat.	Log.	Nat.	Log.	
15° 00′	.2588	9.4130	.9659	9.9849	.2679	9.4281	3.7321	0.5719	75° 00′
10	.2616	4177	.9652	9846	.2711	4331	3.6891	5669	50
20	.2644	4223	.9644	9843	.2742	4381	3.6470	5619	40
30	.2672	4269	.9636	9839	.2773	4430	3.6059	5570	30
40	.2700	4314	.9628	9836	.2805	4479	3.5656	5521	20
50	.2728	4359	.9621	9832	.2836	4527	3.5261	5473	10
16° 00′ ·	.2756	9.4403	.9613	9.9828	.2867	9.4575	3.4874	0.5425	74° 00′
10	.2784	4447	.9605	9825	.2899	4622	3.4495	5378	50
20	.2812	4491	.9596	9821	.2931	4669	3.4124	5331	40
30	.2840	4533	.9588	9817	.2962	4716	3.3759	5284	30
40	.2868	4576	.9580	9814	.2994	4762	3.3402	5238	20
50	.2896	4618	.9572	9810	.3026	4808	3.3052	5192	10
17° 00′	.2924	9.4659	.9563	9.9806	.3057	9.4853	3.2709	0.5147	73° 00′
10	.2952	4700	.9555	9802	.3089	4898	3.2371	5102	50
20	.2979	4741	.9546	9798	.3121	4943	3.2041	5057	40
30	.3007	4781	.9537	9794	.3153	4987	3.1716	5013	30
40	.3035	4821	.9528	9790	.3185	5031	3.1397	4969	20
50	.3062	4861	.9520	9786	.3217	5075	3.1084	4925	10
18° 00′	.3090	9.4900	.9511	9.9782	.3249	9.5118	3.0777	0.4882	72° 00′
10	.3118	4939	.9502	9778	.3281	5161	3.0475	4839	50
20	.3145	4977	.9492	9774	.3314	5203	3.0178	4797	40
30	.3173	5015	.9483	9770	.3346	5245	2.9887	4755	30
40	.3201	5052	.9474	9765	.3378	5287	2.9600	4713	20
50	.3228	5090	.9465	9761	.3411	5329	2.9319	4671	10
19° 00′	.3256	9.5126	.9455	9.9757	.3443	9.5370	2.9042	0.4630	71° 00′
10	.3283	5163	.9446	9752	.3476	5411	2.8770	4589	50
20	.3311	5199	.9436	9748	.3508	5451	2.8502	4549	40
30	.3338	5235	.9426	9743	.3541	5491	2.8239	4509	30
40	.3365	5270	.9417	9739	.3574	5531	2.7980	4469	20
50	.3393	5306	.9407	9734	.3607	5571	2.7725	4429	10
20° 00′	.3420	9.5341	.9397	9.9730	.3640	9.5611	2.7475	0.4389	70° 00′
10	.3448	5375	.9387	9725	.3673	5650	2.7228	4350	50
20	.3475	5409	.9377	9721	.3706	5689	2.6985	4311	40
30	.3502	5443	.9367	9716	.3739	5727	2.6746	4273	30
40	.3529	5477	.9356	9711	.3772	5766	2.6511	4234	20
50	.3557	5510	.9346	9706	.3805	5804	2.6279	4196	10
21° 00′	.3584	9.5543	.9336	9.9702	.3839	9.5842	2.6051	0.4158	69° 00′
10	.3611	5576	.9325	9697	.3872	5879	2.5826	4121	50
20	.3638	5609	.9315	9692	.3906	5917	2.5605	4083	40
30	.3665	5641	.9304	9687	.3939	5954	2.5386	4046	30
40	.3692	5673	.9293	9682	.3973	5991	2.5172	4009	20
50	.3719	5704	.9283	9677	.4006	6028	2.4960	3972	10
22° 00′	.3746	9.5736	.9272	9.9672	.4040	9.6064	2.4751	0.3936	68° 00′
10	.3773	5767	.9261	9667	.4074	6100	2.4545	3900	50
20	.3800	5798	.9250	9661	.4108	6136	2.4342	3864	40
30	.3827	5828	.9239	9656	.4142	6172	2.4142	3828	30
	Nat.	Log.	Nat.	Log.	Nat.	Log.	Nat.	Log.	
Angle	Cosine		Sine		Cotangent		Tangent		Angle

TRIGONOMETRIC FUNCTIONS (*Cont.*)

Angle	Sine		Cosine		Tangent		Cotangent		Angle
	Nat.	Log.	Nat.	Log.	Nat.	Log.	Nat.	Log.	
40	.3854	5859	.9228	9651	.4176	6208	2.3945	3792	20
50	.3881	5889	.9216	9646	.4210	6243	2.3750	3757	10
23° 00′	.3907	9.5919	.9205	9.9640	4245	9.6279	2.3559	0.3721	67° 00′
10	.3934	5948	.9194	9635	.4279	6314	2.3369	3686	50
20	.3961	5978	.9182	9629	.4314	6348	2.3183	3652	40
30	.3987	6007	.9171	9624	.4348	6383	2.2998	3617	30
40	.4014	6036	.9159	9618	.4383	6417	2.2817	3583	20
50	.4041	6065	.9147	9613	.4417	6452	2.2637	3548	10
24° 00′	.4067	9.6093	.9135	9.9607	.4452	9.6486	2.2460	0.3514	66° 00′
10	.4094	6121	.9124	9602	.4487	6520	2.2286	3480	50
20	.4120	6149	.9112	9596	.4522	6553	2.2113	3447	40
30	.4147	6177	.9100	9590	.4557	6587	2.1943	3413	30
40	.4173	6205	.9088	9584	.4592	6620	2.1775	3380	20
50	.4200	6232	.9075	9579	.4628	6654	2.1609	3346	10
25° 00′	.4226	9.6259	.9063	9.9573	.4663	9.6687	2.1445	0.3313	65° 00′
10	.4253	6286	.9051	9567	.4699	6720	2.1283	3280	50
20	.4279	6313	.9038	9561	.4734	6752	2.1123	3248	40
30	.4305	6340	.9026	9555	.4770	6785	2.0965	3215	30
40	.4331	6366	.9013	9549	.4806	6817	2.0809	3183	20
50	.4358	6392	.9001	9543	.4841	6850	2.0655	3150	10
26° 00′	.4384	9.6418	.8988	9.9537	.4877	9.6882	2.0503	0.3118	64° 00′
10	.4410	6444	.8975	9530	.4913	6914	2.0353	3086	50
20	.4436	6470	.8962	9524	.4950	6946	2.0204	3054	40
30	.4462	6495	.8949	9518	.4986	6977	2.0057	3023	30
40	.4488	6521	.8936	9512	.5022	7009	1.9912	2991	20
50	.4514	6546	.8923	9505	.5059	7040	1.9768	2960	10
27° 00′	.4540	9.6570	.8910	9.9499	.5095	9.7072	1.9626	0.2928	63° 00′
10	.4566	6595	.8897	9492	.5132	7103	1.9486	2897	50
20	.4592	6620	.8884	9486	.5169	7134	1.9347	2866	40
30	.4617	6644	.8870	9479	.5206	7165	1.9210	2835	30
40	.4643	6668	.8857	9473	.5243	7196	1.9074	2804	20
50	.4669	6692	.8843	9466	.5280	7226	1.8940	2774	10
28° 00′	.4695	9.6716	.8829	9.9459	.5317	9.7257	1.8807	0.2743	62° 00′
10	.4720	6740	.8816	9453	.5354	7287	1.8676	2713	50
20	.4746	6763	.8802	9446	.5392	7317	1.8546	2683	40
30	.4772	6787	.8788	9439	.5430	7348	1.8418	2652	30
40	.4797	6810	.8774	9432	.5467	7378	1.8291	2622	20
50	.4823	6833	.8760	9425	.5505	7408	1.8165	2592	10
29° 00′	.4848	9.6856	.8746	9.9418	.5543	9.7438	1.8040	0.2562	61° 00′
10	.4874	6878	.8732	9411	.5581	7467	1.7917	2533	50
20	.4899	6901	.8718	9404	.5619	7497	1.7796	2503	40
30	.4924	6923	.8704	9397	.5658	7526	1.7675	2474	30
40	.4950	6946	.8689	9390	.5696	7556	1.7556	2444	20
50	.4975	6968	.8675	9383	.5735	7585	1.7437	2415	10
	Nat.	Log.	Nat.	Log.	Nat.	Log.	Nat.	Log.	
Angle	Cosine		Sine		Cotangent		Tangent		Angle

TRIGONOMETRIC FUNCTIONS (*Cont.*)

Angle	Sine		Cosine		Tangent		Cotangent		Angle
	Nat.	Log.	Nat.	Log.	Nat.	Log.	Nat.	Log.	
30° 00′	.5000	9.6990	.8660	9.9375	.5774	9.7614	1.7321	0.2386	60° 00′
10	.5025	7012	.8646	9368	.5812	7644	1.7205	2356	50
20	.5050	7033	.8631	9361	.5851	7673	1.7090	2327	40
30	.5075	7055	.8616	9353	.5890	7701	1.6977	2299	30
40	.5100	7076	.8601	9346	.5930	7730	1.6864	2270	20
50	.5125	7097	.8587	9338	.5969	7759	1.6753	2241	10
31° 00′	.5150	9.7118	.8572	9.9331	.6009	9.7788	1.6643	0.2212	59° 00′
10	.5175	7139	.8557	9323	.6048	7816	1.6534	2184	50
20	.5200	7160	.8542	9315	.6088	7845	1.6426	2155	40
30	.5225	7181	.8526	9308	.6128	7873	1.6319	2127	30
40	.5250	7201	.8511	9300	.6168	7902	1.6212	2098	20
50	.5275	7222	.8496	9292	.6208	7930	1.6107	2070	10
32° 00′	.5299	9.7242	.8480	9.9284	.6249	9.7958	1.6003	0.2042	58° 00′
10	.5324	7262	.8465	9276	.6289	7986	1.5900	2014	50
20	.5348	7282	.8450	9268	.6330	8014	1.5798	1986	40
30	.5373	7302	.8434	9260	.6371	8042	1.5697	1958	30
40	.5398	7322	.8418	9252	.6412	8070	1.5597	1930	20
50	.5422	7342	.8403	9244	.6453	8097	1.5497	1903	10
33° 00′	.5446	9.7361	.8387	9.9236	.6494	9.8125	1.5399	0.1875	57° 00′
10	.5471	7380	.8371	9228	.6536	8153	1.5301	1847	50
20	.5495	7400	.8355	9219	.6577	8180	1.5204	1820	40
30	.5519	7419	.8339	9211	.6619	8208	1.5108	1792	30
40	.5544	7438	.8323	9203	.6661	8235	1.5013	1765	20
50	.5568	7457	.8307	9194	.6703	8263	1.4919	1737	10
34° 00′	.5592	9.7476	.8290	9.9186	.6745	9.8290	1.4826	0.1710	56° 00′
10	.5616	7494	.8274	9177	.6787	8317	1.4733	1683	50
20	.5640	7513	.8258	9169	.6830	8344	1.4641	1656	40
30	.5664	7531	.8241	9160	.6873	8371	1.4550	1629	30
40	.5688	7550	.8225	9151	.6916	8398	1.4460	1602	20
50	.5712	7568	.8208	9142	.6959	8425	1.4370	1575	10
35° 00′	.5736	9.7586	.8192	9.9134	.7002	9.8452	1.4281	0.1548	55° 00′
10	.5760	7604	.8175	9125	.7046	8479	1.4193	1521	50
20	.5783	7622	.8158	9116	.7089	8506	1.4106	1494	40
30	.5807	7640	.8141	9107	.7133	8533	1.4019	1467	30
40	.5831	7657	.8124	9098	.7177	8559	1.3934	1441	20
50	.5854	7675	.8107	9089	.7221	8586	1.3848	1414	10
36° 00′	.5878	9.7692	.8090	9.9080	.7265	9.8613	1.3764	0.1387	54° 00′
10	.5901	7710	.8073	9070	.7310	8639	1.3680	1361	50
20	.5925	7727	.8056	9061	.7355	8666	1.3597	1334	40
30	.5948	7744	.8039	9052	.7400	8692	1.3514	1308	30
40	.5972	7761	.8021	9042	.7445	8718	1.3432	1282	20
50	.5995	7778	.8004	9033	.7490	8745	1.3351	1255	10
37° 00′	.6018	9.7795	.7986	9.9023	.7536	9.8771	1.3270	0.1229	53° 00′
10	.6041	7811	.7969	9014	.7581	8797	1.3190	1203	50
20	.6065	7828	.7951	9004	.7627	8824	1.3111	1176	40
	Nat.	Log.	Nat.	Log.	Nat.	Log.	Nat.	Log.	
Angle	Cosine		Sine		Cotangent		Tangent		Angle

TRIGONOMETRIC FUNCTIONS (*Cont.*)

Angle	Sine Nat.	Sine Log.	Cosine Nat.	Cosine Log.	Tangent Nat.	Tangent Log.	Cotangent Nat.	Cotangent Log.	Angle
30	.6088	7844	.7934	8995	.7673	8850	1.3032	1150	30
40	.6111	7861	.7916	8985	.7720	8876	1.2954	1124	20
50	.6134	7877	.7898	8975	.7766	8902	1.2876	1098	10
38° 00′	.6157	9.7893	.7880	9.8965	.7813	9.8928	1.2799	0.1072	52° 00′
10	.6180	7910	.7862	8955	.7860	8954	1.2723	1046	50
20	.6202	7926	.7844	8945	.7907	8980	1.2647	1020	40
30	.6225	7941	.7826	8935	.7954	9006	1.2572	0994	30
40	.6248	7957	.7808	8925	.8002	9032	1.2497	0968	20
50	.6271	7973	.7790	8915	.8050	9058	1.2423	0942	10
39° 00′	.6293	9.7989	.7771	9.8905	.8098	9.9084	1.2349	0.0916	51° 00′
10	.6316	8004	.7753	8895	.8146	9110	1.2276	0890	50
20	.6338	8020	.7735	8884	.8195	9135	1.2203	0865	40
30	.6361	8035	.7716	8874	.8243	9161	1.2131	0839	30
40	.6383	8050	.7698	8864	.8292	9187	1.2059	0813	20
50	.6406	8066	.7679	8853	.8342	9212	1.1988	0788	10
40° 00′	.6428	9.8081	.7660	9.8843	.8391	9.9238	1.1918	0.0762	50° 00′
10	.6450	8096	.7642	8832	.8441	9264	1.1847	0736	50
20	.6472	8111	.7623	8821	.8491	9289	1.1778	0711	40
30	.6494	8125	.7604	8810	.8541	9315	1.1708	0685	30
40	.6517	8140	.7585	8800	.8591	9341	1.1640	0659	20
50	.6539	8155	.7566	8789	.8642	9366	1.1571	0634	10
41° 00′	.6561	9.8169	.7547	9.8778	.8693	9.9392	1.1504	0.0608	49° 00′
10	.6583	8184	.7528	8767	.8744	9417	1.1436	0583	50
20	.6604	8198	.7509	8756	.8796	9443	1.1369	0557	40
30	.6626	8213	.7490	8745	.8847	9468	1.1303	0532	30
40	.6648	8227	.7470	8733	.8899	9494	1.1237	0506	20
50	.6670	8241	.7451	8722	.8952	9519	1.1171	0481	10
42° 00′	.6691	9.8255	.7431	9.8711	.9004	9.9544	1.1106	0.0456	48° 00′
10	.6713	8269	.7412	8699	.9057	9570	1.1041	0430	50
20	.6734	8283	.7392	8688	.9110	9595	1.0977	0405	40
30	.6756	8297	.7373	8676	.9163	9621	1.0913	0379	30
40	.6777	8311	.7353	8665	.9217	9646	1.0850	0354	20
50	.6799	8324	.7333	8653	.9271	9671	1.0786	0329	10
43° 00′	.6820	9.8338	.7314	9.8641	.9325	9.9697	1.0724	0.0303	47° 00′
10	.6841	8351	.7294	8629	.9380	9722	1.0661	0278	50
20	.6862	8365	.7274	8618	.9435	9747	1.0599	0253	40
30	.6884	8378	.7254	8606	.9490	9772	1.0538	0228	30
40	.6905	8391	.7234	8594	.9545	9798	1.0477	0202	20
50	.6926	8405	.7214	8582	.9601	9823	1.0416	0177	10
44° 00′	.6947	9.8418	.7193	9.8569	.9657	9.9848	1.0355	0.0152	46° 00′
10	.6967	8431	.7173	8557	.9713	9874	1.0295	0126	50
20	.6988	8444	.7153	8545	.9770	9899	1.0235	0101	40
30	.7009	8457	.7133	8532	.9827	9924	1.0176	0076	30
40	.7030	8469	.7112	8520	.9884	9949	1.0117	0051	20
50	.7050	8482	.7092	8507	.9942	9975	1.0058	0025	10
45° 00′	.7071	9.8495	.7071	9.8495	1.0000	0.0000	1.0000	0.0000	45° 00′
	Nat.	Log.	Nat.	Log.	Nat.	Log.	Nat.	Log.	

| Angle | Cosine | | Sine | | Cotangent | | Tangent | | Angle |

LENGTH OF CHORD FOR CIRCLE ARCS OF 1-IN. RADIUS

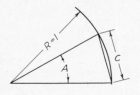

°	0′	10′	20′	30′	40′	50′
0	0.0000	0.0029	0.0058	0.0087	0.0116	0.0145
1	0.0175	0.0204	0.0233	0.0262	0.0291	0.0320
2	0.0349	0.0378	0.0407	0.0436	0.0465	0.0494
3	0.0524	0.0553	0.0582	0.0611	0.0640	0.0669
4	0.0698	0.0727	0.0756	0.0785	0.0814	0.0843
5	0.0872	0.0901	0.0931	0.0960	0.0989	0.1018
6	0.1047	0.1076	0.1105	0.1134	0.1163	0.1192
7	0.1221	0.1250	0.1279	0.1308	0.1337	0.1366
8	0.1395	0.1424	0.1453	0.1482	0.1511	0.1540
9	0.1569	0.1598	0.1627	0.1656	0.1685	0.1714
10	0.1743	0.1772	0.1801	0.1830	0.1859	0.1888
11	0.1917	0.1946	0.1975	0.2004	0.2033	0.2062
12	0.2091	0.2119	0.2148	0.2177	0.2206	0.2235
13	0.2264	0.2293	0.2322	0.2351	0.2380	0.2409
14	0.2437	0.2466	0.2495	0.2524	0.2553	0.2582
15	0.2611	0.2639	0.2668	0.2697	0.2726	0.2755
16	0.2783	0.2812	0.2841	0.2870	0.2899	0.2927
17	0.2956	0.2985	0.3014	0.3042	0.3071	0.3100
18	0.3129	0.3157	0.3186	0.3215	0.3244	0.3272
19	0.3301	0.3330	0.3358	0.3387	0.3416	0.3444
20	0.3473	0.3502	0.3530	0.3559	0.3587	0.3616
21	0.3645	0.3673	0.3702	0.3730	0.3759	0.3788
22	0.3816	0.3845	0.3873	0.3902	0.3930	0.3959
23	0.3987	0.4016	0.4044	0.4073	0.4101	0.4130
24	0.4158	0.4187	0.4215	0.4244	0.4272	0.4300
25	0.4329	0.4357	0.4386	0.4414	0.4442	0.4471
26	0.4499	0.4527	0.4556	0.4584	0.4612	0.4641
27	0.4669	0.4697	0.4725	0.4754	0.4782	0.4810
28	0.4838	0.4867	0.4895	0.4923	0.4951	0.4979
29	0.5008	0.5036	0.5064	0.5092	0.5120	0.5148
30	0.5176	0.5204	0.5233	0.5261	0.5289	0.5317
31	0.5345	0.5373	0.5401	0.5429	0.5457	0.5485
32	0.5513	0.5541	0.5569	0.5597	0.5625	0.5652
33	0.5680	0.5708	0.5736	0.5764	0.5792	0.5820
34	0.5847	0.5875	0.5903	0.5931	0.5959	0.5986
35	0.6014	0.6042	0.6070	0.6097	0.6125	0.6153
36	0.6180	0.6208	0.6236	0.6263	0.6291	0.6319
37	0.6346	0.6374	0.6401	0.6429	0.6456	0.6484
38	0.6511	0.6539	0.6566	0.6594	0.6621	0.6649
39	0.6676	0.6704	0.6731	0.6758	0.6786	0.6813
40	0.6840	0.6868	0.6895	0.6922	0.6950	0.6977
41	0.7004	0.7031	0.7059	0.7086	0.7113	0.7140
42	0.7167	0.7195	0.7222	0.7249	0.7276	0.7303
43	0.7330	0.7357	0.7384	0.7411	0.7438	0.7465
44	0.7492	0.7519	0.7546	0.7573	0.7600	0.7627
45 *	0.7654	0.7681	0.7707	0.7734	0.7761	0.7788

* For angles between 45° and 90°, draw 90° angle and lay off complement from 90° line.

DECIMAL EQUIVALENTS OF INCH FRACTIONS

Fraction	Equiv.	Fraction	Equiv.	Fraction	Equiv.	Fraction	Equiv.
$\frac{1}{64}$	0.015625	$\frac{17}{64}$	0.265625	$\frac{33}{64}$	0.515625	$\frac{49}{64}$	0.765625
$\frac{1}{32}$	0.03125	$\frac{9}{32}$	0.28125	$\frac{17}{32}$	0.53125	$\frac{25}{32}$	0.78125
$\frac{3}{64}$	0.046875	$\frac{19}{64}$	0.296875	$\frac{35}{64}$	0.546875	$\frac{51}{64}$	0.796875
$\frac{1}{16}$	0.0625	$\frac{5}{16}$	0.3125	$\frac{9}{16}$	0.5625	$\frac{13}{16}$	0.8125
$\frac{5}{64}$	0.078125	$\frac{21}{64}$	0.328125	$\frac{37}{64}$	0.578125	$\frac{53}{64}$	0.828125
$\frac{3}{32}$	0.09375	$\frac{11}{32}$	0.34375	$\frac{19}{32}$	0.59375	$\frac{27}{32}$	0.84375
$\frac{7}{64}$	0.109375	$\frac{23}{64}$	0.359375	$\frac{39}{64}$	0.609375	$\frac{55}{64}$	0.859375
$\frac{1}{8}$	0.1250	$\frac{3}{8}$	0.3750	$\frac{5}{8}$	0.6250	$\frac{7}{8}$	0.8750
$\frac{9}{64}$	0.140625	$\frac{25}{64}$	0.390625	$\frac{41}{64}$	0.640625	$\frac{57}{64}$	0.890625
$\frac{5}{32}$	0.15625	$\frac{13}{32}$	0.40625	$\frac{21}{32}$	0.65625	$\frac{29}{32}$	0.90625
$\frac{11}{64}$	0.171875	$\frac{27}{64}$	0.421875	$\frac{43}{64}$	0.671875	$\frac{59}{64}$	0.921875
$\frac{3}{16}$	0.1875	$\frac{7}{16}$	0.4375	$\frac{11}{16}$	0.6875	$\frac{15}{16}$	0.9375
$\frac{13}{64}$	0.203125	$\frac{29}{64}$	0.453125	$\frac{45}{64}$	0.703125	$\frac{61}{64}$	0.953125
$\frac{7}{32}$	0.21875	$\frac{15}{32}$	0.46875	$\frac{23}{32}$	0.71875	$\frac{31}{32}$	0.96875
$\frac{15}{64}$	0.234375	$\frac{31}{64}$	0.484375	$\frac{47}{64}$	0.734375	$\frac{63}{64}$	0.984375
$\frac{1}{4}$	0.2500	$\frac{1}{2}$	0.5000	$\frac{3}{4}$	0.7500	1	1.0000

METRIC EQUIVALENTS

Mm	In.*	Mm	In.	In.	Mm †	In.	Mm
1 = 0.0394		17 = 0.6693		$\frac{1}{32}$ =	0.794	$\frac{17}{32}$ =	13.493
2 = 0.0787		18 = 0.7087		$\frac{1}{16}$ =	1.587	$\frac{9}{16}$ =	14.287
3 = 0.1181		19 = 0.7480		$\frac{3}{32}$ =	2.381	$\frac{19}{32}$ =	15.081
4 = 0.1575		20 = 0.7874		$\frac{1}{8}$ =	3.175	$\frac{5}{8}$ =	15.875
5 = 0.1969		21 = 0.8268		$\frac{5}{32}$ =	3.968	$\frac{21}{32}$ =	16.668
6 = 0.2362		22 = 0.8662		$\frac{3}{16}$ =	4.762	$\frac{11}{16}$ =	17.462
7 = 0.2756		23 = 0.9055		$\frac{7}{32}$ =	5.556	$\frac{23}{32}$ =	18.256
8 = 0.3150		24 = 0.9449		$\frac{1}{4}$ =	6.349	$\frac{3}{4}$ =	19.050
9 = 0.3543		25 = 0.9843		$\frac{9}{32}$ =	7.144	$\frac{25}{32}$ =	19.843
10 = 0.3937		26 = 1.0236		$\frac{5}{16}$ =	7.937	$\frac{13}{16}$ =	20.637
11 = 0.4331		27 = 1.0630		$\frac{11}{32}$ =	8.731	$\frac{27}{32}$ =	21.431
12 = 0.4724		28 = 1.1024		$\frac{3}{8}$ =	9.525	$\frac{7}{8}$ =	22.225
13 = 0.5118		29 = 1.1418		$\frac{13}{32}$ =	10.319	$\frac{29}{32}$ =	23.018
14 = 0.5512		30 = 1.1811		$\frac{7}{16}$ =	11.112	$\frac{15}{16}$ =	23.812
15 = 0.5906		31 = 1.2205		$\frac{15}{32}$ =	11.906	$\frac{31}{32}$ =	24.606
16 = 0.6299		32 = 1.2599		$\frac{1}{2}$ =	12.699	1 =	25.400

* Calculated to *nearest* fourth decimal place.
† Calculated to *nearest* third decimal place.

AMERICAN STANDARD UNIFIED AND AMERICAN THREAD SERIES [a]

Threads per inch for coarse, fine, extra-fine, 8-thread, 12-thread, and 16-thread series [b] [tap-drill sizes for approximately 75 per cent depth of thread (not American Standard)]

Nominal size (basic major diam.)	Coarse-thd. series UNC and NC [c] in classes 1A, 1B, 2A, 2B, 3A, 3B, 2, 3		Fine-thd. series UNF and NF [c] in classes 1A, 1B, 2A, 2B, 3A, 3B, 2, 3		Extra-fine-thd. series UNEF and NEF [d] in classes 2A, 2B, 2, 3		8-thd. series 8N [c] in classes 2A, 2B, 2, 3		12-thd. series 12UN and 12N [d] in classes 2A, 2B, 2, 3		16-thd. series 16UN and 16N [d] in classes 2A, 2B, 2, 3	
	Thd. /in.	Tap drill	Thd. /in.	Tap drill	Thd. /in.	Tap drill	Thd. /in.	Tap drill	Thd. /in.	Tap drill	Thd. /in.	Tap drill
0(0.060)	....	.....	80	$\frac{3}{64}$								
1(0.073)	64	No. 53	72	No. 53								
2(0.086)	56	No. 50	64	No. 50								
3(0.099)	48	No. 47	56	No. 45								
4(0.112)	40	No. 43	48	No. 42								
5(0.125)	40	No. 38	44	No. 37								
6(0.138)	32	No. 36	40	No. 33								
8(0.164)	32	No. 29	36	No. 29								
10(0.190)	24	No. 25	32	No. 21								
12(0.216)	24	No. 16	28	No. 14	32	No. 13						
$\frac{1}{4}$	20	No. 7	28	No. 3	32	$\frac{7}{32}$						
$\frac{5}{16}$	18	Let. F	24	Let. I	32	$\frac{9}{32}$						
$\frac{3}{8}$	16	$\frac{5}{16}$	24	Let. Q	32	$\frac{11}{32}$						
$\frac{7}{16}$	14	Let. U	20	$\frac{25}{64}$	28	$\frac{13}{32}$						
$\frac{1}{2}$	13	$\frac{27}{64}$	20	$\frac{29}{64}$	28	$\frac{15}{32}$	..	...	12	$\frac{27}{64}$		
$\frac{9}{16}$	12	$\frac{31}{64}$	18	$\frac{33}{64}$	24	$\frac{33}{64}$	..	...	12	$\frac{31}{64}$		
$\frac{5}{8}$	11	$\frac{17}{32}$	18	$\frac{37}{64}$	24	$\frac{37}{64}$	..	...	12	$\frac{35}{64}$		
$\frac{11}{16}$	....	.....	..	.....	24	$\frac{41}{64}$	..	...	12	$\frac{39}{64}$		
$\frac{3}{4}$	10	$\frac{21}{32}$	16	$\frac{11}{16}$	20	$\frac{45}{64}$	..	...	12	$\frac{43}{64}$	16	$\frac{11}{16}$
$\frac{13}{16}$	....	.....	..	.....	20	$\frac{49}{64}$	..	...	12	$\frac{47}{64}$	16	$\frac{3}{4}$
$\frac{7}{8}$	9	$\frac{49}{64}$	14	$\frac{13}{16}$	20	$\frac{53}{64}$	..	...	12	$\frac{51}{64}$	16	$\frac{13}{16}$
$\frac{15}{16}$	....	.....	..	.....	20	$\frac{57}{64}$	..	...	12	$\frac{55}{64}$	16	$\frac{7}{8}$
1	....	.....	14	$\frac{15}{16}$	..	.....	8	$\frac{7}{8}$				
1	8	$\frac{7}{8}$	12	$\frac{59}{64}$	20	$1\frac{1}{64}$	..	...	12	$\frac{59}{64}$	16	$\frac{15}{16}$
1 $\frac{1}{16}$	....	.....	..	.....	18	1	..	...	12	$\frac{63}{64}$	16	1
1 $\frac{1}{8}$	7	$\frac{63}{64}$	12	1 $\frac{3}{64}$	18	1 $\frac{5}{64}$	8	1	12	1 $\frac{3}{64}$	16	1 $\frac{1}{16}$
1 $\frac{3}{16}$	....	.....	..	.....	18	1 $\frac{9}{64}$	..	...	12	1 $\frac{7}{64}$	16	1 $\frac{1}{8}$
1 $\frac{1}{4}$	7	1 $\frac{7}{64}$	12	1 $\frac{11}{64}$	18	1 $\frac{3}{16}$	8	1 $\frac{1}{8}$	12	1 $\frac{11}{64}$	16	1 $\frac{3}{16}$
1 $\frac{5}{16}$	....	.....	..	.....	18	1 $\frac{17}{64}$	..	...	12	1 $\frac{15}{64}$	16	1 $\frac{1}{4}$
1 $\frac{3}{8}$	6	1 $\frac{7}{32}$	12	1 $\frac{19}{64}$	18	1 $\frac{5}{16}$	8	1 $\frac{1}{4}$	12	1 $\frac{19}{64}$	16	1 $\frac{5}{16}$
1 $\frac{7}{16}$	....	.....	..	.....	18	1 $\frac{3}{8}$	..	...	12	1 $\frac{23}{64}$	16	1 $\frac{3}{8}$
1 $\frac{1}{2}$	6	1 $\frac{11}{32}$	12	1 $\frac{27}{64}$	18	1 $\frac{7}{16}$	8	1 $\frac{3}{8}$	12	1 $\frac{27}{64}$	16	1 $\frac{7}{16}$
1 $\frac{9}{16}$	....	.....	..	.....	18	1 $\frac{1}{2}$	..	.....	..	.....	16	1 $\frac{1}{2}$
1 $\frac{5}{8}$	....	.....	..	.....	18	1 $\frac{9}{16}$	8	1 $\frac{1}{2}$	12	1 $\frac{35}{64}$	16	1 $\frac{9}{16}$
1 $\frac{11}{16}$	....	.....	..	.....	18	1 $\frac{5}{8}$	..	...	..	.....	16	1 $\frac{5}{8}$

AMERICAN STANDARD UNIFIED AND AMERICAN THREAD SERIES (*Cont.*)

Nominal size (basic major diam.)	Coarse-thd. series UNC and NC[c] in classes 1A, 1B, 2A, 2B, 3A, 3B, 2, 3		Fine-thd. series UNF and NF[c] in classes 1A, 1B, 2A, 2B, 3A, 3B, 2, 3		Extra-fine-thd. series UNEF and NEF[d] in classes 2A, 2B, 2, 3		8-thd. series 8N[c] in classes 2A, 2B, 2, 3		12-thd. series 12UN and 12N[d] in classes 2A, 2B, 2, 3		16-thd. series 16UN and 16N[d] in classes 2A, 2B, 2, 3	
	Thd./in.	Tap drill	Thd./in.	Tap drill	Thd./in.	Tap drill	Thd./in.	Tap drill	Thd./in.	Tap drill	Thd./in.	Tap drill
1 3/4	5	1 9/16	..	.....	16	1 11/66	8[e]	1 5/8	12	1 43/64	16	1 11/16
1 13/16	....	.....	..	.....	..	.....	..	...	..	.....	16	1 3/4
1 7/8	....	.....	..	.....	..	.....	8	1 3/4	12	1 51/64	16	1 13/16
1 15/16	....	.....	..	.....	..	.....	..	...	..	.....	16	1 7/8
2	4 1/2	1 25/32	..	.....	16	1 15/16	8[e]	1 7/8	12	1 59/64	16	1 15/16
2 1/16	....	.....	..	.....	..	.....	..	...	..	.....	16	2
2 1/8	....	.....	..	.....	..	.....	8	2	12	2 3/64	16	2 1/16
2 3/16	....	.....	..	.....	..	.....	..	...	..	.....	16	2 1/8
2 1/4	4 1/2	2 1/32	..	.....	..	.....	8[e]	2 1/8	12	2 11/64	16	2 3/16
2 5/16	....	.....	..	.....	..	.....	..	...	..	.....	16	2 1/4
2 3/8	....	.....	..	.....	..	.....	..	...	12	2 19/64	16	2 5/16
2 7/16	....	.....	..	.....	..	.....	..	...	..	.....	16	2 3/8
2 1/2	4	2 1/4	..	.....	..	.....	8[e]	2 3/8	12	2 27/64	16	2 7/16
2 5/8	....	.....	..	.....	..	.....	..	...	12	2 35/64	16	2 9/16
2 3/4	4	2 1/2	..	.....	..	.....	8[e]	2 5/8	12	2 43/64	16	2 11/16
2 7/8	....	.....	..	.....	..	.....	..	...	12	2 51/64	16	2 13/16
3	4	2 3/4	..	.....	..	.....	8[e]	2 7/8	12	2 59/64	16	2 15/16
3 1/8	....	.....	..	.....	..	.....	..	...	12	3 3/64	16	3 1/16
3 1/4	4	3	..	.....	..	.....	8[e]	3 1/8	12	3 11/64	16	3 3/16
3 3/8	....	.....	..	.....	..	.....	..	...	12	3 19/64	16	3 5/16
3 1/2	4	3 1/4	..	.....	..	.....	8[e]	3 3/8	12	3 27/64	16	3 7/16
3 5/8	....	.....	..	.....	..	.....	..	...	12	3 35/64	16	3 9/16
3 3/4	4	3 1/2	..	.....	..	.....	8[e]	3 5/8	12	3 43/64	16	3 11/16
3 7/8	....	.....	..	.....	..	.....	..	...	12	3 51/64	16	3 13/16
4	4	3 3/4	..	.....	..	.....	8[e]	3 7/8	12	3 59/64	16	3 15/16
4 1/4	....	.....	..	.....	..	.....	8[e]	4 1/8	12	4 11/64	16	4 3/16
4 1/2	....	.....	..	.....	..	.....	8[e]	4 3/8	12	4 27/64	16	4 7/16
4 3/4	....	.....	..	.....	..	.....	8[e]	4 5/8	12	4 43/64	16	4 11/16
5	....	.....	..	.....	..	.....	8[e]	4 7/8	12	4 59/64	16	4 15/16
5 1/4	....	.....	..	.....	..	.....	8[e]	5 1/8	12	5 11/64	16	5 3/16
5 1/2	....	.....	..	.....	..	.....	8[e]	5 3/8	12	5 27/64	16	5 7/16
5 3/4	....	.....	..	.....	..	.....	8[e]	5 5/8	12	5 43/64	16	5 11/16
6	....	.....	..	.....	..	.....	8[e]	5 7/8	12	5 59/64	16	5 15/16

[a] ASA B1.1—1949. Dimensions are in inches.

[b] Bold type indicates unified combinations.

[c] Limits of size for classes are based on a length of engagement equal to the nominal diameter.

[d] Limits of size for classes are based on a length of engagement equal to nine times the pitch.

[e] These sizes, with specified limits of size, based on a length of engagement of 9 threads in classes 2A and 2B, are designated UN.

Note. If a thread is in both the 8-, 12-, or 16-thread series and the coarse, fine, or extra-fine-thread series, the symbols and tolerances of the latter series apply.

AMERICAN STANDARD SQUARE AND HEXAGON BOLTS*
AND HEXAGON CAP SCREWS †

Nominal size (basic major diam.)	Regular bolts			Heavy bolts		
	Width across flats W, sq.‡ and hex.	Height H		Width across flats W	Height H	
		Unfaced sq. and hex.	Semifin. hex., fin. hex., and hex. screw		Unfaced hex.	Semifin. hex. and fin. hex.
1/4	3/8(sq.), 7/16(hex.)	11/64	5/32			
5/16	1/2	7/32	13/64			
3/8	9/16	1/4	15/64			
7/16	5/8	19/64	9/32			
1/2	3/4	11/32	5/16	7/8	7/16	13/32
9/16	13/16	25/64	23/64	15/16	15/32	7/16
5/8	15/16	27/64	25/64	1 1/16	17/32	1/2
3/4	1 1/8	1/2	15/32	1 1/4	5/8	19/32
7/8	1 5/16	37/64	35/64	1 7/16	23/32	11/16
1	1 1/2	43/64	39/64	1 5/8	13/16	3/4
1 1/8	1 11/16	3/4	11/16	1 13/16	29/32	27/32
1 1/4	1 7/8	27/32	25/32	2	1	15/16
1 3/8	2 1/16	29/32	27/32	2 3/16	1 3/32	1 1/32
1 1/2	2 1/4	1	15/16	2 3/8	1 3/16	1 1/8
1 5/8	2 7/16	1 1/16	1	2 9/16	1 9/32	1 7/32
1 3/4	2 5/8	1 5/32	1 3/32	2 3/4	1 3/8	1 5/16
1 7/8	2 13/16	1 7/32	1 5/32	2 15/16	1 15/32	1 13/32
2	3	1 11/32	1 7/32	3 1/8	1 9/16	1 7/16
2 1/4	3 3/8	1 1/2	1 3/8	3 1/2	1 3/4	1 5/8
2 1/2	3 3/4	1 21/32	1 17/32	3 7/8	1 15/16	1 13/16
2 3/4	4 1/8	1 13/16	1 11/16	4 1/4	2 1/8	2
3	4 1/2	2	1 7/8	4 5/8	2 5/16	2 3/16
3 1/4	4 7/8	2 3/16	2			
3 1/2	5 1/4	2 5/16	2 1/8			
3 3/4	5 5/8	2 1/2	2 5/16			
4	6	2 11/16	2 1/2			

* ASA B18.2—1955. All dimensions in inches.

† ASA B18.6.2—1956. Hexagon-head cap screw in sizes 1/4 to 1 1/2 only.

‡ Square bolts in (nominal) sizes 1/4 to 1 5/8 only.

For bolt-length increments, see table, page 720. Threads are coarse series, class 2A, except for finished hexagon bolt and hexagon cap screw, which are coarse, fine, or 8-pitch, class 2A. Minimum thread length: $2D + 1/4$ in. for bolts 6 in. or less in length; $2D + 1/2$ in. for bolts over 6 in. in length; bolts too short for formula, thread entire length.

AMERICAN STANDARD SQUARE AND HEXAGON NUTS *

Nominal size (basic major diam.)	Reg. nuts						Heavy nuts							Reg. sq. nuts	
	Width across flats W	Thickness T					Width across flats W	Thickness T				Slot		Width across flats W	Thickness T
		Reg. hex.	Reg. hex. jam	Semi-fin. and fin. hex. and hex. slotted	Semi-fin. and fin. hex. jam	Semi-fin. hex. thick, thick slotted,† and castle		Reg. sq. and hex.	Reg. hex. jam	Semi-fin. hex. and hex. slotted	Semi-fin. hex. jam	Width	Depth		
1/4	7/16	.....	....	7/32	5/32	9/32	1/2	1/4	3/16	15/64	11/64	5/64	3/32	7/16	7/32
5/16	1/2	.....	....	17/64	3/16	21/64	9/16	5/16	7/32	19/64	13/64	3/32	3/32	9/16	17/64
3/8	9/16	.....	....	21/64	7/32	13/32	11/16	3/8	1/4	23/64	15/64	1/8	1/8	5/8	21/64
7/16	11/16	.....	....	3/8	1/4	29/64	3/4	7/16	9/32	27/64	17/64	1/8	5/32	3/4	3/8
1/2	3/4	.....	....	7/16	5/16	9/16	7/8	1/2	5/16	31/64	19/64	5/32	5/32	13/16	7/16
9/16	7/8	.....	....	31/64	5/16	39/64	15/16			35/64	21/64	5/32	3/16		
5/8	15/16	.....	....	35/64	3/8	23/32	1 1/16	5/8	3/8	39/64	23/64	3/16	7/32	1	35/64
3/4	1 1/8	21/32	7/16	41/64	27/64	13/16	1 1/4	3/4	7/16	47/64	27/64	3/16	1/4	1 1/8	21/32
7/8	1 5/16	49/64	1/2	3/4	31/64	29/32	1 7/16	7/8	1/2	55/64	31/64	3/16	1/4	1 5/16	49/64
1	1 1/2	7/8	9/16	55/64	35/64	1	1 5/8	1	9/16	63/64	35/64	1/4	9/32	1 1/2	7/8
1 1/8	1 11/16	1	5/8	31/32	39/64	1 5/32	1 13/16	1 1/8	5/8	1 7/64	39/64	1/4	11/32	1 11/16	1
1 1/4	1 7/8	1 3/32	3/4	1 1/16	23/32	1 1/4	2	1 1/4	3/4	1 7/32	23/32	5/16	3/8	1 7/8	1 3/32
1 3/8	2 1/16	1 13/64	13/16	1 11/64	25/32	1 3/8	2 3/16	1 3/8	13/16	1 11/32	25/32	5/16	3/8	2 1/16	1 13/64
1 1/2	2 1/4	1 5/16	7/8	1 9/32	27/32	1 1/2	2 3/8	1 1/2	7/8	1 15/32	27/32	3/8	7/16	2 1/4	1 5/16
1 5/8	2 7/16	.....	....	1 25/64	29/32	.....	2 9/16			1 19/32	29/32	3/8	7/16		
1 3/4	2 5/8	.....	....	1 1/2	31/32	.....	2 3/4	1 3/4	1	1 23/32	31/32	7/16	1/2		
1 7/8	2 13/16	.....	....	1 39/64	1 1/32	.....	2 15/16			1 27/32	1 1/32	7/16	9/16		
2	3	.....	....	1 23/32	1 3/32	.....	3 1/8	2	1 1/8	1 31/32	1 3/32	7/16	9/16		
2 1/4	3 3/8	.....	....	1 59/64	1 13/64	.....	3 1/2	2 1/4	1 1/4	2 13/64	1 13/64	7/16	9/16		
2 1/2	3 3/4	.....	....	2 9/64	1 29/64	.....	3 7/8	2 1/2	1 1/2	2 29/64	1 29/64	9/16	11/16		
2 3/4	4 1/8	.....	....	2 23/64	1 37/64	.....	4 1/4	2 3/4	1 5/8	2 45/64	1 37/64	9/16	11/16		
3	4 1/2	.....	....	2 37/64	1 45/64	.....	4 5/8	3	1 3/4	2 61/64	1 45/64	5/8	3/4		
3 1/4	.....	.....	....	.....	.....	.....	5	3 1/4	1 7/8	3 3/16	1 13/16	5/8	3/4		
3 1/2	.....	.....	....	.....	.....	.....	5 3/8	3 1/2	2	3 7/16	1 15/16	5/8	3/4		
3 3/4	.....	.....	....	.....	.....	.....	5 3/4	3 3/4	2 1/8	3 11/16	2 1/16	5/8	3/4		
4	.....	.....	....	.....	.....	.....	6 1/8	4	2 1/4	3 15/16	2 3/16	5/8	3/4		

* ASA B18.2—1955.

† Slot dimensions for regular slotted nuts are same as for heavy slotted nuts.

Thread. Regular and heavy nuts: coarse series, class 2B; finished and semifinished nuts, regular and heavy (all): coarse, fine, or 8-pitch series, class 2B; thick nuts: coarse or fine series, class 2B.

SIZES OF NUMBERED AND LETTERED DRILLS

No.	Size	No.	Size	No.	Size	Letter	Size
80	0.0135	53	0.0595	26	0.1470	A	0.2340
79	0.0145	52	0.0635	25	0.1495	B	0.2380
78	0.0160	51	0.0670	24	0.1520	C	0.2420
77	0.0180	50	0.0700	23	0.1540	D	0.2460
76	0.0200	49	0.0730	22	0.1570	E	0.2500
75	0.0210	48	0.0760	21	0.1590	F	0.2570
74	0.0225	47	0.0785	20	0.1610	G	0.2610
73	0.0240	46	0.0810	19	0.1660	H	0.2660
72	0.0250	45	0.0820	18	0.1695	I	0.2720
71	0.0260	44	0.0860	17	0.1730	J	0.2770
70	0.0280	43	0.0890	16	0.1770	K	0.2810
69	0.0292	42	0.0935	15	0.1800	L	0.2900
68	0.0310	41	0.0960	14	0.1820	M	0.2950
67	0.0320	40	0.0980	13	0.1850	N	0.3020
66	0.0330	39	0.0995	12	0.1890	O	0.3160
65	0.0350	38	0.1015	11	0.1910	P	0.3230
64	0.0360	37	0.1040	10	0.1935	Q	0.3320
63	0.0370	36	0.1065	9	0.1960	R	0.3390
62	0.0380	35	0.1100	8	0.1990	S	0.3480
61	0.0390	34	0.1110	7	0.2010	T	0.3580
60	0.0400	33	0.1130	6	0.2040	U	0.3680
59	0.0410	32	0.1160	5	0.2055	V	0.3770
58	0.0420	31	0.1200	4	0.2090	W	0.3860
57	0.0430	30	0.1285	3	0.2130	X	0.3970
56	0.0465	29	0.1360	2	0.2210	Y	0.4040
55	0.0520	28	0.1405	1	0.2280	Z	0.4130
54	0.0550	27	0.1440				

ACME AND STUB ACME THREADS *

ASA-preferred diameter-pitch combinations

Nominal (major) diam.	Threads/in.	Nominal (major) diam.	Threads/in.	Nominal (major) diam.	Threads/in.	Nominal (major) diam.	Threads/in.
$\frac{1}{4}$	16	$\frac{3}{4}$	6	$1\frac{1}{2}$	4	3	2
$\frac{5}{16}$	14	$\frac{7}{8}$	6	$1\frac{3}{4}$	4	$3\frac{1}{2}$	2
$\frac{3}{8}$	12	1	5	2	4	4	2
$\frac{7}{16}$	12	$1\frac{1}{8}$	5	$2\frac{1}{4}$	3	$4\frac{1}{2}$	2
$\frac{1}{2}$	10	$1\frac{1}{4}$	5	$2\frac{1}{2}$	3	5	2
$\frac{5}{8}$	8	$1\frac{3}{8}$	4	$2\frac{3}{4}$	3		

* ASA B1.5 and B1.8—1952. Diameters in inches.

BUTTRESS THREADS

Recommended diam., in.	Assoc. threads/in.
$\frac{1}{2}$, $\frac{9}{16}$, $\frac{5}{8}$, $1\frac{1}{16}$	20, 16, 12
$\frac{3}{4}$, $\frac{7}{8}$, 1	16, 12, 10
$1\frac{1}{8}$, $1\frac{1}{4}$, $1\frac{3}{8}$, $1\frac{1}{2}$	16, 12, 10, 8, 6
$1\frac{3}{4}$, 2, $2\frac{1}{4}$, $2\frac{1}{2}$, $2\frac{3}{4}$, 3, $3\frac{1}{2}$, 4	16, 12, 10, 8, 6, 5, 4
$4\frac{1}{2}$, 5, $5\frac{1}{2}$, 6	12, 10, 8, 6, 5, 4, 3
7, 8, 9, 10	10, 8, 6, 5, 4, 3, $2\frac{1}{2}$, 2
11, 12, 14, 16	10, 8, 6, 5, 4, 3, $2\frac{1}{2}$, 2, $1\frac{1}{2}$, $1\frac{1}{4}$
18, 20, 22, 24	8, 6, 5, 4, 3, $2\frac{1}{2}$, 2, $1\frac{1}{2}$, $1\frac{1}{4}$, 1

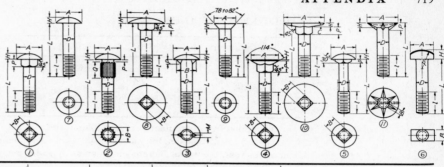

AMERICAN STANDARD ROUND-HEAD BOLTS [a]

Proportions for drawing purposes

Fastener name		Nominal diam.[b] (basic major diam.)	A	H	P or M	B	
Carriage bolts	Round-head square-neck bolt[c]	No. 10, ¼″ to ½″ by (¹⁄₁₆″), ⅝″ to 1″ by (⅛″)	$2D + \frac{1}{16}$	$\frac{D}{2}$	$\frac{D}{2}$	D	
	Round-head ribbed-neck bolt[d]	No. 10, ¼″ to ½″ by (¹⁄₁₆″), ⅝″ and ¾″	$2D + \frac{1}{16}$	$\frac{D}{2}$	$\frac{1}{16}$	$D + \frac{1}{16}$	$Q \begin{cases} \frac{3}{16}″ \text{ for } L = \frac{7}{8}″ \text{ or less} \\ \frac{5}{16}″ \text{ for } L = 1″ \text{ and } 1\frac{1}{8}″ \\ \frac{1}{2}″ \text{ for } L = 1\frac{1}{4}″ \text{ or more} \end{cases}$
	Round-head fin.-neck bolt[c]	No. 10, ¼″ to ½″ by (¹⁄₁₆″)	$2D + \frac{1}{16}$	$\frac{D}{2}$	$\frac{3}{8}D$	$1\frac{1}{2}D + \frac{1}{16}$	
	114° countersunk square-neck bolt[c]	No. 10, ¼″ to ½″ by (¹⁄₁₆″), ⅝″ and ¾″	$2D + \frac{1}{8}$	$\frac{1}{32}$	$D + \frac{1}{32}$	D	
Round-head short square-neck bolt[e]		¼″ to ½″ by (¹⁄₁₆″), ⅝″ and ¾″	$2D + \frac{1}{16}$	$\frac{D}{2}$	$\frac{D}{4} + \frac{1}{32}$	D	
T-head bolt[d]		¼″ to ½″ by (¹⁄₁₆″), ⅝″ to 1″ by (⅛″)	$2D$	$\frac{7}{8}D$	$1\frac{5}{8}D$	D	
Round-head bolt[c] (buttonhead bolt)		No. 10, ¼″ to ½″ by (¹⁄₁₆″), ⅝″ to 1″ by (⅛″)	$2D + \frac{1}{16}$	$\frac{D}{2}$			
Step bolt[c]		No. 10, ¼″ to ½″ by (¹⁄₁₆″)	$3D + \frac{1}{16}$	$\frac{D}{2}$	$\frac{D}{2}$	D	
Countersunk bolt[e] (may be slotted if so specified)		¼″ to ½″ by (¹⁄₁₆″), ⅝″ to 1½″ by (⅛″)	$1.8D$	Obtain by projection			
Elevator bolt, flat head, countersunk[c]		No. 10, ¼″ to ½″ by (¹⁄₁₆″)	$2\frac{1}{2}D + \frac{5}{16}$	$\frac{D}{3}$	$\frac{D}{2} + \frac{1}{16}$	D	Angle $C = 16D + 5°$ (approx.)
Elevator bolt, ribbed head[d] (slotted or unslotted as specified)		¼″, ⁵⁄₁₆″, ⅜″	$2D + \frac{1}{16}$	$\frac{D}{2} - \frac{1}{32}$	$\frac{D}{2} + \frac{3}{64}$	$\frac{D}{8} + \frac{1}{16}$	

[a] The proportions in this table are in some instances approximate and are intended for drawing purposes only. For exact dimensions see ASA B18.5—1951, from which this table was compiled. Dimensions are in inches.

[b] Fractions in parentheses show diameter increments, *e.g.*, ¼ in. to ½ in. by (¹⁄₁₆ in.) includes the diameters ¼ in., ⁵⁄₁₆ in., ⅜ in., ⁷⁄₁₆ in., and ½ in.

Threads are coarse series, class 2A.

Minimum thread length l: $2D + ¼$ in. for bolts 6 in. or less in length; $2D + ½$ in. for bolts over 6 in. in length.

For bolt length increments see table page 720.

[c] Full-size body bolts furnished unless undersize body is specified.

[d] Only full-size body bolts furnished.

[e] Undersize body bolts furnished unless full-size body is specified.

BOLT-LENGTH INCREMENTS *

Bolt diameter		1/4	5/16	3/8	7/16	1/2	5/8	3/4	7/8	1
Length increments	1/4	3/4-3	3/4-4	3/4-6	1-3	1-6	1-6	1-6	1-4 1/2	
	1/2	3-4	4-5	6-9	3-6	6-13	6-10	6-15	4 1/2-6	3-6
	1	4-5	....	9-12	6-8	.....	10-22	15-24	6-20	6-12
	2	....	....	.....	...	.....	22-30	24-30	20-30	12-30

* Compiled from manufacturers' catalogues.

Example. 1/4-in. bolt lengths increase by 1/4-in. increments from 3/4- to 3-in. length. 1/2-in. bolt lengths increase by 1/2-in. increments from 6- to 13-in. length. 1-in. bolt lengths increase by 2-in. increments from 12- to 30-in. length.

AMERICAN STANDARD CAP SCREWS [a]—SOCKET [b] AND SLOTTED HEADS [c]

For hexagon-head screws, see page 716.

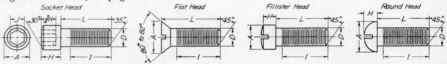

Nominal diam.	Socket head [d]			Flat head [e]	Fillister head [e]		Round head [e]	
	A	H	J	A	A	H	A	H
0	0.096	0.060	0.050					
1	0.118	0.073	0.050					
2	0.140	0.086	1/16					
3	0.161	0.099	5/64					
4	0.183	0.112	5/64					
5	0.205	0.125	3/32					
6	0.226	0.138	3/32					
8	0.270	0.164	1/8					
10	5/16	0.190	5/32					
12	11/32	0.216	5/32					
1/4	3/8	1/4	3/16	1/2	3/8	11/64	7/16	3/16
5/16	7/16	5/16	7/32	5/8	7/16	13/64	9/16	15/64
3/8	9/16	3/8	5/16	3/4	9/16	1/4	5/8	17/64
7/16	5/8	7/16	5/16	13/16	5/8	19/64	3/4	5/16
1/2	3/4	1/2	3/8	7/8	3/4	21/64	13/16	11/32
9/16	13/16	9/16	3/8	1	13/16	3/8	15/16	13/32
5/8	7/8	5/8	1/2	1 1/8	7/8	27/64	1	7/16
3/4	1	3/4	9/16	1 3/8	1	1/2	1 1/4	17/32
7/8	1 1/8	7/8	9/16	1 5/8	1 1/8	19/32		
1	1 5/16	1	5/8	1 7/8	1 5/16	21/32		
1 1/8	1 1/2	1 1/8	3/4					
1 1/4	1 3/4	1 1/4	3/4					
1 3/8	1 7/8	1 3/8	3/4					
1 1/2	2	1 1/2	1					

[a] Dimensions in inches.

[b] ASA B18.3—1954.

[c] ASA B18.6.2—1956.

[d] Thread coarse or fine, class 3A. Thread length l: coarse thread, $2D + 1/2$ in.; fine thread, $1\frac{1}{2}D + 1/2$ in.

[e] Thread coarse, fine, or 8-pitch, class 2A. Thread length l: $2D + 1/4$ in.

Slot proportions vary with size of screw; draw to look well. All body-length increments for screw lengths 1/4 in. to 1 in. = 1/8 in., for screw lengths 1 in. to 4 in. = 1/4 in., for screw lengths 4 in. to 6 in. = 1/2 in.

AMERICAN STANDARD MACHINE SCREWS *

Heads may be slotted or recessed

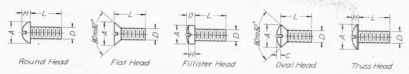

Round Head   Flat Head   Fillister Head   Oval Head   Truss Head

Nominal diam.	Round head A	Round head H	Flat head A	Fillister head A	Fillister head H	Fillister head O	Oval head A	Oval head C	Truss head A	Truss head H
0	0.113	0.053	0.119	0.096	0.045	0.059	0.119	0.021		
1	0.138	0.061	0.146	0.118	0.053	0.071	0.146	0.025	0.194	0.053
2	0.162	0.069	0.172	0.140	0.062	0.083	0.172	0.029	0.226	0.061
3	0.187	0.078	0.199	0.161	0.070	0.095	0.199	0.033	0.257	0.069
4	0.211	0.086	0.225	0.183	0.079	0.107	0.225	0.037	0.289	0.078
5	0.236	0.095	0.252	0.205	0.088	0.120	0.252	0.041	0.321	0.086
6	0.260	0.103	0.279	0.226	0.096	0.132	0.279	0.045	0.352	0.094
8	0.309	0.120	0.332	0.270	0.113	0.156	0.332	0.052	0.384	0.102
10	0.359	0.137	0.385	0.313	0.130	0.180	0.385	0.060	0.448	0.118
12	0.408	0.153	0.438	0.357	0.148	0.205	0.438	0.068	0.511	0.134
$\frac{1}{4}$	0.472	0.175	0.507	0.414	0.170	0.237	0.507	0.079	0.573	0.150
$\frac{5}{16}$	0.590	0.216	0.635	0.518	0.211	0.295	0.635	0.099	0.698	0.183
$\frac{3}{8}$	0.708	0.256	0.762	0.622	0.253	0.355	0.762	0.117	0.823	0.215
$\frac{7}{16}$	0.750	0.328	0.812	0.625	0.265	0.368	0.812	0.122	0.948	0.248
$\frac{1}{2}$	0.813	0.355	0.875	0.750	0.297	0.412	0.875	0.131	1.073	0.280
$\frac{9}{16}$	0.938	0.410	1.000	0.812	0.336	0.466	1.000	0.150	1.198	0.312
$\frac{5}{8}$	1.000	0.438	1.125	0.875	0.375	0.521	1.125	0.169	1.323	0.345
$\frac{3}{4}$	1.250	0.547	1.375	1.000	0.441	0.612	1.375	0.206	1.573	0.410

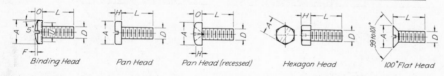

Binding Head   Pan Head   Pan Head (recessed)   Hexagon Head   100° Flat Head

Nominal diam.	Binding head A	Binding head O	Binding head F	Binding head U	Pan head A	Pan head H	Pan head O	Hexagon head A	Hexagon head H	100° flat head A
2	0.181	0.046	0.018	0.141	0.167	0.053	0.062	0.125	0.050	
3	0.208	0.054	0.022	0.162	0.193	0.060	0.071	0.187	0.055	
4	0.235	0.063	0.025	0.184	0.219	0.068	0.080	0.187	0.060	0.225
5	0.263	0.071	0.029	0.205	0.245	0.075	0.089	0.187	0.070	
6	0.290	0.080	0.032	0.226	0.270	0.082	0.097	0.250	0.080	0.279
8	0.344	0.097	0.039	0.269	0.322	0.096	0.115	0.250	0.110	0.332
10	0.399	0.114	0.045	0.312	0.373	0.110	0.133	0.312	0.120	0.385
12	0.454	0.130	0.052	0.354	0.425	0.125	0.151	0.312	0.155	
$\frac{1}{4}$	0.513	0.153	0.061	0.410	0.492	0.144	0.175	0.375	0.190	0.507
$\frac{5}{16}$	0.641	0.193	0.077	0.513	0.615	0.178	0.218	0.500	0.230	0.635
$\frac{3}{8}$	0.769	0.234	0.094	0.615	0.740	0.212	0.261	0.562	0.295	0.762

* ASA B18.6—1947. Dimensions given are maximum values, all in inches.

Thread length: screws 2 in. long or less, thread entire length; screws over 2 in. long, thread length $l = 1\frac{3}{4}$ in. Threads are coarse or fine series, class 2. Heads may be slotted or recessed as specified, excepting hexagon form, which is plain or may be slotted if so specified. Slot and recess proportions vary with size of fastener; draw to look well.

AMERICAN STANDARD MACHINE-SCREW * AND STOVE-BOLT † NUTS ‡

Nominal size	0	1	2	3	4	5	6	8	10	12	1/4	5/16	3/8
"W"	5/32	5/32	3/16	3/16	1/4	5/16	5/16	11/32	3/8	7/16	7/16	9/16	5/8
"T"	3/64	3/64	1/16	1/16	3/32	7/64	7/64	1/8	1/8	5/32	3/16	7/32	1/4

* Machine-screw nuts are hexagonal and square.

† Stove-bolt nuts are square.

‡ ASA B18—1951. Dimensions are in inches.

Thread is coarse series for square nuts and coarse or fine series for hexagon nuts; class 2B.

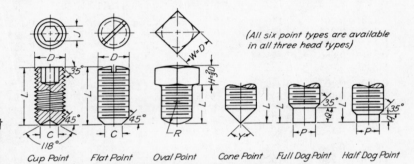

(All six point types are available in all three head types)

Cup Point   Flat Point   Oval Point   Cone Point   Full Dog Point   Half Dog Point

AMERICAN STANDARD HEXAGON SOCKET,* SLOTTED HEADLESS,† AND SQUARE-HEAD ‡ SETSCREWS

Diam. D	Cup and flat-point diam. C	Oval-point radius R	Cone-point angle Y		Full and half dog points			Socket width J
			118° for these lengths and shorter	90° for these lengths and longer	Diam. P	Length Full Q	Length Half q	
5	1/16	3/32	1/8	3/16	0.083	0.06	0.03	1/16
6	0.069	7/64	1/8	3/16	0.092	0.07	0.03	1/16
8	5/64	1/8	3/16	1/4	0.109	0.08	0.04	5/64
10	3/32	9/64	3/16	1/4	0.127	0.09	0.04	3/32
12	7/64	5/32	3/16	1/4	0.144	0.11	0.06	3/32
1/4	1/8	3/16	1/4	5/16	5/32	1/8	1/16	1/8
5/16	11/64	15/64	5/16	3/8	13/64	5/32	5/64	5/32
3/8	13/64	9/32	3/8	7/16	1/4	3/16	3/32	3/16
7/16	15/64	21/64	7/16	1/2	19/64	7/32	7/64	7/32
1/2	9/32	3/8	1/2	9/16	11/32	1/4	1/8	1/4
9/16	5/16	27/64	9/16	5/8	25/64	9/32	9/64	1/4
5/8	23/64	15/32	5/8	3/4	15/32	5/16	5/32	5/16
3/4	7/16	9/16	3/4	7/8	9/16	3/8	3/16	3/8
7/8	33/64	21/32	7/8	1	21/32	7/16	7/32	1/2
1	19/32	3/4	1	1 1/8	3/4	1/2	1/4	9/16
1 1/8	43/64	27/32	1 1/8	1 1/4	27/32	9/16	9/32	9/16
1 1/4	3/4	15/16	1 1/4	1 1/2	15/16	5/8	5/16	5/8
1 3/8	53/64	1 1/32	1 3/8	1 5/8	1 1/32	11/16	11/32	5/8
1 1/2	29/32	1 1/8	1 1/2	1 3/4	1 1/8	3/4	3/8	3/4
1 3/4	1 1/16	1 5/16	1 3/4	2	1 5/16	7/8	7/16	1
2	1 7/32	1 1/2	2	2 1/4	1 1/2	1	1/2	1

* ASA B18.3—1954. Dimensions are in inches. Threads coarse or fine, class 3A. Length increments: 1/4 in. to 5/8 in. by (1/16 in.); 5/8 in. to 1 in. by (1/8 in.); 1 in. to 4 in. by (1/4 in.); 4 in. to 6 in. by (1/2 in.). Fractions in parentheses show length increments; for example, 5/8 in. to 1 in. by (1/8 in.) includes the lengths 5/8 in., 3/4 in., 7/8 in., and 1 in.

† ASA B18.6.2—1956. Threads coarse or fine, class 2A. Slotted headless screws standardized in sizes No. 5 to 3/4 in. only. Slot proportions vary with diameter. Draw to look well.

‡ ASA B18.6.2—1956. Threads coarse, fine, or 8-pitch, class 2A. Square-head setscrews standardized in sizes No. 10 to 1 1/2 in. only.

AMERICAN STANDARD SOCKET-HEAD SHOULDER SCREWS [a]

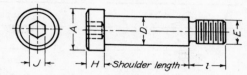

Shoulder diameter D			Head [b]			Thread		Shoulder lengths [d]
Nominal	Max.	Min.	Diam. A	Height H	Hexagon [c] J	Specification E	Length l	
¼	0.2480	0.2460	⅜	3/16	⅛	10-24NC-3	⅜	¾–2½
5/16	0.3105	0.3085	7/16	7/32	5/32	¼-20NC-3	7/16	1 –3
⅜	0.3730	0.3710	9/16	¼	3/16	5/16-18NC-3	½	1 –4
½	0.4980	0.4960	¾	5/16	¼	⅜-16NC-3	⅝	1¼–5
⅝	0.6230	0.6210	⅞	⅜	5/16	½-13NC-3	¾	1½–6
¾	0.7480	0.7460	1	½	⅜	⅝-11NC-3	⅞	1½–8
1	0.9980	0.9960	1 5/16	⅝	½	¾-10NC-3	1	1½–8
1¼	1.2480	1.2460	1¾	¾	⅝	⅞-9NC-3	1⅛	1½–8

[a] ASA B18.3—1947. Dimensions are in inches.

[b] Head chamfer is 30°.

[c] Socket depth = ¾H.

[d] Shoulder-length increments: shoulder lengths from ¾ in. to 1 in., ⅛-in. intervals; shoulder lengths from 1 in. to 5 in., ¼-in. intervals; shoulder lengths from 5 in. to 7 in., ½-in. intervals; shoulder lengths from 7 in. to 8 in., 1-in. intervals. Shoulder-length tolerance ±0.005.

AMERICAN STANDARD WOOD SCREWS *

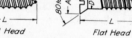
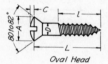

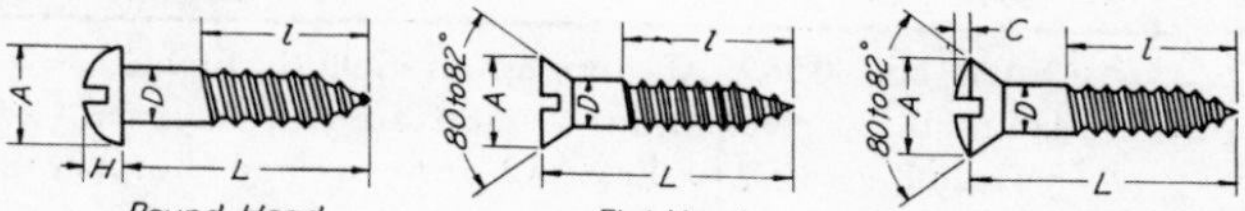

Round Head   Flat Head   Oval Head

Nominal size	Basic diam. of screw D	No. of threads per in. †	Slot width ‡ J (all heads)	Round head		Flat head	Oval head	
				A	H	A	A	C
0	0.060	32	0.023	0.113	0.053	0.119	0.119	0.021
1	0.073	28	0.026	0.138	0.061	0.146	0.146	0.025
2	0.086	26	0.031	0.162	0.069	0.172	0.172	0.029
3	0.099	24	0.035	0.187	0.078	0.199	0.199	0.033
4	0.112	22	0.039	0.211	0.086	0.225	0.225	0.037
5	0.125	20	0.043	0.236	0.095	0.252	0.252	0.041
6	0.138	18	0.048	0.260	0.103	0.279	0.279	0.045
7	0.151	16	0.048	0.285	0.111	0.305	0.305	0.049
8	0.164	15	0.054	0.309	0.120	0.332	0.332	0.052
9	0.177	14	0.054	0.334	0.128	0.358	0.358	0.056
10	0.190	13	0.060	0.359	0.137	0.385	0.385	0.060
12	0.216	11	0.067	0.408	0.153	0.438	0.438	0.068
14	0.242	10	0.075	0.457	0.170	0.491	0.491	0.076
16	0.268	9	0.075	0.506	0.187	0.544	0.544	0.084
18	0.294	8	0.084	0.555	0.204	0.597	0.597	0.092
20	0.320	8	0.084	0.604	0.220	0.650	0.650	0.100
24	0.372	7	0.094	0.702	0.254	0.756	0.756	0.116

* ASA B18.6—1947. Dimensions given are maximum values, all in inches. Heads may be slotted or recessed as specified.

† Thread length $l = \frac{2}{3}L$.

‡ Slot depths and recesses vary with type and size of screw; draw to look well.

SMALL RIVETS *

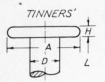

TINNERS'

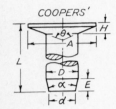

COOPERS'

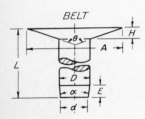

BELT

Tinner's			Cooper's			Belt		
Size No. †	D Diam. body	L Length	Size No.	D Diam. body	L Length	Size No.‡	D Diam. body	L Length
8 oz	0.089	0.16	1 lb	0.109	0.219	7	0.180	From ⅜ to ¾ by ⅛" increments
12	0.105	0.19	1½	0.127	0.256	8	0.165	
1 lb	0.111	0.20	2	0.141	0.292	9	0.148	
1½	0.130	0.23	2½	0.148	0.325	10	0.134	
2	0.144	0.27	3	0.156	0.358	11	0.120	
2½	0.148	0.28	4	0.165	0.392	12	0.109	
3	0.160	0.31	6	0.203	0.466	13	0.095	
4	0.176	0.34	8	0.238	0.571			
6	0.203	0.39	10	0.250	0.606			
8	0.224	0.44	12	0.259	0.608			
10	0.238	0.47	14	0.271	0.643			
12	0.259	0.50	16	0.281	0.677			
14	0.284	0.52						
16	0.300	0.53						

Approx. proportions:

$A = 2.25 \times D$

$H = 0.30 \times D$

Approx. proportions:

$A = 2.25 \times D, \quad d = 0.90 \times D$

$E = 0.40 \times D, \quad H = 0.30 \times D$

Included $\angle \theta = 144°$

$\angle \alpha = 18°$

Approx. proportions:

$A = 2.8 \times D, \quad d = 0.9 \times D$

$E = 0.4 \times D, \quad H = 0.3 \times D$

Tolerances on the nominal diameter:

$+0.002$

-0.004

Finished rivets shall be free from injurious defects.

* ASA B18gl—1942. All dimensions given in inches.
† Size numbers refer to the Trade Name or weight of 1,000 rivets.
‡ Size number refers to the Stubs iron-wire gage number of the stock used in the body of the rivet.

DIMENSIONS OF STANDARD GIB-HEAD KEYS, SQUARE AND FLAT

Approved by ASA *

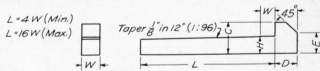

$L = 4W$ (Min.)
$L = 16W$ (Max.)
Taper ⅛" in 12" (1:96)

Diameters of shafts	Square type					Flat type				
	Key		Gib head			Key		Gib head		
	W	H	C	D	E	W	H	C	D	E
½ – 9⁄16	⅛	⅛	¼	7⁄32	5⁄32	⅛	3⁄32	3⁄16	⅛	⅛
⅝ – ⅞	3⁄16	3⁄16	5⁄16	9⁄32	7⁄32	3⁄16	⅛	¼	3⁄16	5⁄32
15⁄16–1¼	¼	¼	7⁄16	11⁄32	11⁄32	¼	3⁄16	5⁄16	¼	3⁄16
1 5⁄16–1⅜	5⁄16	5⁄16	9⁄16	13⁄32	13⁄32	5⁄16	¼	⅜	5⁄16	¼
1 7⁄16–1¾	⅜	⅜	11⁄16	15⁄32	15⁄32	⅜	¼	7⁄16	⅜	5⁄16
1 13⁄16–2¼	½	½	⅞	19⁄32	⅝	½	⅜	⅝	½	7⁄16
2 5⁄16–2¾	⅝	⅝	1 1⁄16	23⁄32	¾	⅝	7⁄16	¾	⅝	½
2 ⅞ –3¼	¾	¾	1 ¼	⅞	⅞	¾	½	⅞	¾	⅝
3 ⅜ –3¾	⅞	⅞	1 ½	1	1	⅞	⅝	1 1⁄16	⅞	¾
3 ⅞ –4½	1	1	1 ¾	1 3⁄16	1 3⁄16	1	¾	1¼	1	1 13⁄16
4 ¾ –5½	1¼	1¼	2	1 7⁄16	1 7⁄16	1¼	⅞	1½	1¼	1
5 ¾ –6	1½	1½	2 ½	1 ¾	1 ¾	1½	1	1¾	1½	1 ¼

* ASA B17.1—1934. Dimensions in inches.

WIDTHS AND HEIGHTS OF STANDARD SQUARE- AND FLAT-STOCK KEYS WITH CORRESPONDING SHAFT DIAMETERS

Approved by ASA *

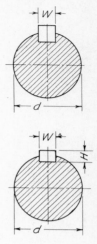

Shaft diam. d (inclusive)	Square-stock keys W	Flat-stock keys, $W \times H$	Shaft diam. d (inclusive)	Square-stock keys W	Flat-stock keys, $W \times H$
$\frac{1}{2} - \frac{9}{16}$	$\frac{1}{8}$	$\frac{1}{8} \times \frac{3}{32}$	$2\frac{7}{8}-3\frac{1}{4}$	$\frac{3}{4}$	$\frac{3}{4} \times \frac{1}{2}$
$\frac{5}{8} - \frac{7}{8}$	$\frac{3}{16}$	$\frac{3}{16} \times \frac{1}{8}$	$3\frac{3}{8}-3\frac{3}{4}$	$\frac{7}{8}$	$\frac{7}{8} \times \frac{5}{8}$
$\frac{15}{16}-1\frac{1}{4}$	$\frac{1}{4}$	$\frac{1}{4} \times \frac{3}{16}$	$3\frac{7}{8}-4\frac{1}{2}$	1	$1 \times \frac{3}{4}$
$1\frac{5}{16}-1\frac{3}{8}$	$\frac{5}{16}$	$\frac{5}{16} \times \frac{1}{4}$			
$1\frac{7}{16}-1\frac{3}{4}$	$\frac{3}{8}$	$\frac{3}{8} \times \frac{1}{4}$	$4\frac{3}{4}-5\frac{1}{2}$	$1\frac{1}{4}$	$1\frac{1}{4} \times \frac{7}{8}$
$1\frac{13}{16}-2\frac{1}{4}$	$\frac{1}{2}$	$\frac{1}{2} \times \frac{3}{8}$	$5\frac{3}{4}-6$	$1\frac{1}{2}$	$1\frac{1}{2} \times 1$
$2\frac{5}{16}-2\frac{3}{4}$	$\frac{5}{8}$	$\frac{5}{8} \times \frac{7}{16}$			

* ASA B17.1—1934. Dimensions in inches.

WOODRUFF-KEY DIMENSIONS

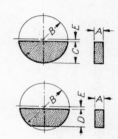

Key * No.	Nominal size $A \times B$	Max. width of key A	Max. diam. of key B	Max. height of key		Distance below center E
				C	D	
204	$\frac{1}{16} \times \frac{1}{2}$	0.0635	0.500	0.203	0.194	$\frac{3}{64}$
304	$\frac{3}{32} \times \frac{1}{2}$	0.0948	0.500	0.203	0.194	$\frac{3}{64}$
305	$\frac{3}{32} \times \frac{5}{8}$	0.0948	0.625	0.250	0.240	$\frac{1}{16}$
404	$\frac{1}{8} \times \frac{1}{2}$	0.1260	0.500	0.203	0.194	$\frac{3}{64}$
405	$\frac{1}{8} \times \frac{5}{8}$	0.1260	0.625	0.250	0.240	$\frac{1}{16}$
406	$\frac{1}{8} \times \frac{3}{4}$	0.1260	0.750	0.313	0.303	$\frac{1}{16}$
505	$\frac{5}{32} \times \frac{5}{8}$	0.1573	0.625	0.250	0.240	$\frac{1}{16}$
506	$\frac{5}{32} \times \frac{3}{4}$	0.1573	0.750	0.313	0.303	$\frac{1}{16}$
507	$\frac{5}{32} \times \frac{7}{8}$	0.1573	0.875	0.375	0.365	$\frac{1}{16}$
606	$\frac{3}{16} \times \frac{3}{4}$	0.1885	0.750	0.313	0.303	$\frac{1}{16}$
607	$\frac{3}{16} \times \frac{7}{8}$	0.1885	0.875	0.375	0.365	$\frac{1}{16}$
608	$\frac{3}{16} \times 1$	0.1885	1.000	0.438	0.428	$\frac{1}{16}$
609	$\frac{3}{16} \times 1\frac{1}{8}$	0.1885	1.125	0.484	0.475	$\frac{5}{64}$
807	$\frac{1}{4} \times \frac{7}{8}$	0.2510	0.875	0.375	0.365	$\frac{1}{16}$
808	$\frac{1}{4} \times 1$	0.2510	1.000	0.438	0.428	$\frac{1}{16}$
809	$\frac{1}{4} \times 1\frac{1}{8}$	0.2510	1.125	0.484	0.475	$\frac{5}{64}$
810	$\frac{1}{4} \times 1\frac{1}{4}$	0.2510	1.250	0.547	0.537	$\frac{5}{64}$
811	$\frac{1}{4} \times 1\frac{3}{8}$	0.2510	1.375	0.594	0.584	$\frac{3}{32}$
812	$\frac{1}{4} \times 1\frac{1}{2}$	0.2510	1.500	0.641	0.631	$\frac{7}{64}$
1008	$\frac{5}{16} \times 1$	0.3135	1.000	0.438	0.428	$\frac{1}{16}$
1009	$\frac{5}{16} \times 1\frac{1}{8}$	0.3135	1.125	0.484	0.475	$\frac{5}{64}$
1010	$\frac{5}{16} \times 1\frac{1}{4}$	0.3135	1.250	0.547	0.537	$\frac{5}{64}$
1011	$\frac{5}{16} \times 1\frac{3}{8}$	0.3135	1.375	0.594	0.584	$\frac{3}{32}$
1012	$\frac{5}{16} \times 1\frac{1}{2}$	0.3135	1.500	0.641	0.631	$\frac{7}{64}$
1210	$\frac{3}{8} \times 1\frac{1}{4}$	0.3760	1.250	0.547	0.537	$\frac{5}{64}$
1211	$\frac{3}{8} \times 1\frac{3}{8}$	0.3760	1.375	0.594	0.584	$\frac{3}{32}$
1212	$\frac{3}{8} \times 1\frac{1}{2}$	0.3760	1.500	0.641	0.631	$\frac{7}{64}$

* Dimensions in inches. Key numbers indicate the nominal key dimensions. The last two digits give the nominal diameter B in eighths of an inch, and the digits preceding the last two give the nominal width A in thirty-seconds of an inch. Thus 204 indicates a key $\frac{2}{32}$ by $\frac{4}{8}$, or $\frac{1}{16}$ by $\frac{1}{2}$ in.

WOODRUFF-KEY-SEAT DIMENSIONS

Key* No.	Nominal size	Key slot			
		Width W		Depth H	
		Max.	Min.	Max.	Min.
204	$\frac{1}{16} \times \frac{1}{2}$	0.0630	0.0615	0.1718	0.1668
304	$\frac{3}{32} \times \frac{1}{2}$	0.0943	0.0928	0.1561	0.1511
305	$\frac{3}{32} \times \frac{5}{8}$	0.0943	0 0928	0.2031	0.1981
404	$\frac{1}{8} \times \frac{1}{2}$	0.1255	0.1240	0.1405	0.1355
405	$\frac{1}{8} \times \frac{5}{8}$	0.1255	0.1240	0.1875	0.1825
406	$\frac{1}{8} \times \frac{3}{4}$	0.1255	0.1240	0.2505	0.2455
505	$\frac{5}{32} \times \frac{5}{8}$	0.1568	0.1553	0.1719	0.1669
506	$\frac{5}{32} \times \frac{3}{4}$	0.1568	0.1553	0.2349	0.2299
507	$\frac{5}{32} \times \frac{7}{8}$	0.1568	0.1553	0.2969	0.2919
606	$\frac{3}{16} \times \frac{3}{4}$	0.1880	0.1863	0.2193	0.2143
607	$\frac{3}{16} \times \frac{7}{8}$	0.1880	0.1863	0.2813	0.2763
608	$\frac{3}{16} \times 1$	0.1880	0.1863	0.3443	0.3393
609	$\frac{3}{16} \times 1\frac{1}{8}$	0.1880	0.1863	0.3903	0.3853
807	$\frac{1}{4} \times \frac{7}{8}$	0.2505	0.2487	0.2500	0.2450
808	$\frac{1}{4} \times 1$	0.2505	0.2487	0.3130	0.3080
809	$\frac{1}{4} \times 1\frac{1}{8}$	0.2505	0.2487	0.3590	0.3540
810	$\frac{1}{4} \times 1\frac{1}{4}$	0.2505	0.2487	0.4220	0.4170
811	$\frac{1}{4} \times 1\frac{3}{8}$	0.2505	0.2487	0.4690	0.4640
812	$\frac{1}{4} \times 1\frac{1}{2}$	0.2505	0.2487	0.5160	0.5110
1008	$\frac{5}{16} \times 1$	0.3130	0.3111	0.2818	0.2768
1009	$\frac{5}{16} \times 1\frac{1}{8}$	0.3130	0.3111	0.3278	0.3228
1010	$\frac{5}{16} \times 1\frac{1}{4}$	0.3130	0.3111	0.3908	0.3858
1011	$\frac{5}{16} \times 1\frac{3}{8}$	0.3130	0.3111	0.4378	0.4328
1012	$\frac{5}{16} \times 1\frac{1}{2}$	0.3130	0.3111	0.4848	0.4798
1210	$\frac{3}{8} \times 1\frac{1}{4}$	0.3755	0.3735	0.3595	0.3545
1211	$\frac{3}{8} \times 1\frac{3}{8}$	0.3755	0.3735	0.4060	0.4015
1212	$\frac{3}{8} \times 1\frac{1}{2}$	0.3755	0.3735	0.4535	0.4485

* Dimensions in inches. Key numbers indicate the nominal key dimensions. The last two digits give the nominal diameter B in eighths of an inch, and the digits preceding the last two give the nominal width A in thirty-seconds of an inch. Thus 204 indicates a key $\frac{2}{32}$ by $\frac{4}{8}$, or $\frac{1}{16}$ by $\frac{1}{2}$ in.

DIMENSIONS OF PRATT AND WHITNEY KEYS

Key No.	L	W	H	D	Key No.	L	W	H	D
1	$\frac{1}{2}$	$\frac{1}{16}$	$\frac{3}{32}$	$\frac{1}{16}$	22	$1\frac{3}{8}$	$\frac{1}{4}$	$\frac{3}{8}$	$\frac{1}{4}$
2	$\frac{1}{2}$	$\frac{3}{32}$	$\frac{9}{64}$	$\frac{3}{32}$	23	$1\frac{3}{8}$	$\frac{5}{16}$	$\frac{15}{32}$	$\frac{5}{16}$
3	$\frac{1}{2}$	$\frac{1}{8}$	$\frac{3}{16}$	$\frac{1}{8}$	F	$1\frac{3}{8}$	$\frac{3}{8}$	$\frac{9}{16}$	$\frac{3}{8}$
4	$\frac{5}{8}$	$\frac{3}{32}$	$\frac{9}{64}$	$\frac{3}{32}$	24	$1\frac{1}{2}$	$\frac{1}{4}$	$\frac{3}{8}$	$\frac{1}{4}$
5	$\frac{5}{8}$	$\frac{1}{8}$	$\frac{3}{16}$	$\frac{1}{8}$	25	$1\frac{1}{2}$	$\frac{5}{16}$	$\frac{15}{32}$	$\frac{5}{16}$
6	$\frac{5}{8}$	$\frac{5}{32}$	$\frac{15}{64}$	$\frac{5}{32}$	G	$1\frac{1}{2}$	$\frac{3}{8}$	$\frac{9}{16}$	$\frac{3}{8}$
7	$\frac{3}{4}$	$\frac{1}{8}$	$\frac{3}{16}$	$\frac{1}{8}$	51	$1\frac{3}{4}$	$\frac{1}{4}$	$\frac{3}{8}$	$\frac{1}{4}$
8	$\frac{3}{4}$	$\frac{5}{32}$	$\frac{15}{64}$	$\frac{5}{32}$	52	$1\frac{3}{4}$	$\frac{5}{16}$	$\frac{15}{32}$	$\frac{5}{16}$
9	$\frac{3}{4}$	$\frac{3}{16}$	$\frac{9}{32}$	$\frac{3}{16}$	53	$1\frac{3}{4}$	$\frac{3}{8}$	$\frac{9}{16}$	$\frac{3}{8}$
10	$\frac{7}{8}$	$\frac{5}{32}$	$\frac{15}{64}$	$\frac{5}{32}$	26	2	$\frac{3}{16}$	$\frac{9}{32}$	$\frac{3}{16}$
11	$\frac{7}{8}$	$\frac{3}{16}$	$\frac{9}{32}$	$\frac{3}{16}$	27	2	$\frac{1}{4}$	$\frac{3}{8}$	$\frac{1}{4}$
12	$\frac{7}{8}$	$\frac{7}{32}$	$\frac{21}{64}$	$\frac{7}{32}$	28	2	$\frac{5}{16}$	$\frac{15}{32}$	$\frac{5}{16}$
A	$\frac{7}{8}$	$\frac{1}{4}$	$\frac{3}{8}$	$\frac{1}{4}$	29	2	$\frac{3}{8}$	$\frac{9}{16}$	$\frac{3}{8}$
13	1	$\frac{3}{16}$	$\frac{9}{32}$	$\frac{3}{16}$	54	$2\frac{1}{4}$	$\frac{1}{4}$	$\frac{3}{8}$	$\frac{1}{4}$
14	1	$\frac{7}{32}$	$\frac{21}{64}$	$\frac{7}{32}$	55	$2\frac{1}{4}$	$\frac{5}{16}$	$\frac{15}{16}$	$\frac{5}{16}$
15	1	$\frac{1}{4}$	$\frac{3}{8}$	$\frac{1}{4}$	56	$2\frac{1}{4}$	$\frac{3}{8}$	$\frac{9}{16}$	$\frac{3}{8}$
B	1	$\frac{5}{16}$	$\frac{15}{32}$	$\frac{5}{16}$	57	$2\frac{1}{4}$	$\frac{7}{16}$	$\frac{21}{32}$	$\frac{7}{16}$
16	$1\frac{1}{8}$	$\frac{3}{16}$	$\frac{9}{32}$	$\frac{3}{16}$	58	$2\frac{1}{2}$	$\frac{5}{16}$	$\frac{15}{32}$	$\frac{5}{16}$
17	$1\frac{1}{8}$	$\frac{7}{32}$	$\frac{21}{64}$	$\frac{7}{32}$	59	$2\frac{1}{2}$	$\frac{3}{8}$	$\frac{9}{16}$	$\frac{3}{8}$
18	$1\frac{1}{8}$	$\frac{1}{4}$	$\frac{3}{8}$	$\frac{1}{4}$	60	$2\frac{1}{2}$	$\frac{7}{16}$	$\frac{21}{32}$	$\frac{7}{16}$
C	$1\frac{1}{8}$	$\frac{5}{16}$	$\frac{15}{32}$	$\frac{5}{16}$	61	$2\frac{1}{2}$	$\frac{1}{2}$	$\frac{3}{4}$	$\frac{1}{2}$
19	$1\frac{1}{4}$	$\frac{3}{16}$	$\frac{9}{32}$	$\frac{3}{16}$	30	3	$\frac{3}{8}$	$\frac{9}{16}$	$\frac{3}{8}$
20	$1\frac{1}{4}$	$\frac{7}{32}$	$\frac{21}{64}$	$\frac{7}{32}$	31	3	$\frac{7}{16}$	$\frac{21}{32}$	$\frac{7}{16}$
21	$1\frac{1}{4}$	$\frac{1}{4}$	$\frac{3}{8}$	$\frac{1}{4}$	32	3	$\frac{1}{2}$	$\frac{3}{4}$	$\frac{1}{2}$
D	$1\frac{1}{4}$	$\frac{5}{16}$	$\frac{15}{32}$	$\frac{5}{16}$	33	3	$\frac{9}{16}$	$\frac{27}{32}$	$\frac{9}{16}$
E	$1\frac{1}{4}$	$\frac{3}{8}$	$\frac{9}{16}$	$\frac{3}{8}$	34	3	$\frac{5}{8}$	$\frac{15}{16}$	$\frac{5}{8}$

Dimensions in inches. Key is $\frac{2}{3}$ in shaft; $\frac{1}{3}$ in hub. Keys are 0.001 in. oversize in width to ensure proper fitting in keyway. Keyway size: width = W; depth = $H - D$. Length L should never be less than $2W$.

AMERICAN STANDARD PLAIN WASHERS *

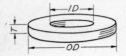

Size	Light			Medium			Heavy			Extra heavy		
	ID	OD	Thickness	ID	OD	Thickness	ID	OD	Thickness	ID	OD	Thickness
0	5/64	3/16	0.020									
1	3/32	7/32	0.020									
2	3/32	1/4	0.020									
3	1/8	1/4	0.022									
4	1/8	1/4	0.022	1/8	5/16	0.032						
5	5/32	5/16	0.035	5/32	3/8	0.049						
6	5/32	5/16	0.035	5/32	3/8	0.049						
7	11/64	13/32	0.049	3/16	3/8	0.049						
8	3/16	3/8	0.049	3/16	7/16	0.049						
9	13/64	15/32	0.049	7/32	1/2	0.049						
3/16	7/32	7/16	0.049	7/32	1/2	0.049	1/4	9/16	0.049			
10	7/32	7/16	0.049	1/4	9/16	0.049	1/4	9/16	0.065			
11	15/64	17/32	0.049	1/4	9/16	0.049	1/4	9/16	0.065			
12	1/4	1/2	0.049	1/4	9/16	0.049	1/4	9/16	0.065			
14	17/64	5/8	0.049	5/16	3/4	0.065	5/16	7/8	0.065			
1/4	9/32	5/8	0.065	5/16	3/4	0.065	5/16	3/4	0.065	5/16	7/8	0.065
16	9/32	5/8	0.065	5/16	3/4	0.065	5/16	7/8	0.065	5/16	7/8	0.065
18	5/16	3/4	0.065	3/8	3/4	0.065	3/8	7/8	0.083	3/8	1 1/8	0.065
5/16	11/32	11/16	0.065	3/8	3/4	0.065	3/8	7/8	0.083	3/8	1 1/8	0.065
20	11/32	11/16	0.065	3/8	3/4	0.065	3/8	7/8	0.083	3/8	1 1/8	0.065
24	13/32	13/16	0.065	7/16	7/8	0.083	7/16	1	0.083	7/16	1 3/8	0.083
3/8	13/32	13/16	0.065	7/16	7/8	0.083	7/16	1	0.083	7/16	1 3/8	0.083
7/16	15/32	59/64	0.065	1/2	1 1/8	0.083	1/2	1 1/4	0.083	1/2	1 5/8	0.083
1/2	17/32	1 1/16	0.095	9/16	1 1/4	0.109	9/16	1 3/8	0.109	9/16	1 7/8	0.109
9/16	19/32	1 3/16	0.095	5/8	1 3/8	0.109	5/8	1 1/2	0.109	5/8	2 1/8	0.134
5/8	21/32	1 5/16	0.095	11/16	1 1/2	0.134	11/16	1 3/4	0.134	11/16	2 3/8	0.165
3/4	13/16	1 1/2	0.134	13/16	1 3/4	0.148	13/16	2	0.148	13/16	2 7/8	0.165
7/8	15/16	1 3/4	0.134	15/16	2	0.165	15/16	2 1/4	0.165	15/16	3 3/8	0.180
1	1 1/16	2	0.134	1 1/16	2 1/4	0.165	1 1/16	2 1/2	0.165	1 1/16	3 7/8	0.238
1 1/8	.....	.....	.....	1 3/16	2 1/2	0.165	1 1/4	2 3/4	0.165			
1 1/4	.....	.....	.....	1 5/16	2 3/4	0.165	1 3/8	3	0.165			
1 3/8	.....	.....	.....	1 7/16	3	0.180	1 1/2	3 1/4	0.180			
1 1/2	.....	.....	.....	1 9/16	3 1/4	0.180	1 5/8	3 1/2	0.180			
1 5/8	.....	.....	.....	1 11/16	3 1/2	0.180	1 3/4	3 3/4	0.180			
1 3/4	.....	.....	.....	1 13/16	3 3/4	0.180	1 7/8	4	0.180			
1 7/8	.....	.....	.....	1 15/16	4	0.180	2	4 1/4	0.180			
2	.....	.....	.....	2 1/16	4 1/4	0.180	2 1/8	4 1/2	0.180			
2 1/4	.....	.....	.....	.....	.....	.....	2 3/8	4 3/4	0.220			
2 1/2	.....	.....	.....	.....	.....	.....	2 5/8	5	0.238			
2 3/4	.....	.....	.....	.....	.....	.....	2 7/8	5 1/4	0.259			
3	.....	.....	.....	.....	.....	.....	3 1/8	5 1/2	0.284			

* ASA B27.2—1949. All dimensions in inches.

AMERICAN STANDARD LOCK WASHERS *

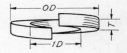

Nominal size	Inside diam., min.	Light		Medium		Heavy		Extra heavy	
		Min. thick-ness	Out-side diam., max.	Min. thick-ness	Out-side diam., max.	Min. thick-ness	Out-side diam., max.	Min. thick-ness	Out-side diam., max.
0.086 (No. 2)	0.088	0.015	0.165	0.020	0.175	0.025	0.185	0.027	0.211
0.099 (No. 3)	0.102	0.020	0.188	0.025	0.198	0.031	0.212	0.034	0.242
0.112 (No. 4)	0.115	0.020	0.202	0.025	0.212	0.031	0.226	0.034	0.256
0.125 (No. 5)	0.128	0.025	0.225	0.031	0.239	0.040	0.255	0.045	0.303
0.138 (No. 6)	0.141	0.025	0.239	0.031	0.253	0.040	0.269	0.045	0.317
0.164 (No. 8)	0.168	0.031	0.280	0.040	0.296	0.047	0.310	0.057	0.378
0.190 (No. 10)	0.194	0.040	0.323	0.047	0.337	0.056	0.353	0.068	0.437
0.216 (No. 12)	0.221	0.047	0.364	0.056	0.380	0.063	0.394	0.080	0.500
1/4	0.255	0.047	0.489	0.062	0.493	0.077	0.495	0.084	0.539
5/16	0.319	0.056	0.575	0.078	0.591	0.097	0.601	0.108	0.627
3/8	0.382	0.070	0.678	0.094	0.688	0.115	0.696	0.123	0.746
7/16	0.446	0.085	0.780	0.109	0.784	0.133	0.792	0.143	0.844
1/2	0.509	0.099	0.877	0.125	0.879	0.151	0.889	0.162	0.945
9/16	0.573	0.113	0.975	0.141	0.979	0.170	0.989	0.182	1.049
5/8	0.636	0.126	1.082	0.156	1.086	0.189	1.100	0.202	1.164
11/16	0.700	0.138	1.178	0.172	1.184	0.207	1.200	0.221	1.266
3/4	0.763	0.153	1.277	0.188	1.279	0.226	1.299	0.241	1.369
13/16	0.827	0.168	1.375	0.203	1.377	0.246	1.401	0.261	1.473
7/8	0.890	0.179	1.470	0.219	1.474	0.266	1.504	0.285	1.586
15/16	0.954	0.191	1.562	0.234	1.570	0.284	1.604	0.308	1.698
1	1.017	0.202	1.656	0.250	1.672	0.306	1.716	0.330	1.810
1 1/16	1.081	0.213	1.746	0.266	1.768	0.326	1.820	0.352	1.922
1 1/8	1.144	0.224	1.837	0.281	1.865	0.345	1.921	0.375	2.031
1 3/16	1.208	0.234	1.923	0.297	1.963	0.364	2.021	0.396	2.137
1 1/4	1.271	0.244	2.012	0.312	2.058	0.384	2.126	0.417	2.244
1 5/16	1.335	0.254	2.098	0.328	2.156	0.403	2.226	0.438	2.350
1 3/8	1.398	0.264	2.183	0.344	2.253	0.422	2.325	0.458	2.453
1 7/16	1.462	0.273	2.269	0.359	2.349	0.440	2.421	0.478	2.555
1 1/2	1.525	0.282	2.352	0.375	2.446	0.458	2.518	0.496	2.654

* ASA B27.1—1950. All dimensions in inches.

Tapers. Taper means the difference in diameter or width in 1 ft of length; see figure below. *Taper pins*, much used for fastening cylindrical parts and for doweling, have a standard taper of ¼ in. per ft.

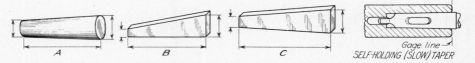

Machine tapers. The American Standard for self-holding (slow) machine tapers is designed to replace the various former standards. The table below shows its derivation. Detailed dimensions and tolerances for taper tool shanks and taper sockets will be found in ASA B5.10—1937.

DIMENSIONS OF TAPER PINS

Taper ¼ in. per ft

Size No.	Diam., large end	Drill size for reamer	Max. length
000000	0.072	53	⅝
00000	0.092	47	⅝
0000	0.108	42	¾
000	0.125	37	¾
00	0.147	31	1
0	0.156	28	1
1	0.172	25	1¼
2	0.193	19	1½
3	0.219	12	1¾
4	0.250	3	2
5	0.289	¼	2¼
6	0.341	9/32	3¼
7	0.409	11/32	3¾
8	0.492	13/32	4½
9	0 591	31/64	5¼
10	0.706	19/32	6
11	0.857	23/32	7¼
12	1.013	55/64	8¾
13	1.233	1 1/64	10¾

All dimensions in inches.

AMERICAN STANDARD MACHINE TAPERS,* SELF-HOLDING (SLOW) TAPER SERIES

Basic dimensions

<table>
<tr><th>Origin of series</th><th>No. of taper</th><th>Taper /ft</th><th>Diam. at gage line</th><th colspan="4">Means of driving and holding</th></tr>
<tr><td rowspan="3">Brown and Sharpe taper series</td><td>0.239</td><td>0.500</td><td>0.239</td><td rowspan="13">Tongue drive with shank held in by friction</td><td colspan="3" rowspan="3"></td></tr>
<tr><td>0.299</td><td>0.500</td><td>0.299</td></tr>
<tr><td>0.375</td><td>0.500</td><td>0.375</td></tr>
<tr><td rowspan="6">Morse taper series</td><td>1</td><td>0.600</td><td>0.475</td><td rowspan="10">Tongue drive with shank held in by key</td><td colspan="2" rowspan="6"></td></tr>
<tr><td>2</td><td>0.600</td><td>0.700</td></tr>
<tr><td>3</td><td>0.602</td><td>0.938</td></tr>
<tr><td>4</td><td>0.623</td><td>1.231</td></tr>
<tr><td>4½</td><td>0.623</td><td>1.500</td></tr>
<tr><td>5</td><td>0.630</td><td>1.748</td></tr>
<tr><td rowspan="10">¾-in./ft taper series</td><td>200</td><td>0.750</td><td>2.000</td><td rowspan="10">Key drive with shank held in by key</td><td rowspan="10">Key drive with shank held in by drawbolt</td></tr>
<tr><td>250</td><td>0.750</td><td>2.500</td></tr>
<tr><td>300</td><td>0.750</td><td>3.000</td></tr>
<tr><td>350</td><td>0.750</td><td>3.500</td></tr>
<tr><td>400</td><td>0.750</td><td>4.000</td><td colspan="2" rowspan="6"></td></tr>
<tr><td>500</td><td>0.750</td><td>5.000</td></tr>
<tr><td>600</td><td>0.750</td><td>6.000</td></tr>
<tr><td>800</td><td>0.750</td><td>8.000</td></tr>
<tr><td>1,000</td><td>0.750</td><td>10.000</td></tr>
<tr><td>1,200</td><td>0.750</td><td>12.000</td></tr>
</table>

* ASA B5.10—1937. All dimensions in inches.

WIRE AND SHEET-METAL GAGES

Dimensions in decimal parts of an inch

No. of gage	American or Brown and Sharpe [a]	Washburn & Moen or American Steel & Wire Co. [b]	Birmingham or Stubs iron wire [c]	Music wire [d]	Imperial wire gage [e]	U.S. Std. for plate [f]
0000000	.....	0.4900	....	.....	0.5000	0.5000
000000	0.5800	0.4615	.....	0.004	0.4640	0.4688
00000	0.5165	0.4305	0.500	0.005	0.4320	0.4375
0000	0.4600	0.3938	0.454	0.006	0.4000	0.4063
000	0.4096	0.3625	0.425	0.007	0.3720	0.3750
00	0.3648	0.3310	0.380	0.008	0.3480	0.3438
0	0.3249	0.3065	0.340	0.009	0.3240	0.3125
1	0.2893	0.2830	0.300	0.010	0.3000	0.2813
2	0.2576	0.2625	0.284	0.011	0.2760	0.2656
3	0.2294	0.2437	0.259	0.012	0.2520	0.2500
4	0.2043	0.2253	0.238	0.013	0.2320	0.2344
5	0.1819	0.2070	0.220	0.014	0.2120	0.2188
6	0.1620	0.1920	0.203	0.016	0.1920	0.2031
7	0.1443	0.1770	0.180	0.018	0.1760	0.1875
8	0.1285	0.1620	0.165	0.020	0.1600	0.1719
9	0.1144	0.1483	0.148	0.022	0.1440	0.1563
10	0.1019	0.1350	0.134	0.024	0.1280	0.1406
11	0.0907	0.1205	0.120	0.026	0.1160	0.1250
12	0.0808	0.1055	0.109	0.029	0.1040	0.1094
13	0.0720	0.0915	0.095	0.031	0.0920	0.0938
14	0.0641	0.0800	0.0£3	0.033	0.0800	0.0781
15	0.0571	0.0720	0.072	0.035	0.0720	0.0703
16	0.0508	0.0625	0.065	0.037	0.0640	0.0625
17	0.0453	0.0540	0.058	0.039	0.0560	0.0563
18	0.0403	0.0475	0.049	0.041	0.0480	0.0500
19	0.0359	0.0410	0.042	0.043	0.0400	0.0438
20	0.0320	0.0348	0.035	0.045	0.0360	0.0375
21	0.0285	0.0317	0.032	0.047	0.0320	0.0344
22	0.0253	0.0286	0.028	0.049	0.0280	0.0313
23	0.0226	0.0258	0.025	0.051	0.0240	0.0281
24	0.0201	0.0230	0.022	0.055	0.0220	0.0250
25	0.0179	0.0204	0.020	0.059	0.0200	0.0219
26	0.0159	0.0181	0.018	0.063	0.0180	0.0188
27	0.0142	0.0173	0.016	0.067	0.0164	0.0172
28	0.0126	0.0162	0.014	0.071	0.0148	0.0156
29	0.0113	0.0150	0.013	0.075	0.0136	0.0141
30	0.0100	0.0140	0.012	0.080	0.0124	0.0125
31	0.0089	0.0132	0.010	0.085	0.0116	0.0109
32	0.0080	0.0128	0.009	0.090	0.0108	0.0102
33	0.0071	0.0118	0.008	0.095	0.0100	0.0094
34	0.0063	0.0104	0.007	0.100	0.0092	0.0086
35	0.0056	0.0095	0.005	0.106	0.0084	0.0078
36	0.0050	0.0090	0.004	0.112	0.0076	0.0070
37	0.0045	0.0085	.....	0.118	0.0068	0.0066
38	0.0040	0.0080	.....	0.124	0.0060	0.0063
39	0.0035	0.0075	.....	0.130	0.0052	
40	0.0031	0.0070	.....	0.138	0.0048	

[a] Recognized standard in the United States for wire and sheet metal of copper and other metals except steel and iron.

[b] Recognized standard for steel and iron wire. Called the "U.S. steel wire gage."

[c] Formerly much used, now nearly obsolete.

[d] American Steel & Wire Company's music or piano wire gage. Recommended by U.S. Bureau of Standards.

[e] Official British Standard.

[f] Legalized U.S. Standard for iron and steel plate, although plate is now always specified by its thickness in decimals of an inch.

Preferred thicknesses for uncoated thin flat metals (under 0.250 in.): ASA B32—1941 gives recommended sizes for sheets.

TABLE OF LIMITS FOR CYLINDRICAL FITS *

Size of hole or external member inclusive †	Clearance fits							
	Class 1, loose fit				Class 2, free fit			
	Hole or external member		Shaft or internal member		Hole or external member		Shaft or internal member	
	+		−	−	+		−	−
0–3/16	0.001	0.000	0.001	0.002	0.0007	0.0000	0.0004	0.0011
3/16–5/16	0.002	0.000	0.001	0.003	0.0008	0.0000	0.0006	0.0014
5/16–7/16	0.002	0.000	0.001	0.003	0.0009	0.0000	0.0007	0.0016
7/16–9/16	0.002	0.000	0.002	0.004	0.0010	0.0000	0.0009	0.0019
9/16–11/16	0.002	0.000	0.002	0.004	0.0011	0.0000	0.0010	0.0021
11/16–13/16	0.002	0.000	0.002	0.004	0.0012	0.0000	0.0012	0.0024
13/16–15/16	0.002	0.000	0.002	0.004	0.0012	0.0000	0.0013	0.0025
15/16–1 1/16	0.003	0.000	0.003	0.006	0.0013	0.0000	0.0014	0.0027
1 1/16–1 3/16	0.003	0.000	0.003	0.006	0.0014	0.0000	0.0015	0.0029
1 3/16–1 3/8	0.003	0.000	0.003	0.006	0.0014	0.0000	0.0016	0.0030
1 3/8–1 5/8	0.003	0.000	0.003	0.006	0.0015	0.0000	0.0018	0.0033
1 5/8–1 7/8	0.003	0.000	0.004	0.007	0.0016	0.0000	0.0020	0.0036
1 7/8–2 1/8	0.003	0.000	0.004	0.007	0.0016	0.0000	0.0022	0.0038
2 1/8–2 3/8	0.003	0.000	0.004	0.007	0.0017	0.0000	0.0024	0.0041
2 3/8–2 3/4	0.003	0.000	0.005	0.008	0.0018	0.0000	0.0026	0.0044
2 3/4–3 1/4	0.004	0.000	0.005	0.009	0.0019	0.0000	0.0029	0.0048
3 1/4–3 3/4	0.004	0.000	0.006	0.010	0.0020	0.0000	0.0032	0.0052
3 3/4–4 1/4	0.004	0.000	0.006	0.010	0.0021	0.0000	0.0035	0.0056
4 1/4–4 3/4	0.004	0.000	0.007	0.011	0.0021	0.0000	0.0038	0.0059
4 3/4–5 1/2	0.004	0.000	0.007	0.011	0.0022	0.0000	0.0041	0.0063
5 1/2–6 1/2	0.005	0.000	0.008	0.013	0.0024	0.0000	0.0046	0.0070
6 1/2–7 1/2	0.005	0.000	0.009	0.014	0.0025	0.0000	0.0051	0.0076
7 1/2–8 1/2	0.005	0.000	0.010	0.015	0.0026	0.0000	0.0056	0.0082

Size of hole or external member inclusive †	Class 3, medium fit				Class 4, snug fit			
	Hole or external member		Shaft or internal member		Hole or external member		Shaft or internal member	
	+		−	−	+		−	−
0–3/16	0.0004	0.0000	0.0002	0.0006	0.0003	0.0000	0.0000	0.0002
3/16–5/16	0.0005	0.0000	0.0004	0.0009	0.0004	0.0000	0.0000	0.0003
5/16–7/16	0.0006	0.0000	0.0005	0.0011	0.0004	0.0000	0.0000	0.0003
7/16–9/16	0.0006	0.0000	0.0006	0.0012	0.0005	0.0000	0.0000	0.0003
9/16–11/16	0.0007	0.0000	0.0007	0.0014	0.0005	0.0000	0.0000	0.0003
11/16–13/16	0.0007	0.0000	0.0007	0.0014	0.0005	0.0000	0.0000	0.0004
13/16–15/16	0.0008	0.0000	0.0008	0.0016	0.0006	0.0000	0.0000	0.0004
15/16–1 1/16	0.0008	0.0000	0.0009	0.0017	0.0006	0.0000	0.0000	0.0004
1 1/16–1 3/16	0.0008	0.0000	0.0010	0.0018	0.0006	0.0000	0.0000	0.0004
1 3/16–1 3/8	0.0009	0.0000	0.0010	0.0019	0.0006	0.0000	0.0000	0.0004
1 3/8–1 5/8	0.0009	0.0000	0.0012	0.0021	0.0007	0.0000	0.0000	0.0005
1 5/8–1 7/8	0.0010	0.0000	0.0013	0.0023	0.0007	0.0000	0.0000	0.0005
1 7/8–2 1/8	0.0010	0.0000	0.0014	0.0024	0.0008	0.0000	0.0000	0.0005
2 1/8–2 3/8	0.0010	0.0000	0.0015	0.0025	0.0008	0.0000	0.0000	0.0005
2 3/8–2 3/4	0.0011	0.0000	0.0017	0.0028	0.0008	0.0000	0.0000	0.0005
2 3/4–3 1/4	0.0012	0.0000	0.0019	0.0031	0.0009	0.0000	0.0000	0.0006
3 1/4–3 3/4	0.0012	0.0000	0.0021	0.0033	0.0009	0.0000	0.0000	0.0006
3 3/4–4 1/4	0.0013	0.0000	0.0023	0.0036	0.0010	0.0000	0.0000	0.0006
4 1/4–4 3/4	0.0013	0.0000	0.0025	0.0038	0.0010	0.0000	0.0000	0.0007
4 3/4–5 1/2	0.0014	0.0000	0.0026	0.0040	0.0011	0.0000	0.0000	0.0007
5 1/2–6 1/2	0.0015	0.0000	0.0030	0.0045	0.0011	0.0000	0.0000	0.0007
6 1/2–7 1/2	0.0015	0.0000	0.0033	0.0048	0.0011	0.0000	0.0000	0.0008
7 1/2–8 1/2	0.0016	0.0000	0.0036	0.0052	0.0012	0.0000	0.0000	0.0008

* Compiled from ASA B4a—1925. All dimensions in inches.

† When nominal value is one of sizes given, use upper line in table.

TABLE OF LIMITS FOR CYLINDRICAL FITS (*Cont.*)

Size of hole or external member inclusive	Interference fits							
	Class 5, wringing fit				Class 6, tight fit			
	Hole or external member		Shaft or internal member		Hole or external member		Shaft or internal member	
	+		+		+		+	+
0–3/16	0.0003	0.0000	0.0002	0.0000	0.0003	0.0000	0.0003	0.0000
3/16–5/16	0.0004	0.0000	0.0003	0.0000	0.0004	0.0000	0.0005	0.0001
5/16–7/16	0.0004	0.0000	0.0003	0.0000	0.0004	0.0000	0.0005	0.0001
7/16–9/16	0.0005	0.0000	0.0003	0.0000	0.0005	0.0000	0.0006	0.0001
9/16–11/16	0.0005	0.0000	0.0003	0.0000	0.0005	0.0000	0.0007	0.0002
11/16–13/16	0.0005	0.0000	0.0004	0.0000	0.0005	0.0000	0.0007	0.0002
13/16–15/16	0.0006	0.0000	0.0004	0.0000	0.0006	0.0000	0.0008	0.0002
15/16–1 1/16	0.0006	0.0000	0.0004	0.0000	0.0006	0.0000	0.0009	0.0003
1 1/16–1 3/16	0.0006	0.0000	0.0004	0.0000	0.0006	0.0000	0.0009	0.0003
1 3/16–1 3/8	0.0006	0.0000	0.0004	0.0000	0.0006	0.0000	0.0009	0.0003
1 3/8–1 5/8	0.0007	0.0000	0.0005	0.0000	0.0007	0.0000	0.0011	0.0004
1 5/8–1 7/8	0.0007	0.0000	0.0005	0.0000	0.0007	0.0000	0.0011	0.0004
1 7/8–2 1/8	0.0008	0.0000	0.0005	0.0000	0.0008	0.0000	0.0013	0.0005
2 1/8–2 3/8	0.0008	0.0000	0.0005	0.0000	0.0008	0.0000	0.0014	0.0006
2 3/8–2 3/4	0.0008	0.0000	0.0005	0.0000	0.0008	0.0000	0.0014	0.0006
2 3/4–3 1/4	0.0009	0.0000	0.0006	0.0000	0.0009	0.0000	0.0017	0.0008
3 1/4–3 3/4	0.0009	0.0000	0.0006	0.0000	0.0009	0.0000	0.0018	0.0009
3 3/4–4 1/4	0.0010	0.0000	0.0006	0.0000	0.0010	0.0000	0.0020	0.0010
4 1/4–4 3/4	0.0010	0.0000	0.0007	0.0000	0.0010	0.0000	0.0021	0.0011
4 3/4–5 1/2	0.0010	0.0000	0.0007	0.0000	0.0010	0.0000	0.0023	0.0013
5 1/2–6 1/2	0.0011	0.0000	0.0007	0.0000	0.0011	0.0000	0.0026	0.0015
6 1/2–7 1/2	0.0011	0.0000	0.0008	0.0000	0.0011	0.0000	0.0029	0.0018
7 1/2–8 1/2	0.0012	0.0000	0.0008	0.0000	0.0012	0.0000	0.0032	0.0020

Size of hole or external member inclusive	Class 7, medium force fit				Class 8, heavy force and shrink fit			
	Hole or external member		Shaft or internal member		Hole or external member		Shaft or internal member	
	+		+	+	+		+	+
0–3/16	0.0003	0.0000	0.0004	0.0001	0.0003	0.0000	0.0004	0.0001
3/16–5/16	0.0004	0.0000	0.0005	0.0001	0.0004	0.0000	0.0007	0.0003
5/16–7/16	0.0004	0.0000	0.0006	0.0002	0.0004	0.0000	0.0008	0.0004
7/16–9/16	0.0005	0.0000	0.0008	0.0003	0.0005	0.0000	0.0010	0.0005
9/16–11/16	0.0005	0.0000	0.0008	0.0003	0.0005	0.0000	0.0011	0.0006
11/16–13/16	0.0005	0.0000	0.0009	0.0004	0.0005	0.0000	0.0013	0.0008
13/16–15/16	0.0006	0.0000	0.0010	0.0004	0.0006	0.0000	0.0015	0.0009
15/16–1 1/16	0.0006	0.0000	0.0010	0.0005	0.0006	0.0000	0.0016	0.0010
1 1/16–1 3/16	0.0006	0.0000	0.0012	0.0006	0.0006	0.0000	0.0017	0.0011
1 3/16–1 3/8	0.0006	0.0000	0.0012	0.0006	0.0006	0.0000	0.0019	0.0013
1 3/8–1 5/8	0.0007	0.0000	0.0015	0.0008	0.0007	0.0000	0.0022	0.0015
1 5/8–1 7/8	0.0007	0.0000	0.0016	0.0009	0.0007	0.0000	0.0025	0.0018
1 7/8–2 1/8	0.0008	0.0000	0.0018	0.0010	0.0008	0.0000	0.0028	0.0020
2 1/8–2 3/8	0.0008	0.0000	0.0019	0.0011	0.0008	0.0000	0.0031	0.0023
2 3/8–2 3/4	0.0008	0.0000	0.0021	0.0013	0.0008	0.0000	0.0033	0.0025
2 3/4–3 1/4	0.0009	0.0000	0.0024	0.0015	0.0009	0.0000	0.0039	0.0030
3 1/4–3 3/4	0.0009	0.0000	0.0027	0.0018	0.0009	0.0000	0.0044	0.0035
3 3/4–4 1/4	0.0010	0.0000	0.0030	0.0020	0.0010	0.0000	0.0050	0.0040
4 1/4–4 3/4	0.0010	0.0000	0.0033	0.0023	0.0010	0.0000	0.0055	0.0045
4 3/4–5 1/2	0.0010	0.0000	0.0035	0.0025	0.0010	0.0000	0.0060	0.0050
5 1/2–6 1/2	0.0011	0.0000	0.0041	0.0030	0.0011	0.0000	0.0071	0.0060
6 1/2–7 1/2	0.0011	0.0000	0.0046	0.0035	0.0011	0.0000	0.0081	0.0070
7 1/2–8 1/2	0.0012	0.0000	0.0052	0.0040	0.0012	0.0000	0.0092	0.0080

AMERICAN STANDARD PIPE [a, b]

Welded wrought iron

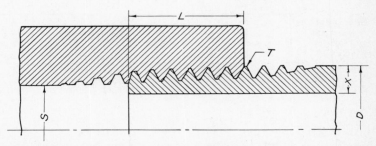

Nominal pipe size	Actual outside diam. D	Tap-drill size S	Thd. /in. T	Distance pipe enters fittings L	Wall thickness X			Weight, lb/ft [f]		
					Standard 40 [c]	Extra strong 80 [d]	Double extra strong [e]	Standard 40 [c]	Extra strong 80 [d]	Double extra strong [e]
⅛	0.405	$1\frac{1}{32}$	27	$\frac{3}{16}$	0.070	0.098	....	0.25	0.32	
¼	0.540	$\frac{7}{16}$	18	$\frac{9}{32}$	0.090	0.122	....	0.43	0.54	
⅜	0.675	$\frac{37}{64}$	18	$\frac{19}{64}$	0.093	0.129	....	0.57	0.74	
½	0.840	$\frac{23}{32}$	14	$\frac{3}{8}$	0.111	0.151	0.307	0.86	1.09	1.714
¾	1.050	$\frac{59}{64}$	14	$\frac{13}{32}$	0.115	0.157	0.318	1.14	1.48	2.440
1	1.315	$1\frac{5}{32}$	11½	$\frac{1}{2}$	0.136	0.183	0.369	1.68	2.18	3.659
1¼	1.660	$1\frac{1}{2}$	11½	$\frac{35}{64}$	0.143	0.195	0.393	2.28	3.00	5.214
1½	1.900	$1\frac{47}{64}$	11½	$\frac{9}{16}$	0.148	0.204	0.411	2.72	3.64	6.408
2	2.375	$2\frac{7}{32}$	11½	$\frac{37}{64}$	0.158	0.223	0.447	3.66	5.03	9.029
2½	2.875	$2\frac{5}{8}$	8	$\frac{7}{8}$	0.208	0.282	0.565	5.80	7.67	13.695
3	3.5	$3\frac{1}{4}$	8	$\frac{15}{16}$	0.221	0.306	0.615	7.58	10.3	18.583
3½	4.0	$3\frac{3}{4}$	8	1	0.231	0.325	....	9.11	12.5	
4	4.5	$4\frac{1}{4}$	8	$1\frac{1}{16}$	0.242	0.344	0.690	10.8	15.0	27.451
5	5.563	$5\frac{5}{16}$	8	$1\frac{5}{32}$	0.263	0.383	0.768	14.7	20.8	38.552
6	6.625	$6\frac{5}{16}$	8	$1\frac{1}{4}$	0.286	0.441	0.884	19.0	28.6	53.160
8	8.625	.....	8	$1\frac{15}{32}$	0.329	0.510	0.895	28.6	43.4	72.424
10	10.75	.....	8	$1\frac{43}{64}$	0.372	0.606	....	40.5	64.4	
12	12.75	.....	8	$1\frac{7}{8}$	0.414	0.702	....	53.6	88.6	
14 OD	14.0	.....	8	2	0.437	0.750	....	62.2	104.	
16 OD	16.0	.....	8	$2\frac{13}{64}$	0.500	....	....	82.2		
18 OD	18.0	.....	8	$2\frac{13}{32}$	0.562	....	....	103.		
20 OD	20.0	.....	8	$2\frac{19}{32}$	0.562	....	....	115.		
24 OD	24.0	.....	8	3						

[a] For welded and seamless steel pipe. See ASA B36.10—1939. Dimensions in inches.

[b] A pipe size may be designated by giving the nominal pipe size and wall thickness or by giving the nominal pipe size and weight per linear foot.

[c] Refers to American Standard schedule numbers, approximate values for the expression $1{,}000 \times P/S$. Schedule 40—standard weight.

[d] Schedule 80—extra strong.

[e] Not American Standard, but commercially available in both wrought iron and steel.

[f] Plain ends.

AMERICAN STANDARD 150-LB MALLEABLE-IRON SCREWED FITTINGS [a]

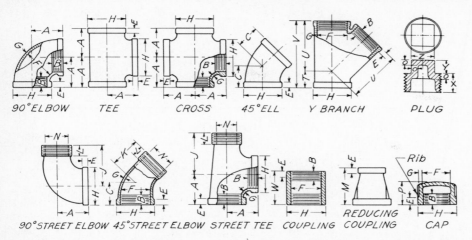

90°ELBOW   TEE   CROSS   45°ELL   Y BRANCH   PLUG

90°STREET ELBOW   45°STREET ELBOW   STREET TEE   COUPLING   REDUCING COUPLING   CAP

Nominal pipe size	A	B	C	E	F	G	H	J	K	L	M
1/8	0.69	0.25	....	0.200	0.405	0.090	0.693	1.00 b	....	0.264	
1/4	0.81	0.32	0.73	0.215	0.540	0.095	0.844	1.19	0.94	0.402	1.00
3/8	0.95	0.36	0.80	0.230	0.675	0.100	1.015	1.44	1.03	0.408	1.13
1/2	1.12	0.43	0.88	0.249	0.840	0.105	1.197	1.63	1.15	0.534	1.25
3/4	1.31	0.50	0.98	0.273	1.050	0.120	1.458	1.89	1.29	0.546	1.44
1	1.50	0.58	1.12	0.302	1.315	0.134	1.771	2.14	1.47	0.683	1.69
1 1/4	1.75	0.67	1.29	0.341	1.660	0.145	2.153	2.45	1.71	0.707	2.06
1 1/2	1.94	0.70	1.43	0.368	1.900	0.155	2.427	2.69	1.88	0.724	2.31
2	2.25	0.75	1.68	0.422	2.375	0.173	2.963	3.26	2.22	0.757	2.81
2 1/2	2.70	0.92	1.95	0.478	2.875	0.210	3.589	3.86	2.57	1.138	3.25
3	3.08	0.98	2.17	0.548	3.500	0.231	4.285	4.51	3.00	1.200	3.69
3 1/2	3.42	1.03	2.39	0.604	4.000	0.248	4.843	5.09 b	....	1.250	4.00
4	3.79	1.08	2.61	0.661	4.500	0.265	5.401	5.69	3.70	1.300	4.38
5	4.50	1.18	3.05	0.780	5.563	0.300	6.583	6.86 b	....	1.406	5.12
6	5.13	1.28	3.46	0.900	6.625	0.336	7.767	8.03 b	....	1.513	5.86

Nominal pipe size	N	P	T	U	V	W	X	Y	Z c	O d	Thickness of ribs on caps, couplings
1/8	0.20	....	....	....	....	0.96	0.37	0.24	9/32	....	0.090
1/4	0.26	....	....	....	....	1.06	0.44	0.28	3/8	....	0.095
3/8	0.37	....	0.50	1.43	1.93	1.16	0.48	0.31	7/16	....	0.100
1/2	0.51	0.87	0.61	1.71	2.32	1.34	0.56	0.38	9/16	0.16	0.105
3/4	0.69	0.97	0.72	2.05	2.77	1.52	0.63	0.44	5/8	0.18	0.120
1	0.91	1.16	0.85	2.43	3.28	1.67	0.75	0.50	13/16	0.20	0.134
1 1/4	1.19	1.28	1.02	2.92	3.94	1.93	0.80	0.56	15/16	0.22	0.145
1 1/2	1.39	1.33	1.10	3.28	4.38	2.15	0.83	0.62	1 1/8	0.24	0.155
2	1.79	1.45	1.24	3.93	5.17	2.53	0.88	0.68	1 5/16	0.26	0.173
2 1/2	2.20	1.70	1.52	4.73	6.25	2.88	1.07	0.74	1 1/2	0.29	0.210
3	2.78	1.80	1.71	5.55	7.26	3.18	1.13	0.80	1 11/16	0.31	0.231
3 1/2	3.24	1.90	....	....	....	3.43	1.18	0.86	1 7/8	0.34	0.248
4	3.70	2.08	2.01	6.97	8.98	3.69	1.22	1.00	2 1/8	0.37	0.265
5	4.69	2.32	....	....	....	....	1.31	1.00	2 5/16	0.46	0.300
6	5.67	2.55	....	....	....	....	1.40	1.25	2 1/2	0.52	0.336

[a] ASA B16c—1939. Street tee not made in 1/8-in. size. Dimensions in inches. Left-hand couplings have four or more ribs. Right-hand couplings have two ribs. [b] Street ell only.

[c] These dimensions are the nominal size of wrench (ASA B18.2—1941). Square-head plugs are designed to fit these wrenches.

[d] Solid plugs are provided in sizes 1/8 to 3 1/2 in. inclusive; cored plugs 1/2 to 3 1/2 in. inclusive. Cored plugs have min. metal thickness at all points equal to dimension O except at the end of thread.

AMERICAN STANDARD CAST-IRON SCREWED FITTINGS *

For maximum working saturated steam pressure of 125 and 250 lb per sq in.

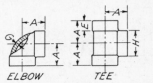

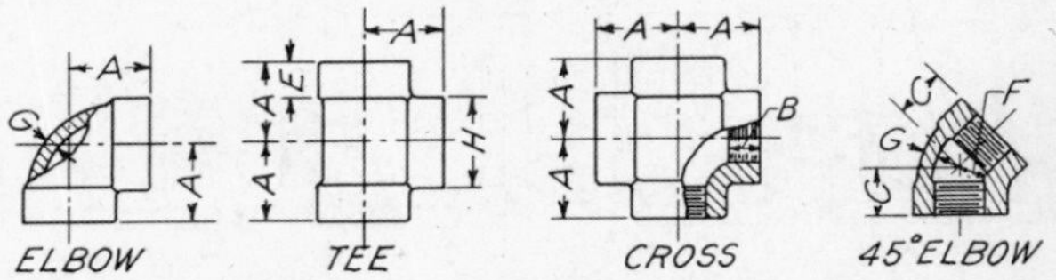

ELBOW   TEE   CROSS   45° ELBOW

Nominal pipe size	A	B min.	C	E min.	F Min.	F Max.	G min.	H min.
¼	0.81	0.32	0.73	0.38	0.540	0.584	0.110	0.93
⅜	0.95	0.36	0.80	0.44	0.675	0.719	0.120	1.12
½	1.12	0.43	0.88	0.50	0.840	0.897	0.130	1.34
¾	1.31	0.50	0.98	0.56	1.050	1.107	0.155	1.63
1	1.50	0.58	1.12	0.62	1.315	1.385	0.170	1.95
1¼	1.75	0.67	1.29	0.69	1.660	1.730	0.185	2.39
1½	1.94	0.70	1.43	0.75	1.900	1.970	0.200	2.68
2	2.25	0.75	1.68	0.84	2.375	2.445	0.220	3.28
2½	2.70	0.92	1.95	0.94	2.875	2.975	0.240	3.86
3	3.08	0.98	2.17	1.00	3.500	3.600	0.260	4.62
3½	3.42	1.03	2.39	1.06	4.000	4.100	0.280	5.20
4	3.79	1.08	2.61	1.12	4.500	4.600	0.310	5.79
5	4.50	1.18	3.05	1.18	5.563	5.663	0.380	7.05
6	5.13	1.28	3.46	1.28	6.625	6.725	0.430	8.28
8	6.56	1.47	4.28	1.47	8.625	8.725	0.550	10.63
10	8.08	1.68	5.16	1.68	10.750	10.850	0.690	13.12
12	9.50	1.88	5.97	1.88	12.750	12.850	0.800	15.47

* ASA B16d—1941. Dimensions in inches.

GLOBE, ANGLE-GLOBE, AND GATE VALVES *

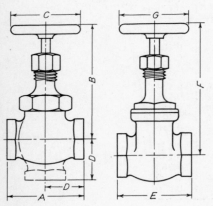

Size	A (globe only)	B (open)	C	D (angle only)	E	F (open)	G
⅛	2	4	1¾	1			
¼	2	4	1¾	1	1⅞	5⅛	1¾
⅜	2¼	4½	2	1⅛	2	5⅛	1¾
½	2¾	5¼	2½	1¼	2⅛	5½	2
¾	3³⁄₁₆	6	2¾	1½	2⅜	6⅝	2½
1	3¾	6¾	3	1¾	2⅞	7⅞	2¾
1¼	4¼	7¼	3⅝	2	3¼	9½	3
1½	4¾	8¼	4	2¼	3½	10⅞	3⅝
2	5¾	9½	4¾	2¾	3⅞	13⅛	4
2½	6¾	11	6	3¼	4½	15⅜	4¾
3	8	12¼	7	3¾	5	17⅞	5⅜

* Dimensions in inches and compiled from manufacturers' catalogues for drawing purposes.

PIPE BUSHINGS *

Dimensions of outside-head, inside-head, and face bushings in inches

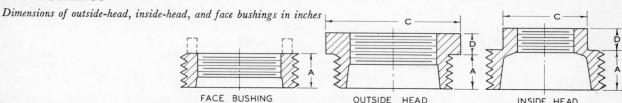

FACE BUSHING   OUTSIDE HEAD   INSIDE HEAD

Size	Length of external thread,† min., A	Height of head, min., D	Width of head,‡ min., C		Size	Length of external thread,‡ min., A	Height of head, min., D	Width of head,† min., C	
			Outside	Inside				Outside	Inside
¼ × ⅛	0.44	0.14	0.64		1½ × ¼	0.83	0.37	....	1.12
⅜ × ¼	0.48	0.16	0.68		2 × 1½	0.88	0.34	2.48	
⅜ × ⅛	0.48	0.16	0.68		2 × 1¼	0.88	0.34	2.48	
½ × ⅜	0.56	0.19	0.87		2 × 1	0.88	0.41	....	1.95
½ × ¼	0.56	0.19	0.87		2 × ¾	0.88	0.41	....	1.63
½ × ⅛	0.56	0.19	0.87		2 × ½	0.88	0.41	....	1.34
¾ × ½	0.63	0.22	1.15		2 × ⅜	0.88	0.41	....	1.12
¾ × ⅜	0.63	0.22	1.15		2 × ¼	0.88	0.41	....	1.12
¾ × ¼	0.63	0.22	1.15		2½ × 2	1.07	0.37	2.98	
¾ × ⅛	0.63	0.22	1.15		2½ × 1½	1.07	0.44	2.68	
1 × ¾	0.75	0.25	1.42		2½ × 1¼	1.07	0.44	....	2.39
1 × ½	0.75	0.25	1.42		2½ × 1	1.07	0.44	....	1.95
1 × ⅜	0.75	0.30	....	1.12	2½ × ¾	1.07	0.44	....	1.63
1 × ¼	0.75	0.30	....	1.12	2½ × ½	1.07	0.44	....	1.34
1 × ⅛	0.75	0.30	....	1.12	3 × 2½	1.13	0.40	3.86	
1¼ × 1	0.80	0.28	1.76		3 × 2	1.13	0.48	3.28	
1¼ × ¾	0.80	0.28	1.76		3 × 1½	1.13	0.48	....	2.68
1¼ × ½	0.80	0.34	....	1.34	3 × 1¼	1.13	0.48	....	2.39
1¼ × ⅜	0.80	0.34	....	1.12	3 × 1	1.13	0.48	....	1.95
1¼ × ¼	0.80	0.34	....	1.12	3 × ¾	1.13	0.48	....	1.63
1½ × 1¼	0.83	0.31	2.00		3 × ½	1.13	0.48	....	1.34
1½ × 1	0.83	0.31	2.00						
1½ × ¾	0.83	0.37	....	1.63					
1½ × ½	0.83	0.37	....	1.34					
1½ × ⅜	0.83	0.37	....	1.12					

* ASA B16.14—1949.

† In the case of outside-head bushings, length A includes provisions for imperfect threads.

‡ Heads of bushings shall be hexagonal or octagonal, except that on the larger sizes of outside-head bushings the heads may be made round with lugs instead of hexagonal or octagonal.

LENGTHS OF PIPE NIPPLES *

Size	Length		Size	Length		Size	Length		Size	Length	
	Close	Short		Close	Short		Close	Short		Close	Short
⅛	¾	1½	½	1⅛	1½	1¼	1⅝	2½	2½	2½	3
¼	⅞	1½	¾	1⅜	2	1½	1¾	2½	3	2⅝	3
⅜	1	1½	1	1½	2	2	2	2½			

* Compiled from manufacturers' catalogues. Dimensions in inches.

Long-nipple lengths: from short-nipple lengths to 6 in. in ½ in. increments; from 6 in. nipple lengths to 12 in. in 1 in. increments; from 12 in. nipple lengths to 24 in. in 2 in. increments.

AMERICAN STANDARD CAST-IRON PIPE FLANGES AND FLANGED FITTINGS *

For maximum working saturated steam pressure of 125 lb per sq in. (gage)

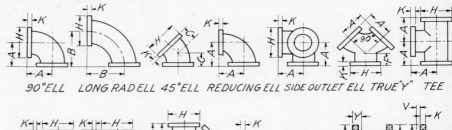

90° ELL   LONG RAD ELL   45° ELL   REDUCING ELL   SIDE OUTLET ELL   TRUE "Y"   TEE

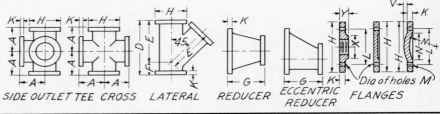

SIDE OUTLET TEE   CROSS   LATERAL   REDUCER   ECCENTRIC REDUCER   FLANGES

Nominal pipe size N	A	B	C	D	E	F	G	H	K min.
1	$3\frac{1}{2}$	5	$1\frac{3}{4}$	$7\frac{1}{2}$	$5\frac{3}{4}$	$1\frac{3}{4}$	....	$4\frac{1}{4}$	$\frac{7}{16}$
$1\frac{1}{4}$	$3\frac{3}{4}$	$5\frac{1}{2}$	2	8	$6\frac{1}{4}$	$1\frac{3}{4}$	....	$4\frac{5}{8}$	$\frac{1}{2}$
$1\frac{1}{2}$	4	6	$2\frac{1}{4}$	9	7	2	....	5	$\frac{9}{16}$
2	$4\frac{1}{2}$	$6\frac{1}{2}$	$2\frac{1}{2}$	$10\frac{1}{2}$	8	$2\frac{1}{2}$	5	6	$\frac{5}{8}$
$2\frac{1}{2}$	5	7	3	12	$9\frac{1}{2}$	$2\frac{1}{2}$	$5\frac{1}{2}$	7	$\frac{11}{16}$
3	$5\frac{1}{2}$	$7\frac{3}{4}$	3	13	10	3	6	$7\frac{1}{2}$	$\frac{3}{4}$
$3\frac{1}{2}$	6	$8\frac{1}{2}$	$3\frac{1}{2}$	$14\frac{1}{2}$	$11\frac{1}{2}$	3	$6\frac{1}{2}$	$8\frac{1}{2}$	$\frac{13}{16}$
4	$6\frac{1}{2}$	9	4	15	12	3	7	9	$\frac{15}{16}$
5	$7\frac{1}{2}$	$10\frac{1}{4}$	$4\frac{1}{2}$	17	$13\frac{1}{2}$	$3\frac{1}{2}$	8	10	$\frac{15}{16}$
6	8	$11\frac{1}{2}$	5	18	$14\frac{1}{2}$	$3\frac{1}{2}$	9	11	1
8	9	14	$5\frac{1}{2}$	22	$17\frac{1}{2}$	$4\frac{1}{2}$	11	$13\frac{1}{2}$	$1\frac{1}{8}$
10	11	$16\frac{1}{2}$	$6\frac{1}{2}$	$25\frac{1}{2}$	$20\frac{1}{2}$	5	12	16	$1\frac{3}{16}$
12	12	19	$7\frac{1}{2}$	30	$24\frac{1}{2}$	$5\frac{1}{2}$	14	19	$1\frac{1}{4}$

Nominal pipe size N	L	M	No. of bolts	Diam. of bolts	Length of bolts	X min.	Y min.	Wall thickness	V
1	$3\frac{1}{8}$	$\frac{5}{8}$	4	$\frac{1}{2}$	$1\frac{3}{4}$	$1\frac{15}{16}$	$1\frac{1}{16}$	$\frac{5}{16}$	$\frac{3}{8}$
$1\frac{1}{4}$	$3\frac{1}{2}$	$\frac{5}{8}$	4	$\frac{1}{2}$	2	$2\frac{5}{16}$	$1\frac{3}{16}$	$\frac{5}{16}$	$\frac{7}{16}$
$1\frac{1}{2}$	$3\frac{7}{8}$	$\frac{5}{8}$	4	$\frac{1}{2}$	2	$2\frac{9}{16}$	$\frac{7}{8}$	$\frac{5}{16}$	$\frac{1}{2}$
2	$4\frac{3}{4}$	$\frac{3}{4}$	4	$\frac{5}{8}$	$2\frac{1}{4}$	$3\frac{1}{16}$	1	$\frac{5}{16}$	$\frac{9}{16}$
$2\frac{1}{2}$	$5\frac{1}{2}$	$\frac{3}{4}$	4	$\frac{5}{8}$	$2\frac{1}{2}$	$3\frac{9}{16}$	$1\frac{1}{8}$	$\frac{5}{16}$	$\frac{5}{8}$
3	6	$\frac{3}{4}$	4	$\frac{5}{8}$	$2\frac{1}{2}$	$4\frac{1}{4}$	$1\frac{3}{16}$	$\frac{3}{8}$	$\frac{11}{16}$
$3\frac{1}{2}$	7	$\frac{3}{4}$	8	$\frac{5}{8}$	$2\frac{3}{4}$	$4\frac{13}{16}$	$1\frac{1}{4}$	$\frac{7}{16}$	$\frac{3}{4}$
4	$7\frac{1}{2}$	$\frac{3}{4}$	8	$\frac{5}{8}$	3	$5\frac{5}{16}$	$1\frac{5}{16}$	$\frac{1}{2}$	$\frac{7}{8}$
5	$8\frac{1}{2}$	$\frac{7}{8}$	8	$\frac{3}{4}$	3	$6\frac{7}{16}$	$1\frac{7}{16}$	$\frac{1}{2}$	$\frac{7}{8}$
6	$9\frac{1}{2}$	$\frac{7}{8}$	8	$\frac{3}{4}$	$3\frac{1}{4}$	$7\frac{9}{16}$	$1\frac{9}{16}$	$\frac{9}{16}$	$\frac{15}{16}$
8	$11\frac{3}{4}$	$\frac{7}{8}$	8	$\frac{3}{4}$	$3\frac{1}{2}$	$9\frac{11}{16}$	$1\frac{3}{4}$	$\frac{5}{8}$	$1\frac{1}{16}$
10	$14\frac{1}{4}$	1	12	$\frac{7}{8}$	$3\frac{3}{4}$	$11\frac{15}{16}$	$1\frac{15}{16}$	$\frac{3}{4}$	$1\frac{1}{8}$
12	17	1	12	$\frac{7}{8}$	$3\frac{3}{4}$	$14\frac{1}{16}$	$2\frac{3}{16}$	$1\frac{3}{16}$	

* ASA B16a—1939. Dimensions in inches.

LENGTHS OF MALLEABLE-IRON UNIONS *

Ground joint

Nominal size......	$\frac{1}{8}$	$\frac{1}{4}$	$\frac{3}{8}$	$\frac{1}{2}$	$\frac{3}{4}$	1	$1\frac{1}{4}$	$1\frac{1}{2}$	2	$2\frac{1}{2}$	3
End to end........	$1\frac{1}{2}$	$1\frac{9}{16}$	$1\frac{5}{8}$	$1\frac{13}{16}$	$2\frac{1}{16}$	$2\frac{1}{4}$	$2\frac{1}{2}$	$2\frac{5}{8}$	3	$3\frac{9}{16}$	$3\frac{15}{16}$

 * Compiled from manufacturers' catalogues. Dimensions in inches.

AMERICAN STANDARD STEEL BUTT-WELDING FITTINGS *, †

Elbows, tees, caps, and stub ends

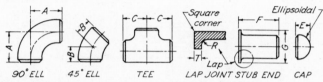

90° ELL   45° ELL   TEE   LAP JOINT STUB END   CAP

Nominal pipe size	Outside diam. at bevel	Center to end			Welding caps E	Lapped-joint stub ends		
		90° welding elbow A	45° welding elbow B	Of run, welding tee C		Lengths F	Radius of fillet R	Diameter of lap G
1	1.310	$1\frac{1}{2}$	$\frac{7}{8}$	$1\frac{1}{2}$	$1\frac{1}{2}$	4	$\frac{1}{8}$	2
$1\frac{1}{4}$	1.660	$1\frac{7}{8}$	1	$1\frac{7}{8}$	$1\frac{1}{2}$	4	$\frac{3}{16}$	$2\frac{1}{2}$
$1\frac{1}{2}$	1.900	$2\frac{1}{4}$	$1\frac{1}{8}$	$2\frac{1}{4}$	$1\frac{1}{2}$	4	$\frac{1}{4}$	$2\frac{7}{8}$
2	2.375	3	$1\frac{3}{8}$	$2\frac{1}{2}$	$1\frac{1}{2}$	6	$\frac{5}{16}$	$3\frac{5}{8}$
$2\frac{1}{2}$	2.875	$3\frac{3}{4}$	$1\frac{3}{4}$	3	$1\frac{1}{2}$	6	$\frac{5}{16}$	$4\frac{1}{8}$
3	3.500	$4\frac{1}{2}$	2	$3\frac{3}{8}$	2	6	$\frac{3}{8}$	5
$3\frac{1}{2}$	4.000	$5\frac{1}{4}$	$2\frac{1}{4}$	$3\frac{3}{4}$	$2\frac{1}{2}$	6	$\frac{3}{8}$	$5\frac{1}{2}$
4	4.500	6	$2\frac{1}{2}$	$4\frac{1}{8}$	$2\frac{1}{2}$	6	$\frac{7}{16}$	$6\frac{3}{16}$

Butt-welding reducers

Nominal pipe size	Outside diam. at bevel		End to end H	Nominal pipe size	Outside diam. at bevel		End to end H
	Large end	Small end			Large end	Small end	
1 × $\frac{3}{4}$		1.050		3 × $2\frac{1}{2}$		2.875	
1 × $\frac{1}{2}$	1.315	0.840	2	3 × 2	3.500	2.375	$3\frac{1}{2}$
1 × $\frac{3}{8}$		0.675		3 × $1\frac{1}{2}$		1.900	
				3 × $1\frac{1}{4}$		1.660	
$1\frac{1}{4}$ × 1		1.315		$3\frac{1}{2}$ × 3		3.500	
$1\frac{1}{4}$ × $\frac{3}{4}$	1.660	1.050	2	$3\frac{1}{2}$ × $2\frac{1}{2}$		2.875	
$1\frac{1}{4}$ × $\frac{1}{2}$		0.840		$3\frac{1}{2}$ × 2	4.000	2.375	4
				$3\frac{1}{2}$ × $1\frac{1}{2}$		1.900	
$1\frac{1}{2}$ × $1\frac{1}{4}$		1.660		$3\frac{1}{2}$ × $1\frac{1}{4}$		1.660	
$1\frac{1}{2}$ × 1	1.900	1.315	$2\frac{1}{2}$	4 × $3\frac{1}{2}$		4.000	
$1\frac{1}{2}$ × $\frac{3}{4}$		1.050		4 × 3		3.500	
$1\frac{1}{2}$ × $\frac{1}{2}$		0.840		4 × $2\frac{1}{2}$	4.500	2.875	4
				4 × 2		2.375	
2 × $1\frac{1}{2}$		1.900		4 × $1\frac{1}{2}$		1.900	
2 × $1\frac{1}{4}$	2.375	1.660	3	5 × 4		4.500	
2 × 1		1.315		5 × $3\frac{1}{2}$		4.000	
2 × $\frac{3}{4}$		1.050		5 × 3	5.563	3.500	5
				5 × $2\frac{1}{2}$		2.875	
$2\frac{1}{2}$ × 2		2.375					
$2\frac{1}{2}$ × $1\frac{1}{2}$	2.875	1.900	$3\frac{1}{2}$				
$2\frac{1}{2}$ × $1\frac{1}{4}$		1.660					
$2\frac{1}{2}$ × 1		1.315					

CONCENTRIC REDUCER

ECCENTRIC REDUCER

 * For larger sizes, see ASA B16.
 † ASA B16.9—1940. Dimensions in inches.

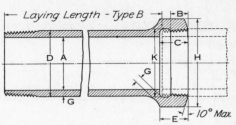

THREADED CAST-IRON PIPE *

Dimension of pipe and drainage hubs

Pipe size	Pipe				Drainage hubs					Nominal weights	
	Nominal diam.		Wall thickness, min.,	Thread length *	Diam. of groove, max.,	End to shoulder †	Min. band		Type A and barrel of type B per foot	Additional weight of hubs for type B
	Outside	Inside					Diam.	Length		
	D	A	G	B	K	C	H	E		
1¼	1.66	1.23	0.187	0.42	1.73	0.71	2.39	0.71	3.033	0.60
1½	1.90	1.45	0.195	0.42	1.97	0.72	2.68	0.72	3.666	0.90
2	2.38	1.89	0.211	0.43	2.44	0.76	3.28	0.76	5.041	1.00
2½	2.88	2.32	0.241	0.68	2.97	1.14	3.86	1.14	7.032	1.35
3	3.50	2.90	0.263	0.76	3.60	1.20	4.62	1.20	9.410	2.80
4	4.50	3.83	0.294	0.84	4.60	1.30	5.79	1.30	13.751	3.48
5	5.56	4.81	0.328	0.93	5.66	1.41	7.05	1.41	19.069	5.00
6	6.63	5.76	0.378	0.95	6.72	1.51	8.28	1.51	26.223	6.60
8	8.63	7.63	0.438	1.06	8.72	1.71	10.63	1.71	39.820	10.00
10	10.75	9.75	0.438	1.21	10.85	1.92	13.12	1.93	50.234	
12	12.75	11.75	0.438	1.36	12.85	2.12	15.47	2.13	60.036	

* ASA A40.5—1943. All dimensions are given in inches, except where otherwise stated. Type A has external threads both ends. Type B as shown.

† The length of thread B and the end to shoulder C shall not vary from the dimensions shown by more than plus or minus the equivalent of the pitch of one thread.

BEAM CONNECTIONS

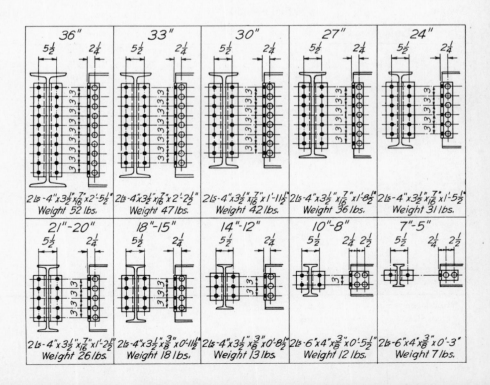

SELECTED STRUCTURAL SHAPES *

Dimensions for detailing

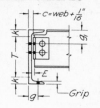

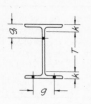

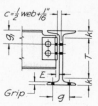

CHANNEL — WF SHAPE — BEAM

Name	Depth of section, in.	Weight per foot, lb	Flange: Width, in.	Flange: Mean thickness, in.	Web: Thickness, in.	Web: Half thickness, in.	Distances: T, in.	Distances: k, in.	Distances: g_1, in.	Distances: c, in.	Grip, in.	Max. flange rivet, in.	Usual gage g, in.
Channels	18	58.0	4 1/4	5/8	11/16	3/8	15 3/8	1 5/16	2 3/4	3/4	5/8	1	2 1/2
	15	40.0	3 1/2	5/8	9/16	1/4	12 3/8	1 5/16	2 3/4	5/8	5/8	1	2
	12	30.0	3 1/8	1/2	1/2	1/4	9 7/8	1 1/16	2 1/2	9/16	1/2	7/8	1 3/4
	10	15.3	2 5/8	7/16	1/4	1/8	8 1/8	15/16	2 1/2	5/16	7/16	3/4	1 1/2
	9	13.4	2 3/8	7/16	1/4	1/8	7 1/4	7/8	2 1/2	5/16	3/8	3/4	1 3/8
	8	18.75	2 1/2	3/8	1/2	1/4	6 3/8	13/16	2 1/4	9/16	3/8	3/4	1 1/2
	7	12.25	2 1/4	3/8	5/16	3/16	5 3/8	13/16	2	3/8	3/8	5/8	1 1/4
	6	10.5	2	3/8	5/16	3/16	4 1/2	3/4	2	3/8	3/8	5/8	1 1/8
	5	9.0	1 7/8	5/16	5/16	3/16	3 5/8	11/16	2	3/8	5/16	1/2	1 1/8
	4	7.25	1 3/4	5/16	5/16	3/16	2 3/4	5/8	2	3/8	5/16	1/2	1
	3	6.0	1 5/8	1/4	3/8	3/16	1 3/4	5/8	...	7/16	5/16	1/2	7/8
WF shapes	21 † (21 1/4)	127	13	1	9/16	5/16	17 3/4	1 3/4	3	3/8	.....	.....	5 1/2
	16 (16 3/8)	96	11 1/2	7/8	9/16	5/16	13 1/8	1 5/8	2 3/4	3/8	.....	.....	5 1/2
	14 (14 1/8)	84	12	3/4	7/16	1/4	11 3/8	1 3/8	2 3/4	5/16	.....	.....	5 1/2
	14 (13 3/4)	48	8	9/16	3/8	3/16	11 3/8	1 3/16	2 1/2	1/4	.....	.....	5 1/2
	12 (12 1/4)	50	8 1/8	5/8	3/8	3/16	9 3/4	1 1/4	2 1/2	1/4	.....	.....	5 1/2
	10 (10)	49	10	9/16	3/8	3/16	7 7/8	1 1/16	2 1/2	1/4	.....	.....	5 1/2
	10 (9 3/4)	33	8	7/16	5/16	3/16	7 7/8	15/16	2 1/4	1/4	.....	.....	5 1/2
	8 (8)	28	6 1/2	7/16	5/16	1/8	6 3/8	13/16	2 1/4	3/16	.....	.....	3 1/2
Beams	24	120.0	8	1 1/8	13/16	7/16	20 1/8	1 15/16	3 1/4	1/2	1 1/8	1	4
	20	85.0	7	15/16	11/16	5/16	16 1/2	1 3/4	3 1/4	3/8	7/8	1	4
	18	70.0	6 1/4	11/16	3/4	3/8	15 1/4	1 3/8	2 3/4	7/16	11/16	7/8	3 1/2
	15	50.0	5 5/8	5/8	9/16	5/16	12 1/2	1 1/4	2 3/4	3/8	9/16	3/4	3 1/2
	12	31.8	5	9/16	3/8	3/16	9 3/4	1 1/8	2 1/2	1/4	1/2	3/4	3
	10	35.0	5	1/2	5/8	5/16	8	1	2 1/2	3/8	1/2	3/4	2 3/4
	8	23.0	4 1/8	7/16	7/16	1/4	6 1/4	7/8	2 1/4	5/16	7/16	3/4	2 1/4
	7	20.0	3 7/8	3/8	7/16	1/4	5 3/8	13/16	2	5/16	3/8	5/8	2 1/4
	6	17.25	3 5/8	3/8	1/2	1/4	4 1/2	3/4	2	5/16	3/8	5/8	2
	5	10.0	3	5/16	1/4	1/8	3 5/8	11/16	2	3/16	5/16	1/2	1 3/4
	4	9.5	2 3/4	5/16	5/16	3/16	2 3/4	5/8	2	1/4	5/16	1/2	1 1/2
	3	7.5	2 1/2	1/4	3/8	3/16	1 7/8	9/16	...	1/4	1/4	3/8	1 1/2

* From Steel Construction Handbook.

† Nominal depth; ( ) indicates actual depth.

DRIVING CLEARANCES FOR RIVETING

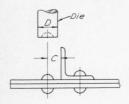

	Diam. of rivet								
	$\frac{1}{2}$	$\frac{5}{8}$	$\frac{3}{4}$	$\frac{7}{8}$	1	$1\frac{1}{8}$	$1\frac{1}{4}$	$1\frac{3}{8}$	$1\frac{1}{2}$
D	$1\frac{3}{4}$	2	$2\frac{1}{4}$	$2\frac{1}{2}$	$2\frac{3}{4}$	3	$3\frac{1}{4}$	$3\frac{1}{2}$	$3\frac{3}{4}$
C	1	$1\frac{1}{8}$	$1\frac{1}{4}$	$1\frac{3}{8}$	$1\frac{1}{2}$	$1\frac{5}{8}$	$1\frac{3}{4}$	$1\frac{7}{8}$	2

Dimensions in inches.

GAGE AND MAXIMUM RIVET SIZE FOR ANGLES

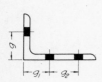

Leg	8	7	6	5	4	$3\frac{1}{2}$	3	$2\frac{1}{2}$	2	$1\frac{3}{4}$	$1\frac{1}{2}$	$1\frac{3}{8}$	$1\frac{1}{4}$	1
g	$4\frac{1}{2}$	4	$3\frac{1}{2}$	3	$2\frac{1}{2}$	2	$1\frac{3}{4}$	$1\frac{3}{8}$	$1\frac{1}{8}$	1	$\frac{7}{8}$	$\frac{7}{8}$	$\frac{3}{4}$	$\frac{5}{8}$
g_1	3	$2\frac{1}{2}$	$2\frac{1}{4}$	2										
g_2	3	3	$2\frac{1}{2}$	$1\frac{3}{4}$										
Max. rivet	$1\frac{1}{8}$	$1\frac{1}{8}$	1	1	$\frac{7}{8}$	$\frac{7}{8}$	$\frac{7}{8}$	$\frac{3}{4}$	$\frac{5}{8}$	$\frac{1}{2}$	$\frac{3}{8}$	$\frac{3}{8}$	$\frac{3}{8}$	$\frac{1}{4}$

Dimensions in inches.

SAE STANDARD COTTER PINS

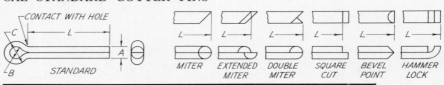

Pin diameter A			Eye diameter, min.		Recommended hole diam., drill size
Nominal	Max.	Min.	Inside B	Outside C	
$\frac{1}{32}$ (0.031)	0.032	0.028	$\frac{1}{32}$	$\frac{1}{16}$	$\frac{3}{64}$ (0.0469)
$\frac{3}{64}$ (0.047)	0.048	0.044	$\frac{3}{64}$	$\frac{3}{32}$	$\frac{1}{16}$ (0.0625)
$\frac{1}{16}$ (0.062)	0.060	0.056	$\frac{1}{16}$	$\frac{1}{8}$	$\frac{5}{64}$ (0.0781)
$\frac{5}{64}$ (0.078)	0.076	0.072	$\frac{5}{64}$	$\frac{5}{32}$	$\frac{3}{32}$ (0.0937)
$\frac{3}{32}$ (0.094)	0.090	0.086	$\frac{3}{32}$	$\frac{3}{16}$	$\frac{7}{64}$ (0.1094)
$\frac{1}{8}$ (0.125)	0.120	0.116	$\frac{1}{8}$	$\frac{1}{4}$	$\frac{9}{64}$ (0.1406)
$\frac{5}{32}$ (0.156)	0.150	0.146	$\frac{5}{32}$	$\frac{5}{16}$	$\frac{11}{64}$ (0.1719)
$\frac{3}{16}$ (0.188)	0.176	0.172	$\frac{3}{16}$	$\frac{3}{8}$	$\frac{13}{64}$ (0.2031)
$\frac{7}{32}$ (0.219)	0.207	0.202	$\frac{7}{32}$	$\frac{7}{16}$	$\frac{15}{64}$ (0.2344)
$\frac{1}{4}$ (0.250)	0.225	0.220	$\frac{1}{4}$	$\frac{1}{2}$	$\frac{17}{64}$ (0.2656)
$\frac{5}{16}$ (0.312)	0.280	0.275	$\frac{5}{16}$	$\frac{5}{8}$	$\frac{5}{16}$ (0.3125)
$\frac{3}{8}$ (0.375)	0.335	0.329	$\frac{3}{8}$	$\frac{3}{4}$	$\frac{3}{8}$ (0.3750)
$\frac{1}{2}$ (0.500)	0.473	0.467	$\frac{1}{2}$	1	$\frac{1}{2}$ (0.5000)

AMERICAN STANDARD GRAPHICAL SYMBOLS

ASA Z14.2—1935

PIPING

Piping, General	(Lettered with name of material conveyed)
Non-intersecting Pipes	

(To differentiate lines of piping on a drawing the following symbols may be used.)

Air	Cold Water	Steam
Gas	Hot Water	Condensate
Oil	Vacuum	Refrigerant

PIPE FITTINGS AND VALVES

	Flanged	Screwed	Bell and Spigot	Welded	Soldered
Joint					
Elbow—90 deg					
Elbow—45 deg					
Elbow—Turned Up					
Elbow—Turned Down					
Elbow—Long Radius					
Side Outlet Elbow Outlet Down					
Side Outlet Elbow Outlet Up					
Base Elbow					
Double Branch Elbow					
Reducing Elbow					
Reducer					
Eccentric Reducer					
Tee-Outlet Up					
Tee-Outlet Down					
Tee					
Side Outlet Tee Outlet Up					
Side Outlet Tee Outlet Down					
Single Sweep Tee					
Double Sweep Tee					
Cross					
Lateral					
Gate Valve					

AMERICAN STANDARD GRAPHICAL SYMBOLS

PIPING

	Flanged	Screwed	Bell and Spigot	Welded	Soldered
Globe Valve					
Angle Globe Valve					
Angle Gate Valve					
Check Valve					
Angle Check Valve					
Stop Cock					
Safety Valve					
Quick Opening Valve					
Float Operating Valve					
Motor Operated Gate Valve					
Motor Operated Globe Valve					
Expansion Joint Flanged					
Reducing Flange					
Union	(See Joint)				
Sleeve					
Bushing					

HEATING AND VENTILATING

Lock and Shield Valve		Tube Radiator	(Plan) (Elev.)	Exhaust Duct, Section	
Reducing Valve		Wall Radiator	(Plan) (Elev.)	Butterfly Damper	(Plan or Elev.) (Elev. or Plan)
Diaphragm Valve		Pipe Coil	(Plan) (Elev.)	Deflecting Damper Rectangular Pipe	
Thermostat	(T)	Indirect Radiator	(Plan) (Elev.)	Vanes	
Radiator Trap	(Plan) (Elev.)	Supply Duct, Section		Air Supply Outlet	
				Exhaust Inlet	

HEAT-POWER APPARATUS

Flue Gas Reheater (Intermediate Superheater)		Steam Turbine		Automatic By-pass Valve	
Steam Generator (Boiler)		Condensing Turbine		Automatic Valve Operated by Governor	
Live Steam Superheater		Open Tank		Pumps Air Service Boiler Feed Condensate Circulating Water Reciprocating	
Feed Heater With Air Outlet		Closed Tank			
Surface Condenser		Automatic Reducing Valve		Dynamic Pump (Air Ejector)	

ELECTRIC SYMBOLS

ASA Z10g2—1934

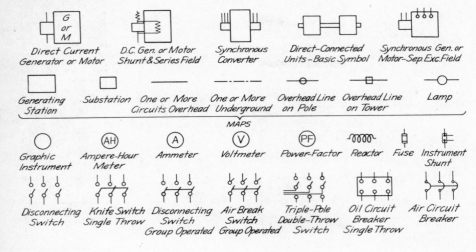

Direct Current Generator or Motor | D.C. Gen. or Motor Shunt & Series Field | Synchronous Converter | Direct-Connected Units – Basic Symbol | Synchronous Gen. or Motor-Sep. Exc. Field

Generating Station | Substation | One or More Circuits Overhead | One or More Underground | Overhead Line on Pole | Overhead Line on Tower | Lamp

MAPS

Graphic Instrument | Ampere-Hour Meter | Ammeter | Voltmeter | Power-Factor | Reactor | Fuse | Instrument Shunt

Disconnecting Switch | Knife Switch Single Throw | Disconnecting Switch Group Operated | Air Break Switch Group Operated | Triple-Pole Double-Throw Switch | Oil Circuit Breaker Single Throw | Air Circuit Breaker

RADIO SYMBOLS

ASA Z10g3—1933

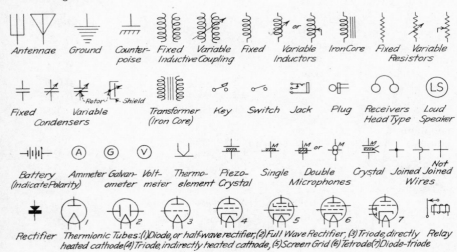

Antennae | Ground | Counterpoise | Fixed Inductive Coupling | Variable | Fixed | Variable Inductors | Iron Core | Fixed | Variable Resistors

Fixed Condensers | Variable | Transformer (Iron Core) | Key | Switch | Jack | Plug | Receivers Head Type | Loud Speaker

Battery (Indicate Polarity) | Ammeter | Galvanometer | Voltmeter | Thermo-element | Piezo-Crystal | Single Double Microphones | Crystal | Joined Wires | Not Joined Wires

Rectifier | Thermionic Tubes: (1) Diode, or half-wave rectifier, (2) Full Wave Rectifier, (3) Triode, directly heated cathode (4) Triode, indirectly heated cathode, (5) Screen Grid (6) Tetrode (7) Diode-triode | Relay

SYMBOLS FOR MATERIALS (EXTERIOR)

Brick

Stone

Transparent Material Glass. Celluloid. Etc.

Wood

SYMBOLS FOR MATERIALS (SECTION)

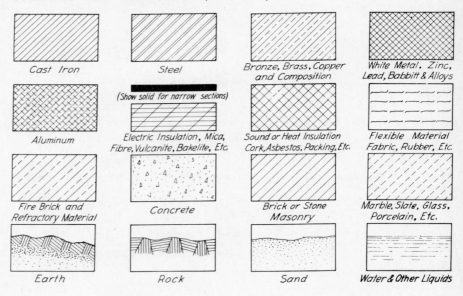

Cast Iron	Steel	Bronze, Brass, Copper and Composition	White Metal, Zinc, Lead, Babbitt & Alloys
Aluminum	*(Show solid for narrow sections)* Electric Insulation, Mica, Fibre, Vulcanite, Bakelite, Etc.	Sound or Heat Insulation Cork, Asbestos, Packing, Etc.	Flexible Material Fabric, Rubber, Etc.
Fire Brick and Refractory Material	Concrete	Brick or Stone Masonry	Marble, Slate, Glass, Porcelain, Etc.
Earth	Rock	Sand	Water & Other Liquids

WEIGHTS OF MATERIALS

Metals	lb/cu in.	Wood	lb/cu in.
Aluminum alloy, cast	0.099	Ash	0.024
Aluminum, cast	0.094	Balsa	0.0058
Aluminum, wrought	0.097	Cedar	0.017
Babbitt metal	0.267	Cork	0.009
Brass, cast or rolled	0.303–0.313	Hickory	0.0295
Brass, drawn	0.323	Maple	0.025
Bronze, aluminum cast	0.277	Oak (white)	0.028
Bronze, phosphor	0.315–0.321	Pine (white)	0.015
Chromium	0.256	Pine (yellow)	0.025
Copper, cast	0.311	Poplar	0.018
Copper, rolled, drawn or wire	0.322	Walnut (black)	0.023
Dowmetal A	0.065		
Duralumin	0.101	*Miscellaneous materials*	*lb/cu ft*
Gold	0.697	Asbestos	175
Iron, cast	0.260	Bakelite	79.5
Iron, wrought	0.283	Brick, common	112
Lead	0.411	Brick, fire	144
Magnesium	0.063	Celluloid	86.4
Mercury	0.491	Earth, packed	100
Monel metal	0.323	Fiber	89.9
Silver	0.379	Glass	163
Steel, cast or rolled	0.274–0.281	Gravel	109
Steel, tool	0.272	Limestone	163
Tin	0.263	Plexiglass	74.3
Zinc	0.258	Sandstone	144
		Water	62.4

ABBREVIATIONS AND WORD SYMBOLS TO BE USED ON DRAWINGS

Alternating current	a-c	Extra fine (screw threads)	EF	Patent	pat
American Standard	Am Std	Fabricate	fab	Pattern	patt
American Standards Association	ASA	Fillister	fil	Perforate	perf
		Fine (screw threads)	F	Perpendicular to	⊥
American wire gage (B & S gage)	Awg	Finish	V or fin or f	Phosphor bronze	phos bro
		Foot, feet	ft or '	Piece(s)	pc, pcs
Angle (structural shape)	∟	Gage	ga	Pitch	P
Approved (by)	App	Gallon	gal	Pitch diameter	PD
Babbitt metal (specified by number)	bab #——	Galvanized iron	GI	Plate	pl
		Grind	gr	Pound	# or lb
Birmingham wire gage	Bwg	Harden	hdn	Pratt and Whitney (key)	P & W
Brass, SAE (specified by number)	br #——	H beam	H	Propeller	prop
		Head	hd	Quart	qt
Brinell hardness number	Bhn	Heat-treatment, SAE (specified by number)	htr #——	Radius	R
Bronze, SAE (specified by number)	bro #——			Required	req
		Hexagonal	hex	Revolutions per minute	rpm
Brown & Sharpe gage	B & S	Horsepower	hp or HP	Revolutions per second	rps
Cast iron	CI	I beam	I	Right hand	RH
Center line	₵ or CL	Impregnate	impreg	Round	rd
Center to center	c to c	Inch(es)	" or in.	Round bar	⌀
Centimeter(s)	cm	Inside diameter	ID	Round bar deformed	ƒ
Chamfer	chfr	Insulate, insulated	insl	Screw	sc
Channel	⊔	Kilowatt	kw	Section	sec
Checked (by)	Ch	Kip	k	Society of Automotive Engineers	SAE
Circular	cir	Laminate	lam		
Circular pitch (gear drawings)	CP	Lateral	lat	Special (screw threads)	S
		Left hand	LH	Square	□ or sq
Coarse (screw threads)	C	Longitudinal	long	Square bar	⊡
Cold rolled steel	CRS	Lubricate, lubrication	lub	Square bar, deformed	⊡
Copper	cop	Machine	mach	Square foot, feet	sq ft or □'
Counterbore	c'bore	Magnetic	mag	Square inch(es)	sq in. or □"
Countersink	csk	Malleable iron	Mal I	Standard	Std
Cubic inches	cu in.	Maximum	max	Steel	Stl
Cylinder, cylindrical	cyl	Meter(s)	m	Steel casting	Stl C
Degree(s) (angular measurement)	° or deg	Millimeter(s)	mm	Tee (structural shape)	T
		Minimum	min	Teeth (on gear drawings)	T
Detail drawing	Dtl dwg	Minute(s) (time)	' or min	Thread(s)	thd, thds
Diagonal	diag	Minute(s) (angular measure)	'	Traced (by)	Tr
Diameter	D			Unified (screw threads)	U
Diametral pitch (gear drawings)	DP	National Electrical Code	NEC	United States Standard (old)	USS
		National form (screw threads)	N		
Die casting	D cast			Wide flange section (structural)	WF
Die stamping	D st	Number	# or no.		
Direct current	d-c	On center (center to center)	oc	Woodruff (key)	spell out or Wdrf
Drawing(s)	Dwg, Dwgs			Wrought iron	WI
Drawn (by)	Dr	Outside diameter	OD	Yard(s)	yd, yds
Drop forging	D forg	Oxidize	ox	Zee (structural shape)	Z
External	ext	Parallel to	‖		

INDEX